D0230209

GOOD BEER GUIDE 1995

EDITED BY JEFF EVANS

BOOKS

Campaign for Real Ale Ltd.
34 Alma Road, St Albans,
Herts. AL1 3BW

CONTENTS

Editor: Jeff Evans. **Deputy Editor:** Jill Adam. **The HQ Team:** Stephen Cox, Iain Loe, Richard
Smith, Malcolm Harding, Jo Bates, Cressida Feiler, Su Tilley, Mike Benner, Jean Jones, Clare
Stevens, Mandi Gilling. **Design:** Rob Howells. **Cover Photograph:** Tom Dobbie. **Pub Sign:**
Clive Armitage Associates. **Maps:** David Perrott.

Published by Campaign for Real Ale Ltd., 34 Alma Road, St Albans, Herts. AL1 3BW. Tel.
(01727) 867201. **Typeset by** Create Publishing Services, Bath. **Printed by** Bath Press, Bath.

ISBN 1 85249 007 1   © **Campaign for Real Ale Ltd.** 1994/95

This guide could not have been produced without the tireless efforts of over 40,000 CAMRA
members. Special thanks once again to CAMRA Regional Directors, to those members who
helped with pub surveys and those who provided information on beers and breweries.

INTRODUCTION

Do we expect too much of our pubs?

PERHAPS THE NAME 'public house' is now a misnomer. To some drinkers, it undoubtedly conveys the impression that such an establishment belongs to them, to use or abuse at will. The 1995 *Good Beer Guide* will hopefully dispel this myth. For the first time in its twenty-two years, the *Guide* takes a good look at pub law and spells out exactly what, legally, the pub is, and how it should be used by its customers. In *You, The Pub and The Law*, licensing law expert Peter Coulson explains the rights of the publican and his clientele, weeding out a few misconceptions along the way. He reveals that the 'public house' is not so public and that the licensee nearly always holds the upper hand.

But if we do not 'own' the pub, we are at least its clients and as such deserve the best of service. Is it unreasonable to request a clean drinking environment, even in the most basic pub? The laws on hygiene are specific and are there to protect the drinker. There can therefore be no support for publicans who allow their staff to smoke behind the bar, to dish out ice cubes with their hands and pat the dog between serving rounds. And is it really too much trouble to clear tables of overflowing ashtrays and floating beer mats, and equip toilets with soap and towels?

Not every pub has the scope to cater specifically for visitors with disabilities, though every publican has a duty to consider this. Perhaps the toilets are a no-go area, because of flights of steps or space restrictions, but why can't a ramp be fixed to one of the doorways to allow wheelchairs in? When most pubs pride themselves on holding charity events and constructing mountains of pennies for good causes, it is shameful just how many have a negative or indifferent attitude to disabled drinkers. What's that about charity beginning at home?

INFORMATION TECHNOLOGY

Sometimes, none of us can get in. The right of the publican to open and close within the set licensing hours is thoroughly respected, but why can't the opening hours be listed outside? This would prevent wasted hours sitting in the car park, wondering if and when a remote country pub is going to lift the latch. Information, as ever, is the key, and it's even more important inside the pub. Despite the law stating that it must be done, it's amazing just how many pubs refuse to display a price list. Would the offending publicans be happy to shop in a supermarket which didn't price its wares? The tradition of drinking in rounds, albeit sociable, tends to obscure the price of individual drinks, so it's imperative that a tariff is clearly visible to the customer.

ASK FOR A TOP-UP!

Together with cleanliness and information, value for money tops the list of customer grumbles in the *Good Beer Guide* postbag. Overpriced, freezer to microwave food is a familiar target, though it is not as angrily attacked as expensive, short-measured, mediocre pints. It seemed that the days of short measures were over when the Government announced that it intended to implement Section 43 of the Weights and Measures Act. This clause stipulates that a pint of beer equals a pint of liquid, with any froth or foam not counted in the measure. Sadly, the President of the Board of Trade, Michael Heseltine, succumbed to heavy lobbying by the brewers and backed away in November 1993. It is now legal for a publican to serve you with 95% beer and 5% froth. If you think you are getting a short measure, you can, according to Mr Heseltine, 'ask for a top-up'. One wonders how often he has tried that tactic in a busy pub at half-past ten on a Friday night.

Cleanliness, consideration, information and value for money: do we expect too much of our pubs? We don't think so.

TRUST THE LANDLORD

The Section 43 climbdown was portrayed as being in line with the Government's 'bonfire of red tape', stripping bureaucracy away from business and letting industry prosper. As a consumer organisation, CAMRA is concerned that such deregulation may work too much in favour of the industry and too much against the customer, as in the case of the full pint. But what is strange is that only certain aspects of licensing law have been deemed fit for deregulation. What about allowing pubs to stay open longer? What about allowing publicans to use their own discretion as to when to call time, instead of making justices enforce arcane licensing hours, especially on Sundays. You can now shop on a Sunday and Scottish landlords are trusted to open on Sunday afternoons, so does the Government not think English, Welsh and Northern Irish landlords are capable of running orderly houses, if they so wish? CAMRA is not campaigning for pubs to be compelled to open at all hours, rather for publicans who want to open to be allowed to do so.

The deregulation theme does not extend as far as children in pubs, either. Indeed, the Government has *introduced* regulation in this department, throwing open pub doors to children but making landlords apply for special certificates to admit them. Yet again, why not hand back control to the landlord and the parents. The landlord should be able to admit accompanied children, if he so wishes, and the parents should be able to decide whether they want their children to visit that particular pub. Why create a new layer of bureaucracy and a raft of new offences to monitor what is a perfectly acceptable arrangement elsewhere in the world?

PUB PROTECTION

CAMRA is a jealous organisation. It is jealous of the reputation of the British pub and recognises the unique position it holds in the world. That is why we continually urge our publicans to provide the service the pub deserves and call on the Government to help preserve the pub as an exceptional social amenity. These are worrying times, however, with many publicans close to the bread line, and both the Government and the brewing industry seemingly eager to shoot themselves in the foot. The Beer Orders of 1989 heralded major changes in the world of brewing. Traditional tenancies were scrapped by many brewers in favour of long lease arrangements for licensees, resulting in higher rents, higher beer prices, the exodus of dedicated publicans and the potential closure of thousands of pubs. The pub needs a lifeline and both the Government and the brewers can help. The most immediate and dramatic way in which the Government can assist is by cutting beer duty.

CLOSING THE FLOODGATES

January 1993 saw the introduction of new, generous allowances for the transportation of beer across European frontiers. As a result, as long as it's declared for 'personal use', anyone can bring back as much beer from France as they or their transit van can carry, and the reason so many people are doing so is the enormous price difference. The duty the French Government levies on its brewers is one-seventh that levied by our own Government on our brewers. On a pint at 5% ABV, the French pay 4p tax and we pay 30p. Consequently, it's one-way traffic for beer sales: millions of gallons of cheap French booze are pouring into Britain, enough, it has been estimated, to supply every pub in Kent or West Yorkshire for a year. The threat to pubs and the smaller breweries is self-evident, and the only way to curb abuse of the system is to remove the incentive, namely the huge price imbalance.

The Government must act to cut beer duty. CAMRA suggests that this should be done in three or four consecutive Budgets, removing, say, 5p beer tax a year until we arrive at the European beer duty average. Indeed, it would make economic sense for the Treasury to do so, as every can of beer which is bought in France delivers not one penny to the British coffers. Even the VAT on the sale goes to the French Government. One estimate has it that the Chancellor is losing around £160 million in revenue to the French beer trade. He could start to reclaim that money if people returned to our pubs instead of quaffing cheap Eurofizz in front of the TV, and our pubs would get the boost they need to stay alive.

CAMRA is at one with the big brewers on this issue, and shares their concern over brewing industry jobs and pub closures. Sadly, the biggest brewers have weakened their hand by lobbing another 5p or so on a pint in the last year. Whilst chastising the Government for keeping beer prices too high, the nationals have been cheerfully frightening away drinkers with yet another price hike. They should take a leaf out of the book of smaller breweries, many of whom have shelved price increases for the time being. If a cut in beer duty is forthcoming, the brewers have promised to pass on any saving directly to the customer. As a consumer group, CAMRA will be watching to ensure that they do.

CAMRA AND THE GOOD BEER GUIDE

All of the above provides ample evidence that there is as great a need as ever for an active consumer voice in the world of beer and pubs. When CAMRA was founded in 1971, it was in response to a tidal wave of brewery take-overs and closures, at a time when pubs were losing character and traditional British beer was on its deathbed. The big breweries were closing down small producers all across the country, choice was diminishing and, in place of much-loved beers brewed for local palates, nationally advertised, brewery processed, at best insipid, keg beers were finding their way onto the bar.

Thankfully, CAMRA won those initial battles. Real ale has regained its prominent position in British pubs and the pace of brewery rationalisation has slowed. The *Good Beer Guide* has been instrumental in bringing about this sea-change. First published in 1974, its primary purpose has been to champion real ale by guiding drinkers to pubs which serve traditionally-brewed beer in top quality condition. In the *Guide*, you will find around 5,000 pubs serving the best real ale in Britain, as well as full details of all breweries and brew pubs currently in operation.

All kinds of pub are featured, from thatched, rural hostelries to noisy, city boozers and they are selected for the *Guide* by CAMRA members. We do not employ inspectors to visit pubs once or twice before making up their minds, nor do we rely simply on reader recommendations. Our surveyors are real enthusiasts who use the pubs in their area all year-round and know just how consistently good or bad they are. The final list of entries for each area is drawn up at a selection meeting of the local CAMRA branch. No payment is ever taken for entry to the *Guide* and no advertising is accepted. Readers' views are, of course, always taken into account. Any recommendations or criticisms are forwarded to the local CAMRA branch and are carefully considered when choosing pubs. Correspondence is very much appreciated, so please continue to write.

All pubs are formally surveyed each year and all the information is checked and updated, right up to the very last minute. As with all guide books, changes are inevitable during the currency of the *Good Beer Guide* and some beers or facilities may be different on your visit. However, major amendments to pub entries are published throughout the year in *What's Brewing*, the monthly CAMRA newspaper, delivered free to all members (see page 528 for more membership details).

HOW THE ENTRIES ARE ARRANGED

Pubs are arranged alphabetically in counties, with English counties first, then Welsh, followed by Scottish regions, Northern Ireland and the offshore islands. All the Yorkshire counties are listed under Y, all the Glamorgans under G, both Sussexes under S and Greater London and Greater Manchester under L and M, respectively.

An at-a-glance guide to reading the pub entries is provided on the inside front cover of the *Guide*, with all the symbols for pub facilities explained. Where meals and accommodation are indicated, no assessment of quality is made, unless mentioned in the pub description. Only the pub's real ales are included, with beers listed by brewery, in alphabetical order. Where more than one beer is available from the same brewery, they are listed in increasing order of original gravity (approximate strength). Seasonal beers, like winter ales, are included but are clearly not available all year-round. Full details of all beers mentioned can be found in the breweries section, and the Beers Index will help to locate the information.

A BLOCKHOUSE ON THE HOME FRONT

Brian Glover looks back 50 years to the end of the Second World War, a conflict which ensured the place of the pub and the pint in the heart of the British people.

WHEN CHURCHILL uttered his wartime words 'This was their finest hour', he was not thinking about the brewing industry. But his famous quote applies just as much to the men and women behind the barrels and bars, as to those manning the barricades against Hitler's army.

And the Government knew it. During the Second World War, beer and those who served it were regarded as a vital morale-boosting part of the war machine. One contributor to the *Grimsby Evening Telegraph* in the dark days of July 1940, reflected a popular view when he wrote:

'The inn has become, since September, a thing of far greater significance than perhaps it has ever been ... it brings people together in a spirit of companionship and cements the common purpose. The inn is a blockhouse on the home front'.

THE TROOPS WERE ALREADY MARCHING TO THE BEAT OF THE BARREL BEFORE THE WAR, ACCORDING TO THIS BREWERS' SOCIETY POSTER OF 1937

This was a far cry from the official attitude in the First World War, when beer and public houses were seen as subversive, a dangerous fifth column inside the country to be imprisoned by regulations. The Defence of the Realm Act of 1914 (DORA) strictly controlled the trade. Licensing hours were curtailed, beer production cut back, prices increased and some pubs and breweries in sensitive military areas like Carlisle even taken over by the state. In part, some measures were justified, since, before 1914, drunkenness had been rife - hardly surprising when an average pint (price 2d) had a power-ful original gravity of 1052, the strength of a strong ale today. By 1918, the gravity had been slashed to 1039, where it remained.

TEMPERING TEMPERANCE

During the inter-war years, the brewing industry worked over-time to make the pub a respectable part of society. Spacious new houses were built with comfortable seating. One writer compared them to Carnegie libraries. Drinking dropped so much that the industry was forced to launch its own collective advertising campaign, *Beer is Best*, during the 1930s. With the drunk having almost staggered off the streets, the dry cries of the temperance lobby for severe restrictions once war was declared in 1939, fell on deaf ears. Lord Woolton, the Minister of Food, declared: 'It is because we are in the position of having a sober and temperate nation, that ... it is wise to allow the present production of beer to continue'.

MP Quintin Hogg firmly rebuffed his local lobby in Oxford:

'The Temperance Council must clearly understand that the national emergency is not a moment to introduce temperance propaganda under the cloak of national necessity. Beer is the inno-cent pleasure of many mil-lions, especially among those who bear the brunt today'. To further safeguard its position, the Brewers' Society donated its collective advertising space to the grateful Government during the war.

This did not mean that there were no restrictions on brewing - but only ones imposed by the growing shortage of materials, rather than any anti-drink policy. First sugar was cut, then malt and hops rationed. Maize and oat flakes found their way into the mash tun. Potatoes followed. At one time it looked as if the supply of hops might run out altogether – until Hitler's bombers dived to the rescue, as the *Brewing Trade Review* recorded in October 1940:

SOME BREWERIES WERE DESTROYED BY GERMAN AIR RAIDS DURING THE WAR, SUCH AS ROBSON'S OF SUNDERLAND AND TOMLINSON'S OF SHEFFIELD. FORTUNATELY, THIS BOMB, WHICH HIT THE ROOF OF GEORGE'S BREWERY IN BRISTOL, DID NOT EXPLODE, BUT JUST PLUNGED THROUGH THE ROOF, MUCH TO THE DISGUST OF THE HEAD BREWER (COURAGE ARCHIVE)

'There was, only a week or two back, considerable doubt whether more than a portion of the hop crop could be picked, owing to the difficulty of getting enough pickers

WOMEN REPLACED
MEN IN MANY
AREAS OF BREWING,
LIKE BOTTLING,
DURING THE WAR
(COURAGE ARCHIVE)

to enter the dangerous zones of Kent and
Sussex. It is, however, an ill wind that blows
nobody any good, and one of the effects of the
recent large-scale bombing attacks on London
has been a sudden change of attitude on the
part of those who normally spend their holidays picking hops, who have flocked to the
gardens as a refuge from their bombed neighbourhoods'.

Strength was slashed again to spin out supplies. Some wartime
beer was barely above the non-alcoholic level. The light bitter and
XX of Steward & Patteson of Norfolk, for instance, was produced
from a diluted original gravity of 1026. Greene King of Suffolk
produced one beer, either light or dark, at 1027.

To finance the massive war effort, excise duty on beer was
increased three times in the first 12 months of the conflict, and regularly thereafter, lifting the price from around 3d to 8d a pint. With
restricted petrol, and wood for crates and casks also severely limited,
beer supplies became erratic. As many key workers were called up
by the armed forces, breweries struggled to keep going, recalling
pensioners and bringing in women to keep the vital ale flowing.

BLITZED BREWERIES

Some were bombed out of brewing altogether. Robson's of
Sunderland was knocked out in an air-raid in 1941. Sheffield
suffered a double blow, with Rawson's Park Street Brewery and
Tomlinson's Anchor Brewery both destroyed. Whitbread's
Chiswell Street brewery, in the City of London, survived in a sea of
rubble, thanks to the bravery and efficiency of its own fire service.

When breweries were hit, their neighbours rallied around to
help. After Devenish's Weymouth brewery was put out of action
for two years, the next-door Grove's Brewery and Eldridge Pope
of Dorchester supplied their pubs. When Groves & Whitnall of
Salford was badly damaged, their Manchester rivals rushed to
their aid.

The Government was not happy when pubs shut because of
shortages, particularly since all other places of entertainment were

closed. Officials feared that the notice 'No Beer' hung in bar windows dented the spirit of the nation. The Home Intelligence Committee, anxiously monitoring morale, told the Cabinet in 1941 that shortages in Rugby 'appear to have more effect upon factory workers than any naval disaster; they interpret this shortage to mean that we are in a worse position than is being disclosed'.

Pubs were given priority. When Canterbury was heavily blitzed in two nights in 1942, Mackeson's lorries, with special police permission, were the only ones allowed on the scene the next morning, supplying their houses through the rubble. Many pubs were destroyed.

By 1944, it was estimated that 3,000 public houses had been bombed out of business. Many more battled against tremendous odds just to stay open.

Pubs also led the way in fundraising, with many landlords organising 'lend and defend' clubs. Altogether 10,000 war savings groups were set up in licensed premises, more than any other industry. Astonishing amounts were collected, one London suburban house raising £3,400 during War Weapons Week alone.

CASKS AWAY - STRONG'S ALE READY FOR LIFT-OFF TO THE TROOPS
(WHITBREAD ARCHIVE)

Some pubs became more directly involved in the conflict. The Bell at Sandwich had an anti-tank gun installed in one of its bathrooms. Others became the unofficial mess rooms of pilots, soldiers and sailors. A few gained official recognition. The White Hart at Salisbury was for a time the headquarters of Southern Command, while the walls of the Royal Hotel at Bideford, Devon, and the Golden Lion at Southwick in Hampshire protected many of the secrets of the D-Day landings in Normandy.

MORALE VICTORIES

Beer was seen as vital for the armed forces. A special committee was set up to supervise the supply of beer to the troops. 'I remember how the chaps (the fighter pilots) used to flock up to the mess at the end of each day's fighting, flop down on the hall floor, just as they were, straight from their aircraft, and call for their beer', recalled Air Vice Marshall Sir Cecil Bouchier, commander of the Hornchurch fighter section in the Battle of Britain. 'This was their one great relaxation, the beer they had dreamt about all day. Often a leader bringing his squadron home, fearful of being late, would radio from halfway across the channel - 'Keep the bar open, we'll be down in 20 minutes'.

Once the troops had landed in Normandy on D-Day, the ale followed. Two days after the first men hit the beaches, bitter from the Star Brewery of Eastbourne was flown out in specially adapted tanks mounted on a Hurricane. Casks of Strong's ale from Romsey were fixed under fighters' wings. Much more was shipped out in bottle, its value appreciated right at the top. Winston Churchill, in a note to the Secretary of State for War in 1944, following thirsty

MANY LANDLORDS HAD OTHER WARTIME DUTIES. JACK CLIFFE IS SEEN OFF FROM THE WAGGONERS, NEAR LONDON, BY HIS WIFE AND CUSTOMERS, AS HE GOES TO WORK AS AN OBSERVER, WATCHING FOR ENEMY PLANES (WHITBREAD ARCHIVE)

complaints from Italy, thundered: 'Make sure that the beer - four pints a week - goes to the troops under fire before any of the parties in the rear get a drop'.

Beer was almost as important as bullets, it seemed, when it came to defeating the enemy. And at home the pub was viewed as the first line of defence, the fortress protecting the nation's morale.

The conflict settled two scores. During the 1930s, Hitler had threatened in Europe and prohibition had been introduced in the United States. The war had routed them both, preventing either gaining a foothold in Britain. The *Brewing Trade Review* could confidently reflect as early as 1943: 'The war has broken up many old prejudices and dispelled many deep-rooted illusions. None, perhaps, has been more completely shattered than the idea that the devil lurks at the bottom of every glass of beer'.

Brian Glover is a former editor of CAMRA's newspaper, What's Brewing, and the author of many books on beer. His Prince of Ales - The History of Brewing in Wales won the gold tankard at the 1993 British Guild of Beer Writers awards.

ALE AND HEARTY

Wine may be fine, but beer can be better.
Susan Nowak abandons the wine list
and suggests some perfect beers for an
alternative dining experience.

T
O START, I'll have red onion tartlets with leek purée, followed by roast haunch of venison...and then the crème caramel.'

'And to drink, Madame?' Gold pen poised in immaculately white-gloved hand, he was all attentiveness... 'I think a spicy wheat beer just sour enough to offset the sweetness in the onions - Hoegaarden White, if you've got it. That touch of coriander won't come amiss.'

'Certainly, and might I suggest a vinous barley wine with the venison? Robinson's Old Tom, perhaps? Or something a little more rounded and mouth-filling? Bateman's Victory Ale is drinking well...'

Choices, choices. Port-like Old Tom packs the punch for well-hung game, but would Victory provide a better balance? 'I'll stick with Victory because it has to be Thomas Hardy's Silver Anniversary '93 with dessert.' That brittle burnt-butterscotch crust cries out for the toffee malt and bitter chocolate of this sensuous sip, but at 12% it might be a bit much after Old Tom. The beer waiter leant towards me conspiratorially: 'We still have a little Hardy '91...'

And then I woke up! But is it so eccentric to fancy the hop a serious alternative to the grape with food? Today's ale is a tipple of stunning variety and complexity, displaying all the character you demand to complement your dinner. From oat beer through to cherry beer, porter to pilsner, Xmas ale to IPA, mild to stout, barley wine to bitter; golden, amber, black, chestnut, syrupy, citric, hoppy, malty, yeasty, fruity, spicy, nutty ... truly, a beer for all seasons and all menus.

Beer as a food partner is more feasible as it becomes more available. Just as you once bunged a bottle of Beaujolais in the trolley, so you now find beer on the supermarket shelves. Slender, elegant vessels with wired 'champagne' corks jostle with neat little nips as chains like Oddbins lead the way. Cask-conditioned ales are just as accessible to the home gourmet, taken-away from the pub or brewery, so diners can

indulge their taste for draught and bottled all in the space of a meal.

Right, let's beckon the beer waiter. This is eclectic territory; forget any preconceptions along the lines of 'white with fish and poultry, red with meat.' Would you serve the same white wine with sole as with musky tuna? Does red equally partner a delicate pork escalope as it does roast leg and crackling? So it is with beer. There may be merit in launching a meal with a weaker bevy and 'working up' to a post-prandial barley wine instead of a brandy, but marrying flavour and texture matters more. Let's face it, even the strongest beers are weaker than most moderate wines. The highest gravity ale in the country, the aforementioned Hardy's, twice the strength of most bitters, is only just as strong as wine. And if you serve beer as it should be served with food, by the wine glass or tumbler instead of the tankard, potency is even less important.

WETTING THE APPETITE

Time for an aperitif. Go for either a piquant little number to get those juices flowing or, in contrast, a palate cleanser. A mild makes a good appetite rouser; dark Tetley Mild at only 3.2% has a hint of hops with a slightly nutty, dry finish that could take the place of sherry - or Harvey's delicate XX Mild might titillate the tastebuds. If you want something more astringent, try Ridleys IPA with its lightly lemon opening and bitter finish. Très chic is bottled Jenlain French bière de garde blonde. Chilled slightly, it effervesces up champagne flutes like the real thing, and sweetly elusive vanilla undertones make it a great 'pudding wine', too.

Starters don't necessarily demand a restrained beer. Again, be guided by the dish itself. Blander soups, light fish mousses and avocado might well indicate staying with a creamy, dry mild, or choose a delicately hoppy and flowery brew. A more robust first course - rich liver pâté, duck terrine, game soup or earthy fungus -

13

wants something with a bit more welly, like the dark malty fruitiness and bitter finish of Palmers Tally Ho! or the full taste found in Young's Special. In a bottle, I could happily settle for a glass of peppery Chimay White from Belgium.

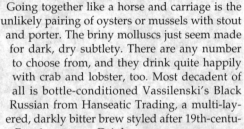

Going together like a horse and carriage is the unlikely pairing of oysters or mussels with stout and porter. The briny molluscs just seem made for dark, dry subtlety. There are any number to choose from, and they drink quite happily with crab and lobster, too. Most decadent of all is bottle-conditioned Vassilenski's Black Russian from Hanseatic Trading, a multi-layered, darkly bitter brew styled after 19th-century Russian stouts. Drink it in a large wine glass with your oysters - and it's equally handsome with steak and smoked oyster pie. My husband likes the dry flavour with beef, but, in my view, our traditional Sunday roast calls for an English bitter - or perhaps specifically a Yorkshire bitter, for the sake of the pud - such as the full-mouthed and fruity Timothy Taylor Landlord. Who needs Burgundy!

Fish calls for a little finesse on the ale front. White fillets might benefit from a delicate dry bitter with citrus undertones; Hook Norton's Best at 3.3% comes to mind. Cod in beer batter or a thick haddock steak wants a rounded bitter like Marston's. As for smoked haddock kedgeree, the bottled IPA from Ushers is complex and spicy enough to oblige. It might well go with real curries, too, though there is some merit in the assertion of an Asian publican in the West Midlands that M&B Mild is best with Balti.

A PINT OF COOKING

I never feel any obligation to drink the same beer with a dish as I have used in preparing it, especially as cooking alters its character. Game marinated in a chewy, coffee-toned mild might produce a pie that calls for a barley wine; lamb braised with apricots in a fruity bitter needs something a little more tannic alongside. But I was sold on pork hock slowly turned to deep toffee crispness in Schneider's wheat beer, Aventinus from Bavaria, served with more of the aromatic same - and German wheat beers, especially those with a smoky tang, are marvellous with their sausages and sauerkraut.

Devotees of duck with cherry could forget the sauce and instead drink Lindemans bottled pink kriek from Belgium, also luscious with dessert - contrarily enough with plain chocolate mousse. Equally at home with duck or goose is something weighty and vinous enough to cut across the grease - Theakston Old Peculier springs to mind, or even Harvey's bottled Elizabethan barley wine.

Beer is at its best with cold cuts. Slices of ham with their sweet saltiness are superb with a bittersweet beer sporting a dry edge, especially if the rind has been scored and caramelised in a treacly beer. Ringwood's Old Thumper with pork pie and beer mustard is sheer bliss!

Vegetarians might look to Ross's organic Saxon Strong Ale (also bottled), while beautifully-balanced Golden Promise from Caledonian, using 100% organic malted barley, could be right for a cheese and onion quiche. A nut roast with chestnuts finds its mate in a sweetish fruit 'n' nuts taste like Adnams Broadside, and a simple bubble and squeak goes with a medium bitter. When you slow cook red cabbage with nutmeg and cinnamon you might match it with the mixed spice of a winter ale.

FINISHING TOUCHES

'Pudding beers' stretch from a palely zestful Belgian framboise with tart fruit desserts to the coffee and chocolate tones in creamy milds with vanilla ice-cream. Fruity, dark ales, like Marston's Owd Rodger, go with bread pudding, and the stout used to soak the raisins in rich fruit cake drinks with it, too. Burton Bridge bottle-conditioned Porter is perfect with treacle pud, or try a light, pale bitter with citrus notes for lemon meringue.

With cheese you can indulge in the heavyweights. The roundness of farmhouse mature Cheddar is complemented by the biscuity finish of Elgood's Winter Warmer, or heavenly, mahogany-hued Chiltern's Three Hundreds Old Ale (bottled). With Stilton you want to echo port and find it triumphantly in Gibbs Mew Bishop's Tipple at 6.5% and Young's Winter Warmer - serve it in a port glass and fool your guests.

After all this, what could be better than to stretch your toes towards the fire with an after-dinner tipple - S&N's Gordons Highland Scotch Ale (imported from Belgium) for malt whisky lovers; McMullen's Stronghart, 'liquid Christmas pudding'; Chiltern's Bodgers Barley Wine at 8.5%; Woodforde's Headcracker at 7% to make you mellow; or Courage's bottle-conditioned Imperial Russian Stout, matured in oak casks, flirting with liquorice, dark fruit, bitter chocolate and hops, but ending like angels dancing on your tongue?

Susan Nowak is author of CAMRA's Good Pub Food,
a guide to pubs which serve the best food as well as real ale.
It is available from all good bookstores, or direct from
CAMRA (post-free) at £9.95

15

YOU, THE PUB AND THE LAW

We all think we know our rights as pub customers. But just what do we know? *Peter Coulson* has been called to the bar and has the facts.

THESE DAYS, it's the bar room rather than the barrack room which provides scope for amateur lawyers. Much pontification over a pint in my local on 'common law rights' and so on. A tremendous amount of misinformation, as it's now called, is issued with the gravitas that only the true amateur can muster when he doesn't know what the hell he's talking about. It's been my job to sort it all out on both sides of the bar. So here, for what it's worth (if only to settle a few arguments), is a quick guide to the main bones of contention between Mine Host and his friendly customers.

RIGHTS, WHAT RIGHTS?

Contrary to the expectations of a vast majority of the drinking fraternity, a public house is not a public place, and you cannot demand entry or demand to be served. The holder of the licence is entitled to accept or reject whoever he pleases, subject to statutory controls on discrimination. But even these will not cover the stroppy customer, of whatever race or sex. If the landlord says 'you're barred', you are. For the technically-minded, the contract of sale is only made when the trader accepts the offer to purchase made by the customer. Up to that point, opening the doors of the pub is termed an 'invitation to treat' and does not bind the publican to serve you, even if you're wearing a tie and have the money for a pint.

What about the obligations of an innkeeper? It is true that such a mortal 'shall not unreasonable refuse to accommodate travellers', but this obligation applies mainly to hotels and premises offering both board and lodging, not to your local when you pop in for a pint. Commuters calling in at the Railway Hotel on their way home from the office are not entitled thereby to call for instant service and hay for the horse. Nor can you demand a glass of water. This is an interesting extension of the requirement for holders of restaurant or residential licences to have 'suitable beverages, including drinking water' available for customers. But nothing in the statute binds a publican to offer free water, though many do, if asked nicely. Neither do you have the right to use the pub loos, if you are not a customer. There is no condition on a pub licence requiring landlords to supplement local authority conveniences.

So what rights does a customer have? I don't think landlords would welcome customers who come in with confrontation in mind, so I'm not giving any hostages to fortune. You have a right to be treated fairly and to be supplied with exactly what you ask for, or told why not. So the law covers adequate information on quantities, strengths, prices and hygiene. It is the job of the local trading standards officer or environmental health department to check and monitor these matters, and if you are really dissatisfied with your treatment, you can take a trip to the Town Hall to complain. But you should only do this if there is a real problem, not a minor blip.

MEASURES

The law on draught beer and cider measures has been yo-yoing in the last couple of years, and has now been firmly settled in limbo. In fact, you are allowed to receive 95% of a pint, plus a head, unless you are in a pub with metered dispense, in which case you get a full pint, plus or minus six millilitres. But if you are not satisfied with the hand-pumped quantity, you may ask for it to be topped up, which request should not be unreasonably refused. From 1 January 1995, the old 'sixth of a gill' for spirit measures will have been ousted, to make way for the metric measures of 25 ml (slightly more than a sixth) and 35 ml (mainly for Scotland). The quantity should be marked on the automatic pourer. Remember that this only applies to gin, rum, vodka and whisky. Other spirits are not controlled.

PRICES AND HYGIENE

The law maintains that the product sold must be 'of the nature, substance and quality' demanded by the purchaser, and, as beer is classified as 'food', all the food regulations apply to the bar. So, you can expect a clean glass every time, a beer that is drinkable and the one coming from the pump should be what the label states, at the strength which is correct for the product. As far as price is concerned, the current regulations require a 'representative' list of products (which need not be more than 30) to be shown with their unit price and their alcohol by volume. In fact, all pump clips should now give ABV information to comply with labelling regulations. Some give original gravities (OGs) as well, although this is not a legal requirement. You should be able to check on a list which is immediately available whether you have been correctly charged. A price list must be on view to customers, not just behind the bar for staff. Food hygiene laws also require bar staff to refrain from smoking while they are handling 'food'. So the device of stepping through the bar door to smoke on the customer's side is simply not good enough.

DISCRIMINATION

The management of a famous wine bar in Fleet Street bore the brunt of feminist ire some years ago when they refused to amend their house rule that ladies would only be served at tables and could not stand at the bar. They lost their case, and with it went 'men only' bars. Workingmen's and golf clubs are now the last bastions of legal anti-female prejudice, but I understand that even this is weakening. More recently, a publican received a dressing down for refusing to serve pints to women - the sex discrimination rules outlaw making a distinction in service purely on the grounds of sex. However, bar staff must by law refuse to serve you if they think you are drunk, or getting that way. They face a serious penalty if they continue to provide you with liquor: it's not merely the fact that you may get violent and smash the place up. So read this sober and you may just remember it when you are pleading for your eighth pint.

HOURS

The day of the 24-hour pub is still a long way off and, meanwhile, Sid and his staff are entitled to some time off, if they can prise you out of the premises. Currently, permitted hours in England and Wales are fixed by the Government and on weekdays are from 11am to 11pm, and on Sundays from 12 noon until 3pm and then from 7pm to 10.30pm. However, these can be 'nudged' by the local licensing bench, either generally by allowing an extra hour from 10am in the morning, or specifically over holiday periods, when they might grant one or two extensions. There's no national system of bank holiday extensions. Some clever catering pubs get a restaurant extension to cover the Sunday afternoon break, but you must take a meal. The same goes for the extra restaurant hour from 11pm to midnight on weekdays and from 10.30 to 11.30pm on Sundays. There is no obligation on a licensee to open all these hours, and no right for a customer to thump on the door to demand service. Similarly, there's no obligation for a publican to put a notice as to his hours of opening outside the premises, though many do for the information of potential patrons. Although the general licensing hours in Scotland are now broadly similar (11 to 11 on weekdays and 12.30 to 2.30pm and 6.30 until 11pm on Sundays), a system of 'regular extensions' has been widely used to create even further extended hours. In addition, the so-called night club extension (until 2am on weekdays; 3am in central London) can apply to some pubs which provide entertainment.

A couple more myths take a bashing. There is no legal duty on the landlord to call 'last orders', and you can't complain if, when you get to the bar, he refuses to serve you. Nor can you query the time on his clock, because, as mentioned earlier, he has no obligation to serve you anyway. If you have managed to get in a last pint, you'll want to know how long you've got to finish it. There are, in fact, two drinking up times in operation for all public houses. The licensee must stop serving at the terminal hour, whether the drink has been paid for or not (because it is the 'supply' which is illegal). Customers may then consume drinks without penalty for 20 minutes in England and Wales, or 15 minutes in Scotland. Thereafter, it is the customer, not the landlord, who commits an offence. However, if the drink is supplied as an ancillary to a meal, anywhere in the premises (not just in a restaurant), the diner has 30 minutes drinking up time. The same rule applies in Scotland.

The reason Mine Host turns off all the lights, Hoovers your legs and lets Fang out of the cellar is to avoid being found guilty of 'aiding and abetting' your wickedness. There is no direct offence of permitting consumption outside hours. The only people allowed either to purchase or consume drinks during non-permitted hours are residents, the holder of the licence or the manager of the premises. Non-resident staff cannot buy drinks for themselves or friends, nor can you put money behind the bar during normal time to pay for late drinks. More licences are lost through allowing 'lates' than for any other reason.

MINORS

What about kids? There are now two types of pubs catering for families - the traditional ones with a children's room, patio or garden where everyone can sit and drink together, and those with a new-style children's certificate, which allows youngsters under 14 into the bar. There may be an evening curfew imposed by the justices, so be prepared to be asked to move, if you're in late. There's no obligation to take a meal, but you may be required to sit in a semi-dining area. Remember also that the landlord sets the rules, and if he doesn't want Jimmy on a bar stool or playing the fruit machine, then you must comply. Normally, children under 14 are prohibited from bars, and both parents and landlord can be prosecuted. They can pass through a bar to reach the toilets or some other area, however, and they can stay in a part of the bar that's exclusively used for meals. Between 14 and 18 they can sit in the bar (again, at the landlord's behest) and may consume non-alcoholic drinks. Do not buy them alcohol for consumption in a bar. You may find yourself in court. The publican has the right to refuse service to anyone he considers looks under 18. There is no redress. An identity card may help, but has no legal authority. If he is in doubt, he won't serve.

YOUR RESPONSIBILITIES

So landlords have rights too? You wouldn't expect me to be anything but even-handed, would you? Yes, they do, and customers have certain legal responsibilities. Basically, you contract to behave yourself and not become drunk, quarrelsome or disorderly, at which point he can turf you out. If you refuse to go, he can call the police to have you ejected. You can be prosecuted for consuming after hours, buying a drink for someone who is drunk, being drunk, betting or gaming on licensed premises and several other offences. When you book a restaurant table, for example, you are making a binding contract. If you fail to turn up, the proprietor can sue you for the loss of profit, where he can show that he turned away other customers because of your reservation. The same would be true if you hired a room, or he prepared a buffet and you cancelled at the last minute.

If you have read this far, you will recognise what a complex set of laws and regulations govern the running of public houses. And you might have a little more patience and respect for the poor souls who have to remember them in case some officious copper or pompous magistrate hauls them over the coals. Happy drinking!

Peter Coulson LL.B is a specialist on licensing law and contributes regularly to The Publican and The Licensee and Morning Advertiser. He is also Secretary of the British Guild of Beer Writers.

BREWING - IN A NUTSHELL

ALL BEERS ARE DIFFERENT. Each brew has its own character: the result of a finely-honed recipe, or the unique touch a brewer brings to his work. Malts - pale or dark, hops - bitter or aromatic, water - varying in mineral content, and yeasts - distinctive to each brewery, all add their influence to the flavour of beers. Over 1,000 different real ales are now brewed in the UK, yet they are all produced in basically the same way, using the same, relatively simple brewing process. Of course, equipment varies from brewery to brewery, from Heath Robinson systems to high-tech machinery, but this, in a nutshell, is how brewing takes place.

THE INGREDIENTS

MALT: Malt is barley which has been partially germinated to release the sugars held inside. These sugars are vital to the flavour of the beer and its fermentability. The malt is also kilned, or baked, to prevent germination continuing, and the degree of kilning affects its taste. Heavily kilned malt turns dark and chocolatey, and can be used for dark, bitter beers; gentler treatment results in lighter, more delicate malts, ideal for paler, subtler brews. Sometimes extra sugars are added to build up the fermentability of the brew and other cereals are also used in brewing. The Germans specialise in wheat beers, for instance, but in the UK, too, cereals like maize are added to help provide a fuller head on the pint. Malt extract, a commercially-prepared, treacly derivative, is often used by the smallest breweries and brew pubs to save the labour and expense of full-mash brewing.

HOPS: The hop is an intriguing plant, a wild-running relative of the nettle which is cherished in brewing circles for its varied qualities. Primarily, it adds bitterness to beer, but it also acts as a preservative and helps prevent protein haze. It provides aromas and tastes which vary from the spicy to the floral. Various species of hop are used in British brewing, the most common being Fuggles (for bitterness) and Goldings (for aroma), and they may be added at various stages of brewing. Many brewers now use hop pellets or, more controversially, hop oils instead of whole hop flowers.

WATER: Known as liquor in the trade, water is the primary ingredient of beer. Some breweries use their own spring water; others use mains supplies. However, many ensure that the water is treated before brewing, to guarantee the correct chemical balance for the beer. One trend is to Burtonise the water, in other words to recreate the mineral composition of the water of Burton upon Trent, home of the world's finest pale ales. It was Burton's gypsum-heavy water which made it such a brewing Mecca.

YEAST: Each brewery maintains its own distinctive yeast strain. Yeast is a single-celled fungus which digests the sweet sugars in the brew and turns them into alcohol and carbon dioxide. Use a differ-

How Real Ale Is Brewed

A step-by-step guide to the technicalities of brewing

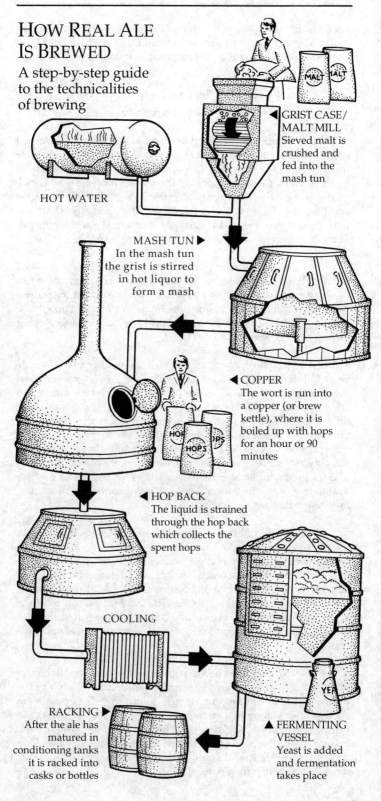

HOT WATER

GRIST CASE/ MALT MILL
Sieved malt is crushed and fed into the mash tun

MASH TUN ▶
In the mash tun the grist is stirred in hot liquor to form a mash

◀ COPPER
The wort is run into a copper (or brew kettle), where it is boiled up with hops for an hour or 90 minutes

◀ HOP BACK
The liquid is strained through the hop back which collects the spent hops

COOLING

RACKING ▶
After the ale has matured in conditioning tanks it is racked into casks or bottles

▲ FERMENTING VESSEL
Yeast is added and fermentation takes place

21

ent yeast in a beer and you will invariably end up with a different taste. Move a yeast to a new environment and its character changes. It's as delicate an organism as that, and it is vital to the identity of a brewery.

THE BREWING PROCESS

1. Sieved malt is crushed in the grist case and malt mill.

2. The grist (crushed malt) is fed into a mash tun, where it is steeped and stirred in hot liquor for an hour or two, to form a porridge-like mash. (Lager brewers may use a more complicated 'decoction' system, which involves pumping the mash from vessel to vessel, gradually increasing the heat.) The mash is strained through the grist and the sweet liquid which is run off is called wort. To extract any remaining sugars, the grist is sprayed – or sparged – with hot water. The grist is then spent and is taken away for animal fodder.

3. The wort is run into a copper (or brew kettle), where it is boiled up with hops for an hour or 90 minutes. The hops may be introduced at various stages and some sugar may be added to increase the fermentability. After boiling, the liquid is strained through the hop back (which collects the spent hops) and cooled, before being passed into the fermenting vessels.

4. Yeast is added (pitched) and fermentation takes place. An ale yeast (top-fermenting) sits on top of the wort, whilst a lager yeast (bottom-fermenting) sinks to the bottom. (Lager fermentation also takes place at a much lower temperature than that for ales and lasts up to a couple of weeks longer.) After a few days of primary fermentation, most of the yeast is removed and the beer is allowed to mature for a while in separate conditioning tanks (much longer for lager styles). Some yeast is reprocessed for future brews; the rest is sold for products like Marmite. The yeast which remains in the beer continues to work in the conditioning tanks, rounding off most of the harsher flavours.

5. Real ale is left unfiltered and, with some finings (an extract from the sturgeon fish) added to make the yeast settle and clear the beer, it is racked into casks (or bottles). Some sugar is sometimes included to encourage a strong secondary fermentation and extra hops may be added for aroma (dry hopping). Keg beers (and most British-brewed lagers) are chilled, filtered and pasteurised at this stage, before being racked into pressurised containers (kegs). (Continental-brewed lagers are filtered to remove solids, but are not always pasteurised.)

6. The real ales are dispatched to pub cellars for secondary fermentation (cask-conditioning) before serving (at around 55°F/13°C) by use of a simple handpump, an electric pump, by air pressure (in Scotland), or simply by opening the tap on the cask (gravity). No extra gas is needed. Keg beers and British lagers are dead, do not mature any further, and can be served immediately, often after flash cooling. However, they do need to be pumped to the bar by carbon dioxide (hence their fizzy nature).

A BEER FOR ALL SEASONS

Suddenly, quality is back in fashion. Brewers have been bending over backwards to offer drinkers unusual, limited-edition beers, with the emphasis on prime ingredients. *Roger Protz* reviews a year of remarkable special brews.

BRITAIN NOW HAS a beer for all seasons. The once staid world of mild and bitter, with winter warmers for the Christmas period, has been embellished and enlivened by a flood of new beers. Brewers are dusting off ancient recipes and generating new ones in a rush to produce a plethora of brews that are seasonal or occasional. The thinking behind the development is the need to get people back into pubs, to cash in on the now inexorable rise of cask ale, and to generate interest in the subject of beer.

The pace was set by Marston's, brewers of the famous Pedigree Bitter. Head brewer Paul Bayley, who deserves the praise of every beer lover for his commitment to the Burton Union system of fermentation, has produced a wide portfolio of new ales, the most successful of which may become regular brews. His Head Brewer's Choice has included a mild, a porter, a stout and a magnificently sulphurous India Pale Ale, Burton brewing at its best.

IPA FEVER

The interest in genuine IPAs has been one of the most fascinating developments. Prompted by CAMRA and the British Guild of Beer Writers, many brewers have turned to old brewery books and recreated the great pale ales that made Britain the powerhouse of brewing in the 19th century.

Carlsberg-Tetley's Burton brewery has named its new pilot brewhouse after its founder, Samuel Allsopp, who, legend claims, brewed beer in a teapot in the last century in an attempt to produce a pale ale. The company no longer has recipes dating back that far but its recent Samuel Allsopp's IPA was based on a 1935 brew. At 4.4% alcohol, it had a pleasing amber colour, a flowery hop aroma from traditional Fuggles and Goldings, tart citric fruit in the mouth and a refreshing, bittersweet finish. Ushers of Trowbridge has also joined the IPA fray with a bottled beer which, though pasteurised, has a powerful peppery hops aroma and a deep fruity and hoppy palate.

THINKING BEER

Two centuries ago, Whitbread became a famous brewing name as a result of porter, but it also turned a hand to pale ale as fashions changed in Victorian Britain. In 1994, the group's splendidly traditional Castle Eden Brewery in County Durham brewed an impressively hoppy and tangy IPA as part of a series of new occasional ales labelled 'The Beer Thinkers - New Classics from Whitbread'. Behind the portentous title lies a massive market research initiative that has concluded that ale needs the excitement and élan of New World wines if it is to appeal to a new generation of drinkers. Whitbread launched its new breed with Glorious Goldings (4%). As the name implies, it used Goldings hops, and the company described the beer as 'a single varietal hop ale'. It was also made exclusively from Maris Otter barley, a tried and trusted variety that has been overtaken in recent years by new breeds that produce more per acre. Many regional brewers have remained faithful to Otter but all the big brewers rejected it on the grounds of increased cost, which worked out at a fraction of a penny a pint. It is good to see it once again in a Whitbread mash tun as the group chooses quality rather than quantity.

Glorious Goldings, an appealing pale gold-coloured beer, packed with tart, citric character from the hops, has, by now, been followed by varietal brews using Czech Saaz and English Fuggles hops, with more beers to come in 1995. As with Marston's, beers that find particular favour may become regular brews.

AROUND BRITAIN

Regional brewers, too, have hurried to join the scramble for new beers. McMullen launched its series of Special Reserve ales and Ushers announced a new range of seasonal beers, starting with a spring ale that used 25% oat malt in its make-up. Bateman and Eldridge Pope, spotting the burgeoning success of Belgian and German wheat beers, brought out their own versions in cask-conditioned form. Both Robinson's of Stockport and Gale's of Hampshire produced new ales - Frederic's and Gold - that were pale gold in colour. Perhaps they had noticed the success of Whitbread's Boddingtons Bitter and felt that lager-coloured beers were the best way to appeal to a younger generation bored with fake European fizz. Fuller's, too, introduced a pale summer ale and Gale's has also started its own beer club, offering a series of special, limited-edition brews to licensees who join.

Whatever the motives, brewers are providing greater choice and variety for cask beer drinkers. They have learned from CAMRA that getting people to discuss beer is the best way to boost enjoyment. Information about ingredients and the aromas and flavours to be teased out from beer remove ale from the dangerous minefields of wine snobbery and take the drink to a wider and more appreciative audience. In spite of the best efforts of chancellors and bootleggers, 1994 proved to be a good year for beer, with more fresh brews on the horizon in 1995.

Roger Protz is editor of What's Brewing, CAMRA's monthly newspaper, and the author of many books on beer and pubs.

THE BAD BEER GUIDE

Ever been served a lousy pint but not
known why it was so undrinkable?
Just how can you complain to ignorant bar
staff? Should we simply put up with bad
beer and abysmal service? *Keith Thomas*
has the answers.

I T MAY SEEM UNLIKELY, but, somewhere in the country,
there must be a training centre for incompetent bar staff,
especially aimed at the *Fawlty Towers* of the beer world. If
not, how else can the extent of bad service and cellarmanship be
explained?

At this institution, staff are probably given instruction in the
best ways of ruining a pint of well-produced cask ale, and in the
fastest ways to alienate customers. Specialist courses possibly
address more complex skills such as short measuring and the intri-
cacies of returning waste beer back into the cask. And homework is
no doubt centred on developing proficiency in verbal abuse.

To gauge the success of this institution one has only to enter a
pub which has grudgingly installed handpumps in response to
financial inducements rather than a desire to promote better beer.
The first indication that all is not well comes when, at a request for
a pint of bitter, bar staff reach for a line of half-filled glasses lurking
in the vicinity of the beer engine. At best, these glasses are likely to
contain beer line drainings from earlier cleaning; at worst, they
could be the residue from a previously dissatisfied customer. With
the briefest of top-ups from the handpump, a head is added and
the pint offered. Naturally, this should be refused. Such cre-
ations will undoubtedly be warm, flat and oxidised – and only fit
for the sink. Freshness is a transient and precious character which
should not be sacrificed for the sake of a publican's ignorance and
meanness. Once a beer is exposed to the air, a number of important
flavours are quickly lost, particularly hoppiness which sharply
degenerates as a beer ages. When present, hoppiness does indicate
that a bitter is fresh and well-kept, and negligible hop aroma suggests a poor rotation of stock at the very least. More likely, poor
hop flavour results from low sales, with casks left open too long
(which also causes loss of condition, or fizz). However, bear in
mind that not all styles have a strong, pungent hop character and
make allowances accordingly.

A WARM WELCOME

Further faults may be found in the beer's temperature. One particularly obvious, but common, sin is to use a fresh glass straight
from the dishwasher. While cleanliness is admirable, a steaming
hot glass not only warms up the contents but encourages oxidation

and flavour loss. UHT milk is bad enough, but boiled beer is fit only for shampoo. A less evident, but more subtle, fault is the serving of warm beer which has sat in the lines through a hot afternoon. Ideally, beer should reach the glass at cellar temperature, i.e. 11-13°C. Bar temperature is usually between 18 and 25°C and will rapidly warm up beer lying in uninsulated pipes. When this happens, all manner of flavours may change, giving the beer a stale and insipid character somewhat akin to tepid tea. For rounds containing pints and halves, to reduce the effect of heat, a pint should always be served before a half. In a perfect world, a slow moving beer would be regularly pulled through the lines in any case, just to keep it in peak condition.

CLOUDING OVER

Before paying for a pint, quickly check its clarity. This will indicate whether the beer has been handled correctly in the cellar and whether it might be infected. Real ale contains live yeast and does have the potential to be served cloudy. However, a very yeasty pint will have a quite different taste from a clear one and should be refused, and any excuses about it being 'natural' or a 'healthier pint' should be rejected. Some beers such as continental wheat styles are intended to be served cloudy, but this does not apply to real ale, which contains finings to clear the beer. In most cases, cloudy beer is the result of poor cellar control and usually indicates that the cask has been started too soon. In a few instances, cloudiness may result from settled casks being disturbed in the cellar, usually because of bad positioning. So, if you are served with a yeasty beer (often detectable by a background flavour of Marmite), request a replacement brand and, if that carries a similar hue, seek an alternative venue.

OFF FLAVOURS

Occasionally, cloudy beer results from infection with bacteria or wild yeasts. These micro-organisms are a brewer's nightmare but are not infrequently a publican's way of life, since they grow particularly well in dirty cellars. They can also produce some pretty undesirable flavours, ranging from parsnip, sweetcorn and toffee (not to be confused with caramel from crystal malt), to sulphury or drain-like smells and, worst of all, the distinctive aroma of stale sweat. Certain beer styles may deliberately exhibit such flavours, arising from traditional yeast activity and handling, but, with experience of beer types, drinkers can quickly identify a rogue pint. Acetic and lactic acid are the most common indicators of bacterial infection. They may be confused with bitterness by the unwary, and also by misleading bar staff. To learn to recognise acid infection try gargling with diluted vinegar. Convincing sceptical bar staff is a different matter, though, and it is indeed a persuasive complainant who can induce the manager to sample the condiment tray in the interests of adjudication.

One of the most intriguing off flavours found in bad beer is that of a phenolic or TCP character, giving rise to a beer more at home in a hospital than a pub. This flavour is not detected equally by different people, meaning that a faulty beer may be acceptable to many drinkers but an abomination to a few. As a result, the oft-repeated excuse that 'no one else has complained' carries some credence here, but the beer should still be replaced.

Indeed, excuses for bad beer are legion and are no doubt worthy of special attention on the training course. 'It's fresh today' is a common euphemism for a week-old cask being reconnected after more recent casks have run out. Local experts are quickly called into disputes over beer quality. 'Albert's been drinking Pancreatic Porter for 50 years' is a common cry, usually resulting in Albert downing most of your pint without contributing positively to the debate. 'It's always like that - sulphury like' is a good way of directing attention back to the brewery and allows the barman to sneer at the customer's 'ignorance'.

Sadly, however, although some beers are outstandingly bad, many are just off-colour, possibly due to a slight over-ageing or a degree of adulteration caused by adding slops back to the cask. Such mixing of beers is impossible to detect from the bar, but keep an eye out for part-filled buckets or sleight of hand with unfinished pints, particularly at closing time. Only beer drawn through pipes whilst cleaning, or lost in tapping, may be returned to the cask. Anything already in a drip tray should go straight into the sink.

Finally, should you meet your match in an honours graduate of the bad beer school, and decide that the pint you looked forward to just wasn't up to it, vote with your feet. There are some 5,000 excellent beer pubs in this guide alone, and plenty of other pubs where service with a smile is not a thing of the past. But, before you leave, do remember to dispose of any remnants in a suitable receptacle. You wouldn't want them joining the queue beside the drip tray, would you?

Dr Keith Thomas is Director of Brewlab, a specialist laboratory and training service for breweries, based at the University of Sunderland. He also devised the Good Beer Guide's system of tasting notes.

THE BAD BEER CHECKLIST

APPEARANCE	LIKELY CAUSE
Warm to the taste	Slow turnover, warm beer lines
Warm to the touch	Newly washed glass
Flat and insipid – lacks expected character	Old cask
Hazy (but fresh taste – often apples or sulphur)	Possibly fresh cask still to settle
Cloudy (often with undesirable tastes)	Yeast/bacteria in suspension; old cask
Unusual/undesirable tastes (sour, parsnip, celery, sweat)	Bacterial infection
Other unusual/undesirable tastes (TCP, sewers, woody, plastic, creosote)	Wild yeast infection

HAVE GUIDES, WILL TRAVEL

ANYONE who finds the *Good Beer Guide* a useful ally on British beer hunts will be pleased to discover its two sister publications, the *Good Beer Guide to Belgium and Holland*, and the *Good Beer Guide to Munich and Bavaria*.

Seasoned travellers will know that, however fond we are of our classic British ales, good beer is truly international. The Low Countries are amazing hunting grounds, offering a mind-boggling variety of beer styles which range from mysterious, rich monastic brews to quirky wild yeast and fruit beers. Tim Webb's *Good Beer Guide to Belgium and Holland* (£9.99) is now in its second edition, fully updated and providing details of all the two countries' breweries and their best bars.

Joining it on the bookshelves is the *Good Beer Guide to Munich and Bavaria* (£8.99), by CAMRA founder member Graham Lees, who has lived in southern Germany for many years. This is likely to prove an invaluable travelling companion for those visiting the world's greatest beer drinking region, with all its colourful brews and larger than life beer festivals.

Both titles are available from good bookstores, or direct from CAMRA at 34 Alma Road, St Albans, Herts. AL1 3BW (post-free) - tel. (01727) 867201. Discounts are available for CAMRA members.

Avon

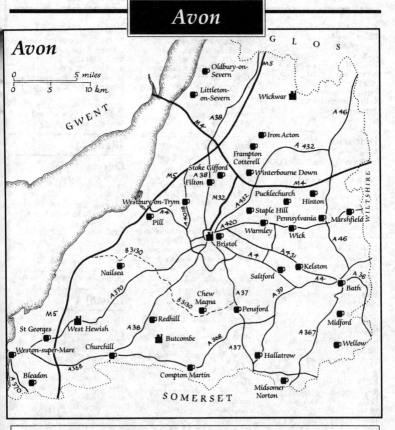

Avon

0 — 5 miles
0 — 5 — 10 km

G L O S

GWENT

Oldbury-on-Severn
Littleton-on-Severn
Wickwar
Iron Acton
Frampton Cotterell
Winterbourne Down
Stoke Gifford
Filton
Pucklechurch
Hinton
Westbury-on-Trym
Staple Hill
Pennsylvania
Marshfield
Pill
Warmley
Wick
Bristol
Kelston
Nailsea
Saltford
Bath
Chew Magna
Pensford
Midford
St Georges
West Hewish
Redhill
Weston-super-Mare
Churchill
Butcombe
Wellow
Bleadon
Compton Martin
Hallatrow
Midsomer Norton

WILTSHIRE

SOMERSET

Butcombe, Butcombe; **Hardington, Hope & Anchor**, Bristol; **RCH**, West Hewish; **Ross, Smiles**, Bristol; **Wickwar**, Wickwar

---

Bath

Bell Inn
103 Walcot Street
☎ (01225) 460426
11.30–11
Courage Best Bitter, Directors; Fuller's London Pride; Greene King Abbot; Smiles Best Bitter, Exhibition H
Open-plan bar renowned for its jazz and soul music. Games include chess and backgammon.
❀ ♣

Belvedere
25 Belvedere, Lansdown Road
☎ (01225) 330264
12–3, 5.30–11
Bass Charrington IPA, Draught Bass H
Welcoming, unpretentious local with a quiet lounge bar.
Q ⊕ ♣

Bladud Arms
Gloucester Road, Lower Swainswick (A46)
☎ (01225) 420152
11–3, 7–11
Draught Bass; Butcombe Bitter; Marston's Pedigree; Wadworth 6X; Wickwar Brand Oak; guest beer (occasional) H
Long, lounge bar local with a public bar section. Skittle alley and garden patio area, below the main road. No food Sun.
❀ ◑ ⊕ ♣ P

Cross Keys Inn
Midford Road, Combe Down (B3110) ☎ (01225) 832002
11–2.30 (3 Sat), 6–11
Courage Best Bitter; John Smith's Bitter; Ushers Best Bitter, Founders H
Attractive Bath stone building with two traditional bars and a no-smoking area. Large aviary in the beer garden. Interesting and good food.
🛏 Q ❀ ◑ ▶ P ✂

Fairfield Arms
1 Fairfield Park Road, Fairfield
☎ (01225) 310594
11–2.30 (3 Sat), 6–11
Courage Best Bitter; Ushers Best Bitter H
Welcoming local with an award-winning garden, in the north-eastern outskirts of the city. ❀ ⊕ ♣

Foresters Arms
Bradford Road, Combe Down
☎ (01225) 837671
11–2.30, 5–11
Courage Best Bitter; Otter Bitter, Ale, Head; Wadworth 6X H
Comfortable lounge bar with an adjacent skittle alley behind a chintzy set of curtains. The spartan public bar is dominated by a pool table. No food Sat. ◑ ⊕ ♣ P

Golden Fleece
1–3 Avon Buildings, Lower Bristol Road ☎ (01225) 429572
11–2.30 (3 Sat), 5.30 (4.30 Fri)–11

Avon

Courage Bitter Ale, Best Bitter; guest beer [H]
Very popular, street-corner local where the enterprising landlord changes his guest beer on a day to day basis. The range includes Eldridge Pope Hardy Country alternating with Wadworth 6X and Marston's Pedigree. No food Sat or Sun. ◖ ⊞ ♣ P

Hatchetts
6–7 Queen Street (off SE corner of Queen Sq) ☎ (01225) 425045
11–11
Beer range varies [H]
Popular side-street free house with four, usually higher gravity beers, which change on a day to day basis. No food Sun. ◖ ⇌ (Spa)

Kings Arms
1 Monmouth Place
☎ (01225) 425418
11–11
Courage Best Bitter, Directors; Wadworth 6X; guest beer [H]
Former coaching inn on the last leg of the London to Bristol mailcoach run. A popular weekend music venue for its mainly local clientele. Lunches Sun. ❀ 🛏 ⊞ ♣

Larkhall Inn
St Saviours Road, Larkhall (400 yds from A4/A46 jct)
☎ (01225) 425710
11–2 (2.30 Fri), 6–10.30 (11 Fri & Sat); 12–2, 7–10.30 Sun
Courage Best Bitter, Directors [H]
Distinctive suburban local with unusual brass beer engines. No entry after 10.30pm Fri and Sat.
⌂ Q ❀ ⊞ ♣

Old Crown
1 Crown Hill, Weston
☎ (01225) 423371
11–2.30 (3 Sat), 6 (6.30 Sat)–11
Courage Best Bitter; John Smith's Bitter; Wadworth 6X [H]
Originally a staging post during the Civil War, this pleasant village local has a single, spacious bar and a walled garden, popular with families in summer. ❀ ◖ ◗ ♣

Old Farmhouse
1 Lansdown Road
☎ (01225) 316162
12–11
Draught Bass; Butcombe Bitter; Hall & Woodhouse Tanglefoot; Wadworth 6X [H]
Lively local of great character where the unusual pub sign is a caricature of its landlord. Live jazz Wed, Thu and Fri. No meals Sun. Tiny car park.
⌂ ❀ ◖ ◗ ⊞ ♣ P

Pig & Fiddle
2 Saracen Street
☎ (01225) 460868
12–3, 5–11
Ash Vine Bitter, Challenger, Black Bess Porter, Hop & Glory; guest beer [H]
Extremely popular, city-centre pub. No food Sun. Bar billiards played.
❀ ◖ ⇌ ♣ ⌓

Porter Butt
York Place, London Road
☎ (01225) 425084
12–3, 5.30–11; 12–11 Sat
Courage Bitter Ale, Best Bitter, Directors; Fuller's London Pride; Marston's Pedigree [H]
Enthusiastically-run, two-bar local with an upstairs meeting room and regular live music in the 'Walcot Palais' downstairs. Located next to the bus depot. No meals Sun. ❀ ◖ ⊞ ♣ P

Pulteney Arms
37 Daniel Street, Bathwick
☎ (01225) 463923
11.30–2.30, 5.30–11; 11–3, 5–11 Fri; 11–11 Sat
John Smith's Bitter [H]**; Smiles Best Bitter** [G]**; Ushers Best Bitter; Wadworth 6X; guest beer** [H]
Comfortable city pub near Henrietta Park. The single main bar is a shrine to rugby union. The smaller overspill room is popular with university students. Eve meals served till 8.45. ◖ ◗ ⊞ ♣ ⌓

Rising Sun
4 Grove Street
☎ (01225) 425584
11–2.30, 6–11
Courage Best Bitter, Directors [H]
Traditional, twin-bar local tucked away behind Bath's historic Pulteney Bridge.
Q ◖ ◗ ⊞ ⇌ (Spa) ♣

Rose & Crown
6 Brougham Place, Larkhall (400 yds NW of A4/A46 jct)
☎ (01225) 425700
11–11
Smiles Bitter, Best Bitter, Bristol Stout, Exhibition; guest beer [H]
Tastefully refurbished suburban local with a friendly, relaxed atmosphere. Taunton cider served. ❀ ◖ ⊞ ♣ ⌓

Smith Brothers
11–12 Westgate Buildings
☎ (01225) 330470
11–3, 5.30–11
Eldridge Pope Dorchester, Hardy Country, Royal Oak [H]
Spacious, one-bar, central pub with a public bar section.
◖ ⇌ ♣

Star Inn
23 The Vineyards (on Paragon, A4, ½ mile NE of city centre)
☎ (01225) 425072
12 (11 Sat)–2.30, 5.30–11
Draught Bass [G]**; Butcombe Bitter; Wadworth 6X; guest beer**
Enjoy the atmosphere in this classic town pub where Bass is served from the jug. Q ⊞ ♣

Bleadon

Queens Arms
Celtic Way (off A370)
☎ (01934) 812080
11–3, 7–11
Ringwood (beer varies) [G]**; Whitbread Flowers IPA** [H]**; guest beers** [G]
Little white-washed, olde-worlde gem with three drinking areas. Skittles and darts are popular. All the Ringwood beers are available in rotation. Q ⛾ ❀ ◖ ♣ P

Bristol

Brewery Tap
8 Upper Maudlin Street
☎ (0117) 9213668
11–11; 7–10.30 Sun, closed Sun lunch
Smiles Bitter, Best Bitter, Exhibition [H]
Small, friendly, wood-panelled pub with a horseshoe bar. A new no-smoking extension has been opened to offer more space, but it can still get very crowded in the eve. Serves breakfasts from 8–11am and hot food 12–8pm. Smiles Bristol Stout (or a guest ale) is also available. Q ⅄

Bristol Brewhouse
117–119 Stokes Croft
☎ (0117) 9420306
11–11
Ross Picton's Pleasure, Hartcliffe, SPA; guest beers [H]
Large, main-road brew pub with a central bar, very popular in the eve. Annual beer festival. New/occasional Ross brews also regularly sold. Music can be loud.
◖ ⇌ (Montpelier) ⌓

Highbury Vaults
164 St Michael's Hill, Kingsdown ☎ (0117) 9733203
12–11
Brains SA; Smiles Bitter, Best Bitter, Bristol Stout, Exhibition; guest beers [H]
Highly original and popular with all, a pub with Victorian/Edwardian fittings and a tiny snug. Eve meals Mon–Fri (till 8.30). Q ❀ ◖ ◗

Hobgoblin
2 Upper Byron Place, Triangle, Clifton ☎ (0117) 9299322

11–11; 7–10.30 Sun, closed Sun lunch

John Smith's Bitter;
Wadworth 6X; Wychwood Fiddlers Elbow, Best, Hobgoblin Ⓗ
Popular drinking place frequented by young people. Regular discos supplement the excellent rock music system and satellite TV and pinball machines are in evidence. Not the pub for a quiet eve drink! Beware the fake cider handpump.

Howlin' Wolf
155 St Michael's Hill, Kingsdown ☎ (0117) 9735960
11–11
Courage Best Bitter, Directors; Wychwood Best, Dr Thirsty's Draught Ⓗ
For blues in Bristol, in an electric pub atmosphere, this cannot be beaten: a wonderful, one-room pub, filled with jazz and blues memorabilia. Can get studenty, but many older regulars, too. ♨ ◖ ♿ ⏃

Kellaway Arms
140 Kellaway Avenue, Horfield ☎ (0117) 9497548
11–2.30 (3 Fri & Sat), 6–11
Courage Best Bitter; Marston's Pedigree; Smiles Best Bitter Ⓗ
Comfortable, friendly, two-bar local close to Horfield Common: a deceptively large public bar and a smaller lounge. Slides in the garden. No food Sun. Q ✿ ◖ ◗ ♣

Kings Head
60 Victoria Street
☎ (0117) 9277860
11–3 (not Sat), 5.30 (7.30 Sat)–11; 12–3, 7.45–10.30 Sun
Draught Bass; Courage Bitter Ale, Best Bitter Ⓗ
Small Victorian gem, restored but unspoilt, boasting a superb barback and a tramcar bar, full of character. Four-pint beer jug discount. Highly praised lunch snacks. Q ⇌ (T Meads)

Knowle Hotel
Leighton Road
☎ (0117) 9777019
12–2.30, 5.30–11; 11–3, 6–11 Sat
Ind Coope Burton Ale; Smiles Best Bitter; Tetley Bitter; guest beer Ⓗ
Brick-built, two-bar pub with a friendly atmosphere and extensive views over Bristol. Good value food. Several sports teams fielded.
Q ✿ ◖ ♣

Market House Tavern
13 St Nicholas Street
☎ (0117) 9496663
11–8 (3 Sat); closed Sun
Draught Bass; Smiles Best Bitter; Whitbread Boddingtons Bitter; guest beers Ⓗ

Small, city-centre pub in historic St Nicholas Market. Popular with the business community. Wide selection of West Country cheeses. Q ◖ ◗

Phoenix
15 Wellington Road, Broadweir ☎ (0117) 9558327
11.30–11
Draught Bass; Oakhill Best Bitter Ⓗ, Yeoman Ⓖ; Smiles Best Bitter Ⓗ; Wadworth 6X Ⓖ; Wickwar Coopers WPA Ⓗ; guest beers Ⓖ & Ⓗ
Very popular, unspoilt corner local, for all ages. Large collection of bottled beers and old photos of Bristol. ✿ ♿

Ropewalk Inn
Bedminster Parade, Bedminster ☎ (0117) 9535552
11–11
Draught Bass; Butcombe Bitter; Fuller's London Pride; McEwan 80/–; S&N Theakston Old Peculier Ⓗ
Refurbished, large Georgian pub offering excellent value beer in a friendly atmosphere. Regular discos and live bands.
♨ ✿ ◖ ◗ ♿
⇌ (T Meads) ♣ P

Rose of Denmark
6 Dowry Place, Hotwells
☎ (0117) 9290472
11–11
Ind Coope Burton Ale; Smiles Bitter; Tetley Bitter; guest beers Ⓗ
Pub with a classic, listed Georgian exterior and a friendly atmosphere. Excellent value beer and food.
Q ✿ ♨ ◖ ▲ ♣

Swan With Two Necks
12 Little Ann Street, St Judes (near end of M32)
☎ (0117) 9551893
11.30–3, 5–11; 11.30–11 Fri; 12–11 Sat
Hardington Bitter, Best Bitter, Jubilee, Moonshine, Old Ale; guest beer Ⓗ
Currently Hardington's only pub, a popular one-bar local refurbished in traditional, basic style. Unusual guest beers. Hardington Old Lucifer and Special Pale Ale are available occasionally. Regular mini-beer festivals. Live jazz alternate Suns. Q ◖ ♣

White Lion
Quay Head, Colston Avenue (opp. cenotaph)
☎ (0117) 9496602
11.30–11
Draught Bass; Butcombe Bitter; Smiles Best Bitter; Wadworth 6X; Wickwar Coopers WPA; guest beer (occasional) Ⓗ
Small, city-centre pub with a wood-burning stove, recently

refurbished to expose antique pine panelling. Gents beware of the spiral staircase from the old Bristol prison. Occasional guest beer at the expense of one of the regulars. Good value lunch snacks. ♨ ✦

Try also: Cadbury House, Richmond Rd (Inntrepreneur); **King Charles**, Kings Sq Ave (Free); **Ship**, Lower Park Row (Greenalls)

Chew Magna

Bear & Swan
South Parade
☎ (01275) 332577
11–3, 6–11; 11–11 Sat
Courage Bitter Ale, Best Bitter; Mole's Tap Ⓗ
Cosy, stone-built pub with two bars. The lounge bar extends through an alcove, giving extra space plus a real fire, while the other bar includes a TV. Good food.
♨ Q ✿ ◖ ◗ ♣ P

Try also: New Inn, Church St, Blagdon (Wadworth)

Churchill

Crown Inn
The Batch, Skinners Lane (off A38, S of A368/A38 jct)
☎ (01934) 852995
11.30–3.30, 5.30–11
Draught Bass; Butcombe Bitter; Eldridge Pope Hardy Country; Palmers IPA; RCH PG Steam; guest beers Ⓖ
Unspoilt country pub on the edge of the Mendip Hills: two bars with real log fires. Always a wide selection of ales, mainly from south-western independents. Batch Bitter, the house beer, is brewed by Cotleigh. Dress restrictions.
♨ Q ♿ ✿ ◖ ▲ P

Try also: Churchill Inn, Bristol Rd (Whitbread)

Compton Martin

Ring o' Bells
Bath Road ☎ (01761) 221284
11.30–2.30, 6.30–11
Draught Bass; Butcombe Bitter Ⓗ; Wadworth 6X Ⓖ; guest beer (occasional)
Very pleasant, old, two-bar roadside pub offering good value food. Large family room with toys; spacious garden.
♨ Q ♿ ✿ ◖ ◗ ▲ ♣ P

Filton

Filton Recreation Centre
Elm Park ☎ (0117) 9791988
12–2 (11.30–2.30 Thu & Fri; 11.30–2 Sat), 6.30 (4 Sat)–11

31

Butcombe Bitter; Furgusons
Dartmoor Best Bitter; Ind
Coope Burton Ale; Tetley
Bitter; guest beer H
Part of Filton Recreation
Centre but open to the public.
The landlord is a Burton
Master Cellarman. Guest beer
once a week. Q & ♣ P

Frampton Cotterell

Rising Sun
43 Ryecroft Road
☎ (01454) 772330
11.30–3, 7–11
Draught Bass; Hall &
Woodhouse Tanglefoot;
Smiles Best Bitter; Wadworth
6X; Wickwar Coopers WPA;
guest beer H
Six ales are always available at
this genuine free house, with a
single bar and a skittle alley.
Q ❀ ◖) ♣ P

Hallatrow

Old Station Inn
Wells Road (A39, 400 yds from
A37 jct) ☎ (01761) 452228
11–3, 5 (6 Sat)–11
Bass Worthington BB,
Draught Bass; Oakhill Best
Bitter; Otter Ale H
Old railway hotel on the
disused GWR North Somerset
line: a busy free house which
retains its friendly, local
atmosphere.
🏚 Q ⛺ ❀ 🛏 ◖) ♣ P

Hinton

Bull
1½ miles SW of M4 jct 18
☎ (0117) 9372332
11.30–2.30, 7 (6 summer)–11
Draught Bass; Wadworth IPA,
6X H, Old Timer G
Mature, unspoilt country local
with a large garden for
children: an attractive bar and
lounge with full meals served
in the restaurant.
🏚 Q ❀ ❀ ◖) ⊟ ▲ ♣ P

Iron Acton

Rose & Crown
High Street ☎ (01454) 228423
5–11; 12–2.30; 6–11 Sat
Draught Bass; Hook Norton
Old Hooky; Marston's
Pedigree; Whitbread Exhibition;
Whitbread WCPA H
Friendly, 17th-century village
pub with two bars. Table
skittles. Closed lunchtime
Mon–Fri. 🏚 Q ❀ 🛏 ♣

Kelston

Old Crown
Bath Road ☎ (01225) 423032
11.30–2.30 (3 Sat), 5–11

Draught Bass; Butcombe
Bitter; Smiles Best Bitter;
Wadworth 6X, Old Timer H
Attractive, 18th-century
coaching inn with a large
garden, a flagstone floor and
original beer engines. No
lunches Sun; eve meals served
Thu–Sat. 🏚 Q ❀ 🛏 ◖) ♣ P

Littleton-on-Severn

White Hart
☎ (01454) 412275
11.30–2.30, 6–11; 11.30–11 Sat
Smiles Bitter, Best Bitter,
Exhibition; Wadworth 6X;
guest beer H
17th-century country pub,
sympathetically enlarged and
popular. A winner of many
awards. The home-cooking
includes daily specials.
🏚 Q ⛺ ❀ 🛏 ◖) ♣ P ✗

Marshfield

Catherine Wheel
High Street ☎ (01225) 892220
11–2.30 (not Mon), 6–11
Courage Bitter Ale H, Best
Bitter G; Ruddles Best Bitter;
Wadworth 6X H; Old Timer G
Thriving 17th-century local
with a warm welcome. The
new rear lounge bar was
formerly the coal cellar. No
food Mon.
🏚 Q 🛏 ◖) ⊟ ♣ P

Midford

Hope & Anchor
On B3110 ☎ (01225) 832296
11–3, 6.30–11
Draught Bass; Butcombe
Bitter H
Nestling between the old
Somerset and Dorset railway
line and the disused Somerset
Coal Canal, this 300-year-old
country pub is given a touch
of the exotic by its cheerful
Spanish landlord. One large
bar, split into pub and
restaurant areas. 🏚 ❀ ◖)

Midsomer Norton

White Hart
The Island ☎ (01761) 418270
11–3, 5.30–11
Draught Bass G
Victorian establishment with
many rooms, a minor classic.
Skittles played. No food Sun.
🏚 ⛺ ◖) ♣ ⛺

Nailsea

Blue Flame
West End OS449690
☎ (01275) 856910
12–3, 6–11
Draught Bass; Oakhill Best
Bitter; Smiles Best Bitter,

Exhibition; guest beers
(summer) G
Wonderful, small, cottage-
style pub. Very popular with a
mixed local clientele. Warm
welcome.
🏚 Q ❀ & ▲ ♣ ⛺ P

Oldbury-on-Severn

Anchor Inn
Church Road
☎ (01454) 413331
11.30–2.30 (3 Sat), 6.30 (6 Sat)–11
Bass Worthington BB H,
Draught Bass G; Butcombe
Bitter; Marston's Pedigree;
S&N Theakston Best Bitter H,
Old Peculier G
Converted 16th-century mill
near the river. Excellent food
with a daily, changing menu
in the bar and restaurant.
Deservedly popular, with a
friendly atmosphere. Avon
CAMRA *Pub of the Year* 1993.
🏚 Q ❀ ◖) ⊟ ♣ P

Pennsylvania

Swan Inn
On A46, ¼ mile N of A420 jct
☎ (01225) 891022
12–3, 5.30–11 (12–11 Easter–mid-
Sept); 12–2.30, 7–10.30 Sun
Archers Village; Draught
Bass; Courage Bitter Ale;
Marston's Pedigree; Morland
Old Speckled Hen; guest
beer H
Excellent free house in a rural
area, featuring a comfortable,
split-level interior with a busy,
but not too crowded, bar and a
quieter lounge/eating area.
Courage Bitter Ale is sold as
Harry's Bitter Ale. No eve
meals Mon, except bank hols.
🏚 ❀ ◖) ♣ P

Pensford

Rising Sun
Church Street
☎ (01761) 490402
11.30–2.30, 7–11
Ind Coope Burton Ale; Tetley
Bitter; Wadworth 6X H
15th-century stone pub with a
garden leading down to the
River Chew (unfenced); cosy,
comfortable and friendly.
Good value food but no eve
meals Sun or Mon; book Sun
lunch. 🏚 ❀ ◖) & ♣ ⛺ P

Pill

Star
Rank Place ☎ (01275) 374926
12–4, 7–11
Butcombe Bitter; guest
beers H
Single-bar pub with a lively
atmosphere and a constant
range of changing real ales
(often unusual). 🏚 ♣ P

Pucklechurch

Rose & Crown
68 Parkfield Road
☎ (0117) 9372351
11–2.30, 6.30–11
Draught Bass H; **Hall & Woodhouse Tanglefoot** G; **Wadworth IPA, 6X, Farmer's Glory** (summer) H, **Old Timer** G
Large, attractive, two-bar village local: a small public bar and a large lounge with a restaurant. Small garden with a children's play area. Unusual fireplace in the lounge. No food Sun or Mon eves. Worth a visit. ♨ Q ❀ ◖ ▶ ♣ P

Redhill

Bungalow
Winford Lane (from Bristol, 1st left after Lulsgate airport)
☎ (01275) 472386
10.30–4.30, 6–11
Draught Bass E; **Wadworth IPA, 6X** H
50-year-old, brick-built bungalow with a cosy, friendly atmosphere. Large function room. Good value food (no Sun lunch).
♨ Q ❀ ◖ ৬ ♣ P

St Georges

Woolpack Inn
Shepherds Way (off M5 jct 21)
☎ (01934) 521670
12–2.30, 6–11
Courage Best Bitter; guest beers H
17th-century coaching house and wool-packing station on the old Bristol road: a friendly, two-bar pub with a separate restaurant. Varying guest beers – five in summer, three in winter. Booking advised for eve meals (good value).
♨ ❀ ◖ ৬ ♨ ▲ ♣ P

Saltford

Bird in Hand
High Street ☎ (01225) 873335
11–2.30 (3 Sat), 6.30 (6 Fri & Sat)–11
Draught Bass; Courage Best Bitter; Wadworth 6X H
Large, food-oriented pub on the Bristol to Bath cycle track, close to the River Avon. Especially popular in summer. No eve meals Sun in winter.
Q ❀ ◖ ▶ ᠔ P

Staple Hill

Humpers Off-Licence
26 Soundwell Road
☎ (0117) 9565525
12–2, 4.30–10.30; 11–10.30 Sat; 12–2, 7–10.30 Sun

Draught Bass; Smiles Best Bitter, Exhibition; Wickwar Brand Oak H; **guest beers** G
Lively, street-corner off-licence offering the widest range of beers for miles, at probably the lowest prices in the Bristol area. The guest beers (three usually) are often strong and from independent breweries. Richards cider. Polypins at Xmas. ৬ ᠔

Stoke Gifford

Parkway Tavern
43 North Road
☎ (0117) 9690329
11–2.30, 5–11; 11–11 Fri & Sat
Banks's Mild, Bitter E; **Camerons Strongarm; Marston's Pedigree** H
Large, modern pub on the northern edge of Bristol. Two large bars serve local residents and increasing numbers of office workers. Also very handy as a secondary waiting room for Parkway station. No meals Sat or Sun.
❀ ◖ ⇌ (Parkway) ♣ P

Warmley

Midland Spinner
London Road
☎ (0117) 9674204
11–11
Draught Bass; Courage Best Bitter; John Smith's Bitter; Marston's Pedigree; Wadworth 6X H
Pleasant pub with a railway theme, near the old Midland line, which is regularly used by walkers and cyclists. Popular with all ages. Genial landlord. ♨ ❀ ◖ ♣ P

Wellow

Fox & Badger
Railway Lane (2 miles W of B3110 at Hinton Charterhouse)
☎ (01225) 832293
11–3, 6–11
Butcombe Bitter; Exmoor Ale; Wadworth 6X H
Pretty Wellow's only pub, a two-bar local where, unusually, the public bar is carpeted and the lounge bar flagstoned. It can be difficult to park. ♨ ◖ ▶ ⊞ ♣

Westbury-on-Trym

Post Office Tavern
17 Westbury Hill
☎ (0117) 9401233
11–3, 5–11
Draught Bass; Courage Best Bitter; Oakhill Best Bitter; Otter Ale; Ruddles Best Bitter; Smiles Best Bitter; guest beers H
Interesting pub featuring lots of old GPO memorabilia. Up

to five guest beers available and the good menu includes substantial, home-made pizzas (no other meals eves). Reasonable standard of dress required. ◖ ▶ ৬

Prince of Wales
84 Stoke Lane
☎ (0117) 9623715
11–3, 5.30–11; 11–11 Sat
Courage Bitter Ale, Best Bitter; Hardington Best Bitter, Ushers Best Bitter H
Friendly pub in a residential area, with lots of royal memorabilia and sporting items on display. Very popular in summer, with a large garden (barbecues). Ask for 'Boys' when drinking Bitter Ale. Q ❀ ◖ ᠔ ♣ ৬

Weston-super-Mare

Elm Tree Hotel
64 Meadow Street
☎ (01934) 621213
12–3, 7–11; 12–11 Thu–Sat
Bass Worthington BB; guest beer H
Small, traditional, one-bar local near the main shopping area, with a games room. Thatcher's cider served. ♣ ᠔

Wick

Rose & Crown
High Street ☎ (0117) 9372198
11.30–2.30, 5.30–11
Courage Best Bitter, Directors; John Smith's Bitter; Wadworth 6X H
Large village inn dating back to 1640, with original oak beams and three log fires. Deservedly popular for its varied and reasonably priced food (book Sun lunch; no food Sun eve). Recently acquired by S&N so its range may change. Families welcome in one bar.
♨ Q ❀ ◖ ♣ P ৬

Winterbourne Down

Cross Hands
Down Road ☎ (01454) 772777
12 (11 Sat)–11
Courage Bitter Ale, Best Bitter; Morland Old Speckled Hen; Smiles Best Bitter, Exhibition; John Smith's Bitter; Wadworth 6X; Wickwar Brand Oak; guest beers H
Carefully extended and refurbished old village local, with a single bar and a no-smoking family room, decorated with a large collection of old sewing machines. The large garden has animals and ponds.
♨ ♋ ❀ ◖ ৬ ♣ ᠔ ৬

Bedfordshire

Bedfordshire

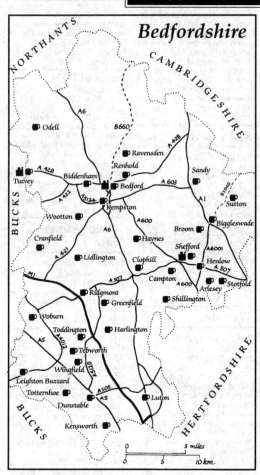

Banks & Taylor, *Shefford;* **Nix Wincott**, *Turvey;* **Wells**, *Bedford*

Arlesey

True Briton
27 Hospital Road (off Station Rd) ☎ (01462) 731264
5.30–11; 11–3.30, 6–11 Sat
Adnams Broadside; Fuller's London Pride; Tetley Bitter Ⓗ
Traditional village pub with a very friendly atmosphere, featuring a collection of old photographs of the village. Open-plan, but with two bars, one including a pool table. Small car park. ♿ ♣ P

Bedford

Castle
17 Newnham Street (E of A6, High St) ☎ (01234) 353295
11–3, 5.30 (7 Sat)–11; 11–11 Fri
Adnams Broadside; Morland Old Speckled Hen; Wells Eagle Ⓗ
A country pub in town, with a delightful walled garden, busy at weekends. Excellent meals served Mon–Sat lunchtime and Mon–Thu eves.
♿ ⇄ ◖ ▶ ⊟ ♿ P

Clarence
13 St Johns Street (over town bridge from High St, 400 yds) ☎ (01234) 352781
11–11
Ansells Mild; Draught Bass; Courage Directors; Ind Coope Benskins Best Bitter; Tetley Bitter Ⓗ
Large, two-roomed, town pub with a lounge/dining room popular with office workers at lunchtime. Busy with games-

playing regulars in the eve. Good value bar food.
♿ ◖ ▶ ⇌ (St Johns) ♣ P

Fleur de Lis
12 Mill Street (E off A6, High St) ☎ (01234) 211004
10.30–2.30 (4 Sat), 5.30 (7 Sat)–11; 10.30–11 Thu & Fri; 12–2, 7–10.30 Sun
Adnams Broadside *or* **Hall & Woodhouse Tanglefoot** *or* **Morland Old Speckled Hen; Wells Eagle** Ⓗ
Very well-run, one-bar, town-centre pub with a mixed clientele. Upstairs meeting room. Parking difficult lunchtimes. Lunches served Mon–Fri. ◖

Three Cups
45 Newnham Street (down Mill St and past the church) ☎ (01234) 352153
11–11; 10.30–4, 7–11 Sat
Greene King XX Mild, IPA, Rayments Special, Abbot Ⓗ
Fine, traditional pub near the town centre, with oak-panelled bars. The wide range of food at lunchtime includes daily specials and a full breakfast menu. No meals Sun. ♿ ◖ ⊟ ♣ P

Biddenham

Three Tuns
Main Road (S of A428, village loop) ☎ (01234) 354847
11.30–2.30, 6–11
Greene King IPA, Rayments Special, Abbot Ⓗ
Delightful village inn with an excellent range of home-cooked food (children permitted in the dining area). No food Sun and Mon eves. Table skittles played.
♿ ◖ ▶ ⊟ ♣ P

Biggleswade

Yorkshire Grey
140 London Road ☎ (01767) 313222
11–2.30, 5.30–11
Greene King XX Mild, IPA, Rayments Special, Abbot Ⓗ
Large, open-plan bar with a separate games area. Very mixed clientele: business trade at lunchtimes; popular with youngsters at weekends. Enclosed garden with swings, climbing frames and tables. Varied menu.
♿ ◖ ▶ ⇌ ♣ P ✗

Broom

Cock
23 High Street ☎ (01767) 314411
12–3, 6–11
Greene King IPA, Abbot Ⓖ
Pub with several small rooms

off a central corridor. With no bar, beer is served from the cellar steps, straight out of the cask. Table skittles played. Good value meals, with game a speciality (no food Sun eve). Well worth a visit.
🏚 Q ⬥ ❀ ◖ ▲ ♣ P

Campton

White Hart
Mill Lane (off A507)
☎ (01462) 812657
4.30 (11 Sat)–11
Hook Norton Best Bitter; Marston's Pedigree; Morland Old Speckled Hen; S&N Theakston Best Bitter; Wadworth 6X; guest beer Ⓗ
Popular, three-bar, open-plan village free house with a comfortable lounge and dining area. Games dominate the public bar, which has a flagstone floor and an inglenook. Petanque played all year. 🏚 ❀ ◗ ⅃ ♣ P

Clophill

Stone Jug
Back Street (2nd right N of A6/A507 roundabout)
☎ (01525) 860526
11–3, 6–11
Banks & Taylor Shefford Bitter; Courage Directors; John Smith's Bitter; guest beers Ⓗ
Deservedly popular free house where two guest beers complement the regular range. Check before arriving with children. No food Sun.
⬥ ❀ ◖

Cranfield

Cross Keys
159 High Street
☎ (01234) 750213
11–3.30, 6–11; 11–11 Fri & Sat
Banks's Mild; Whitbread Boddingtons Bitter, Castle Eden Ale; guest beers Ⓗ
Popular, large, central village pub with a good range of bar food and a separate restaurant. Rebuilt in 1923 and recently refurbished.
Q ❀ ◖ ◗ ⅃ ♣ P

Dunstable

Highwayman
London Road (A5)
☎ (01582) 601122
11–2.30, 6–11; 11–11 Sat
Wells Eagle, Bombardier Ⓗ
Recently refurbished lounge bar of a medium-sized, two-star hotel, one mile south of the town centre on the A5. Food available at all times. Comfortable restaurant with an extensive menu.
🛏 ◖ ◗ ⅃ ♣ P

Greenfield

Compasses
44 High Street
☎ (01525) 713144
12–11
Morland Old Speckled Hen; Wells Eagle; guest beer Ⓗ
A friendly atmosphere in a T-shaped, split-level bar, a butcher's shop till the early 1900s (the curing and smoking implements remain in a detached rear building). Live music Fri–Sun eves. Successful tug-of-war team. Excellent menu (eve meals Mon–Sat; book for Sun lunch)
🏚 ❀ ◖ ⅃ ▲ ♣ P

Harlington

Carpenters Arms
Sundon Road
☎ (01525) 872384
12–2.30, 5.30–11; 11–11 Sat
Banks's Bitter; Courage Best Bitter; Wadworth 6X Ⓗ
17th-century village pub featuring a low-ceilinged lounge with copper-topped tables and a small snug. The public bar has pool, darts, etc. The recommended upstairs restaurant does not open Sun or Mon eves. No bar meals Sun eve. 🏚 ❀ ◖ ◗ ≷ ♣ P

Haynes

Greyhound
68 Northwood End Road
☎ (01234) 381239
11–3, 5.30–11
Greene King IPA, Rayments Special, Abbot Ⓗ
Friendly village pub providing good food and a convivial atmosphere. Outdoor/indoor games available.
⬥ ❀ ◖ ◗ ⅃ ⅃ ▲ ♣ P

Henlow

Engineers Arms
68 High Street
☎ (01462) 812284
3 (12 Sat)–11
Hook Norton Best Bitter; Sarah Hughes Ruby Mild; S&N Theakston Best Bitter, Old Peculier; Tetley Bitter; Younger Scotch; guest beers Ⓗ
Ex-Charles Wells pub. Although the regular beers come from S&N, many of the guest ales are rare to this area. Two beer festivals a year add to the variety. Very mixed clientele in two bars and a separate pool room. Regular music nights. 🏚 ❀ ♣

Try also: Five Bells, High St (Greene King)

Kempston

King William IV
56 High Street
☎ (01234) 854533
11.30 (11 Sat)–3, 5.30 (6.30 Sat)–11
Wells Eagle, Bombardier; guest beers Ⓗ
Attractive, genuine oak-beamed building which caters for a mixed clientele with one bar and a games room. Swings and slides in the nicely landscaped garden. No eve meals Sun. ❀ ◖ ◗ ♣ P

Try also: Griffin, Bedford Rd (Greene King)

Kensworth

Farmer's Boy
216 Common Road
☎ (01582) 872207
11–11
Fuller's London Pride, ESB Ⓗ
Lively, two-bar village local with a comfortable lounge (note the original Mann, Crossman & Paulin leaded windows) and separate dining area (excellent, home-cooked food available at all times). Children's play area in the garden. 🏚 ❀ ◖ ◗ ⅃ P

Leighton Buzzard

Black Lion
High Street ☎ (01525) 382510
11–2.30, 5.30–11
Ind Coope Burton Ale; Tetley Bitter; guest beers Ⓗ
One-bar, split-level, town-centre pub appealing to all ages and tastes. A video jukebox packs them in Fri nights; popular with office workers lunchtimes. No food Sun. The venue of the annual Leighton Buzzard beer festival. ❀ ◖ ⅃ ♣

Stag
Heath Road ☎ (01525) 372710
12 (11 Sat)–2.30, 6–11
Fuller's Hock, Chiswick, London Pride, Mr Harry, ESB Ⓗ
Heavily renovated, wedge-shaped pub, a ten-minute walk from the town centre. The landlord devises daily witticisms for the blackboard outside. No food Sun. Tiny car park. ◖ ◗ ♣ P

Star
Heath Road ☎ (01525) 377294
11–2.30 (3 Sat), 5.30 (6 Sat)–11
Adnams Bitter; Draught Bass; Ind Coope ABC Best Bitter; Wadworth 6X Ⓗ
Large, smart out-of-town pub, catering unashamedly for the food trade but still a welcoming spot for a quiet

drink. Interesting artefacts adorn every nook and cranny. No food Sun. Q ✿ ◖ ▷ P

Try also: Globe, Stoke Rd (Free)

Lidlington

Green Man
High Street ☎ (01525) 402869
12–2.30, 6 (6.30 Sat)–11
Greene King IPA, Abbot Ⓗ
17th-century, thatched pub and restaurant in a quiet village, hosting traditional games plus petanque. Cosy lounge with an attached restaurant area (good varying menu: food not available Sun and Mon eves). Handy for ramblers on the Greensand Ridge Path.
🚗 ✿ ◖ ▷ ᐃ ᐁ ⇌ ♣ P

Luton

Bird & Bush
Hancock Drive, Bushmead (off A6, behind Barnfield College)
☎ (01582) 480723
12–2.30, 6–11; 12–11 Sat
Adnams Bitter; Bass Charrington IPA, Worthington BB, Draught Bass; guest beer Ⓗ
Opened in May 1991, a 'community tavern' with attractive Yorkshire flagstone and quarry-tiled floors. The good bar food includes vegetarian options; no food Sun. Wheelchair WC.
✿ ◖ ᐃ ♣ P

Boater
121 Icknield Way (off A6)
☎ (01582) 575191
11–11
Greene King IPA, Abbot Ⓗ
The area's most patronised pub, catering for all age groups and situated on the northern outskirts of town. Well-managed, with a comfortable, large lounge and a public bar.
✿ ◖ ▷ ᐁ ♣ P

Two Brewers
43 Dumfries Street
☎ (01582) 23777
11–11
Banks & Taylor Shefford Bitter; guest beers Ⓗ
Friendly, back-street local, popular with bricklayers, bankers and bikers. Yard for outdoor drinking. ✿ ◖ ▷ ♣

Wheelwrights Arms
34 Guildford Street
☎ (01582) 20023
10.30–11
Fuller's London Pride, ESB; guest beers Ⓗ
Lively, one-bar, town-centre

free house, handy for the bus and rail stations, and Arndale shoppers. Ever-changing selection of guest beers, often unusual for the area. No food Sun. ◖ ⇌ ♣

Try also: Bat & Barrel, Park St (Wells)

Odell

Mad Dog
Little Odell (W end of village)
☎ (01234) 720221
11–2.30, 6–11
Greene King IPA, Rayments Special, Abbot Ⓗ
Thatched pub near Harrold-Odell Country Park. A ghost is seen occasionally near the inglenook. Generous home-cooked food includes vegetarian dishes and the pub can be busy at mealtimes. Children's roundabout in the garden. Q ✿ ◖ ▷ P

Ravensden

Blacksmith's Arms
Bedford Road (B660, 3½ miles from Bedford)
☎ (01234) 771496
11–3, 6–11
Greene King IPA, Abbot; Whitbread Boddingtons Bitter; guest beers Ⓗ
Countryside pub and restaurant with lounge and public bars. Family-run, with up to five guest beers from an extensive range sold. Wheelchair WC.
Q ✿ ◖ ▷ ᐁ ᐃ ᐃ ♣ P

Renhold

Three Horseshoes
42 Top End (1 mile N of A428)
☎ (01234) 870218
11–2.30, 6–11; 11–11 Sat
Greene King XX Mild, IPA, Abbot Ⓗ
Friendly village local with a children's play area in the garden. The pub has traditional games plus satellite TV. Good value food includes fresh steaks and home-made soup. No eve meals Sun or Tue. A rare outlet for mild.
🚗 Q ✿ ◖ ▷ ᐁ ♣ P

Ridgmont

Rose & Crown
89 High Street
☎ (01525) 280245
10.30–2.30, 6–11
Adnams Broadside; Mansfield Riding Bitter; Wells Eagle, Bombardier Ⓗ
Popular, welcoming pub with a restaurant (open weekends only). The public bar has a games area, whilst the large

grounds offer facilities for camping and caravanning, and barbecues in summer. In every edition of this guide.
🚗 ✿ ◖ ▷ ᐁ ᐃ ♣ P

Sandy

Bell
Station Road (50 yds S of B1042) ☎ (01767) 680267
12–2.30 (4 Sat), 5 (6 Sat)–11
Greene King IPA, Rayments Special Ⓗ
Friendly one-bar local opposite the station and handy for the RSPB HQ. Extensive range of free bar-top food Sun lunchtimes (eve meals end at 8.30; no meals Sun). Newly added function room at the rear for hire.
🚗 ✿ ◖ ▷ ⇌ ♣ P

Shefford

White Hart Hotel
2 Northbridge Street (A507/A600 jct)
☎ (01462) 811144
11–3, 6.30 (7 Sat)–11
Greene King XX Mild, IPA, Rayments Special, Abbot Ⓗ
Original coaching inn with letting accommodation. Bar snacks and a full menu are available in either the bar or restaurant. Games include darts, dominoes, crib, bar billiards and petanque.
🚗 Q ✿ ⌂ ◖ ▷ ᐁ ᐃ ♣ P

Try also: Black Swan (Free)

Shillington

Musgrave Arms
Aspley End Road
☎ (01462) 711286
11–11
Greene King IPA, Rayments Special, Abbot Ⓖ
Unspoilt, country local: a cosy, low-beamed 'public bar' end. Good range of food, including game; no eve meals Sun. Large garden with a children's play area. Wheelchair WC.
🚗 Q ✿ ◖ ▷ ᐃ ᐃ ♣ P

Stotfold

Stag
Brook Street ☎ (01462) 730261
12–2.30, 5–11; 12–11 Fri & Sat
Beer range varies Ⓗ
Home of the Stotfold Nail Game, a pub with a beer festival every week (over 250 different ales again last year, including Marston's Head Brewer's Choice and the full Titanic range). Many unusual beers, and many rare to this area. No food Sun eve.
🚗 ✿ ◖ ▷ ᐃ ♣ ⌂ P

Sutton

John o' Gaunt
30 High Street
☎ (01767) 260377
12–3, 7–11
Greene King IPA, Abbot H
Attractive village pub near the
golf course of the same name.
Good range of bar food (Sun
lunches now served). Table
skittles played; floodlit boules
court in the garden.
🏰 Q ❀ ◗ ♣ P

Tebworth

Queen's Head
The Lane ☎ (01525) 874101
11–3 (3.30 Sat), 6–11
Adnams Broadside G; **Wells
Eagle** H
Very welcoming, good-
humoured pub with two
small, popular bars. Good-
value food (no meals Sun).
Quizzes, darts and
conversation provide the
entertainment. 🏰 ❀ ◗ ▶ P

Toddington

Angel
1 Luton Road
☎ (01525) 872380
11–3, 5.30–11; 11–11 Sat & Easter–
Aug Bank Hol
**Courage Best Bitter; John
Smith's Bitter; guest beers** H
Dating in part from the 16th
century, a lively and
enterprising pub where the
lounge bar is decorated with
musical instruments. The
Stable Bar is the venue for live
jazz (Thu and Sun lunch) and
other occasional live
events, including blues and
theatre. Cream teas.
Restaurant open Tue–Sat eves.
Ring before arriving with
children.
🏰 🛏 ❀ ◗ ▶ ⅙ ♣ P

Bedford Arms
64 High Street
☎ (01525) 873503
12–3, 6–11
**Adnams Broadside; Morland
Old Speckled Hen; Wells
Eagle** H
Attractive pub both outside
and in, with a large rambling
garden to the rear and two
warm and comfortable lounge
bars. No food Sun eve. Guest
beers occasionally replace the
Adnams or Morland.
🏰 ❀ ◗ ▶ ♣ P

Sow & Pigs
19 Church Square
☎ (01525) 873089
11–11
**Greene King IPA, Rayments
Special, Abbot** H
Unpretentious and
unpredictable pub where the
bar area features a number of
pigs (even flying!), golf
memorabilia, a piano, an
harmonium and a bar billiards
table. A Victorian dining room
is available for group
bookings. Customers may find
a sense of humour useful!
Good food.
🏰 Q ❀ ◗ ▶ ♣ P

Totternhoe

Old Bell
Church Road
☎ (01582) 662633
12–3, 6–11
**Greene King IPA; Hook
Norton Old Hooky; Palmers
IPA; Wadworth 6X; guest
beers** H
Comfortable, friendly village
free house, offering a good
choice of ales, normally
including some that are rare to
the area. The above range may
alter, with up to three guest
beers served. Bar billiards and
shove-ha'penny played. Eve
meals to 8.30 only (no meals
Sun). Occasional cider.
🏰 ❀ ◗ ▶ ♣ ⌂ P

Old Farm Inn
16 Church Road
☎ (01582) 661294
11–3, 6–11
**Fuller's Hock, Chiswick,
London Pride** H
Old village pub: a popular,
traditional public bar with a
low, boarded ceiling, and a
quiet, comfortable lounge with
a large inglenook. No meals
Sun.
🏰 Q ❀ ◗ ♣ P

Turvey

Three Cranes
High Street (off A428)
☎ (01234) 881305
11–3, 6–11
**Draught Bass; Fuller's
London Pride, ESB; Hook
Norton Best Bitter; Taylor
Landlord; guest beer** H
17th-century coaching inn
offering an excellent range of
food, including vegetarian
dishes, in all bars and a
restaurant area. Sun eve
quizzes. 🏰 Q ❀ 🛏 ◗ ▶ P

Three Fyshes Inn
Bridge Street ☎ (01234) 881264
11.30–2.30, 5.30–11
**Nix Wincott Old Cock Up,
Turvey Bitter, Two Henrys
Bitter, THAT, Old Nix,
Winky Wobbler** H
Old riverside inn, at the west
end of the village, home of Nix
Wincott Brewery. The main
bar has a flagstone floor, an
inglenook and cats and dogs
a-plenty. The public bar has a
skittles table. The wide-
ranging food menu includes
blackboard specials. Wilkins
cider. The car park is 25 yards
up the road.
🏰 Q ❀ ◗ ▶ ♣ ⌂ P

Wingfield

Plough
Tebworth Road
☎ (01525) 873077
12–3, 6–11
**Banks & Taylor Shefford
Bitter; Fuller's London Pride;
guest beers** H
Attractive and friendly,
thatched village free house
with a children's/pool room.
Three ever-changing guest
beers normally available.
South Beds CAMRA *Pub of the
Year* 1993. Good food, but no
meals Sun eves.
🏰 🛏 ❀ ◗ ▶ P

Woburn

Royal Oak
George Street
☎ (01525) 290610
11–11
**Greene King IPA, Rayments
Special, Abbot** H
Multi-roomed, low-ceilinged
pub of character. Good food
(no meals Tue eve).
🏰 Q 🛏 ❀ ◗ ▶ ♣

Wootton

Chequers Inn
Hall End Road
☎ (01234) 768394
11–3, 5.30–11
**Wells Eagle, Bombardier;
guest beer** H
16th-century coaching inn
boasting three real fires, oak
beams and brasses. Large
garden. No eve meals Sun in
winter. Boules played in
summer.
🏰 Q ❀ ◗ ▶ 🍴 ♣ P

Updates to the *Good Beer Guide* are published in CAMRA's
newspaper, *What's Brewing*. Join CAMRA and receive a free copy
each month.

Berkshire

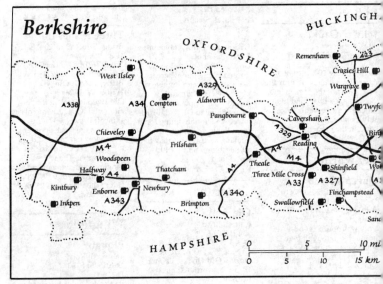

Aldworth

Bell
☎ (01635) 578272
11–3, 6–11; closed Mon, except bank hols
Arkell's 3B, Kingsdown; Hall & Woodhouse Badger Best Bitter; Hook Norton Best Bitter; Morrells Mild H
Small, friendly two-bar pub set amidst tranquil surroundings. Walk in and you go back in time to the old traditional pub. National CAMRA *Pub of the Year* 1990. The hot rolls are well worth a try.
🏨 Q 🍽 🏵 ♣ P

Binfield

Jack O'Newbury
Terrace Road North (off B3018) ☎ (01344) 54881
11–2.30 (3 Sat), 6–11
Old Luxters Barn Ale; Rebellion IPA, ESB; Wychwood Dr Thirsty's Draught, Hobgoblin; guest beers H
Interesting free house with a detached skittle alley. Guns, jugs and teapots are on display. The attractive Wendy house appeals to the younger element. A house beer, Binfield Bitter, is not brewed here. 🏨 🏵 ◗ ♣ P

Try also: Victoria Arms, Terrace Rd North (Fuller's)

Bracknell

Old Manor
High Street (opp. Met Office roundabout) ☎ (01344) 304490
11–11

S&N Theakston Best Bitter, XB; Wadworth 6X; Younger Scotch; guest beers H
Tastefully refurbished, town-centre Wetherspoon house. Originally the old manor house, it is now split into two distinct bars, with separate areas, each with its own period theme. Children always welcome. Open for food all day Sun.
Q 🏵 🍽 🏵 ◗ ♿ ≒ 🛏 P ✗

Brimpton

Three Horseshoes
School Road ☎ (01734) 712183
11–3 (4 Sat), 6–11
Adnams Bitter; Fuller's London Pride, ESB H
Pleasant, early Victorian, two-bar village pub, built by Mays of Basingstoke. The panelled, brass-filled lounge, with its fine old clock and old prints, is generally quiet. The larger bar offers darts, pool and a jukebox. The Adnams may alternate with Wadworth 6X. 🏨 Q 🏵 ◗ ♣ P

Try also: Rising Sun, Woolhampton (Free)

Caversham

Clifton Arms
12 Gosbrook Road
☎ (01734) 471775
11–3, 6–11
Brakspear Bitter, Special H
Friendly, traditional, three-roomed pub near the town centre. The landlord is one of the brewery's longest standing

tenants. No food Sun eve.
🏵 ◗ ▶ ♣ P

Chieveley

Olde Red Lion
Green Lane (½ mile NW of M4 jct 13)
☎ (01635) 248379
11–3, 6 (5.30 Fri & Sat)–11
Arkell's 2B, Mash Tun Mild, 3B, Kingsdown H
Chieveley services with a difference! A comfortable pub rescued by Arkell's, which, while popular with passing trade, remains a village local. Northants skittles played.
🏨 🏵 🏨 ◗ ▶ ♣ P

Compton

Swan Hotel
Cheap Street
☎ (01635) 578269
11–3, 5.30–11; 11–11 Fri & Sat; 12–3, 7.30–10.30 Sun
Adnams Broadside; Morland Bitter, Old Speckled Hen H
Sympathetically refurbished pub drawing clientele from near and far. A strikingly large pub which offers something for everyone yet remains cosy when required.
🏵 🏨 ◗ ▶ ♿ ♣ P

Crazies Hill

Horns
On road between A4 and A423 towards Warren Row
OS799809 ☎ (01734) 401416
11–2.30, 5.30–11
Brakspear Mild, Bitter, Old, Special, OBJ (winter) H

Wonderful country pub, well worth finding for all Brakspear's beers. CAMRA regional *Pub of the Year* 1994. No piped music or machines. Lunches Tue–Sat; eve meals Fri and Sat only, if booked.
🏚 Q 🌣 ❀ ◖ ▮ Å ♣ P

Enborne

Craven Arms

OS427647 ☎ (01635) 253336
12–2.30, 6–11; 11–3, 6–11 Sat
Hall & Woodhouse Tanglefoot; Wadworth IPA, 6X, Farmer's Glory, Old Timer; guest beer H
Rambling, secluded, early-17th century, multi-room pub near the site of a Civil War battle. Oak beams, settles and chintz furniture feature. High chairs for infants; large garden for toddlers. Regular discos and live music. A welcome for dogs and good food for all. A pub for everyone.
🌣 ❀ ◖ ▮ Å ♣ P

Eton

Watermans Arms

Brocas Street ☎ (01753) 861001
11–2.30 (3 Fri & Sat), 6–11
Brakspear Bitter; Courage Best Bitter, Directors; Morland Old Speckled Hen; Ruddles County; Wadworth 6X H
Cosy, single-bar pub with a low ceiling and an intimate atmosphere. A conservatory covers the old courtyard and is suitable for children. 🏚 🌣 ◖ ▮ ➧ (Central/Riverside) ♣ ✕

Eton Wick

Pickwick

32 Eton Wick Road
☎ (01753) 861713
11.30 (12 Sat)–2.30, 5.30 (6 Sat)–11
Young's Bitter, Special, Winter Warmer H
One-bar pub, the only Young's house in Berkshire, well-known for its Malaysian food (no eve meals Sun/Mon). Live music every other Fri; Mon crib; Sun night quiz. An award-winner for its floral displays and its herb garden.
❀ ◖ ▮ ♣ P

Try also: Greyhound (Morland)

Finchampstead

Queens Oak

Church Lane (opp. church)
OS794639 ☎ (01734) 734855
11.30–2.30, 6–11; 12–3, 6–11 Sat
Brakspear Bitter, Old, Special, OBJ H
Old two-bar pub, popular with walkers. Aunt Sally played; a haunt of morris dancers in summer. Great garden for kids (barbecues held). Separate, well-established no-smoking bar. 🏚 Q ❀ ◖ ▮ Å ♣ P ✕

Frilsham

Pot Kiln

On Yattendon to Bucklebury road; not in Frilsham village.
OS552731 ☎ (01635) 201366
12–2.30, 6.30–11
Arkell's 3B; Morland Bitter, Old Speckled Hen; guest beers H
Unspoilt pub in Flemish brickwork, with views over farmland; an intimate, rustic bar and a comfortable lounge. The pub dates back over 200 years, the building to the 15th century. Good range of food, including vegetarian. Hot filled rolls only Sun and Tue.
🏚 Q 🌣 ❀ ◖ ▮ ♣ P ✕

Halfway

Halfway Inn

Bath Road (A4)
☎ (01488) 58215
11.30–3, 5.30–11
Hall & Woodhouse Badger Best Bitter, Hard Tackle, Tanglefoot; Wadworth 6X H
18th-century, oak-beamed pub, decorated with farming implements and frequented by all ages. Good food choice, including vegetarian, snacks and children's portions. A cosy, separate restaurant opens on to a barbecue area. 53 miles from both Bath and

London—hence its name.
🏚 ❀ ◖ ▮ ♿ P

Holyport

Belgian Arms

Holyport Street (E end of the green) ☎ (01628) 34468
11–2.30, 5.30 (7.30 winter)–11
Brakspear Bitter, Old, Special H
Old wisteria-clad local just off the green, by the village pond, renamed during WWI after German prisoners held locally saluted the pub sign (it was the Eagle at the time). An upper room was used as a Wesleyan chapel until 1835. A Brakspear pub for 98 years. No food Sun eve. 🏚 Q ❀ ◖ ▮ P

Inkpen

Swan

Craven Road, Lower Green (Hungerford to Combe Road)
☎ (01488) 668326
12–2.30, 6.30–11; closed Mon
Brakspear Bitter; Marston's Pedigree; Ringwood Best Bitter; Thwaites Bitter H
Large, 16th-century inn near Combe Gibbet. Far-eastern dishes feature prominently on the menu. Three open fires.
🏚 ❀ ◖ ▮ P

Kintbury

Dundas Arms

53 Station Road
☎ (01488) 58263
11–2.30, 6–11; 12–2.30, 7–10.30 Sun
Fuller's London Pride; Morland Bitter; Wells Bombardier H
Attractive 18th-century inn by the Kennet and Avon canal (lock 78). Named after Lord Dundas, who opened the canal in 1810. Separate high quality restaurant. Good bar food.
Q ❀ 🏚 ◖ ▮ ⊟ ♿ ➧ P

Maidenhead

Cricketers Arms

16 Park Street (behind town hall) ☎ (01628) 38332
11–3, 5.30–11
Morland Bitter, Old Masters H
Two-bar pub with bar billiards in the small public bar. Ring the bell there for service. Lunches served in the more spacious saloon. No food Sun.
Q ◖ ▮ ⊟ ♿ ✕

Hand & Flowers

15 Queen Street
☎ (01628) 23800
10.30–3, 5.30–11
Brakspear Bitter, Old, Special, OBJ H
Small Victorian pub in the

town centre. Popular with office workers at lunchtime; relaxing atmosphere in the eve. Mild is occasionally available. Eve meals on request. ♨ Q ◖ ▶ ≉

Hobgoblin
34 High Street
☎ (01628) 36510
11–11
Wychwood Best, Hobgoblin, Dr Thirsty's Draught, Black Wych Stout; guest beers Ⓗ
Lively, refurbished town-centre pub where the jukebox is well-used. Popular with the young; live music some nights. Mini-beer festivals are planned. ♨ ❀ ◖ ≉ ♣

Moneyrow Green

White Hart
☎ (01628) 21460
11–11
Morland Bitter, Old Speckled Hen Ⓗ
Over 400 years old and originally a hunting lodge in Windsor Royal Forest: a picturesque pub with leaded-light windows. The saloon is wood-panelled, its decor adding an air of class. The public is panelled in light oak and resounds to the sound of dominoes and bar billiards. No food Sun.
♨ Q ❀ ◖ ⊟ & ♣ P

Newbury

Lock, Stock & Barrel
104 Northbrook Street (just off the main street, by canal bridge) ☎ (01635) 42730
11–11
Fuller's Hock, Chiswick, London Pride, Mr Harry, ESB Ⓗ
Spacious pub converted from a coffee shop on the banks of the Kennet & Avon Canal: a listed building which was a brewery and tap at the turn of the century. Open at 10am for coffee. ❀ ◖ ▶ ≉

Try also: Coopers Arms, Bartholomew St (Arkell's)

Oakley Green

Old Red Lion
Oakley Green Road (B3024, off A308) ☎ (01753) 863892
11–11
Brakspear Bitter; Greene King IPA; Ind Coope Friary Meux Best Bitter Ⓗ
400-year old country inn where Aunt Sally can be played in the garden. The separate restaurant boasts an extensive menu of home-cooked food (eve meals Tue–Sat); bar snacks also available. Q ❀ ◖ ▶ ♣ P

Old Windsor

Oxford Blue
Crimp Hill (off A308)
☎ (01753) 861954
11–11
Brakspear Bitter; Ind Coope Burton Ale; Tetley Bitter Ⓗ
300-year-old, verandah-fronted pub with an adventure playground at the rear. The back bar is an aviation enthusiast's paradise. The restaurant is very popular and provides home-cooked food. The longest serving licensee in the area (14 years).
Q ❀ ⇔ ◖ ♣ P

Pangbourne

Cross Keys
Church Road
☎ (01734) 843268
11–3, 6–11
Courage Best Bitter; Morland Bitter, Old Speckled Hen Ⓗ
Super, unspoilt, 17th-century village pub where the patio garden backs on to the River Pang. Small aviary. Just south of Whitchurch bridge on the Thames. Tiny car park.
♨ Q ⏳ ❀ ◖ ⊟ ≉ ♣ P

Pinkneys Green

Robin Hood
Furze Platt Road (A308, facing the green) ☎ (01628) 26686
11–2.30 (3.30 Sat), 5 (6 Sat)–11
Morland Bitter, Old Masters; Wells Bombardier Ⓗ
Small, busy, out-of-town pub, built as a greengrocer's in the 17th century. Mind your head on the ceiling. ❀ ◖ ♣ P

Stag & Hounds
1 Lee Lane (SW corner of the green) ☎ (01628) 30268
11–2.30, 6–11
S&N Theakston Best Bitter, XB, Old Peculier; guest beers Ⓗ
Originally a Nicholson's beer house from the 1820s. The raised, open porch leads to the bar; the lounge area is used by diners only at weekends. Off-road parking opposite.
♨ Q ❀ ◖

Waggon & Horses
112 Pinkney Road (S of green)
☎ (01628) 24429
11–3, 5–11
Morland Bitter, Old Masters; guest beers Ⓗ
Very welcoming and popular locals' pub where the quiet saloon is accessed via the alley to the right. The public is plain but can get very busy. No meals weekends.
♨ Q ❀ ♣

Reading

Butler
89–91 Chatham Street
☎ (01734) 391635
11.30–11
Fuller's Hock, Chiswick, London Pride, Mr Harry, ESB Ⓗ
Popular pub with a horseshoe-shaped bar and a friendly atmosphere. The background music is not overpowering. Guinness was once bottled on the premises.
♨ Q ❀ ◖ ▶ & P

Dove
119 Orts Road (near canal, behind Reading College)
☎ (01734) 352556
11–2.30, 5.30–11; 11–11 Sat
Brakspear Mild, Bitter, Old, Special, OBJ Ⓗ
Friendly town pub with a great community spirit. Irish and blues music eves. ◖ ♣ P

Eldon Arms
19 Eldon Terrace
☎ (01734) 573857
10.30 (11 Sat)–3, 6.30–11
Adnams Broadside; Hall & Woodhouse Tanglefoot; Wadworth IPA, 6X, Old Timer Ⓗ
Friendly, two-room, back-street boozer, which welcomes all: a quiet lounge and a much livelier public. Curry night Mon; live folk music Wed; no food at weekends. Well worth seeking out, but parking is not easy. Q ◖

Horse & Jockey
120 Castle Hill (just outside ring road, near police station)
☎ (01734) 590172
11–11
Courage Directors; Gale's HSB; Ruddles Best Bitter; Shepherd Neame Bishops Finger; Young's Special Ⓗ
Relaxed, friendly local with a horse racing theme. Conversation is still the order of the day. Occasional discos at weekends. Families welcome in summer.
♨ ⏳ ❀ ◖ P

Sweeney & Todd
10 Castle Street (off St Mary's Butts) ☎ (01734) 586466
11–11; 12–3 Sun, closed Sun eve
Adnams Bitter; Eldridge Pope Blackdown Porter, Royal Oak Ⓗ; Gibbs Mew Salisbury, Wake Ale Ⓖ; Wadworth 6X Ⓗ
Small bar at the back of a pie shop, above a cellar restaurant (but drinkers are warmly welcomed). Try the interesting, home-made pies and the house wines and port.
Q ⏳ ❀ ◖ ▶

Wallingford Arms

2 Caroline Street (off ring road, near swimming pool)
☎ (01734) 575272
11 (12 Fri)–11
Morland Bitter, Old Masters, Old Speckled Hen; Wells Bombardier; guest beer H
Reading CAMRA *Town Pub of the Year*: a two-bar, back-street pub involved in crib, bar billiards and darts leagues. Smart and tidy dress required in the lounge bar. No food Sun. Cuddly pub dog.
❀ ◖ ♣ P

Remenham

Two Brewers

Wargrave Road (A321/A423 jct, just before Henley bridge)
☎ (01491) 574375
11–3, 6–11
Brakspear Bitter, Special (summer), **OBJ** (winter) H
Pleasant, near-riverside pub within sight of the brewery. Just a short walk from, and a good base for visiting, Henley. Children welcome if eating.
♨ ❀ ⌂ ◖ ≠ (Henley–not winter Sun) ♣ P

Sandhurst

Rose & Crown

108 High Street
☎ (01252) 872332
12–3, 5.30–11; 12–11 Sat
John Smith's Bitter; Ushers Best Bitter H
Friendly locals' pub on a site licensed since 1729.
♨ ❀ ◖ ▶ ≠ ♣ P

Shinfield

Bell & Bottle

School Green
☎ (01734) 883563
11–11
Gale's XXXD, 5X; Hook Norton Best Bitter; S&N Theakston Best Bitter, XB; guest beers H
Enthusiastically-run village pub with a changing range of guest beers. Traditional two-bar layout with a dartboard and other games.
♨ Q ❀ ◖ ▶ ♣ P

Slough

Rising Sun

20 Windsor Road
☎ (01753) 554877
11–11
Bass Worthington BB; Fuller's London Pride H
One-bar, town-centre tavern. There has been a pub on this site since the 1800s. Live music weekends. The beer range may vary. No food Sun.
◖ & ≠ ♣

Swallowfield

Crown

The Street (off old A33)
☎ (01734) 883260
11–3, 6–11
Morland Bitter, Old Masters, Old Speckled Hen H
Two-bar village pub which has been run by the same family for 30 years. Very much the centre of local life, with a good regular trade and a keen following for the various games on offer. Eve meals Thu–Sat. ♨ ❀ ◖ ▶ ⌂ ♣ P

Thatcham

Old Chequers

36 The Broadway
☎ (01635) 863312
11–11
Tetley Bitter; Wadworth 6X; guest beer H
Warmly atmospheric, 17th-century building with wood floors and low beams, popular lunchtimes and eves. The guest beer changes every two weeks. Separate dining area (lunches seven days). Quiz nights. ❀ ◖ P

Theale

Falcon

High Street ☎ (01734) 302523
10.30–11
Archers Best Bitter; Courage Best Bitter; Wadworth 6X H
Old, two-bar coaching inn near the site of the former Blatch's Brewery and close to Theale swing bridge on the Kennet and Avon Canal. Park through the classic archway. No meals weekends.
Q ❀ ◖ ≠ ♣ P

Three Mile Cross

Swan

Basingstoke Road (½ mile S of M4 jct 11, on old A33)
☎ (01734) 883674
11–11
Courage Best Bitter, Directors; Marston's Pedigree; Wadworth 6X; Webster's Yorkshire Bitter H
17th-century coaching inn in a quiet village setting, with oak beams and an inglenook. Small, homely lunchtime restaurant (renowned for freshly home-cooked food).
♨ Q ❀ ◖ P

Twyford

Duke of Wellington

High Street ☎ (01734) 340456
11.30–3, 5–11
Brakspear Mild, Bitter, Old, Special, OBJ H

Friendly, 16th-century village pub: a popular public bar and a quieter lounge. Large sheltered garden and patio area. Q ❀ ◖ ⌂ ≠ ♣ P

Wargrave

Bull

High Street ☎ (01734) 403120
11–3, 6–11
Brakspear Bitter, Special H
15th-century inn located in a picturesque village. Brass and beams abound. Extensive and interesting menu (no food Sun eve). ♨ Q ❀ ◖ ▶ ≠ (not winter Sun)

West Ilsley

Harrow

Off A34 ☎ (01635) 28160
11–3, 6–11
Morland Bitter, Old Masters, Old Speckled Hen H
Beautifully refurbished village pub in the Berkshire downs. Cricket can be viewed on the ground opposite without leaving the front garden. Handy for walkers on the nearby Ridgeway. Very good food: home-made rabbit pie is a speciality.
♨ Q ❀ ◖ & ♣ P

White Waltham

Beehive

Waltham Road
☎ (01628) 822877
11–3, 5.30–11
Brakspear Bitter; Whitbread WCPA, Flowers IPA, Original; guest beers H
Deservedly popular country local opposite the cricket pitch. Friendly regulars make all feel welcome and the enterprising landlord arranges trips to breweries and beer festivals. Petanque and a menagerie in the fine back garden. No eve meals Sun/Mon.
♨ Q ❀ ◖ ▶ ⌂ & ♣ ⌂

Windsor

Prince Albert

2 Clewer Hill Road (B3022 SW of centre) ☎ (01753) 864788
11–11
Courage Best Bitter; Marston's Pedigree; John Smith's Bitter; Wadworth 6X H
Cosy and comfortable, two-bar pub: a former 19th-century hunting lodge in the Great Park. No food Sun.
Q ❀ ◖ ⌂ ♣ P

Prince Christian

11 Kings Road
☎ (01753) 864788
11–3, 5–11

Brakspear Bitter; Fuller's
London Pride; S&N
Theakston Best Bitter Ⓗ
Windsor's longest established
free house, just a short stroll
from the main tourist area and
reasonably priced for the
locality. No food Sat/Sun.
Ɑ ⇌ (Central)

Vansittart Arms

Vansittart Road
☎ (01753) 865988
11–11
Fuller's Hock, London Pride,
ESB Ⓗ
Pub split into three distinct,
cosy areas in Victorian style.
The back section is an olde-
worlde public bar, with an
area for pool. Lots of nice
wood provides character. All
food is home-cooked (no food
Sun eve). ♨ ☻ Ɑ ▶ ⇌ ♣

Winkfield Row

Old Hatchet

Hatchet Lane (A330) OS922713
☎ (01344) 882303
11–11
Bass Charrington IPA,
Draught Bass; Fuller's
London Pride Ⓗ
A sensitive conversion from
three woodcutters' cottages
has produced a welcoming ale
house serving a range of food
in either the two-part bar or
the separate restaurant. Very
friendly atmosphere; well
worth finding. ♨ ☻ Ɑ ▶ P

Wokingham

Crooked Billet

Honey Hill (off B3430, 2 miles
SE of Wokingham) OS826667
☎ (01734) 780438
11–11
Brakspear Bitter, Old,
Special Ⓗ
A gem of a traditional ale
house on the outskirts of
Wokingham; well worth
seeking out for both food and
drink. The ramp access and a
real fire typify the welcome.
No eve meals Sun/Mon.
♨ Q ☻ Ɑ ▶ ♣ P

Dukes Head

56 Denmark Street
☎ (01734) 780316
11.30–3, 5.30 (4.30 Fri, 6 Sat)–11
Brakspear Bitter, Special,
OBJ Ⓗ
Town pub popular with
business and passing trades,
converted from three cottages
in 1795. Separate area with
games; comfortable,
well-furnished lounge.
No food Sun. ☻ Ɑ ⇌ P

Queens Head

23 The Terrace (A329, top of
Station Rd)
☎ (01734) 781221
11–3, 5.30–11
Morland Bitter, Old Masters,
Old Speckled Hen Ⓗ
Superb, basic hostelry where

the local and business regulars
take an active role in the many
pub sports activities. No food
Sun. ☻ Ɑ ⇌ ♣

Ship Inn

104–108 Peach Street (main
Bracknell road)
☎ (01734) 780389
11.30–3 (4 Sat), 5 (6.30 Sat)–11;
11.30–11 Fri
Fuller's Hock, Chiswick,
London Pride, ESB Ⓗ
As its name suggests, a pub
with a nautical theme in two
separate bars and a games
room (16th-century in part).
Lively and bustling at
weekends. Home-cooking (no
food Fri, Sat or Sun eves).
☻ Ɑ ▶ ♣ P

Woodspeen

Five Bells

Lambourn Road OS451687
☎ (01635) 48763
11.30–2.30 (3 Sat), 6–11
Morland Bitter, Old Speckled
Hen; S&N Theakston XB or
Draught Bass or Wells
Bombardier Ⓗ
Small, early Victorian pub at
the bottom end of the
Lambourn valley, near the
famous Watermill Theatre, in
an area soon to be wrecked by
Newbury's bypass. Recently
purchased from Courage and
extended to resemble a
restaurant.
☻ ⛺ Ɑ ▶ ⅄ ♣ P ⚥

CZECH MATES?

The term 'Pilsner' originally denoted a beer from the town of Pilsen in the Czech republic. Similarly, 'Budweiser' meant beer from the Czech town of Ceske Budejovice. In 1874, Adolphus Busch founded a brewery in St Louis, USA, and began to brew his own beer called Budweiser. Anheuser Busch is now the world's biggest brewery. However, there is still a brewery in Ceske Budejovice that brews a beer called 'Budweiser': Budweiser Budvar—a fine traditional Czech lager. For most of this century, the two breweries have been in a dispute over the trademark and Britain is one of the few countries where both beers are available. Now, with the privatisation of many companies in the Czech republic, Anheuser Busch is poised to pounce. By buying a stake in the Czech brewery, the trademark dispute can be settled.

But CAMRA is concerned that once this fine brewery's independence is lost, there is no guarantee that the beer will remain the same, or its current markets secure. Independence is the only safeguard any brewery can have. Look at the hundreds of breweries taken over and closed down in Britain alone. Budvar deserves the support of the discerning drinker. Its continued independence will safeguard one of the world's classic beers, and send a message to the international brewing corporations.

Buckinghamshire

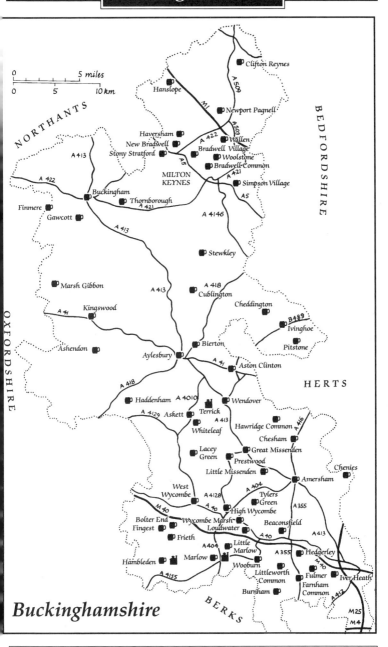

Buckinghamshire

Chiltern, *Terrick*; **Old Luxters**, *Hambleden*; **Rebellion**, *Marlow*

Amersham

Eagle
High Street ☎ (01494) 725262
11–3, 6–11

Fuller's London Pride; Greene King IPA; Tetley Bitter Ⓗ Traditional, old-town pub with a narrow frontage: comfortable, friendly and often dominated by diners at lunchtimes. Footbridge access to the attractive garden. Eve meals Sat only. 🏨 Q ⊛ ◑ ♣

Try also: Kings Arms, High St (Free)

Buckinghamshire

Ashendon

Red Lion
Lower End (lane by church)
☎ (01296) 651296
12–2.30, 7–11
Adnams Bitter; Hall & Woodhouse Badger Best Bitter; Wadworth IPA, 6X; guest beer H
400-year-old building once a courtroom, on a hill overlooking the northern Vale of Aylesbury. Imaginative food. 🛏 🕮 ◖ ▶ P

Askett

Three Crowns
☎ (01844) 343041
12–2.30, 5.30–11
Bass Worthington BB; Hancock's HB; Marston's Pedigree H
An enigma!: a plain, basic village pub from the 17th century. Superior, freshly-cooked food (featuring Thai and Indian Dishes). No reservations; no food Mon.
🛏 🕮 ◖ ▶ P

Aston Clinton

Rothschild Arms
82 Weston Road (B4544)
☎ (01296) 630320
12–2.30, 5.30–11; 12–11 Fri & Sat
Bass Worthington BB; M&B Highgate Dark; Marston's Pedigree H
Friendly, one-bar, mid-terrace local with a function room. Meals till 8.30pm (8 Sat); no food Sun. Summer barbecues.
🕮 🛏 ◖ ♣ P

Aylesbury

Grapes
Market Square ☎ (01296) 83735
10.30–11
Courage Best Bitter, Directors; S&N Theakston Best Bitter, XB H
Narrow bar next to the civic centre. Wooden floorboards and Victorian decor provide a pleasant atmosphere. Upstairs restaurant (group bookings only for eve meals). ◖ ⇌

Old Plough & Harrow
Stoke Road ☎ (01296) 23306
11–11
Courage Best Bitter, Directors; Gale's HSB; Marston's Pedigree; Ruddles County; Wadworth 6X H
Popular, comfortable pub on a busy gyratory road system. Strong local trade; games emphasis. 🛏 🕮 ◖ ▶ ⇌ ♣ P

Try also: Aristocrat, Wendover Rd (Fuller's)

Beaconsfield

Greyhound
Windsor End
☎ (01494) 673823
11–2.30, 5.30–11
Courage Best Bitter; Fuller's London Pride; Wadworth 6X; guest beer H
Small, charming, unspoilt pub with a cosy snug bar. Home-cooked food in the bar or restaurant. Q 🕮 ◖ ▶ 🍺

Bierton

Bell
191 Aylesbury Road
☎ (01296) 436055
11–3, 6–11; 11–11 Sat
Fuller's Hock, Chiswick, London Pride, ESB H
A much-improved pub since becoming a Fuller's house: a comfortable lounge bar and a small public bar. Live jazz Sun nights but no meals Sun eve.
🕮 ◖ ▶ 🍺 ♠ ♣ P

Bolter End

Peacock
On B482 ☎ (01494) 881417
11.45–2.30, 6–11
Ansells Mild; Draught Bass; Ind Coope ABC Best Bitter; Tetley Bitter H
Pub with one large room and several distinct areas, located just west of Lane End and dating from 1620. The emphasis is on home-cooked bar meals (no food Sun eve).
🛏 Q 🕮 ◖ ▶ ♣ P

Buckingham

Whale
Market Hill ☎ (01280) 815537
10–11
Fuller's Hock, Chiswick, London Pride, ESB H
Welcoming, traditional market town pub where gas lights are a feature of the bar. The lounge doubles as a restaurant.
🛏 🕮 🛏 ◖ ▶ ♣

Burnham

Old Five Bells
14 Church Street (just off High St) ☎ (01628) 604276
11–11
Brakspear Bitter; Whitbread Boddingtons Bitter, Flowers Original, Winter Royal H
Pub mentioned in the *Domesday Book*: one large bar. Good value food (no lunches Sun, no eve meals Fri or Sat). Very comfortable children's room. The beer range may vary. 🌣 🕮 ◖ ♣

Cheddington

Rosebery Arms
Station Road ☎ (01296) 668222
11.30–2.30, 5.30–11
Brakspear Special; Wells Eagle, Bombardier; guest beer H
Fine, old ex-hotel, now a free house, offering good value food and drink near the scene of the Great Train Robbery. No food Sun eve. 🕮 ◖ ▶ ⇌ ♣ P

Chenies

Red Lion
Off A404 ☎ (01923) 282722
11–2.30, 5.30–11
Adnams Bitter; Ind Coope Benskins Best Bitter; Wadworth 6X; guest beer (occasional) H
Friendly, busy village free house, which attracts drinkers and diners from near and far and is notable for its complete lack of machines. Find the amazing 'snug', to the rear of the dining room. Q 🕮 ◖ ▶ P

Chesham

Black Horse
Chesham Vale (2 miles N of Chesham on Cholesbury road)
☎ (01494) 784656
11–2.30, 6–11
Adnams Bitter; Ind Coope Benskins Best Bitter, Burton Ale; Rebellion IPA; Tring Ridgeway H
Comfortable old inn with an enormous garden. The accent is on food, but drinkers are also very welcome. Watch out for the low beam. 🕮 ◖ ▶ ⅋ P

Queens Head
Church Street (B485)
☎ (01494) 783773
11–2.30, 5 (6 Sat)–11
Brakspear Bitter, Special; Fuller's Hock, London Pride H
A public bar and a comfortable, airy lounge make this an excellent old-town local. Brakspear's Old is an occasional winter visitor. No meals Sun. 🛏 🕮 ◖ ▶ ⊖ ♣ P

Clifton Reynes

Robin Hood
☎ (01234) 711574
11.30–2.30, 6.30–11; 12–2.30, 7–10.30 Sun
Greene King IPA, Abbot H
Welcoming, two-bar village pub, a little off the main road but worth finding. Spacious garden with camping. Good variety of well-priced food.
🛏 🌣 🕮 ◖ ▶ ♠ P

Buckinghamshire

Cublington

Unicorn
High Street ☎ (01296) 681261
12–3, 5.30–11
Beer range varies Ⓗ
Low-beamed village local with open fires at each end of a long bar. Separate dining room (no meals Sun eve). Five ales served from a changing range.
🏚 Q ❀ ◑ ♪ ▲ P

Farnham Common

Yew Tree
Collinswood Road (A355, N of village) ☎ (01753) 643723
11–11
Morland Bitter, Old Masters, Old Speckled Hen; guest beer Ⓗ
Small country pub, 300 years old, where locals enjoy country sports. Meals served in the lounge bar; breakfasts from 8am. Emphasis on game.
🏚 Q ❀ ◑ ♪ 🖼 ▲ ♣ P

Fingest

Chequers
☎ (01491) 638335
11–3, 6–11
Brakspear Bitter, Special, Old Ⓗ
Friendly, 15th-century pub opposite the church. The emphasis is on food. The restaurant is closed Sun eve (but a cold buffet is available in the bar as usual).
🏚 Q ❀ ◑ ♪ P

Finmere

Red Lion
Mere Road (W of village)
☎ (01280) 847836
12–3, 6–11
Fuller's Hock, London Pride, ESB Ⓗ
17th-century, stone and thatch pub: a single bar with an inglenook and beams.
🏚 ❀ ◑ ♪ ♣ P ⚹

Frieth

Prince Albert
Moors End (100 yds from Lane End road) ☎ (01494) 881683
11–3, 5.30–11
Brakspear Mild, Bitter, Old, Special, OBJ Ⓗ
The sort of pub you don't want to tell others about, enjoying a superb atmosphere, location and hospitality. Josie's platefuls are a bonus lunchtime (Tue–Sat).
🏚 Q ❀ ◑ ♣

Fulmer

Black Horse
Windmill Road
☎ (01753) 663183
11–2.30, 5.30–11
Courage Best Bitter, Directors Ⓗ
Early 17th-century, three-bar pub. Note the naked figurine handpump in the saloon. Snacks only Sun.
🏚 Q ❀ ◑ ♪ ♣ P

Gawcott

Cuckoo's Nest
New Inn Lane
☎ (01280) 812092
10.30–3 (not Mon), 6–11
Adnams Broadside; Hook Norton Best Bitter; guest beer (occasional) Ⓗ
Friendly and welcoming, two-bar 18th-century village local. 🏚 ❀ 🖼 ♣ P

Great Missenden

Cross Keys
High Street ☎ (01494) 865373
11–3, 5.30–11
Fuller's Hock, Chiswick, London Pride, ESB Ⓗ
About 450 years old, the oldest pub in town. The licensee insists on no dining in the bar in the eve, thus retaining a good pub atmosphere (eve meals in the dining area Mon–Sat). High-backed settles feature. 🏚 ❀ ◑ ⇌ ♣ P

Haddenham

Rising Sun
Thame Road ☎ (01844) 291744
11–3, 7–11; 11–11 Fri
Wells Eagle; guest beers Ⓗ
Small and friendly, one-bar village local. No lunches Sun. Cider in summer.
Q ❀ ◑ ♪ ♣ ⌂

Hambleden

Stag & Huntsman
☎ (01491) 571227
11–2.30, 6–11
Brakspear Bitter, Special; Old Luxters Barn Ale; Rebellion IPA; Wadworth 6X, Old Timer Ⓗ
Unspoilt, three-bar pub in a picturesque, brick and flint NT village. Extensive menu (not Sun eve), with seafood a speciality; fish and chip specials Tue eve in winter.
🏚 ❀ 🛏 ◑ ♣

Hanslope

Globe
50 Hartwell Road, Long Street
☎ (01908) 510336
12–2.30, 6–11
Banks's Mild, Bitter Ⓔ; **Marston's Pedigree** Ⓗ
Very pleasant pub north of the village with a good garden and play area (zoo). Booking advised for meals weekends. No food Mon eve.
Q ❀ ◑ ♪ 🖼 ♣ P

Haversham

Greyhound
High Street ☎ (01908) 313487
11.30–2.30, 5.30–11; 12–3, 6.30–11 Sat
Greene King XX Mild, IPA, Abbot Ⓗ
Attractive, 17th-century village inn, with two cosy bars. No food Sun; no eve meals Tue or Wed. Q ❀ ◑ ♪ ♣ P

Hawridge Common

Full Moon
OS936069 ☎ (01494) 758262
12–3, 6–11
Courage Best Bitter; Morrells Bitter, Graduate; Ruddles Best Bitter; Wadworth 6X; guest beer Ⓗ
Fine old country pub, licensed for over 300 years and once a 'house of dubious repute'! Radically extended in recent years. No eve meals Sun.
🏚 Q ❀ ◑ ♪ 🖼 ♣ P

Hedgerley

One Pin
One Pin Lane
☎ (01753) 643035
11–4, 5.30–11
Courage Best Bitter, Directors Ⓗ
Traditional, two-bar pub with an air of class in the saloon. The landlord has been in residence for 30 years. No food Sun. ◑ ♣

Try also: **White Horse** (Free)

High Wycombe

Hobgoblin
High Street ☎ (01494) 526533
11–11
Courage Best Bitter, Directors; Wychwood Best, Hobgoblin Ⓗ
Refurbished town-centre pub, a listed building from the 18th/19th century. Business trade lunchtimes; students in the eve. Usually busy and noisy. No food weekends.
🏚 ❀ ◑ ⇌

Rose & Crown
Desborough Road
☎ (01494) 527982
11–11
Chiltern Beechwood; Gale's HSB; Marston's Pedigree;

45

Buckinghamshire

Morland Old Speckled Hen; Webster's Green Label; Young's Special; Wycombe's most interesting selection of beers, in an L-shaped, corner pub with busy office lunchtime trade (no meals weekends).
🏚 ◖ ⇌ ♣ ⌂

Iver Heath

Black Horse

Slough Road ☎ (01753) 653044
11–3, 5 (7 Sat)–11
Adnams Bitter; Fuller's London Pride; Marston's Pedigree; Old Luxters Barn Ale; Tetley Bitter; Wychwood Hobgoblin; guest beers Ⓗ
Pub with a single bar that still has some of its original character, and two smart restaurant areas. No eve food Sun. 🏚 ❀ ◖ ◗ P

Ivinghoe

Rose & Crown

Vicarage Lane (turn opp. church, then 1st right)
☎ (01296) 668472
12–2.30, 6–11
Adnams Bitter; Greene King IPA; Morrells Mild; guest beer Ⓗ
Hard to find, but worth the effort, this street-corner local has a comfortable lounge and a lively public bar on different levels. 🏚 ◖ ◗ ♣

Kingswood

Crooked Billet

Ham Green ☎ (01296) 770239
11–11; 11–3, 5–11 Mon & Thu
Draught Bass; Ind Coope Burton Ale; Tetley Bitter; guest beer Ⓗ
Deceptively large, 17th-century, single-storey pub on the A41 with a spacious garden, a restaurant and a function room. Popular with ramblers, car clubs and hot air balloonists.
🏚 ⛺ ❀ ◖ ◗ ▲ ♣ P

Lacey Green

Pink & Lily

Pink Road, Parslows Hillock (1 mile from village) OS828019
☎ (01494) 488308
11.45–3, 6–11
Brakspear Bitter; Chiltern Beechwood; Courage Directors; Wadworth 6X; Whitbread Flowers Original; Wychwood Hobgoblin Ⓗ
Lively and popular country pub noted for its choice of beers and food (no chips!). No meals Sun eve. The original snug is dedicated to the poet Rupert Brooke.
🏚 ❀ ◖ ◗ ♣ P

Little Marlow

King's Head

Church Road
☎ (01628) 484407
11–3, 5.30–11
Brakspear Bitter; Marston's Pedigree; Whitbread Boddingtons Bitter; Young's Special; guest beer Ⓗ
14th-century village pub: two bars with much character. Varied, home-cooked meals always available. Function room; new separate dining room. Wheelchair WC.
🏚 ⛺ ◖ ◗ ﴾ P

Little Missenden

Crown

Off A413 ☎ (01494) 862571
11–2.30, 6–11; 12–2.30, 7–10.30 Sun
Draught Bass; Hook Norton Best Bitter; Morrells Varsity Ⓗ; **guest beer** Ⓖ
Authentic old village pub with a genuine welcome. The single, small bar enjoys a two-bar atmosphere and is decorated with brass and farm implements. No food Sun.
🏚 Q ❀ ◖ ♣ ⌂ P

Littleworth Common

Blackwood Arms

Common Lane (SE of Burnham–Beaconsfield road, near Beech Tree pub)
OS937863 ☎ (01753) 642169
11–2.30, 5.30–11; 11–11 Fri & Sat
Beer range varies Ⓗ
Outstanding free house in idyllic woodland surroundings, with one of the fastest changing range of beers in the country – 752 in 1993, all from independent breweries. Good value food. Local CAMRA *Pub of the Year* 1993.
🏚 Q ❀ ◖ ◗ ▲ ⌂ P

Loudwater

Derehams Inn

Derehams Lane (just N of A40)
OS903907 ☎ (01494) 530965
11–3, 5.30–11
Beer range varies Ⓗ
Cosy and hard to find and mainly catering for local trade. Six ales on sale. Lunches weekdays only. Small car park. 🏚 ❀ ◖ ♣ P

Marlow

Carpenters Arms

15 Spittal Street
☎ (01628) 473649
11–11
Morrells Bitter, Mild, Varsity Ⓗ

Thriving workingman's local of character, acquired by Morrells in 1992. Q ⇌ ♣

Prince of Wales

Mill Road (off Station Rd)
☎ (01628) 482970
11–11
Brains Bitter; Young's Special; guest beer
Friendly, back-street local with two connecting bars: a comfortable public, and a lounge with a dining area (families welcome). No food Sun eve. ❀ ◖ ⇌ ♣ P

Try also: Clayton Arms, Oxford Rd (Brakspear)

Marsh Gibbon

Greyhound

West Edge ☎ (01869) 277365
12–3.30, 6–11
Fuller's London Pride; Greene King IPA, Abbot; Hook Norton Best Bitter Ⓗ
Listed building, probably of Tudor origin, rebuilt after a fire in 1740. It still has the fire plaque of Sun Insurance. Thai cuisine a speciality; popular for quick business lunches.
🏚 Q ❀ ◖ ◗ P

Milton Keynes: *Bradwell Common*

Countryman

Bradwell Common Boulevard
☎ (01908) 676346
11–11
Ansells Mild; Enville Ale; Ruddles Best Bitter; Webster's Yorkshire Bitter; guest beers
Popular new pub offering the best selection of beers in the area: 12 handpumps. Good food. Regular beer festivals.
❀ ◖ ◗ ﴾ ⇌ (M Keynes) P

Bradwell Village

Prince Albert

Vicarage Road, Old Bradwell
☎ (01908) 312080
11–2.30 (4.30 Sat), 5.30 (6 Sat)–11
Wells Eagle, Bombardier; guest beers Ⓗ
Friendly Victorian pub with a village atmosphere and a children's outdoor play area. Excellent food. The guest beers change regularly. ❀ ◖ ◗ P

New Bradwell

New Inn

2 Bradwell Road
☎ (01908) 312094
11–11; 11–4, 6.30–11 Sat
Adnams Broadside; Wells Eagle; guest beers Ⓗ

Lively, canalside inn with good value bar food, plus a separate restaurant. Ideal for narrowboaters. 🏕 Q ❀ ◑ ▶ 🍴 ⇌ (Wolverton) ♣ P

Simpson Village

Plough
Simpson Road
☎ (01908) 670015
11–11
Hall & Woodhouse Tanglefoot; Morland Old Speckled Hen; Wells Eagle, Bombardier; guest beer H
Two-bar village pub in a prominent position. The large garden backs on to the Grand Union Canal. Good value, home-cooked food. Separate dining room. ❀ ◑ ▶ 🍴 ♣ P

Stony Stratford

Vaults/Bull
High Street ☎ (01908) 567104
11–11
Bass Worthington BB, Draught Bass; Brakspear Special; Fuller's London Pride; Hook Norton Best Bitter; guest beers H
Flagstone-floored bar of character attached to an old coaching inn. Folk music Sun lunch. With the Cock Hotel next door, it is said to be the origin of the cock and bull story. 🏕 🍴 ◑ ▶ ♿ ♣ P

Willen

Ship Ashore
Granville Square
☎ (01908) 609998
11–2.30 (3 Sat), 5 (6 Sat)–11
Draught Bass; Fuller's London Pride H
Modern pub with a comfortable lounge decorated to a nautical theme, plus a family room and a children's play area outside. Wheelchair WC. No food Sun. ♿ ❀ ◑ ▶ ♿ P ✂

Woolstone

Cross Keys
Newport Road
☎ (01908) 679404
11–11
Wells IPA, Bombardier; guest beers H
Thatched, two-bar village pub at the heart of a modern housing estate. Open Sun afternoon for food.
❀ ◑ ▶ ♣ P

Newport Pagnell

Green Man
92 Silver Street (off High St)
☎ (01908) 611914
12–3, 6–11; 12–11 Sat

Banks's Mild, Bitter; Camerons Strongarm; Marston's Pedigree H
A plain exterior hides this traditional gem with its cheery public bar and quiet lounge, with intriguing bric-a-brac. A basic, honest, back-street boozer. 🏕 Q ♣

Pitstone

Duke of Wellington
Cook's Wharf
☎ (01296) 661402
12–2.30 (3 Sat), 6–11
Butcombe Bitter; Fuller's London Pride; Marston's Pedigree H
Friendly, one-bar, country pub, half-way between Pitstone and Cheddington. The Grand Union Canal passes behind. Special rates for senior citizens' meals.
🏕 ❀ ◑ ▶ ♣ P

Prestwood

Kings Head
188 Wycombe Road
☎ (01494) 862392
11–11
Adnams Broadside; Brakspear Mild, Bitter, Old, Special, OBJ; Greene King Abbot; Tring Old Icknield Ale G
The antidote to the modern pub: traditional decor and atmosphere – no machines, music, draught lager or meals (snacks only).
🏕 Q ❀ 🍴 ♣ 🍵 P

Stewkley

Swan
High Street North
☎ (01525) 240285
12–3, 6–11
Courage Best Bitter, Directors; Marston's Pedigree H
Fine, beamed Georgian village pub with a good atmosphere. No food Sun eve. ❀ ◑ ▶ ♣ P

Thornborough

Lone Tree
Buckingham Road
☎ (01280) 812334
11–3, 5–11
Chiltern Ale; Samuel Smith OBB; guest beers H
Smart roadside pub with an ever-changing range of beers (four guests). The menu is equally varied (booking advised). 🏕 ❀ ◑ ▶ ♿ ✂

Tylers Green

Horse & Jockey
Church Road (off B474)
☎ (01494) 815963
11–2.30, 5.30–11

Ansells Mild; Fuller's London Pride; Ind Coope Burton Ale; Tetley Bitter; guest beer H
Spacious pub serving food at all times. Fine collection of horse brasses and livery.
❀ ◑ ▶ ♣ P

Wendover

King & Queen
South Street ☎ (01296) 623272
12–3, 6–11; 12–11 Sat
Greene King IPA; Tetley Bitter; Whitbread Flowers Original H
Small, 16th-century, two-bar pub with a stone-flagged public bar and an inglenook. Ask for Scrumpy to get real cider. Eve meals on request.
🏕 ❀ ◑ 🍴 ⇌ 🍵 P

West Wycombe

George & Dragon
☎ (01494) 464414
11–2.30, 5.30–11; 11–11 Sat
Courage Best Bitter, Directors; Young's Special H
18th-century coaching inn with an original timbered bar, in a NT village. Noted for food. Excellent garden.
🏕 Q ♿ ❀ 🍴 ◑ ▶ P

Whiteleaf

Red Lion
Upper Icknield Way (near A4010) ☎ (01844) 344476
11.30–3, 5.30 (6 Sat)–11
Brakspear Bitter; Hook Norton Best Bitter; Morland Bitter, Old Speckled Hen; Wadworth 6X H
Attractive and secluded, 17th-century, village pub with low ceilings. Well-known for food. 🏕 ❀ 🍴 ◑ ▶ P

Wooburn

Queen & Albert
The Green ☎ (01628) 520610
11–3, 5.30–11
Ind Coope Benskins Best Bitter, Burton Ale H
Friendly local, popular with all ages. Meals not available Sun, nor Mon and Tue in winter.
◑ ▶ ⇌ ♣

Wycombe Marsh

General Havelock
114 Kings Mead Road (parallel to A40) ☎ (01494) 520391
11–2.30 (3 Fri), 5.30 (5 Fri)–11
Fuller's Hock, Chiswick, London Pride, ESB H
Traditional family pub, smart, friendly and noted for its lunches. 🏕 ❀ ◑ ♣ P

Cambridgeshire

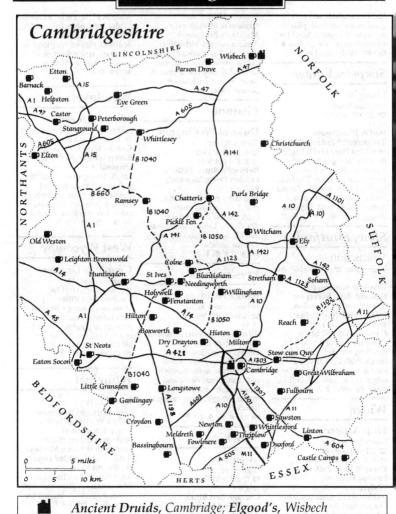

Cambridgeshire

Ancient Druids, *Cambridge*; **Elgood's**, *Wisbech*

Barnack

Millstone
Millstone Lane
☎ (01780) 740296
11–2.30, 6–11
Adnams Bitter; Everards Tiger, Old Original; Ridleys IPA; guest beer H
High standards are maintained here as a recent refurbishment shows; the bar area has been moved but you wouldn't know. Excellent, home-made food (eve meals Tue–Sat). ⚅ ✿ ◑ ▶ ᐈ & P ⤬

Bassingbourn

Pear Tree
North End (right off A1098 onto the Causeway)

☎ (01763) 44068
11–2.30, 6–11; 11–11 Sat
Bass Worthington BB; Eldridge Pope Royal Oak; Greene King IPA; Whitbread Boddingtons Bitter H
Village-centre pub with a social club—discount for OAPs. The two bars are quite different, the public bar being lively and the lounge bar quieter. ⚅ ✿ ◑ ▶ ᐈ ✦ P

Bluntisham

White Swan
High Street ☎ (01487) 842055
12.30–2.30, 7–11
Draught Bass; Greene King IPA; Tetley Bitter H
Two-bar fenland pub with a friendly atmosphere.
⚅ ✿ ◑ ▶ ᐈ ✦ P

Boxworth

Golden Ball
High Street ☎ (01454) 267397
11.30–2.30, 6.30–11
Greene King IPA; guest beers H
Pub offering a friendly welcome, an ever-changing choice of home-cooked food, and three guest beers.
⚇ ✿ ◑ ▶ &

Cambridge

Cambridge Blue
85–87 Gwydir Street
☎ (01223) 61382
12–2.30, 6–11
Nethergate IPA, Bitter, Old Growler; guest beers H
Pub run by Nethergate

48

Brewery as a free house. The comfortable, no-smoking back bar boasts a collection of hats. The lively main bar leads to a new extension with pictures of trains to complement the model railway in the garden. Children welcome till 9pm.

Cow & Calf
14 Pound Hill
☎ (01223) 311909
12 (2.30 Sat)–3, 5.30 (7 Sat)–11
Draught Bass; Courage Best Bitter; Elgood's Cambridge Bitter; Nethergate IPA; Shepherd Neame Best Bitter; Young's Special H
Traditional pub atmosphere in one of the few genuine free houses in Cambridge. The beer range varies. Lunches weekdays only.

Empress
72 Thoday Street (off Mill Rd)
☎ (01223) 247236
11–2.30, 6.30–11
Marston's Pedigree; Whitbread Castle Eden Ale; guest beers
Popular bustling, street-corner pub: four different drinking areas within a basically open-plan layout.

Free Press
Prospect Row ☎ (01223) 68337
12–2.30 (3 Sat), 6–11
Greene King IPA, Abbot H
Busy, no-smoking pub serving outstanding food. No machines.

Haymakers
54 High Street, Chesterton
☎ (01223) 67417
11–2.30 (3 Sat), 6–11
Ind Coope Burton Ale; Tetley Bitter; guest beers H
Welcoming, one-bar community pub serving good value food (no meals Sun). Live music staged Fri and usually Sat.

Live & Let Live
40 Mawson Road (off Mill Rd)
☎ (01223) 460261
12–2.30, 6–11
Adnams Bitter; Everards Tiger; Felinfoel Double Dragon; Morland Old Speckled Hen; Shepherd Neame Bishops Finger; guest beers H
Plentiful use of wood and other natural materials gives this little pub a really cosy atmosphere. Excellent reputation for food.

Mitre Tavern
17 Bridge Street
☎ (01223) 358403
11–11

Adnams Bitter; Ind Coope Burton Ale; Tetley Bitter; Wadworth 6X; guest beers H
Attractively de-modernised in a non-clichéd ale house style, with usually eight beers on tap. Open for meals Sun afternoons; limited eve menu in winter.

Red Bull
11 Barton Road
☎ (01223) 352788
11–11
Brakspear Bitter; Morland Old Speckled Hen; S&N Theakston Best Bitter; Wadworth 6X; Whitbread Boddingtons Bitter; guest beers H / G
Pub offering up to seven beers on handpump plus two on gravity. A full menu is served lunchtime, Cheddar and Stilton platters from 3pm and basket suppers after 8.30 (no food Sun eve).

St Radegund
129 King Street
☎ (01223) 311794
12–3, 5.30–11; 12–11 Fri & Sat
Bateman XB; Fuller's London Pride; Nethergate Bitter, Old Growler H
Cambridge CAMRA *Pub of the Year 1994*: it makes up in character what it lacks in size. Ask about Veil Ale. Greek meze and huge crusty sandwiches are available Thu and Fri. The ceiling makes interesting reading.

Tap & Spile
13–14 Mill Road
☎ (01223) 357026
11–11
Beer range varies H
Bare brick and floorboards and plenty of wood in a straightforward ale house-style pub offering a range of eight, constantly changing beers from independent breweries. Crones cider. No food Sun.

Wrestlers
337 Newmarket Road
☎ (01223) 358777
11–11
Adnams Broadside; Hall & Woodhouse Tanglefoot; Mansfield Riding Bitter; Morland Old Speckled Hen; Wells Eagle, Bombardier H
Bustling, buoyant main road pub essentially one to experience rather than scrutinise. The character is formed by the clientele, not the fixtures and fittings. Authentic Thai bar meals or take-aways available 12–3 and 5–9 (no food Sun). Live music twice a week.

Castle Camps

Cock
High Street ☎ (01799) 584207
12–2, 7–11; 12–11 Sat
Greene King IPA, Abbot; Nethergate Bitter H
Pleasant, two-bar country local. Collections of horse brasses and porcelain adorn the main bar where food is served (blackboard menu). Note the outstanding mural of a cock in an alcove.

Castor

Royal Oak
Peterborough Road
☎ (01733) 380217
11–2.30, 6–11
Ind Coope Burton Ale; Tetley Bitter; guest beer H
Listed building with a thatched roof and considerable charm. The cosy atmosphere is enhanced by a low, beamed ceiling. Small area at the front for summer drinking.

Chatteris

Honest John
South Park Street
☎ (01354) 692698
11–2.30, 5.30–11
Whitbread Boddingtons Bitter, Fremlins Bitter, Wethered Bitter; guest beers H
Former labour exchange, built in the 1950s, featuring model ship and car collections. The landlord is a bit of a poet.

Walk the Dog
34 Bridge Street
☎ (01354) 693695
12–2.30, 6.30–11
Adnams Bitter; Bass Charrington IPA, Draught Bass H
One L-shaped room in a building which dates from the 1850s. No dogs.

Christchurch

Dun Cow
☎ (01354) 638323
11–11
Elgood's Cambridge Bitter; guest beers H
One-room village pub which is reputedly haunted, a 200-year-old former coaching inn. Live C&W music Sat.

Colne

Green Man
East Street ☎ (01487) 840368
12–3, 7–11

Greene King IPA; Ind Coope Burton Ale H
Comfortable and friendly, two-bar village pub, that dates back to the 17th century. Take care with the deep step down into the pub and the low, uneven door to the lounge.
❀ ◐ ◑ ⊞ ♣ P

Croydon

Queen Adelaide
High Street ☎ (01233) 208278
11.30–3, 6–11 (11–3, 5.30–11 summer)
Greene King IPA, Rayments Special; Mansfield Riding Bitter; guest beer (occasional) H
Large country pub near Royston. The remains of a wall between the dining area and the bar gives a cosier atmosphere than most pubs of this size. Home-cooked food.
⛫ ♉ ❀ ◐ ◑ ♣ P

Dry Drayton

Black Horse
Park Street (signed off main road) ☎ (01954) 781055
11–2.30, 6.30–11
Greene King IPA; guest beers H
Pleasant, 300-year-old pub, popular for food and committed to real ale (three, regularly changing guest beers). ⛫ Q ◐ ◑ ▲

Duxford

Plough
50 St Peters Street
☎ (01223) 833170
11–3, 5.30–11
Adnams Bitter; Everards Beacon, Tiger, Old Original; guest beers (occasional) H
17th-century, refurbished, thatched house offering a warm welcome. Excellent pub food is served at reasonable prices. Ideally situated for the Air Museum. ⛫ ❀ ◐ ◑ P

Eaton Socon

Crown
Great North Road (off A45, St Neots bypass)
☎ (01480) 212232
11–2.30, 5–11; 11–11 Sat
Draught Bass; Tetley Bitter; guest beer H
Ivy-clad free house, just off the A1 with at least six real ales on offer. Bookings are advised for the restaurant. ❀ ◐ ◑ ▲ ♣ P

Elton

Crown
Duck Street ☎ (01832) 280232
11.30–2.30, 6–11
Greene King IPA, Rayments Special, Abbot; guest beers H
Stone-built, thatched, village pub with great character. The ambience is delightful and the food excellent. The attached restaurant is renowned locally. No food Mon eve.
⛫ ❀ ◐ ◑ ♣ P

Ely

Prince Albert
62 Silver Street
☎ (01353) 663494
11.30–2.30 (3 Fri, 3.30 Sat), 6.30–11
Greene King XX Mild, IPA, Abbot H
The emphasis is firmly on good ale and good company at Cambridge CAMRA's *Pub of the Year* 1993. Delightful, award-winning garden; public car park across the street (entrance in Barton Rd). No food Sun. ⛫ Q ❀ ◐ ♣

West End House
West End ☎ (01353) 662907
11.30–2.30, 6–11
Draught Bass; Courage Directors; Marston's Pedigree; Ruddles Best Bitter; Webster's Yorkshire Bitter H
Four drinking areas with a plethora of beams and low ceilings. ⛫ ❀ ♣

Etton

Golden Pheasant
1 Main Street (Helpston turn off A15, then 1st right)
☎ (01733) 252387
11–11
Draught Bass; Bateman XXXB; Butcombe Bitter; Greene King IPA; Ruddles County; guest beers H
Former 19th-century manor farmhouse, with a large, comfortable lounge bar, a family room and a restaurant. The local artists' paintings on display are for sale. The large garden seats up to 230 and is very popular in summer (aviary). Petanque played.
⛫ Q ♉ ❀ ◐ ◑ ♿ ▲ ♣ P ⊭

Eye Green

Greyhound
41 Crowland Road (A1073)
☎ (01733) 222487
11–2.30, 7–11
Wells Eagle, Bombardier; guest beers H
Two-bar village local, popular with all. Large garden.
⛫ Q ❀ ♿ ♣ P

Fenstanton

King William IV
High Street (off A604)
☎ (01480) 462467
11–3.30, 6–11
Greene King IPA, Rayments Special, Abbot H
Village pub opened up, but separated into eating and drinking areas by original beams and settles. It is pleasantly situated on the village green, which is complete with a clock tower and pond. ❀ ◐ ◑ ♿ ♣ ⊭

Fowlmere

Chequers
High Street ☎ (01763) 208369
12–2.30, 6–11
Tetley Bitter; Tolly Cobbold Original H
16th-century coaching inn serving good food. Local aviation history features.
⛫ Q ❀ ◐ ◑

Fulbourn

Six Bells
High Street ☎ (01223) 880244
11.30–3, 6.30–11
Ind Coope Burton Ale; Tolly Cobbold Mild; Whitbread Flowers IPA; guest beer H
Village-centre pub, revitalised by a return to basics. Traditional values are reflected in the front-of-house presence as well as the menu (all home-cooked), available as bar meals or in the restaurant (7–9.30). No food Sun or Mon eves. ⛫ ❀ ◐ ◑ ▲ ♣ P

Gamlingay

Hardwicke Arms
The Cross ☎ (01767) 50727
11.30–3, 7 (5.30 Fri & Sat)–11
Draught Bass; Hook Norton Best Bitter; Whitbread Boddingtons Bitter; guest beers H
Comfortable pub and restaurant on the village crossroads. The lounge bar features an impressive inglenook. ⛫ Q ♣ P

Great Wilbraham

Carpenters Arms
High Street ☎ (01223) 880202
11.30–2.30, 6.30–11
Greene King XX Mild, IPA, Rayments Special, Abbot H
Two-bar country local with an active ghost. Home-cooked bar meals are available till 9.30; collection of malt whiskies. Friendly forthright conversation is the norm at the bar. ⛫ ❀ ◐ ◑ ♣ P

Helpston

Blue Bell
10 Woodgate
☎ (01733) 252394
11–2.30, 6–11; 12–2, 7–10.30 Sun

Draught Bass; Bateman XXXB; Ruddles Best Bitter; John Smith's Magnet; Webster's Yorkshire Bitter H
Pub dating from the 1600s. Its wood-panelled lounge features a collection of teapots and Toby jugs; simple public bar. John Clare, the peasant-poet, was born next door and used to be the pub's pot boy. No keg bitter.
🏚 Q ✿ 🖂 ⊞ ♣ ➾ P

Hilton

Prince of Wales
Potton Road (B1040)
☎ (01480) 830257
11–2.30, 6–11
Adnams Bitter; Fuller's London Pride; guest beer (occasional) H
Village free house which still retains a public bar. A warm welcome and good value food are assured (no meals Mon).
🏚 ✿ 🖂 ◑ ▶ ♣ P

Histon

Rose & Crown
2 Glebe Way ☎ (01223) 232448
11–3, 5–11
Adnams Bitter; Everards Tiger; guest beer H
A friendly ghost makes its presence felt at this 400-year-old pub with a cosy, traditional atmosphere.
🏚 Q ◑ ▶ ⊞

Holywell

Ferry Boat Inn
Take A1123 to Needingworth and follow signs OS343707
☎ (01480) 463227
11–3, 6–11
Adnams Broadside; Bass Charrington IPA; Fuller's London Pride; John Smith's Bitter; Webster's Yorkshire Bitter H
Partly thatched, riverside pub, reputedly haunted by a ghost called Juliet; now very much a lounge bar pub. Popular with rivergoers in the summer, it features in the *Guinness Book of Records* as one of England's oldest pubs. Much extended.
🏚 ☔ ✿ 🖂 ◑ ▶ P ✄

Huntingdon

Old Bridge Hotel
High Street (ring road next to river bridge) ☎ (01480) 52681
11–11
Adnams Bitter; Banks & Taylor Shefford Bitter; guest beer H
Imposing riverside pub offering many dining and function rooms. The small bar may seem a bit upmarket for some. 🏚 Q ✿ 🖂 ◑ ▶ ➾ P

Leighton Bromswold

Green Man
The Avenue (off A14)
OS113754 ☎ (01480) 890238
12–2.30 (not Mon–Thu), 7–11; closed Mon
Hall & Woodhouse Tanglefoot; Mitchell's Best Bitter; S&N Theakston Old Peculier; Taylor Landlord; guest beer H
Welcoming, comfortable rural free house with a collection of brewery memorabilia, stocking a wide and ever-changing range of guest beers. Hood skittles are played. The food is good value. Beware the Scrumpy Jack keg cider fake handpump. ☔ ✿ ◑ ▶ ♣ P

Linton

Crown
High Street ☎ (01223) 891759
12–2.30 (4 Sat), 5.30 (6.30 Sat)–11
Whitbread Boddingtons Bitter, Flowers IPA; guest beers H
Comfortable, orderly, narrow pub at the top of a fine village High Street. The exciting food range tastes as good as it reads (no meals Sun eve). Independents' guest beers.
🏚 ✿ 🖂 ◑ P

Little Gransden

Chequers
71 Main Road (B1046)
☎ (01767) 677348
7 (11 Sat)–11
Beer choice varies H
Small, two-bar village pub with absolutely no frills; simply a good place to enjoy a drink. A different real ale each week. 🏚 Q ⊞ ⚅ ♣ P

Longstowe

Golden Miller
54 High Street (B1046)
12–2.30, 7 (6.30 Sat)–11
Adnams Bitter; Bateman XXXB; Greene King IPA H
Named after the 1934 Grand National winner, this one-bar village pub offers a warm welcome. Separate dining room (no food Tue eve).
✿ ◑ ▶ ♣ P

Meldreth

British Queen
94 High Street
☎ (01763) 260252
11–3, 5.30–11
Adnams Bitter; Whitbread Boddingtons Bitter, Best Bitter, Flowers IPA; guest beers H

Friendly, pleasant and comfortable village local. The food is good and excellent value. 🏚 Q ✿ ◑ ▶ ➾

Milton

Waggon & Horses
39 High Street
☎ (01223) 860313
12–2.30, 5–11; 12–11 Sat
Bateman XB; Nethergate Bitter; guest beers H
Pub offering two constantly changing guest beers, plus a curry night Fri and a traditional Sun roast lunch. No food Sat lunch or Sun eve.
🏚 ✿ ◑ ▶ ➾ P

Needingworth

Queens Head
30 High Street (A1128)
☎ (01480) 463946
12–11
Hop Back Summer Lightning; Taylor Landlord; Woodforde's Wherry; guest beers H
Friendly, two-bar village local, with a strong domino following in the public bar. It always stocks a good range of guest beers. Note: the handpumps are in the public bar. ✿ ▶ ⊞ ♣ ➾ P

Newton

Queens Head
☎ (01223) 870436
11.30 (11 Sat)–2.30, 6–11; 12–2, 7–10.30 Sun
Adnams Bitter, Old, Broadside G
This pub has appeared in every edition of this *Guide*. An idyllic village pub, it serves simple but delicious food to complement the ale.
🏚 Q ✿ ◑ ▶ ⚅ ▲ ♣ ➾ P

Old Weston

Swan
Main Street (B660)
☎ (01832) 239400
12–3 (not Mon or Tue), 7–11; 11–11 Sat
Adnams Bitter; Greene King Abbot; Hook Norton Old Hooky; Morland Old Speckled Hen; Nethergate Old Growler; Webster's Yorkshire Bitter H
Olde-worlde free house and restaurant with beams and a low ceiling. 🏚 ✿ ◑ ▶ ♣ P

Parson Drove

Swan
Main Road (B1166/B1187 jct)
☎ (01945) 700291
12–2 (3 Sat), 7–11

Cambridgeshire

Elgood's Cambridge Bitter; guest beers H
Largely unspoilt Fen village pub built in 1541. The regulars are known to walk several miles for a pint here. The lounge is named after Samuel Pepys, whose uncle's horse was stolen the night he stayed at this inn. Bar billiards in the public bar. A friendly welcome and good food are assured. No meals Tue lunchtime.
⌂ Q ❀ 🛏 ◖ ◗ ⊞ ♣ P

Peterborough

Blue Bell
6 The Green, Werrington (½ mile off A15)
☎ (01733) 571264
11–3, 6.30–11
Elgood's Cambridge Bitter, GSB; guest beers H
Considered the best Elgood's pub in the city by the local CAMRA branch, this large whitewashed pub has a modern interior and offers an excellent food menu. Elgood's occasional brews and monthly guest ales feature. Family-run.
Q ❀ ◖ ◗ ⊞ ♿ ♣ P

Bogart's Bar & Grill
17 North Street
☎ (01733) 349995
11–11; closed Sun
Draught Bass; Bateman XB, Valiant; guest beers H
Once the Ostrich pub, then a home-brew shop, this is now an oasis in the real ale desert of Peterborough city centre. It combines an interesting lunch menu and a lively night-time atmosphere. Numerous guest beers. ❀ ◖ ≹ ⌓

Charters Café Bar
Town Bridge (steps down from S end of bridge)
☎ (01733) 315700
12–3, 5–11 (may vary in summer; closed football eves)
Adnams Broadside; Draught Bass; Fuller's London Pride; M&B Highgate Dark; guest beers H
Peterborough's real ale flagship is a converted Dutch barge, moored against the town bridge, providing the town's largest and busiest venue. An extensive range of up to four guest beers includes milds and porters. The informal atmosphere appeals to all ages. ❀ ◖ ◗ ≹

Dragon
Hodgson Avenue, Werrington
☎ (01733) 322675
12–3.30, 5.30–11
Wells Eagle, Bombardier; guest beer H
Modern, but pleasant and friendly estate pub, opened in 1988. The restaurant area is popular for Sun lunches.
❀ ◖ ♿ ♣ P

Fountain
2 Burghley Road (500 yds from centre, by Park Rd jct)
☎ (01733) 54533
11–2.30, 7–11
Courage Directors; Everards Beacon, Tiger, Old Original; guest beers H
Former Grand Met pub now in the care of a leasing company. The landlord has really dragged the pub back from the dead, offering an ever-changing range of guest beers. A local CAMRA seasonal pub award recipient.
Q ❀ ◖ ⊞ ≹ ♣ P

Hand & Heart
12 Highbury Street (300 yds from old A15 in Millfield area)
☎ (01733) 69463
10.30–2.30 (3 Sat), 6–11
Courage Best Bitter, Directors; John Smith's Bitter, Magnet; Wilson's Mild; guest beer H
1930s, back-street local with original Warwicks' Brewery windows; the quintessence of a pub. It boasts a lively bar, snug lounge, good prices and occasional quiz nights; an all-round gem. Bottled Imperial Russian Stout is available.
⌂ Q ⊞ ♣ ⌓

Old Ramblewood Inn
The Village, Orton Longueville
☎ (01733) 391111
11.30–2.30, 5.30–11; 11.30–11 Sat
Adnams Bitter, Broadside; Draught Bass; Fuller's London Pride; Greene King IPA; guest beers H
Formerly the stables of Orton Hall, itself now a hotel. A pub with a comfortable, cosy atmosphere, very attractive gardens, plus a highly regarded, good value restaurant. Hotel rooms at Orton Hall; camping at Nene Valley.
❀ 🛏 ◖ ◗ ♿ ▲ P

Royal Oak
1099 Lincoln Road, Walton (A15) ☎ (01733) 571032
11–3, 6.30–11
Draught Bass; John Smith's Bitter; Wells Bombardier; Whitbread Boddingtons Bitter; guest beer H
1930s local: two bars and a function room (children admitted). The local BMF motorcycle club meets here.
⌂ Q ☺ ❀ ⊞ ♿ ♣ P

Try also: Coopers, South Bretton (Whitbread); **Palmerston Arms**, Oundle Rd (Courage); **Royal Arms**, Eye Rd (Elgood's)

Pickle Fen

Crafty Fox
London Road (B1050)
☎ (01354) 692266
11–3, 5.30–11; 11–11 Sat
Draught Bass; John Smith's Bitter H
Small, isolated pub with a restaurant (home-cooked food), and a large covered vineyard area. Children are welcome in the conservatory.
⌂ Q ☺ ❀ ◖ ◗ P

Purls Bridge

Ship
OS477868 ☎ (01354) 680578
12–3, 7–11; closed Mon
Greene King IPA H
Isolated fenland pub, two miles from Manea boat moorings on the Old Bedford river. Access to the RSPB reserve at Welches Dam.
⌂ ◖ ◗ ♿ P

Ramsey

Three Horseshoes
Little Whyte
☎ (01487) 812452
11–2.30, 6–11
S&N Theakston Best Bitter; Younger IPA; guest beer H
Busy, back-street pub with a distinct northern flavour. Lunch available Sun only; eve meals must be booked.
🛏 ◗ ⊞ ♣

Try also: Jolly Sailor (Pubmaster)

Reach

Kings
Fair Green ☎ (01638) 741745
12–3, 7–11; closed Mon lunch, except bank hols
Greene King IPA; Nethergate Bitter; guest beers H
Comfortable beamed pub by the village green. Interesting menu. ⌂ ❀ ◖ ◗ ♣ P

St Ives

Aviator
Ramsey Road (near church, W end of town) ☎ (01480) 464417
11–2.30, 6–11
Courage Directors; Webster's Yorkshire Bitter; guest beers H
When quiet, this has a continental café atmosphere, but, when busy, especially when the piano is playing, it has a good pub feel. Good food is available until 10pm and there are always at least five guest beers (the range varies). ❀ 🛏 ◖ ◗ P

Oliver Cromwell

Wellington Street (off Bridge St, along the quay)
☎ (01480) 465601
10.30–2.30, 6–11
Adnams Broadside; Elgood's Cambridge Bitter; Greene King IPA H
Busy, one-bar pub, largely unchanged in recent years, near the riverside quay and historic bridge. Note the ornate wrought iron sign bracket outside, once part of the Ship, a former quayside pub. The pub clock keeps to GMT. Q

St Neots

Wheatsheaf

3 Church Street
☎ (01480) 477435
11–2.30, 7 (6 Fri)–11
Greene King XX Mild, IPA, Abbot H**, Winter Ale** G
Terraced town-centre local, enjoying strong sales of the excellent XX Mild. Its traditional atmosphere is rare for pubs in the centre of town. Successful quiz team. ♠

Sawston

Kings Head

19 High Street
☎ (01223) 833541
11–2.30, 7–11
Greene King XX Mild, IPA, Abbot H
Two-bar, 18th-century pub—a landmark in the village street. The public bar, with its low beams and ornamental inglenook, is functional, warm and welcoming, and especially popular with teachers. The resplendent gardens feature children's amusements. Function room. ❀ ◖ ♣ P

Soham

Carpenters Arms

Brook Street (off Staple Lane from Fordham Rd roundabout) ☎ (01353) 720869
11–11
Greene King IPA; guest beers H
Edge-of-town free house: an L-shaped bar with a lounge beyond, plus a pool room at the back. Warm and welcoming, it offers extremely good value beer and food. Beer fests provide focal points for the year. Two guest beers (one strong). No food Sun. ❀ ◖ P

Stanground

Coach & Horses

High Street (1½ miles from centre, towards Whittlesey)
☎ (01733) 343400
11.30–2.30, 6–11; 11–11 Sat
Marston's Pedigree; Ruddles Best Bitter; John Smith's Bitter; guest beer H
Friendly local, consisting of two contrasting bars. Regularly changing guest beer. Q ❀ ◖ ▶ ♣ P

Stow cum Quy

Prince Albert

Newmarket Road (A1303, off A45 at Quy roundabout)
☎ (01223) 811294
11.30–3, 5–11
Greene King IPA; guest beers H
The 1992 CAMRA Cambridge *Pub of the Year*; over 800 different beers sold of all strengths. Essentially a roadhouse, but the hospitality ensures all are catered for. Book for eve meals.
🏠 ❀ ◖ ▶ ♣ P

Stretham

Red Lion

18 High Street
☎ (01353) 648132
11–3, 6.30–11
Ansells Mild; Greene King IPA; Ind Coope Burton Ale; Nethergate Old Growler; Tetley Bitter; guest beer H
Superbly renovated and extended village inn. Run with style and imagination, it appeals to all. Teenagers' amusements are available in the first floor club room. Good food at all times.
🏠 🛏 ❀ 🚪 ◖ ▶ 🍴 & ♣ P ✗

Thriplow

Green Man

2 Lower Street
☎ (01763) 208855
12–3, 6–11
Bateman XB; Hook Norton Best Bitter; Nethergate Old Growler; Taylor Landlord; guest beers H
Small, carpeted bar area plus a public bar-type room and a dining area. Note the outstanding old Adnams posters. Enormous trade can be expected on the annual daffodil weekend. No food Sun eve. ❀ ◖ ▶ ♣ P

Whittlesey

Boat

2 Ramsey Road
☎ (01733) 202488
11–2 (not winter Mon), 7–11
Elgood's Cambridge Bitter; guest beers H
Ancient pub, catering for locals and fishermen. One of the main calling points at the Straw Bear Festival in early Jan. Elgood's seasonal brews stocked.
🏠 ❀ 🚪 ≠ ♠ P

Whittlesford

Bees in the Wall

36 North Road
☎ (01223) 834345
12–2, 6–11
Bateman XB; Fuller's London Pride; Hook Norton Best Bitter; Morland Old Speckled Hen; Wadworth 6X H
There really are bees in the wall of this two-bar pub at the north end of the village, where visitors are most likely to feel comfortable in the pleasantly appointed lounge. Large, paddock-style garden. Food might be re-introduced.
🏠 Q ❀ 🍺 ♣ ◠ P

Willingham

Three Tuns

Church Street
☎ (01954) 260437
11–2.30, 6–11; 12–2.30, 7–10.30 Sun
Greene King XX Mild, IPA, Abbot H
Classic village local offering good company and basic lunchtime snacks.
Q ❀ 🍺 ♣

Wisbech

Rose Tavern

53 North Brink
☎ (01945) 588335
12–3, 5.30–11
Butterknowle Conciliation Ale; Cains FA; guest beers H
Cosy, one-roomed pub on the riverside: a listed, 200-year-old building and the closest pub to Elgood's Brewery. The present landlord reinstated the original name. The only pub in Wisbech selling no keg bitter.
❀ 🚪 & ♣

Try also: Red Lion, North Brink; **Three Tuns**, Norwich Rd (both Elgood's)

Witcham

White Horse

7 Silver Street
☎ (01353) 778298
12–3 (not Mon), 6.30–11
Adnams Bitter; Greene King IPA; guest beers H
Small village local with a large dining room. The reputation for food has not dulled the enthusiasm for real ale. No meals Sun eve/Mon lunch.
❀ ◖ ▶ ♣ P

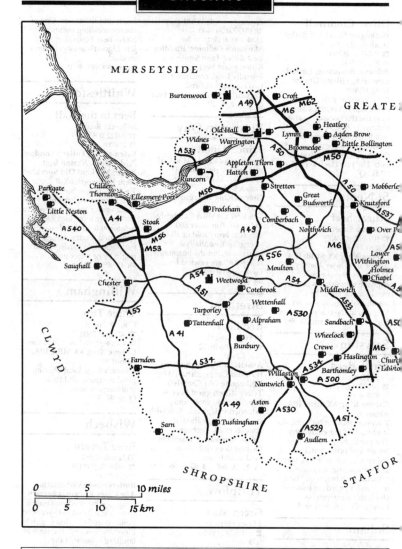

Burtonwood, *Burtonwood*; **Coach House**, *Warrington*; **Weetwood**, *Weetwood*

Agden Brow

Wheatsheaf
Higher Lane (A56, 300 yds from B5159 jct)
☎ (01925) 752567
11.30–3, 5.30–11
Hydes' Anvil Mild, Bitter E
Pub with one modern bar, but the drinking area is pleasantly sub-divided. A grassed playground is set aside for supervised toddlers. Good value meals (eves Thu–Sun only, till 9pm). ☀ ◑ ▶ ♣ P

Alpraham

Travellers Rest
Chester Road (A51)
☎ (01829) 260523
6–11; 12–3, 6–11 Sat
McEwan 70/-;
Tetley Walker Mild,
Bitter H
In this guide for years and largely unchanged, still a quiet village local on a main road. Own bowling green.
 Q ☀ ♣ P

Appleton Thorn

Appleton Thorn Village Hall
Stretton Road
☎ (01925) 261187
8.30–11; 8.30–10.30 Sun; closed Mon–Wed eves and every lunchtime, except 1st Sun of month (12–3)
Beer range varies H
Award-winning, cosy lounge attached to the village hall, run by a charitable trust in old school buildings. It stocks six guest beers, including a mild;

MANCHESTER

Handforth Disley

Wilmslow Bollington

Prestbury A523

Higher Hurdsfield

Henbury Macclesfield

Eaton

Wincle

Buglawton

Congleton

Timbersbrook

Newbold

Cheshire

the house beer is from Coach
House. Note the restricted
hours. Boules pitch.
Q ❀ ♿ ♣ P

Aston

Bhurtpore Inn
Wrenbury Road (off A530)
OS610469 ☎ (01270) 780917
12–2.30, 6–11
**Hanby Drawwell; guest
beers** H
Former farmhouse displaying
photos of local interest. The
name is a town in India with
connections to Lord
Combermere, a local dignitary.
The six guest beers normally
include a mild; it also stocks a
selection of bottled beers.
Local CAMRA *Pub of the Year*
1993. ♨ Q ❀ ♿ ▮ ♣ ⌂ P

Audlem

Bridge
Shropshire Street
☎ (01270) 811267
11–3 (4 Sat), 5.30–11
**Banks's Mild; Marston's
Bitter, Pedigree**
One of four pubs in a small
village, catering for locals and
passing canal users.
♨ ❀ ♿ ▲ ♣ P

Try also: **Lord Combermere**,
The Square (Free)

Barthomley

White Lion
Audley Road (off B5078)
☎ (01270) 882242
11.30–3, 6–11; 11.30–11 Sat
**Burtonwood Mild, Bitter,
Forshaw's, Top Hat** H
Popular, black and white,
thatched pub at the centre of a
small, picturesque village.
Dated 1614, it displays a list of
just 18 landlords. The church
opposite was the scene of a
massacre during the Civil War.
♨ Q ☎ ❀ ♿ ♣ P

Bollington

Church House
Chapel Street
☎ (01625) 574014
12–2.30 (3 Sat), 5.30–11
**Ind Coope Burton Ale;
Jennings Bitter; S&N
Theakston Best Bitter;
Thwaites Bitter; Whitbread
Boddingtons Bitter** H
Popular and busy corner-
terrace pub with a reputation
for good food at all times.
Renovated church pews make
attractive seating in the
lounge. ♨ Q ⌂ ♿ ▮

Cotton Tree
3–5 Ingersley Road
☎ (01625) 576883
11–11
**Vaux Bitter, Samson; Wards
Mild** H
Stone-built corner local. The
Bollington Building Society
met here in the 1830s, when
such societies were simple,
friendly organisations.
Recently taken over by Vaux,
it has been pleasantly
decorated throughout and is
now a good village pub.
♨ Q ♿ ▮ ⌂ ♿ ♣

Vale
29–31 Adlington Road
☎ (01625) 575147
11.30–3 (not Mon), 7–11
**Taylor Landlord; Thwaites
Best Mild, Bitter** H
Once three terraced houses,
now a comfortable one-room

pub, with a large bar topped
with Westmorland slate. Live
jazz Mon nights; thriving golf
society. Handy for the
Macclesfield Canal. No food
Mon lunch or Sun.
♨ Q ❀ ♿ ▮ P

Broomedge

Jolly Thresher
Higher Lane (A56/B5159 jct)
☎ (01925) 752265
11.30–3 (4 Fri & Sat), 5.30 (6 Sat)–11
Hydes' Anvil Mild, Bitter E
Pub with an opened-out
lounge and a small darts
room, plus a restaurant for
functions. A large crown
bowling green stands at the
rear. The manager holds a
long-standing CAMRA
commendation from a
previous tenancy. No food Sun
eve or Mon. ❀ ♿ ▮ ♣ P

Buglawton

Church House
Buxton Road (A54)
☎ (01260) 272466
11.30–3, 6–11
**Robinson's Hatters Mild, Best
Bitter** E
Classic between-the-wars,
roomy pub which caters for
local, passing and canal trade
(½ mile away), and offers
excellent bar meals and a
restaurant (closed Sat eve).
The unusual pub sign is
combined with a pigeon cote.
Very good outside facilities for
children.
♨ Q ⌂ ❀ ♿ ▮ ♣ P

Bunbury

Dysart Arms
College Lane (opp. church)
☎ (01829) 260183
12–3.30, 5.30–11; 12–11 Sat
**Tetley Walker Bitter;
Thwaites Bitter** H
Stone-floored, public bar and a
lounge with a large fireplace
and an aquarium in an 18th-
century, former farmhouse.
Wheelchair access is via the
back door.
♨ Q ⌂ ❀ ♿ ▮ ♿ ♣ P

Burtonwood

Bridge Inn
Phipps Lane ☎ (01925) 225709
11.30–11
**Burtonwood Mild, Bitter,
Forshaw's** H
Four-roomed pub, oriented
towards sports; the licensee's
mementos from his Rugby
League playing days are
displayed. It has a bowling
green and a children's play
area. No food Sat.
⌂ ❀ ♿ ♣ P

Cheshire

Chester

Albion
4 Park Street ☎ (01244) 340345
11.30–3, 5.30–11
Cains Bitter; Greenalls Mild, Bitter, Original; Stones Best Bitter H
Typical, back-street pub, notable for its collection of old enamelled signs and sewing machine tables. It serves an out-of-the-ordinary choice of pub grub; eve meals Fri and Sat. No admittance after 10.30 Fri and Sat. ♨ Q ◐ ▶ ⊟

Centurion
Oldfield Drive, Vicars Cross (off A51, 1 mile from centre) ☎ (01244) 347623
11.30–3, 5.30–11; 11–11 Sat
Cains Bitter; Jennings Bitter; Robinson's Best Bitter; Tetley Walker Mild, Bitter; guest beer H
Energetic, modern pub holding regular beer festivals and quizzes, plus charity fund-raising events. The beer range may vary.
❀ ⊟ ዲ ♣ P

Clavertons
Lower Bridge Street ☎ (01244) 316316
11.30–11
Lees Bitter, Moonraker H
Popular bar in the cellar of an historic building. Doormen at weekends prevent over-crowding. No meals after 5.30. ◐ ዲ

Mill Hotel
Milton Street ☎ (01244) 350035
11–11
Weetwood Best Bitter; Whitbread Boddingtons Bitter; guest beers H
Hotel bar that is popular with visitors and locals alike. The guest beers always include a mild. Join the fitness club next door to work off the ale. Meals served until 10pm. A rare local outlet for Weetwood.
❀ ⊯ ◐ ▶ ዲ ⇌ P

Old Custom House
Watergate Street ☎ (01244) 324435
11–3, 5.30–11
Bateman Mild; Marston's Bitter, Pedigree H
Reassuringly constant and friendly: three rooms with ornate fireplaces, unsullied by kitsch. This long-time *Guide* entry is home to many sports teams. ♨ Q ◐ ⊟ ♣

Pop-In (Off-Licence)
43 Boughton ☎ (01244) 320013
12–10
Beer range varies G

Off-licence specialising in foreign and cask beers, something like the old 'Jug and Bottle'. It also stocks a good selection of strong and bottle-conditioned beers, plus occasional ciders in summer. ⇌

Try also: Boot, Eastgate St (Samuel Smith); **Union Vaults**, Egerton St (Boddington Pub Co.)

Childer Thornton

White Lion
New Road (200 yds off A41) ☎ (0151) 339 3402
11.30–3, 5–11; 11.30–11 Fri & Sat
Thwaites Best Mild, Bitter H
Unspoilt, two-roomed country local with a warm reception for all. The snug is used by families at lunchtime but can get busy at weekends. No food Sun. ♨ Q ❀ ◐ P

Church Lawton

Lawton Arms
Liverpool Road West (A50, near B5077 jct) ☎ (01270) 873743
11.30–3, 5.30 (4.30 Fri, 7 Sat)–11
Robinson's Hatters Mild, Best Bitter E
Georgian local with a snug and a games room.
♨ Q ❀ ♣ P

Comberbach

Drum & Monkey
The Avenue ☎ (01606) 891417
11.30–3, 5.30–11
Tetley Walker Bitter H
Friendly, single-roomed village local. ◐ P

Congleton

Moss Inn
140 Canal Road ☎ (01260) 273583
11–11
Marston's Bitter, Pedigree H
Warm and welcoming, cosy pub whose walls are laden with interesting artefacts. A thriving local trade is boosted by cyclists, walkers and boaters from the canal (100 yards away). Effective smoke filter and extraction system. Eve meals 6–8, Tue and Fri.
❀ ◐ ዲ ⇌ ♣ P

Cotebrook

Alvanley Arms
Forest Road ☎ (01829) 760200
11.30–3, 5.30–11
Robinson's Hatters Mild, Best Bitter H
Country pub with decor and furnishings to suit: two

comfortable lounges and a small dining room. Excellent value and quality meals tend to predominate. Handy for Oulton Park (motor racing).
♨ ❀ ⊯ ◐ ▶ P

Crewe

Albion
1 Pedley Street ☎ (01270) 256234
12–3 Sat; not Wed & Thu), 7–11; 12–11 Fri
Tetley Walker Dark Mild, Bitter; guest beer H
Good example of a street-corner local. The bar has an emphasis on darts and dominoes; separate pool room. Quiz night is Wed. Frequently changing guest beer.
⇌ ♣ ♨

British Lion
58 Nantwich Road ☎ (01270) 214379
12–3 (4 Mon & Thu), 7–11; 12–11 Fri & Sat
Ind Coope Burton Ale; Tetley Walker Dark Mild, Bitter H
Lively local, known almost universally as the Pig. A useful watering hole if changing trains, just 300 yards west of the station. ♨ ⇌ ♣

Crown
25 Earle Street ☎ (01270) 257295
11–5 (may vary), 7–11
Robinson's Hatters Mild, Best Bitter H
Small, multi-roomed, town-centre pub which recently celebrated its centenary. Customers are mostly local regulars, but some visitors come from the nearby Railway Heritage Centre. ⅙ ♣

Kings Arms
56 Earle Street ☎ (01270) 584134
11.30 (11 Sat)–3.30 (4.30 Mon, Fri & Sat), 7–11
Whitbread Chester's Mild, Best Bitter, Boddingtons Bitter, Trophy H
Multi-roomed, town-centre pub with rooms for all tastes, and a friendly atmosphere. Threatened with demolition due to a road widening scheme. ⊟ ዲ ♣

Croft

General Elliot
51 Lord Street ☎ (01925) 763264
12–11
Tetley Walker Bitter; guest beers H
Pub with a split-level, comfortable lounge, plus a conservatory which serves as an eating area and family room. Children's play area

outside. Good variety of guest beers. Food served all day Sun. Q ❀ ◁ ❶ ⚑ ✦ P ⌖

Disley

White Horse Hotel
Buxton Old Road
☎ (01663) 762397
11–3, 5.30–11
Robinson's Hatters Mild, Best Bitter Ⓗ
Imposing building at the village centre. It dates from 1869, although its open-plan interior now conforms to the Robinson's format. A sedate pub which suffers few vices, and smoke is kept to a low level, thanks to good ventilation. Good value food.
⌂ ◁ ❶ ⅋ ≽ ✦ P

Eaton

Waggon & Horses
Manchester Road (A34)
☎ (01260) 224229
11–3, 5.30 (6 Sat)–11
Robinson's Hatters Mild, Best Bitter Ⓗ
Pleasant, two-bar pub on the main road, with a large dining room. The meeting place for an MG owners' club. The popular bar menu offers children's portions.
🏠 Q ⌂ ❀ ◁ ❶ ✦ P

Try also: Plough, Macclesfield Rd (Banks's)

Ellesmere Port

Grosvenor
2 Upper Mersey Street (below M53, nr jct 9)
☎ (0151) 355 1810
5 (12 Thu–Sat)–11
Burtonwood Bitter, Forshaw's Ⓗ
Large, under-utilised, two-bar workingman's boozer, close to the Boat Museum. ≽ ✦ P

Straw Hat
Hope Farm Road, Great Sutton (off A41) ☎ (0151) 356 3335
12–11
Courage Directors; John Smith's Bitter; guest beer (occasional) Ⓗ
Modern, sports-oriented, estate pub, offering live music four nights a week. Pleasant and popular.
✦ P

Try also: Sir Robert, Overpool Rd (Whitbread); **Sutton Way**, Thelwell Rd (Courage)

Farndon

Greyhound Hotel
High Street ☎ (01829) 270244
5.30–11; 12–3, 7–11 Sat
Greenalls Mild, Bitter, Original Ⓗ

Friendly hotel, 100 yards from the River Dee, with a pottery attached. Beware the keg cider on a fake pump. Note restricted opening hours.
🏠 Q ❀ ⌸ ❶ ✦ P

Try also: Farndon Arms (Free)

Frodsham

Rowlands Bar
31 Church Street
☎ (01928) 733361
11–11
Weetwood Best Bitter; Whitbread Boddingtons Bitter; guest beers Ⓗ
Busy, single-bar pub with a friendly atmosphere. It stocks at least 12 different guest beers per week, four at any one time. The food is recommended, with daily bar snacks and an excellent upstairs bistro (booking advised). A local CAMRA award-winner. Q ◁ ❶ ≽

Great Budworth

George & Dragon
High Street ☎ (01606) 891317
11.30–3.30, 6.30–11
Tetley Walker Bitter; guest beers Ⓗ
Award-winning pub, opposite the church in a picturesque village. It usually has two guest beers. Beware the sharp, blind bend on exiting.
🏠 ⌂ ❀ ◁ ❶ ⅋ P

Handforth

Railway
Station Road ☎ (01625) 523472
11–3, 5.30–11
Robinson's Hatters Mild, Best Bitter Ⓔ
Large, multi-roomed pub facing the station: a thriving local, popular with all. No food Sun. Q ◁ ❶ ≽ ✦ P

Haslington

Hawk
137 Crewe Road
☎ (01270) 582181
11–11
Robinson's Hatters Mild, Best Bitter Ⓔ
15th-century, multi-roomed inn. An original wattle wall is on display behind a glass panel and Dick Turpin is believed to have stayed here. Eve meals Wed–Sat.
🏠 ⌂ ❀ ◁ ❶ P

Hatton

Hatton Arms
Hatton Lane ☎ (01925) 730314
11–11
Greenalls Mild, Bitter, Original Ⓗ

Traditional, rural village pub based on old cottages, retaining multiple rooms and real fires. It is run by a caring village-born couple.
🏠 Q ❀ ◁ ❶ ✦ P

Heatley

Railway
Mill Lane (B5159)
☎ (01925) 752742
12–11
Cains Mild; Whitbread Boddingtons Bitter; guest beer Ⓗ
Large, multi-roomed, old-style pub catering for most tastes: an ideal base for a stroll along the River Bollin plain on the Trans-Pennine Trail. Large, open garden and play area. Sandwiches are served at all times; no meals Sun. Folk club Thu. Q ❀ ◁ ✦ P

Henbury

Cock Inn
Chelford Road (A537)
☎ (01625) 423186
11–3, 5–11
Robinson's Hatters Mild, Best Bitter, Old Tom Ⓗ
Comfortable, main road pub with both local and passing trade, situated just outside Macclesfield. Children are welcome in the restaurant. No coaches. Q ❀ ◁ ❶ ❶ ✦ P

Higher Hurdsfield

George & Dragon
61 Rainow Road (B5470, Whaley Bridge road, ½ mile from canal) ☎ (01625) 424300
12–3 (not Sat), 7–11
John Smith's Bitter; guest beers Ⓗ
Small, friendly pub, built of local stone and set back off the main road at the far end of Higher Hurdsfield. Part of the pub is 400 years old. Bus stop outside the front door.
◁ ❶ ⅋ ✦

Holmes Chapel

Swan
29 Station Road
☎ (01477) 532259
11–3, 4.30–11; 11–11 Fri & Sat
Samuel Smith OBB, Museum Ⓗ
Former coaching inn serving good food; very large pizzas are a speciality. Note the old black stove. The car park is reached by driving under the pub. 🏠 ❀ ⌸ ◁ ❶ ❶ ≽ P

Knutsford

Builders Arms
Mobberley Road (just off A537) ☎ (01565) 634528
11.30–3, 5.30–11; 12–2, 7–10.30 Sun

Banks's Mild; **Marston's Bitter, Pedigree** H
Delightful pub in an attractive terrace on the outskirts of the town centre. A former Taylors Eagle Brewery house, it is busy, with a keen games emphasis. Best approached from the road opposite the Legh Arms. Q ❀ ⊟ ⇌

White Lion
94 King Street
☎ (01565) 632018
11.30–11
Tetley Walker Bitter; guest beers (occasional) H
Black and white timbered, town-centre building probably dating from the mid-17th century. Certainly the pub was in existence long before a party of soldiers was billeted here at the time of the 1745 Jacobite rebellion. No food Sun. ⋈ Q ❀ ◑ ⇌ ♣

Little Bollington

Swan With Two Nicks
Park Lane (off A57)
☎ (0161) 928 2914
11.30–3, 5.30–11
Whitbread Boddingtons Bitter, Flowers IPA, Castle Eden Ale H
Typical rural Cheshire pub, licensed since 1880, now much extended into a large restaurant at the rear. Next to the Bridgewater Canal and Dunham Deer Park.
⋈ ❀ ◑ ♣ P

Little Neston

Harp Inn
19 Quayside, Marshlands (from Burton Rd, down Marshlands Rd, left along Marsh Rd) ☎ (0151) 336 6980
11–11
Taylor Landlord; Whitbread Flowers IPA, Trophy; guest beer H
Delightful, two-room pub, served by one bar. The public bar, with a real fire and low beams, is superb. Quiz night Wed. Difficult to get to but a joy when you find it; beware high tides! ⋈ Q ⌂ ❀ ◑ P

Lower Withington

Red Lion
Trap Street, Dicklow Cob (B5392) ☎ (01477) 71248
11.45–2.30 (3 Sat), 5.30–11
Robinson's Dark Mild, Best Bitter H
Large, rural pub with a restaurant, a lounge bar and a tap room for locals, near the Jodrell Bank radio telescope. Even though the pump clip says Robinson's Best Mild,

it is actually a very rare outlet for the Dark Mild.
⋈ ❀ ◑ ⇐ ⚲ ♣ P

Lymm

Spread Eagle
Eagle Brow (A6144)
☎ (0192 575) 5939
11.30–11
Lees GB Mild, Bitter H, **Moonraker** (winter) E
Ornate, old village pub near Lymm Cross and canal moorings, comprising three varying rooms: a large, plush, split-level lounge; a cosy snug, particularly popular with locals early eve; and a basic bar extended into the cottage next door. ⋈ Q ◑ ⊟

Macclesfield

Baths
40 Green Street (off A537)
6.30–11; 11–4, 6.30–11 Sat
Banks's Hanson's Mild, Bitter; Whitbread Boddingtons Bitter H
Small, but thriving local, a few minutes' walk uphill from the station. A local bowling green inspired its original name, Bowling Green Tavern, and a public baths its current one. The pub has outlived both.
⊟ ⇌ ♣

Chester Road Tavern
18 Chester Road
☎ (01625) 424683
11–3 (4 Fri & Sat), 6–11
Greenalls Mild, Bitter; Stones Best Bitter H
Popular pub, on a now quiet street since the opening of the ring road. Home of a keen domino school along with other pub games, plus an excellent draw on Sun. ⊟ ♣

George & Dragon
Sunderland Street
☎ (01625) 421898
11–3 (4 Thu, 5 Sat), 5.30 (7 Sat)–11; 11–11 Fri
Robinson's Hatters Mild, Best Bitter E
Friendly pub serving good value food (until 6.45; not Sun). Pool, darts and skittles are played. Close to both bus and railway stations.
Q ❀ ◑ ⇌ ♣

Old Millstone
66 Waters Green
☎ (01625) 422684
11–11
Marston's Bitter, Pedigree H
Recently modernised, split-level pub opposite a public car park. It offers a good selection of food at lunchtimes (not Sun). The jukebox is switched off until 7pm. Very busy at times. ◑ ⇌ ♣ P

Ox-Fford
73 Oxford Road
☎ (01625) 422092
12–3.30, 5–11; 11–11 Fri & Sat
S&N Theakston Best Bitter, XB; guest beer H
Detached, brick-built pub on the busy through-road to Congleton. Recently refurbished, it was called the Oxford before being renamed after a ford which crossed the road many years ago.
❀ ◑ ⊟ ♣

Queens
5 Albert Place
☎ (01625) 422328
11–11
Holt Mild, Bitter H
Large Victorian inn, opposite the station. The original brickwork has been restored by the brewery. Now an honest drinking house, serving very cheap beer. ⋈ ⊟ ⇌ ♣

Middlewich

Big Lock
Webbs Lane (off A530, Northwich Road, turn down Finneys Lane)
☎ (01606) 833489
11.30–11
Bass Worthington BB, Draught Bass; guest beer H
Former, run-down, Allied pub, now enjoying a revival as a free house. It offers good food (not served Mon eve), and is handy for canal-users.
⌂ ❀ ◑ ⚲ ♣ P

Cheshire Cheese
Lewin Street (A533)
☎ (01606) 832097
11–4.30, 6.30–11
Cains Mild, Bitter; Whitbread Boddingtons Bitter; guest beers H
Small, friendly, town pub, located near the canal. Formerly a Tetley keg pub, sold to Boddingtons in 1990.
❀ ♣ P

Mobberley

Bulls Head
Town Lane (off B5085, in old village) ☎ (01565) 873134
11–11
Tetley Walker Mild, Bitter; Whitbread Boddingtons Bitter H
Large, detached pub of late-17th-century origin, with a bowling green to the rear. The open-plan lounge has a central fireplace. Occasional beer festivals; no food Sun.
⋈ Q ❀ ◑ P

Moulton

Lion
Main Road ☎ (01606) 592451
12–4 (4.30 Fri, 5 Sat), 7–11

Tetley Walker Bitter; guest beers Ⓗ
Large pub in the village centre. The landlord's Rugby League medals are displayed at the bar. 🍴 ♦ P

Nantwich

Rifleman
68 James Hall Street
☎ (01270) 629977
12–4, 6.30–11; 12–11 Fri; 11–11 Sat
Robinson's Hatters Mild, Best Bitter Ⓔ
Small, brick-built pub in a back-street residential area, close to the town centre. Predominantly an open-plan lounge, it has a small bar and a pool room. 🍴 ❄ ◐ ♣ P

Try also: Wilbraham Arms, Welsh Row (Courage)

Newbold

Horseshoe
Fence Lane (left off A34 at Astbury church, right after ½ mile, follow bends for 1½ miles) OS863602
☎ (01260) 272205
11–3, 6–11
Robinson's Hatters Mild, Best Bitter Ⓔ
Isolated country pub, formerly part of a farmhouse and still enjoying a farming atmosphere. The superb children's play area has swings, a see-saw and climbing frames. It draws a good local trade and offers a welcome to walkers and canal-users. Hard to find, but worth the effort. No meals Mon eve.
🍴 Q 🛏 ❄ ◐ ♣ P

Northwich

Beehive
High Street
11–11
Greenalls Mild, Bitter, Original; Stones Best Bitter Ⓗ
Attractive, red-brick, town-centre pub with an open, split-level interior. Popular throughout the day: the excellent value lunches and congenial atmosphere entice both locals and shoppers. ◐

Old Hall

Bewsey Farm
Bewsey Farm Close (off A57, W of Warrington)
☎ (01925) 33705
12–3.30, 5.30–11; 12–11 Fri & Sat
Cains Bitter; Tetley Walker Bitter; Whitbread Boddingtons Bitter; guest beer Ⓗ

Long, open-plan pub, converted from old farm buildings in the 1980s to serve new estates, near Bewsey Old Hall. An interesting blend of woodwork and brick, it displays ornaments reflecting its former use. Quiz night Tue; barbecues in summer.
❄ ◐ ♣ P

Over Peover

Parkgate Inn
Stocks Lane ☎ (01625) 861455
11–3, 5–11; 11–11 Sat
Samuel Smith OBB Ⓗ
Very smart, ivy-clad, old pub with several small, wood-panelled rooms, including a tap room. Good food.
🍴 Q 🛏 ❄ ◐ ▮ ◪ ⚄ ♣ P

Parkgate

Red Lion
The Parade ☎ (0151) 336 1548
12–11
Ind Coope Burton Ale; Walker Mild, Best Bitter, Winter Warmer Ⓗ
A pub since at least 1822, offering a traditional lounge and a bar with a pool table and a dartboard. It draws mainly local people during the winter, but has a good passing trade in summer, taking advantage of the excellent views of Wales. A goat guards the orchard. Q ◐ ♣

Prestbury

Admiral Rodney
New Road (A538)
☎ (01625) 828078
11–3, 5.30–11
Robinson's Hatters Mild, Best Bitter Ⓗ
Popular inn, in an attractive village terrace. A Grade II-listed building, the original front door became the back door when the new road was built through the village.
🍴 Q ◐ ⇌ P

Runcorn

Windmill
Windmill Hill (off A558, 1½ miles from A56 jct)
☎ (01928) 710957
11.30–3, 5–11; 11.30–11 Fri & Sat
Hydes' Anvil Light, Bitter Ⓔ
Large 1980s pub, with views across the valley towards Warrington. Note its unusual octahedral shape.
🛏 ❄ ◪ ♣ P

Sandbach

Crown
The Square ☎ (01270) 762161
11–3, 4.30–11

Robinson's Hatters Mild, Best Bitter Ⓔ
Old town pub, on a cobbled square, facing the Saxon Crosses. 🛏 ❄ ◐ P

Lower Chequers
Crown Banks
☎ (01270) 762569
12–3 (not Mon or Tue), 5.30–11; 12–11 Sat
Ruddles Best Bitter; guest beers Ⓗ
Former money-changing house which dates from the 16th century. It boasts a striking frontage and an unusual interior. Up to five guest beers are available, but they can be expensive for the area. 🍴 ❄ ◐

Sarn

Queens Head
Sarn Bridge (off B5069, S of Threapwood) OS440447
☎ (0194 881) 244
11–3, 5–11
Banks's Mild; Marston's Bitter Ⓗ
Small country pub by a stream which forms the English/Welsh border, worth the search. Meals by order only.
🍴 Q ❄ ◐ ♣ P

Saughall

Greyhound Inn
Seahill Road ☎ (01244) 880205
12–3 (may extend Sat), 6–11
Whitbread Boddingtons Bitter, Castle Eden Ale; guest beers Ⓗ
Pleasantly refurbished local in the village centre, worth the bus ride from Chester. Several cosy drinking areas and usually two guest beers may delay your 200-yard trip to the Welsh border. Q ❄ ◐ ▮ ♣ P

Stoak

Bunbury Arms
Little Stanney Lane
☎ (01244) 301665
11.30–3, 6–11.30
Cains Bitter; Whitbread Boddingtons Bitter, Higsons Bitter Ⓗ
Traditional local set amidst motorway junctions and the Shropshire Union Canal. It offers a friendly atmosphere in the lounge and games in the snug. Meals Mon–Fri.
Q ❄ ◐ P

Stretton

Ring O'Bells
Northwich Road, Lower Stretton (nr M56 jct 10)
☎ (01925) 730556
12–3 (3.30 Sat), 5.30 (7 Sat)–11

Greenalls Mild, Bitter, Original H
Small, welcoming roadside pub, once a row of cottages, and still recognisable as such. Getting more popular every year. 🏚 Q ❀ P

Tarporley

Rising Sun
38 High Street
☎ (01829) 732423
11–3, 5.30–11
Robinson's Hatters Mild, Best Bitter H
Rambling old inn of character. Excellent value meals and local sports teams mean the pub is generally packed. One bar is reserved for diners, plus a bookable dining room (children allowed); no food Sun eve. Pity about the fake fires. In every edition of the *Guide*. ◖ ▶ P

Tattenhall

Letters Inn
High Street ☎ (01829) 70221
11–3, 5.15–11; 11–11 Sat
Cains Bitter; Morland Old Speckled Hen; Wadworth 6X; Whitbread Boddingtons Bitter; guest beers H
Traditional country inn where bar meals are available at all times. The 'Post Room' is a no-smoking restaurant area. Collection of blow lamps.
🏚 ❀ ◖ ▶

Timbersbrook

Coach & Horses
Dane in Shaw Bank OS890618
☎ (01260) 273019
11–3, 6–11
Robinson's Hatters Mild, Best Bitter E
Situated high in the hills above Congleton, this small brick-built pub with associated farm buildings is half hidden from the main road as it winds upwards from the A537. The interior is mainly a large through-lounge, but there is a tiny tap room.
🏚 ꝏ ❀ ◖ ▶ ⌂ & ♿ P

Tushingham

Blue Bell Inn
Just off A41, 4 miles N of Whitchurch ☎ (01948) 662172
12–3, 6–11
Hanby Drawwell, Treacleminer; guest beers H
This delightful country pub deservedly won CAMRA's regional *Pub of the Year* award, 1994. Three timber-beamed rooms have a welcome for

locals and visitors, children included. 🏚 ❀ ◖ ▶ & ♿ P

Try also: Wheatsheaf Inn, Noman's Heath (S&N)

Warrington

Lower Angel
27 Buttermarket Street
☎ (01925) 633299
11–4, 7–11
Ind Coope Burton Ale; Walker Mild, Bitter, Best Bitter, Winter Warmer; guest beer H
Small, popular pub offering up to ten guest beers per week. A multi-award-winner from the local CAMRA branch.
🚋 (Central) ♣

Manx Arms
31 School Brow
☎ (01925) 230791
12–3.30 (4.30 Sat), 7–11
Vaux Samson; Wards Mild; guest beer H
A welcome return to the *Guide* for this ex-Tetley pub, a friendly back-street local near the town centre. It is a rare survivor in a town decimated by so-called 'development'. Regularly changing guest beers come from the Vaux stable. ◖ ⊟ 🚋 (Central) ♣

Old Town House
95 Buttermarket Street
☎ (01925) 413892
12–3 (5 Fri), 7–11; 7–10.30 Sun, closed Sun lunch
Courage Directors; John Smith's Bitter; guest beers H
Single-bar, open-plan pub in a Georgian building set back from the road. The modern decor is due to be replaced by a more traditional one; the opening hours may change afterwards. Up to four guest beers. ❀ ◖ 🚋 (Central) ⌂

Wettenhall

Boot & Slipper
Long Lane OS625613
☎ (01270) 73238
11.30–3.30, 5.30–11
M&B Highgate Dark; Marston's Pedigree E / H
Friendly, 16th-century country inn and restaurant.
🏚 ❀ 🍴 ◖ ♣ P

Wheelock

Cheshire Cheese
466–468 Crewe Road
☎ (01270) 760319
12–11
Banks's Mild, Bitter H
Canalside pub with a loyal local clientele, some of whom are portrayed on the walls in caricature form. Marston's Pedigree or Camerons

Strongarm occasionally served. 🏚 ❀ ◖ ▶ ♣ P

Try also: Commercial, Crewe Rd (Free)

Widnes

Millfield
Millfield Road
☎ (0151) 424 2955
11–11; 11–5, 7–11 Sat
Webster's Yorkshire Bitter, Wilson's Mild; guest beers H
Busy, back-street local. The landlord also runs the Commercial in the town. ♣

Willaston

Horseshoe
Newcastle Road (A500)
☎ (01270) 69404
12–3, 6–11; 12–11 Fri
Robinson's Hatters Mild, Bitter, Best Bitter, Old Tom H
Roadside cottage pub, a rare outlet for Robinson's ordinary bitter. This former brew pub has a small bar and a wood-panelled lounge. Eve meals Wed–Sun. 🏚 Q ❀ ◖ ▶ P

Wilmslow

Farmers Arms
71 Chapel Lane
☎ (01625) 532443
11–11
Whitbread Boddingtons Mild, Bitter; guest beer H
Traditional Victorian town pub. Several rooms abound with brasses and antiques; the family room is upstairs. Note the eye-catching finery around the etched lounge windows. The garden is kept in beautiful condition. No meals Sun.
🏚 Q ⏣ ❀ ◖ ⊟ P

George & Dragon
Church Street
☎ (01625) 522802
11.30–3.30 (3 Thu), 6–11; 11–11 Wed & Fri
Bass Worthington BB, Draught Bass; Stones Best Bitter; guest beers H
Excellent, large, multi-roomed community pub next to the church, with a very large garden. Keen emphasis on sport. 🏚 ❀ ◖ ▶ ⊟ 🚋 ♣ P

Wincle

Wild Boar
On A54 ☎ (01260) 227219
12–3, 7–11
Robinson's Hatters Mild, Best Bitter H
Traditional, welcoming stone-built pub, high on the moors. Fortnightly clay-pigeon shoots make Sun lunchtimes very busy. 🏚 Q ❀ ◖ ▶ P

Cleveland

 Camerons, *Hartlepool;* **North Yorkshire,** *Middlesbrough*

Acklam

Coronation at Acklam
Acklam Road (A1032/A1130 jct) ☎ (01642) 817599
11–11.30 (11 Sat)
Camerons Strongarm H
Inter-war, brick-built pub, recently refurbished as a Wolverhampton & Dudley house, with a bar, lounge and function room. ◐ ⚭ ♿ ♣ ⚲

Try also: Master Cooper, Acklam Rd (Samuel Smith)

Brotton

Green Tree
High Street (100 yds from hospital) ☎ (01287) 76377
11–1, 7–11
Camerons Strongarm H
Stone-built former manor house on a street corner. The bar has been recently enlarged, but smaller rooms and cosy corners have been retained. Strong local trade. Quiz nights; occasional live entertainment. Sun lunches served.
🍴 Q ♿ ⚭ ♣

Egglescliffe

Pot & Glass
Church Road
☎ (01642) 780145
11–3, 5.30–11

Bass Worthington BB, Draught Bass H
Charming village pub with two bars and a separate children's/function room. The ornate bar fronts were carved from furniture by a former licensee. A pub with a long and interesting history and a resident ghost. Eve meals on request. Q ⚭ ⚖ ◐ ⊞
≷ (Allens West) ♣ ⚲

Try also: Eagle, Durham Lane (Camerons)

Elwick

McOrville Arms
The Green ☎ (01429) 273344
11.30–3, 7–11; 11–11 Fri & Sat
Whitbread Boddingtons Bitter, Castle Eden Ale, guest beers H
Country tavern on the village green. Excellent, home-cooked lunch menu, with eves set aside for drinkers. Live jazz monthly. Fine collection of pigs. Two guest beers always available. 🍴 ⚭ ◐ ⚖ ♣ P

Guisborough

Tap & Spile
Westgate (near market cross)
☎ (01287) 632983
11–3, 5.30–11; 11–11 Thu–Sat
Beer range varies H
Old town-centre pub, refurbished in traditional style,

with a separate room at the rear, available for small functions. Eight beers on sale. Lunches every day in summer; Thu–Sun only in winter.
Q ⚭ ⚖ ◐ ⚖ ♣ ⚲

Hartburn

Masham
☎ (01642) 580414
11–11
Draught Bass; guest beer H
Classic village local whose origins as a 'public house' can still be clearly seen. Warm and comfortable interior with several drinking areas. The guest beer has been Butterknowle Conciliation.
Q ⚭ ⚖ P

Try also: Parkwood Hotel, Darlington Lane (Vaux); **Sutton Arms,** Elton (Free)

Hartlepool

Causeway
Elwick Road, Stranton
☎ (01429) 273954
11–11
Banks's Bitter; Camerons Bitter, Strongarm H
Unspoilt pub, once part of the Tap & Spile chain, standing next to the Camerons brewery. No lunches Sun.
Q ⚭ ⚖ ◐ ≷ ♣

Try also: Brewer & Firkin, Whitby St (Whitbread)

Cleveland

Gillen Arms
Clavering Road (off A690)
☎ (01429) 860218
11.30–3.30, 6.30–11.30; 11–11 Wed, Fri
& Sat
**Whitbread Boddingtons
Bitter, Castle Eden Ale; guest
beer** Ⓗ
Modern estate pub with a
strong local following,
indulging in many community
events. Children welcome in
the conservatory. ⏷ ◖ ♣ P

Jackson Arms
Tower Street ☎ (01429) 862413
12–3, 6–11; 12–11 Fri & Sat
**Draught Bass; S&N
Theakston XB, Old Peculier;
Stones Best Bitter; Whitbread
Boddingtons Bitter; guest
beer** Ⓗ
Two-room pub, typical of the
Fitzgerald chain in its antique
touches. Quiet lounge.
🏧 Q Ⓔ ⇌ ♣

New Inn
Durham Street
☎ (01429) 267797
11–4, 7–11
Camerons Strongarm Ⓗ
Classic, two-bar, street-corner
local—Cleveland's record
holder for *Good Beer Guide*
entries. Not to be missed!
Ⓔ ♣

High Leven

Fox Covert
Low Lane (A1044, between
Yarm and Thornaby)
☎ (01642) 760033
11–3, 5–11
**Vaux Samson, Double
Maxim** Ⓗ
A distinctive cluster of whitewashed brick buildings of
obvious farmhouse origin,
with a comfortable, open-plan
interior and a warm welcome
for all. Large function room
upstairs. Strong emphasis on
food. 🏧 ❀ ◖ ▶ ♣ P

Lazenby

Nags Head
High Street ☎ (01642) 440149
11.30–3 (5 Sat), 7–11
**Bass Worthington BB,
Draught Bass** Ⓗ
Cosy, spacious local decorated
with rural scenes, photographs
and paintings, popular for
lunchtime meals (not served
Sat). Eve meals available
Thu–Sat. Q ◖ ▶ ♣ P

Maltby

Pathfinders
High Lane ☎ (01642) 590300
11–11
**Whitbread Boddingtons
Bitter, Castle Eden Ale,
Flowers Original; guest
beer** Ⓗ

Large, one-roomed bar with a
separate area for meals.
❀ ◖ ▶ & P

Marske-by-the-Sea

Frigate
Hummershill Lane (opp.
cricket ground)
☎ (01642) 484302
11–3, 7–11; 11–11 Fri; 12–11 Sat
**John Smith's Bitter,
Magnet** Ⓗ
Pleasant estate pub with a
large lounge. Live
entertainment every Tue night,
and Fri night once a month.
Quiet room at the rear.
Q Ⓔ ⇌ ♣ P

Zetland Hotel
9 High Street
☎ (01642) 483973
2 (12 Sat)–11
**Vaux Samson, Double
Maxim; Wards Thorne Best
Bitter** Ⓗ
Large, spacious lounge and
bar with a friendly regular
clientele. Quiz nights, folk and
domino eves held in the
lounge, bar and upstairs room.
Sandwiches available all day;
lunches Sun. Adjacent to the
rail station. Local CAMRA *Pub
of the Year* 1992.
Q Ⓔ ⇌ ♣ P

Marton

Apple Tree
38 The Derby (off A172)
☎ (01642) 310564
11–11
**Bass Worthington BB,
Draught Bass** Ⓗ
Modern pub in an area of
suburban housing. Better
designed than most, with
quieter areas available.
Something for everyone!
⏷ ❀ ◖ Ⓔ & ♣ P

Try also: Rudds Arms, Marton
Rd (Whitbread)

Middlesbrough

Hogshead
228 Linthorpe Road
☎ (01642) 242559
11–11
**S&N Theakston XB;
Whitbread Boddingtons
Bitter, Castle Eden Ale; guest
beer** Ⓗ
Pub with ultra basic decor,
popular with young people.
The regular beers are
moderately priced, but guests
can be pricey. Wheelchair WC.
❀ 🏠 ◖ & ◠

Malt Shovel
97 Corporation Road (just off
A66 near Odeon cinema)
☎ (01642) 213213
11–11

**North Yorkshire Best Bitter,
Yorkshire Brown, Yorkshire
Porter, Erimus Dark, Flying
Herbert, Dizzy Dick; guest
beers** Ⓗ
Recently renovated pub built
in 1886. Wide ranging
clientele; popular with office
workers lunchtime. Quiz Tue
night; live entertainment Wed
night and Sat afternoon. Six
guest beers; three real fires.
Large car park nearby.
🏧 Q ❀ ◖ & ⇌ ♣ ◠

Star & Garter
14 Southfield Road
☎ (01642) 245307
11–11
**Bass Worthington BB,
Draught Bass; Butterknowle
Conciliation Ale; S&N
Theakston XB, Old Peculier** Ⓗ
Pub popular with students,
with a large screen TV in the
bar. A CAMRA pub
preservation award-winner.
One beer a week is sold at a
low price; free pint with Sun
lunch. Q ❀ ◖ ▶ Ⓔ ⇌ ♣ P

Tap'n'Barrel
86 Newport Road (near bus
station) ☎ (01642) 219995
11–11; 11–4.30, 7–11 Sat
**North Yorkshire Best Bitter,
Yorkshire Brown, Erimus
Dark, Dizzy Dick; guest
beer** Ⓗ
Cosy pub near the centre of
town, converted from a shop.
Victorian-style eating/function
room upstairs (eve meals
served). Gaslit bar. A total of
nine beers is on sale.
Q ⏷ ◖ & ⇌ ♣

Try also: Brody's, Vancouver
House (Free); **Rumpole's**,
Cleveland Centre (Free);
Westminster, Parliament Rd
(John Smith's)

Normanby

Poverina
45 High Street (B1380)
☎ (01642) 440521
11–11
Camerons Strongarm Ⓗ
Old roadhouse, much
extended in the postwar years
and taking its name from a
racehorse. Recently
refurbished in typical
Wolverhampton & Dudley
style. Strong local patronage.
No lunches Sat; eve meals
served Mon–Fri.
❀ ◖ ▶ & ♣ P

Try also: Parklands, Skippers
Lane (Whitbread)

Redcar

Yorkshire Coble
West Dyke Road (S end of
racecourse) ☎ (01642) 482071
11–3 (4 Fri & Sat), 6–11

Samuel Smith OBB H
Large estate pub with a strong
regular clientele: a comfortable
lounge, a large, functional bar
and a games room. Food
available all day.
❀ ◖ ▶ ☖ ⇌ (Central) ♣ P

Try also: Elgins, High St
(Whitbread)

Saltburn-by-the-Sea

Churchills
47 Marine Parade (top of
promenade, corner of
Diamond St) ☎ (01287) 624010
11–11
**Eldridge Pope Royal Oak;
Liquid Assets Potter's Pride;
Taylor Landlord; Tetley
Bitter; guest beer** H
Large Victorian pub, offering a
comfortable lounge, a bar with
a pool table and a private
function room with a bar. Free
Sun night quiz; summer and
winter beer festivals. Eve
meals available if booked, but
not Sun. ❀ ◖ ☖ ▲ ⇌ ♣ ◠

Try also: Victoria, Dundas St
(Tetley)

Skelton Green

Green Inn
Boosbeck Road (top of steep
hill leading to Skelton)
☎ (01287) 650475
11–4, 7–11 (may extend in the
afternoon)
Camerons Strongarm H
Terraced pub with a large bar,
a separate pool room and a
strong local trade.
Photographs of old Skelton
Green in the bar. Pie and
ploughman's type food served
(eve meals finish early). Be
sure to order beer straight
from the pump!
Q ⋟ ❀ ◖ ▶ ☖ ♣

Stainton

Stainton Inn
☎ (01642) 599902
11–3, 6–11
Camerons Strongarm H
Imposing, Victorian redbrick

pub in the centre of the village.
Extended in 1987 into cottages
next door. Strong emphasis on
food. ❀ ◖ ▶ ☖ ♣ P

Stockton-on-Tees

Cricketers
Portrack Lane (off Maritime
Rd) ☎ (01642) 675468
11–11
**Whitbread Trophy; guest
beers** H
Popular, old street-corner local
with a warm, friendly
atmosphere. Quiz Fri night;
band box Sat night.
♨ Q ◖ ♣ P

Fitzgeralds
9–10 High Street (opp. Mecca
bingo hall) ☎ (01642) 678220
11–3 (3.30 Fri, 4.30 Sat), 6.30–11
**Draught Bass; McEwan 80/-;
S&N Theakston Old Peculier;
Taylor Landlord; guest
beers** H
Imposing stone-built pub with
granite pillar fronts. The
split-level, open-plan interior
has typical Fitzgerald fittings.
Much-frequented by younger
patrons (jukebox). Local
CAMRA *Pub of the Year* 1993.
Occasional ciders. ◖ ⇌ ♣

Sun
Knowles Street
☎ (01642) 615676
11–4, 5.30–11; 11–11 Wed, Fri & Sat
Draught Bass H
Classic town-centre boozer,
which claims to sell more
Draught Bass than any other
pub in Britain. A legend in its
own lifetime. Folk club Mon.
⇌ ♣

Waterfront
Castlegate Quay (off main
riverside road)
☎ (01642) 674309
12–3, 5–11 (1am Thu–Sat)
**McEwan 80/-; S&N Theakston
Best Bitter; Younger No. 3;
guest beers** H
Modern pub on two floors of
an old riverside warehouse.
The conservatory and terrace
overlook the fast-improving
River Tees tourist area. Note
the late opening. Can be noisy

and full of younger patrons.
No meals weekends.
◖ ⇌ (Thornaby) P

Try also: Clarendon, Dovecot
St (Camerons); **Senators**,
Bishopton Rd (Vaux)

Thornaby-on-Tees

Oddfellows Arms
500 Thornaby Road
☎ (01642) 763091
11.30–11
Camerons Strongarm H
Classic brewers' Tudor pub set
on a crossroads, almost
opposite the gate of a former
RAF station. Refurbished in
Wolverhampton & Dudley
style and none the worse for it.
Eve meals finish at 8.30.
❀ ◖ ▶ ☖ ♣ P

Wolviston

Wellington Inn
31–33 High Street
☎ (01740) 644439
12–3, 5.30–11; 11–11 Fri & Sat
**Bass Worthington BB,
Draught Bass; guest beers** H
Friendly, traditional village
pub with a welcoming
atmosphere: a tiny 'Farmers'
bar' along with two separate,
larger rooms. Folk club
upstairs Thu nights; function
room available. Eve meals
Mon–Fri. Wheelchair access is
via the rear car park.
Q ❀ ◖ ☖ ♣ P

Try also: Smiths Arms,
Billingham (Camerons)

Yarm

Black Bull
High Street ☎ (01642) 780299
11–11
Draught Bass H
One of several fine old
coaching inns in the village
conservation area: a popular,
high street local with a long-
standing commitment to real
ale. ❀ ◖ ▶ ☖ ♣ P

Try also: Ketton Ox, High St
(Vaux)

OPENING HOURS

Permitted opening hours in England and Wales are 11–11, though not
all pubs choose to take advantage of the full session and many close in
the afternoons. Some pubs have special licences and there are
sometimes special local arrangements for market days and other
events. Standard Sunday hours are 12–3, 7–10.30. Scottish licensing
laws are more generous and pubs may stay open longer.

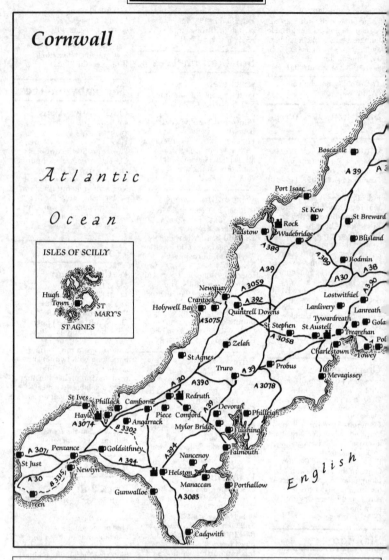

Cornwall

Atlantic

Ocean

ISLES OF SCILLY

Hugh Town
ST MARY'S
ST AGNES

English

 Bird in Hand, Hayle; **Blue Anchor**, Helston; **Redruth**, Redruth; **St Austell**, St Austell; **Sharp's**, Rock

---

Albaston

Queens Head
½ mile S of A390
☎ (01822) 832482
11–3, 6–11
Draught Bass;
Courage Best Bitter;
Morland Old Speckled Hen H
Excellent village local on the edge of the Tamar valley: an unspoilt pub run by the same family for many years. Good value beer and bar snacks;

Taunton cider. ♨ Q ✿ ⬚
⇌ (Gunnislake) ♣ ➥ P

Altarnun

Rising Sun
Off A30, on Camelford road,
1 mile N of village
☎ (01566) 86332
11–3, 5.30–11
Exmoor Ale; Marston's
Pedigree; Otter Ale;
Whitbread Flowers Original;
guest beer H

Lively, 16th-century country inn on the edge of Bodmin Moor, offering ever-changing guest beers and good fare. Popular.
♨ ⌘ ✿ ⬚ ⬚ ◗ ➤ ♣ P

Angarrack

Angarrack Inn
32 Steamers Hill (off A30, N of Hayle) ☎ (01736) 752380
11–2.30, 6–11; 12–2, 7–10.30 Sun
St Austell Bosun's, XXXX
Mild, HSD H

Cornwall

Very welcoming and comfortable village pub offering an extensive and good value menu of home-prepared food (vegetarian option).
🏚 ❀ ◑ ▲ P

Blisland

Royal Oak
Village Green
☎ (01208) 850739
12–3, 6–11
Draught Bass; guest beers Ⓗ
A welcoming pub in an attractive moorland village: a comfortable lounge, a simple public bar, a spacious family room and a patio. No food Sun eve. 🏚 Q ☺ ❀ ◑ ▶ 🗗 ♣ P

Bodmin

Masons Arms
5–9 Higher Bore Street (A389)
☎ (01208) 72607
11–3, 5–11; 11–11 Fri & Sat
Bass Worthington BB, Draught Bass; Fuller's London Pride; Wadworth 6X; guest beers Ⓗ
Historic town pub, reputed to hold the oldest continuous licence in the Duchy. Good value food and a friendly atmosphere. The lounge is quiet.
Q ☺ ❀ 🗗 ◑ ▶ 🗗 ♣ P

Boscastle

Wellington Hotel
The Harbour ☎ (01840) 250202
11–3, 5.30–11
Draught Bass; St Austell HSD; Whitbread Flowers IPA; guest beers Ⓗ
Fine, listed Georgian coaching inn. In the long bar hang some stained-glass windows, dating from 1846, and some lamps from St Juliot church, put there by Thomas Hardy. Excellent food. Regular live folk music.
🏚 ☺ ❀ 🗗 ◑ ▶ ♣ ◔ P

Try also: Cobweb (Free)

Botus Fleming

Rising Sun
Off A388, 4 miles from Tamar Bridge ☎ (01752) 842792
12–3, 6–11 (may vary)
Draught Bass; Morland Old Speckled Hen; guest beer Ⓗ
Unspoilt and unpretentious country pub with 12th-century origins. Tucked away in a quiet village on the outskirts of Saltash. Now in the third generation of family ownership. Good value cider.
🏚 ❀ 🗗 ▲ ♣ ◔ P

Cadgwith

Cadgwith Cove Inn
☎ (01326) 290513
12–2.30, 7–11 (11–11 summer)
Devenish Cornish Original; Marston's Pedigree; Whitbread Castle Eden Ale, Flowers Original; guest beers Ⓗ
17th-century, unspoilt old smuggling inn in the heart of a famous fishing village. It has a main bar, plus a small lounge. The fishermen's choir sings Fri. 🏚 ❀ 🗗 ◑ ▲

Callington

Coach Makers Arms
Newport Square
☎ (01579) 82567
11–2.30, 6.30–11

Draught Bass; Fuller's London Pride; Greene King Abbot; guest beer Ⓗ
17th-century coaching inn with a friendly atmosphere and good food. Popular public bar area; reasonable beer prices. Q 🗗 ◑ ▶ ♣ P

Calstock

Tamar Inn
The Quay ☎ (01822) 832487
11.30–3.30, 6–11 (11–11 summer)
Wadworth 6X; Whitbread Boddingtons Mild, Bitter, Flowers IPA, Original Ⓗ;
guest beers
17th-century riverside pub popular with locals and visitors, especially river boat custom. Featuring an open-plan layout, the pub is ideally set in the Tamar valley, with a striking view of the Calstock viaduct.
🏚 🗗 ❀ ◑ ▶ & ▲ ⇌ ♣ P

Camborne

Tyacks Hotel
Commercial Street
☎ (01209) 612424
11–11
St Austell Bosun's, XXXX Mild, Tinners, HSD Ⓗ
18th-century former coaching inn, providing a very high standard of comfort and offering a good range of ales, wines and excellent cuisine.
Q ❀ 🗗 ◑ ▶ & ⇌ ♣ P

Charlestown

Rashleigh Arms
☎ (01726) 73635
11–11
Draught Bass; Ruddles County; St Austell Tinners; Tetley Bitter; Wadworth 6X; Whitbread Boddingtons Bitter; guest beers Ⓗ
Large, friendly inn overlooking the famous port, comprising two large bars, a restaurant and a family room. AA 3-star accommodation.
🗗 ❀ 🗗 ◑ ▶ 🗗 & ▲ ♣ P

Comford

Fox & Hounds
On A393 Falmouth–Redruth road ☎ (01209) 820251
11–3, 6–11
Draught Bass; St Austell Tinners, HSD, Winter Warmer Ⓖ
Comfortable country pub with a restaurant. An old frieze in the snug is being restored to its former glory after being hidden by wallpaper for over ten years.
🏚 ❀ ◑ ▶ 🗗 ▲ ♣ P

Cornwall

Crantock

Old Albion
Langurroc Road
☎ (01637) 830243
11–11
Courage Best Bitter; John Smith's Bitter; guest beers H
Quaint, thatched village pub by the church lychgate, offering good food. Well-set for walks. Live music often at weekends. Popular with summer visitors.
🏾 Q ⚘ ✿ ◑ ▶ ▲ ♣ P

Devoran

Old Quay Inn
St John's Terrace (off A39)
☎ (01872) 863142
11–3, 6–11
Whitbread Boddingtons Bitter, Flowers IPA, Original H
Friendly pub benefiting from fine views over Devoran Quay and Creek. A good local which serves good food.
🏾 ⚘ 🛏 ◑ ▶ ♣ P

Falmouth

Quayside Inn
Arwenack Street
☎ (01326) 312113
11–11
Draught Bass; Ruddles County; Whitbread Boddingtons Bitter, Flowers IPA, Original H**; guest beers** G
Large, two-bar pub overlooking the Custom House Quay and Falmouth Harbour. The upstairs bar boasts 175 whiskies, while the downstairs bar has a wide range of guest beers, plus live music on Fri and Sat eve. Twice-yearly beer festivals. No food Sun eve. Cider in summer. ⚘ ◑ ▶ ⇌ (The Dell) ↺

Seven Stars
The Moor ☎ (01326) 312111
11–3, 6–11
Draught Bass G**; Ruddles County; John Smith's Bitter** H**; St Austell HSD; guest beers** H
Unspoilt by 'progress', a pub in the same family for five generations; the current landlord is an ordained priest. The lively tap room has barrels on display; the rear snug is quiet. Q ⚘ ⊞

Flushing

Royal Standard
St Peter's Hill (off A393 at Penryn) ☎ (01326) 374250
11–2.30 (3 Fri & Sat), 6.30–11; 12–2, 7–10.30 Sun (varies winter)

Draught Bass; Whitbread Boddingtons Bitter, Flowers IPA H
Friendly local near the entrance to the village. Beware of swans and high spring tides. 🏾 ⚘ ◑ ▶ ♣

Fowey

Ship Inn
Trafalgar Square
☎ (01726) 832230
11–3, 6–11 (11–11 Easter & summer)
St Austell XXXX Mild, Tinners, HSD H
This comfortable, one-bar, town-centre pub was once the family home of the Rashleighs and has historic connections with Drake and Raleigh. Parking is difficult.
🏾 Q ⚘ 🛏 ◑ ▶ ▲ ♣

Golant

Fisherman's Arms
Fore Street ☎ (01726) 832453
11–3, 6–11
Courage Best Bitter; Ushers Best Bitter, Founders H
Charming village pub in a delightful waterside setting, with views across the River Fowey. Try the home-cooked food. Riverside parking is available (at low tide!)
🏾 Q ⚘ ◑ ▶ ♣ P

Goldsithney

Crown
Fore Street ☎ (01736) 710494
11–3, 6–11
St Austell Bosun's, XXXX Mild, HSD H
Attractive, comfortable, village pub with a warm atmosphere, and a very popular restaurant (bookings advisable). It also serves excellent home-cooked bar meals. 🏾 ⚘ 🛏 ◑ ▶ ▲

Gunwalloe

Halzephron
2½ miles SW of A3083 jct
☎ (01326) 240406
11–3, 6.30–11
Fergusons Dartmoor Best Bitter, Strong H
Welcoming, comfortable inn with woodwork partly from old shipwrecks. It takes its name from the nearby cliff, and was once the haunt of smugglers. A well-appointed, cosy pub.
🏾 Q ⚘ ⚘ 🛏 ◑ ▶ ⚅ ▲ ♣ P

Hayle

Bird in Hand
Trelissick Road
☎ (01736) 753974
12–3, 7–11 (11–11 summer)

Courage Directors; Paradise Bitter, Miller's Ale, Artists Ale; John Smith's Bitter; Wadworth 6X H
Set in a former coach house, with its own brewery, this imposing pub stands adjacent to Paradise Park bird gardens. Good range of ales; friendly, relaxed atmosphere. Live music most weekends. Children welcome. Meals in summer only. ⚘ ◑ ▶ ⇌ ♣ P

Helston

Blue Anchor
Coinagehall Street
☎ (01326) 562821
11–3, 6–11
Blue Anchor Middle, Best, Special H
An inn for all reasons. A superb, unspoilt, rambling, granite and thatch, 15th-century building. The famous 'Spingo' beers come from the old brewhouse, whilst two friendly bars offer good chat (no jukebox). 🏾 Q ⚘ ▲

Holywell Bay

Treguth Inn
Holywell Road (off A3075)
☎ (01637) 830248
11.30–2.30, 7–11 (11–11 summer)
Courage Best Bitter, Directors; Ruddles County; John Smith's Bitter H
Thatched pub with low beams drawing a good mix of locals and holidaymakers, who enjoy the cooked meals and occasional entertainment. A choice of camping or self-catering sites nearby.
🏾 Q ⚘ ⚘ ◑ ▶ ▲ ♣ P

Isles of Scilly: *St Mary's*

Bishop & Wolf
Main Street, Hugh Town
☎ (01720) 22790
11–11
St Austell XXXX Mild, HSD, Tinners H
Named after the two famous local lighthouses, this lively pub features marine decor. It has a large bar, a pool room and an upstairs restaurant. The beer is fined at the pub after its sometimes arduous sea crossing! ⚘ ◑ ▶ ▲ ♣

Try also: **Turks Head**, St Agnes (Carlsberg-Tetley)

Kilkhampton

New Inn
On A39 ☎ (01288) 82488
11–2.30, 7–11
Draught Bass; St Austell HSD; guest beers H

Cornwall

15th-century, comfortable village inn which formerly had its own brewhouse: a quiet front bar and a spacious main bar, with an adjoining family room/skittle alley. Good selection of home-made food; good, friendly atmosphere.
🏚 Q ✿ 🛏 ◖ ▶ ♣ P

Kingsand

Rising Sun
The Green ☎ (01752) 822840
11–3, 7–11
Draught Bass; Courage Best Bitter; guest beer (summer) H
A former customs house, this Grade II-listed building stands in a village of narrow streets. On a coastal path, it is popular, quiet, and offers excellent food. A national finalist in a *Best Pub Sandwich* competition.
🏚 Q ✿ ◖ ▶ ♦ ▲ ♣

Lanlivery

Crown Inn
Off A390, 1½ miles W of Lostwithiel ☎ (01208) 872707
11–3, 6–11
Bass Worthington BB; Draught Bass; guest beer (summer) H
Comfortable and old-fashioned pub, a listed building. The restaurant has an inglenook and a low-beamed ceiling. Good accommodation in pleasant country village surroundings.
🏚 Q ✿ ✿ 🛏 ◖ ▶ 🖴 ♦ ▲ ♣ P

Lanreath

Punch Bowl Inn
Off B3359 ☎ (01503) 220218
11–3, 6–11
Draught Bass; Whitbread Boddingtons Bitter; guest beer H
Chaises-longues in the lounge and a large flagstoned kitchen (now the public bar) are the key features of this historic coaching house. Excellent food.
🏚 Q ✿ ✿ 🛏 ◖ ▶ 🖴 ♦ ▲ ♣ P

Launceston

Bakers Arms
Southgate Street
☎ (01566) 772510
11–3, 7–11; 11–11 Sat
Courage Directors; John Smith's Bitter; Wadworth 6X H**; guest beers** (occasional)
Popular town pub, adjacent to the historic Southgate Arch: a cosy wood-panelled lounge bar, and a busy, games-oriented public bar. Good value, home-cooked pub grub.
🏚 Q 🛏 ✿ ◖ ▶ ♣ P

Lostwithiel

Royal Oak
Duke Street ☎ (01208) 872552
11–11
Draught Bass; Fuller's London Pride; Marston's Pedigree; Whitbread Flowers Original, London Pride; guest beers H
Busy 13th-century inn, renowned for food. A stone floor in the public contrasts with the comfortable lounge and restaurant. Guest beers from small independent breweries.
🏚 Q ✿ 🛏 ◖ ▶ 🖴 ⇌ P

Manaccan

New Inn
☎ (01326) 231323
11–3, 6–11
Whitbread Flowers IPA, Castle Eden Ale; guest beer G
Very traditional, thatched village pub which has always provided home-cooked food and has no jukebox or fruit-machines. 🏚 Q ✿ ◖ ▶ P

Mevagissey

Fountain Inn
St Georges Square
☎ (01726) 842320
11–11
St Austell XXXX Mild, Tinners H**, Winter Warmer** G
Traditional, olde-worlde inn, licensed for 500 years. The two bars, with a slate floor and wood beams, display historic photos. A separate restaurant is open March–Oct.
🏚 Q 🛏 🛏 ◖ ▶ ▲ ♣

Mylor Bridge

Lemon Arms
Off A393 ☎ (01326) 373666
11–3, 6–11
St Austell Tinners, HSD H
Friendly, one-bar village-centre pub, serving good food.
🏚 ✿ ◖ ▶ ▲ ♣ P

Nancenoy

Trengilly Wartha
Off B3291, Constantine–Gweek road OS731282
☎ (01326) 40332
11–3, 6–11 (may vary)
Furgusons Dartmoor Best Bitter; St Austell XXXX Mild G**; Tetley Bitter** H**; guest beers** G
Delightful, remote country pub with beer-loving owners who ring the changes with guest beers. Renowned for its food. Excellent walks.
🏚 Q ✿ 🛏 ◖ ▶ 🖴 ♣ P

Newlyn

Fisherman's Arms
Fore Street ☎ (01736) 63399
10.30–2.30, 5.30–11
St Austell XXXX Mild, Tinners, HSD H
Popular old local boasting superb views over the busy fishing harbour and Mount's Bay. Note the inglenook and memorabilia display. Good value, simple food. Limited parking. 🏚 ✿ ◖ ▶ ♣ P

Newquay

Tavern
Mellanvrane Lane
☎ (01637) 873564
11–11
Bass Worthington BB, Draught Bass; Stones Best Bitter; guest beers H
Pub partly dating back to the 14th century, original manor house, which is now surrounded by modern dwellings. It stands apart from the more brash tourist traps of this popular seaside resort.
🛏 ✿ ◖ ▶ ▲ ♣ P

Padstow

Old Ship Hotel
Mill Square ☎ (01841) 532357
11–3, 6–11 (11–11 summer)
Draught Bass; Brains SA H
Set back from the road, just off the harbour, with tables outside, this is a pleasant haven in a busy fishing port. The wood-panelled public bar has high ceilings. Regular live music. Q 🛏 ✿ 🛏 ◖ ▶ 🖴 ♣

Penzance

Mount's Bay Inn
The Promenade, Werrytown
☎ (01736) 63027
11–2.30, 5.30–11
Draught Bass; guest beers H
Small, friendly, free house found towards Newlyn on the sea front. The open bar has an eating area to one side. Ever-changing guest ales.
🏚 Q ◖ ▶

Phillack

Bucket of Blood
☎ (01736) 752378
11–2.30, 6–11
St Austell Bosun's, XXXX Mild, HSD H
Historic village inn close to Hayle beaches, with a cosy, friendly atmosphere. Meals served and families welcome in summer.
🏚 Q 🛏 ✿ ◖ ▶ ♣ P

Cornwall

Philleigh

Roseland Inn
2 miles off A3078, on King Harry Ferry road
☎ (01872) 580254
11.30–3, 6–11
Devenish Cornish Original; Marston's Pedigree; Whitbread Flowers Original H
Classic pub in the heart of the Roseland peninsula: an unspoilt 17th-century inn featuring slate floors, beams and lots of character. Excellent, home-cooked fare; separate restaurant. It also has a locals' snug. ♨ Q ✿ ◑ ▶ ▲ P

Piece

Countryman
On the Four Lanes–Pool road
☎ (01209) 215960
11–11
Courage Best Bitter, Directors; Ruddles County; John Smith's Bitter; Wadworth 6X; guest beer H
Former count house for the local tin mining community, this popular country pub is said to be haunted by three maidens. Warm welcome; variety of entertainments.
♨ ✿ ◑ ▶ ♿ ▲ ♣ P

Polperro

Blue Peter
The Quay ☎ (01503) 72743
11–11
St Austell Tinners, HSD; guest beers H
The smallest pub in Polperro, reached by a steep flight of steps adjacent to the harbour. Wonderful atmosphere; good food; wide variety of guest ales. ♨ ➴ ◑ ▶ ᗒ

Polruan

Lugger
The Quay ☎ (01726) 870007
11–3, 6–11 (11–11 summer)
St Austell Bosun's, XXXX Mild, Tinners, HSD H
Situated near the quay, serving the Fowey passenger ferry, the Lugger has nautical decor and a friendly atmosphere.
♨ ➴ ◑ ▶ ⊞ ▲ ♣

Porthallow

Five Pilchards
☎ (01326) 280256
11–2.30, 6–11
Courage Directors; Devenish Cornish Original; Greene King Abbot H; guest beers (summer)
Attractive, rural pub on the beach, with views across to Falmouth. It boasts a fine collection of brass ships'
lamps, model ships and wreck histories. ♨ ✿ ◪ ◑

Port Isaac

Golden Lion
Fore Street ☎ (01208) 880336
11–11 (12–3, 6–11 winter)
St Austell Tinners, HSD H
Splendid, 18th-century pub overlooking the harbour, comprising several drinking areas. Pleasantly decorated, with ornate plasterwork on the ceiling. Can get busy in summer. ♨ ➴ ◑ ▶ ⊞ ♣

Probus

Hawkins Arms
Fore Street ☎ (01726) 882208
11–3, 5.30–11
St Austell Bosun's, XXXX Mild, Tinners, HSD H
Typical Cornish pub run by a landlord who enjoys his beers and home-cooking: a large bar and a dining room.
♨ Q ➴ ✿ ◪ ◑ ▶ ♿ ♣ P

Quintrell Downs

Two Clomes
East Road (A392)
☎ (01637) 873485
12–2.30, 7–11
Beer range varies H
18th-century free house which takes its name from the old clome ovens either side of the open log fire. Self-catering chalets. The beer range provides a mini-beer festival.
♨ Q ➴ ✿ ◪ ◑ ▶ ♿ ▲ ⇄ ♣ P

Redruth

Tricky Dickie's
Tolgus Mount (off old Redruth bypass) ☎ (01209) 219292
11–3, 6–11 (midnight Tue & Thu)
Greene King Abbot; Tetley Bitter; Wadworth 6X; guest beer H
This renovated old tin mine smithy offers squash/exercise facilities, plus jazz on Tue. The emphasis is on restaurant and bar meals; children welcome.
✿ ◑ ▶ ♿ ▲ ♣ P

Rilla Mill

Manor House Inn
Off B3254 at Upton cross
☎ (01579) 62354
12–2.30, 7–11
Draught Bass; Greene King Abbot; guest beer H
Comfortable, 17th-century inn and restaurant in the Lynher valley. Excellent, home-cooked food. Self-catering cottages, plus a heated outdoor swimming pool.
Q ✿ ◪ ◑ ▶ ⊞ ♿ ▲ ♣ P

St Agnes

Driftwood Spars
Trevaunance Cove (100 yds from beach) ☎ (01872) 552428
11–11 (midnight Fri & Sat)
Draught Bass; Ind Coope Burton Ale; Tetley Bitter; guest beers H
17th-century inn with a nautical theme. The cosy bar has a fine collection of whiskies. The restaurant offers an extensive menu. Lively bands Fri and Sat eve. Busy in the summer and at weekends. Family room in summer only.
♨ ➴ ✿ ◪ ◑ ▶ ▲ P

St Austell

Carlyon Arms
Sandy Hill (1 mile E on Bethel Rd) ☎ (01726) 72129
11–3, 5–11
St Austell XXXX Mild, Tinners, HSD H
Friendly local on the eastern suburbs of St Austell, serving good home-cooked food. It attracts a lively eve clientele; live music Wed and Fri.
♨ ✿ ◪ ◑ ▶ ♣ P

St Breward

Old Inn
Churchtown OS098773
☎ (01208) 850711
12–3, 6–11
Draught Bass; Ruddles County; John Smith's Bitter; guest beer H
Ancient pub that has seen some changes: one of the internal granite walls was originally an external wall. The large fireplace is very welcoming in winter. Fine selection of malts.
♨ Q ➴ ✿ ◑ ▶ ♣ P

St Ive

Butchers Arms
On A390 ☎ (01597) 82298
11–3, 5–11
Courage Best Bitter; Ruddles County; John Smith's Bitter H
Picturesque, 16th-century roadside inn, midway between Callington and Liskeard. The mainly locals' bar has a flagstone floor and pool table. There is also a comfortable lounge and an extensive play area for children. Prize-winning flower displays. Cider in summer.
♨ Q ➴ ✿ ◪ ◑ ▶ ⊞ ♣ ◔ P

St Ives

Sloop Inn
The Wharf ☎ (01736) 796584
11–11

Courage Best Bitter; Morland Old Speckled Hen; Ruddles County; John Smith's Bitter; Whitbread Boddingtons Bitter H

Old harbourside inn with three bars, two without music. Extensive seafood menu.

Q ⌂ ⊯ ⬤) ⩘ ≋ ♣

St John

St John Inn

3 miles S of Torpoint
☎ (01752) 822280
12–3, 6–11
Bass Worthington BB, Draught Bass H

Traditional, 17th-century village local: one bar plus a family snug. Quiet and welcoming, it nestles in a picturesque hamlet on the edge of the Tamar estuary. Good, home-cooked food.

⌂ Q ⌂ ⊛ ⬤) & ▲ ♣ P

St Just

Star

Fore Street ☎ (01736) 788767
11–3, 5.30–11
St Austell Tinners, HSD H

Old and atmospheric bar where beer from the wood is served by friendly staff. Set in a once-great tin mining area.

⌂ ⌂ ⊛ ⊯ ⬤

St Kew

St Kew Inn

Churchtown (1 mile off A39)
☎ (01208) 84259
12–2.30, 6–11
St Austell Tinners, HSD G

A pub since 1729, an inn which once had its own brewery and now has a very comfortable lounge and a popular public bar with a worn slate floor and an open range. Excellent food. Large garden. ⌂ Q ⊛ ⬤) ⊟ P

St Stephen

Queens Head

The Square (A3058)
☎ (01726) 822407
11–3, 6–11; 11–11 Fri & Sat
St Austell Bosun's, XXXX Mild, HSD H; Winter Ale G

Old coaching house, a listed building, with a traditional Cornish granite frontage. The interior has been opened out to form a large bar. Friendly village atmosphere; lively on music nights (Fri and Sat).

⌂ ⊛ ⊯ ⬤) ▲ ♣ ⌂ P

Saltash

Two Bridges

Albert Road ☎ (01752) 848952
12–11

Courage Best Bitter, Ushers Best Bitter, Founders; guest beer H

Lively pub with a cosy, country cottage interior. The large garden benefits from river views. Live music Wed and Fri; barbecues summer Sat. ⌂ ⊛ ≋ ♣

Seaton

Olde Smugglers Inn

Tregunnick Lane
☎ (01503) 5646
12–3, 6.30–11 (11–11 in summer)
Draught Bass; Wadworth 6X; guest beer H

Refurbished pub, with 17th-century origins, at the heart of a small village. It lies on the coastal path, with woods behind. Home-cooked food.

⌂ Q ⌂ ⊛ ⬤) ▲ ♣ ⌂ P

Stratton

Kings Arms Inn

Howells Road (A3092)
☎ (01288) 352396
11–3, 6–11 (may extend in summer)
Butcombe Bitter; Exmoor Gold; Fuller's London Pride; Hook Norton Best Bitter; Mansfield Riding Bitter; Morland Old Speckled Hen H

Delightful, 17th-century village pub, with a sense of fun. Two cosy bars with slate flags are complemented by a dining area. A sociable, old-fashioned pub. Good value pub meals; live jazz.

⌂ Q ⊛ ⊯ ⬤) ⊟ & ▲ ♣ ⌂ P

Tideford

Rod & Line

Church Road
☎ (01752) 851323
11–3, 5.30–11
Ushers Best Bitter, Founders H

Old Cornish farmhouse, converted to a pub around 1840. This typical working country inn retains traditional values; wellies welcomed! Music most Fri nights.

⌂ Q ⬤) & ▲ ♣ P

Treen

Logan Rock Inn

☎ (01736) 810495
10.30–3, 5.30–11
St Austell Tinners, HSD H

Good, small pub near Minack Open Air Theatre. The characterful bar offers good food. Try a stiff walk to the cliffs. ⌂ ⌂ ⊛ ⬤)

Tregrehan

Britannia Inn

On A390 ☎ (01726) 812889
11–11

Bass Worthington BB, Draught Bass; Greene King Abbot; St Austell Tinners H; guest beer

16th-century, large inn, open for food and drink all day. Large, safe garden and play area. Separate restaurant.

Q ⌂ ⊛ ⬤) ⊟ & ▲ P

Truro

City Inn

Pydar Street (N of cathedral)
☎ (01872) 72623
11–11
Courage Best Bitter, Directors; Morland Old Speckled Hen; John Smith's Bitter; Wadworth 6X; guest beer (occasional) H

Lively town pub with a central, square bar and three drinking areas. CAMRA Cornwall *Pub of the Year* 1992.

⊛ ⊯ ⬤) ≋ ♣ ⌂ P

Rising Sun

Mitchell Hill (100 yds off A39 at Trafalgar roundabout)
☎ (01872) 73454
11–3, 5–11; 11–11 Fri & Sat
Fuller's Chiswick; Whitbread Boddingtons Bitter H; guest beers

Friendly, two-bar local offering good, home-cooked food. Large dining area. Six guest beers. Q ⬤) & ♣ P

Tywardreath

New Inn

Fore Street ☎ (01726) 813901
11–2.30, 6–11
Draught Bass G; St Austell XXXX Mild, Tinners H, Winter Warmer G

Popular village local near the coast, with a large, secluded garden and a room for games. In the *Guide* for over 20 years. Q ⊛ ⊟ ▲ ≋ (Par) ♣ ⌂ P

Wadebridge

Swan Hotel

The Platt ☎ (01208) 812526
11–11
St Austell Tinners, HSD H

Pub whose attractive and brightly painted exterior opens on to one spacious bar, with alcoves.

⌂ ⊯ ⬤) ♣

Zelah

Hawkins Arms

High Road ☎ (01872) 540339
11–3, 6–11
Butcombe Bitter; Fergusons Dartmoor Best Bitter; Ind Coope Burton Ale; Tetley Bitter; guest beers H

Old coaching inn providing excellent value beer and food. Dining area for non-smokers.

⌂ Q ⌂ ⊛ ⬤) & ♣ ⌂ P

Cumbria

Cumbria

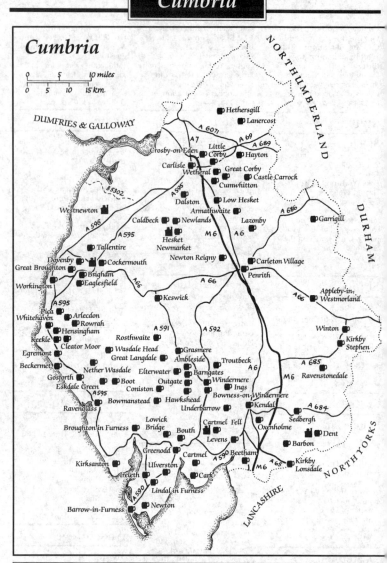

0   5   10 miles
0   5   10   15 km

NORTHUMBERLAND

DUMFRIES & GALLOWAY

DURHAM

Hethersgill
Lanercost
Crosby-on-Eden · Little Corby
A 6071 · A 69 · A 689
Hayton
Carlisle · Wetheral · Great Corby
Castle Carrock
Cumwhitton
Dalston · Low Hesket
Armathwaite · Lazonby
A 686 · Garrigill
Westnewton
Caldbeck · Newlands
Hesket Newmarket
Newton Reigny · Carleton Village
Tallentire
Dovenby · Cockermouth
Great Broughton · Brigham · Eaglesfield
Workington
Penrith
Appleby-in-Westmorland
Pica · Arlecdon
Whitehaven · Rowrah
Hensingham
Keswick
Keekle · Cleator Moor · Rosthwaite
Egremont
Winton
Kirkby Stephen
Beckermet · Nether Wasdale · Wasdale Head · Great Langdale
Grasmere · Ambleside · Troutbeck
Gosforth · Boot · Elterwater · Barngates · Ings
Eskdale Green · Coniston · Outgate · Windermere
Bowmanstead · Hawkshead · Bowness-on-Windermere
Ravenglass · Underbarrow · Kendal
Broughton in Furness · Lowick Bridge · Bouth · Cartmel Fell · Oxenholme
Sedbergh
Barbon · Dent
Greenodd · Cartmel · Levens · Beetham
Kirksanton · Ulverston · Cark
Ireleth · Lindal in Furness
Kirkby Lonsdale
Barrow-in-Furness · Newton

NORTH YORKS

LANCASHIRE

 Dent, Dent; **Hesket Newmarket,** Hesket Newmarket; **Jennings,** Cockermouth; **Masons Arms,** Cartmel Fell; **Yates,** Westnewton

Ambleside

Golden Rule

Smithy Brow
(off A591, signed to Kirkstone)
☎ (0153 94) 32257
11–11
Robinson's Hatters Mild, Bitter, Hartleys XB, Best Bitter H
The sort of pub which is becoming an endangered species; unchanged from the 1974 *Guide*. It remains deservedly popular for the beer and 'crack'. No jukebox or food smells (just pork pies and rolls daily). The patio can be a suntrap. ♨ Q ✿ ♣ P

Appleby-in-Westmorland

Golden Ball

High Wiend ☎ (0176 83) 51493
11.30–3, 7–11; 11.30–11 Sat (may vary)
Jennings Bitter, Cumberland Ale H
The licensee has changed, but this is still a fine example of an honest, no-frills, town-centre 'boozer'. Sandwiches always available. ♫ ⇌ ♣

Royal Oak

Bongate ☎ (0176 83) 51463
11–3, 6–11
S&N Theakston Best Bitter; Yates Bitter, Premium; Younger Scotch; guest beers H

70

Well-appointed, former coaching inn on the southern edge of town, comprising a splendid, panelled tap room, a separate lounge and a dining room. Up to four guest beers are available. CAMRA Cumbria *Pub of the Year* 1992. Prize-winning food. Not to be missed.
🍴 Q ❀ 🛏 ◑ ▶ ⇌ ♣ P

Arlecdon

Sun Inn
☎ (01946) 862011
11.30–2.30, 6–11
Jennings Bitter; Tetley Bitter; guest beer H
Friendly, village local serving good food. Children welcome. 🍴 ◑ ▶ ♣ P

Armathwaite

Fox & Pheasant
9 miles S of Carlisle; off A6
☎ (0169 74) 72400
11–11
Hesket Newmarket Doris's 90th Birthday Ale; Mitchell's ESB H
Coaching inn featuring an oak-beamed lounge and a slate-floored stable bar. Good food. 🍴 Q ❀ 🛏 ◑ ▶ ⇌ ♣ P

Try also: Duke's Head (Whitbread)

Barbon

Barbon Inn
☎ (0152 42) 76233
12–3, 6.30–11
S&N Theakston Best Bitter, Old Peculier H
17th-century, former coaching inn. The cosy front bar boasts a fine cast iron range; the lounge has comfortable armchairs. The restaurant serves good value, home-cooked meals using local produce. Q ❀ 🛏 ◑ ▶ P

Barngates

Drunken Duck
Off B5286 OS351012
☎ (0153 94) 36347
11.30–3, 6–11
Jennings Bitter; S&N Theakston XB, Old Peculier; Whitbread Boddingtons Bitter; Yates Bitter; guest beer H
One of the best known, but most difficult to find, pubs in the Lake District, reputed to be some 400 years old. An amusing legend about its name can be read inside. It is nearly always busy, especially in summer. Good food.
🍴 Q ❀ 🛏 ◑ ▶ ▲ P

Barrow-in-Furness

Albion Hotel
29 Dalton Road
☎ (01229) 820089
11–3, 5.30–11; 11–11 Fri & Sat (may vary)
S&N Matthew Brown Bitter, Theakston Best Bitter; Younger No. 3; guest beer H
Large, town-centre pub with a distinctive atmosphere in each room: a traditional local offering enough variety to appeal to all. Lunches Mon–Fri. Q ❀ 🛏 ◑ ♣

Beckermet

Royal Oak
☎ (01946) 841551
11–11
Jennings Bitter, Cumberland Ale H
Many-roomed pub, with a strong local following. Children welcome in the pool room. 🍴 ❀ 🛏 ◑ ▶ ▲ ♣ P

Beetham

Wheatsheaf Hotel
☎ (0153 95) 62123
11–3, 6–11
Thwaites Bitter; Whitbread Boddingtons Bitter H
Popular, three-roomed village hotel with a stone-flagged tap room. Good value meals are available and families are welcome until 8.30pm.
🍴 🛏 ◑ ▶ 🍲 ♿ ♣ P

Boot

Burnmoor Inn
OS176010 ☎ (0194 67) 23224
11–2.45, 4.45–11
Jennings Bitter, Cumberland Ale H
Picturesque, comfortable pub in the Upper Eskdale Valley, a peaceful situation. Austrian food is a speciality.
🍴 Q ❀ 🛏 ◑ ▶ ♣ P

Bouth

White Hart
☎ (01229) 861229
12–3, 6–11; 12–11 Thu, Fri, Sat & summer
Ruddles County; John Smith's Bitter; Tetley Bitter; Whitbread Boddingtons Bitter; guest beers H
17th-century coaching inn, popular with tourists and locals. It hosts live music and quizzes and has a games room. The food is good.
🍴 ❀ 🛏 ◑ ▶ P

Bowmanstead

Ship Inn
On A593, just S of Coniston

☎ (0153 94) 41224
12–3, 5.30–11; 12–11 Sat
Robinson's Hartleys XB H
Comfortable old local with a warm welcome. The snug adjoining the bar is used as a family/games room. Bed and breakfast is very popular, so book.
🍴 Q ❀ 🛏 ◑ ▶ ▲ ♣ P

Bowness-on-Windermere

Hole in T'Wall (New Hall Inn)
Lowside
☎ (0153 94) 43488
11–11
Robinson's Hatters Mild, Hartleys XB, Best Bitter H
This former smithy is probably the oldest Bowness tavern. It has split-level ground floor bars, plus a games/family room upstairs. The large patio is very popular in summer. Spontaneous entertainment. Self-catering flat available.
🍴 🐕 ❀ 🛏 ◑ ♣

Westmorland Arms
Lake Road (near Royalty cinema) ☎ (0153 94) 45678
11–11
Jennings Mild, Bitter, Cumberland Ale, Sneck Lifter; guest beers H
Built as a Victorian house, and converted to a restaurant in the 1960s, this then became a pub (the Cabin, then the Robbie Burns). It was bought and renamed by Jennings in 1993. Jazz Fri/Sat eves (bar closes 12.30am). Lunchtime snacks in summer.
🛏 ♣

Brigham

Lime Kiln
Low Road ☎ (01900) 825375
12–3, 6.30–11
Robinson's Hartleys XB H
Pleasant, two-roomed village pub. No food Mon.
Q ❀ 🛏 ◑ ▶ ▲ ♣ P

Broughton in Furness

Manor Arms
The Square
☎ (01229) 716286
2 (12 Fri, Sat & summer)–11
Jennings Cumberland Ale; Taylor Landlord; Yates Bitter, Premium; guest beers H
Children are welcome at this friendly, popular village local, which offers changing guest beers and snacks at all times. Local CAMRA *Pub of the Year* for the last four years.
🍴 Q ❀ 🛏 ▲ ♣

Cumbria

Caldbeck

Oddfellows Arms
☎ (0169 74) 78227
12–3, 6.30–11
Jennings Bitter, Cumberland Ale; guest beer (occasional) H
Formerly known as the John Peel, the Oddfellows has undergone a major refurbishment. It now has a comfortable bar area, with a spacious restaurant to the rear, serving high quality food.
🏠 Q ❀ ◑ ▶ ♣ P

Cark

Engine Inn
☎ (0153 95) 58341
12–4, 6–11 (12–11 summer)
S&N Theakston Mild, Best Bitter, XB or **Old Peculier; Younger Scotch; guest beer** (summer/Christmas) H
Comfortable, 18th-century ale house near the Old Mill House. Accommodation is in self-contained flats. Near Holker Hall.
🏠 ❀ 🛏 ◑ ▶ ♿ ▲ ⇌ ♣ P

Carleton Village

Cross Keys
On A686 ☎ (01768) 66233
11–3, 6–11
Vaux Samson; Wards Best Bitter H
Comfortable old village inn just off the main road, on the outskirts of Penrith. Caravan Club approved campsite nearby. 🏠 Q ❀ ◑ ▶ ▲ ♣

Carlisle

Caledonian Cask House
Botchergate ☎ (01228) 30460
11–11; 7–10.30 Sun, closed Sun lunch
Whitbread Boddingtons Bitter, Castle Eden Ale; guest beers H
Carlisle's premier cask ale house, much transformed. It now features stone-flagged and wooden floors and lots of railway memorabilia. Up to five guest beers are available, changed regularly. Good value bar meals. ◑ ⇌

Carlisle Rugby Club
Warwick Road
☎ (01228) 21300
7 (5.30 Fri, 6 Sat)–11 (12.30–11 Sat during rugby season)
Tetley Bitter; Yates Bitter; guest beer H
Welcoming, friendly club with a cosy lounge and a large bar, often crowded when Carlisle Utd are at home. The bar is decorated with rugby memorabilia. Show this *Guide*

or CAMRA membership to be signed in.
🏠 🛏 ❀ ♣ P

Chaplins
4 Crosby Street
☎ (01228) 29055
11–3, 7–11; 7–10.30 Sun, closed Sun lunch
S&N Theakston Best Bitter; Younger No. 3 H
Deservedly popular city-centre bar offering excellent value bar meals along with daily specials; the self-service salad bar is highly recommended. The upstairs restaurant is open eves. ❀ ◑ ⇌ ♣ ♠

Crown Inn
23 Scotland Road, Stanwix (A6) ☎ (01228) 512789
11–11
S&N Theakston Best Bitter; Younger Scotch H
Ex-State Management pub retaining some of Redfern's superb original wood panelling. It stands on the line of Hadrian's Wall, just a pleasant walk from the city centre across the River Eden. Good value, home-cooked lunches. ◑ ♣

Howard Arms
Lowther Street
☎ (01228) 32926
11–11
S&N Theakston Best Bitter, XB H
A regular *Guide* entry. Numerous partitions give the pub a multi-roomed effect, but it's usually a squeeze to get in. Unchanged for many years, it bears evidence of the State Management scheme in the old bottles lining the shelves. ❀ ◑ ⇌

Maltsters Arms
John Street, Caldewgate (A595) ☎ (01228) 20499
11–11
Jennings Cumberland Ale; guest beer H
Convivial local where the customer matters. ◑ ▶ ♿ ♣

Cartmel

Cavendish Arms
Off the square through the arch ☎ (0153 95) 36240
11–11
Bass Worthington BB, Draught Bass; Butterknowle Conciliation Ale; John Smith's Bitter; guest beers H
Roomy, comfortable village pub with a warm welcome. Short breaks and guided fell walks are available. Specific guest beers can be stocked on request. Regular beer festival Aug. Brewing is a possibility.
🏠 ❀ 🛏 ◑ ▶ ♿ ▲ P

Cartmel Fell

Masons Arms
Strawberry Bank (between Gummers How and Bowland Bridge) OS413895
☎ (0153 95) 68486
11.30–3, 6–11
Lakeland Amazon Bitter, Great Northern, Big Six, Damson H
Extremely popular brew pub which stocks an enormous range of bottled beers from all over the world, and offers a wide range of food. Always busy; large parties are discouraged. Accommodation is self-catering.
🏠 Q 🛏 ❀ 🛏 ◑ ▶ ▲ ♣ ⏛ P

Castle Carrock

Duke of Cumberland
☎ (01228) 70341
12–3, 7–11 (may vary)
Jennings Bitter, Cumberland Ale; S&N Theakston Best Bitter H
A former Marston's house, now re-opened, boasting a comfortable lounge area, and a pool room behind the bar.
🏠 ❀ ◑ ▶ ▲ ♣

Cleator Moor

Crown
1 Bowthorn Road
☎ (01946) 810136
11–4, 7–11; 11–11 Fri & Sat
Robinson's Hatters Mild, Hartleys XB, Best Bitter H
Pleasant, well-thought-out local. No meals Tue.
🛏 ◑ ▶ ♣

Cockermouth

Bush Hotel
Main Street
☎ (01900) 822064
11–3.30, 5.30–11; 11–11 Fri & summer
Jennings Mild, Bitter, Cumberland Ale, Oatmeal Stout, Sneck Lifter; guest beers H
Town-centre pub, the first Jennings house to sell guest beers. A large variety of bottled beers is also available. A local CAMRA branch special award-winner and Western Lakes *Pub of the Year*. Children are welcome when it's not too busy. 🏠 ◑ ♣

Swan Inn
Kirkgate ☎ (01900) 822425
11–3, 7–11
Jennings Bitter, Oatmeal Stout, Sneck Lifter H
Popular pub on a cobbled Georgian square, near All Saints church. Q ▲ ♣

Coniston

Sun Hotel
☎ (0153 94) 41248
11–11
**Ind Coope Burton Ale;
Jennings Bitter; Tetley
Bitter** H
Comfortable, well-appointed
16th-century hotel with a
popular public bar, convenient
for the fells. No meals Jan.
⚌ ❀ ⇙ ◖ ▮ P

Crosby-on-Eden

Stag Inn
☎ (01228) 573210
11–2.30, 6–11
**Jennings Mild, Bitter,
Cumberland Ale** H
Superb, olde-worlde pub with
low-beamed ceilings and
stone-flagged floors. Good
value, home-cooked food is
served in both the bar and the
upstairs restaurant.
⚌ Q ❀ ◖ ♣ P

Cumwhitton

Pheasant Inn
Off A69 at Warwick Bridge
☎ (01228) 560102
12–3, 5.30–11; 11–11 Sat (may vary)
**Jennings Cumberland Ale,
Sneck Lifter; Marston's
Pedigree; S&N Theakston
Best Bitter; guest beer**
(occasional) H
Fine old country pub, built in
1690. A large, warming real
fire complements the fine food
and friendly atmosphere and
the pub retains many original
features, particularly the
flagged floor and beams.
⚌ Q ❀ ◖ ▮ ▲ ♣ P

Dalston

Bridge End Inn
Bridge End (B5299, just S of
village) ☎ (01228) 710161
11–3, 5.30–11; 11–11 Sat & summer
Greenalls Original H
Interesting watering-hole near
the northern end of the
Cumbria Way. Good basic
food includes a take-away
menu that serves the village.
Good outdoor play area for
children.
⚌ Q ⇙ ❀ ◖ ▮ ▲ ⇌ ♣ P

Dent

Sun
Main Street ☎ (0153 96) 25208
11–2, 7–11; 11–11 Sat & summer
**Dent Bitter, Ramsbottom,
T'Owd Tup; Tetley Bitter** H
Unspoilt, traditional pub in the
cobbled main street of this
picturesque village. The bar

area buzzes with local 'crack'.
Games room. Twice voted
CAMRA Westmorland *Pub of
the Year*.
⚌ Q ❀ ⇙ ◖ ▲ ♣ P ✄

Dovenby

Ship Inn
On A594 ☎ (01900) 828097
11–3, 5.30–11; 11–11 Sat
Jennings Bitter H
Friendly village pub with a
garden play area for children.
⚌ Q ❀ ⇙ ◖ ♣ P

Eaglesfield

Black Cock
☎ (01900) 822989
11–3.30, 6–11; 11–11 Sat
Jennings Bitter H
Cosy, panelled and brass-hung
village local. An unspoilt gem.
⚌ Q ♣ P

Egremont

Blue Bell
Market Place ☎ (01946) 820581
11–3, 6–11
**Robinson's Hartleys XB, Best
Bitter** H
Light and airy modernisation
with a fly-fishing theme. The
long, enclosed garden at the
rear is safe for children, and
can be reached from the public
car park behind. ⚌ ❀ ♣

Elterwater

Britannia
☎ (0153 94) 37210
11–11
**Jennings Mild, Bitter;
Whitbread Boddingtons
Bitter; guest beers** H
Unspoilt pub at the centre of
an unspoilt village in one of
the best areas of Lakeland. The
flagstoned patio is so popular
on sunny days that the
adjacent green is often needed
as an overflow. Small back bar.
⚌ Q ❀ ⇙ ◖ ▮ ▲ ♣

Eskdale Green

King George IV
☎ (0194 67) 23262
11–3 (not weekdays Jan–Feb), 6–11
**Draught Bass; S&N
Theakston Best Bitter, XB;
guest beer** (summer) H
Picturesque pub in the Eskdale
valley. The beer range may
vary.
⚌ ⇙ ❀ ⇙ ◖ ▲ ♣ P

Garrigill

George & Dragon
☎ (01434) 381293
12–3, 7–11 (12–11 summer; may vary)

**McEwan 70/-; S&N Theakston
Best Bitter, XB, Old Peculier;
guest beer** H
Excellent free house and
restaurant, popular with fell
walkers.
⚌ Q ⇙ ⇙ ◖ ▲ ♣ P

Gosforth

Wheatsheaf Inn
The Square ☎ (0194 67) 25821
12–3, 5.30–11 (12–11 summer)
**Bass Worthington BB,
Draught Bass; guest beer** H
Comfortable, popular local.
The menu caters for children
and vegetarians. Table
football. ⚌ ❀ ◖ ♣

Grasmere

Travellers Rest
On A591 ½ mile N of village
☎ (0153 94) 35604
11–11
**Jennings Bitter, Cumberland
Ale, Sneck Lifter** H
Roadside pub, noted for its
good value meals. The small
bar is popular with Coast-to-
Coast walkers and there are
games/family and dining
rooms. Open Sun afternoon for
meals only. The beer range
may vary. Splendid views.
⚌ ⇙ ❀ ⇙ ◖ ▮ ▲ ♣ P

Great Broughton

Punchbowl Inn
Main Street ☎ (01900) 824708
11–3 (not Mon, except bank hols),
6.30–11 (may vary)
Jennings Bitter H
Small, friendly village pub
with a cosy atmosphere and a
warm welcome. ⚌ ♣ P

Great Corby

Queen Inn
The Village Green
☎ (01228) 560731
12–2.30 (not winter weekdays), 7 (5
winter)–11; 12–3, 7–11 Sat
Draught Bass; guest beer H
Superb village pub with a
warm welcome. A very
sporting pub. The guest beer
changes regularly. ⚌ Q ❀
⚿ ▲ ⇌ (Wetheral) ♣ P

Great Langdale

Old Dungeon Ghyll
☎ (0153 94) 37272
11–11
**Jennings Cumberland Ale;
Marston's Pedigree; S&N
Theakston Mild, XB, Old
Peculier; Yates Bitter; guest
beer** H
Deservedly popular Lakeland
climbers'/walkers' bar. No
carpet, jukebox or machines;
the modest improvements are

Cumbria

barely noticeable. Informal live music Fri eve. The beer range may vary. Views from the patio are magnificent.
🏚 Q ✿ 🛏 ◖ ▶ ▲ ♣ ↺ P

Greenodd

Machells Arms
☎ (01229) 861246
12–3, 6–11
Greenalls Original; Ind Coope Burton Ale; Tetley Bitter H
Small, friendly village local offering good, home-cooked food and reasonably priced bed and breakfast. The landlord can always find time for a good 'crack'.
🏚 Q 🛏 ◖ ▶ ♣ P

Hawkshead

Kings Arms Hotel
☎ (0153 94) 36372
11–11
Greenalls Original; S&N Theakston Best Bitter, Old Peculier; Tetley Bitter H
Cosy, olde-worlde pub and restaurant with beams, set in a picturesque village. Self-catering accommodation. Occasional live music.
🏚 ✿ 🛏 ◖ ▶ ▲ ♣

Hayton

Stone Inn
☎ (01228) 70498
11–3, 5.30–11; 11–11 Sat
Federation Buchanan's Original; Jennings Cumberland Ale, Oatmeal Stout; Maclay 70/- H
Popular, friendly village local with an attractive stone bar and fireplace. The beer range varies. 🏚 ♣ P

Hensingham

Sun Inn
Main Street ☎ (01946) 695149
12–4, 6.30–11
Jennings Bitter H
Traditional pub with loyal regulars. Q ♣

Hesket Newmarket

Old Crown
☎ (0169 74) 78288
12–3 (not Mon–Fri, except school hols), 5.30–11 (may vary)
Hesket Newmarket Great Cockup Porter, Skiddaw Special, Blencathra, Doris's 90th Birthday Ale, Old Carrock H
Superb fellside village pub, with fine home cooking and its own brewery (book for a tour and a meal). 🏚 Q ▶ ♣

Hethersgill

Black Lion
Off A6071, 2½ miles NE of Smithfield ☎ (01228) 75318
11–3, 7–11; 11–11 Sat
Draught Bass; Maclay 60/-; Younger Scotch H
Welcoming village local which also serves as the Post Office. Good value snacks. A self-catering cottage is available. The Maclay beer choice varies.
🏚 ✿ & ♣ P

Ings

Watermill Inn
Just off A591 ☎ (01539) 821309
12–2.30, 6–11
Lees Moonraker; S&N Theakston Best Bitter, XB, Old Peculier; guest beers H
Welcoming, family-run pub, popular for the largest choice of guest beers in Cumbria, and its good value meals. The recently refurbished lounge bar has a no-smoking area. Twice voted Westmorland CAMRA *Pub of the Year*, since opening four years ago.
🏚 Q ✿ 🛏 ◖ ▶ & ♣ ↺ P ✗

Ireleth

Bay Horse
Ireleth Brow ☎ (01229) 463755
8 (7 Wed–Sat)–11; 7–10.30 Sun, closed Sun lunch
Jennings Mild, Bitter, Cumberland Ale, Oatmeal Stout, Sneck Lifter H
Impressive, 18th-century pub on the top of a hill: a popular local, offering a friendly welcome. Parking limited.
🏚 🚲 ≠ (Askam) ♣ P

Keekle

Keekle Inn
Keekle Terrace
☎ (01946) 815451
7–11; 12–3, 7–11 Sat
Draught Bass H
Traditional Cumberland, two-roomed local offering a welcome to all, including children. There is a splendid seven-arched viaduct across the road, with a small nature/play area beneath. Sun lunch by arrangement.
🏚 Q ✿ 🛏 ♣

Kendal

Black Swan
8 Allhallows Lane
☎ (01539) 724278
11–3, 6–11; 11–11 Sat & summer
Beer range varies H
No-nonsense, no-jukebox pub dating from 1764; off the main tourist beat. The three beers

come from the Pubmaster range. 🏚 Q ✿ 🛏 ◖ ♣ P

Burgundy's Wine Bar
Lowther Street
☎ (01539) 733803
11–2.30, 6.30–11; 7–10.30 Sun, closed Sun lunch; closed Mon
Draught Bass; Courage Directors; guest beers H
Pleasant, bistro-style bar with a continental feel. It normally stocks two guest beers, but may extend. Eve meals May–Sept, and by arrangement in winter. Q ◖ ▶ ≠

Ring O'Bells
Kirkland
☎ (01539) 720326
12–3, 6–11 (11–11 summer)
Vaux Lorimers Best Scotch, Samson; Wards Best Bitter H
Largely unspoilt pub standing in the (consecrated) grounds of the fine parish church. The snug is a real gem.
🏚 Q ✿ 🛏 ◖ ♣

Keswick

Bank Tavern
Main Street ☎ (0176 87) 72663
11–11
Jennings Mild, Bitter, Cumberland Ale, Sneck Lifter H
Popular local in the town centre, but with a village atmosphere. Food all year round. Q 🚲 ✿ 🛏 ◖ ▶ ▲ ♣

Kirkby Lonsdale

Red Dragon
Main Street ☎ (0152 42) 71205
11–11
Jennings Bitter, Cumberland Ale, Sneck Lifter H
Family-run pub with a splendid fireplace. The open-plan bar area offers plenty of room to sit and enjoy the beer; the range may vary and often includes Mild. The dining area serves good value meals.
🏚 🛏 ◖ ▶ & ▲ ♣ P

Kirkby Stephen

White Lion
4 Market Street
☎ (0176 83) 71481
10.30–3, 5.30–11 (may vary)
Jennings Bitter, Cumberland Ale H
Two-bar, town-centre local, strong on darts and dominoes. The range of Jennings beers increases in summer.
◖ ▶ ▲ ♣

Kirksanton

King William IV
☎ (01229) 772009
11–3, 7–11

Jennings Bitter, Cumberland Ale; guest beer H
Popular community local, with a friendly atmosphere. The guest beer varies but the price is fixed. The walls are adorned with photos of Old Millom and the RAF base. The menu offers children's portions.
🏠 ❀ 🛏 🌓 🛡 ♣ P

Lanercost

Abbey Bridge Inn (Blacksmith's Bar)

2 miles from Brampton, off A69 ☎ (0169 77) 2224
12–2.30, 7–11
Yates Bitter; guest beers H
Superb country pub/diner, in a beautiful rural setting, close to Lanercost Priory. Three pumps serve ever-changing guest beers. Quality food is served in the restaurant, reached by a spiral staircase. Miss this place at your peril.
🏠 Q ❀ 🛏 🌓 ▶ ▲ ♣ P

Lazonby

Joiners Arms

☎ (01768) 898728
11–11
Draught Bass; Stones Best Bitter; guest beer H
Excellent village pub, with good food and a friendly welcome. The guest beer changes regularly. Handy for the Settle–Carlisle railway line.
🏠 ❀ 🛏 🌓 ≷ ♣ P

Levens

Hare & Hounds

Causeway End (400 yds off A590) ☎ (0153 95) 60408
11–3, 6–11
Vaux Samson; Wards Thorne Best Bitter, Best Bitter H
Village local dating from 1714 where the lounge is for diners and families. It also has a tap room, and a games room in the former cellar. No eve food Mon or Tue, Oct–Mar.
Q ❀ 🌓 ♣ P

Lindal in Furness

Railway Inn

London Road
☎ (01229) 462889
7.30 (12 Sat)–11
Tetley Bitter; guest beers H
Very friendly village local offering changing guest beers. Children's play area at the rear. 🏠 ❀ ♣ ♠

Little Corby

Haywain

☎ (01228) 560598
12–3, 7–11 (may vary)

Robinson's Hartleys XB, Best Bitter H
Friendly village local, with a comfortable lounge and a bar. It stages regular live entertainment and numerous village clubs meet here. Good value food. Q ❀ 🌓 ▶ ♣

Low Hesket

Rose & Crown

☎ (0169 74) 73346
12–3, 7–11
Jennings Mild, Bitter, Cumberland Ale H
Comfortable pub, right next to the A6. Good value food.
🏠 ❀ 🌓 ▶ P

Lowick Bridge

Red Lion

☎ (01229) 885366
11.30–3, 6–11
Robinson's Hatters Mild, Hartleys XB, Best Bitter H
Quiet, country pub with low-beamed ceilings and a welcoming atmosphere. Good food. Enjoy the mountain views. 🏠 Q ❀ 🌓 ▶ ▲ ♣ P

Nether Wasdale

Screes Hotel

☎ (0194 67) 26262
12–3 (may vary in winter), 6–11
Jennings Bitter; S&N Theakston Best Bitter, Old Peculier; Yates Bitter; guest beer (summer) H
Ideally situated for activities in Wasdale, this homely, split-level pub is popular with younger drinkers.
🏠 ❀ 🛏 🌓 ▶ 🛡 ▲ ♣ P

Newlands

Swinside Inn

In Swinside hamlet near Derwentwater OS243218
☎ (0176 87) 78253
12–3, 6–11 (11–11 summer)
Jennings Bitter, Cumberland Ale H
Comfortable, multi-roomed inn in enviable surroundings.
🏠 Q ❀ 🛏 🌓 ▶ ♣ P

Newton

Farmers Arms

☎ (01229) 462607
11–3 (not Mon–Fri except summer & bank hols), 6.30–11 (may vary)
Thwaites Best Mild, Bitter; Whitbread Boddingtons Bitter, Bentley's Yorkshire Bitter H
Large, rural village pub. Beams and stone fireplaces complement the welcoming atmosphere. Very popular for meetings, games and food.
🏠 Q 🛏 🌓 ♣ P

Newton Reigny

Sun

Off B5288 ☎ (01768) 67055
11–3, 6–11; 11–11 Sat
Beer range varies H
Excellent free house, with a large lounge. Usually up to four beers are available, with current and forthcoming beers displayed on a blackboard.
🏠 🛞 🛏 🌓 ▶ 🛡 ▲ ♣ P

Outgate

Outgate

☎ (0153 94) 36413
11–3, 6–11
Robinson's Hartleys XB, Best Bitter H
Friendly, rural pub serving generous helpings of good value food. Live trad jazz is performed Fri nights: arrive early if you want a seat.
🏠 Q 🛞 🛏 🌓 ▶ ♣ P

Oxenholme

Station

☎ (01539) 724094
11–3, 6–11
S&N Theakston Best Bitter; Whitbread Boddingtons Bitter, Flowers Original H
Two-room local near the station. A Whitbread 'Cask Collection' beer is also usually available. There is a play area in the garden. No food Mon eve in winter.
❀ 🛏 🌓 ▶ ▲ ≷ ♣ P

Penrith

Grey Bull

Scotland Road
☎ (01768) 62374
11–3, 6–11; 11–11 Sat
Thwaites Best Mild, Bitter, Craftsman H
Cosy, two-roomed local on the main A6, north of the centre. It boasts a superb wood-panelled bar area with horse brasses, brass taps et al. A rare Thwaites outlet in this area.
❀ ▲ ♣ P

Try also: Agricultural, Castlegate (Jennings)

Pica

Greyhound

1 mile E of Pica
☎ (01946) 830366
12–2, 6–11
Jennings Mild, Bitter, Cumberland Ale, Sneck Lifter; guest beer H
Cosy, roadside pub with a warm welcome, offering first-class, home-cooking and accommodation at reasonable rates. 🏠 ❀ 🛏 🌓 ▲ P

Cumbria

Ravenglass

Ratty Arms
☎ (01229) 717676
11–3, 6–11 (11–11 summer)
Jennings Bitter; Ruddles Best Bitter; Webster's Yorkshire Bitter; guest beer H
Popular local in old railway buildings, convenient for the La'al Ratty Steam Railway.
🏚 ⊛ ◑ ▶ ▲ ⇌ P

Ravenstonedale

Black Swan Hotel
☎ (0153 96) 23204
12–3, 6–11
Robinson's Hartleys XB, Best Bitter; S&N Theakston Best Bitter; Younger Scotch; guest beers H
Well-appointed hotel with a locals' bar, a comfortable lounge and a dining room. Three bedrooms are suitable for guests with disabilities.
🏚 Q ⊛ 🛏 ◑ ▶ ⊟ & ▲ P

Rosthwaite

Scafell Hotel (Riverside Bar)
☎ (0176 87) 77208
11–11
S&N Theakston Mild (summer), Best Bitter, XB, Old Peculier H
Refurbished bar at the rear of a country hotel in a beautiful valley. Children, walkers, climbers (boots and all) are welcome. It opens 8.30am for breakfasts, sandwiches and flask-filling. Live folk music.
🏚 Q ⴲ 🛏 ◑ ▶ ▲ P

Rowrah

Stork Hotel
☎ (01946) 861213
11–3, 6–11
Jennings Bitter; Whitbread Boddingtons Bitter; guest beer (occasional) H
Family-run local, close to a karting track and the Coast-to-Coast walk. Hunting memorabilia. Limited parking.
🏚 Q ⊛ 🛏 ▲ ♣ P

Sedbergh

Red Lion
Finkle Street
☎ (0153 96) 20433
11–11
Jennings Mild, Bitter, Cumberland Ale, Sneck Lifter (summer)
Former Marston's pub which remains popular with the locals and visitors to this area of great natural beauty. Unusual covered patio at the rear. ⊛ 🛏 ◑ ▶ ▲ ♣

Tallentire

Bush Inn
☎ (01900) 823707
12–3 (not Tue), 7–11
S&N Theakston XB H
Friendly village local and Post Office combined (limited hours). Note the extensive matchbox collection. Another S&N beer is available. No food Tue. 🏚 Q ⊛ ◑ ▶ ♣ P

Troutbeck

Queens Head Hotel
Townhead (A592)
☎ (0153 94) 32174
11–11
Mitchell's ESB; Tetley Bitter; Whitbread Boddingtons Bitter; guest beers H
Pub where a high quality refurbishment has retained the four-poster bed in the bar and the two huge fireplaces. The part-stone-flagged floor is handy for those in boots. Well above average food is served in the many nooks and crannies, as well as in the Mayor's Parlour. Fine views.
🏚 ⊛ 🛏 ◑ ▶ ▲ ♣ P

Ulverston

Stan Laurel Inn
The Ellers (just S of A590)
☎ (01229) 582814
12–3, 7–11; 12–11 Thu
Jennings Bitter, Cumberland Ale, Sneck Lifter H
Friendly local near the former Hartleys Brewery, with lots of Stan Laurel memorabilia (he was born in Ulverston).
🏚 ⴲ ◑ ▶ ⊟ ⇌ P

Underbarrow

Punch Bowl
☎ (0153 95) 68234
11–3 (4 Sat), 6–11 (may vary summer)
Draught Bass; Whitbread Boddingtons Bitter; guest beers H
Former Jonas Alexander/Dutton's pub, built circa 1640. Now a free house, it retains interesting rooms and levels. Fish and chips (Fri afternoon) and pizzas are very popular. A stopping-off point on the Westmorland Walk. Caravans can be parked overnight.
🏚 Q ⊛ ◑ ▶ ♣ P

Wasdale Head

Wasdale Head
OS186088 ☎ (0194 67) 26229
11–11 (winter weekends: 6–11 Fri; 11–3, 5.30–11 Sat; 12–3 Sun)
Jennings Bitter; S&N Theakston Best Bitter, Old Peculier; Yates Bitter; guest beer (summer) H

Magnificently situated, award-winning hotel with a climbers' bar. Varied home-cooking.
🏚 Q ⴲ ⊛ 🛏 ◑ ▶ ▲ ♣ P

Wetheral

Wheatsheaf
☎ (01228) 560686
12–3, 6–11
Greenalls Bitter, Original H
Comfortable and friendly village pub. Excellent home-cooked food.
🏚 Q ⊛ ◑ ▶ ⇌ ♣ P

Whitehaven

Golden Fleece
Chapel Street ☎ (01946) 63194
11–11
Jennings Bitter, Oatmeal Stout, Sneck Lifter H
Lively drinkers' pub offering the best bar prices around. Oil portraits of regulars hang on the walls and this 200-year-old pub hosts occasional live music. The Jennings beer range may vary. ⊛ ⇌ ♣

Windermere

Grey Walls Hotel (Greys Inn)
Elleray Road
☎ (0153 94) 43741
11–11
S&N Theakston Mild, Best Bitter, XB, Old Peculier; guest beers H
Late-Victorian former doctor's house and surgery. Now a popular pub, it enjoys a reputation for guest beers and good value food (all day Sat).
🏚 ⴲ ⊛ 🛏 ◑ ▶ ⇌ ♣ P

Winton

Bay Horse
Off A685 ☎ (0176 83) 71451
12–2, 6.30–11 (12–11 summer)
Jennings Bitter; S&N Theakston Best Bitter; Younger Scotch; guest beers H
Traditional village local overlooking the green, with a flagged bar (dogs allowed), a dining room and a games area. The salad bar is always open.
🏚 Q ⊛ 🛏 ◑ ▶ P

Workington

George IV
Stanley Street (near harbour, behind station)
☎ (01900) 602266
11–3, 7–11
Jennings Bitter H
Cosy, end-of-terrace, quiet local, on probably the oldest street in town. Convenient for the rugby league, football and greyhound stadia. Children welcome. 🏚 Q ⇌

Derbyshire

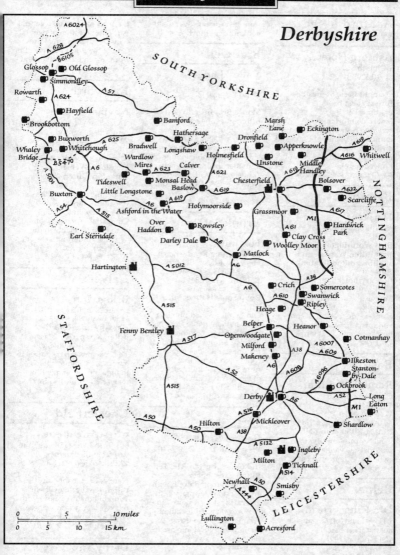

 Black Bull, *Fenny Bentley*; **Brunswick, Flamingo & Firkin**, *Derby*; **John Thompson Inn/Lloyds**, *Ingleby*; **Townes**, *Chesterfield*; **Whim**, *Hartington*

Acresford

Cricketts Inn
Burton Road ☎ (01283) 760359
11–3, 6.30–11; 12–2.30, 7–10.30 Sun
Draught Bass; Marston's Pedigree; guest beer H
18th-century former coaching inn near the county boundary. Its name means 'wooded copse' and is not derived from an insect or game. Tidy basic bar; smart lounge. Good reputation for food (not available Mon eve in winter).
🏨 ❀ ◑ ● 🍴 ♣ P

Apperknowle

Yellow Lion
High Street ☎ (01246) 413181
12–2 (3 Sat), 6–11
Greene King Abbot; Stones Best Bitter; Tetley Bitter; guest beers H
Busy, stone-built village free house with a comfortable lounge and a separate, no-smoking restaurant. The extensive menu includes vegetarian dishes. Winner of several CAMRA awards.
Q ❀ ◑ ● P

Derbyshire

Ashford in the Water

Ashford Hotel
1 Church Street
☎ (01629) 812725
11–11
Draught Bass; Stones Best Bitter; guest beers (summer) Ⓗ
Smart, comfortable pub with a separate restaurant. The cosy lounge has plenty of brass and a welcoming log fire. Popular in summer. House beer (not brewed here).
🏨 Q ☎ ⊛ ⌖ ⌂ ◗ ▶ ௹ ♣ P ⊀

Bamford

Derwent
Main Road ☎ (01433) 651395
11–11
Bass Worthington BB; Stones Best Bitter; Wards Best Bitter; Whitbread Boddingtons Bitter Ⓗ
Country hotel dating from 1890, with a tap room, two lounge areas and a dining room. Reasonably-priced home-made food. A friendly and unspoilt haven in the heart of the Peak District.
☎ ⌖ ⌂ ◗ ▶ 🍺 ▲ ⇌ ♣ P

Baslow

Robin Hood Inn
Chesterfield Road
☎ (01246) 583186
11.30–3.30; 11.30–11 Sat
Mansfield Riding Mild, Riding Bitter, Old Baily Ⓗ
Country pub catering for motorists as well as hikers (who have their own bar at the rear). 🏨 ⊛ ◗ ▶ ௹ ▲ ♣ P

Belper

Old King's Head
1 Days Lane (off Cheapside near Market Place)
☎ (01773) 821497
12–4, 7–11; 11–11 Sat
Banks's Mild; Marston's Pedigree Ⓗ
Multi-roomed local built in the early 15th-century: a centre of much local activity on a quiet lane. Marston's Head Brewer's Choice beers usually available. Parking can be difficult. Meals Thu–Sat. 🏨 Q ☎ ◗ ⇌ ♣

Bolsover

Black Bull
3 Hill Top (A632/B6419 jct)
☎ (01246) 822337
11.30–3.30, 7–11
Burtonwood Forshaw's, Top Hat Ⓗ
Olde-worlde pub with a friendly atmosphere, 200 yards from historic Bolsover Castle. Book for Sun lunch. ◗ ♣ P

Bradwell

Valley Lodge
Church Street
☎ (01433) 620427
12–3, 7–11
Stones Best Bitter; Wards Best Bitter; guest beers Ⓗ
Large pub in a scenic Peak District village, with three bars, a tap room with pool, a large, comfortable lounge and a smaller foyer bar in-between. A lively pub with a warm welcome. CAMRA E Midlands *Pub of the Year* 1992.
🏨 ⊛ ⌂ ◗ ▶ ௹ ▲ ♣ P

Brookbottom

Fox Inn
Brookbottom Road (end of High Lea Rd, off St Mary's Rd, New Mills) OS985864
☎ (0161) 427 1634
11.30–3, 7 (5.30 summer)–11
Robinson's Hatters Mild, Best Bitter Ⓗ
Old, whitewashed pub in a quiet hamlet a mile from New Mills centre: a comfortable, beamed lounge with original features, and a basic games room. Access (on foot only) from Strines station, along part of Goyt Way. Families catered for till early eve. 🏨 ☎ ◗ ▶ ▲ ⇌ (Strines) ♣ P

Buxton

Bakers Arms
West Road ☎ (01298) 24404
12–3, 6 (7 Sat)–11
Ind Coope Burton Ale; Tetley Bitter; guest beers Ⓗ
Cosy, two-roomed pub with an ivy-clad exterior. A Tetley and a 'Tapster's Choice' guest beer are changed fortnightly. Frequented by sporting factions and located close to the market place.
⊛ ௹ ⇌ ♣ P

Sun Inn
High Street ☎ (01298) 23452
12 (1.30 winter)–11
Banks's Mild; Marston's Bitter, Pedigree Ⓗ
Pub with a white exterior, just beyond the market place in Buxton's best drinking area. No food, frills, or distractions; no music or TV in the lounge. Games room. Q ⊛ ⇌ ♣ P

Swann Inn
40 High Street
☎ (01298) 23278
12–11
Ind Coope Burton Ale; Tetley Bitter; guest beers Ⓗ
Nicely presented pub with three rooms around a central bar. Fine selection of over 60 whiskies and two real fires. One of the guest beers is often from Coach House. No food Sun. 🏨 ◗ ௹ ⇌ ♣ P

Buxworth

Navigation Inn
Canal Basin (100 yds off B6062, near village centre)
☎ (01663) 732072
11–11
Marston's Pedigree; Taylor Landlord; Webster's Yorkshire Bitter; guest beers Ⓗ
Stone pub alongside the only remaining canal tramway interchange in the UK. Comfortable and welcoming, with food available in the separate restaurant area or as snacks in the bar.
🏨 ☎ ⊛ ⌂ ◗ ▶ ௹ ▲ P

Calver

Bridge Inn
On A623 ☎ (01433) 630415
11.30–3 (4.30 Sat), 5.30 (6 Sat)–11
Hardys & Hansons Best Bitter, Kimberley Classic Ⓗ
Large, roadside village local. The spacious tap room has a games area; comfortable lounge (no-smoking at the rear). No eve meals Sun/Mon.
🏨 Q ⊛ ◗ ▶ ௹ ௹ ▲ ♣ P ⊀

Chesterfield

Chesterfield Bowl
Storforth Lane (150 yds from A61 jct at Birdholme)
☎ (01246) 550092
11–11
Hardys & Hansons Best Bitter, Kimberley Classic Ⓗ
Ten pin bowling centre with a relaxed family atmosphere. Food available from 9am to 10.30pm. ☎ ⊛ ◗ ▶ ௹ P

Derby Tup
387 Sheffield Road, Whittington Moor
☎ (01246) 454316
11.30–3, 5.30–11
Exmoor Gold; Marston's Pedigree; S&N Theakston XB, Old Peculier; Taylor Landlord; Tetley Bitter; guest beers Ⓗ
Superb, unspoilt, corner free house with three rooms. Fifteen guest beers a week, including a mild. Eve meals till 7.30pm. Q ◗ ▶ ௹ ௹ ♣

Royal Oak
43 Chatsworth Road (A617, opp. B&Q) ☎ (01246) 277854
11.30–11

78

S&N Theakston Best Bitter, XB, Old Peculier; Younger No. 3; guest beers H
Lively pub with a friendly atmosphere. Events include beer festivals, live music and quiz nights. A Bateman's beer is available, plus continental bottled beers.
🏨 👪 ≠ ♣ ⛘ P

Star Inn

422 Chatsworth Road (A627)
☎ (01246) 277714
12–4 (5 Sat), 5.30 (6.30 Sat)–11
Ind Coope Burton Ale; Stones Best Bitter; Tetley Bitter; guest beers H
Tastefully refurbished local on the outskirts of town, with an unusually long bar. ♣ P

Sun Inn

13 West Bars ☎ (01246) 273963
11–11
Mansfield Riding Mild, Riding Bitter, Bitter, Old Baily H
Large, popular town-centre pub with an impressive frontage. Car parking and no-smoking areas lunchtime. Wheelchair access to the gents' WC only. ♿ ❀ ◑ ♿ P ⊁

Victoria

21–23 Victoria Street West, Brampton (off A619, near mini-roundabout)
☎ (01246) 273832
12–3.30, 7–11
Wards Thorne Best Bitter, Best Bitter; guest beers (occasional) H
Two-roomed, traditional local with a warm welcome. Guest beers come from the Vaux group. A winner of brewery and CAMRA awards.
Q ❀ ⊞ ⅃ ♣

Clay Cross

Prince of Wales

8 Thanet Street
☎ (01246) 865698
12–4 (4.30 Sat), 7–11
Bass Worthington BB; Stones Best Bitter H
Comfortable, small village pub with a lounge and a public bar. No gimmicks, just a great atmosphere. ❀ ⊞ ♣

Royal Volunteer

63 Market Street (A6175)
11–11; 11–3, 7–11 Wed
Stones Best Bitter; Tetley Bitter H
Large games pub, very popular with the locals, but also boasting a cosy snug for those who like a quiet pint. Wheelchair WC. 🏨 ❀ ⅃ ♣

Cotmanhay

Bridge Inn

Bridge Street ☎ (0115) 9322589
11–11

Hardys & Hansons Best Mild, Best Bitter E
Traditional village local by the Erewash Canal, frequented by locals, fishermen and boaters. Regular visitors include eagles and goats. No swearing in the bar. A rare find.
Q ❀ ⊞ ♣ P

Crich

Cliff Inn

Cromford Road (NW of village) OS345548
☎ (01773) 852444
11–3, 6–11
Hardys & Hansons Best Mild, Best Bitter, Kimberley Classic H
Friendly, popular, stone-built local with two rooms, very close to the National Tramway Museum. ❀ ◑ ▶ ⊞ P

Darley Dale

Grouse Inn

Dale Road North (A6)
☎ (01629) 734357
12–3, 7–11
Hardys & Hansons Best Mild, Best Bitter H
Roadside local, renovated but keeping a traditional atmosphere. Popular with all ages and handy for tourists. Good children's playground.
🏨 ♿ ◑ ▶ ⅃ ♣ P

Derby

Alexandra Hotel

203 Siddals Road
☎ (01332) 293993
11–2.30, 4.30 (6 Sat)–11
Bateman Mild, XB; Courage Bitter Ale; Marston's Pedigree; guest beers H
E Midlands CAMRA *Pub of the Year 1994:* a friendly pub with two rooms, subtle decor and wooden floors. Bottled beer collection and train photos in the bar. Usually at least five guest beers, with over 600 sold in 1993. Guest ciders, too.
Q ❀ ◑ ⅃ ≠ ⛘ P

Brunswick Inn

1 Railway Terrace
☎ (01332) 290677
11–11
Brunswick Recession, First Brew, Old Accidental; Marston's Pedigree H; **S&N Theakston Old Peculier** G; **Taylor Landlord; guest beers** H
The oldest purpose-built railwayman's pub, where 14 handpumps serve beers from all around the country, as well as from the on-site brewery. Annual beer festival first week of Oct; winter ales week Feb.
Q ♿ ❀ ◑ ⅃ ≠ ♣ ⛘ ⊁

Crompton Tavern

46 Crompton Street
☎ (01332) 292259
11–11
Marston's Pedigree; Taylor Landlord; Wards Best Bitter; guest beers H
Lively and friendly, mid-terraced pub. A U-shaped room caters for and welcomes all. Three guest beers. Snacks usually available. ❀ ♣

Dolphin

Queen Street ☎ (01332) 349115
10.30–11
Bass Worthington BB, Draught Bass; M&B Highgate Dark, Brew XI; Marston's Pedigree; Stones Best Bitter; guest beers H
The oldest and most picturesque pub in the city, built in 1530, the same year as the cathedral tower. One of the four rooms is devoted to Offiler's Brewery memorabilia. Food available 11.30–7.45, all week. Q ❀ ◑ ▶ ♣ P

Drill Hall Vaults

1 Newlands Street
☎ (01332) 248073
12–2.30, 7–11
Marston's Pedigree H
Friendly, comfortable multi-section, one-roomed pub with brass items on the walls. Pool table in one section. 🏨 ◑ ♣

Flowerpot

25 King Street
☎ (01332) 204955
11–11
Draught Bass; Bateman Mild; Marston's Pedigree H; **S&N Theakston Old Peculier** G; **Taylor Landlord; Wards Best Bitter** H
Recently refurbished, friendly, one-roomed pub where the original back bar fitting has been tastefully refurbished and relocated. Eight beers usually available. Q ❀ ♿

Station Inn

Midland Road
☎ (01332) 360114
11.30–3, 5.30–11; 11–11 Fri
Draught Bass H
Friendly, narrow pub, used mostly by postal workers. Pool table off the main bar. Large function room. ≠ ♣

Victoria Inn

12 Midland Place (opp. station) ☎ (01332) 345156
3–11
Bass Worthington BB, Draught Bass; M&B Highgate Dark H
Friendly, popular, music-oriented local: a U-shaped bar area with a function room. Regular live music nights,

with most styles catered for.
Marston's Pedigree available
at weekends. ❀ ⇌

York Tavern

23 York Street (off Vernon St,
off Friargate) ☎ (01332) 362849
12–3, 6–11
**Marston's Pedigree; guest
beers** H
Busy, friendly, back-street
local, near the old greyhound
stadium: a U-shaped pub with
a pool table and a darts area.
Varying guest beers. ❀ ◖ ♣

Dronfield

Old Sidings

91 Chesterfield Road
☎ (01246) 410023
12–11
**Banks's Mild; Bass
Worthington BB; Fuller's
London Pride; Marston's
Pedigree; Stones Best Bitter** H
Lively pub with an L-shaped
lounge on two levels,
comfortably furnished with a
railway theme. Restaurant in
the basement. ❀ ◖ ▶ ⇌ ♣ P

Victoria

5 Stubley Lane
☎ (01246) 412117
12–11
**Banks's Mild, Bitter;
Marston's Pedigree** H
Genuine locals' pub with a
comfortable L-shaped lounge
and a darts area at one end.
🏠 Q ❀ ◖ ⇌ ♣

Earl Sterndale

Quiet Woman

☎ (01298) 83211
11–3, 6–11
**Banks's Mild; Marston's
Bitter, Pedigree, Owd
Rodger** H
A superb example of a village
local, overlooking the green.
The bar and games room both
have real fires; dominoes
tables can be found in the
low-beamed lounge and
free-range eggs and local
cheeses can be bought over the
bar. A classic.
🏠 Q ❀ ♠ ♣ P

Eckington

White Hart

32 Church Street
☎ (01246) 434855
12–3.30, 7–11
**Home Bitter; Marston's
Pedigree; S&N Theakston
Mild, XB** H
Historic inn next to the church.
A traditional tap room with a
pool table and a comfortable
lounge. Live music some
nights, including jazz on Mon.
Q ❀ 🏚 ◖ ⊟ ♠ ♣ P

Glossop

Crown Inn

42 Victoria Street
☎ (01457) 862824
11.30–11
Samuel Smith OBB, Museum
(winter) H
A regular *Guide* entry for 11
years, a pub with two small,
comfortable snugs, an active
games room and an attractive
central bar. Strong local,
friendly atmosphere.
🏠 Q ❀ ♠ ⇌ ♣ ✂

Friendship

3 Arundel Street
☎ (01457) 855277
12–3 (4 Sat), 5 (7 Sat)–11
**Robinson's Hatters Mild, Best
Bitter** H
Corner-of-terrace pub, just off
the main shopping street, with
always a pleasant atmosphere.
Families are made especially
welcome. Typical Robinson's
decor, with wood panelling.
🏠 ❀ ⇌ ♣

Prince of Wales

Milltown (off A57 on way to
Snake Pass) ☎ (01457) 864679
11.30–3, 5–11; 11.30–11 Sat
**Banks's Mild; Marston's
Bitter, Pedigree** H
Cosy, characterful, stone-built,
end-terraced pub which keeps
out the worst of Glossop
winters. Marston's Head
Brewer's Choice available. Eve
meals Thu–Sat.
🏠 ❀ ◖ ▶ ♠ ♣ ⇌ ♣ P

Grassmoor

Boot & Shoe

302 North Wingfield Road
☎ (01246) 850251
12–4, 7–11
Mansfield Riding Bitter H
Friendly, two-roomed village
local, catering for all age
groups. Organist at weekends.
Skittles outside. ❀ ♠ ♣ P

Hardwick Park

Hardwick Inn

1 mile S of M1 jct 29
☎ (01246) 850245
11.30–3, 6.30–11
**S&N Theakston XB; Younger
Scotch; guest beers** H
17th-century inn owned by the
NT, at the exit gates of
Hardwick Hall. Excellent food.
🏠 Q ♠ ◖ ▶ P

Hathersage

Scotsman's Pack Inn

School Lane ☎ (01433) 650253
12–3, 6–11; 11–11 Sat
**Burtonwood Mild, Bitter,
Forshaw's** H

Comfortable village pub with
three lounge areas served by a
central bar. A feature is 'Little
John's Chair', made for a
giant, but perhaps not the one
buried in the nearby
churchyard. 🏠 Q ♠
❀ 🏚 ◖ ▶ ♠ ♣ ⇌ ♣ P

Hayfield

Royal Hotel

Market Street
☎ (01663) 742721
12–3, 6–11; 12–11 Sat
**Marston's Pedigree; John
Smith's Bitter; Webster's
Yorkshire Bitter; guest
beers** H
Centrally located pub, next to
the river and cricket ground, a
former vicarage, with original
oak panels and church pews.
Regular live music, including
jazz every Sun lunch. Beer
festival in Oct.
🏠 Q ♠ ❀ 🏚 ◖ ▶ ♠ ♣ ♣ P

Sportsman

Kinder Road (½ mile out of
village) ☎ (01663) 741565
12–3 (not Mon–Thu in winter), 7–11
**Thwaites Best Mild, Bitter,
Craftsman** H
Comfortable, welcoming
hostelry used by walkers after
a descent off Kinder. Noted for
fine food, log fires and its
antique furnishings. Always 30
single malt whiskies available.
🏠 Q ♠ ❀ 🏚 ◖ ▶ ♠ ♣ ♣

Heage

Black Boy

Old Road (set back from
B6013) ☎ (01773) 856799
12–3 (not Mon), 6.30–11
**Mansfield Riding Bitter,
Bitter, Old Baily** H
Modernised, large, open-plan,
bright and friendly lounge-
based pub. Restaurant open
eves. 🏠 ❀ ◖ ♣ P

White Hart

2 Church Street (off B6374 and
B6013) ☎ (01773) 852302
11.30–3, 5 (7 Sat)–11
Draught Bass H
Welcoming and friendly, large,
attractive pub: an early
17th-century building with
many cosy rooms.
◖ ▶ 🏚 ♣ P

Heanor

Derby Arms

High Street ☎ (01773) 713508
11–4, 7–11; 12–2, 7–10.30 Sun
Home Mild, Bitter E
Traditional, two-roomed beer
drinkers' pub, small and
friendly. TV in the bar.
Popular for darts, dominoes
and pool. ❀ 🏚 ♣

Derbyshire

Hilton

White Swan
Eggington Road (A5132)
☎ (01283) 732305
11.30–11
Bass Worthington BB,
Draught Bass; M&B Highgate
Dark, Brew XI; Marston's
Pedigree; guest beers H
100-year-old country pub, with
feature fireplaces and original
beams. Famed for its meals,
including the Desperate Dan
Pie (no eve food Sun/Mon).
Children's assault course in
the garden. Usually seven or
eight beers served.
🏨 ✿ ◖ ▲ ♣ P ✕

Holmesfield

Travellers Rest
Main Road ☎ (0114) 2890446
12–4, 7–11
Home Bitter; Stones Best
Bitter; Younger No. 3 H
Pleasant pub with a pool table
in the tap room and a spacious
lounge. Live entertainment
Thu. ✿ 🍴 ▲ ♣ P

Holymoorside

Lamb Inn
Loads Road ☎ (01246) 566167
12–3 (not Mon–Thu), 7–11
Draught Bass; Home Bitter;
S&N Theakston XB; guest
beers H
Unspoilt village pub offering a
variety of guest beers and a
warm welcome. Popular with
locals. 🏨 Q ✿ 🍴 ᕂ ♣ P

Ilkeston

Middleton
Station Street (off A6096
between river and railway
bridges) ☎ (0115) 9329684
11.30–3, 7–11
Ind Coope Burton Ale; Tetley
Bitter; Wards Best Bitter;
guest beers H
Old, unchanged Victorian
boozer, known locally as the
Dewdrop. It has a small bar
with pool table, but the cosy
snug/lounge is the focal point,
hosting impromptu sing-
alongs. Excellent value food.
Cheap B&B. An ex-Strettons
house worth finding.
🏨 Q ☞ ✿ 🍴 ◖ 🍴 ♣ ◔

Spring Cottage
1 Fulwood Street
☎ (0115) 9323153
11–3 (4 Fri, 5 Sat), 6 (7 Sat)–11
Draught Bass; guest beers H
Genuine, traditional local in a
back street, with a good mix of
friendly locals. Sky TV and
pool in the bar but the
atmosphere remains sociable

and relaxing.
🏨 ☞ ◖ 🍴 ♣ P

Ingleby

John Thompson Inn
☎ (01332) 862469
10.30–2.30, 7–11
Draught Bass; JTS XXX,
Porter H
Pub opened in 1969, a
conversion from a 15th-
century farmhouse. The
interior consists of a wealth of
oak and displays a large
collection of paintings and
antiques. The pub is up-
market and motorcyclists are
not welcome. Brewery in the
car park. 🏨 ☞ ✿ 🍴 ᕂ ♣ P

Little Longstone

Packhorse
Main Street ☎ (01629) 640471
11–3, 5 (6 Sat)–11
Marston's Bitter, Pedigree H
Ancient, unspoilt village local,
a pub since 1787. The small,
comfortable lounge has an
adjoining intimate dining
room (open Wed–Sat). The tap
room is used by ramblers and
offers live folk sessions Wed.
🏨 Q ✿ 🍴 🍴 ▲ ♣

Long Eaton

Hole in the Wall
Regent Street (off Market
Place) ☎ (0115) 9734920
11–3, 6–11; 11–11 Mon, Fri & Sat
Bass Worthington BB,
Draught Bass; guest beers H
Friendly, two-roomed, side-
street pub: a bar with Sky TV
and pool, a pleasant, narrow
lounge, plus an off-sales hatch.
Nice back garden with an
aviary and skittle alley.
✿ 🍴 🍴 ♣ ◔

Longshaw

Grouse
On B6054 ☎ (01433) 630423
12–3, 6 (7 winter)–11
Vaux Double Maxim; Wards
Best Bitter H
Pub originally built as a
farmhouse in 1804, the hayloft,
barn doors and stone trough of
which survive. A comfortable
lounge at the front leads to a
conservatory overhung with
vines, and an adjoining bar.
No eve meals Mon/Tue.
🏨 Q ☞ ✿ 🍴 ◖ ♣ P

Lullington

Colvile Arms
Coton Road ☎ (01827) 373212
12–3 (not Mon–Fri), 7–11
Draught Bass; Marston's
Pedigree; guest beer
(weekends) H

18th-century village pub: a
basic wood-panelled bar, a
smart lounge, plus a function
room. Bowling green in the
garden. 🏨 ✿ ♣ P

Makeney

Hollybush
Hollybush Lane
☎ (01332) 841729
12–3, 6–11; 12–11 Sat
Marston's Pedigree H, Owd
Rodger G; Ruddles County;
Taylor Landlord; guest
beers H/G
Old pub with many rooms,
housed in a Grade II-listed
building. Some beer is brought
up from the cellar in jugs (four
or five guests). Very popular,
especially in summer.
🏨 Q ☞ ✿ ♣ P

Marsh Lane

Fox & Hounds
Main Road ☎ (01246) 432974
12–3, 7 (6 summer)–11
Burtonwood Bitter,
Forshaw's H
Pub with a comfortable lounge
and a tap room, plus a large
garden and play area.
Extensive menu (no hot food
Wed). Q ✿ ◖ 🍴 ᕂ ♣ P

Matlock

Thorn Tree
48 Jackson Road (on hillside N
of town, behind county offices)
☎ (01629) 582923
11.30–3 (not Mon or Tue), 7–11
Draught Bass; Mansfield
Bitter, Old Baily H
18th-century, two-roomed
local with a warm welcome
and comfortable surroundings.
Excellent views. Well worth
seeking out. No food Sun.
Q ✿ 🍴 🍴 ♣

Mickleover

Honeycomb
Ladybank Road
☎ (01332) 515600
11.30–2.30 (3 Fri & Sat), 6.30–11
Everards Beacon, Tiger, Old
Original; guest beers H
Busy, honeycomb-shaped pub
on two levels, with friendly
staff. Popular with all. Pool
table and darts in the lower
section. No meals Sun. 🍴 ♣ P

Middle Handley

Devonshire Arms
Westfield Lane (off B6052)
☎ (01246) 432189
1.30–3, 7–11
Stones Best Bitter H
Friendly, popular, traditional
village local. Q ✿ ♣ P

81

Derbyshire

Milford

King William IV
The Bridge, Derby Road (A6)
☎ (01332) 840842
12–2.30, 7–11
**Fuller's London Pride;
Marston's Pedigree; guest
beers** (weekends) Ⓗ
Traditional, one-roomed
country pub, with stone walls
and a beamed ceiling, standing
by the River Derwent. No
meals Sun eve. 🚲 ◖ ▶

Milton

Swan Inn
Main Street ☎ (01283) 703188
12–2.30, 7–11
Marston's Pedigree Ⓗ
Popular and friendly village
pub with a smart lounge and a
locals' bar. Well worth
visiting. No food Mon.
🚲 ❀ ◖ ▶ ♣ P

Monsal Head

Monsal Head Hotel
☎ (01629) 640250
11–11
**Marston's Pedigree; Ruddles
Best Bitter; S&N Theakston
Old Peculier; John Smith's
Bitter** Ⓗ
150-year-old country hotel
with an elegant, genteel
lounge in the main building.
Most of the real ales are in the
rear stable bar, once part of the
long-gone Bull's Head. A large
inglenook, stall seating and a
manger all feature.
🚲 Q ❀ 🚲 ◖ ▶ ▲ ♣ P

Newhall

Thorntree Inn
59 Bretby Road
☎ (01283) 216902
12–3, 6–11; 12–11 Sat; 12–2.30,
7–10.30 Sun
**Draught Bass; Marston's
Pedigree; guest beer** Ⓗ
19th-century local in a former
coal mining area, particularly
busy weekend eves and
reputedly haunted by the
friendly ghost of a former
landlord. Satellite TV in the
public bar. Mini-beer festival
in July. 🚲 ❀ ♿ ♣ P

Ockbrook

Royal Oak
Green Lane ☎ (01332) 662378
11.30–2.30, 7–11
Draught Bass; guest beer Ⓗ
Friendly, characterful, village
meeting place offering many
small and cosy rooms. No
meals Sun. 🚲 Q ❀ ◖ ♣ P

Old Glossop

Bull's Head
102 Church Street
☎ (0145 785) 3291
12–11
**Robinson's Hatters Mild, Best
Bitter, Old Tom** (winter) Ⓗ
Listed, 16th-century inn, with
a friendly village atmosphere,
at the foot of the Pennines
(hikers welcome). Renowned
for its curries. Sun lunches
served. Free parking nearby.
🚲 ❀ ▶ ▲ 🚆 (Glossop) ♣

Openwoodgate

Bull's Head
2 Kilburn Lane (A60)
☎ (01773) 822669
11–2.30, 6.30–11
**Hardys & Hansons Best Mild,
Best Bitter** Ⓔ, **Kimberley
Classic** Ⓗ
Exceptionally well-run,
hospitable village local: a
two-roomed pub with live
music in the bar at weekends.
Club room for families and
meetings. 🚲 🍴 ♣ P

Over Haddon

Lathkill Hotel
½ mile S off B5055
☎ (01629) 812501
11.30–3, 6–11
**Wards Mild, Thorne Best
Bitter** Ⓗ
Free house in an idyllic
setting, overlooking one of the
Peak's most picturesque dales,
with a fine oak-panelled bar
and traditional-style leather
and wood furnishings.
Excellent food. Family room
lunchtime only.
🚲 Q 🚲 ❀ 🚲 ◖ ▶ ♣ P

Ripley

Sitwell Arms
60 Wall Street
☎ (01773) 742727
1–3, 7.30–11
**Hardys & Hansons Best Mild,
Best Bitter** Ⓗ
Basic, friendly, multi-roomed
pub, a popular local. Pool
table in the back room; skittles
in the yard. ❀ ♣

Three Horseshoes
Market Place
☎ (01773) 743113
11–3 (4 Sat), 5 (7 Sat)–11
**Vaux Samson; Wards Mild,
Best Bitter; guest beer** Ⓗ
Market town-centre pub in
open-plan style. Pool table in
one section off the main room;
TV in the front bar.
❀ ◖ ♣ P

Rowarth

Little Mill Inn
Signed off the road out of
Mellor ☎ (01663) 743178
11–11
**Banks's Bitter; Bateman
XXXB; Camerons Strongarm;
Marston's Pedigree** Ⓗ
Huge, multi-roomed pub of
great character, boasting huge
log fires and good food. A
fully working water wheel is a
feature. Meals and a good
choice of beer every day (even
Christmas Day).
🚲 Q 🚲 ❀ 🚲 ◖ ▶ ▲ P

Rowsley

Grouse & Claret
Main Road ☎ (01629) 733233
11–3, 5.30–11; 11–11 Sat & Easter–Oct
**Mansfield Riding Mild,
Riding Bitter, Bitter, Old
Baily** Ⓗ
Over 100-year-old imposing
stone pub, comfortably
refurbished but retaining
many old features and a
separate tap room (hikers
welcome). Large range of
traditional, home-cooked food,
plus special food eves. Family
room in summer, and on
winter weekends.
🚲 🚲 ❀ 🚲
◖ ▶ ♿ ▲ ♣ P ✗

Scarcliffe

Elm Tree
Station Road ☎ (01246) 823213
12–3, 7–11; 12–2.30, 7–10.30 Sun
**Bass Worthington BB;
Mansfield Bitter; Stones Best
Bitter; guest beers** Ⓗ
Unspoilt village local, playing
host to a classic motorbike
club on Tue. ❀ ◖ ♣ P

Horse & Groom
Mansfield Road (B6417)
☎ (01246) 823152
12–3, 7–11
**Home Bitter; S&N Theakston
XB** Ⓗ
Beamed coaching inn with a
play area. Good home cooking
(extensive menu).
❀ ◖ ♣ P

Shardlow

Malt Shovel
The Wharf (off A6 at
Navigation pub)
☎ (01332) 799763
11–3, 5–11
**Ansells Mild; Marston's
Bitter, Pedigree** Ⓗ
Characterful, multi-level
canalside tavern converted
from old maltings and popular
with the boating fraternity in
summer. Dogs are welcome.
🚲 Q ❀ ◖ ♣ P

Simmondley

Hare & Hounds

☎ (01457) 852028
12–3, 5.30–11; 12–11 Sat
Ind Coope Burton Ale; Tetley Mild, Bitter H
Former 19th-century textile mill, with extensive views. The landlord is a Burton Ale *Master Cellarman*. Beer festival in June. ✿ ◖ ▶ ♣ P

Smisby

Smisby Arms

Main Street ☎ (01530) 412677
11 (11.30 Sat)–3, 5.30 (7 Sat)–11
Greene King Abbot; Marston's Pedigree; Morland Old Speckled Hen; guest beers H
Old village pub, sympathetically extended, with a welcoming atmosphere. Cosy snug in the original rooms. Marston's Head Brewer's Choice. Interesting menu. ❧ Q ♒ ◖ ▶ P

Somercotes

Horse & Jockey

Leabrooks Road
☎ (01773) 602179
11–3, 7–11
Home Mild, Bitter; S&N Theakston XB H
Popular, multi-roomed, unspoilt local. Lunchtime snacks. Parking difficult. ✿

Stanton-by-Dale

Chequers

Dale Road
11–2.30 (3 Thu–Sat), 7–11
Draught Bass; M&B Mild E**; Marston's Pedigree** H
Excellent, cottage-style pub of exceptional character, with a raised lounge area where an old water pump takes pride of place. Lunches of the highest quality, all home-made (no meals Sun). Q ✿ ◖ ♿ ♣ P

Swanwick

Boot & Slipper

The Green ☎ (01773) 606052
12–3 (11–4 Sat), 7–11
Mansfield Riding Bitter, Old Baily H
Friendly, one-roomed, old-fashioned local. Pool table and TV upstairs; skittles outside. Lunches Tue–Sat. ❧ ◖ ♣ P

Gate Inn

The Delves ☎ (01773) 602039
11.30–3, 7–11
Courage Directors; Marston's Pedigree; John Smith's Bitter H

Smart, open-plan pub with a bar (pool table), lounge and eating area (eve meals Thu–Sat). ◖ ▶ ♣ P

Ticknall

Chequers

High Street ☎ (01332) 864392
12–2.30, 6–11
Marston's Pedigree; Ruddles Best Bitter, County H
Small and friendly, two-roomed local. The bar houses a feature fireplace and many games. ❧ Q ♒ ♣ P

Staff of Life

High Street ☎ (01332) 862479
11.30–2.30, 6 (7 winter)–11
Marston's Pedigree, Owd Rodger; Moorhouse's Pendle Witches Brew; S&N Theakston XB H**, Old Peculier** G**; Shepherd Neame Bishops Finger** H**; guest beers** H / G
Food-oriented pub with a large bar. Everards and Taylor beers also available, plus at least five guests. ✿ ◖ ▶ P

Tideswell

George

Commercial Road
☎ (01298) 871382
11–3, 7–11
Hardys & Hansons Best Mild, Best Bitter, Kimberley Classic H
Substantial stone-built hotel adjacent to the village church—'The Cathedral of the Peaks'. Comfortable lounge with an adjacent dining room; small snug, leading to a tap room with a pool table.
❧ Q ⌂ ◖ ▶ ♿ ▲ ♣ P

Unstone

Inn on the Green

Birch Hall Golf Club, Sheffield Road ☎ (01246) 291979
11–11
John Smith's Bitter; Stones Best Bitter; guest beers H
Comfortable, well-furnished, 19th hole, primarily a pub. Genial landlord. Eve meals for groups if arranged. ◖ P

Wardlow Mires

Three Stags' Heads

At A623/B6465 jct
☎ (01298) 872268
7–11; 11–11 Sat, summer & bank hols
Hoskins & Oldfield Old Navigation; Kelham Island Pale Rider, Bête Noir; Springhead Bitter; guest beer H
Carefully restored, 17th-century farmhouse pub with two rooms. The bar is heated by an ancient range. Popular with hikers; dogs welcome.
❧ Q ✿ ◖ ▲ P

Whaley Bridge

Shepherd's Arms

7 Old Road (off old A6)
☎ (01663) 732384
11.30–3, 7.30–11
Banks's Mild; Marston's Bitter, Pedigree H
Ageless local above the main street. The lounge is softly lit and quiet, in contrast with the excellent vault with its flagged floor.
❧ Q ✿ ♿ ▲ ⇌ ♣ P

White Horse

1 Lower Macclesfield Road (old A6/B6570 jct)
☎ (01663) 732617
11–3, 5–11; 11–11 Wed, Fri & Sat
Whitbread Boddingtons Mild, Bitter; guest beers H
Sociable lounge-style Victorian pub in local stone, offering a relatively rare mild. Handy for the Goyt Valley. Look for the Timex. ✆ ✿ ▲ ⇌ ♣ P

Whitehough

Oddfellows Arms

Whitehead Lane (½ mile downhill from Chinley station)
☎ (01663) 750306
12–3, 5–11 (12–11 summer)
Marston's Bitter, Pedigree H
A proper country pub, attracting a cross-section of the community. A timber and stained-glass dividing screen creates two or three rooms. Marston's Head Brewer's Choice. ❧ ✿ ◖ ▶ ▲ ⇌ (Chinley) ♣ P

Whitwell

Jug & Glass

Portland Street
☎ (01909) 720289
11–3, 6.30–11
John Smith's Bitter, Magnet H
Unspoilt, two-roomed stone local with a timber bar, doors and matching fireplace: a listed building at the centre of the old village (a genuine mining community). All welcome. ❧ ✿ ♿ ♣ P

Woolley Moor

White Horse

White Horse Lane
☎ (01246) 590319
11.30–2.30 (3 Sat), 6.30 (6 Sat)–11
Draught Bass; M&B Highgate Dark; guest beers H
250-year-old village pub with an excellent reputation for ale and food (no meals Sun eve). Separate bar. Family area Sun eve. Q ✿ ◖ ▶ ♿ ♣ P

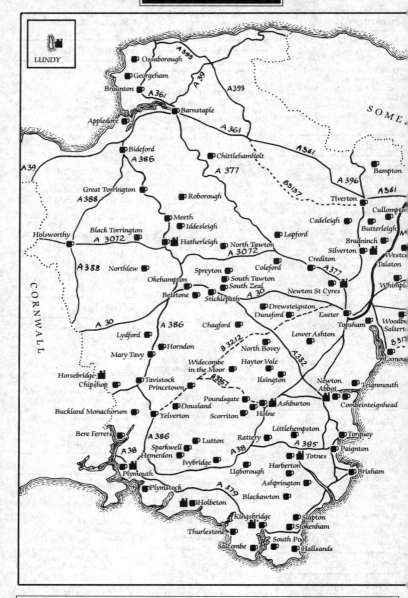

LUNDY

Beer Engine, Newton St Cyres; **Blackawton**, Totnes;
Branscombe Vale, Branscombe; **Exe Valley**, Silverton;
King's Head, Plymouth; **Lundy**, Lundy Island;
Mildmay, Holbeton; **Mill**, Newton Abbot; **Otter**,
Mathayes, Luppitt; **Royal Inn**, Horsebridge; **Ship &
Plough**, Kingsbridge; **Summerskills**, Sutton,
Plymouth; **Tally Ho**, Hatherleigh; **Teignworthy**,
Newton Abbot; **Thompson's**, Ashburton

Devon

Appledore

Beaver Inn
Irsha Street ☎ (01237) 474822
11–3.30, 6–11 (11–11 summer)
Draught Bass; Whitbread Flowers IPA; guest beers (occasional) Ⓗ
Fairly modern riverside inn with views across the Torridge estuary. Cider in summer.
❀ ◖ ▶ ♿ ▲ ♣ ⌂

Champion of Wales
Meeting Street
☎ (01237) 424500
11–11
Draught Bass; Oakhill Best Bitter, Yeoman Ⓗ; **guest beers** (occasional)
Small, side-street local, with a piano. ⚏ ♣

Royal George
Irsha Street ☎ (01237) 474335
11–11
Draught Bass; Ind Coope Burton Ale Ⓗ
Unspoilt riverside pub, with excellent views from the restaurant across the estuary: one main bar with nooks and crannies.
Q ☂ ❀ ◖ ▶ ▲ ♣ P

Ashburton

London Hotel
West Street ☎ (01364) 652478
11–2.30, 5.30–11
Thompson's Best Bitter, IPA, Man of War (summer), **Figurehead** Ⓗ; **guest beers** (occasional)
15th-century coaching house with two bars and a large restaurant. Thompson's brewery is situated to the rear.
⚏ Q ⊨ ◖ ▶ ⌂

Ashprington

Durant Arms
☎ (01803) 732240
11–2.30, 6–11
Draught Bass; Exmoor Ale; Palmers IPA Ⓗ
Friendly, 18th-century inn, once owned by the Durant family. Wide range of meals.
⚏ Q ☂ ❀ ◖ ▶ ▲

Axminster

Axminster Inn
Silver Street ☎ (01297) 34947
11–11
Palmers BB, IPA, Tally Ho! Ⓗ
Originally a farmers' local, a lively town pub, just behind the church.
⚏ Q ☂ ❀ ♿ ⇌ ♣ ⌂ P

Millwey
Chard Road ☎ (01297) 32774
11–2.30, 7–11
Palmers BB, IPA Ⓗ
Cheerful carpet-town pub in a residential suburb, featuring a collection of Toby jugs. Meals Tue–Sat. ☂ ❀ ◖ ▣ ♣ P

Axmouth

Ship Inn
Church Street ☎ (01297) 21838
11–2 (2.30 Sat), 6–11
Devenish Cornish Original; guest beer Ⓗ
Well-known pub serving excellent food in a large dining room. Convalescing owls make unusual drinking companions. One of only three pubs in Devon in every edition of the *Guide*. Family room and cider in summer only. ⚏ Q
☂ ❀ ◖ ▶ ▣ ♿ ▲ ♣ ⌂ P

Bampton

Exeter Inn
Tiverton Road (1 mile from Bampton)
☎ (01398) 331345
11–2.30, 6–11
Exmoor Ale Ⓗ, **Beast; Freetraders Twelve Bore; Shepherd Neame Spitfire** Ⓖ; **guest beer**
15th-century Devon Longhouse inn, serving good food, in a friendly atmosphere. Speciality food days held. ⚏
Q ☂ ❀ ⊨ ◖ ▶ ♿ ♣ ⌂ P

Barnstaple

Rolle Quay Inn
Rolle Quay
☎ (01271) 45182
11–11
Draught Bass; Ushers Best Bitter Ⓗ
Spacious, well-run, two-bar pub at the northern edge of town, handy for the rugby and soccer grounds. Families welcome; excellent food; skittle alley. Annual beer festivals are held.
Q ❀ ◖ ▶ ♿ ▲ ⇌ ♣ ⌂

Belstone

Tors Inn
The Torrs
☎ (01837) 840689
11–2.30, 6–11
Butcombe Bitter; Otter Ale; guest beers Ⓗ
Large, old granite building with a more modern interior, on the edge of Dartmoor. Cider in summer.
⚏ Q ❀ ⊨ ◖ ▶ ▲ ♣ ⌂

Bere Ferrers

Old Plough
Signed from Bere Alston, off A386 ☎ (01822) 840358
12–3 (4 Sat), 7–11
Courage Best Bitter; Summerskills Best Bitter; Whitbread Boddingtons Bitter, Flowers IPA; guest beer Ⓗ
16th-century village inn, by the River Tavy in an area of outstanding beauty; 1991 local seafood *Pub of the Year*. Moorings for visitors; check first. Cider in summer.
⚏ Q ❀ ◖ ▶ ⇌ ♣ ⌂

Devon

Bideford

Joiners Arms
Market Square
☎ (01237) 472675
12–3, 7–11; 11–11 Sat
Draught Bass G; Courage Best Bitter; guest beer H
Excellent, convivial, well-run local, popular for its quiz (Sun), impromptu sing-songs and occasional live music. No food Sun eve.
🏠 ⛲ ✿ 🛏 🍽 ♣

Kings Arms
The Quay ☎ (01237) 475196
11–11
Wadworth 6X; Whitbread Boddingtons Bitter, Flowers IPA H
Quayside pub that has changed little. The bar is below sea level on high spring tides and can flood. Pictures show Bideford's seafaring history. 🏠 🛏 🍽 ♣

Portobello
Silver Street ☎ (01237) 472991
11–3, 6–11; 11–11 Fri & Sat
Ushers Best Bitter, Founders H
Rambling old pub in the market square, named after an 18th-century naval battle in the Caribbean. ⛲ ♣

Blackawton

Normandy Arms
Chapel Street (1 mile from A3122) ☎ (01803) 712316
12–2.30, 7–11 (11.30–3, 6.30–11 summer)
Draught Bass; Blackawton Bitter, 44; Ruddles Best Bitter H
A pub since 1836, renamed in 1952 to commemorate the Normandy landings. It hosts the international Worm-Charming Festival (early May); Blackawton Wiggly X is brewed for the event.
🏠 Q ⛲ ✿ 🛏 🍽 🅰 ♣ P

Black Torrington

Torridge Inn
Broad Street ☎ (01409) 23243
12–2.30 (not Mon & Wed), 7–11
Whitbread Boddingtons Bitter; guest beers H
With 18th-century origins, now modernised into one bar, this pub is the centre of village activity. Annual beer festival in the games room.
🏠 Q ⛲ ✿ 🛏 🍽 🍺 P

Bradninch

Castle Inn
1 Fore Street ☎ (01392) 881378
12–2.30, 6–11

Furgusons Dartmoor Best Bitter; Ind Coope Burton Ale H
Old coaching inn with atmosphere and comfortable surroundings. Good value, home-cooked meals; families welcome. ✿ 🛏 🍽 ⅙ ♣ P

Branscombe

Fountain Head
☎ (0129 780) 359
11–2.30 (2 winter), 6.30–11 (10.30 winter)
Branscombe Vale Branoc, Olde Stoker H
14th-century pub warmed by huge log fires in winter. The lounge bar was formerly the village blacksmith's shop and the forge now forms the central fireplace. Good food at sensible prices.
🏠 Q 🛏 🍽 🍺 🅰 ♣ P

Braunton

Mariners Arms
South Street ☎ (01271) 813160
11–3.30, 5–11; 11–11 Sat
Courage Directors; Exmoor Ale; guest beers H
Busy local whose landlord has a miraculous memory for faces and their favourite tipple. Low prices too! 🛏 🍽 🅰 ♣

New Inn
Silver Street ☎ (01271) 817800
11–3.30, 5–11; 11–11 Sat
Cotleigh Harrier; Morland Old Speckled Hen; Ruddles Best Bitter; Ushers Best Bitter H
Former coaching house, beside Braunton's lovely old church: a quintessential local. Welcoming atmosphere; no loud music. 🏠 🅰 ♣ P

Brixham

Blue Anchor
Fore Street ☎ (01803) 859373
11–11
Blackawton Headstrong; Furgusons Dartmoor Strong H
Historic, 16th-century harbourside pub, where the food is very reasonably priced. The building used to be a sail loft, and its nautical character survives. Live music. Popular with tourists. 🏠 Q 🍽 ♣

Broadhembury

Drewe Arms
☎ (0140 484) 267
11–2.30, 6–11
Draught Bass; Otter Bitter, Ale, Head G
A picturesque exterior and an old-fashioned interior at an inn which is full of character. This largely unspoilt village

pub stands amongst thatched, whitewashed cottages, next to the church. No meals Sun eve.
🏠 ⛲ ✿ 🛏 🍽 ♣ 🍺

Buckland Monachorum

Drake Manor Inn
The Village ☎ (01822) 853892
11.30–2.30, 6.30–11
Courage Best Bitter; John Smith's Bitter; Ushers Best Bitter, Founders H
16th-century pub in a picturesque village. Note the original beams and collection of cups in the snug. The lively locals' bar offers pub games. The beer has to be drawn across the road by handpump.
🏠 Q ⛲ ✿ 🛏 🍽 ♣ 🍺 P

Butterleigh

Butterleigh Inn
☎ (01884) 855407
12–2.30, 6 (5 Fri)–11; 12–2.30, 7–10.30 Sun
Cotleigh Harrier, Tawny, Old Buzzard; guest beer (occasional) H
Friendly village inn with a stained-glass porch, popular for food and accommodation.
🏠 ✿ 🛏 🍽 ⅙ ♣ P

Cadeleigh

Cadeleigh Arms
2 miles W of Bickleigh
☎ (01884) 855238
11–11
Bass Charrington IPA, Draught Bass; Cotleigh Tawny; Exe Valley Exeter Old; Fuller's London Pride; Wadworth 6X H
Comfortable village pub with a warm, friendly atmosphere and wonderful views across the Exe and Dart valleys. Cream teas in summer.
⛲ ✿ 🛏 ⅙ ♣ P

Chagford

Globe
High Street ☎ (01647) 433485
11–3, 7–11
Draught Bass; Courage Best Bitter; guest beer H
Friendly, 16th-century, two-bar coaching inn in a stannery town. 🏠 🛏 🍽

Chipshop

Chipshop Inn
Off A384, W of Tavistock
OS437751 ☎ (01822) 832322
12–2.30, 7 (6.30 Fri & Sat)–11
Draught Bass; Exmoor Ale; guest beers H
Welcoming, one-bar pub on a remote crossroads. Skittle alley. 🏠 Q 🛏 🅰 ♣ P

Devon

Chittlehamholt

Exeter Inn
Off A377 ☎ (01769) 540281
11.30–2.30, 6–11
Furgusons Dartmoor Best
Bitter; Tetley Bitter; guest
beer H
Friendly, 16th-century,
thatched inn, on the edge of
Exmoor. ❀ ⌂ ⫟ ◗ ⌂ P

Clayhidon

Half Moon Inn
☎ (01823) 680291
12–2.30, 7–11
Draught Bass; Cotleigh
Tawny, Old Buzzard; guest
beers (occasional) H
Old, well-cared-for village
local which has a reputation
for good value meals. Superb
views across the Culm valley.
⚄ Q ⭗ ❀ ◗ ▲ ♣ ⌂ P

Colaton Raleigh

Otter Inn
Exmouth Road
☎ (01395) 568434
11–2.30 (3 summer), 6–11
Ruddles Best Bitter, County;
John Smith's Bitter;
Wadworth 6X H
Friendly village pub, with an
'otter' theme, well-known for
its food. A large games room,
and a children's room
supplement the safe garden.
Q ⭗ ❀ ◗ ◗ ⬤ ⬥ ▲ ♣ P

Coleford

New Inn
☎ (01363) 84242
11.30–2.30, 6–11
Otter Ale; Wadworth 6X;
Whitbread Flowers IPA; guest
beer H
Large, well-appointed,
pub/restaurant, with one bar;
a 13th-century Grade II-listed
building boasting a splendid
thatched roof. Rather
expensive, but worth a visit.
⚄ ❀ ❀ ◗ ◗ ▲ P

Combeinteignhead

Wild Goose
☎ (01626) 872241
11.30–2.30, 6.30–11
Cotleigh Old Buzzard; Exe
Valley Exeter Old; Exmoor
Gold; Mill Janner's Ale;
Wadworth 6X H
17th-century farmhouse in a
quiet village, near the River
Teign. Jazz Mon. Good food.
⚄ Q ⭗ ❀ ◗ ◗ ▲ ⌂ P

Crediton

Crediton Inn
28a Mill Street
☎ (01363) 772882

11–11
Draught Bass; guest beer H
Lively town-centre local, built
in 1852. The sign depicts St
Boniface. Skittle alley.
⭗ ◗ ◗ ⬥ ♣

Cullompton

White Hart
19 Fore Street ☎ (01884) 33260
11–11 (may vary)
Courage Best Bitter,
Directors; John Smith's
Bitter H
Recently modernised, town-
centre pub with good value
food. ⚄ ❀ ◗ ◗ ⬤ ⬥ ♣ P

Dousland

Burrator Inn
☎ (01822) 853121
11–11
Bass Worthington BB,
Draught Bass; St Austell
HSD; Wadworth 6X; guest
beers H
Former Victorian hotel in
Dartmoor National Park, near
the Burrator reservoir. Ideal
for walkers, it has a large
garden and play area and
serves food all day.
⚄ ⭗ ❀ ❀ ◗ ◗ ⬥ ▲ ♣ P

Drewsteignton

Drewe Arms
The Square ☎ (01647) 21224
11–2.30, 6–11; 12–2, 7–10.30 Sun
Whitbread Flowers IPA G
Thatched village pub,
untouched for a century, run
by the oldest (99), and longest
serving landlady in the
country. It is one of three pubs
in Devon in every edition of
the Guide. Near good walks.
⚄ Q ⭗ ▲ ♣ ⌂

Dunsford

Royal Oak
☎ (01647) 52256
11.30–2.30 (3 Fri & Sat), 6.30 (6 Fri &
Sat)–11
Draught Bass; Brains Bitter;
Greene King Abbot;
Whitbread Flowers Original;
guest beer H
Popular local in a small Devon
village, with a well-decorated,
Victorian interior. Various
entertainments; two beer
festivals (March and Nov).
⚄ ⭗ ❀ ❀ ◗ ◗ ▲ ♣ ⌂ P

East Budleigh

Rolle Arms
Exmouth Road
☎ (01395) 442012
11–2.30, 6–11
Branscombe Vale Branoc;
Whitbread Boddingtons
Bitter, Flowers Original H

Pleasant, one-bar village pub,
on a crossroads. The dining
room serves excellent food.
⭗ ❀ ◗ ◗ ▲ ♣ P

Exeter

Brook Green Tavern
31 Well Street
☎ (01392) 496370
11–2.30, 6–11
Devenish Cornish Original;
Otter Ale; guest beer H
Friendly, two-bar pub near the
football ground.
◗ ⬤ ⬥ (St James) ♣ P

Cowick Barton Inn
Cowick Lane, St Thomas
☎ (01392) 70411
11–3, 6.30–11
Draught Bass; Courage Best
Bitter; Ruddles County H;
guest beers G
Converted Elizabethan house,
a country pub within the city
boundary, consisting of an
attractive old lounge, a newish
public bar and a large garden.
⚄ Q ⭗ ❀ ◗ ⬤ ⬥ P

Double Locks
Canal Banks, Marsh Barton
(follow lane by incinerator,
over canal) ☎ (01392) 56947
11–11
Adnams Broadside; Eldridge
Pope Royal Oak G; Everards
Old Original H; Exe Valley
Dob's Best Bitter G; Greene
King Abbot H; guest beers
Highly successful, slightly
eccentric, canalside pub with a
huge outdoor area and two
rooms suitable for families,
plus an atmospheric old bar.
Good value food. ⚄ ⭗
❀ ◗ ◗ ⬤ ⬥ ▲ ♣ ⌂ P

Exeter & Devon Arts Centre
Bradninch Place, Gandy Street
☎ (01392) 219741
12–2.30, 5–11; closed Sun
Branscombe Vale Branoc;
Furgusons Dartmoor Strong;
Wadworth 6X H
Friendly, small bar with
excellent food (eve meals until
8.30pm). Frequent events in
the Theatre Bar.
◗ ◗ ⬥ ⬥ (Central) ⬥

Jolly Porter
St David's Hill
☎ (01392) 54848
11–11
Courage Best Bitter,
Directors; John Smith's Bitter;
guest beer H
Long, narrow pub on several
levels, popular with students.
Good value food; jazz club
Wed. ◗ ◗ ⬥ (St Davids) ♣

Mill on the Exe
Bonhay Road
☎ (01392) 214464
11–3, 6–11; 11–11 Fri, Sat & summer

87

St Austell Bosun's, XXXX Mild, Tinners, HSD H
Busy riverside pub in a converted mill. Exeter Folk Club meets here. No food Sun eve. 🛏 ❀ ◖ ◗ ♿
⇌ (St Davids) P

North Bridge Inn
St David's Hill
☎ (01392) 56296
11–3 (not Mon–Thu winter), 6–11; 12–11 Fri & Sat
Beer range varies H
One-bar pub between the main railway stations and the city centre, featuring local, independent brewers. It was the first outlet in Exeter to use oversized, lined glasses.
⇌ (St Davids/Central) ♣

Prospect Inn
The Quay
☎ (01392) 422303
11–2.30, 5.30–11 (11–11 summer)
Draught Bass; Eldridge Pope Royal Oak; Whitbread Boddingtons Bitter H
Popular pub on the quay. A family room is open at lunchtime only.
🛏 ◖ ◗ ⇌ (St Thomas)

Well House
Cathedral Yard
☎ (01392) 58464
11–2.30, 5–11; 7–10.30 Sun, closed Sun lunch
Draught Bass; guest beers H
Popular pub, serving five independent beers (mainly local), next to the Cathedral Green. The ancient cellar is inhabited by a victim of the Black Death.
◖ ⇌ (Central)

Exmouth

Country House Inn
Withycombe Village Road
☎ (01395) 263444
11–2.30 (3.45 Sat), 5–11
Devenish Royal Wessex; Whitbread Boddingtons Bitter, Flowers Original H
Village-style local (formerly a blacksmith's), with an aviary in the large garden. Barbecues in summer. Excellent food, especially Sat eve (book); lunches Mon–Fri.
🛏 ❀ ◖ ◗ ⊞ ♣ ⌓

Grove
The Esplanade (near docks)
☎ (01395) 272101
11–3, 5.15–11 (11–11 May–Sept)
Brakspear Special; Greene King Abbot; Wadworth 6X; Whitbread Boddingtons Bitter, Flowers IPA H
Friendly, seafront pub with a traditional bar and timber decor/furniture. Good food. Monthly mini-beer festivals, Oct–May.
Q ❀ ◖ ◗ ⇌ P

Feniton

Nog Inn
Ottery Road
☎ (01404) 850210
11–3, 6–11
Branscombe Vale Branoc; Cotleigh Tawny; guest beer H
Genuine village local with a friendly landlord and a squash court. Cider in summer.
🏰 Q ❀ 🛏 ⊞ ⇌ ♣ ⌓ P

Georgeham

Rock
Rock Hill ☎ (01271) 890322
12–3.30, 6–11; 12–11 Sat (& summer if busy)
Fuller's ESB; Marston's Pedigree; Morland Old Speckled Hen; Ruddles County; Tetley Bitter; Wadworth 6X; guest beers H
An absolute gem. This charming, 16th-century inn carries eight real ales and enjoys an irresistible sense of good cheer. Cider in summer.
🏰 🛏 ❀ 🛏 ◖ ◗ ♿ ♣ ⌓ P

Great Torrington

Black Horse Inn
High Street
☎ (01805) 22121
11–3, 6–11
Courage Directors; John Smith's Bitter; Ushers Best Bitter; Wadworth 6X; guest beer H
Attractive town-centre inn with one bar plus a lounge. It was used by General Fairfax during the Civil War. One independent's beer is always sold.
🏰 Q 🛏 🛏 ◖ ◗ ▲ ♣

Hunters Inn
Well Street ☎ (01805) 23832
11–3, 5.30–11
John Smith's Bitter; Wadworth 6X; Whitbread Flowers Original H
Popular pub, close to the town centre; an old building of traditional Devon style, inside and out. 🏰 🛏 ♣ ⌓ P

Hallsands

Hallsands Hotel
Off A379, in Stokenham, follow signs to N Hallsands OS818387 ☎ (0154 851) 264
11–11
Draught Bass G/H**; guest beer** (summer) H
Isolated, old coaching inn on the South Devon coastal path, built in 1906 to replace the London Inn, washed into the sea in 1903. Impressive sea views. Cider in summer.
🏰 ❀ 🛏 ◖ ◗ ♣ ⌓ P

Harberton

Church House Inn
☎ (01803) 863707
12–2.30 (11.30–3 Sat), 6–11
Draught Bass; Courage Best Bitter; guest beers H
Beautiful, 12th-century pub, originally a chantry house owned by the neighbouring church. Friendly atmosphere; ever-changing guest beers.
🏰 Q 🛏 ◖ ◗ ▲ ♣ ⌓ P

Hatherleigh

George Hotel
Market Street
☎ (01837) 810454
11–3.30, 6–11
Draught Bass; Whitbread Boddingtons Bitter, Flowers Original; guest beer (occasional) H
Large, thatched coaching inn with its main bar at the rear, past a beautiful courtyard. The front two bars have been knocked into one.
🏰 Q 🛏 ❀ 🛏 ◖ ◗ ⌓ P

Tally Ho
14 Market Street
☎ (01837) 810306
11–3, 6–11
Tally Ho Mild, Potboiler's Brew, Tarka's Tipple, Nutters, Thurgia, Janni Jollop H
Welcoming and cosy brew pub, in a market village. The comfortable bar has two wood burners. 🏰 ❀ 🛏 ◖ ◗ ♣ P

Haytor Vale

Rock Inn
☎ (01364) 661305
11–3, 6.30–11
Draught Bass; Eldridge Pope Dorchester, Hardy Country, Royal Oak H
Superb, 200-year-old village inn, offering excellent food and accommodation.
🏰 Q ❀ 🛏 ◖ ◗ ⚡

Hemerdon

Miners Arms
On Newham (Plympton)–Cornwood road
☎ (01752) 343232
11.30–2.30 (3 Sat), 5.30–11
Draught Bass H/G**; Ruddles County; Whitbread Boddingtons Bitter; guest beers** H
Former tin miners' pub on a hill overlooking Plympton. Good facilities for children.
🏰 Q 🛏 ❀ ◖ ♿ ♣ P

Holbeton

Dartmoor Union
Fore Street ☎ (0175 530) 288
11.30–3, 6–11

Summerskills Best Bitter; Wadworth 6X H
Ancient former workhouse and cider press which celebrated its 200th birthday in 1993 and is noted for its food. Good family room.
🏠 Q ⛱ 🕯 ◁ ▶ ▲ 🍴 P

Holcombe Rogus

Prince of Wales
☎ (01823) 672070
11.30–3, 6.30–11
Draught Bass; Cotleigh Tawny, Old Buzzard; guest beer H
Pleasant country pub with cash register handpumps. The restaurant serves excellent food. Beer festivals every bank hol. Cider in summer. 🏠 Q
⛱ 🕯 ◁ ▶ 🚻 ▲ 🍴 🍴 P

Holne

Church House Inn
OS705695 ☎ (0136 43) 208
11.30 (12 winter)–3, 6.30 (7 winter)–11
Blackawton Bitter; Furgusons Dartmoor Best Bitter, Dartmoor Strong; Palmers IPA H
14th-century traditional inn on the edge of Dartmoor offering a variety of good value, home-cooked meals (no chips). It also has a restaurant, a public bar and two lounge areas, one for families. 🏠 Q
⛱ 🕯 🍴 ◁ ▶ ▲ 🍴 🍴 P

Holsworthy

Kings Arms
The Square ☎ (01409) 253517
11–11
Draught Bass; Wadworth 6X H
Traditional, late-Victorian town pub with two main bars; one has a snob screen partition to form a quiet snug. Very popular with locals.
🏠 Q ◁ 🍴

White Hart Hotel
Fore Street ☎ (01409) 253475
11–11 (may close afternoons)
Draught Bass; Eldridge Pope Hardy Country, Royal Oak; guest beers H
Hotel whose landlord is trying to wean locals on to the real thing. It has a cellar bar and a restaurant. 🍴 ◁ ▶ 🍴

Honiton

Red Cow
High Street ☎ (01404) 47497
11–3, 6–11
Courage Directors; Freetraders Twelve Bore; Otter Ale; John Smith's Bitter; guest beer H
Charming, friendly town pub with a superb stone front,

dating back to the 16th century. 🏠 🍴 ◁ ▶ ▲ ≈

Vine Inn
Vine Passages ☎ (01404) 42889
11–3, 6–11; 11–11 Sat
Otter Ale H
Town local, fielding keen skittles, darts and crib teams.
🏠 Q ⛱ 🍴 ▲ ≈ 🍴 P

Horndon

Elephants Nest
Off A386, 1½ miles E of Mary Tavy ☎ (01822) 810273
11–2.30, 6.30–11
Palmers IPA; St Austell HSD; Whitbread Boddingtons Bitter; guest beers H
Popular, 16th-century moorland pub offering an extensive menu.
🏠 Q ⛱ 🍴 🍴 ◁ ▶ 🍴 🍴 P

Iddesleigh

Duke of York
☎ (01837) 810253
11.30–3, 6.30–11
Cotleigh Tawny; Hook Norton Old Hooky; guest beers (occasional) G
12th-century inn of unspoilt character, featuring a large log fire. An attractive garden at the rear gives good views of Dartmoor. Children welcome.
🏠 Q ⛱ 🍴 ◁ ▶ 🍴

Ilsington

Carpenters Arms
☎ (01364) 661215
11–2.30, 6–11
Whitbread Flowers IPA G
A farmers' and villagers' local, run at a leisurely pace in a small village on the edge of Dartmoor. 🏠 Q ⛱ ◁ ▶ 🍴

Ivybridge

Imperial
28 Western Road
☎ (01752) 892269
11–3.30, 5–11; 11–11 Fri, Sat & summer
Courage Bitter Ale, Best Bitter; Ruddles County; guest beers H
Friendly pub serving high quality food and a wide range of guest beers. Barbecues and cider in summer.
🏠 ⛱ 🍴 ◁ ▶ 🚻 ▲ 🍴 🍴

Kilmington

New Inn
The Hill ☎ (01297) 33376
11–3, 7–11 (11–11 summer)
Palmers BB, IPA E
Palmers' western outpost is a fine, friendly village inn just off the A35. Enjoy the superb views from the garden. 🏠 Q
⛱ 🍴 ◁ ▶ 🍴 ▲ 🍴 P

Kingsbridge

Ship & Plough
The Quay ☎ (01548) 852485
11–11
Draught Bass; Blewitts Best Bitter H; **guest beers**
Popular, large, one-room pub near the town centre, with a friendly atmosphere. The guest beers are often special brews from Blewitts Brewery, based here. Good value food; welcoming landlord. 🍴 ◁ ▶

Lapford

Old Malt Scoop Inn
☎ (01363) 83330
11.30–3, 6–11
Adnams Broadside G; **Draught Bass; Wadworth 6X** H; **guest beer** G
Real village inn (17th-century), with a wooden stillage behind the bar, an inglenook, and a stone-flagged floor. Wheelchair access to gents' WC only. 🏠 ⛱ 🍴 🍴 ◁ ▶
🍴 🍴 🍴 P

Littlehempston

Tally Ho!
☎ (01803) 862316
11–3, 6–11; 12–2.30, 7–10.30 Sun
Furgusons Dartmoor Best Bitter; Wadworth 6X H
14th-century house, beside the main railway line in an otherwise peaceful village. Curios cover the natural stonework. Most tables are for diners. 🏠 Q ⛱ ◁ ▶ P

Lower Ashton

Manor Inn
Just E of B3193
☎ (01647) 52304
12–2.30, 6–11; closed Mon
Draught Bass; Cotleigh Tawny H; **Wadworth 6X** G; **guest beer** H
Typical, unspoilt country pub. The public bar comprises a few tables and chairs, a dartboard, an open fire and a small bar area. The lounge is much more comfortable but retains a rustic atmosphere. Reputation for food. CAMRA SW *Pub of the Year* 1993.
🏠 Q ⛱ 🍴 ◁ ▶ 🍴 ▲ 🍴 🍴 P

Lutton

Mountain Inn
Off A38 at Plympton
☎ (01752) 537247
11–3, 6 (7 Mon–Wed winter)–11
Furgusons Dartmoor Best Bitter; Summerskills Best Bitter; Wadworth 6X; guest beers H

Exposed cob walls and a large fireplace make this a pub worth visiting, with families very welcome. Ind Coope Burton Ale is sold as Mountain Ale. Cider in summer.
🏚 Q ♿ 🌞 ⓓ ▶ ▲ ♣ ⌂ P

Lydford

Castle
☎ (01822) 82242
11.30–3, 6–11
Draught Bass; Furgusons Dartmoor Best Bitter H**; Palmers IPA; guest beers** G
Pleasant, 16th-century inn, next to the castle, featuring low, bowed ceilings, slate floors, large stone fireplaces, and many curios. 🏚 Q ♿ 🌞 🏩 ⓓ ▶ ⌂ ♣ P

Mucky Duck
Lydford Gorge
☎ (01822) 82208
11–11
Draught Bass; Butcombe Bitter; guest beers H
Accommodating, multi-roomed inn with slate floors, exposed stone walls, and large family rooms. Live music Sun night. Cider in summer. 🏚
Q ♿ 🌞 🏩 ⓓ ▶ ♣ ⌂ P

Marsh

Flintlock Inn
Just off A303 on Somerset border ☎ (01460) 234403
11–2.30, 6.30–11
Fuller's London Pride; Furgusons Dartmoor Best Bitter; guest beer H
17th-century inn with rustic ceiling timbers and exposed stonework. The inglenook includes a baker's oven.
🏚 ⓓ ▲ ⌂ P ✂

Mary Tavy

Mary Tavy Inn
Lane End (A386)
☎ (01822) 810326
11.30 (11 summer)–3, 6–11
Draught Bass; St Austell XXXX Mild, HSD; Wadworth 6X; guest beers H
Charming, 16th-century inn on the western edge of Dartmoor. Good value food.
🏚 Q 🌞 🏩 ⓓ ▶ ⌂ ♣ P

Meeth

Bull & Dragon
☎ (01837) 810325
12–3, 7–11 (11–5, 6.15–11 summer)
Butcombe Bitter; Furgusons Dartmoor Best Bitter H
16th-century thatched inn of character, almost destroyed by fire some years ago but wonderfully restored. The beer range may vary.
🏚 ♿ 🌞 ⓓ ▶ ♣ P

Newton Abbot

Dartmouth Inn
East Street (opp. hospital)
☎ (01626) 53451
11–11
Draught Bass H**; guest beers**
Reputed to be the oldest pub in the town, specialising in guest beers (over 1000 tried). CAMRA S Devon *Pub of the Year* 1992 and 1994. 🚲 ♣ ⌂

Newton St Cyres

Beer Engine
☎ (01392) 851282
11.30–2.30, 6–11; 11–11 Sat & bank hols
Beer Engine Rail Ale, Piston, Sleeper H
Friendly and deservedly popular brew pub near the station. At weekends the downstairs bar is opened and the brewery may be viewed. Good value food includes locally-made sausages. Live entertainment weekends.
🏚 Q 🌞 ⓓ ▶ ▲ 🚲 P

North Bovey

Ring of Bells
☎ (01647) 40375
11–3, 6–11 (11–11 summer)
Furgusons Dartmoor Best Bitter; Ind Coope Burton Ale; Wadworth 6X; guest beers (summer) H
Rambling, low-beamed, 13th-century thatched pub in an attractive Dartmoor village. Good food.
🏚 Q ♿ 🌞 🏩 ⓓ ▶ 🍺 ▲ ⌂

Northlew

Green Dragon
12–3 (not winter Mon–Fri), 5–11 (not winter Thu–Fri); 12–11 Sat
Courage Dartmoor Ale, Best Bitter; Whitbread Boddingtons Bitter H
A rare outlet in W Devon for Courage BA. This warm and friendly village inn and restaurant has been opened-out. Note the large stained-glass dragon over the door.
🏚 🌞 ⓓ ▶ 🍺 ♣ P

North Tawton

Copper Key
Fore Street ☎ (01837) 82357
11–3, 7–11
Draught Bass; Fuller's London Pride; Wadworth 6X H
Pub which was previously a cider house, dating back to 1520. It has a heavy involvement in the Civil War Society. 🏚 ♿ 🌞 🏩 ⓓ ▶ 🍺 ▲ ♣ ⌂ P

Okehampton

Plume of Feathers
38 Fore Street ☎ (01837) 52815
10.30–11
Draught Bass; Courage Best Bitter; Wadworth 6X; guest beers H
Fairly large, two-bar town pub with a skittle alley. The two guest beers mostly come from south-western independent breweries. Occasional beer festivals. Q 🏩 ⓓ ▶ ▲ ♣ P

Ossaborough

Mill
Near Woolacombe
☎ (01271) 870237
12–3.30, 6–11
Beer range varies H
Tasteful mill conversion with its own 'Ale Room', offering some eight beers.
🏚 ♿ 🌞 ⓓ ▶ 🍺 ▲ ⌂ P

Ottery St Mary

London Inn
Gold Street ☎ (01404) 814763
11–11
Draught Bass; Furgusons Dartmoor Best Bitter H
18th-century coaching house with genuine oak beams and horse brasses, a restaurant, two function rooms, a skittle alley and a pool room.
🏚 Q ⓓ ▶ ♣ ⌂ P

Paignton

Polsham Arms
Lower Polsham Road
☎ (01803) 558360
11–11
Draught Bass; Whitbread Boddingtons Bitter, Flowers IPA, Winter Royal; guest beers H
Whitbread 'Cask Ale' house hosting mini-beer festivals in summer, plus live music and discos. Games include pool and a bowling alley. The lounge is friendly and quiet.
Q 🌞 🍺 ♣ P

Plymouth

Clifton Hotel
35 Clifton Street, Greenbank
☎ (01752) 266563
5–11; 11.30–11 Fri; 11.30–3, 7–11 Sat
Draught Bass; Morland Old Speckled Hen; Summerskills Best Bitter H**, Ninjabeer** G**; Tetley Bitter** H**; guest beers**
Warm, friendly pub fielding numerous teams. The guest beers are unusual. ♿ 🚲 ♣

Dolphin Hotel
The Barbican ☎ (01752) 660876
10–11
Draught Bass; M&B Highgate Old; guest beers G

Historic pub untouched by brewery developers, and frequented by fishermen and serious drinkers. The Tolpuddle Martyrs stayed here on their return to the UK. ♨ Q ♣

Fisherman's Arms

31 Lambhay Street, Barbican
☎ (01752) 661457
11–11
St Austell XXXX Mild, Tinners (summer), **HSD** H
Hospitable, 200-year-old pub, the only pub in the area selling St Austell beers. Families welcome. ◑ ▶ ♣ ◔

Little Mutton Monster

240 James Street, Mutton Cove, Devonport
☎ (01752) 560938
11.30–2.30, 6–11
Courage Best Bitter; Marston's Pedigree; Morland Old Speckled Hen; Wadworth 6X; guest beers H
Large, 200-year-old, one-bar pub by the dockyard. Good value food (not served Tue eve). ❀ ◑ ▶ ♣

London Inn

8 Church Road, Plympton St Maurice
☎ (01752) 337025
12–2.30 (11–3 May–Dec), 7–11
Courage Best Bitter; Ruddles County; John Smith's Bitter; Summerskills Indiana's Bones; Sutton Plymouth Porter; guest beers H
17th-century coaching pub, reputedly haunted by Roundheads and Cavaliers who died here after a local Civil War battle. The lounge has not been altered since 1945. ♨ ◑ ▲ ♣ P

Prince Maurice

3 Church Hill, Eggbucland (off B3413)
☎ (01752) 771515
11–3, 7 (6 Fri)–11; 11–11 Sat
Draught Bass; Eldridge Pope Royal Oak; Fuller's London Pride; S&N Theakston Mild, Old Peculier; guest beers H
Small, two-bar house, popular with locals, next to the church in a village swallowed by Plymouth. ♨ ❀ ♣ P

Pym Arms

16 Pym Street, Devonport
☎ (01752) 561823
11–3, 6–11
Bass Worthington BB, Draught Bass; St Austell XXXX Mild H**, HSD; Wadworth 6X** G**;** guest beers
Beer drinkers' haunt, heavily populated with students during termtime.
⇌ (Devonport) ♣ ◔

Royal Albert Bridge Inn

930 Wolseley Road, St Budeaux ☎ (01752) 361108
11–11
Draught Bass; Courage Best Bitter H
Friendly, riverside local in the shadow of Brunel's bridge, with picturesque views across the Tamar to Cornwall. Opposite stands a D-Day monument to the American V and VII corps. ❀ ◑ ▶
⇌ (St Budeaux/Ferry Rd) ♣

Shipwrights Arms

13 Sutton Road, Coxside
☎ (01752) 665804
11–3, 6 (5.30 Fri)–11
Courage Best Bitter, Directors H
Convivial one-bar pub near the city centre, a ten-minute walk from the Barbican.
♨ Q ❀ ◑ ♣ P

Stopford Arms

172 Devonport Road, Stoke
☎ (01752) 562195
11–2.30 (3 Sat), 6–11
Courage Best Bitter; Ind Coope Burton Ale H
Smart, two-bar pub used by locals. Q ⇌ (Devonport) ◔

Swan Inn

Cornwall Beach, Devonport
☎ (01752) 568261
12–3, 7–11 (12 Thu–Sat)
Draught Bass; Ruddles County; St Austell HSD; Wadworth 6X; Whitbread Boddingtons Bitter; guest beers H
Riverside pub with yacht moorings nearby. Live bands play Thu–Sat (extension). Popular with dockyard employees at lunchtime.
♨ Q ❀ ◑ ▶ ♣

Thistle Park Tavern

32 Commercial Road, Coxside
☎ (01752) 667677
11–11
Greene King Abbot; St Austell HSD; Summerskills Best Bitter; Sutton XSB, Plymouth Porter; guest beers H
Warm, friendly pub which holds regular beer festivals. The Sutton Brewery is based next door. ♨ ♣

Unity

50 Eastlake Street
☎ (01752) 262622
11–11; 7–10.30 Sun, closed Sun lunch
Furgusons Dartmoor Best Bitter; Ind Coope Burton Ale H
Single room on two levels (the lower has a vaulted ceiling), popular with shoppers. The landlady is a member of the Guild of Master Cellarmen

and ensures a good welcome. Unaccompanied women feel comfortable. Coffee served from 9am. ◑ ✄

Plymstock

Boringdon Arms

Boringdon Terrace, Turnchapel ☎ (01752) 402053
11–3, 5.30–11; 11–11 Fri, Sat & summer
Draught Bass; Butcombe Bitter; Fuller's London Pride; Summerskills Best Bitter; guest beers H
Welcoming local, centre of the village community. Beer festivals bimonthly. Plymouth CAMRA *Pub of the Year* 1993.
♨ Q ➳ ❀ ♨ ◑ ♣

Poundsgate

Tavistock Inn

On B3352 ☎ (0136 43) 251
11–2.30, 6–11
Courage Best Bitter; Ushers Best Bitter, Founders H
700-year-old, unspoilt pub in a small Dartmoor village, with a cosy front bar. Very popular in summer. ♨ Q ➳ ❀ ◑ ▶ P

Princetown

Plume of Feathers

The Square ☎ (01822) 890240
11–11
Draught Bass; St Austell HSD; guest beer H
Reputedly Princetown's oldest building, with slate floors, exposed beams, granite walls, a camp site and an adventure play area for children. Used by walkers. ♨ ➳ ❀ ♨ ◑ ▶ ◐
▲ ♣ ◔ P

Rattery

Church House Inn

☎ (01364) 42220
11–2.30, 6–11
Ind Coope Burton Ale; Furgusons Dartmoor Best Bitter; guest beer H
One of England's most historic inns, dating from 1028. A large fireplace and a grandfather clock enhance the bar area. Interesting range of home-cooked food. ♨ Q ◑ ▶ P

Roborough

Olde Inn

Off B3227 ☎ (0180 53) 247
7–11; 11–3, 7–11 Sat & bank hols
John Smith's Bitter; Wadworth 6X H
16th-century, thatched inn with a garden at the front. It was recently altered to accommodate a food area and a skittle alley, but retains its character. ♨ Q ❀ ◑ ▶ ♣ P

Devon

Salcombe

Ferry Inn
Ferry Steps, High Street
☎ (01548) 844000
11–11
Palmers BB, IPA, Tally Ho! Ⓗ
Two-bar pub with its own
bistro and large garden,
offering superb views over the
estuary. Palmers BB is sold as
Ferry Bitter. 🏚 Q ✿ ◖ ▶ ♣

Scorriton

Tradesman's Arms
Top of hill from Buckfast
Abbey, right at Round Cross,
2 miles ☎ (0136 43) 206
12–2 (3 Sat), 7–11
**Bass Worthington BB,
Draught Bass** Ⓗ; **guest beers**
(occasional)
Quiet pub inside Dartmoor
National Park. No food Mon.
🏚 Q ⌚ ✿ ◖ ▶ ⌣ P

Seaton

Hook & Parrot
The Esplanade
☎ (01297) 20222
11–11
**Draught Bass; Devenish
Royal Wessex; Whitbread
Flowers Original** Ⓗ
Seafront pub with a terrace, a
cellar bar (eve only) and an
adjoining coffee shop.
Splendid sea vistas.
Q ⌚ ◖ ▲ ♣

Silverton

Silverton Inn
Fore Street ☎ (01392) 860196
12–3, 5.30–11; 11–11 Sat
**Draught Bass; Exe Valley
Bitter, Dob's Best Bitter,
Exeter** Ⓗ
One-bar village local, with no
silly frills. It is best to book for
the restaurant (Thu–Sat eves
and Sun lunch). Q ◖ ▶ &

Slapton

Queens Arms
☎ (01548) 580800
11.30–3, 6–11
**Blackawton Headstrong;
Exmoor Ale; Furgusons
Dartmoor Best Bitter; Palmers
IPA; guest beers** Ⓗ
14th-century inn in the village
centre. The garden is a
suntrap, whilst, inside, old
local photos are displayed. The
friendly landlord offers good
quality and value food.
🏚 Q ◖ ▶ ▲ ♣ ⌣ P

South Pool

Millbrook Inn
1½ miles S of Frogmore
☎ (01548) 531581

11–3, 5 or 6 (or earlier, depending on
tides)–11
Draught Bass Ⓖ; **Ruddles Best
Bitter; John Smith's Bitter** Ⓗ
Small, cosy pub with two bars,
situated beside a small brook,
and decorated with nautical
prints and assorted collections.
The bar food comes highly
recommended. Q ✿ ◖ ▶ ⌣

South Tawton

Seven Stars
The Square ☎ (01837) 840292
11–2, 6–11
**Whitbread Boddingtons
Bitter; guest beers** Ⓗ
Stone village pub with one bar
and a restaurant. Families are
welcome. Games include pool.
Folk eve last Sun of the month.
🏚 Q ✿ 🛏 ◖ ▶ & ▲ ♣ ⌣

South Zeal

Oxenham Arms
Off old A30 at Sticklepath
☎ (01837) 840244
11–2.30, 6–11
**Draught Bass; Furgusons
Dartmoor Best Bitter** Ⓖ
First licensed in 1477, but a
monolith in the lounge dates
back 5,000 years, and the
building is listed as an ancient
monument. A settle stands in
the bar corner by the fire.
Cider in summer.
Q ⌚ ✿ 🛏 ◖ ▶ ▲ ♣ ⌣ P

Sparkwell

Treby Arms
Off A38, at Plympton jct
☎ (01752) 837363
11–3, 6.30–11
**Draught Bass; Wadworth 6X;
Whitbread Boddingtons
Bitter; guest beers** Ⓗ
Pub dating from around 1750
and standing next to Dartmoor
Wildlife Park. Compact and
cosy. No eve meals winter
Mon. 🏚 Q ◖ ▶ & ▲ ♣ P

Spreyton

Tom Cobley Tavern
☎ (01647) 231314
12–2.30, 6 (7 Mon)–11 (winter hours
may be shorter)
**Cotleigh Tawny; Exe Valley
Dob's Best Bitter; guest
beer** Ⓖ
Quiet village local, where
beers are fetched from an
adjoining 'cob'-built cellar. A
function/family room boasts
an indoor barbecue. Home-
cooked food (no meals Mon).
🏚 Q ⌚ ✿ 🛏 ◖ ▶ & ♣ P

Sticklepath

Devonshire Inn
☎ (01837) 840626
11–3, 5.30–11; 11–11 Sat & summer

**Draught Bass; St Austell
XXXX Mild, Tinners, HSD,
Winter Warmer** Ⓖ
Pub where the casks are
stillaged against the back,
cooled by a mill leat. Lots of
Civil War armour and other
curios are displayed.
🏚 Q ⌚ ✿ ▶ ▲ ♣ ⌣ P

Stockland

Kings Arms
☎ (01404) 881361
12–3, 6.30–11
**Exmoor Ale; Hall &
Woodhouse Badger Best
Bitter; Ruddles County;
Ushers Best Bitter** Ⓗ
17th-century coaching inn,
popular with locals and
tourists alike in the
comfortable Farmers' Bar and
the Coachman's Haunt dining
room (no food Sun lunch).
Skittle alley. 🏚 Q ⌚
✿ 🛏 ◖ ▶ 🂡 & ♣ P

Stokenham

Tradesman's Arms
50 yds N of A379
☎ (01548) 580313
12–2.30 (3 summer), 7–11; closed
Sun–Thu eves in winter
**Draught Bass; Hook Norton
Best Bitter; guest beer** Ⓗ
Small, 15th-century, thatched
cottage inn in an attractive
setting. The restaurant offers
fish specialities at weekends
and curry on Sun. Over 100
whiskies; cider in summer.
🏚 Q ✿ ◖ ▶ ▲ ⌣ P

Talaton

Talaton Inn
☎ (01404) 822214
12–2.30, 7–11
**Branscombe Vale Branoc;
Wadworth 6X** Ⓗ
Friendly village local with
good food in the
lounge/restaurant. Skittle
alley. 🏚 ⌚ ✿ ◖ ▶ 🂡 ♣ P

Tavistock

Tavistock Inn
Brook Street ☎ (01822) 612661
11.30–3, 5.30–11; 11.30–11 Fri & Sat;
12.30–3, 7–10 Sun
**Courage Best Bitter; Ushers
Best Bitter, Founders** Ⓗ
Friendly locals' town pub next
to the former site of Tavistock
Brewery. The single bar has a
recently enlarged pool area,
plus a dining area. 🏚 ◖

Teignmouth

Blue Anchor
Teign Street (near quay)
☎ (01626) 772741
11–11

Adnams Broadside; Greene
King Abbot; Marston's
Pedigree; S&N Theakston
Old Peculier; Wadworth 6X;
Whitbread Boddingtons
Bitter; guest beers H
Large, one-room pub with a
friendly atmosphere.
Runner-up in Devon CAMRA
Pub of the Year 1993.
🏠 ☀ ◑ ▶ & ≉ ♣ ⌂ P

Golden Lion

85 Bitton Park Road (A381)
☎ (01626) 776442
11–2.30, 5.30–11; 11–11 Sat
Beer range varies H
Friendly local: a two-roomed
pub with two constantly
changing guest beers. Pool and
darts feature in the main bar,
and town memorabilia in the
lounge bar. Q ≉ ♣ ⌂ P

Thurlestone

Village Inn

☎ (01548) 560382
11.30–2.30, 6–11
**Draught Bass; Palmers IPA;
Wadworth 6X** H
Two-bar, beamed pub with a
family dining area, owned by
the adjacent hotel. It also
stocks foreign bottled beers.
No Sun eve meals in winter.
Q ⌇ ☀ ◑ ▶ & ▲ ⌂ P

Tiverton

Racehorse

Wellbrook Street
☎ (01884) 252606
11–11
**Ruddles County; Ushers Best
Bitter; Webster's Yorkshire
Bitter** H
Popular local with a friendly
atmosphere. Meals are served
all day. 🏠 ⌇ ☀ ◑ ▶ & ♣ P

White Horse

Gold Street ☎ (01884) 252022
11–11
**Bass Worthington BB,
Draught Bass** H
Small, friendly, town-centre
pub, with good value food.
⌇ ☀ 🏠 ◑ ▶ & ♣

Topsham

Lighter Inn

The Quay ☎ (01392) 875439
11–11
**Hall & Woodhouse Badger
Best Bitter, Tanglefoot** H
Roomy pub near the river; the
only Hall & Woodhouse tied
house in Devon. Good food.
⌇ 🏠 ◑ ▶ ≉ P

Torquay

Crown & Sceptre

2 Petitor Road, St Marychurch
☎ (01803) 328290
11–3, 5.30–11; 11–11 Sat

Courage Best Bitter,
Directors; Marston's Pedigree;
Morland Old Speckled Hen;
Ruddles County; John
Smith's Bitter; guest beer H
200-year-old, stone-walled
coaching inn adorned with
chamber pots. Regular folk
and jazz music; interesting
guest beers. No food Sun.
🏠 ⌇ ☀ ◑ ▶ & ▲ ♣ P

Devon Dumpling

108 Shiphay Lane, Shiphay
(near hospital)
☎ (01803) 613465
11–2.30, 5.30–11; 11–11 Sat
**Courage Best Bitter; Ruddles
County; John Smith's Bitter;
Wadworth 6X; guest beers** H
16th-century converted
farmhouse, very popular with
locals. Good range of food.
The family room is upstairs.
🏠 ⌇ ☀ ◑ ▶ & ♣ P

Wig & Pen

168–170 Union Street
☎ (01803) 213848
11–11
**Courage Best Bitter,
Directors; Morland Old
Speckled Hen; John Smith's
Bitter; guest beer** H
Busy, town-centre pub,
popular with the business
community at lunchtimes and
a younger clientele eves.
Friendly. ◑ ≉ (Torre) ♣

Totnes

Kingsbridge Inn

9 Leechwell Street
☎ (01803) 863324
11–3, 7–11
**Draught Bass; Blackawton
Bitter; Furgusons Dartmoor
Best Bitter; S&N Theakston
Old Peculier; guest beer** H
A superb example of a pub,
with excellent food. South
Devon CAMRA *Pub of the Year*
1993. 🏠 Q ◑ ▶ ≉ ⌂ ⊬

Rumour

High Street ☎ (01803) 864682
10–11
**Draught Bass; Wadworth 6X;
guest beers** H
Dutch-style 'Brown Café',
being both a café and a pub
and opening early for
breakfast. Cider in summer.
⌇ ◑ ▶ & ▲ ≉ ⌂ ⊬

Ugborough

Anchor Inn

1 Lutterburn Street
☎ (01752) 892283
11–11
Draught Bass G**; Wadworth
6X; guest beers** H
Lively, traditional public bar at
the centre of village life. The
lounge restaurant enjoys an
excellent reputation. Local
cider in summer and local

guest beers all year. 🏠 ☀
🏠 ◑ ▶ & ▲ ♣ ⌂ P

Westcott

Merry Harriers

On B3181 ☎ (01392) 881254
12–2.30, 7–11; 12–2, 7–10.30 Sun
Draught Bass H
Friendly pub serving possibly
the best Bass in the area. Good
food in the restaurant and the
bar (not Sun). Skittle alley.
🏠 ⌇ ◑ ▶ & ♣ P

Whimple

New Fountain Inn

Church Road
☎ (01404) 822350
11–3, 6–11
**Furgusons Dartmoor Best
Bitter; Oakhill Bitter; guest
beer** H
Family-run local, with a warm,
friendly atmosphere, serving
good value food.
🏠 ⌇ ☀ ◑ ▶ ⊡ ≉ ♣ ⌂ P

Widecombe in the Moor

Rugglestone Inn

¼ mile S of village OS721766
☎ (0136 42) 327
11.30 (11 summer)–2.30 (3 Sat), 7
(6.30 summer)–11
Draught Bass; guest beer G
A classic Dartmoor pub,
unspoilt and popular with
locals and walkers. Eve meals
by arrangement only in
winter. 🏠 Q ☀ ◑ ▶ ♣

Woodbury Salterton

Diggers Rest

☎ (01395) 232375
11–2.30, 6.30–11
**Draught Bass; Furgusons
Dartmoor Best Bitter; Tetley
Bitter; Whitbread Flowers
IPA** H
14th-century thatched pub,
well-known for its food.
Unusual handpumps; large
games room at the rear.
🏠 Q ⌇ ☀ ◑ ▶ ♣ ⌂ P

Yelverton

Rock Inn

On Princetown road, near
roundabout ☎ (01822) 852022
11–11
**Draught Bass; Fuller's
London Pride; St Austell
HSD; Wadworth 6X;
Whitbread Boddingtons
Bitter; guest beers**
(summer) H
Pub incorporating the oldest
building in Yelverton, dating
back to the 16th-century. Three
bars plus a family room with
videos. Children's menu.
🏠 Q ⌇ ◑ ▶ & ♣ P

Dorset

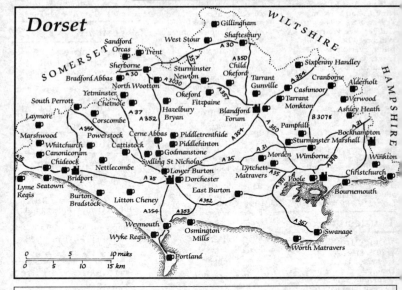

 Cook's, *Bockhampton*; **Eldridge Pope**, **Goldfinch**, *Dorchester*; **Hall & Woodhouse**, *Blandford Forum*; **Palmers**, *Bridport*; **Poole**, *Poole*

Alderholt

Churchill Arms
Daggons Road
☎ (01425) 652147
11–3, 6–11
Hall & Woodhouse Badger Best Bitter; Wells Eagle Ⓗ
Convivial and comfortable village pub featuring a wood-panelled front bar with a pool room, plus a skittle alley.
🛏 ☕ ✿ Ⓠ Ⓓ ♣ P

Ashley Heath

Struan Hotel
Horton Road (½ mile N of A31/A338) ☎ (01425) 473553
11–3, 6–11
Hall & Woodhouse Badger Best Bitter, Tanglefoot; Wells Eagle Ⓗ
1920s manor house licensed in 1954. A friendly atmosphere prevails in the smart lounge bar and a jazz band plays every Thu eve. Wells Eagle is sold as Struan Bitter.
🛏 ✿ ✿ Ⓠ Ⓓ P

Blandford Forum

Half Moon Inn
16 Whitecliff Mill Street
☎ (01258) 452318
10–11
Hall & Woodhouse Badger Best Bitter; Wells Eagle Ⓗ

Basic town pub with a public bar atmosphere and a separate games room for pool. Q ☕ P

Kings Arms
Whitecliff Mill Street (up Salisbury St from Market Sq)
☎ (01258) 452163
11–11
Bass Worthington BB, Draught Bass; Ringwood Best Bitter Ⓗ
Historic Georgian hotel with a comfortable, newly renovated interior. The former site of JL Marsh brewery.
🛏 ✿ 🛌 Ⓠ Ⓓ A P

Bournemouth

Cottonwood Hotel
Grove Road ☎ (01202) 553183
11–3, 5–11
Draught Bass; Ringwood Best Bitter; guest beer (winter) Ⓗ
Hotel bar, open to non-residents, on the East Clifftop, with views to the Purbeck Hills. ✿ 🛌 ✿ ⇌ P

Porterhouse
113 Poole Road, Westbourne
☎ (01202) 768586
11–3 (4 Sat), 6–11
Ringwood Best Bitter, XXXX Porter, Fortyniner, Old Thumper; guest beer Ⓗ
The best example of a proper pub in Bournemouth (although previously a cinema

and a wine bar). Reasonable prices. Ⓠ Ⓓ ⇌ (Branksome)

Punch & Judy
Poole Hill (¼ mile from square) ☎ (01202) 290016
11–11
Marston's Bitter, Pedigree Ⓗ
Lively well-kept pub on the edge of the town centre. Good value food. Beware the fake cider handpump. Ⓠ ✿

Bradford Abbas

Rose & Crown
Church Road ☎ (01935) 74506
12–3, 6.30–11
Eldridge Pope Dorchester, Hardy Country, Royal Oak Ⓗ
Historic building on the southern edge of the village, serving good reasonably priced food. It can get quite lively. Respectable dress is appreciated. Inch's cider.
🛏 ✿ 🛌 Ⓠ Ⓓ ♣ A ♣ ☕ P

Bridport

George Hotel
4 South Street
☎ (01308) 423187
10–11
Palmers BB, IPA, Tally Ho! Ⓗ
Cosy, main-street hotel with a good local trade. It opens at 8.30am for coffee. No meals Sun. 🛏 Q ☕ 🛌 Ⓠ A ✂

94

Burton Bradstock

Dove Inn
Southover (off B3157, E of village) ☎ (01308) 897897
11.30–2.30 (3 Sat), 7 (6 Sat)–11
Exmoor Ale; Wadworth 6X; guest beer H
Pretty stone-built, 300-year-old smuggling inn: three bars, plus a carvery. Popular with camping tourists in summer. Snug in winter. No food Sun eve or Mon. ♨ Q ⌛ ❀ ⊯
◑ ▶ ⊞ ▲ ♣ ⇨ P

Three Horseshoes
Mill Street ☎ (01308) 897259
11–2.30, 6–11 (7–11.30 holiday weekends)
Palmers BB, IPA, Tally Ho! H
Lovely thatched pub with suntrap seats at the front. Very good food. Popular with families using the beach.
♨ ⌛ ❀ ⊯ ◑ ▶ ⅙ ▲ P

Cashmoor

Cashmoor Inn
On A354 ☎ (01725) 552230
11–3, 6.30–11
Hall & Woodhouse Badger Best Bitter, Tanglefoot H
Former coaching inn which dates back to 1667, with two different bars.
♨ Q ❀ ⊯ ◑ ▶ ⊞ ♣ ⇨ P

Cattistock

Fox & Hounds
Duck Street ☎ (01300) 20444
12–2.30 (not Mon), 7–11
Beer range varies H
Former medieval longhouse opposite the church. Two large fireplaces dominate the main bar and the flagstone floor, panelling and window seats add to the unspoilt atmosphere. Cider in summer.
♨ ⌛ ❀ ⊯ ◑ ▶ ⊞ ⅙ ▲ ♣ P

Cerne Abbas

Red Lion
Long Street ☎ (01300) 341441
11.30–3, 6.30–11
Wadworth IPA, 6X; guest beers H
Pub with a striking Victorian frontage at the centre of a picturesque village, near the famous giant. Interesting menu. ♨ Q ❀ ◑ ▶ ⅙ ▲ ♣

Chetnole

Chetnole Inn
☎ (01935) 872337
11–2.30 (4 Sat), 6.30–11
Hook Norton Best Bitter; Mole's Tap; Palmers IPA; guest beers H

Pub in an attractive village setting, opposite the church: a lively public bar and a quiet lounge. Perries served.
♨ Q ⌛ ❀ ⊯ ◑ ▶ ⅙ ▲ ⇥ ♣ P

Chideock

George Inn
On A35 ☎ (0129 74) 89419
11–2.30, 6–11
Palmers BB, IPA, Tally Ho!, 200 E
Traditional Dorset inn with a splendid horseshoe bar. Much enlarged in recent times, it retains its original character.
♨ ⌛ ❀ ◑ ▶ ⅙ ▲ ♣ P

Child Okeford

Saxon Inn
Gold Hill (end of narrow lane, N end of village)
☎ (01258) 860310
11.30–2.30, 7–11
Draught Bass; Butcombe Bitter; guest beer H
Converted from two cottages in 1949, but looks older: a pub with wildlife in the garden. No meals Tue or Sun eve.
♨ ⌛ ❀ ◑ ▶ ▲ ♣ P

Christchurch

Old George Inn
2a Castle Street
☎ (01202) 479383
11–2.30 (3 Sat), 6–11
Ringwood Fortyniner; Whitbread Strong Country, Flowers Original; guest beer H
Old Tudor coaching inn comprising two cosy bars and a pleasant courtyard. Folk Wed and jazz Thu night.
Q ❀ ◑ P

Corscombe

Fox Inn
☎ (01935) 891330
12–2.30, 7–11
Exmoor Ale G**; Fuller's London Pride; Palmers BB** H
Traditional, thatched village pub featuring a stone-flagged floor and a slate bar. Quality home-cooked food.
♨ ⌛ ❀ ◑ ▶ ⊞ ♣ ⇨ P

Cranborne

Sheaf of Arrows
4 The Square ☎ (01725) 517456
11.30–3 (4 summer), 6–11
Ringwood Best Bitter; Smiles Best Bitter; guest beer H
Thriving, traditional local with two contrasting bars: a large, rather noisy locals' public, and a small, quiet lounge. Skittle alley. Q ❀ ⊯ ◑ ▶ ⊞ ▲ ♣

Dorchester

Bakers Arms
140 Monmouth Road
☎ (01305) 264382
11–2.30, 6–11
Eldridge Pope Dorchester, Hardy Country, Royal Oak H
Comfortable, corner local, overlooking the railway. Formerly a bakehouse, its old ovens can still be seen in the bar. ❀ ◑ ▶ ⇥ ♣ P

Tom Brown's
47 High East Street
☎ (01305) 264020
11–3, 6–11; 11–11 Fri
Goldfinch Tom Brown's, Flashman's Clout, Midnight Blinder H
Wooden-floored home of the Goldfinch brewery. Popular, especially on Fri and Sat nights. Well-used jukebox.
⊯ ◑ ▶ ♣

East Burton

Seven Stars
East Burton Road
☎ (01929) 462292
11–3, 6.30 (6 summer)–11
Ind Coope Burton Ale; Tetley Bitter; Whitbread Castle Eden Ale; guest beer H
Large, slightly out of place, free house in a country location. Friendly atmosphere; good value food.
♨ ❀ ◑ ▶ ♣ P

Gillingham

Dolphin
Peacemarsh (B3095)
☎ (01747) 822758
11–3, 6–11
Hall & Woodhouse Badger Best Bitter, Tanglefoot H
Small, friendly 18th-century pub on the outskirts of town, retaining many original features. Interesting food.
♨ Q ❀ ◑ ▶ ⅙ ▲ ⇥ ♣ ⇨ P

Godmanstone

Smiths Arms
☎ (01300) 341236
11–3, 6–11
Ringwood Best Bitter G
The smallest pub in England, granted a licence by Charles II when he stopped here to have his horse shod. Riverside garden. ♨ Q ❀ ◑ ▶ ⅙ P

Hazelbury Bryan

Antelope
Pidney (1 mile E of B3143)
OS745091 ☎ (01258) 817295
11–2.30, 6–11
Hall & Woodhouse Badger Best Bitter G

Dorset

One of Dorset's finest unspoilt country pubs. The simply furnished single bar has changed little over the years. The handpumps are for show.
🚲 Q ❀ 🛏 ◑ ▶ ♣ ⌂ P

Laymore

Squirrel
On B3162, 2 miles SE of Winsham ☎ (01460) 30298
11–2.30, 6–11
Cotleigh Harrier; Oakhill Yeoman; guest beers H
Brick pub, in beautiful countryside: a good local, offering two or three guest beers each week.
🚲 Q ❀ 🛏 ◑ ▶ ♿ ▲ ♣ ⌂ P

Litton Cheney

White Horse
☎ (01308) 482539
11–2, 6.30–11
Palmers BB, IPA, Tally Ho! H
Flint and brick pub on the edge of the village, beside a stream. Very accommodating for walkers, it also provides hearty food (lunches in summer only). 🚲 Q ❁ ❀
🛏 ◑ ▶ ♿ ♣ ⌂ P

Lower Burton

Sun Inn
½ mile N of Dorchester
☎ (01305) 250445
11–2.30, 6.30–11
Fuller's London Pride; Hook Norton Best Bitter; Smiles Bitter; guest beer H
Former Devenish pub, extensively refurbished, on the old Sherborne road. The landlord's motto is: 'Good food, good beer and good cheer'. Wheelchair WC.
🚲 ❀ ◑ ▶ ♿ ♣ P

Lyme Regis

Angel Inn
Mill Green (down Monmouth St, off High St)
☎ (01297) 443267
11–2.30, 7–11
Palmers BB, IPA G
Back-street, basic local which is a *Guide* regular; one of the few places serving Palmers on gravity. ❁ ❀ ▲ ♣ P

Lytchett Matravers

Chequers
High Street ☎ (01202) 622215
11–2.30 (3 Sat), 6–11
Draught Bass; Ringwood Fortyniner; guest beer H
Large, one-bar pub and restaurant in a rural setting on the conurbation's edge. The garden has children's play equipment and farm animals. New conservatory. 🚲 Q ❁
❀ 🛏 ◑ ▶ ♿ ♣ P ✕

Marshwood

Bottle Inn
On B3165 ☎ (01297) 678254
11–2 (3 summer), 6–11
Exmoor Ale; Hook Norton Best Bitter; Ruddles Best Bitter; Wadworth 6X H
Unspoilt pub in beautiful countryside. Not all the ales listed may be available.
🚲 Q ❁ ❀ 🛏 ◑ ▶ ♿ ▲ ♣

Morden

Cock & Bottle
On B3075 ☎ (01929) 459238
11–2.30 (3 Sat), 6–11
Hall & Woodhouse Badger Best Bitter, Hard Tackle (summer), Tanglefoot; Wells Eagle H
Friendly, village pub in a rural setting. A restaurant has been built on but is in keeping with the character of this 400-year-old inn. 🚲 Q ❀ ◑ ▶ ♣ ⌂ P

Nettlecombe

Marquis of Lorne
OS956517 ☎ (01308) 485236
11–3, 6–11
Palmers BB H, **IPA** G, **Tally Ho!** H
This 16th-century country inn has the feel of a private front room in the bar; separate dining room. Peaceful garden.
🚲 Q ❁ ❀ 🛏 ◑ ▶ ▲ ♣ ⌂ P

North Wootton

Three Elms
☎ (01935) 814881
11–2.30, 6.30 (6 Fri & Sat)–11
Fuller's London Pride; Greene King Abbot; Hook Norton Mild; Hop Back Summer Lightning; Whitbread Boddingtons Bitter; guest beers H
Popular, country free house, well-known for its food. Wide range of bottled beers from many countries. The house beer is Ash Vine Bitter.
🚲 Q ❀ 🛏 ◑ ▶ ♣ P ✕

Okeford Fitzpaine

Royal Oak
Lower Street ☎ (01258) 860308
11–2.30, 6.30–11
Brakspear Special; Ringwood Best Bitter; Wadworth 6X H
Locals' pub in an expanding but picturesque village. No meals Wed. Skittle alley.
🚲 ❁ ❀ ◑ ▶ 🍴 ♿ ♣ ⌂ P

Osmington Mills

Smugglers Inn
Off A353 ☎ (01305) 833125
11–2.30 (3 weekends), 6.30–11 (11–11 summer)

Courage Best Bitter; guest beers H
Spacious pub close to the cliff top, on the coastal path. The beer range varies, but beware, strong beers are sold at strong prices! It can be crowded in summer. Good restaurant.
🚲 Q ❀ 🛏 ◑ ▶ ♿ ▲ ♣ P

Pamphill

Vine Inn
Vine Hill (off B3082, near Wimborne) OS995004
☎ (01202) 882259
11–2.30, 7–11
Whitbread Strong Country H; **guest beer** G
Split-level country pub built into the hillside and owned by the NT. Two very small bars, with a stairway leading to an area with darts. Q ❀ ♣ ⌂

Piddlehinton

Thimble Inn
☎ (01300) 348270
12–2.30, 7–11
Eldridge Pope Hardy Country; Hall & Woodhouse Badger Best Bitter, Hard Tackle; Ringwood Old Thumper H
Friendly country inn, spanning the River Piddle. Good food.
🚲 ❁ ❀ ◑ ▶ ♣ P

Piddletrenthide

Piddle Inn
☎ (01300) 348468
11.30–2.30, 7–11 (11–11 summer)
Courage Best Bitter; Wadworth 6X H
Riverside local, with a collection of chamber pots.
🚲 ❁ ❀ ◑ ▶ ♿ P

Poole

Albion
470 Ringwood Road, Parkstone ☎ (01202) 732197
11–3, 5–11; 11–11 Sat
Hall & Woodhouse Badger Best Bitter, Tanglefoot H
Two-bar pub on a main road into town. Q ❀ ◑ ▶ ♿ ♣ P

Beehive
234 Sandbanks Road, Lilliput
☎ (01202) 708641
11–2.30, 5.30–11 (11–11 summer)
Eldridge Pope Dorchester, Hardy Country, Royal Oak H
Plush pub/restaurant with a dining area for families. Handy for the beach and Sandbanks ferry.
🚲 ❀ ◑ ▶ ♿ P

Bermuda Triangle
Parr Street ☎ (01202) 748087
11.30–2.30, 5.30 (5 Fri)–11; 11–11 Sat
Beer range varies H

A true free house, offering three constantly changing real ales, and over 30 bottled beers. Pricey but friendly.
❀ ◖ ⇌ (Parkstone)

Branksome Railway Hotel

429 Poole Road, Parkstone (A35) ☎ (01202) 769555
11–11
Whitbread Boddingtons Bitter, Flowers Original; guest beers Ⓗ
Rather like a city pub, with high ceilings and a large family room. ⛄ ❀ ◖
⇌ (Branksome) ♣ P

Conjurors Half Crown

Commercial Road, Parkstone (A35) ☎ (01202) 740302
11–3, 5 (6 Sat)–11 (may vary in summer)
Hall & Woodhouse Badger Best Bitter, Hard Tackle, Tanglefoot Ⓗ
Large food pub with many levels, alcoves and low beams. Handy for Poole Park.
❀ ◖ ⇌ (Parkstone) P

Inn in the Park

26 Pinewood Road, Branksome Park
☎ (01202) 761318
11–2.30 (3 Sat), 5.30 (6 Sat)–11
Adnams Bitter; Draught Bass; Wadworth 6X Ⓗ
Plush, comfortable inn in an exclusive residential area near Branksome beach. A dining area welcomes children at lunchtime (no eve meals Sun). The beers may vary.
🍴 Q ❀ 🛏 ◖ ▶ P

Lord Nelson

The Quay ☎ (01202) 673774
11–11
Hall & Woodhouse Badger Best Bitter, Hard Tackle, Tanglefoot; Wells Eagle Ⓗ
Busy pub with nautical artefacts and flagstone floors. Live bands and blues/rock music; comfortable family room. No food Sun.
🍴 ⛄ ❀ ◖ &

Portland

Corner House

49 Straits, Easton
☎ (01305) 822526
11–3, 6–11
Eldridge Pope Dorchester, Hardy Country, Royal Oak; guest beer Ⓗ
Unchanged, 19th-century ale house with a cosy bar and a games room. ❀ 🛏 ♣

Powerstock

Three Horseshoes

OS961516 ☎ (01308) 848532
11–3, 6–11

Palmers BB, IPA, Tally Ho! Ⓗ
Pub at the foot of Eggardon Hill (lovely views). The menu offers many fish dishes (no eve meals winter Sun), but the beers are a little pricey. 🍴 Q
❀ 🛏 ◖ ▶ & ▲ ♣ ⌂ P

Sandford Orcas

Mitre Inn

☎ (01963) 220271
11.30–3, 7 (6 Sat)–11
Wiltshire Stonehenge; guest beers Ⓗ
Flagstone-floored gem of a rural, 18th-century local, in the hills. Enjoy a quiet pint or boisterous skittles. Excellent value home cooking (no meals Mon eve). 🍴 Q ⛄ ❀ 🛏
◖ ▶ & ▲ ♣ ⌂ P

Seatown

Anchor

Turn left off A35 in Chideock
OS420917 ☎ (01297) 89215
11–2.30, 7–11 (may vary); 11–11 summer
Palmers BB, IPA, Tally Ho! Ⓖ, 200 Ⓖ
Small, cosy pub overlooking Lyme Bay. Very busy in summer, and popular with trekkers. No meals Sun eve.
🍴 ⛄ ❀ 🛏 ◖ ▶ ▲ ♣ P ⌞

Shaftesbury

Fountain Inn

Breach Lane, Enmore Green
☎ (01747) 52062
11–3, 6.30–11; 11–11 Sat
Fuller's London Pride; Wadworth 6X; guest beers Ⓗ
Comfortable split-level bar patronised by the young. Live music every other Thu. Skittle alley. ❀ ◖ ▶ ♣ ⌂ P

Olde Two Brewers

St James Street (near foot of Gold Hill) ☎ (01747) 54211
11–3, 6–11
Courage Best Bitter, Directors; Wadworth 6X; guest beers Ⓗ
Popular, well-run pub nestling below the town. It comprises many different drinking areas and has a secluded garden with superb views. Excellent, home-cooked food. ❀ ◖ ▶ P

Sherborne

Digby Tap

Cooks Lane (near abbey)
☎ (01935) 813148
11–2.30 (3 Sat), 5.30–11
Beer range varies Ⓗ
Unpretentious and unspoilt, side-street tap room: stone-flagged floors and wood panelling. Five beers.
🍴 Q ⛄ ◖ ⇌ ♣ ⌂

Skippers

Horsecastle ☎ (01935) 812753
11–2.30, 5.30–11; 12–2.30, 7–10.30 Sun
Draught Bass; Wadworth IPA, 6X; guest beers Ⓗ
A long bar in a long, narrow room: a good drinking pub, also offering a sizeable menu.
Q ❀ ◖ ▶ ⇌ ♣ P

Sixpenny Handley

Roebuck

High Street ☎ (01725) 552002
11–2.30, 6.30–11
Ringwood Best Bitter, XXXX Porter, Fortyniner; guest beer (occasional) Ⓗ
Upmarket, L-shaped bar with a cosy fireside. The beer is often fetched from the cellar in a jug. No food Mon.
🍴 Q ⛄ ❀ 🛏 ◖ ▶ ♣ P

South Perrott

Coach & Horses

☎ (01935) 891270
12–3, 7–11
Exmoor Ale Ⓗ; **guest beer** (summer)
Open-plan roadside pub in a small village. Taunton cider.
🍴 ⛄ ❀ ◖ ▶ & ▲ ♣ P

Sturminster Marshall

Red Lion

Church Street (1 mile E of A350) ☎ (01258) 857319
11–2.30, 6–11
Hall & Woodhouse Badger Best Bitter, Hard Tackle Ⓗ
Excellently-run, one-bar village local, the last Hall & Woodhouse pub to switch to real ale. The skittle alley doubles as a family room.
🍴 Q ⛄ ❀ ◖ ▶ & ♣ P

Sturminster Newton

Bull

The Bridge ☎ (01258) 472435
11–3, 6–11; 11–11 Sat
Hall & Woodhouse Badger Best Bitter Ⓗ
Thatched, 16th-century pub close to the medieval town bridge and working mill. Popular with skittlers.
🍴 ⛄ ❀ ◖ ▶ & ♣ P

Swanage

Black Swan

High Street ☎ (01929) 422761
11.30–3, 6.30–11 (11–11 summer)
Courage Directors; Wiltshire Stonehenge Ⓗ
Traditional Purbeck-style building where the stables have been converted to an extensive children's area. The

Dorset

comfortable bar has an adjoining room serving mainly as a dining area.
ॐ ❀ ♨ ◁ ◗ ▲ P

Red Lion
High Street ☎ (01929) 423533
11–11 (may vary winter)
Ringwood Fortyniner; Whitbread Strong Country, Flowers Original G
Popular, down-to-earth, two-bar pub. The public bar adjoins the ground floor cellar from where the beers are dispensed. A lounge leads to a large garden and a children's room. Eve meals Fri/Sat only (steak nights).
ॐ ❀ ◁ ◗ ♣ ◔ P

Sydling St Nicholas

Greyhound Inn
☎ (01300) 341303
11–2.30 (3 Sat), 6.30–11
Tetley Bitter; Wadworth 6X; guest beers H
Large, one-bar free house and restaurant. Two guest beers are normally available. Skittle alley. ॐ ❀ ◁ ◗ ▶ P

Tarrant Gunville

Bugle Horn
Off A354 ☎ (01258) 830300
11.30–3, 6–11
Wadworth 6X; guest beer H
Comfortable village local on the edge of Cranborne Chase. The large garden makes an ideal retreat. Beware the keg cider handpump.
♨ Q ❀ ◁ ◗ ♣ P

Tarrant Monkton

Langton Arms
☎ (01258) 830225
11.30–3, 6–11; 11.30–11 Sat
Beer range varies H
Traditional, 17th-century country pub with four changing ales in the lounge bar and on request in the public bar. Mystery Ale Night on Thu. Extensive children's play areas, a skittle alley and a varied menu.
♨ Q ॐ ❀ ◁ ◗ ॐ ♣

Trent

Rose & Crown
Off A30 ☎ (01935) 850776
12–2.30, 7–11
Oakhill Best Bitter; Shepherd Neame Spitfire; guest beers H
Converted farmhouse, now a fine village local. Its warm welcome and cuisine have made it popular: a *Guinness Pub Food* regional award-winner. Cider in summer.
♨ Q ॐ ❀ ◁ ◗ ◔ P ✕

Verwood

Albion Inn
Station Road ☎ (01202) 825267
11–2.30, 5 (6 Sat)–11; 12–2.30, 7–10.30 Sun
Gibbs Mew Salisbury, Deacon, Bishop's Tipple H
Built in 1866: East Dorset CAMRA *Pub of the Year* 1993. A cosy pub on the edge of town. ♨ Q ❀ ◁ ◗ ◁ P

West Stour

Ship
☎ (01747) 838640
11–3, 6–11
Draught Bass; Oakhill Best Bitter; guest beer H
Handsome 18th-century coaching inn on a bend of the A30. The bar area is divided into snug sections. Good food; cider in summer. ♨ Q ॐ ❀
◁ ◗ ◔ ▲ ♣ ◔ P ✕

Weymouth

Weatherbury
7 Carlton Road (off Dorchester Rd) ☎ (01305) 786040
11–3, 5.30–11; 11–11 Fri & Sat
Draught Bass; guest beers H
Large, modern lounge bar in a residential area, stocking four guests. Good value food.
❀ ◁ ◗ ◔ ॐ ♣ P

Whitchurch Canonicorum

Five Bells Inn
Off A35 at Morecombelake ☎ (01297) 89262
12–2.30, 6–11
Palmers BB, IPA H
Traditional country inn in an unspoilt village. The nearby church is well worth a visit. Caravan and camping at the rear. ♨ Q ❀ ◁ ◗ ▲ ♣ ◔ P

Wimborne

Crown & Anchor
Wimborne Road, Walford (B3078) ☎ (01202) 841405
10.30–3, 6–11
Hall & Woodhouse Badger Best Bitter H
Pleasant, friendly, out-of-town local, by the River Allen. No food winter Sun.
♨ Q ❀ ◁ ◔ ▲ ♣ P

Lost Keys
1 Victoria Road (B3082) ☎ (01202) 881021
11–3, 5.30–11; 11–11 Fri & Sat
Draught Bass; Wadworth 6X; guest beer H
Small, enterprising free house with a dining room and many alcoves. The name comes from

a legend of a nun who lost the keys to a nearby church.
Q ❀ ◁ ◗ ♣ P

Winkton

Fishermans Haunt
☎ (01202) 477283
10.30–2.30 (3 Sat), 6–11
Draught Bass; Ringwood Best Bitter, Fortyniner; Wadworth 6X H
Friendly, 17th-century, Avon valley hotel. A good tourist base, ideal for country lovers, offering good value food. Children welcome in one lounge. ♨ Q ◁ ◗ P

Lamb Inn
Burley Road ☎ (01425) 672427
11–2.30, 5–11; 11–11 Sat & bank hols
Draught Bass; Fuller's London Pride; Ringwood Best Bitter, Old Thumper H; **guest beers**
Superb, popular free house in a green field setting, offering seven ever-changing, interesting guest ales. Good value bar food.
♨ ❀ ◁ ◗ ◁ ◔ ▲ ♣ P

Worth Matravers

Square & Compass
Off B3069 OS977777 ☎ (01929) 439229
11–3, 6–11; 11–11 Sat
Whitbread Strong Country, Castle Eden Ale, Porter (summer), **Winter Royal** G
In every edition of the *Guide* and run by the fourth generation of the Newman family. Full of beachcombing finds, with stone floors and serving hatches. Superb sea views. ♨ Q ❀ ▲ ♣ ◔ P

Wyke Regis

Wyke Smugglers
76 Portland Road ☎ (01305) 760010
11–2.30, 6–11
Courage Directors; Whitbread Boddingtons Bitter, Flowers Original; guest beers H
Popular local on the fringe of Weymouth, a venue for many games teams. Frequent, often unusual, guest beers.
ॐ ❀ ◁ ◔ ♣ P

Yetminster

White Hart
High Street ☎ (01935) 872338
11.30 (11 Sat)–2.30, 7–11
Draught Bass; Ringwood Best Bitter H
Splendid, 500-year-old, thatched inn. Note the original low beams and huge inglenook in the lounge. Good value food; skittle alley.
Q ॐ ❀ ◁ ◗ ◁ ▲ ॐ ♣ P

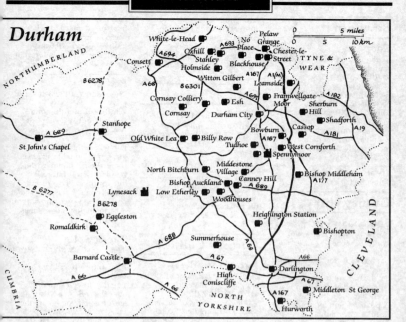

Durham

NORTHUMBERLAND

White-le-Head · Pelaw Grange · No Place
Oxhill · Chester-le-Street · *TYNE & WEAR*
Consett · Stanley · Blackhouse
Holmside
Witton Gilbert · A1(M) · Leamside
B6301 · Framwellgate Moor · Sherburn Hill
Cornsay Colliery · Esh · Shadforth
Cornsay · Durham City · Cassop
Stanhope · Old White Lea · Billy Row · Bowburn · A181
St John's Chapel · Tudhoe · West Cornforth
Spennymoor
North Bitchburn · Middlestone Village · Carney Hill · Bishop Middleham
Lynesack · Bishop Auckland · Low Etherley · Woodhouses
Eggleston · Heighington Station · Bishopton
Romaldkirk · Summerhouse
Barnard Castle · Darlington
High Coniscliffe · Middleton St George
NORTH YORKSHIRE · Hurworth
CUMBRIA · *CLEVELAND*

 Butterknowle, Lynesack; **Whitworth Hall**, Spennymoor

Barnard Castle

King's Head
Market Place
☎ (01833) 690333
11–3 (4 Sat), 6–11 (11–11 Sat in summer)
Courage Directors; Ruddles County; John Smith's Bitter, Magnet Ⓗ
Imposing one-time hotel, now a pub with a nursing home above and a coffee shop attached. Dickens stayed here in 1838 while researching *Nicholas Nickleby*. Two large oak-panelled lounge bars.
Ⓓ ▶ & P

Billy Row

Royal George
Well Bank (B6298)
☎ (01388) 764765
7 (12 Sat)–11
Ind Coope Burton Ale; Stones Best Bitter Ⓗ
Large, two-roomed village inn where the lounge decor is based on a railway theme, with steam memorabilia and a replica engine cab. Lunches Sat and Sun.
❀ ▶ & ♣ P

Try also: Farrers Arms, Crook (Federation)

Bishop Auckland

Sportsman Inn
Market Place ☎ (01388) 607376
11.30–3, 7–11
Tetley Bitter; Whitbread Boddingtons Bitter, Castle Eden Ale, Flowers Original; guest beer Ⓗ
All are welcome in this old inn with its own ghost. Loud and lively at weekends, it is quiet weekday lunchtimes. The only Irish bar in town! The landlord claims to have been booed off every football league ground.
❀ Ⓓ ⇌ ♣

Try also: Post Chaise, Market Place (John Smith's)

Bishop Middleham

Olde Fleece Inn
27 Bank Top (off A177, Sedgefield to Coxhoe road)
☎ (01740) 652392
12–3 (4 Sat), 5.30–11
Draught Bass; Whitbread Boddingtons Bitter, Castle Eden Ale; guest beer Ⓗ
Family pub with a friendly atmosphere, offering bar meals and a traditional Sun carvery. Usually frequented by couples and friendly locals. Quiet background music played.
❀ ⊠ Ⓓ ▶ P

Bishopton

Talbot
The Green
☎ (01740) 630371
11–3, 6–11
Camerons Strongarm; Ind Coope Burton Ale; Tetley Bitter Ⓗ
Pleasant village local with a growing trade from out-of-town diners. In this guide for 21 consecutive editions, with the same landlord in charge all that time.
❀ Q ❀ Ⓓ ▶ ♣ P

Blackhouse

Charlaw Inn
On B6532
☎ (01207) 232085
11–3, 6–11
S&N Theakston Best Bitter, XB; guest beer Ⓗ
Very large pub consisting of five rooms, including a restaurant and a conservatory for family groups. An L-shaped outdoor play area has swings and a play frame. The bar area features a large collection of soccer memorabilia, plus lively bar games. Excellent meals.
Q ⊠ ❀ Ⓓ ⎕ & ♣ P ✕

99

Durham

Bowburn

Cooperage
Durham Road (near A177
roundabout over A1M)
☎ (0191) 377 9473
11.30–11
**S&N Theakston Best Bitter,
Newcastle Exhibition,
Theakston XB; guest beers** H
Tidy pub with friendly staff.
Very spacious, with a central
bar area, it is becoming
increasingly popular.
🛏 ❀ 🍴 🍺 ▶ P

Try also: Avenue, High
Shincliffe (Vaux)

Canney Hill

Sportsman Inn
(A689, 1½ miles E of town)
☎ (01388) 603847
11.30–3, 7–11
**Camerons Bitter, Strongarm;
guest beer** H
On the edge of town: a pub
with a small snug with a fire, a
lively bar and a lounge.
Popular for Sun lunches.
Regular quiz nights.
🛏 Q ❀ 🍺 ♣ P

Cassop

Victoria Inn
Front Street, North Cassop (off
A181) ☎ (01429) 821410
11–2 (not Tue or Wed), 6.30–11
**Bass Worthington BB,
Draught Bass; guest beer** H
Friendly pub, frequented by
local characters: good food
and good conversation.
Witness the panoramic view of
the vale, with Durham
Cathedral five miles distant.
🛏 ⛵ ❀ 🍺 🍴 ▲ ♣

Chester-le-Street

Market Tavern
South Burns (opp. market
place) ☎ (0191) 388 4749
11–11.30
**Whitbread Boddingtons
Bitter, Castle Eden Ale; guest
beers** H
Recently modernised, two-
roomed pub just off the high
street, lively at weekends.
Known locally as the Joiners
Arms. Usually five ales are
served. No food Sun. 🍺 ⇌

Consett

Bellamys
Newmarket Street (near
Derwentside College)
☎ (01207) 503654
11–3, 6–11; 11–11 Sat
**Butterknowle Conciliation
Ale; Whitbread Boddingtons
Bitter** H

Attracting both locals and
students from the nearby
college, a pub with a central
bar and a small annexe
doubling as a dining room.
Thu night quiz; Fri night live
music. 🍺 ▶ 🍴 ▲ ♣

Cornsay

Blackhorse Inn
Main Street (2 miles W of
B6301, Cornsay Colliery road)
☎ (0191) 373 4211
7–11; 12–2.30, 7–10.30 Sun
Tetley Bitter; guest beer H
Smart, remote West Durham
village pub with a separate
eating area. Popular for Sun
lunches (no-smoking area in
the restaurant). Picturesque
view of the Gladdow Valley.
Q ❀ P

Cornsay Colliery

Firtree (Monkey)
Hedley Hill Lane Ends (B3601,
½ mile S of village)
☎ (0191) 373 3212
7–11 (not Tue); 12–2, 7–10.30 Sun
Vaux Lorimers Best Scotch H
A century-old, basic, one-room
boozer with a family room at
the front where local crafts are
sometimes displayed. Warm
up by the welcoming coal fire
in the small bar room.
🛏 Q ⛵ ♣ P

Darlington

Central Borough
Hopetown Lane
☎ (01325) 468490
11–11
Camerons Strongarm H
Small, street-corner local in an
area of terraced housing, run
by the same tenants since 1956
and with a justifiably loyal
clientele. The nearby Railway
Museum is housed in one of
the world's oldest stations – on
the original Stockton &
Darlington Railway.
Q 🍺 ⇌ (North Rd) ♣

Cricketers Hotel
53 Parkgate ☎ (01325) 384444
11.30–3.30, 5.30–11
**Black Sheep Best Bitter; John
Smith's Magnet** H
Small, town-centre pub/hotel
with a warm and friendly
public bar. Close to the Civic
Theatre. 🛏 🍺 ▶ ⇌ P

Glittering Star
Stonebridge ☎ (01325) 353191
11.30–3.30, 5.30–11; 11–11 Fri & Sat
**Samuel Smith OBB,
Museum** H
Local which has been
faithfully remodelled on
traditional pub design
principles, with not a hint of

pastiche or gimmickry
introduced. Hard to believe it
was a boarded-up empty shell
for five years until Sam
Smith's revived its interest in
1993. 🍺 ⇌ ♣

Red Lion
Priestgate ☎ (01325) 467619
11–11
**Whitbread Boddingtons
Bitter, Trophy, Castle Eden
Ale, Flowers Original; guest
beers** H
Pub where the fine, stained-
glass, traditional frontage is
somewhat let down by the
standardised Whitbread
interior decor. Two secluded
'semi-rooms' have survived at
one end however, and harbour
occasional dominoes games.
🍺 ⇌ ♣

Tap & Spile
99 Bondgate ☎ (01325) 381679
11.30–11
**Big Lamp Bitter; guest
beers** H
Popular, town-centre pub,
after the style of a Victorian
alehouse – if you ignore the
video machines, TV, taped
music and live rock bands
upstairs and down! Up to
eight real beers and regular
farmhouse ciders offered.
🍺 ♣ 🍴 🗞

Traveller's Rest
West Auckland Road,
Cockerton (A68, 1 mile W of
centre) ☎ (01325) 468177
11.30–11
**John Smith's Bitter,
Magnet** H
Attractive, 1920s, two-roomed
local in an urbanised village. A
comfortable music-free lounge
and a bustling public bar, built
for the long-defunct Haughton
Road Brewery Co. Q 🍺 🍴 ♣

Turk's Head
22 Bondgate ☎ (01325) 463191
11–11
**Camerons Strongarm;
Marston's Pedigree** H
A pub with some interesting
spaces – especially the former
smoke room, but did
Camerons really have to
remodel the interior of this
pair of listed town houses as a
fake West Country cottage?
Music can be loud at
weekends. ❀ 🍺 🍴

Durham City

Brewer & Firkin
58 Saddler Street
☎ (0191) 386 4134
12–11
**Whitbread Boddingtons
Bitter, Castle Eden Ale; guest
beers** H
Formerly the Buffalo's Head,

100

this is the closest pub to the cathedral and is popular with tourists, students and locals. Bands perform two nights per week. One of the guest ales is always a local independent brew. Real cider is occasionally stocked. Eve meals in summer. ◑ ▶ ≷

Bridge Inn
40 North Road (under viaduct)
☎ (0191) 386 8090
11–11
McEwan 80/-; Marston's Pedigree; S&N Theakston Best Bitter, Newcastle Exhibition, Theakston XB, Old Peculier; Younger No. 3; guest beer H
Former darts-playing local, now renovated as part of the T&J Bernard chain, with the same decor as every other T&J Bernard. Food is available until 7pm (9pm Sun). Conveniently close to the station. Q ◑ ▶ ≷ ○

Dun Cow
37 Old Elvet (opp. Shire Hall)
☎ (0191) 386 9219
11–11
Whitbread Boddingtons Bitter, Castle Eden Ale; guest beer H
Friendly, town-centre pub, popular with both students and locals and often crowded in the eve. Sky TV in the front bar. Bar snacks are available lunch and eve. 🍴 & ≷ ♣

Elm Tree
12 Crossgate
☎ (0191) 386 4621
12–3, 6–11; 12–11 Sat
Vaux Samson; guest beers H
Friendly, city-centre pub, popular with all. Regular rotation of guest beer from the Vaux/Wards range. Handy for the bus station and cinema.
Q ❀ 🍴 ◑ ≷ ♣ P

Half Moon
New Elvet ☎ (0191) 386 4528
11–11
Bass Worthington BB, Draught Bass; guest beer H
A *Good Beer Guide* regular for many years, named after its crescent-shaped, split-level bar. Sandwiches and toasties available. Q ≷

Victoria Hotel
86 Hallgarth Street (near Dunelm House)
☎ (0191) 386 5269
11–3, 6–11; 12–2, 7–10.30 Sun
McEwan 80/-; S&N Theakston Best Bitter, Newcastle Exhibition; guest beer H
Typical Victorian pub, dating from 1899: three rooms retaining original features. The bar has a collection of Toby

jugs, plus a large selection of whiskies. 🍴 Q 🍴 ≷ ♣ P

Try also: Colpitts Hotel, Hawthorne Tce (Samuel Smith); **Court Inn,** Court Lane, Old Elvet (Free); **Garden House,** North Rd (Vaux); **New Inn,** Church St Head (Bass)

Eggleston

Three Tuns
Church Bank
☎ (01833) 650289
11.30–3 (not Mon; 2.30 winter), 7–11
Whitbread Boddingtons Bitter, Castle Eden Ale; guest beer H
Solid, stone Teesdale inn, looking out over a cobbled forecourt to the village green. The large, carpeted lounge almost hides a gem of a public bar beyond it (the 'Regulars' Retreat', with flagged floor, low beams and well-used pewter jugs). Separate dining room. 🍴 Q ◑ ▶ 🍴 ♣ P

Esh

Board Inn
Hill Top ☎ (0191) 373 6914
11–11
Marston's Pedigree; S&N Theakston Best Bitter, Newcastle Exhibition; guest beers H
Previously an annex to a seminary, and used as a boarding house for priests. Its rural location makes it popular with locals from surrounding villages. Enjoy the convivial atmosphere and wonderful views across the valley.
🍴 Q ❀ ◑ ▶ & ♣ P

Framwellgate Moor

Marquis of Granby
Front Street (old Great North Road, off A167)
☎ (0191) 386 9382
11–4, 6–11
Samuel Smith OBB H
Popular community local with traditional decor, a *Guide* regular: two rooms and a snug; one bar. The pool/games room has a TV but noise does not intrude into the main bar. The beer prices are the best around. ❀ ♣ P

Tap & Spile
27 Front Street (old Great North Road, off A167)
☎ (0191) 386 5451
11.30–3, 6–11
Beer range varies H
The third pub in the Tap & Spile chain, refurbished in traditional style. Opened in 1988, it has stocked over 500 guest cask ales to date and the figure is still rising (usually

nine on at a time). Some foreign bottled beers are also available. No food Sun.
Q ⌚ ◑ ♣ ○ ✗

Try also: Lambton Hounds, Pity Me (Vaux)

Heighington Station

Locomotion One
Heighington Lane, Newton Aycliffe (1 mile W of A167 at Aycliffe) ☎ (01325) 320132
11–11
Butterknowle Conciliation Ale; Morland Old Speckled Hen; S&N Theakston Best Bitter, Old Peculier; John Smith's Magnet; Young's Special H
Historic, 1860s railway station converted into a pub of character. George Stephenson placed his engine *Locomotion* on the lines of the Stockton–Darlington railway here in Sept 1825. Trains still run to the door. 🍴 ◑ ▶ ≷ P

High Coniscliffe

Duke of Wellington
☎ (01325) 374283
11–3, 6–11
Camerons Strongarm; Whitbread Castle Eden Ale H
Traditional, one-roomed village local standing opposite a popular riverside beauty spot. Quoits played.
🍴 Q ❀ ◑ & ♣ P

Holmside

Wardles Bridge Inn
Front Street (¾ mile off B6532)
☎ (0191) 371 0926
11–11
Draught Bass; guest beer H
The only pub in a small village. Its lively bar is quite large, with an arch splitting the room and many curios displayed. The lounge/restaurant is very popular for Thai meals. Friendly landlady.
🍴 Q ⌚ ❀ ◑ ▶ 🍴 & ▲ ♣ P

Hurworth

Bay Horse
45 The Green
☎ (01325) 720663
11–11
John Smith's Bitter, Magnet H
Attractive village pub in 18th-century cottages: a plain bar, a cosier lounge and a small conservatory/restaurant at the rear. The central archway beneath the sundial (from 1738) leads to a small car park and garden.
Q ❀ ◑ ▶ 🍴 ♣ P

Durham

Leamside

Three Horse Shoes

Pithouse Lane (off A690, West Rainton–Gt Lumley road)
☎ (0191) 584 2394
12–3 (not Mon or Tue), 7–11
S&N Theakston Best Bitter, Newcastle Exhibition; Whitbread Boddingtons Bitter; guest beers H
Friendly, country inn comprising a large bar with a lounge at one end and a family room off the other. Regular charity nights. Changing guest beers. 🍺 ❀ ◖ ▶ ᵫ ♣ P

Try also: **Warriors Arms**, Gt Lumley (Pubmaster)

Low Etherley

Dog & Gun

114 Low Etherley (A688, ½ mile from Toft Hill)
☎ (01388) 832448
11–3, 6–11; 12–2, 7–11 Sun
Draught Bass H
Excellent family pub, very friendly and homely, offering a varied menu daily. Open-plan in design, but still cosy. ◖ ▶ ᵫ ♣ P

Try also: **Blue Bells**, Etherley (John Smith's)

Middlestone Village

Ship Inn

Low Row (between A688 and A167) ☎ (01388) 814092
7–11; 12–3, 7–11 Sat & summer
Vaux Samson; guest beers H
Small village pub with a high reputation for good food and a friendly, conscientious landlord. No jukebox or bandit, just darts, dominoes and conversation. Watch out for George Formby and Vera Lynn together, with a guest appearance by the ghost. Spot the theme of the memorabilia and collectables.
🍺 Q ❀ ⇌ ◖ ▶ ᵫ ▲ ♣ P

Middleton St George

Fighting Cocks

Darlington Road
☎ (01325) 332327
11.30–2.30, 5.30–11; 11–11 Sat
Vaux Samson, Double Maxim; Wards Best Bitter H
Arguably the oldest railway ticket sales office still in existence, being on the original alignment of the Stockton–Darlington railway. Now much updated, it concentrates on food, with a small bar area tucked away to the rear. No meals Sun eve. ❀ ◖ ▶ ♣ P

No Place

Beamish Mary Inn

600 yds off A693
☎ (0191) 370 0237
12–3, 6–11; 12–11 Fri & Sat
McEwan 80/–; S&N Theakston Best Bitter, Newcastle Exhibition, Theakston XB, Old Peculier; guest beers H
The lively focal point of an ex-mining community. Excellent value food is served in the Victorian/Edwardian lounge/diner (no meals Sun eve). Regular live rock and blues are staged in the stables bar; folk club Wed. Annual beer festival. The No Place BSB house beer is brewed by Big Lamp. National CAMRA *Pub of the Year* 1994.
🍺 Q ❀ ⇌ ◖ ▶ ᵫ ▲ ♣ ☙ P

North Bitchburn

Red Lion

North Bitchburn Terrace (1 mile from A689, Crook–Bishop Auckland road)
☎ (01388) 763561
12–3, 7–11
Courage Directors; John Smith's Bitter, Magnet; guest beer H
Friendly, traditional village pub with a bar, a pool room and a lounge where meals are served. A regular guest is the pub's own Mane Brew, brewed by Hambleton. Note the interesting fireplace in the bar. 🍺 Q ❀ ◖ ▶ ♣ P

Old White Lea

Dun Cow (Cow's Tail)

Leave Billy Row village at the Royal George (no signs)
OS148373 ☎ (01388) 762714
7.30–11; 7.30–10.30 Sun
Black Sheep Special Strong; Vaux Extra Special H
Building dating from 1740 which has been a pub since 1830, always in the same family – the present landlord is only the fifth. A small traditional local with bar and lounge, it has real fires in both. Children are allowed until 9pm. Folk nights one Fri per month. Note: closed lunchtimes.
🍺 Q ❀ ♣ P ✄

Oxhill

Ox Inn

On A693, ¾ mile W of Stanley
☎ (01207) 233626
7–11; 12–4, 7–11 Fri; 12–5, 7–11 Sat
Bass Worthington BB, Draught Bass; guest beer H

Pub with a large bar with a high ceiling and a small conservatory leading on to a patio and play area/garden, easily spotted from the main road. Live music at weekends.
Q 🍺 ❀ ▲ ♣ P

Pelaw Grange

Wheatsheaf

On A167, Chester-le-Street–Birtley road ☎ (0191) 388 3104
11–11
Bass Worthington BB, Draught Bass; Stones Best Bitter; guest beer H
Traditional 16th-century coaching inn with its original mounting steps outside. It has a traditional bar, and a quieter lounge with an emphasis on food, where families are welcome (open to 3.30 Sun for food – all day Sun in winter). Reputedly haunted by a friendly ghost. Children's playground.
🍺 ❀ ◖ ▶ 🍴 ᵫ ♣ P

Romaldkirk

Kirk Inn

The Green ☎ (01833) 50260
12–2.30, 6–11
Black Sheep Best Bitter; Butterknowle Conciliation Ale; Whitbread Boddingtons Bitter, Castle Eden Ale; guest beer H
Charming, single-room pub, with a warm and welcoming atmosphere, situated on the village green. It doubles as a part-time post office.
🍺 Q ❀ ◖ ▶ ♣

St John's Chapel

Golden Lion

Market Place (A689, Stanhope–Alston road) ☎ (01388) 537231
11–3, 7–11; 11–11 Sat & summer
Ruddles County; John Smith's Bitter; guest beer H
Unusual E-shaped pub, welcoming and friendly, with good meals. Holiday flats to let – ideal for walking in Weardale. No-smoking dining room. 🍺 Q ❀ ⇌ ◖ ▶ ▲ ♣ P

Try also: **Blue Bell** (Tetley)

Shadforth

Plough Inn

South Side ☎ (0191) 372 0375
12–3 (not Mon–Wed), 7–11
Draught Bass; Stones Best Bitter; guest beers H
17th-century pub in a pretty village near Durham. Good food in a pub that welcomes visitors but is still at heart a village local. Up to five guest beers at a time. 🍺 ◖ ▶ P

Sherburn Hill

Moor Edge
Front Street (B1283, above Sherburn village)
☎ (0191) 372 1618
12–3 (11–4 Fri & Sat), 7–11
Vaux Samson; Wards Best Bitter; guest beer H
Two-bar pub in a typical Durham village. Character has gradually been restored to the lounge bar, and it is a past local CAMRA *Best Pub* award-winner. Quoits played. Guest beers are on rotation from the Vaux range.
🍴 Q ✿ ♣ ♣ P

Spennymoor

Frog & Ferret
Coulson Street (½ mile from A167 towards centre)
☎ (01388) 818312
11–11
Courage Directors; Samuel Smith OBB; S&N Theakston XB; Whitbread Boddingtons Bitter; guest beers H
Cosy, one-roomed bar; not really a family pub.
Q & P

Hillingdon
Clyde Terrace
☎ (01388) 814425
11–3, 6–11; 11–11 Sat
Bass Worthington BB, Draught Bass H
Pub with a 1980s-style bar featuring metal, mirrors and formica, but a more traditional lounge. With possibly the friendliest bar staff for miles, it suits all tastes.
✿ & ♣ P

Stanhope

Queens Head
89 Front Street (A689)
☎ (01388) 528160
12–3, 7–11 (11–11 Fri & Sat in summer)
S&N Theakston Best Bitter, XB H
Small, friendly, two-roomed local near the market place. The lounge is decorated with photos of old Stanhope. Can get busy Sun lunchtime. 🚪 ◗
◗ ≠ (limited service) ♣

Stanley

Blue Boar Inn
Front Street (400 yds off A693)
☎ (01207) 231167
11–3, 7–11; 11–11 Thu–Sat

Bass Worthington BB, Draught Bass; Stones Best Bitter; guest beers H
Very popular pub at the top of the main street. One of the oldest in town, formerly a coaching inn. Always busy at lunchtime. The entertainment room (entrance at the rear) is busy Fri and Sat nights. Regular changes of guest beers (three on at a time).
🍴 Q ✿ ◗ & ♣ ▲ P

Try also: Smiths Arms, Catchgate (S&N)

Summerhouse

Raby Hunt
On B6279
☎ (0132 574) 604
11.30–3, 6.30–11
Marston's Bitter, Pedigree; guest beer H
Neat, welcoming, old stone free house in a pretty white-washed hamlet, with a homely lounge and busy locals' bar. Good home-cooked lunches (not served Sun). Raby Castle is worth a visit, just five miles away.
🍴 ✿ ◗ ⊟ ♣ P

Tudhoe

Green Tree
The Green (½ mile from A167 on the outskirts of Spennymoor)
☎ (01388) 815679
11–11
Vaux Samson; Wards Best Bitter H
Typical village pub, very homely, with an excellent restaurant and good quality pub lunches. Its friendly and cosy atmosphere makes it popular with the locals. Twice winner of the Vaux *Pub in Bloom* competition.
🍴 Q ✿ ◗ ▶ P

West Cornforth

Square & Compass
7 The Green (near A1(M), off A688 at Bowburn)
☎ (01740) 654606
12 (11 Sat)–3, 7–11
Bass Worthington BB, Draught Bass; Stones Best Bitter H
Pleasant, welcoming pub on the edge of the village green: the traditional decor includes a pictorial history of the village on the walls.
Q ✿ ◗ & P

White-le-Head

Highlander
Front Street (B6311)
☎ (01207) 232416
7–11; 12–2.30, 7–10.30 Sun
Belhaven 80/-; guest beers H
Popular pub in a hilltop village: a lively bar and an intimate lounge with a small dining room. Music is performed at weekends: folk, rock, jazz and blues. Note: closed lunchtime Mon–Sat.
Q ⬙ ✿ ▶ ⊟ & ▲ ♣ P ✗

Witton Gilbert

Glendenning Arms
Front Street (A691, Consett road) ☎ (0191) 371 0316
11–4, 7–11
Vaux Samson H
Very friendly staff and a relaxing atmosphere in this warm and welcoming pub which has appeared for 19 years in the *Guide*. An unspoilt local, with two comfortable rooms in traditional style. Racing memorabilia features in the bar. 🍴 Q ♣ P

Travellers Rest
Front Street (A691, Consett road) ☎ (0191) 371 0458
11–3, 6–11
McEwan 80/-; S&N Theakston Best Bitter, Newcastle Exhibition, Theakston XB, Old Peculier; Younger Scotch, No. 3; guest beer H
A good example of a contemporary village pub, with a split-level, no-smoking area. The rear conservatory is ideal for children, and pleasant in summer. A huge variety of meals is served in the bar and restaurant. Petanque pitch at the rear.
🍴 Q ⬙ ✿ ◗ ▶ ♣ P ✗

Try also: Centurion, Langley Park (Vaux)

Woodhouses

Bay Horse
Saint Helens (between Tindale Cres and Etherley)
☎ (01388) 603422
11–1.30, 7–11
John Smith's Bitter, Magnet H
Friendly village pub comprising an open-plan bar area with a large fire at one end, plus an adjoining dining area. The walls are adorned with pictures of old Auckland and LNER lines.
🍴 ✿ ◗ ▶ & ♣

Protect your pleasure — Join CAMRA (see page 528)

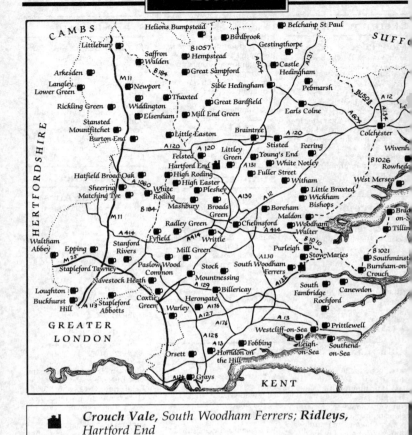

Crouch Vale, *South Woodham Ferrers;* **Ridleys,** *Hartford End*

Ardleigh

Lion
The Street (B1029)
☎ (01206) 230083
12 (11.30 Sat)–3, 7–11
Tolly Cobbold Mild, Original Ⓗ
Friendly, unpretentious village pub with many oak beams; a 400-year-old former coaching inn. On a well-served bus route. Lunches served on request. Q ✿ ♣ P

Arkesden

Axe & Compasses
2 miles N of B1038
☎ (01799) 550272
12–2.30, 6–11
Greene King IPA, Abbot Ⓗ
Superb, 17th-century traditional local with a thriving food trade: a welcoming pub in a picturesque village.
🏚 Q ✿ ◑ ▶ ♣ P

Belchamp St Paul

Cherry Tree Inn
Knowl Green OS784413
☎ (01787) 237263
12–3, 7–11; 12–11 Sat; closed Tue
Adnams Bitter; Greene King IPA; guest beer Ⓗ
Cosy, isolated, 16th-century pub, comfortably refurbished and serving good value beer and food. Good play area.
🏚 Q ✿ 🛏 ◑ ▲ ♣ P

Billericay

Coach & Horses
36 Chapel Street (near B1007)
☎ (01277) 622873
10–4, 5.30–11; 10–11 Fri, Sat & busy days
Greene King IPA, Rayments Special, Abbot; guest beer Ⓗ
Traditional, one-bar local on the site of the former Crown brewery tap, with a friendly, longstanding landlord. Good value meals (no food Sun).
🏚 ✿ ◑ 🍴 ♣ P

Birdbrook

Plough
The Street ☎ (0144 085) 336
11–2.30, 6–11
Adnams Bitter; Greene King IPA; Wells Eagle Ⓗ
Village local enjoying a friendly atmosphere. No food Sun eve. 🏚 ✿ ◑ ▶ 🍴 ♣ P

Boreham

Queens Head
Church Road ☎ (01245) 467298
10.30–2.30, 6–11
Greene King IPA, Abbot Ⓗ
Excellent, friendly, village local, in the same family for over 55 years. Good value in every way. No food Sun.
Q ✿ ◑ ♣ P

Bradwell-on-Sea

Green Man
Waterside ☎ (01621) 776226
11.30–4, 6.30–11 (11–11 summer)

K

Harwich

rdleigh A 120

Little Oakley

A 133

Walton-on-the-Naze

tlingsea Little Clacton

Great Clacton

St Osyth Heath

St Osyth

5   10 miles

5   10   15 km

Essex

Two separate, old-fashioned bars near the waterfront. Railway memorabilia features in the front bar; pub games in the back bar. Five guest ales.
🏚 Q 🔥 ❀ ▲ ♣ ⊂ P

Broads Green

Walnut Tree

1 mile W of B1008
☎ (01245) 360222
11.30–2.30, 6.30–11; 12–2.30, 7–10.30 Sun
Ridleys IPA H& G,
Witchfinder Porter G
Friendly three-bar local facing the village green: a well-furnished lounge and a public bar. The entrance is through the cosy middle snug. Essex 'Huffers' are served lunchtimes and early eve. Local CAMRA *Pub of the Year* 1993. 🏚 Q ❀ ♣ P

Buckhurst Hill

Warren Wood

Epping New Road (A104)
☎ (0181) 505 3737
11–11
Courage Best Bitter, Directors; Ruddles Best Bitter, County; guest beer H
Busy, thriving pub on the edge of Epping Forest, with a great country view at the rear and a warm, friendly atmosphere. Webster's Wonderful Wallop is brewed by Nethergate.
❀ ◑ ♿ P

Burnham-on-Crouch

Olde White Harte

The Quay ☎ (01621) 782106
11–3, 6–11; 11–11 Sat
Adnams Bitter; Tolly Cobbold Bitter H
Old riverside pub, frequented by locals and yachtsmen; it can be crowded and noisy in summer. Superb views from the jetty. 🏚 Q ❀ ⛴ ◑ ▶ P

Ostend George

16 Maldon Road, Ostend (B1010) ☎ (01621) 784552
12–3 (not Mon), 6–11
Ridleys IPA; guest beer H
Large free house on the outskirts, comprising two bars, one with a restaurant. Extensive menu; snacks at lunchtime. 🏚 ❀ ▶ ♣ P

Burton End

Ash

1 mile E of Stansted village
OS532237 ☎ (01279) 814841
11.30–2.30, 5.30–11
Greene King IPA, Rayments Special, Abbot H
15th-century pub, extended to

provide a lounge bar/dining room and a larger quarry-tiled public bar. Near the airport, but it retains a quiet, rural atmosphere. No food winter Sun. 🏚 ❀ ◑ ▶ ♣ P

Canewdon

Chequers

High Street ☎ (01702) 258251
12 (11.30 Sat)–3, 7–11
Greene King IPA, Abbot; Wadworth 6X; guest beer H
Superb, traditionally furnished inn with a snug family room. Crib and dominoes are played in this quiet village pub which is welcoming to visitors. Sun roasts recommended (book) and good bar meals served. No eve meals Sun or Mon.
🔥 ◑ ♣ P

Castle Hedingham

Bell Inn

10 St James Street (B1058)
☎ (01787) 60350
11.30–3, 6–11
Greene King IPA, Abbot G
Excellent, genuine, timbered pub with casks behind the bar. Good value food (not Mon eve, except bank hols). 🏚 Q 🔥 ❀ ◑ ▶ 🍴 ▲ ♣ P ⚥

Chelmsford

Endeavour

351 Springfield Road (A1113, 1 mile NE of centre)
☎ (01245) 257717
11–11; 12–2, 7–10.30 Sun
Greene King IPA, Abbot; guest beer (occasional) H
Quiet, three-roomed, suburban pub. The pub sign shows the sailing ship *Endeavour* on one side and the spacecraft on the other. No-smoking dining area; no eve meals Sun.
🏚 Q ◑ ▶ 🍴 ♣

Partners

30 Lower Anchor Street
☎ (01245) 265181
11–3, 5.30–11; 11–11 Sat
Crouch Vale Best Bitter; Greene King IPA; Wadworth 6X; guest beer H
Friendly, often busy, street-corner local, near the football and cricket grounds. A games room doubles (triples!) as a family/meeting room. Three guest beers, often from small breweries. 🔥 ❀ ◑ ≒ ♣ P

Red Lion

147 New London Road
☎ (01245) 354092
10.30–11
Ridleys IPA, ESX, Witchfinder Porter H
Popular, traditional, street-corner pub, with a comfortable

Ridleys IPA, ESX; Wickwar Brand Oak; guest beer H
15th-century, unspoilt riverside inn originally used by smugglers. Sit at the undertaker's table and try to solve the riddle above the superb fireplace.
🏚 Q 🔥 ❀ ⛴ ◑ ▶ 🍴 ▲ ♣ P

Braintree

Wagon & Horses

53 South Street (B1256)
☎ (01376) 553356
11–3, 5.30 (6 Sat)–11
Greene King XX Mild, IPA, Abbot H, **Winter Ale** G
Well-renovated pub with a large lounge bar, a raised dining area and a friendly snug. Booking is essential for Wed eve food.
❀ ◑ ≒ ♣ P

Brightlingsea

Railway Tavern

58 Station Road (near B1029)
☎ (01206) 302581
11–3 (not winter Mon–Thu, except bank hols), 5.30–11
Mauldons Bitter; guest beers H

105

lounge and a long, basic, public bar (prices equal).
🏾 ◖ ▶ ♣

White Horse

25 Townfield Road (near A138) ☎ (01245) 269556
11–3, 5.30 (7 Sat)–11
Courage Directors; S&N Theakston Best Bitter; John Smith's Magnet; guest beer H
Roomy, friendly, one-bar pub with a good range of games. Over 500 guest beers have been offered in the last two years (up to six at a time). CAMRA's Essex *Pub of the Year* 1992. ◖ ⇌ ♣

Colchester

British Grenadier

67 Military Road
☎ (01206) 770654
11–2.30, 6–11; 11–11 Sat
Adnams Mild, Bitter, Old; guest beer H
Popular, workingman's pub with a pool table in the back bar. Happy hour 6–7pm.
Q ⇌ (Town) ♣

Dragoon

82 Butt Road ☎ (01206) 673464
11–3 (4 Sat), 5.15 (7 Sat)–11; 11–11 Fri
Adnams Mild, Bitter; Tetley Bitter; guest beer H
Very popular pub, close to the town centre. A comfortable, quiet saloon bar contrasts with a public bar with pool and darts. Good value food (no food Sun). The beer range is always changing; five guest beers. 1994 local CAMRA *Pub of the Year*.
🏾 ◖ 🍺 ⇌ (Town) ♣

Odd One Out

28 Mersea Road (B1025)
☎ (01206) 578140
11–3 (4 Sat; not Mon–Thu), 5.30 (6 Sat)–11
Archers Best Bitter; Mauldons Bitter; Ridleys IPA; guest beer H
Formerly the Mermaid, this excellent pub has a friendly atmosphere in its comfortable lounge and basic public bars. Parking difficult. Four guest beers, one a mild; Crones cider.
🏾 Q ⇌ (Town) ◔ ✂

Rose & Crown Hotel

East Street ☎ (01206) 866677
11–2.30, 6–11
Tetley Bitter; Tolly Cobbold Original, Old Strong, Tollyshooter H
Unspoilt 15th-century hotel with low-beamed ceilings.
🏾 Q 🛏 ◖ ▶ ⇌ (Hythe) P

Siege House

75 East Street
☎ (01206) 867121
11–11

Whitbread Boddingtons Bitter, Flowers Original; Wadworth 6X; guest beers H
Revamped, 16th-century building in typical Beefeater style. The bar is separated into smaller units. Popular with the younger set at weekends. Two guest beers. ◖ ▶ P

Stockwell Arms

18 West Stockwell Street
☎ (01206) 575560
10.30–11; 10.30–3.30, 6.30–11 Sat
Marston's Pedigree; Nethergate Bitter; Ruddles Best Bitter, County; John Smith's Bitter H
Old timber-framed pub in the Dutch quarter. Popular with white-collar workers weekday lunchtimes, otherwise it is quiet.
🏾 ◖ ▶ ⇌ (Town) ♣

Tap & Spile

123 Crouch Street
☎ (01206) 573572
11–2.30, 5.30–11
Adnams Bitter; Marston's Pedigree; Mauldons Bitter; Nethergate Bitter; guest beer H
Popular pub with strong rugby connections. Five guest beers; over 600 different ales have been sold since it became a Tap & Spile. Good food.
🏾 ◖ ♣ ◔

Coxtie Green

White Horse

173 Coxtie Green Road (1 mile W of A128) OS564959
☎ (01277) 372410
11–3, 5.30–11
Beer range varies H
Cosy, friendly, country pub. The very large garden has swings, etc. Usually six ales are available, including two house beers by Tolly Cobbold. Occasional beer festivals and dog shows. No food Sun. 🏾 ◖ ▶ ♣ P

Earls Colne

Bird in Hand

Coggeshall Road (B1024)
☎ (01787) 222557
12–2.30, 6–11; 12–2.30, 7–10.30 Sun
Ridleys IPA, Mild H
Pleasant old pub with pictures in the bar showing connections with the former USAAF base nearby. 🏾 Q 🏾 ◖ 🍺 ♣ P

Castle

High Street ☎ (01787) 222694
12–11
Greene King XX Mild, IPA, Abbot H
Beamed pub with log fires. The front bar has a piano. No food Sun eve or Mon.
🏾 Q 🏾 ◖ ▶ ♣ P

Elsenham

Crown

High Street ☎ (01279) 812827
11–3, 6–11; 12–2.30, 7–10.30 Sun
Smiles Best Bitter; Tetley Bitter; guest beer H
Deservedly popular, friendly, village pub with a pargetted exterior and a good reputation for food (not served Sun). Guest beers come from independent brewers.
🏾 🏾 ◖ ▶ ♣ P

Epping

Forest Gate Inn

Theydon Road, Bell Common (near B1393) OS451011
☎ (01992) 572312
10–3, 5.30–11
Adnams Bitter, Broadside; Greene King Abbot; Ridleys IPA; guest beer H
On the edge of Epping Forest, a traditionally decorated pub with a small bar, which can be very busy. 🏾 Q 🏾 ◖ ◔ P

Feering

Sun Inn

3 Feering Hill (B1024)
☎ (01376) 570442
11–3, 6–11 (may be 11–11 Sat)
Wadworth 6X; guest beers H
Refurbished, charming, timbered pub with exposed beams and brickwork, offering a wide range of home-made food. A huge open fire and a nice garden are features. Four guest ales. 🏾 ⛺ 🏾 ◖ ▶ ♿ 🅰
⇌ (Kelvedon) ♣ ◔ P

Felsted

Chequers

Braintree Road (B1417)
☎ (01371) 820226
11–11 (11–3, 6–11 Mon–Fri, Jan–Mar)
Ridleys IPA, ESX H
Imposing Victorian pub next to a public school. Two bars, with a strong sports theme in the convivial saloon. In the same family for 39 years, it offers good value pub grub and summer barbecues. Smart meeting/children's room.
🏾 Q ⛺ 🏾 ◖ ▶ 🍺 P

Fobbing

White Lion

Lion Hill (B1420, 1 mile S of Five Bells interchange on A13)
☎ (01375) 673281
11–2.30 (4 Sat), 5 (6.30 Sat)–11
Ind Coope Burton Ale; Taylor Walker Best Bitter; Tetley Bitter; guest beer (occasional) H
Traditional coaching inn which feels like a country pub,

despite the proximity of Basildon, and enjoys a pleasant position on the brow of a hill. Unspoilt and friendly. No food Sun, or Sat eve.
🏴 Q ◖ ● P

Fuller Street

Square & Compasses

1½ miles E of A131 OS748161
☎ (01245) 361477
11–3, 6–11
Ridleys IPA H
Welcoming country pub with good food, known locally as the 'Stoke Hole'. Note the unusual 'Pitch-Penny' stool in the public bar. First Fri of each month is folk night. No eve meals Thu or Sun.
🏴 Q ✿ ◖ ▲ ♣ P

Fyfield

Queens Head

Queen Street (by B184)
☎ (01277) 899231
11–3, 6–11; 11–11 Sat
Adnams Bitter; Greene King IPA; Wells Bombardier; Whitbread Boddingtons Bitter; guest beer H
Friendly village pub, popular with all ages: one bar with alcoves. A regularly changing guest beer is served. No meals Sat eve. 🏴 ◖ ● P

Gestingthorpe

Pheasant

Audley End ☎ (01787) 61196
11–3, 6–11
Adnams Bitter, Broadside; Greene King IPA H; **Nethergate Bitter** G; **guest beer** G/ H
Multi-roomed pub which is the focal point of the village. Good food includes an extensive vegetarian menu (book weekends).
🏴 ⛺ ✿ ◖ ▲ ♣ ⌂ P

Grays

Theobald Arms

141 Argent Street (near A126)
☎ (01375) 372253
10.30–3, 5.30–11; 10.30–11 Fri & Sat
Courage Best Bitter, Directors H
Two-bar pub near the yacht club, with a pleasant interior. A hexagonal pool table is an unusual feature. A good range of food is served—not Sun.
✿ ◖ ● ⛁ ♿ ⇌ ♣ P

Great Bardfield

Vine

Vine Street ☎ (01371) 810355
11–3, 6–11
Ridleys IPA, Mild, Witchfinder Porter H

Friendly family pub in an historic and beautiful village. Good value food is served in large portions. Play area for children. ✿ ◖ ● ⛁ ♣ P

Great Clacton

Robin Hood

211 London Road (A133)
☎ (01255) 421519
11–11 (11–3, 5.30–11 winter)
Adnams Bitter *or* **Fuller's London Pride; Bass Charrington IPA, Draught Bass** H
Spacious, low-ceilinged and comfortable pub, with an imaginative menu, on the edge of Clacton-on-Sea.
🏴 Q ◖ ● ♿ P ⚲

Great Sampford

Red Lion Inn

Finchingfield Road (B1053)
☎ (01799) 586325
12–3, 5.30–11
Ridleys IPA, ESX, Witchfinder Porter (winter) H
Pleasant local with a varied menu in the bar. The dining room is used for 'theme food' eves. 🏴 ✿ ⛺ ◖ ♣ P

Harwich

Alma Inn

25 Kings Head Street
☎ (01255) 503474
11–3 (extends if busy), 7 (6 Fri)–11
Greene King IPA; Tolly Cobbold Mild; guest beer H
One large bar with a tiny private bar alongside in a pub built in Elizabethan times and refronted by the Georgians. Live trad jazz monthly.
🏴 Q ✿ ◖ ⇌ (Town) ♣

Hanover Inn

65 Church Street
☎ (01255) 502927
10.30–3 (extends busy Sats), 6.30–11
Tolly Cobbold Mild, Old Strong H
Cosy, timbered fisherman's pub with Admiralty charts in the front bar. Pool and darts are played in the back bar. Two other Tolly beers are usually available, including a house beer, Harwich Bitter.
🏴 ⛁ ⇌ (Town) ♣

Hatfield Broad Oak

Cock

High Street ☎ (01279) 718273
12–3, 5.30–11
Adnams Bitter, Broadside; guest beer H
Friendly village local with bare floorboards, a large collection of pictures and ancient beams. Handpainted 16th-century walls feature in the board-

room. The imaginative food menu often has a theme.
🏴 Q ⛺ ✿ ◖ ♣ P ⚲

Helions Bumpstead

Three Horseshoes

Water Lane OS650414
☎ (01440) 730298
11.45–2.30, 7–11; 12–2, 7–10.30 Sun
Greene King IPA, Abbot H
Fine, friendly, remote old pub, offering good value food (not served Mon/Tue eves or Sun). Award-winning gardens.
🏴 Q ✿ ◖ ● ⛁ ▲ ♣ P

Hempstead

Bluebell

High Street ☎ (01799) 599486
11.30–3, 6.30–11
Greene King IPA, Rayments Special; guest beer H
Excellent, welcoming, 16th-century, listed building in a delightful village. The dining area offers a comprehensive range of good value food. The birthplace of Dick Turpin.
🏴 Q ⛺ ✿ ◖ ♣ P

Herongate

Olde Dog

Billericay Road (1 mile E of A128) OS641910
☎ (01277) 810337
11.30–2.30, 6–11
Adnams Extra; Greene King IPA, Abbot; Ridleys IPA, ESX H; **guest beer** H/ G
Attractive, timber-beamed pub, with several distinct drinking areas; largely unspoilt. Various Mauldons and Crouch Vale guest beers are offered. No food Sun eve.
🏴 ⛺ ✿ ◖ ● P

High Easter

Cock & Bell

The Street ☎ (01245) 231296
12–2.30, 7–11
Bateman Valiant; Ruddles County; guest beers H
14th-century Grade II-listed building, steeped in history.
🏴 Q ✿ ◖ ● P

High Roding

Black Lion

The Street ☎ (01279) 872847
10.30–3, 6–11
Ridleys IPA, ESX H
15th-century pub with a timber-framed interior. No jukebox or games machines intrude. The landlord's garden at the rear supplies most of the vegetables for his renowned cooking. 🏴 Q ✿ ◖ ● ♣ P

Essex

Horndon on the Hill

Bell
High Road ☎ (01375) 672451
11–2.30 (3 Sat), 6–11
Bass Charrington IPA, Draught Bass H
Popular, 15th-century coaching inn in a picturesque village with a 94-year old hot cross bun collection! Quality food is served in the pub and restaurant. Good views from the patio. ♨ Q ☀ 🛏 ◁ ▶ P

Langley Lower Green

Bull
☎ (01279) 777307
12–2.30, 6–11
Adnams Bitter, Broadside; Greene King IPA; guest beer H
Classic pub in a very small village, with a local clientele. A pitch-penny game is concealed under a bench in the saloon bar. ♨ Q ☀ ♣ P

Lawford

Manningtree Station Buffet
Station Road ☎ (01206) 391114
10.30–11
Adnams Bitter, Extra; Exmoor Gold; Marston's Pedigree; St Austell HSD H
Excellent station buffet in a listed Victorian building. Superb food is available, especially Sun lunch (book). Tiny dining room and a small patio. ☀ ◁ ▶ ⇌ P

Leigh-on-Sea

Crooked Billet
51 High Street, Old Leigh
☎ (01702) 714854
11.30–3, 6–11 (11–11 summer)
Adnams Bitter; Ind Coope Burton Ale; Taylor Walker Best Bitter; Tetley Bitter; Wadworth 6X; Young's Bitter; guest beers H
16th-century listed pub, once frequented by smugglers and now a Taylor Walker Heritage pub. Superb views of the estuary. No food Sun. Six guest beers.
♨ Q ☀ ◁ 🚃 ⇌ ♣

Little Braxted

Green Man
Green Man Lane (1½ miles SE of village) ☎ (01621) 891659
11.30–3, 6–11
Ridleys IPA, ESX, Winter Ale H

Traditional village pub in an idyllic setting, with a pleasant garden. ♨ Q ☀ 🛏 ◁ ▶ 🚃 ♣ P

Littlebury

Queens Head Inn
High Street ☎ (01799) 522251
12–11
Bass Worthington BB; Courage Directors; John Smith's Bitter; guest beer H
600-year-old village local with traditional features and good accommodation. Regular guest beers feature micro breweries and Marston's Head Brewer's Choice; Easter beer festival. Excellent value food.
♨ Q ☎ ☀ 🛏 ◁ ▶ ♣ P

Little Clacton

Apple Tree
The Street ☎ (01255) 861026
11–11
Draught Bass; Courage Directors; Crouch Vale Woodham IPA; Nethergate Old Growler; S&N Theakston Old Peculier; guest beers H
Probably the real ale oasis of Clacton: four regular beers and up to four guests. It also makes an effort in the live music department (late licence). Q ☀ ◁ P

Little Easton

Stag
Duck Street (1 mile W of B184)
☎ (01371) 870214
11–2.30 (extends if busy), 6–11
Ridleys IPA H
Friendly village pub with plain wooden tables and benches in the public bar, contrasting with a refurbished, extended and comfortable saloon (no price difference). Fine views from the large garden. ♨ ☀ ◁ ▶ ▲ ♣ P

Little Oakley

Olde Cherry Tree
Clacton Road (B1414)
☎ (01255) 880333
11–2.30, 7–11
Adnams Bitter, Broadside H
Comfortable old pub with a central log fire; a meeting place for many local groups. Eve meals Sat or by arrangement weekdays.
♨ Q ☀ ◁ ▶ ♣ P

Littley Green

Compasses
OS699172 ☎ (01245) 362308
11–3, 6–11
Ridleys IPA, Mild, ESX, Witchfinder Porter, Winter Ale G

Victorian cottage-style pub, Ridleys brewery tap. Difficult to find but well worth the effort. Local CAMRA *Pub of the Year* three times.
♨ Q ☀ ⚓ P

Loughton

Last Post
227 High Road (A121)
☎ (0181) 532 0751
11–11
Courage Directors; Wadworth 6X; Younger Scotch; guest beer H
Standard Wetherspoon decor features in this converted former Post Office. Beer festivals are held around St George's Day and Guy Fawkes' Night.
☀ ◁ ▶ ⚓ ⊖

Maldon

Jolly Sailor
Church Street, The Hythe
☎ (01621) 853463
11–3, 6–11
Courage Directors; Morland Old Speckled Hen; Ruddles Best Bitter H
Traditional quayside pub in a superb position overlooking the Blackwater Estuary, offering fine views of Thames barges. Near Promenade Park.
☀ 🛏 ◁ ▶ P

Queen's Head
The Hythe ☎ (01621) 854112
10.30–11
Greene King IPA, Abbot H
Unspoilt, three-bar pub with a strong nautical atmosphere, overlooking the estuary.
♨ Q ☀ 🚃 ♣ P

White Horse
High Street ☎ (01621) 851708
10.30–3, 5.30–11
Courage Best Bitter; Tolly Cobbold Old Strong, Tollyshooter; Wadworth 6X; guest beers H
Modernised, 16th-century coaching house which specialises in guest beers and holds occasional real ale festivals. A single long bar.
◁ ▶ ♣ ⊖

Mashbury

Fox
Fox Road OS650127
☎ (01245) 231573
11–2.30 (not Mon or Tue), 6.30–11
Ridleys IPA, ESX G
350-year-old, cottage-style pub in a quiet rural area with a friendly atmosphere and a good value menu (not served Mon lunch or Tue). Folk music first Sun of the month. Worth finding. ♨ Q ☀ ◁ ▶ ▲ P

Matching Tye

Fox
The Green ☎ (01279) 731335
12–3, 6–11
Draught Bass; Fuller's London Pride; Greene King IPA; guest beer H
Old village pub with three rooms and foxy artefacts. Petanque in the large garden. Camping by arrangement.
⌂ ❀ ◖ ◗ ▲ ♣ P

Mill End Green

Green Man
E of B184 OS619260
☎ (01371) 870286
11.30–3, 6–11
Adnams Bitter; Greene King IPA; Ridleys IPA H
Very pleasant, 15th-century country pub with oak studwork and excellent gardens. Separate outdoor drinking area for families. No food Sun eve.
⌂ Q ❀ ⛟ ◖ ◗ ▲ ♣ P

Mill Green

Viper
Mill Green Road (2 miles NW of Ingatestone) OS641019
☎ (01277) 352010
11–2.30 (3 Sat), 6–11
Beer range varies H
Unspoilt country pub in a picturesque woodland setting, popular with walkers. The range of three beers changes monthly. No price difference between the three bars.
⌂ Q ❀ ◖ ♣ P

Mountnessing

Prince of Wales
199 Roman Road (B1002)
☎ (01277) 353445
11–3, 6–11 (11–11 some summer Sats)
Ridleys IPA, Mild, ESX H**, Witchfinder Porter** (occasional)**, Winter Ale** G
Old, timber-beamed roadside pub with two distinct drinking areas. An imaginative menu includes children's portions. Mentioned in the *Domesday Book*. ⌂ ❀ ◖ ◗ ♣ P

Navestock Heath

Plough Inn
Sabines Road OS538970
☎ (01277) 372296
11–3.30, 6–11
Brains Dark; Cotleigh Tawny; Taylor Landlord; guest beers H
Superb pub with a friendly atmosphere offering 11 ales, always including a mild. It hosts trad jazz on alternate Sun eves and occasional quiz nights. Local CAMRA *Pub of the Year* for the last three years. Good value beer and food.
⌂ ⛟ ❀ ◖ ◗ ♿ ♣ ⌓ P

Newport

Coach & Horses
Cambridge Road (B1383)
☎ (01799) 540292
11–3, 6–11
Tolly Cobbold Original; Whitbread Flowers IPA, Original; guest beer H
Warm and welcoming, 16th-century coaching inn offering excellent restaurant and bar food.
⌂ Q ❀ ◖ ◗ ▲ ⇌ ♣ P ⚟

Orsett

Foxhound
High Road ☎ (01375) 891295
11–3.30, 6–11; 11–11 Sat
Courage Best Bitter, Directors; Crouch Vale Woodham IPA H
Classic, unchanging local. The saloon has lots of foxhound memorabilia and fox hounds patterns in the carpet; basic public bar. Charity quiz nights. Book eve meals.
⌂ Q ❀ ◖ ◗ ⊞ ♣ P

Paslow Wood Common

Black Horse
Stondon Road OS588017
☎ (01277) 821915
11.30–3.30, 6–11
Adnams Bitter; Bateman XB; Fuller's ESB; Greene King IPA; Morland Old Speckled Hen; Wadworth 6X; guest beer (occasional) H
Country pub which organises events, particularly in summer. ⌂ ❀ ◖ ◗ ▲ ♣ P

Pebmarsh

Kings Head
The Street ☎ (01787) 269306
11–3, 7–11
Whitbread Boddingtons Bitter; Greene King IPA; Nethergate Bitter; Sarah Hughes Ruby Mild; guest beers H
A high turnover of beers gives a good selection in this spacious local-type bar with a high, beamed ceiling. Pool in the public bar. Occasional cider. ⛟ ❀ ◖ ◗ ♿ ▲ ♣ ⌓

Pleshey

White Horse
The Street ☎ (01245) 237281
11–3, 7–11
Beer range varies H
Pleasant old timber-framed pub in an historic village, with a number of areas, though space is limited for those just drinking. Families welcome.
⌂ Q ❀ ◖ ◗ ▲ P

Prittlewell

Spread Eagle
267 Victoria Avenue (A127)
☎ (01702) 348383
11.30–11
Bass Charrington IPA, Worthington BB; Hancock's HB; guest beer H
Two-bar local, offering darts and pool, plus live music Fri and bank hol beer festivals. Close to Southend FC.
❀ ⇌ ♣

Purleigh

Bell
The Street (near B1010)
☎ (01621) 828348
11–3, 6–11
Adnams Bitter; Greene King IPA; Ind Coope Benskins Best Bitter; guest beer H
Old, traditional country pub, very spacious, comfortable, and popular for food. Beautiful views. Local CAMRA *Pub of the Year 1993*.
⌂ Q ◖ ◗ ♣ P

Radley Green

Thatchers Arms
½ mile N of A414 OS622054
☎ (01245) 248356
12–2.30, 6–11
Ridleys IPA, ESX, Witchfinder Porter H
Secluded, friendly, one-bar local with a large caravan and camping area. Snacks only Sun lunch. ⌂ Q ❀ ◖ ◗ ▲ ♣ P

Rickling Green

Cricketers' Arms
½ mile W of B1383
☎ (0179 988) 322
11–3, 6–11
Whitbread Flowers IPA; guest beer G
Enlarged pub in an idyllic setting overlooking the cricket green. Guest beers always include a mild or dark beer and a strong ale. Excellent and imaginative food (restaurant open 12–7 on Sun).
⌂ ⛟ ❀ ⛟ ◖ ◗ ♣ P

Rochford

Golden Lion
35 North Street
☎ (01702) 545487
12–11 (may close 3–5 if quiet)
Fuller's London Pride; Greene King IPA, Abbot; guest beers H
300-year-old ex-tailor's shop; a compact, often-crowded free house with a variety of guest

Essex

beers, including mild. Local
CAMRA *Pub of the Year*
awards are displayed.
🍴 🍺 ⇌ ♣ ⌣

Milestone
Union Lane (near B1013)
☎ (01702) 544229
10–11
**Greene King IPA, Abbot;
guest beer** H
Good recent pub conversion in
traditional style, with darts
and pool in the upstairs games
room. Hidden away in a
cul-de-sac. ⛭ 🍴 ⇌ ♣

Rowhedge

Walnut Tree
Fingringhoe Road
☎ (01206) 728149
7–11; 12–3, 7–11 Sat
**Brakspear Special; Hall &
Woodhouse Hard Tackle;
Smiles Bitter; Tolly Cobbold
Old Strong** H
Lively, rural pub on the
outskirts of Colchester,
featuring a rock jukebox. The
beer range varies, but one beer
is always sold cheaply. Join
the 'Cheese Club' on Fri eve
from 9pm. 🍴 🍺 ♣ P

Saffron Walden

Gate
74 Thaxted Road (B184)
☎ (01799) 522321
11–3, 6–11 (11–11 summer)
**Greene King XX Mild, IPA,
Rayments Special, Abbot** H
Busy, friendly local with an
excellent outside play area for
children. Petanque played;
keen darts following. Good
value food.
🍴 ⛭ 🍺 🍴 ♣ P

St Osyth

White Hart
71 Mill Street
☎ (01255) 820318
12–3, 7–11
Adnams Bitter; guest beer H
Friendly, family-run pub with
a commitment to guest beers
(changed weekly). The family
room has animals.
🍴 Q 🍺 🍴 ♣ P

St Osyth Heath

Beehive
Heath Road OS139185
☎ (01255) 830396
11–3, 7–11
**Adnams Bitter; Greene King
IPA; Tetley Bitter** H
Pub built in 1993 on the site of
the original Beehive. The
open-plan lounge around the
central bar has a period feel.
Meals planned.
🍴 Q 🍺 ⛭ 🍴 ♣ P

Sheering

Crown
The Street ☎ (0127 989) 203
11–3.30, 5–11; 11–11 Sat
**Adnams Mild, Bitter; Courage
Best Bitter** H
Well-laid-out bar with settees
as well as tables and chairs.
The spacious restaurant serves
good value food. ⛭ 🍴 ♦ P

Sible Hedingham

Sugar Loaves
175 Swan Street (A4064)
☎ (01787) 462720
11.30–11
Greene King IPA H;
Mauldons White Adder G;
**Whitbread Boddingtons
Bitter, Flowers IPA** H
15th-century, oak-beamed inn,
recently restored; a friendly
local with two bars, regular
music quizzes and live music
fortnightly. Thai food is a
speciality. Sun lunch is served,
but no eve meals Sun/Mon.
🍴 ⛭ 🍴 ▲ ♣ P

Southend-on-Sea

Baker's Bar
15–17 Alexandra Street
☎ (01702) 390403
12–midnight (1am Fri & Sat)
**Courage Directors; Ridleys
IPA** H; **Shepherd Neame
Bishops Finger; Tolly Cobbold
Original; Woodforde's Norfolk
Nog** G; **guest beers**
Lively, late night underground
bar, housed in a Victorian
baker's cellar. It offers a very
good range, but ales served on
gravity can be pricey
(reductions Tue nights). The
authentic interior boasts many
original fittings. ⛭ 🍴 ♦
⇌ (Central) ⌣ P

Cork & Cheese
363 Chartwell Square, Victoria
Circus ☎ (01702) 616914
11–11; closed Sun
Beer range varies H
Pub serving a constantly-
changing range of beers from
independent breweries. Much
improved, it offers about 200
beers annually—hence local
CAMRA *Pub of the Year* 1995.
The Cork & Cheese Bitter
comes from Tolly Cobbold.
🍴 ⇌ (Victoria/Central)
♣ ⌣

Falcon Hotel
45 Marine Parade (B1016)
☎ (01702) 466302
11–11 (11–3, 5–11 winter)
**Ridleys IPA, ESX,
Witchfinder Porter** (winter) H
Ridleys' Southend outpost, as
close to the sea as you will get.
⛭ 🍴 🍴 ⇌ (Central) ♣

Liberty Belle
10–12 Marine Parade (B1016)
☎ (01702) 466936
10–11
**Courage Best Bitter,
Directors; Ruddles County;
guest beer** H
Situated on the 'Golden Mile',
close to the pier, this frequent
Guide entry provides a
welcome contrast to the disco
pubs nearby. Large regular
trade; pool and darts at the rear.
🍴 ⛭ 🍴 ⇌ (Central) ♣

Railway Hotel
Clifftown Road
☎ (01702) 343194
12–11
**Bass Worthington BB,
Draught Bass; Fuller's
London Pride; Greene King
IPA** H
Pub convenient for the town
centre and High Street. No
food Sun. Function room.
🍴 ⇌ (Central/Victoria)

South Fambridge

Anchor Hotel
Fambridge Road
☎ (01702) 203535
11–3, 6–11; 11–11 Sat
**Crouch Vale Woodham IPA;
Greene King Abbot; Tetley
Bitter; guest beer** H
Traditional free house near the
River Crouch, offering regular
guest beers and a range of
food at reasonable prices.
Separate bar for pool and
darts. No eve meals Sun/Mon;
cider in summer.
⛭ 🍴 🍴 ♣ ⌣ P

Southminster

Station Arms
39 Station Road (near B1020/
B1021) ☎ (01621) 772225
12–3, 5.30–11; 11–11 Sat
**Crouch Vale Best Bitter; guest
beer** H
Weatherboarded High Street
pub and restaurant where
good beer and conversation
are the most important
features. Regular beer festivals
are held in the pub yard. Local
CAMRA *Pub of the Year* 1992.
No eve meals Wed or Sun.
🍴 Q 🍺 ⛭ 🍴 ⇌ ♣ ⌣

South Woodham Ferrers

Curlew
80 Gandalf's Ride
☎ (01245) 321371
12–3, 6–11; 12–11 Sat
**Shepherd Neame Master
Brew Bitter, Spitfire, Bishops
Finger; guest beer** H
Friendly, modern estate pub
with a lively atmosphere.
Convenient for Marsh Farm
Country Park. 🍴 ♦ P

Stanford Rivers

Drill House
Toot Hill Road (near Greensted) OS532025
☎ (01277) 362298
11–3, 6–11
Courage Best Bitter; Crouch Vale Best Bitter; guest beer H
Large country pub. Regular barbecues are held on summer eves, and the large garden and paddock has ponies, etc. to interest the kids. Unusual guest beers from small breweries. No meals Mon eve, otherwise a good choice.
Q ✿ ◑ ♣ P

Stansted Mountfitchet

Dog & Duck
Lower Street (B1351)
☎ (01279) 812047
10–2.30, 5.30 (6 Sat)–11
Greene King IPA, Rayments Special, Abbot H
Typical Essex timbered village local, offering a genuinely friendly welcome. Snacks Mon–Sat lunch.
Q ✿ ⊟ ⇌ ♣

Stapleford Abbotts

Rabbits
Stapleford Road (B175)
☎ (01708) 688203
11–2.30 (3 Fri & Sat), 6–11
Adnams Bitter; Ind Coope Benskins Best Bitter, Burton Ale; Tetley Bitter H
Friendly local with a children's play area in the garden. A good range of home-cooked food is served (no meals Sun eve). ⚓ Q ✿ ◑ ▶ P

Stapleford Tawney

Moletrap
Tawney Common, Theydon Mount (left 1 mile W of Toot Hill village) OS501014
☎ (01992) 522394
12 (11 summer)–2.30 (3 summer), 7 (6 summer)–11
McMullen AK, Country; guest beer (summer) H
400-year-old free house, converted from two cottages and named by the inventor of an unusual mole trap who bought it. Very much a local, hard to find—you'll need the OS map! Q ✿ ◑ P

Stisted

Dolphin
Coggeshall Road (A120)
☎ (01376) 321143
11–3, 6–11
Ridleys IPA, ESX G

Traditional beamed pub with two bars, one retaining a public bar atmosphere. Well-run, it offers good value beer and food (no eve meals Tue or Sun). ⚓ ✿ ◑ ▶ P

Onley Arms
The Street (1 mile N of A120)
☎ (01376) 325204
11–3 (extends if busy), 7–11
Ridleys IPA, ESX, Witchfinder Porter H
Cosy, one-bar, rural village pub, built in 1853. A petanque league is held Wed eve in summer. All food is home-cooked; the dining room is open Wed–Sat. Meals are served in the bar at other times. ⚓ Q ✿ ◑ ♣ P

Stock

Bear
16 The Square (near B1007)
☎ (01277) 840232
11.30–3, 6–11
Adnams Bitter; Ind Coope Friary Meux Best Bitter; Tetley Bitter; guest beer H
Popular, 14th-century, snug, two-bar pub and restaurant, offering an excellent range of local food and ample seating in the bar areas.
Q ✍ ◑ ◑ P

Hoop
High Street ☎ (01277) 841137
10–11
Adnams Bitter H; **Brains SA; Courage Best Bitter** G; **Greene King Abbot** H; **Wadworth 6X** G; **Whitbread Boddingtons Bitter** H; **guest beers** G
Very popular small bar, holding an annual beer festival in May. A good range of well-priced hot food is always available as well as usually at least six guest ales, and off-sales in polypins. Large garden. Q ✿ ◑ ▶ & ♣ ⌂

Stow Maries

Prince of Wales
Woodham Road OS830993
☎ (01621) 828971
11–11
Beer range varies H
Beautifully restored and extended rural gem, with a working Victorian bakery and a changing range of esoteric ales (including mild). It is the 'Big Ears' beer agency flagship and CAMRA's East Anglian *Pub of the Year* 1994. Folk night first Mon in the month.
⚓ Q ✍ ✿ ◑ ▲ ♣ ⌂ P

Thaxted

Rose & Crown Inn
31 Mill End (near B184)
☎ (01371) 831152

11 (12 winter)–2.30, 6–11
Ridleys IPA, ESX, Witchfinder Porter; guest beer H
Friendly, well-run local in an historic town with a magnificent church, Guildhall and windmill. It is believed to have been built on the site of a monks' hostelry. The cosy dining area offers excellent, home-cooked food.
✿ ⚓ ▶ ⊟ ▲ ♣ P

Star
Mill End (B184)
☎ (01371) 830368
11–3 (may vary), 5.30–11 (11–11 summer)
Adnams Mild, Bitter, Broadside; guest beer H
Popular local with a keen darts following. Exposed beams and vast brick fireplaces feature and there is a safe play area for children. Good value food.
⚓ ✿ ◑ ♣ P

Tillingham

Cap & Feathers
8 South Street (B1021)
☎ (01621) 779212
11.30–3, 6–11
Crouch Vale Woodham IPA, Best Bitter, Essex Porter, Willie Warmer (winter); **guest beer** H
Unspoilt 15th-century inn with a smoke house for fish and meat. Crouch Vale's only tied house; their other beers are sometimes available. Home-made food; traditional pub games. CAMRA national *Pub of the Year* 1989. ⚓ Q ✍ ✿ ⚓ ◑ ♣ ⌂ P ⊬

Waltham Abbey

Crown
4 Romeland (near A121)
☎ (01992) 701481
10 (11 Sat)–2.30 (3.30 Sat), 6–11
McMullen AK, Country H
Friendly local near the abbey at the town centre.
✿ ◑ ♣

Walton-on-the-Naze

Royal Marine
3 Old Pier Street (near B1034)
☎ (01255) 674000
11–11
Adnams Bitter, Broadside; Marston's Pedigree; Morland Old Speckled Hen; Whitbread Boddingtons Bitter E / G
This pleasant drinking pub has strong links with the RNLI. Note the unusual beer dispense—the casks are kept in an upstairs cellar.
⚓ Q & ⇌

Essex

Warley

Brave Nelson
138 Woodman Road (off B186)
☎ (01277) 211690
12–3, 5.30–11; 12–11 Sat
**Courage Directors;
Nethergate Bitter; Ruddles
Best Bitter; Webster's
Yorkshire Bitter** H
Comfortable, pleasant local
with wood panelling in both
bar areas and many nautical
pictures. A rare outlet for
Nethergate in this area. No
food Sun. ▲ ✿ ◐ P

Westcliff-on-Sea

Cricketers
228 London Road (A13)
☎ (01702) 343168
11–11
**Greene King IPA, Abbot;
guest beer** H
Large, three-bar local in which
the Sportsman's Bar (not open
weekday lunch) boasts three
dartboards, a pool table and a
huge TV set. Food is served in
generous portions.
◐ ♿ ♣ P

Palace Theatre Centre
430 London Road (A13)
☎ (01702) 347816
12–2.30, 6–11; 12–2.30, 7–10.30 Sun
**Courage Directors; Greene
King IPA; John Smith's
Bitter; guest beers** H
There's free, live music Sun
lunch and eve in this
comfortable theatre foyer bar.
✿ ♿ ⇌ ¼

West Mersea

Fountain Hotel
6 Queens Corner (B1025)
☎ (01206) 382080
11–3 (4 Sat), 6 (7 Sat)–11
**Greene King IPA; Mauldons
Suffolk Punch; Ruddles Best
Bitter; Tolly Cobbold Bitter;
guest beer** H
Large, friendly pub on Mersea
Island, an area popular for
watersports. The guest beer
comes from local breweries.
✿ ➤ ◐ ♿ ♣ P

White Notley

Cross Keys
1 The Street ☎ (01376) 583297
11–3, 6.30 (7 Sat)–11
Ridleys IPA, Mild, ESX H
Unspoilt, 14th-century village
local, formerly belonging to
Chappells Brewery. A public
bar and a cosy saloon are
complemented by a restaurant
area (rolls only Tue lunch; eve
bar meals Fri and Sat).
▲ ✿ ◐ ⇌ ♣ P

White Roding

Black Horse
Chelmsford Road (A1060)
☎ (01279) 876322
11.30–3, 6–11
**Ridleys IPA, ESX,
Witchfinder Porter** (winter) H
Former multi-purpose village
building which gradually
turned into a pub and is
reputedly haunted.
▲ Q ✿ ◐ ▲ ♣ P

Wickham Bishops

Mitre
2 The Street ☎ (01621) 891378
11–3, 5.30–11; 11–11 Sat
Ridleys IPA, Mild, ESX H
Lively village local with a
busy restaurant. The public
bar has been refurbished.
▲ Q ✿ ◐ ⊟ ♣ P

Widdington

Fleur de Lys
High Street ☎ (01799) 540659
11–3, 6–11
**Adnams Bitter; Draught Bass;
Wadworth IPA, 6X;
Whitbread Flowers Original;
guest beer** H
Friendly, well-run village
local, offering a good choice of
ales and an extensive range of
good value, home-cooked
dishes. Live folk music Fri eve.
Comfortable family room.
▲ Q ⛻ ✿ ◐ ♿ ▲ ♣ P

Witham

George
36 Newland Street (B1389/
B1018) ☎ (01376) 511098
10–2.30, 5.30–11; 10–11 Fri & Sat
**Ridleys IPA, Mild, ESX,
Witchfinder Porter, Winter
Ale** H
Good value, welcoming, town
pub with a public bar and a
quiet, comfortable saloon.
Occasional special offers on
beer. Limited parking.
Q ⛻ ◐ ⇌ ♣ P

Victoria
Faulkbourne Road, Powers
Hall End ☎ (01376) 511809
11–3 (3.30 Sat), 6–11
**Ridleys IPA, ESX,
Witchfinder Porter** G
Spacious, renovated country
house on the edge of town: a
large locals' public bar and a
comfortable lounge. Regular
eve events. No food Sun.
▲ ⛻ ✿ ◐ ⊟ ♣ P

Wivenhoe

Black Buoy
Black Buoy Hill (near B1028)
☎ (01206) 822425
11–2.30 (3 Sat), 6–11
**Tolly Cobbold Bitter, Old
Strong; Whitbread Flowers
Original; guest beer** H
Pub in Old Wivenhoe, used by
the boating fraternity and
students. Framed drawings
and cartoons adorn the walls.
▲ Q ✿ ◐ ▶ ⇌ P

Flag Inn
Colchester Road (B1028)
☎ (01206) 822830
11–3, 6–11
**Bass Charrington IPA,
Draught Bass; Courage Best
Bitter; Marston's Pedigree;
John Smith's Bitter;
Wadworth 6X** H
Beamed local on the northern
edge of town, with a smart-
casual lounge bar. A small
beer festival is held each year.
✿ ➤ ◐ ▶ ⊟ ♿ P

Horse & Groom
53–55 The Cross (B1028)
☎ (01206) 824928
10.30–3, 5.30 (6 Sat)–11
Adnams Mild, Bitter, Old H
Popular, two-bar local, with a
strong darts following. Beer
prices are the same in both
bars. Q ✿ ◐ ♣ P

Woodham Walter

Bell
The Street
☎ (01245) 223437
12–3, 6.30 (7 Sat)–11
**Adnams Bitter; Ind Coope
Benskins Best Bitter;
Wadworth 6X; guest beer** H
Lovely, 16th-century, timber-
framed coaching inn, in a
pleasant village setting.
▲ Q ⛻ ✿ ◐ ▶ P

Writtle

Wheatsheaf
70 The Green (A122)
☎ (01245) 420695
11–2.30 (3 Fri, 4 Sat), 5.30–11
**Courage Directors; Greene
King IPA, Abbot; Ridleys
Mild** G
Small, cottage-style, friendly
local, retaining a public bar
and a saloon.
Q ✿ ◐ ♣ P

Young's End

Green Dragon
Upper London Road (A131)
☎ (01245) 361030
11–3, 6–11
Greene King IPA, Abbot H
Pub retaining its original
public bar, but the modernised
lounge has been extended to
form a restaurant area (well-
deserved reputation). Spacious
outdoor play area for children.
Q ✿ ◐ ▶ ♣ P

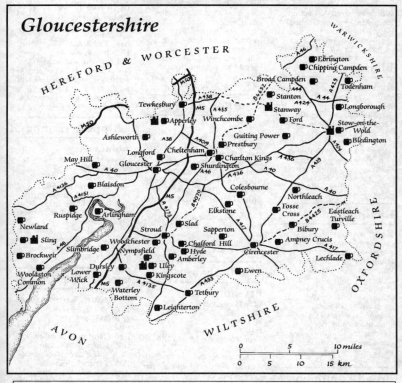

Gloucestershire

Donnington, *Stow-on-the-Wold*; **Farmers Arms**, *Apperley*; **Freeminer**, *Sling*; **Stanway**, *Stanway*; **Uley**, *Uley*

Amberley

Black Horse
At N end of village
☎ (01453) 872556
12–3, 6–11; 11–11 Sat
Archers Best Bitter; Hook Norton Best Bitter; Tetley Bitter; guest beer Ⓗ
Lively local in a village in the middle of Minchinhampton Common, with a conservatory-style extension. Lunches at weekends and bank hols only.
🏨 Q ❀ 🐾 ◑ ▸ Ⅰ ♣ ⚲

Ampney Crucis

Crown of Crucis
On A417 ☎ (01285) 851806
11–11
Archers Village; Ruddles County; S&N Theakston Best Bitter Ⓗ
Attractive country hotel with a very popular separate bar and restaurant. Excellent food in both areas, though the bar can get very crowded. Riverside garden. Families welcome.
🏨 ❀ 🛏 ◑ ▸ ⚲ P

Apperley

Coal House Inn
Gabb Lane (off B4213)
☎ (01452) 780211
11–2.30, 6–11
Draught Bass; Smiles Best Bitter; Wadworth 6X; guest beer Ⓗ
Originally a coal wharf, now a welcoming local on the banks of the Severn, half a mile from the village centre. The road is liable to flooding in winter. Mooring for rivercraft.
🏨 ❀ ◑ ▸ 🍴 Ⅰ & Ⅰ ♣ P

Arlingham

Red Lion
The Cross ☎ (01452) 740269
12–3, 7–11; 11–11 Sat
Draught Bass; Hook Norton Best Bitter; John Smith's Bitter; Uley Bitter; guest beer Ⓗ
Large, two-bar village pub, partly 16th century. Horse brasses and false beams in the lounge; parquet flooring in the public bar. Cider in summer.
🏨 ❀ ◑ ▸ Ⅰ ▲ ♣ ⟲ P

Ashleworth

Boat Inn
The Quay (beyond the tithe barn on the road to 'The Quay') ☎ (01452) 700272
11–2.30, 6–11
Arkell's 3B; Oakhill Yeoman; Smiles Best Bitter; guest beer Ⓖ
Delightful old pub beside the Severn owned by the same family for over 400 years. The interior has hardly changed in a century. Lunchtime snacks. Quoits played. Q ❀ ♣ ⟲ P

Bibury

Catherine Wheel
Arlington (B4425)
☎ (01285) 740250
11–11 (11–2.30, 6–11 Nov–Mar)

Gloucestershire

Courage Best Bitter;
Whitbread WCPA, Castle
Eden Ale, Flowers Original H
Busy 16th-century pub with an
excellent family room. Food
emphasis. ⚃ 🍴 ◖ ▶ 🍺 ♣ P

Blaisdon

Red Hart
☎ (01452) 830477
12.30–2.30, 7–11
S&N Theakston Best Bitter;
Tetley Bitter; guest beers H
Attractive, stone-flagged,
one-bar pub at the heart of the
village: a former Whitbread
pub, pleasantly refurbished.
Good range of home-cooked
food. Two guest beers. Well-
behaved children welcome.
🏚 Q ❀ ◖ ▶ Ꭽ ▲ ♣ ⌂ P

Bledington

King's Head
On B4450 ☎ (01608) 658365
11–2.30, 6–11; 12–2.30, 7–10.30 Sun
Hook Norton Best Bitter;
Wadworth 6X; guest beer H
Delightful, 16th-century,
stone-built inn overlooking the
village green. It specialises in
food, with booking at
weekends essential (no-
smoking area in the
restaurant). Monthly-changing
guest beers. Cider in summer.
🏚 Q ❀ 🍴 ◖ ▶ Ꭽ
⇌ (Kingham) ♣ ⌂ P

Broad Campden

Baker's Arms
Off B4081 ☎ (01386) 840515
11.30–3, 5.30 (6 winter)–11
Donnington BB; Stanway
Stanney Bitter; guest beer H
Fine, old country pub boasting
exposed Cotswold stone walls
and oak beams. Folk music
monthly (third Tue).
🏚 Q ❀ ◖ ♣ P

Brockweir

Brockweir Country
Inn
Off A466 by bridge
☎ (01291) 689548
11.30–3, 6–11; 11.30–11 Sat
Draught Bass; Freeminer
Bitter; Hook Norton Best
Bitter H
Lovely country pub 50 yards
from the Wye, close to Tintern
Abbey. It features oak beams
from a ship built in Brockweir
years ago. Home-cooked food
in generous portions. Cider in
summer.
🏚 Q ❀ 🍴 ◖ ▶ 🍺 ♣ ⌂ P

Chalford Hill

Old Neighbourhood Inn
Midway ☎ (01453) 883385
11–3, 6–11

Archers Best Bitter; Wickwar
Coopers WPA, Brand Oak;
guest beer
Superb village inn. Very
welcoming, with oak flooring
and pine furniture. Large patio
with good views. Coopers and
Brand Oak are sold under
house names.
🏚 Q ❀ ◖ ▶ 🍺 Ꭽ ♣ P ⅀

Charlton Kings

Little Owl
Cirencester Road (A435)
☎ (01242) 529404
11–2.30 (3 Sat), 5.30–11
Brains Bitter; Hook Norton
Best Bitter; Morland Old
Speckled Hen; Wadworth 6X;
Whitbread Boddingtons
Bitter, Flowers Original; guest
beer H
Pub named after a winner of
the Gold Cup. Large interior,
with several sections,
including a restaurant.
🏚 Q ⚃ ❀ ◖ ▶ ♣ P

Cheltenham

Bayshill Inn
92 St George's Place
☎ (01242) 524388
11–3, 5–11
Hall & Woodhouse
Tanglefoot; Wadworth IPA,
6X; guest beer H
Very popular, town-centre pub
without frills, situated near the
bus station. Good value
lunches; hot snacks only in the
eve. Pinball, cribbage and quiz
nights are popular. Fortnightly
guest beers. 🍺 ◖ ♣ ⌂

Beaufort Arms
184 London Road (A40)
☎ (01242) 526038
11–2.30, 6–11
Hall & Woodhouse
Tanglefoot; Wadworth IPA,
6X, Farmer's Glory, Old
Timer H
Excellent local on the main
road, featuring a bistro. A
racing theme pervades the
pub, which has a family
room-cum-skittle alley.
Limited parking. No food Sun
eve. Q 🍺 ◖ ▶ Ꭽ ♣ ⌂ P

Hogshead
Montpellier Walk
☎ (01242) 523431
11–11
Hook Norton Old Hooky G;
Morland Old Speckled
Hen H; Stanway Stanney
Bitter H; Taylor Landlord;
Uley Bitter; Wadworth 6X H;
guest beer G/H
Pub with a basic, scrubbed-
wood look downstairs and a
Berni restaurant upstairs.
Guest beers change frequently.
Bar meals till 7pm; open for
food all day Sun. ◖ ▶ ♣ ⌂

St James Hotel
Ambrose Street
☎ (01242) 522860
11–2.30, 5–11
Arkell's 2B, Mash Tun Mild,
3B, Kingsdown H
Rejuvenated, Victorian,
city-centre pub, impressively
decorated, and furnished with
country-style chairs. Good
selection of food. Loud music
some eves. 🍺 ◖ ▶ Ꭽ Ꭽ

Chipping Campden

Volunteer
Lower High Street
☎ (01386) 840688
11.30–3, 7–11
Bass Worthington BB,
Draught Bass; Hook Norton
Best Bitter; M&B Brew XI;
S&N Theakston XB; Stanway
Stanney Bitter H
Stone building, slightly away
from the village centre, a pub
since 1709. Special food nights
monthly. 🏚 🍺 ◖ ▶ 🍺 ▲ ♣

Cirencester

Corinium Court Hotel
12 Gloucester Street
☎ (01285) 659711
11–3, 6–11
Hook Norton Best Bitter H,
Old Hooky G; Wadworth
6X H; guest beer (occasional)
16th-century hotel with a
charming courtyard entrance
and a superb, small, flagstoned bar open to a smart,
comfortable lounge. Attractive
garden (safe for young
children).
🏚 Q ❀ 🍺 ◖ ▶ ▲ P

Drillman's Arms
34 Gloucester Road, Stratton
(A417) ☎ (01285) 653892
11–3, 5.30–11; 11–11 Sat
Archers Village, Best Bitter;
Wadworth 6X; Whitbread
Boddingtons Bitter; guest
beer H
Popular Georgian inn with a
small, convivial lounge, a
public bar and a skittle alley.
Once an Archers tied house,
now free. Archers Village is
sold as a house beer.
🏚 ⚃ ❀ ◖ ▶ 🍺 ▲ ♣ P

Golden Cross
20 Blackjack Street (near
Corinium Museum)
☎ (01285) 652137
11–3, 6–11
Arkell's 2B, 3B H
A real pub without gimmicks,
relying on good beer, friendly
and efficient service, and good
company. Arkell's seasonal
beers sold. Full-size snooker
table. Families welcome in the
skittle alley if it is not in use.
⚃ ❀ 🍺 ◖ ▲ ♣

114

Colesbourne

Colesbourne Inn
On A435 ☎ (01242) 870376
11–3, 6–11
Wadworth IPA, 6X, Farmer's Glory, Old Timer; guest beer H
Large, 200-year-old inn: a warm and comfortable lounge with a public bar area, but with an emphasis on food.
🏚 Q ❀ ◖) ● ⬡ ♣ P

Dursley

Old Spot Inn
Hill Road ☎ (01453) 542870
11–11
Bass Worthington BB, Draught Bass; Uley Old Spot H
Built in 1776 as a farm cottage, this has been a pub most of this century: a convenient watering hole on the Cotswold Way. Cajun cooking; doorstep sandwiches at all times. Car park opposite.
🏚 Q ❀ ◖) ♣ ✂

Eastleach Turville

Victoria
☎ (0136 785) 277
10.30–2.30 (3 Sat), 7–11
Arkell's 3B, Kingsdown H
Comfortable, 16th-century pub overlooking this Cotswold village. L-shaped bar layout, with a restaurant off the rear of the lounge section. Book Sun lunch. 🏚 ❀ ◖) ♣ ⬡ P

Ebrington

Ebrington Arms
Off B4035 ☎ (01386) 78223
11–2.30, 6–11
Donnington SBA; Hook Norton Best Bitter; guest beers H
Stone-built village pub, with a lovely old entrance door and a preserved open fireplace in the dining room.
🏚 Q ❀ ➤ ◖) ● ⬡ ♣ ⬡ P

Elkstone

Highwayman Inn
Beech Pike (A417)
☎ (01285) 821221
11–2.30, 6–11
Arkell's 2B, 3B, Kingsdown H
Comfortable roadhouse of 16th-century origins: a long bar, a restaurant and a family room. Good selection of food.
🏚 Q ❂ ➤ ◖) ● Å ♣ P

Ewen

Wild Duck Inn
Drakes Island
☎ (01285) 770310
11–11

Draught Bass; Fuller's London Pride; S&N Theakston XB, Old Peculier H
Superb country hotel with a beautiful exterior and gardens. Built in 1563, it retains a rustic feel, with panelling, settles, old paintings and an Elizabethan fireplace. Duck Pond Bitter is Archers Village. 🏚 ❀ ➤ ◖)
≋ (Kemble) ♣ ⬡ P

Ford

Plough Inn
On B4077 ☎ (0138673) 215
11–11
Donnington BB, SBA H
Splendid, unspoilt country pub with a racing theme. The cellar used to be a gaol. Wooden fort in the children's area. No eve meals Sun.
🏚 ❀ ➤ ◖) Å ♣ P

Fosse Cross

Hare & Hounds
On A429 ☎ (01285) 720288
11–3, 6–11
Everards Tiger; Hook Norton Best Bitter; S&N Theakston Old Peculier; Wadworth 6X; guest beers H
Comfortable, 400-year-old stone-built pub with an L-shaped bar, licensed since at least 1772. Children's and vegetarian meals in the bar and restaurant. Caravan site adjacent.
🏚 Q ❀ ◖) & Å ♣ P

Gloucester

Black Swan Inn
68–70 Southgate Street
☎ (01452) 523642
11–2.30, 6–11
Arkell's 2B, Kingsdown; Fuller's London Pride H
Very reasonably-priced hotel undergoing refurbishment. The two-roomed bar is decorated in neo-colonial style. Comes alive in Cheltenham Festival week.
Q ❖ ➤ ◖) ≋ ♣ P

Imperial Inn
59 Northgate Street
☎ (01452) 529918
11–11; 11–5, 7–11 Sat
Draught Bass; S&N Theakston Old Peculier; Stones Best Bitter H
Listed, Victorian M&B pub, with an original tiled frontage. Converted from three small rooms to a large single bar in 1985, but given Victorian styling. A popular city-centre boozer. ≋ ♣

Linden Tree
73–75 Bristol Road (A430, ¾ mile S of centre)
☎ (01452) 527869
11–2.30, 5.30 (6 Sat)–11

Draught Bass; Hall & Woodhouse Tanglefoot; Hook Norton Best Bitter; Wadworth 6X, Farmer's Glory; guest beer H
Excellent pub in a Grade II-listed building, offering good food (no meals Sun eve) and fine accommodation. New skittle alley/function room. Tiny car park.
🏚 ➤ ◖) ♣ P

Old Crown
81–83 Westgate Street (close to cathedral) ☎ (01452) 310517
11–11
Samuel Smith OBB, Museum H
Highly commended in CAMRA's *Pub Design* competition, this building began life again as a pub in 1990. Traditional public bar downstairs; comfortable lounge upstairs (the latter closed Sun/Mon eves).
❀ ◖) ⬡ & ≋ ♣

Whitesmith's Arms
81 Southgate Street
☎ (01452) 414770
11–3, 6–11; 11–11 Sat
Arkell's 2B, 3B, Kingsdown H
Named after maritime metal-workers, this pub stands opposite the historic city docks. Fitting maritime decor. Eve meals in summer only.
🏚 ◖) ● ≋ ♣

Guiting Power

Farmer's Arms
☎ (01451) 850358
11.30–2.30, 5.30–11 (may extend in summer)
Donnington BB, SBA H
Ivy-clad pub in the centre of a typical Cotswold village. Cider in summer. Families allowed in the skittle alley. 🏚 Q ☙
❀ ➤ ◖) & Å ♣ ⬡ P

Hyde

Ragged Cot
Cirencester Road OS887012
☎ (01453) 884643
11–2.30, 6–11 (11–11 summer)
Marston's Pedigree; S&N Theakston Best Bitter; Uley Old Spot; Wadworth 6X; guest beer H
Very busy, comfortable, 16th-century free house in open Cotswold countryside.
🏚 Q ❀ ➤ ◖) & Å P

Kingscote

Hunters Hall
On A4135 ☎ (01453) 860393
11–2.30, 6.30–11
Draught Bass; Hook Norton Best Bitter; Uley Old Spot; Wadworth 6X H

Gloucestershire

16th-century coaching inn with several small, separate bars, with stone-flagged floors, oak settles and open fireplaces. Welcoming for families.
🏨 Q ⇌ ◑ ▶ & ♣ P

Lechlade

Trout Inn
St John's Bridge (A417)
☎ (01367) 252313
11–3, 6–11
Courage Best Bitter; John Smith's Bitter; guest beer H
Attractive, 13th-century inn on the Thames, originally the alms house of a priory. A flagstone floor and a low ceiling are features. Public bar in a separate building.
🏨 Q ⚲ ❀ ◑ ▶ ⊞ ▲ ♣ P

Leighterton

Royal Oak
The Street ☎ (01666) 890250
12–2.30, 7–11
Butcombe Bitter; Crown Buckley Rev. James; Hook Norton Best Bitter; S&N Theakston Old Peculier H
300-year-old free house, much modernised: one bar with a restaurant off. No meals Mon eve. 🏨 Q ❀ ◑ ▶ ♣ P

Longborough

Coach & Horses
☎ (01451) 830325
11–2.30, 7–11 (11–11 bank hols)
Donnington BB, XXX (winter), SBA (summer) H
Friendly, one-bar pub in a village with morris dancing connections. Lunches in summer only. Parking can be difficult. 🏨 ❀ ◑ ♣

Longford

Queen's Head
84 Tewkesbury Road (A38)
☎ (01452) 301882
11–2.30 (3 Sat), 5–11
Marston's Pedigree; Morland Old Speckled Hen; Wadworth 6X; Whitbread WCPA, Boddingtons Bitter, Flowers Original H
18th-century inn with original beams and a stone-flagged public bar area. Excellent selection of bar meals. Colourful flower baskets outside. ❀ ◑ ▶ ⊞ P

Lower Wick

Pickwick Inn
Off A38 OS712958
☎ (01453) 810259
11–2.30, 6–11
Draught Bass; Smiles Bitter, Best Bitter, Exhibition H
Refurbished pub with a stone-flagged floor. Near M5 junction 14 and well worth the detour. Excellent menu.
🏨 Q ❀ ◑ ▶ ⊞ ▲ ♣ P

May Hill

Glasshouse Inn
Off A40 W of Huntley
OS709213 ☎ (01452) 830529
11.30–2.30, 6–11; 12–2, 7–10.30 Sun
Butcombe Bitter; Whitbread WCPA; guest beer H
Unspoilt country pub with an original quarry tiled floor. The outdoor drinking area has an old cider press. Quoits played.
🏨 Q ❀ ♣ P

Newland

Ostrich
On B4231 ☎ (01594) 833260
12–2.30, 6.30–11
Exmoor Gold; Freeminer Speculation; Marston's Pedigree; Ringwood Old Thumper; Shepherd Neame Spitfire; Whitbread Boddingtons Bitter; guest beer H
Charming and unspoilt, traditional English pub, with friendly staff and owners. Wide range of good food. A true free house (the beer range may vary), with a wealth of beams. 🏨 Q ❀ ⇌ ◑ ▶ ▲

Northleach

Red Lion
Market Square
☎ (01451) 860251
11–3.30, 6–11
Courage Best Bitter, Directors; John Smith's Bitter; Ushers Founders H
Cosy hostelry opposite the historic market place, with its 16th- and 17th-century wool houses and inns. The pub doubles as the local job centre. Welcoming atmosphere.
🏨 Q ❀ ⇌ ◑ ▶ ⊞ & ♣ P

Nympsfield

Rose & Crown
The Cross ☎ (01453) 860240
11.45–2.30, 5.30–11
Brakspear Bitter; S&N Theakston Old Peculier; Uley Bitter, Old Spot; Wadworth 6X; Whitbread Boddingtons Bitter H
300-year-old village local with much original character. Large fireplace at one end of the main bar; cosy stove at the other. Noted for its floral display. Quoits played.
🏨 Q ❀ ⇌ ◑ ▶ ⊞ ♣ P ✗

Prestbury

Royal Oak
The Burgage ☎ (01242) 522344
11–2.30 (3 Fri & Sat), 6–11

Archers Best Bitter; Brains Bitter; Whitbread WCPA, Winter Royal; guest beer H
Two-bar pub serving home-made lunchtime food (not Sun). Hops hang from the beam in the lounge bar.
Q ❀ ◑ ▶ ♣ P

Ruspidge

New Inn
On B4227 ☎ (01594) 824508
7 (12 Sat)–11
Archers Golden; Wye Valley Hereford Bitter; guest beer H
Fairly basic village pub open in the eve only during the week. Separate games room.
🏨 Q ❀ ♣ ⌂ P

Sapperton

Daneway Inn
Daneway ☎ (01285) 760297
11–2.30 (3 Sat), 6.30–11
Archers Best Bitter; Draught Bass H; Wadworth 6X G; guest beer
Superb old inn set in an idyllic position near the western end of the Sapperton canal tunnel. The lounge boasts a Dutch carved fireplace; no-smoking family room; large garden. The house beer is from Archers. 🏨
Q ⚲ ❀ ◑ ▶ ♣ ⌂ P ✗

Shurdington

Bell
Shurdington Road (A46)
☎ (01242) 862245
11–3, 5–11; 11–11 Fri & Sat
Marston's Pedigree; Morland Old Speckled Hen; Whitbread WCPA, Boddingtons Bitter, Flowers Original; guest beer H
Once the village bakery, a friendly pub overlooking a sports field. Wide range of food available in the conservatory dining area (Sun roast). Children's play area.
🏨 Q ❀ ◑ ▶ ⊞ ▲ ♣ ⌂ P

Slad

Woolpack
On B4070 ☎ (01452) 813429
12 (11 summer)–3, 6–11
Uley Old Spot, Pig's Ear; Wadworth 6X; Whitbread Boddingtons Bitter, Flowers Original H
Authentic 16th-century pub, clinging to the side of the Slad valley, offering splendid views. Made famous by Laurie Lee in Cider with Rosie (the author can still be found here). Quoits played.
🏨 Q ⚲ ❀ ◑ ▶ ⊞ ♣ ⌂ P

Slimbridge

Tudor Arms
Shepherds Patch (W of village)
☎ (01453) 890306
11–2.30, 7 (6 Sat)–11 (11–11 Sat in summer)
**Hook Norton Best Bitter;
Oakhill Bitter; Uley Bitter;
Wadworth 6X; Whitbread
Boddingtons Bitter; guest
beer** H
Attractive, well-run, large country pub near the canal on the way to the Wildfowl Trust. Separate restaurant. The family room is a no-smoking area and has a nursing facility.
⌂ ✿ ⌸ ① ▶ A ♣ P ✗

Sling

Miners Arms
On B4228 ☎ (01594) 836632
11–11
Freeminer Bitter, Speculation; guest beers H
Basic, one-bar pub. Freeminer's first tied house.
⌸ ✿ ♣ ⌐ P

Stanton

Mount Inn
Old Snowshill Road
☎ (01386) 73316
11–3, 6–11 (11–11 summer)
Donnington BB, SBA H
Popular pub perched on a hill above the village, with an expansive view. The large garden is pleasant on summer eves.
⌸ Q ✿ ① ▶ ♣ ⌐ P

Stow-on-the-Wold

Queens Head
The Square
☎ (01451) 830563
11–2.30 (3 Sat), 6–11
Donnington BB, SBA H
Fine, old Cotswold pub, popular with tourists and locals. The only pub in the county in every *Good Beer Guide* to date. No food Sat eve or Sun; check for eve meals in winter. Park in the square.
Q ✿ ① ▶ ⌸ A ♣ ⌐

Stroud

Pelican
Union Street ☎ (01453) 763817
11.30–11
**Courage Directors; Eldridge Pope Hardy Country;
Marston's Pedigree; Morland Old Speckled Hen; Ruddles Best Bitter; Wadworth 6X; guest beer** H
Popular town pub close to the covered market. A long, split-level main bar with a

pool table on a lower level, plus the Courtyard Bar, open Fri and Sat eves. It runs its own 50-seat theatre. Live music twice a week. Tiny car park.
⌸ ✿ ① ⌐ ♣ ⌐ P

Tetbury

Crown
Gumstool Hill
☎ (01666) 502469
11–3, 5.30–11
**Fuller's London Pride;
Whitbread Boddingtons Bitter, Flowers IPA, Original; guest beer** H
Busy town pub with a lounge bar and a conservatory.
⌸ Q ✿ ① ▶ P

Tewkesbury

Berkeley Arms
8 Church Street (A38)
☎ (01684) 293034
11–2.30, 5–11; 11–11 Fri & Sat
**Hall & Woodhouse Tanglefoot; Wadworth IPA,
6X, Farmer's Glory, Old Timer** H
Ancient pub of character: the most northerly Wadworth pub. Access to the lounge is through an unusual alley way.
Q ⌸ ① ▶ ⌸

Old Black Bear
High Street ☎ (01684) 292202
11–11
Whitbread Boddingtons Bitter H; **guest beers** G
The oldest inn in the county: a rambling pub with a pleasant terrace overlooking the River Avon. Food is available most times when open, except Sun and Mon eves. Wide selection of guest beers. ✿ ① ▶ ⌸

Todenham

Farriers Arms
☎ (01608) 50901
12–3, 7–11
Hook Norton Best Bitter, Old Hooky (summer) H
Pub next to the blacksmith's shop and the church, formerly an iron foundry. Aunt Sally in the car park (75 yards away).
⌸ Q ✿ ⌸ ① ▶ ⌸ ♣ P

Uley

Old Crown
The Green ☎ (01453) 860502
11.30–2.30 (3 Sat), 7–11
**Uley Bitter, Old Spot;
Whitbread WCPA,
Boddingtons Bitter** H
Single-bar, Cotswold village pub, built in 1638 as cottages and recently improved internally. ✿ ⌸ ① ▶ ♣ P

Waterley Bottom

New Inn
OS758964 ☎ (01453) 543659
12–2.30, 7–11
Cotleigh Tawny; Greene King Abbot H; **S&N Theakston Old Peculier** G; **Smiles Best Bitter** H, **Exhibition** G; **guest beer**
Large, friendly free house in a beautiful setting, surrounded by steep hills. A large-scale map is advisable for first-time visitors (it is best attempted from N Nibley – follow signs). The house beer (Cotleigh WB) is a variation of Harrier SPA.
⌸ Q ⌸ ① ▶ ⌸ ♣ ⌐ P

Winchcombe

Bell Inn
Gretton Road
☎ (01242) 602205
11–11
Draught Bass; Donnington BB; Wadworth 6X H
Very much a locals' local, also serving Weston's cider.
⌸ Q ✿ ⌸ ① ♣ ⌐ P

White Hart
High Street ☎ (01242) 602359
11–11
Marston's Pedigree; Stanway Stanney Bitter; Whitbread WCPA, Boddingtons Bitter H
Busy town pub catering for most tastes and age groups. Live music. Small car park.
⌸ ① ▶ A ♣ P

Woodchester

Royal Oak
Church Road (400 yds uphill from A46) ☎ (01453) 872735
12–3, 7–11
**Draught Bass; Tetley Bitter;
Wadworth IPA, 6X** H
300-year-old pub in an old Roman village, with oak beams, tasteful decor and a cosy atmosphere. Busy weekends.
⌸ ⌸ ① ▶ ⌸ ♣ P ✗

Woolaston Common

Rising Sun
1 mile off A48 OS590009
☎ (01594) 529282
12–2.30, 6.30–11
**Hook Norton Best Bitter;
S&N Theakston Best Bitter;
Thwaites Bitter** H
Lovely country pub with excellent views and a friendly landlord. Authentic Indian curries (no food Wed). Beautiful floral displays. Garden swings.
⌸ Q ✿ ① ▶ ⌸ A ♣ P

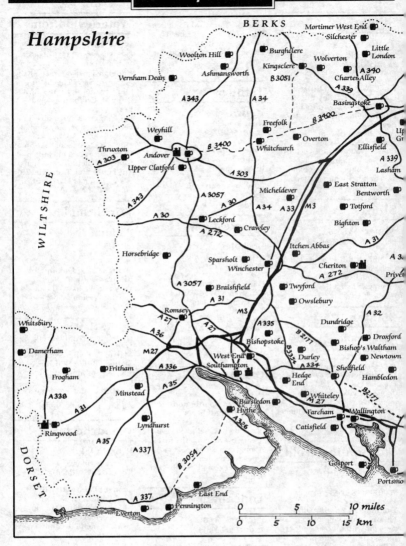

Hampshire

Cheriton, Cheriton; **Gale's**, Horndean; **Hampshire**, Andover; **Hedgehog & Hogshead**, Southampton; **Newale**, Andover; **Ringwood**, Ringwood; **Worldham**, East Worldham

Aldershot

Red Lion
24 Ash Road (A323)
☎ (01252) 23050
12–11
Courage Best Bitter, Directors; Hogs Back TEA;

Marston's Pedigree; Wadworth 6X H
Prominent roadside, two-bar pub catering for drinkers and chatterers alike. It enjoys a huge real ale following, with always one dark ale available. No food at weekends.
 🏠 ❀ ◑ ▶ ⇌ ♣ P

Alton

Eight Bells
33 Church Street
☎ (01420) 82417
12–3, 6–11; 11–11 Fri & Sat
Hampshire Lionheart; Marston's Pedigree;

Worldham Barbarian;
Wychwood Blackwych ⒣
Cosy pub with chamberpots
and assorted items hanging
from the low-beamed ceiling.
It retains a rural charm, yet is
only five minutes from the
town centre. ⒟ ⒟ ⇌

Wheatsheaf Inn
Market Square
☎ (01420) 83316
11–3 (4 Sat), 5 (6 Sat)–11
**Courage Best Bitter,
Directors; Ushers Best Bitter,
Founders** ⒣
Busy, comfortable, two-bar
market square pub. It holds an
extremely popular Sun night
quiz, when no eve meals are
served. 🏠 ⒟ ⒟ ⒝ ⇌ ♣

Andover

White Hart
Bridge Street
☎ (01264) 352266/7
11–2.30, 6–11; 12–2.30, 7–10.30 Sun
**Courage Best Bitter;
Ringwood Fortyniner; guest
beer** (occasional) ⒣
Cosy, characterful town-centre
hotel with plenty of room to
relax. Pub, brewery, and town
memorabilia feature on the
walls. This former coaching
inn on the London–Exeter
route is open all day Sat for
coffee and buns. Chess played.
Q ⒲ 🏠 ⒟ ⇌ ♣ P ⑂

Ashmansworth

Plough
Off A343 ☎ (01635) 253047
12–2.30 (not Mon or Tue); 12–3 Sat &
bank hol Mon), 6–11
**Archers Village, Best Bitter,
Golden; guest beer** ⒢
215 years old and full of
character, one of North
Hampshire's finest rural locals.
The warm and friendly single
bar is simply furnished. The
beer is served straight from
casks behind the bar (cooled in
summer). The highest pub in
the county, 770ft above sea
level. Children's den in the
yard. 🏠 Q ⒲ ⒟ ▲ ♣ P

Basingstoke

Bounty
81 Bounty Road (250 yds SE of
market square)
☎ (01256) 20071
11–2.30, 5.30–11; 11–11 Fri & Sat
**Courage Best Bitter; Ushers
Best Bitter, Founders** ⒣
Former Mays Brewery pub
next to the cricket ground: a
real pub, with character in its
two distinctive bars. Enclosed
family garden.
🏠 Q ⒲ ⒲ ⒟ ⒝ ♣ P

Queens Arms
Bunnian Place
☎ (01256) 465488
11–3, 5–11; 11–11 Fri & Sat
**Courage Best Bitter,
Directors; John Smith's Bitter;
Wadworth 6X; guest beer** ⒣
Pleasant, busy, town pub,
popular with locals and
business people: a typical
Victorian pub, a stone's throw
from the station. Unusual
guest beers often featured.
⒟ ⇌ P

Bentworth

Sun
Off A339, 1 mile S of Lasham
OS661401 ☎ (01420) 562338
12–3, 6–11

**Draught Bass; Courage Best
Bitter; Cheriton Diggers
Gold; Marston's Pedigree;
Ringwood Best Bitter;
Wadworth 6X** ⒣
Built in 1635 and tastefully
extended recently, this country
inn is hidden down a narrow
lane. A wealth of rural
artefacts, plus old pine and
fresh flowers, add to its charm.
Space may be limited so no
under-tens admitted after
8pm. 🏠 Q ⒲ ⒟ ⒝ ♣ P

Try also: Star (Free)

Bighton

Three Horseshoes
Off A31/B3047 OS616344
☎ (01962) 732859
11–2.30, 6–11; 12–2, 7–10.30 Sun
**Gale's XXXD, BBB, 5X,
HSB** ⒣
Friendly, traditional, two-bar
local, well off the beaten track.
A pub since 1612, it has a
quiet, relaxing atmosphere.
Note the country crafts
collection and the old pub sign
in the bar. Handy for Mid-
Hants Steam Railway (Ropley
station 2 miles). No food Mon.
🏠 Q ⒲ ⒟ ⒝ ⒜ ♣ P

Bishopstoke

Foresters Arms
1 Stoke Common Road
☎ (01703) 620287
11–3, 6–11; 11–11 Sat
**Gibbs Mew Salisbury, Wake
Ale, Deacon, Bishop's Tipple;
Tetley Bitter** ⒣
Genuine community pub, with
a team or society for everyone:
a lively public bar and a quiet
lounge, split into two by an
archway, with one end acting
as a TV area. Meals provided
if ordered in advance. Inch's
cider. 🏠 ⒲ 🏠 ♣ ⒪ P

Bishop's Waltham

Bunch of Grapes
St Peter's Street
☎ (01489) 892935
10–2 (2.30 Sat), 6–11; 12–2, 7–10.30
Sun
Courage Best Bitter ⒢**; Ushers
Best Bitter, Founders** ⒣
Situated in narrow medieval
street leading to the parish
church, this small one-bar pub
has been unaltered for many
years and run by the same
family for over 80 years. It has
its own golf society. Ushers
guest beers are to be
introduced. Q ⒲ ♣

Braishfield

Newport Inn
Newport Lane
☎ (01794) 368225
11–2.30, 6–11

119

Hampshire

Gale's BBB, Best Bitter, 5X, HSB H
A survivor from a former era, a gem worth finding. Customers come from miles around for the famous sandwiches. On Sun nights be ready to join in the singing around the piano. Large, sheltered garden.
🏠 Q ❀ 🍺 ♣ P

Burghclere

Queen
Hart's Lane (1 mile E of A34)
☎ (01635) 278350
11–3, 6–11
Adnams Bitter, Broadside; Arkell's 3B H
Turn-of-the-century, traditional local. A good atmosphere and a friendly welcome are assured, especially if you like horseracing at nearby Newbury. This large, one-bar pub is comfortable, spacious and difficult to leave. Busy on darts nights. No food Sun lunch. ❀ 🍺 ♣ P

Buriton

Five Bells
High Street ☎ (01730) 263584
11–2.30 (3 Fri & Sat), 5.30–11
Ballard's Best Bitter; Ind Coope Friary Meux Best Bitter, Burton Ale; Ringwood XXXX Porter, Old Thumper; Tetley Bitter; guest beers (summer) H
Traditional, old, beamed free house: a two-bar pub, with imposing fireplaces. Excellent range of ales and food, including fresh fish and game in season.
🏠 Q ❀ 🍺 🅐 ♣ P

Bursledon

Linden Tree
School Road (off A27/A3025)
☎ (01703) 402356
11–2.30 (3 Sat), 6 (5 Fri)–11
Draught Bass; Wadworth IPA, 6X, Farmer's Glory (summer), **Old Timer** H
Excellent, comfortable, one-bar pub with no obtrusive gaming machines. A children's play area and pergola make it ideal for summer; a blazing log fire extends a warm welcome in winter. Try the high quality, home-cooked lunches (not served Sun). Friendly atmosphere. 🏠 ❀ 🍺 ♣ P

Vine Inn
High Street, Old Bursledon
☎ (01703) 403836
11–3, 6–11; 11–11 Sat
Marston's Bitter, Pedigree H
Smart, cosy local on a winding

lane in *Howards Way* country. Darts night is Mon, quiz night Tue. A recent extension features a new dining room and patio. Park 100 yds away in Lands End Rd.
Q ❀ 🍺 🅐 🚃

Catisfield

Limes at Catisfield
34 Catisfield Lane
☎ (01329) 842926
12–2.30, 5–11; 11–3, 7–11 Sat
Gale's HSB; Gibbs Mew Salisbury H, **Deacon** G, **Bishop's Tipple** H; **Ringwood Fortyniner, Old Thumper** G
Large Victorian building converted to a pub. The public bar has unusual panelling and can get very busy, but the lounge has a more relaxed atmosphere. The petanque terrain in the garden justifies bar extensions in summer. Children welcome at weekends only. ❀ 🍺 ♣ P

Charter Alley

White Hart
White Hart Lane OS595576
☎ (01256) 850048
12–2.30 (3 Sat), 7–11
Brakspear Bitter; Fuller's London Pride; guest beers H
Large, friendly, two-bar, busy village pub: a quiet lounge bar, and a back bar with a skittle alley and games area. Cider in summer. The guest beers change regularly.
🏠 Q ❀ 🍺 🅐 ♣ ♧ 🍶 P

Cheriton

Flower Pots Inn
W off B3046/N of A272
☎ (01962) 771318
11.30–2.30, 6–11
Cheriton Pots Ale, Best Bitter, Diggers Gold G
A real village focal point— with its own brewery: good conversation and food; ale direct from the cask. Other occasional brews are also featured. A fine stop for walkers of the Wayfarers or Downs Ways; a mile from the site of a 1644 civil war battle. No food Sun eve. 🏠 Q ⏳ ❀ 🏠 🍺 ♣ 🅐 ♧ P

Cove

Old Court House
80 Cove Road (B3014)
☎ (01252) 543031
11–11
Bass Worthington BB, Draught Bass; Fuller's London Pride, ESB; M&B Highgate Dark H
16th-century pub, with an extensive horseshoe bar,

refurbished to reveal historic beams. Varied home-cooked food (not served Sun). Skittle alley for hire. ❀ 🍺 ♣ P

Crawley

Rack & Manger
Stockbridge Road (A272)
☎ (01962) 776281
11–3, 5–11; 11–11 Fri & Sat
Marston's Bitter, Pedigree, Owd Rodger H
Large pub, midway between Winchester and Stockbridge. The public bar is lively, but the lounge quieter, with an eating area (good range of pub grub). Popular with local agricultural college students.
🏠 ❀ 🍺 🍶 🍺 🅐 ♣ P

Crondall

Castle
Croft Lane (off A287)
☎ (01252) 850892
11.30–2.30, 6–11
Fuller's Hock, Chiswick, London Pride, Mr Harry, ESB H
Proper village local, serving excellent quality food; the licensee is a Dorchester Hotel-trained chef. No food Mon eve; lunches served on Sun only in summer. Skittle alley for hire.
🏠 Q ❀ 🍶 ♣ P

Hampshire Arms
Pankridge Street (off A287)
☎ (01252) 850418
11–3, 5.30–11
Morland Bitter, Old Speckled Hen; Worldham Old Dray H
Deservedly popular village local with a strong food emphasis. It caters well for families, but has a proper pub atmosphere, too. Thriving petanque club.
Q ⏳ ❀ 🍶 🍺 ♣ P

Crookham Village

Black Horse
The Street ☎ (01252) 616434
11–2.30 (3 Fri & Sat), 5.30–11
Courage Best Bitter, Directors; Fuller's London Pride; Wadworth 6X H
Popular, beamed village hostelry with a welcoming atmosphere. The children's garden features a tree house. No food Sun. Q ❀ 🍺 ♣ P

Damerham

Compasses Inn
On B3078, 2 miles W of Fordingbridge
☎ (01725) 518231
11–2.30, 6–11; 11–11 Sat
Ind Coope Burton Ale; Ringwood Best Bitter; Wadworth 6X; guest beers H

Attractively refurbished free house in a quiet village: a large garden, a lively public bar and a smart, relaxed lounge/dining room.
🍺 Q ❀ 🛏 ◁ ▷ ▲ ♣ P

Droxford

White Horse Inn

South Hill (A32)
☎ (01489) 877490
11–2.30, 6–11; 11–11 Sat
Burts Nipper, VPA; Morland Old Speckled Hen; Wadworth 6X, Old Timer H
Traditional, 16th-century coaching inn with contrasting lounge and public bars. The gents' boasts a well. One of the few pubs in the Meon Valley that has not become a restaurant that sells beer, but serves good food all the same (no-smoking dining area). The beer range may vary.
🍺 Q ❀ ⛄ 🍴 ◁ ▷ ♣ P

Dundridge

Hampshire Bowman

Dundridge Lane (1 mile off B3035) OS578185
☎ (01489) 892940
11–2.30, 6–11
Archers Village, Golden; Cheriton Best Bitter; King & Barnes Festive; Ringwood Fortyniner; guest beers G
Excellent country pub along a winding country lane. The beers are served from a cask stillage behind the brick-floored bar, which is heated by an open log burner. Well-regarded food (not served Mon, or Sun eve); quiz Mon.
🍺 Q ❀ ◁ ▷ ▲ ♣ P

Durley

Robin Hood Inn

Durley Street
☎ (01489) 860229
11–2.30, 6–11
Banks's Mild; Marston's Bitter, Pedigree H
Ex-17th-century coaching inn, now a good village local with a lounge. The large garden features a children's play area. Good value, traditional home-cooked food includes barbecues in summer. See the barrel racing on Aug Bank Hol Mon. 🍺 Q ❀ ◁ ▷ 🍴 ♣ P

East End

East End Arms

Lymington Road (3 miles E of IoW ferry) OS362968
☎ (01590) 65223
11.30–3, 6–11
Adnams Broadside; Ringwood Best Bitter, Fortyniner, Old Thumper G; **guest beers** H

Popular country pub used mainly by locals. A basic public contrasts with a comfortable lounge which has patio doors to the garden. Traditional country game pies served. Occasional ciders.
🍺 ❀ ◁ ▷ ⛄ ♣ P

East Stratton

Plough

½ mile from A33, 5 miles S of Basingstoke ☎ (01962) 89241
11–3 (not Mon), 6.30–11
Gale's BBB, HSB; Ringwood Fortyniner H
Thatched, 18th-century village pub, the former bakery, facing the village green: a basic, happy public bar, a tiny lounge, and a skittle alley. The landlady's own recipes and fresh ingredients guarantee a good, interesting menu in the dining room or bar.
🍺 Q ⛄ ❀ ◁ ▷ ⛄ ♣ P

East Worldham

Three Horseshoes

Cakers Lane (B3004)
☎ (01420) 83211
11–2.30, 6–11
Gale's BBB, Best Bitter, HSB H
Pleasant village roadside pub with unusual barrel seats. The Sun lunchtime roasts are recommended (book in advance; no meals Sun or Mon eves). Close to the Worldham brewery. Q ❀ ◁ ▷ P

Ellisfield

Fox

Green Lane ☎ (01256) 381210
11.30–2.30, 6.30–11
Fuller's London Pride; Hall & Woodhouse Tanglefoot; Hampshire King Alfred's; Marston's Pedigree; S&N Theakston Old Peculier; Wadworth 6X H
Two-bar country pub with an emphasis on food. Despite its proximity to Basingstoke, it is hard to find; situated on a quiet lane some way from the village centre. Persist—a welcoming atmosphere awaits you. No food Mon eve.
🍺 Q ❀ ◁ ▷ ⛄ ♣ P

Emsworth

Coal Exchange

21 South Street
☎ (01243) 375866
10.30–3, 5.30–11; 10.30–11 Sat
Gale's BBB, 5X, HSB, Festival Mild; guest beers (summer) H
Excellent, popular, small old pub with a tiled frontage, concealing one comfortable bar with a good atmosphere.

Good, varied food, including a speciality sausage menu. Public car park adjacent.
🍺 Q ❀ ◁ ▷ & ≈ ♣

Fairfield

125 New Brighton Road
☎ (01243) 373304
11–3, 6–11
Gale's Best Bitter, HSB H
Elegant, Regency-style building with two bars, pool area and a restaurant. Live entertainment at weekends. Regional winner of a 1994 *Cellarcraft* award.
Q ⛄ ❀ ◁ ▷ ⛄ & ≈ ♣ P

Milkman's Arms

55 North Street
☎ (01243) 373356
11–3, 6–11; 11–11 Sat
Gale's BBB, HSB, Festival Mild H
One-bar, convivial local, recently refurbished. Pub games and social events are encouraged. 🍺 ❀ ≈ ♣

Everton

Crown Inn

Old Christchurch Road
☎ (01590) 642655
11–2.30, 6–11
Draught Bass; Fuller's London Pride; Whitbread Strong Country, Flowers Original; guest beers H
19th-century, traditional village inn, offering a good selection of home-cooked fare. The lively but friendly public bar has an excellent jukebox. Note the prize-winning floral displays in summer. No food Sun–Wed in winter.
🍺 Q ❀ ◁ ▷ ⛄ & ▲ ♣ ⌂ P

Fareham

Delme Arms

1 Cams Hill (off A27)
☎ (01329) 232638
11–3 (4 Fri & Sat), 7 (6 summer)–11
Bass Worthington BB, Draught Bass; Burts VPA; M&B Brew XI H
Friendly local welcoming families Sun lunchtime (but no food is served on Sun). Don't be deceived by the posh exterior. Dog owners also welcome. ❀ ◁ ▲ ♣

Turnpike

71 Old Turnpike (off A32, from Wickham take signs to leisure centre)
☎ (01329) 313003
12–3, 6–11; 12–11 Sat (may vary)
Wadworth 6X; guest beers H / G
Partially listed building with a pool table in the large public bar, and a comfortable, small lounge. The majority of the

Hampshire

food is freshly prepared (book
Sun lunch; limited menu Sun
eve). 🏠 Q ✿ ◖ ▶ ♣ P

Farnborough

Imperial Arms
12 Farnborough Street
☎ (01252) 542573
11.30–2.30, 5–11; 11.30–11 Fri & Sat
**Courage Best Bitter; John
Smith's Bitter; guest beer** H
A listed building in a quiet
locality, with three recently
refurbished bars. A sporting
theme dominates one (with TV
and music), and there's also a
pool room, and a fine, low-
ceilinged, tiled-floor bar, alive
with conversation. Interesting
guest beers; no food Sun.
Q ◖ ▶ ⇌ (North) ♣ P

Prince of Wales
184 Rectory Road
☎ (01252) 545578
11.30–2.30, 5.30–11
**Brakspear Bitter; Fuller's
London Pride; Hall &
Woodhouse Badger Best
Bitter, Tanglefoot; Hogs Back
TEA; Ringwood Fortyniner;
guest beers** H
The best free house for miles,
offering a wide range of guest
beers. Convivial, traditional
and invariably busy, it stages
occasional small brewery
promotions, including for
mild. Friendly staff and
excellent lunches (not served
Sun).
Q ◖ ⇌ (North) P

Farringdon

Rose & Crown
Crows Lane (1½ miles from
A32 jct) ☎ (0142 058) 231
11–3, 6–11
**Bass Worthington BB,
Draught Bass; Marston's
Bitter, Pedigree; Ringwood
Old Thumper; Worldham Old
Dray** H
Attractive village free house
whose old ceiling is adorned with
old saws. The beer range
varies. No food Sun eve.
🏠 Q ✿ ◖ ▶ P

Freefolk

Watership Down
On B3400 ☎ (01256) 892254
11.30–3, 5.30–11 (may be 11.30–11
summer)
**Archers Best Bitter; Brakspear
Bitter; guest beers** H
Very welcoming, 19th-century
free house, named after the
book which was set locally.
This one-bar pub happily
mixes diners, locals, and
games/quiz players. Guest
beers change regularly and
always include a mild. The
large garden offers many
facilities. 🏠 ✿ ◖ ▶ ♣ ○ P

Fritham

Royal Oak
1½ miles SW of B3078
OS232141 ☎ (01703) 812606
11–3, 6–11
Beer range varies G
In a class of its own—a tiny,
unspoilt, thatched pub in the
heart of the New Forest: a
small front bar and even
smaller rear snug. Strong
support for all country sports
and activities. 🏠 Q ✿ ▲ ♣

Frogham

Foresters Arms
Abbotswell Road (signed E of
A338) OS173129
☎ (01425) 652294
11–2.30, 6–11
**Draught Bass; Whitbread
Boddingtons Bitter; guest
beers** H
On the fringe of the New
Forest, this friendly pub offers
a range of beers rarely seen in
this area. Three guest beers are
available on rotation and a
mini-beer festival is held
during the Frogham Fair (Aug
Bank Hol). 🏠 ⛺ ✿ ◖ ▶ P

Froxfield

Trooper
Alton Road OS727273
☎ (01730) 827293
12–3, 5.30–11
**Ballard's Best Bitter; Draught
Bass; Gibbs Mew Local Line,
Deacon** H
Interesting, unusual and
atmospheric, two-room local
in an isolated, relaxing
downland setting. The music
comes courtesy of the
landlord's eclectic CD
collection. The beer range
varies; small but varied food
menu. 🏠 Q ✿ ◖ ▲ ♣ P

Froyle

Prince of Wales
Lower Froyle ☎ (01420) 23102
11–2.30, 6–11
**Fuller's London Pride, ESB;
Ruddles County; Whitbread
Boddingtons Bitter; guest
beer** H
Edwardian country pub in a
scenic village. Family owned
and run, it serves a varied
selection of home-cooked food
(separate eating area). No
meals Sun eve. Continually
changing range of beers.
🏠 ✿ ◖ ▶ ♣ P

Golden Pot

Golden Pot
Odiham Road (A32)
☎ (01420) 84130
11–3.30, 5.30–11

**Morland Bitter, Old Speckled
Hen, Old Masters; Wells
Bombardier** H
Friendly, rural roadside pub
with a family welcome.
Formerly drovers' lodgings, it
now has a skittle alley, plus
camping and caravan facilities.
Named after a local Roman
treasure. No eve meals
Sun/Mon.
🏠 Q ✿ ◖ ▲ ♣ P

Gosport

Queen's Hotel
143 Queens Road
☎ (01705) 525518
11.30–2.30, 7–11; 11–11 Sat
**Archers Village; Hook Norton
Old Hooky; Ringwood
Fortyniner; guest beers** H
Popular, street-corner pub, the
local CAMRA *Pub of the Year*
1993. Two regularly changing
guest beers and a cider are
usually available and the pub
specialises in beer from
outside the area. Hot and cold
snacks (not Sun). 🏠 ₺ ♣ ○

Hambledon

New Inn
West Street ☎ (01705) 632466
12–2.30, 7–11
**Ballard's Trotton; Ringwood
Fortyniner, Old Thumper;
Wadworth 6X** H
Pleasant, two-bar pub with no
frills, just good drinking and
socialising at reasonable
prices. At over 450 years, it is
the oldest pub in the village.
Function room.
🏠 Q ✿ ₺ ♣ P

Vine
West Street ☎ (01705) 632419
11.30–2.30 (3 Sat), 6–11
**Burts Nipper; Gale's BBB,
HSB; Wells Bombardier** H;
guest beers
Pleasant old pub with two
bars and wooden beams. The
quiet, welcoming atmosphere
is enhanced by an unusual real
fire, a well, and intimate areas
in the lounge. Ideal for cricket
lovers. Eve meals Mon–Sat.
🏠 Q ✿ ◖ ▶ ₺ ♣ P

Hammer Vale

Prince of Wales
Hammer Lane (off A3, signed
Bulmer Hill) OS867326
☎ (01428) 652600
11–3, 6–11
**Gale's BBB, Best Bitter, 5X,
HSB** G
Impressive, isolated 1920s
red-brick roadhouse, largely
unchanged; one long bar, with
jacketed casks on stillage,
serves three drinking areas.
Stained-glass windows in the

locals' bar advertise Ameys Petersfield Brewery. No food Sun eve. 🏰 Q ❀ ◐ ◗ ♣ P

Hartley Wintney

Waggon & Horses

High Street ☎ (01252) 842119
11–11
Courage Best Bitter, Directors H; guest beers
Small, friendly traditional pub, with a public bar for games and a cosy lounge with a fire. Enterprising guest beers. No food Sun. 🏰 Q ❀ ◐ ♣

Havant

Robin Hood

6 Homewell ☎ (01705) 482779
11–11
Gale's BBB, Best Bitter, 5X, HSB G
Excellent old pub of unspoilt character which can get busy at lunchtime. Beware the cider on a fake handpump.
🏰 ◐ ♿ ⇌ P

Hawkley

Hawkley Inn

Pococks Lane (follow signs from Liss) OS747291
☎ (01730) 827205
12–2.30 (3 Sat), 6–11
Ballard's Trotton, Best Bitter; Cheriton Pots Ale; Oakhill Yeoman; Ringwood XXXX Porter, Fortyniner H
Busy village free house attracting a varied clientele including walkers. Furnished in a very individual style; the decor includes a moose head over the fire. The beers may vary. No food Sun night. Occasional live music.
🏰 Q ❀ ◐ ◗ ♣ ⅟

Hedge End

Barleycorn

2 Lower Northam Road
☎ (01489) 784171
11–2.30 (3.30 Sat), 5.30 (5 Fri, 6 Sat)–11
Banks's Mild; Marston's Bitter, Pedigree H
Located in the original village centre, a busy, good value pub with a good community feel. Although only a single bar, it has several drinking areas. Marston's Head Brewer's Choice stocked. No food Sun.
❀ ◐ ♣ P

Horndean

Ship & Bell Hotel

6 London Road
☎ (01705) 592107
10–11
Gale's BBB, Best Bitter, 5X, HSB, Festival Mild H
The Gale's brewery tap: a spacious 300-year-old hotel catering for all, with its contrasting lounge and public bars. No food Sun eve.
🏰 🛏 ◐ ◗ ▲ ♣ P ⅟

Horsebridge

John O'Gaunt

½ mile W of A3057, S of King's Somborne ☎ (01794) 388394
11.30–2.30 (11–3 Sat), 6–11
Adnams Bitter; Palmers IPA; Ringwood Fortyniner H
Fine village pub in the lovely Test Valley—superb walking country—offering exceptional value for money. Guest beers sometimes replace the Adnams. The shove-ha'penny is taken seriously. No food Tue eve. 🏰 Q ❀ ◐ ◗ ♣ P

Hythe

Lord Nelson

5 High Street
☎ (01703) 842169
11–11
Ringwood Best Bitter, XXXX Porter; Wadworth 6X; Whitbread Strong Country, Flowers Original; guest beers H
Small, waterfront pub with quaint bars. Its gardens overlook Southampton Water and yacht marina (convenient for the ferry). The good value menu includes daily specials.
🏰 Q ❀ ◐ ♿

Itchen Abbas

Trout

Main Road (B3047)
☎ (01962) 779537
11–3, 6–11
Marston's Bitter, Pedigree H
Lively, country local, formerly the Plough; the new name reflects its situation overlooking the River Itchen. The two bars are adorned with breweriana and local views. It also has a restaurant and games area. A good menu and Marston's Head Brewer's Choice feature.
🏰 ❀ 🛏 ◐ ◗ ♣ P

Kingsclere

Swan Hotel

Swan Street ☎ (01635) 298314
11–3, 5.30 (6 Sat)–11
Hampshire Lionheart, Pendragon; S&N Theakston XB; Tetley Bitter H
Spacious, traditional inn with beamed ceilings, in part dating back to 1459. Extensive menu (not served Sat or Mon lunch, or Sun eve).
🏰 Q 🛏 ◐ ◗ ♣ P

Lasham

Royal Oak

Off A339 ☎ (01256) 381213
11–2.30 (3 Sat), 6–11
Hampshire King Alfred's; Ringwood Best Bitter; guest beers H
Popular, two-bar pub at the village centre, serving good-value food and interesting guest ales. Well worth a visit, it is handy for the local airfield, a major gliding centre with a small aircraft museum (open Sun).
🏰 Q ❀ ◐ ◗ ♿ ♣ P

Leckford

Leckford Hutt

On A30, 3 miles E of Stockbridge OS405367
☎ (01264) 810738
11–2.30, 6.30–11
Marston's Bitter, Pedigree H
Full of character, a pub in a remote location, beside the A30. Dating back to the 18th century, with its own 200-ft-deep well inside, it has a paddock for grazing customers' horses and space for camping and games. Full of brewing and pub memorabilia. Marston's Head Brewer's Choice available.
🏰 Q ❀ ◐ ◗ ▲ ♣ P

Little London

Plough

Silchester Road (1 mile E of A340) ☎ (01256) 850628
11 (12 winter Mon–Fri)–2.30 (3 Sat), 6–11
Greene King Abbot; Ringwood Best Bitter; Whitbread Wethered Bitter; guest beer H
Unspoilt, classic country pub with a strong local following, but a warm welcome for all. A path from the garden leads to the 478-acre nature reserve of Pamber Forest. Simple snacks and bar meals are available on request. 🏰 Q ❀ ♣ P

Long Sutton

Four Horseshoes

The Street OS748471
☎ (01256) 862488
11–2.30, 6–11
Gale's BBB, Best Bitter, 5X, HSB H
Isolated country pub with a friendly, relaxed atmosphere and a good blend of locals and foodies who travel miles for the beer and food (not served Sun eve). The enclosed verandah is used as a family room. Camp in an adjacent field.
🏰 Q ❀ ◐ ◗ ▲ ♣ P

Hampshire

Lyndhurst

Mailman's Arms
71 High Street
☎ (01703) 284196
11-2.30, 6-11
Bateman Mild; Marston's Bitter, Pedigree H
Friendly, comfortable pub which stages occasional live entertainment, plus barbecues in summer. Good value lunches and an extensive eve pizza menu.
🏠 Q ⊛ ◑ ♣

Micheldever

Dever Arms
Winchester Road (off A33)
☎ (01962) 774339
11.30-3, 6-11
Cheriton Pots Ale; Gale's HSB; Hall & Woodhouse Badger Best Bitter; Hook Norton Mild; Hop Back Summer Lightning; Ringwood XXXX Porter; guest beer H
Tastefully refurbished pub in a pretty village, popular for its upmarket food, particularly at weekends. Children are welcome in the games room. The restaurant has a no-smoking area. Occasional ciders. Wheelchair WC.
🏠 ⑃ ⊛ ◑ ੬ ▲ ⇌ ♣ ⇔ P

Minstead

Trusty Servant Inn
Just off A31 OS281110
☎ (01703) 812137
11-3, 6-11 (11-11 summer)
Hook Norton Best Bitter; Wadworth 6X; Whitbread Boddingtons Mild H
Picturesque village local in the middle of the New Forest whose restored pub sign is based on old Winchester College servants' lore. Sir Arthur Conan Doyle is buried in the local churchyard. Barbecues are held in summer, and a beer festival early Aug.
⊛ 🏚 ◑ ◪ ▲ P

Mortimer West End

Red Lion
Church Road
☎ (01734) 700169
11-11
Hall & Woodhouse Badger Best Bitter, Tanglefoot; Wadworth 6X H
Circa 1549 building where nooks and crannies add to the charm. Very much a food-oriented house.
🏠 ⑃ ⊛ 🏚 ◑ ੬ P

Newtown

Travellers Rest
Church Road OS613123
☎ (01329) 833263
11-3, 6-11
Gibbs Mew Wiltshire, Salisbury H**, Deacon** G**, Bishop's Tipple** H**; guest beer** G
Picturesque, converted, 18th-century cottage in a pastoral setting. A relaxing unspoilt lounge has a low, matchboard ceiling and there is a popular public bar. Camping and caravan site in the grounds.
🏠 Q ⑃ ⊛ ◑ ◪ ▲ ♣ P

North Camp

Old Ford
Lynchford Road (A3011)
☎ (01252) 544840
11-11
Courage Best Bitter; Hogs Back TEA; Marston's Pedigree; John Smith's Bitter; Wadworth 6X H
Built in the 1850s and architecturally part of North Camp station. The sympathetically refurbished interior has a dining room and a pool room. Summer barbecues are held in the riverside garden, which has a play area and pets corner.
⑃ ⊛ ◑ ⇌ ♣ P

Oakhanger

Red Lion
The Street (B3004)
☎ (01420) 472232
11-3, 6-11
Courage Best Bitter, Directors; Worldham Old Dray H
A true village local, the closest outlet for Worldham beers. Renowned for its high quality food. 🏠 Q ⊛ ◑ ◑ P

Overton

Old House at Home
Station Road ☎ (01256) 770335
11-3, 5.30-11; 11-11 Fri & Sat
Courage Best Bitter; Ushers Best Bitter, Founders H
No-nonsense local boozer, though the new children's outdoor play area may widen its appeal in summer. Live entertainment most weekends; no snacks Sun. ⊛ ⇌ ♣ P

Owslebury

Ship Inn
1 mile N of B2177 OS511232
☎ (01962) 777358
11-3, 6-11

Bateman Mild; Marston's Bitter, Pedigree H
Lively, friendly community local, with a restaurant and an extensive garden, including a children's area and horse park. Marston's Head Brewer's Choice also stocked.
🏠 Q ⑃ ⊛ ◑ ੬ ▲ ♣ P

Pennington

Musketeer
26 North Street
☎ (01590) 676527
12 (11.30 Sat)-3, 5.30-11
Draught Bass; Brakspear Bitter; Gale's HSB; Ringwood Best Bitter; guest beer H
Traditional, friendly, one-bar pub in the village centre, very much a local. The bar is full of medieval weaponry, and the pub sign of a bronze musketeer is based on an original sculpture. Its 17th year in the *Guide*. No food Sun.
🏠 Q ⊛ ◑ P

Portsmouth

Artillery Arms
Hester Road, Milton, Southsea
☎ (01705) 733610
11-3, 6-11
Gale's BBB, Best Bitter, HSB; Hampshire King Alfred's; Hop Back Summer Lightning; Ind Coope Burton Ale; guest beers H
Welcoming, back-street local, with good beer prices. The public bar has pool and darts; there are also a quieter lounge and a new family room. This genuine Pompey boozer is a regular *Guide* entry, with the same landlord for 24 years.
⑃ ◪ P

Connaught Arms
119 Guildford Road, Fratton
☎ (01705) 646455
11.30-2.30 (3.30 Fri), 6-11; 11-11 Sat
Marston's Pedigree; Wadworth 6X; guest beers H
Large, friendly, single-bar local, tucked away in the back streets. It stages a quiz every other Mon, and offers constantly-changing guest beers, plus home-made food (not served Sun).
⊛ ◑ ⇌ (Fratton) ♣ ⇔

Dolphin
41 High Street, Old Portsmouth
☎ (01705) 823595
11-11
Draught Bass; Gale's HSB; Gibbs Mew Bishop's Tipple; Ringwood Fortyniner H**, Old Thumper** G**; Whitbread Flowers Original; guest beers** H

Built in 1630, this former coaching inn overlooks the Anglican Cathedral and its green. Inside, wooden panels and a slate floor reflect its antiquity. At least ten real ales always available.
🏨 ❀ ◑ ▶ ⇌ (Harbour) ♣ ◌

Eldon Arms

15–17 Eldon Street, Southsea
☎ (01705) 851778
11–2.30 (3.30 Sat), 6–11
Eldridge Pope Dorchester, Blackdown Porter, Hardy Country, Royal Oak; guest beers H
It's unusual for an Eldridge Pope pub to have a tiled exterior, but this one was possibly influenced by the United Brewery pubs in the city (the brewery was situated opposite). A high-ceilinged interior leads to a collection of lower-ceilinged extensions. A short walk from the Guildhall. No food Sun eve.
❀ ◑ ▶ ⇌ ♣ ◌ ⎯

Electric Arms

192 Fratton Road, Fratton
☎ (01705) 610910
11–3, 6–11; 11–11 Fri & Sat
Burts Nipper; Ind Coope Burton Ale H
Main road pub, with a glazed tile facade. A busy local, it has a lively public bar and a small quiet, unspoilt lounge. The name is derived from the long-gone trams that used to pass by. Snacks available, except Sun.
🍺 ⇌ (Fratton) ♣

Fifth Hants Volunteer Arms

74 Albert Road, Southsea
☎ (01705) 827161
12–11
Gale's BBB, Best Bitter, 5X, HSB H
Small, two-bar pub with a strong local emphasis. Weekly darts eves and a regular Irish band on Tue night combine to make this a real community pub. Refurbished at the time of the D-Day anniversary. No food Sun. ◑ ♣

Florist

324 Fratton Road, Fratton
☎ (01705) 820289
11–3, 6–11; 11–11 Sat
Wadworth IPA, 6X, Farmer's Glory, Old Timer H
Small, two-bar pub: the front public bar has darts and pool; a comfortable lounge stands at the rear. The exterior is an excellent example of Cogswell's pub design, with half-timbering and a 'witch's hat' tower.
Q 🍺 ⇌ (Fratton) ♣

Golden Eagle

1 Delamere Road, Southsea
☎ (01705) 821658
11 (5.30 Mon & Tue)–11
Gale's BBB, 5X, HSB H
Back-street, corner local: two bars with a pool table in the lounge, and darts in the public. ⇌ (Fratton) ♣

Oyster House

291 Locksway Road, Milton, Southsea ☎ (01705) 827456
12–3 (summer only), 6 (12 Sat)–11
Greene King Abbot; Wadworth 6X; Whitbread Boddingtons Mild, Bitter; guest beers H
Large pub drawing a varied clientele, with family and games rooms. Two real ciders and low prices. Near the only remaining section of the Portsea Canal.
🍺 ❀ ◑ ♣ ◌ P

Red White & Blue

150 Fawcett Road, Southsea
☎ (01705) 780013
11–11
Gale's BBB, Best Bitter, 5X, HSB H
This compact, patriotic (to two countries) local offers a selection of pub games (ask at the bar). The XXXD also makes a guest appearance, and is commonly known as 'Gnome'. Ask about meals.
◑ ⇌ (Fratton) ♣

Sir Loin of Beef

152 Highland Road, Eastney, Southsea ☎ (01705) 820115
10.30–11
Tetley Bitter; Wadworth 6X H**; guest beers**
Ex-Eldridge Pope pub, now a vastly improved free house, handy for the Royal Marines Museum and the seafront. The main bar is divided into two areas and there is a cosy snug bar. Always one real mild and two ciders available. Eve meals Thu–Sun. Frequent live music (jazz Thu).
◑ ▶ ♣ ◌

Tap

17 London Road, North End
☎ (01705) 614861
10.30–11
Arundel Stronghold; Courage Best Bitter, Directors; Gale's HSB; Hall & Woodhouse Tanglefoot H**; Ringwood Best Bitter, Old Thumper** G
Opened in 1985 as a brewery tap to the now defunct Southsea Brewery: an enterprising and successful, genuine free house, offering a good choice of ten real ales, usually including a mild, plus a real cider and occasionally a real perry. Local CAMRA *Pub of the Year 1992.* ❀ ◑ ☖ ◌

Wine Vaults

43–47 Albert Road, Southsea (opp. Kings Theatre)
☎ (01705) 864712
11.30–3.30, 5.30–11; 11–11 Sat
Draught Bass; Eldridge Pope Blackdown Porter; Hop Back Summer Lightning, Wheat Beer; Otter Ale; Ringwood Best Bitter; guest beers H
Lively free house with a wide range of ales; very popular and often crowded. Reduced prices on selected beers; regular beer festivals. The meals represent excellent value and include a vegetarian menu. ◑ ▶ ☖ ♣

Priors Dean

White Horse (Pub With No Name)

400 yds off main road, signed East Tisted OS714290
☎ (01420) 588387
11–2.30 (3 Sat), 6–11
Ballard's Best Bitter; Courage Directors; King & Barnes Mild, Sussex; Ringwood Fortyniner; S&N Theakston Old Peculier H
Famous old pub, hidden down a gravel track in a field. Very difficult to find, as the pub sign is missing. It offers ten real ales, two being house beers (the stronger one is brewed by Ringwood). Beware of the pond in the car park.
🏨 Q ❀ ◑ ▲ P

Privett

Pig & Whistle

Gosport Road (A32)
☎ (01730) 828421
11–11
Ringwood Best Bitter, Fortyniner, Old Thumper; Ruddles County; guest beers H
Large roadside hostelry, part of the Lawns Hotel complex. The single, spacious bar has a games area and food is served all day. The Lawns disco bar is open until 12.30 Fri/Sat nights (£2 entry charge—one real ale).
🏨 ❀ ☖ ◑ ▶ ☖ ♣ P

Ringwood

Inn on the Furlong

12 Meeting House Lane
☎ (01425) 475139
11–3, 5–11; 11–11 Sat
Ringwood Best Bitter, XXXX Porter, Fortyniner, Old Thumper; guest beer H
Excellent, thriving local in the centre of a market town. A central bar serves the two-roomed pub with flagstones and traditional wooden

Hampshire

furnishings. Pleasant
conservatory/dining area.
Live music Tue; beer festival
Easter weekend. 🏠 🏮 ◖ P ⊁

Romsey

Tudor Rose
3 Cornmarket
☎ (01794) 512126
10–11
**Courage Best Bitter,
Directors** H
Tiny, 15th-century ale house,
just 250 square feet, in a single
bar—a haven from the town
bustle, with a yard for summer
drinking. Folk music alternate
Sun. The only Hampshire pub
in every edition of the *Guide*.
Lunchtime snacks.
🏠 Q 🏮 ♣

Rotherwick

Falcon
The Street ☎ (01256) 762586
12–3, 5.30–11 (12–11 summer Sat)
**Brakspear Bitter; Hogs Back
TEA; Taylor Landlord;
Wadworth 6X; Whitbread
Flowers Original; guest
beers** H
Recently renovated, friendly,
two-bar village local, offering
an ever-changing range of
interesting beers (up to three
guests) and excellent value
food (not served Mon/Sun
eves). Not to be missed.
🏠 Q 🛏 🏮 ◖ ▶ 🔥 ♣ P

Shedfield

Sams Hotel
Upper Church Road (off
B2177) ☎ (01329) 832213
11.30–2 (3.30 Sat), 4.30 (6 Sat)–11
**Banks's Mild; Marston's
Bitter, Pedigree** H
Unspoilt, traditional country
inn with three bars, a cosy
lounge with a real fire and a
traditional jug and bottle. It is
reputed to be the birthplace of
British petanque (boules), and
hosts many tournaments.
Darts and bar billiards also
played. Marston's Head
Brewer's Choice available.
🏠 Q 🏮 🍴 ♣ P

Silchester

Calleva Arms
☎ (01734) 700305
11–2.30, 5–11; 11–11 Sat
**Gale's BBB, Best Bitter, 5X,
HSB** H
Popular, two-bar pub, by the
village green, with a no-
smoking conservatory added.
Handy for Calleva Roman
town, which is slowly being
restored. Good country walks.
🏠 🛏 🏮 ◖ ▶ 🔥 ♣ P ⊁

Southampton

Bosun's Locker
Castle Square, Upper Bugle
Street ☎ (01703) 333364
11–3, 6–11; 11–11 Sat
**Hampshire Pendragon; Poole
Bosun; Whitbread
Boddingtons Bitter, Porter** H;
guest beers
Surprisingly large, two-bar,
wood-panelled pub near the
city centre, convenient for
shops and museums. The bar
sports a nautical theme and
offers good, varied, home-
cooked fare (no meals Sun
eve). 🏠 Q 🏮 🛏 ◖ ▶ 🚆

Freemantle Arms
33 Albany Road, Freemantle
(W of A3057)
☎ (01703) 320759
10.30–3, 6–11; 10.30–11 Sat
**Banks's Mild; Marston's
Bitter, Pedigree** H
Friendly, two-bar local in a
quiet cul-de-sac, featuring a
popular, colourful garden and
patio. The venue for the
annual Freemantle Leek and
Vegetable Show (first Sat in
Sept). A good boozer, stocking
Marston's Head Brewer's
Choice. 🏮 ♣

Gate
138–140 Burgess Road, Bassett
(A35) ☎ (01703) 678250
11–3, 7–11
**Eldridge Pope Blackdown
Porter, Hardy Country, Royal
Oak; guest beers** H
Large, open-plan pub close to
the university, popular with
locals and students. It can be
loud and lively, but has a good
atmosphere. Sky TV is very
popular for sport. Eve meals
by arrangement (no food Sat).
Small meeting room.
🏮 ◖ ▶ ♣ P

Hobbit
134 Bevois Valley Road
☎ (01703) 232591
6 (12 Sat)–11
**Brakspear Bitter; Hop Back
Summer Lightning, Wheat
Beer; Whitbread Boddingtons
Mild, Flowers Original; guest
beers** H
Thriving young people's pub,
hosting live music most nights
in the downstairs bar. The
guest beers come from small
breweries. It can be crowded.
Sun lunch served.
🏮 🚆 (St Denys)

Humble Plum
73 Commercial Street, Bitterne
☎ (01703) 437577
11–2.30 (11.30–3 Sat), 6–11
**Bass Worthington BB,
Draught Bass; M&B Brew XI;
Wadworth 6X; Whitbread
Flowers Original; Wychwood**

Dr Thirsty's Draught H; guest
beers
Comfortable, one-bar pub in
quiet, residential Bitterne,
providing a reasonable beer
choice for this part of the
city.Formerly the Commercial
Inn. Q 🏮 ◖ P

Marsh
42 Canute Road (under A3025,
Itchen Bridge)
☎ (01703) 635540
11–11
**Banks's Mild; Marston's
Bitter, Pedigree** H
Characteristic docklands pub,
once a lighthouse, hence the
semi-circular bars. A brisk
lunchtime trade comes from
the nearby Ocean Village and
local businesses. Pool room.
Marston's Head Brewer's
Choice is stocked. 🏮 ◖ ▶
🍴 🛏 🚆 (Woolston) ♣

New Inn
16 Bevois Valley Road
☎ (01703) 228437
11.45–3, 6.45–11; 11–11 Sat
**Gale's XXXD (summer), BBB,
Best Bitter, 5X, HSB; guest
beers** H
Excellent, bustling drinkers'
pub with its own rugby union
team. Large range of Belgian
beers and over 100 malt
whiskies. Good value lunches.
◖ ♣

Park Inn
37 Carlisle Road, Shirley (off
A3057) ☎ (01703) 787835
11–3 (3.30 Sat), 5 (6 Sat)–11
**Hall & Woodhouse
Tanglefoot; Wadworth IPA,
6X, Farmer's Glory, Old
Timer; guest beer** H
Popular, friendly local, close to
the shops. It maintains a
two-bar feel and has some
interesting mirrors. Slightly
more upmarket than most
side-street pubs. 🏮 ◖ ♣

Richmond Inn
108 Portswood Road,
Portswood
☎ (01703) 554523
11–11
**Banks's Mild; Marston's
Bitter, Pedigree** H
Friendly hostelry in a busy
shopping district, with a basic
public bar and a plusher
lounge. Note the wonderful
old LSD cash register and the
excellent whisky selection. Tue
is cribbage night. Marston's
Head Brewer's Choice
available.
🏮 🛏 🚆 (St Denys) ♣

Wellington Arms
56 Park Road, Freemantle
☎ (01703) 227356
11.30–2.30, 5.30 (7 Sat)–11; 12–2.30,
7–10.30 Sun

Courage Directors; Fuller's London Pride; Hampshire Lionheart; Ringwood Best Bitter, Old Thumper; Wadworth 6X; guest beers H
Busy, comfortable, back-street free house with two lounges and a mass of Iron Duke memorabilia. No food Sun.
❀ ◁ ⇌ (Central)

Sparsholt

Plough
Main Road ☎ (01962) 776353
11–3, 6.30–11
Wadworth IPA, 6X H; guest beers
Large village inn, formerly a farmhouse, recently converted to one bar, but keeping many different areas. Strong food emphasis: the menu includes children's and vegetarian choices. The big garden boasts a summerhouse.
🏚 Q ⚞ ❀ ◁ ▶ ⑆ ♣ P

Standford

New Robin Hood Inn
Standford Lane (B3004)
☎ (01428) 751508
11–3, 5.30–11 (11–11 summer)
Draught Bass; Gibbs Mew Local Line, Deacon, Bishop's Tipple H
From the outside, this 1904 pub looks like a railway station, with superb etched windows, but the interior is reminiscent of a wooden paddle steamer (possibly influenced by the nearby working water mill).
🏚 Q ❀ ◁ ▶ ⑆ ▲ ♣ P

Thruxton

White Horse
Off A303 (westbound)
☎ (01264) 772401
11–3 (3.30 Sat), 6–11
Butcombe Bitter; Fuller's London Pride; Smiles Best Bitter H
Pretty, thatched village inn. Fortunate to escape the construction of the trunk road which towers over it, it retains all that is best in character and welcome. Children are allowed in the dining room. No food Sun/Mon eves.
🏚 Q ❀ ◁ ▶ ♣ P

Totford

Woolpack
On B3046 S of Brown Candover ☎ (01962) 732101
11.30–3, 6–11
Cheriton Pots Ale; Eldridge Pope Dorchester; Hardy Country; Gale's HSB; Palmers IPA H

Friendly, 16th-century pub and restaurant with more recent additions, set in a tiny hamlet, unlikely to be on your road map! The garden features a duckpond. Near the Grange (NT). 🏚 Q ❀ 🛏 ◁ ▶ ♣ P

Twyford

Phoenix
High Street (B3335)
☎ (01962) 713322
11.30–2.30 (3 Sat), 6–11
Marston's Bitter, Pedigree H
Busy, friendly village inn, serving good value food. Accommodation is available in nearby village houses. Skittle alley/function room. Marston's Head Brewer's Choice available. 🏚 ❀ ◁ ▶ ⇌ (Shawford) ♣ P

Upper Clatford

Crook & Shears
Off A343 ☎ (01264) 361543
12–3, 6–11; 12–11 Sat
Fuller's Chiswick; Hogs Back TEA; Morland Old Speckled Hen; Ringwood XXXX Porter; Whitbread Flowers Original H
Pretty, 17th-century village inn with a cheerful public bar and a cosy lounge. The huge fireplace was originally a baker's oven. Skittle alley and pleasant courtyard. Good choice of local sausages (no food Sun eve).
🏚 Q ❀ ◁ ▶ ⑆ ♣

Try also: Eagle, Abbotts Ann (Ushers)

Upton Grey

Hoddington Arms
☎ (01256) 862371
11–2.30, 6 (7 Sat)–11; 12–2.30, 7–10.30 Sun
Morland Old Speckled Hen; guest beer H
18th-century, listed building in a pretty village. Excellent cuisine; separate dining area. Note the unusual lattice ceiling in the bar billiards room. Good family room, too. Genuinely friendly. 🏚 ⚞ ❀ ◁ ▶ ♣ P

Vernham Dean

George
Off A343 W of Hurstbourne Tarrant ☎ (01264) 87279
11–2.30 (3 Sat), 6–11
Marston's Bitter, Pedigree H
Super, 16th-century, timber and brick inn, featuring low beams and a large inglenook. Popular with locals, it is arguably one of the prettiest pubs in Hampshire. Note the embroidery depicting local scenes. No food Wed/Sun eves. 🏚 Q ⚞ ❀ ◁ ▶ P

Wallington

White Horse
44 North Wallington (off M27 jct 10/A32/A27)
☎ (01329) 235197
11–3, 5 (7 Sat)–11
Draught Bass; guest beers G
Pub by the River Wallington, with a patio garden. Well-renovated, its two bars each have a different character, with fresh flowers on the tables. The restaurant serves as a family room Sun lunchtime.
🏚 ❀ ◁ ♣

West End

Master Builder
Swaythling Road (A27)
☎ (01703) 472426
11–2.30, 6 (5.30 Fri)–11; 11–11 Sat
Draught Bass; Whitbread Boddingtons Bitter; guest beers H
Large, comfortable roadside pub with many drinking areas, two of which are no-smoking. Four regularly changing guest beers are stocked. The menu carries the *Heartbeat Award* (and includes children's choices); eve food until 9pm, but not Sun/Mon. No fruit machines. ⚞ ❀ ◁ ▶ P ✄

Weyhill

Weyhill Fair
Weyhill Road (A342)
☎ (01264) 773631
11–2.30, 6 (5 Fri, 6.30 Sat)–11
Morrells Bitter, Varsity, Graduate; guest beers H
Free house, 11 years in the *Guide* and twice local CAMRA *Pub of the Year*. An imaginative, constantly-changing selection of three guest beers includes a mild. Good value beer and food; no meals Sun eve. Upstairs function room.
🏚 Q ⚞ ❀ ◁ ▶ ⑆ P

Whitchurch

Prince Regent
104 London Road
☎ (01256) 892179
11–11
Archers Best Bitter; Hop Back GFB, Summer Lightning; guest beer H
Down-to-earth, genuine local; a good traditional pub, well worth a visit. Food is available all day. 🏚 ❀ ◁ ▶ ⇌ ♣ P

Red House
London Street
☎ (01256) 892066
11.30–3, 5.30–11; 11–11 Fri & Sat
Wadworth 6X; guest beers H

Hampshire

Large village pub, painted white, not red! The flagstone-floored public is reminiscent of a student bar: busy, friendly and atmospheric, with a rock/blues jukebox. The lounge, by comparison, is quiet and sedate. Fine garden. No food Sun eve. Inch's cider in summer.
🍺 ❀ ◖ ▌ ⊟ ⇌ ♣ ▭ P

Whiteley

Parsons Collar
Rookery Avenue, Solent Business Park (just off M27 jct 9) ☎ (01489) 880035
11–2.30, 5 (6 Sat)–11
Thwaites Bitter, Craftsman H
Large, comfortable pub, built in 1990, with a stone-flagged floor. The family dining room offers a children's menu or half-portions (no food Sun eve). Accommodation is in the adjacent Solent Hotel.
🍺 ❀ ⇆ ◖ ▌ ⅙ P

Whitsbury

Cartwheel
Whitsbury Road (signed from A338) OS129188
☎ (0172 53) 362
11–2.30 (3 Sat), 6–11
Beer range varies H
Remote, though thriving free house with a games area and a dining room. Six real ales are usually available, offering an excellent selection from far and wide. 🍺 ❀ ◖ ▌ ♣ P

Winchester

Bell
83 St Cross Road, St Cross
☎ (01962) 865284
11–2.30, 5–11; 11–11 Sat
Bateman Mild; Marston's Bitter, Pedigree H
Fine old inn, adjacent to the 12th-century Hospital of St Cross (England's oldest charitable body). Contrasting bars provide a quiet lounge for

conversationalists and a more down-to-earth public bar. Marston's Head Brewer's Choice available.
🍺 Q ❀ ◖ ⊟ ♣ P

Crown & Anchor
168 High Street
☎ (01962) 854897
10 (10.30 Sat)–11
Marston's Bitter, Pedigree H
King Alfred overlooks the bay-windowed facade of this refurbished pub where the award-winning rear patio is an excellent refuge from the bustle of the High Street. Live jazz Mon eve. Marston's Head Brewer's Choice stocked.
❀ ◖ ▲

Eagle Hotel
1 Andover Road (opp. station)
☎ (01962) 853108
11–3, 5–11
Cheriton Best Bitter; Hampshire King Alfred's; Hop Back Summer Lightning; Tetley Bitter; guest beer H
Hotel where the landlady has returned after an absence of 20 years to take it by the scruff of its neck. Now reasonably-priced ales from local small breweries are always available; plus occasional beer festivals. Book for meals eves and Sun.
🍺 Q ⇆ ◖ ▲ ⇌ P

Fulflood Arms
28 Cheriton Road (off A272)
☎ (01962) 865356
12–2, 5 (6 Fri & Sat)–11
Marston's Bitter, Pedigree H
Traditional, corner local in a quiet back street. The tiled frontage still proclaims 'Winchester Brewery'. Marston's Head Brewer's Choice sold.
Q ❀ ⊟ ⇌ ♣

Hyde Tavern
57 Hyde Street
☎ (01962) 862592
11–2.30, 5.30–11
Marston's Bitter, Pedigree H
Double gable-fronted, two-bar pub below street level; the

oldest pub in town. The very homely interior features brass ornaments, low ceilings and low door-frames.
Q ⊟ ▲ ⇌ ♣

Queen Inn
28 Kingsgate Road
☎ (01962) 853898
11.30–2.30, 6–11
Marston's Bitter, Pedigree H
A country cottage in the city, comprising two small bars: a dark wood-panelled public and a 'Laura Ashley' lounge, plus an extensive garden. It lies adjacent to Winchester College and the water meadows. Marston's Head Brewer's Choice available.
🍺 Q ❀ ◖ ▌ ⊟ P

Wolverton

George & Dragon
Off A339 ☎ (01635) 298292
12–3, 5.30–11
Brakspear Special; Fuller's London Pride; Hampshire King Alfred's; Wadworth IPA, 6X H
Open-plan, country inn with a games room to one side of the single bar. A large open fire is a feature. Separate skittle alley.
🍺 ❀ ◖ ▌ ⅙ ♣ P

Woolton Hill

Rampant Cat
Broad Layings (off A343; then road opp. 'The Stores' in village centre)
☎ (01635) 253474
12–3 (not Mon), 7–11
Archers Best Bitter; Arkell's 3B, Kingsdown; guest beers H
Pleasant country pub with a large, L-shaped bar area and ample seating. The restaurant leads on to a raised patio and a large garden with a play area. Near NT woodlands, it is popular with ramblers. Guest beers include winter brews.
🍺 ❀ ♣ P

Try also: **Coopers Arms** (Ushers)

<table>
<tr><td colspan="4" align="center">THE SYMBOLS</td></tr>
<tr><td>🍺</td><td>real fire</td><td>⅙</td><td>easy wheelchair access</td></tr>
<tr><td>Q</td><td>quiet pub (at least one bar)</td><td>▲</td><td>camping facilities at the pub</td></tr>
<tr><td>❄</td><td>indoor room for children</td><td></td><td>or nearby</td></tr>
<tr><td>❀</td><td>garden or other outdoor drinking</td><td>⇌</td><td>near British Rail station</td></tr>
<tr><td></td><td>area</td><td>Ɵ</td><td>near underground station</td></tr>
<tr><td>⇆</td><td>accommodation</td><td>♣</td><td>pub games</td></tr>
<tr><td>◖</td><td>lunchtime meals</td><td>▭</td><td>real cider</td></tr>
<tr><td>▌</td><td>evening meals</td><td>P</td><td>pub car park</td></tr>
<tr><td>⊟</td><td>public bar</td><td>⚥</td><td>no-smoking room or area</td></tr>
</table>

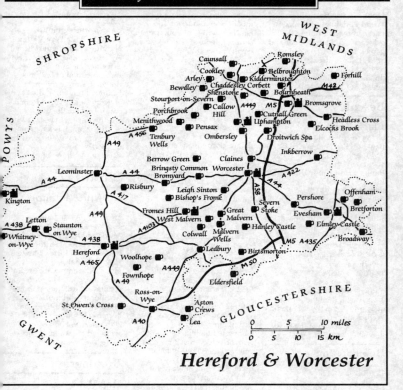

Hereford & Worcester

Cannon Royall, Uphampton; **Evesham**, Evesham;
Jolly Roger, Worcester; **Red Cross**, Bromsgrove;
Solstice, Kington; **Wheatsheaf**, Fromes Hill; **Wye
Valley**, Hereford

Arley

Harbour Inn
Station Bank (down hill from
SVR station, over footbridge
from village) ☎ (01299) 401204
12–3, 7–11 (11–11 summer Sat)
**Bass Worthington BB,
Draught Bass; M&B Mild;
Stones Best Bitter** E
Cosy, free house with a
restaurant at the rear, and a
large garden housing a
children's farmyard. Near the
River Severn. 🏚 ⏰ ❀ ◑ ▶ ㊒
⇌ (SVR summer) ♣ P

Aston Crews

White Hart
Signed just off B4222, Lea–
Newent road
☎ (01989) 750203
11–3, 7–11
**Wye Valley Hereford Bitter;
guest beers** H

300-year-old village local,
mainly catering for an older
clientele. With its adventurous
guest beer policy, it is always
worth a visit. Good food is
served in the restaurant or on
the terrace, with lovely views
over hilly farmland.
Q ❀ ◑ ▶ P

Belbroughton

Holly Bush
Stourbridge Road (A491)
☎ (01562) 730207
11–3, 6–11 (11–11 bank hols)
**Ansells Mild; HP&D Bitter,
Entire; Tetley Bitter; guest
beers** (occasional) H
Traditional roadside inn where
a single bar serves three
distinct areas, one of which is
the dining room. A popular
pianist entertains the locals
Wed, Fri and Sat eves. No
food Sun eve.
🏚 Q ❀ ◑ ▶ ㊒ P

Olde Horseshoe
High Street (B4188)
☎ (01562) 730233
11–3 (4 Sat), 5.30 (6 Sat)–11
**S&N Theakston Mild, Best
Bitter, XB, Old Peculier; guest
beer** H
At one time the only
brewhouse in the village, this
old pub stopped brewing in
1948. It now comprises a very
small lounge and a larger bar
with a pool table. An excellent
menu includes a wide range of
vegetarian food. Often busy
with diners; no meals Mon
eve. ❀ ◑ ▶ ㊒ ♣ ⏰ P

Try also: **Queens**, Queens Hill
(Marston's)

Berrow Green

Admiral Rodney
Take B4197 from Knightwick
OS748584 ☎ (01886) 21375
12–3, 6–11 (may be 12–11 in summer)

129

Hereford & Worcester

Hook Norton Best Bitter; Wood Parish; guest beers H
Large, rambling pub with self-contained lounge, bar and games areas, plus a skittle alley. It has a strong nautical feel but is in no sense a 'theme' pub. No food Mon eve. ⚓ Q ◐ ▮ ▲ ♣ P

Bewdley

Black Boy
50 Wyre Hill (follow Sandy Bank, off B4194 at Welch Gate) ☎ (01299) 403523
12–3, 7–11
Banks's Hanson's Mild, Mild, Bitter E; Marston's Pedigree H
Friendly, welcoming local, more than 400 years old, situated near the top of a steep climb from the centre of town. ⚓ Q ⏳ ◐ ♣

Cock & Magpie
Severnside North ☎ (01299) 403748
11–3, 6–11; 11–11 Sat & summer
Banks's Mild, Bitter E
Two-bar local on the former quayside of the River Severn. Wellies are recommended to reach the pub when the river floods! Q ⇌ (SVR) ♣

Hop Pole Inn
Cleobury Road ☎ (01299) 402127
11–2.30, 6–11
Banks's Mild; Marston's Bitter, Pedigree H
Popular, two-roomed inn situated almost a mile above the town. Meals are served Tue–Sun. Marston's Head Brewer's Choice is featured. Q ◐ ◐ ▮ ◱ ♣ P

Birtsmorton

Farmers Arms
Birts Street ☎ (01684) 833308
11–2.30, 6–11
Hook Norton Best Bitter, Old Hooky; guest beer H
Black and white pub, tucked away down a country lane: a small, low-beamed, lounge and a basic bar with darts. The garden has swings and views of the Malvern Hills—ideal for summer. Reasonably-priced, wholesome food. ⚓ Q ◐ ◐ ▮ ♣ P

Bishop's Frome

Chase Inn
On B4214 ☎ (01885) 490234
12–3.30, 5.30–11; 12–11 Sat
Hook Norton Best Bitter; Wye Valley Hereford Bitter; guest beer H
Uncomplicated and comfortable pub and restaurant opposite the village

green. Two bars offer a good mix of beer and food. The landlord will read your Tarot cards on request. The house beer is brewed by Wye Valley. ⚓ Q ◐ ◐ ◱ ▮ ▲ ♣ P

Green Dragon
Off B4214 ☎ (01885) 490607
12–2.30, 5–11; 11–11 Sat
Robinson's Old Tom; Taylor Golden Best, Landlord; Tetley Bitter; guest beers H
Multi-roomed, old village inn that once commanded a cult following, but is still popular for its good value food and up to seven beers on tap. Original flagstones, an inglenook and low ceilings contrast with the small restaurant and the games bar, popular with village youngsters. ⚓ ◐ ◐ ◱ ♣ P

Bournheath

Gate
Dodford Road (off B4551) OS946741 ☎ (01527) 878169
11–2.30, 6–10.30 (11 Fri & Sat)
Smiles Best Bitter, Exhibition; Whitbread Boddingtons Bitter; guest beer H
Converted nailer's cottage with an added restaurant and conservatory; stylish decor. The emphasis is clearly on the excellent, wide range of food with Mexican/Cajun specialities, plus Balti night (Mon). ⚓ ◐ ◐ ▮ ◱ P

Try also: Nailer's, Dodford Rd (Allied)

Bretforton

Fleece
The Cross (100 yds S of B4035) ☎ (01386) 831173
11–2.30, 6–11; 12–2.30, 7–10.30 Sun
Everards Beacon; Hook Norton Best Bitter; M&B Brew XI; Uley Hogshead, Old Spot H
Famous old inn, owned by the NT. The interior has remained untouched for many years, and includes inglenooks, antiques and a world-famous pewter collection. The family room (no-smoking) is in keeping with the rest of the pub. No crisps! ⚓ Q ⏳ ◐ ◐ ▮ ▲ ⇌ (Honeybourne) ♣ ◱ ✗

Try also: Thatch Tavern, Honeybourne (Whitbread)

Bringsty Common

Live & Let Live
Off A44; at pub sign follow right-hand track on common OS699547 ☎ (01886) 21462

12–3 (not winter Tue), 6–11; 11–11 Fri & Sat
Bass Worthington BB, Draught Bass; Wye Valley Hereford Bitter; guest beer H
A compass and a four-wheel drive vehicle are recommended to find this unspoilt, simple inn on the common, but a friendly welcome and many original features make the trek worthwhile. A five-star anachronism, it offers two ciders on gravity dispense but no food. ⚓ Q ◐ ◱ ▲ ♣ ◱ P

Broadway

Crown & Trumpet
Church Street ☎ (01386) 853202
11–2.30 (3 summer), 5–11
Morland Old Speckled Hen; Wadworth 6X; Whitbread Boddingtons Bitter, Flowers IPA, Original H
Fine, 17th-century Cotswold stone inn, complete with oak beams and log fires, popular with locals and tourists alike. The welcoming interior has been bypassed by most of the 20th century. Food can be arranged for walking parties. ⚓ ◐ ◪ ◐ ▮ ▲ ♣ ◱

Bromsgrove

Hop Pole
78 Birmingham Road ☎ (01527) 870100
12–2.30 (3 Sat), 5.30 (7 Sat)–11
Bass Worthington BB; Red Cross Nailer's OBJ H
Pleasant, street-corner local standing opposite the Rovers' football ground: an L-shaped bar and a simple, but comfortable lounge serving good value lunches (not Sun). Many local societies meet here. OBJ, brewed by the licensee, is occasionally replaced by a guest ale. ◐ ◐

Try also: Merlin, Stourbridge Rd (Free)

Bromyard

Bay Horse Hotel
21 High Street ☎ (01885) 482635
11–11
Draught Bass; Hobsons Best Bitter H
One-bar, comfortable town pub with much wood panelling, that has survived a knock-through quite well. A priest hole, piano and a restaurant feature in this friendly pub. The beer range can vary, but always includes a Bass beer. No meals Sun lunch. ⚓ ◐ ◪ ◐ ▮ ♣ P

Crown & Sceptre

Sherford Street
☎ (01885) 482441
11.30–3, 6.30–11
S&N Theakston Best Bitter, XB; guest beers H
Pleasant, popular free house with various drinking areas and a restaurant. The bars are furnished with maps and old adverts. The guest beers can be quite adventurous. No meals Wed eve. 🏨 🏵 🖼 🌙 ♣ P

Callow Hill

Royal Forrester

On A456, near Kidderminster
☎ (01299) 266286
11–11
Greene King Abbot; John Smith's Bitter H
Pleasant, popular main-road inn, where families are welcome. A cosy lounge stands at the front, with a games room at the rear. Forest Mild is a house beer (not brewed here).
🏨 Q 🐾 🏵 ᵬ ♣ P

Caunsall

Anchor Inn

☎ (01562) 850254
12–4, 7–11
Draught Bass; M&B Mild; Stones Best Bitter H
Pleasant, two-roomed village pub, a short walk from the Staffs and Worcs Canal.
Q 🐾 🏵 ⌂ P

Chaddesley Corbett

Swan

High Street ☎ (01562) 777302
11–4.30 (3.30 Mon), 7–11
Batham Mild, Best Bitter, XXX H
Spacious country pub with a lively, popular bar, a large open lounge, a children's room and a restaurant. It is well worth a visit to this pretty, historic village. Eve meals Wed–Sat; barbecues in summer; jazz Thu.
🏨 🐾 🏵 🌙 🖼 ᵬ ♣ ⌂ P

Try also: Fox Inn, A448 (S&N Theakston)

Claines

Mug House

Claines Lane ☎ (01905) 56649
12–2.30 (3 Sat), 5–11
Banks's Mild E, **Bitter** E/ H
Ancient and unspoilt pub, occasionally used by local schools as an example of old rural architecture. It is worth asking for the bitter from the handpump rather than the electric meter.
🏨 Q 🐾 🏵 ᵬ A ♣

Colwall

Chase Inn

Chase Road, Upper Colwall (200 yds off B4218, Wyche Rd, signed 'British Camp')
☎ (01684) 40276
12–2.30 (not Tue), 6–11; 12–2.30, 7–10.30 Sun
Donnington BB, SBA; Wye Valley HPA, Hereford Supreme H
Quiet, relaxing and original free house, tucked away in a backwater of the Malvern Hills. A limited, but exceptionally wholesome menu is served (not Sun). No muzak; occasional Elgar! Q 🏵 🌙 ♣

Cookley

Bull's Head Hotel

Bridge Road ☎ (01562) 850242
11.30–3, 6–11; 11–11 Sat
Banks's Mild, Bitter E
Large village local, situated over Cookley Canal tunnel. It boasts family rooms and a garden with play area at the rear. Access to the canal is via a steep, twisting path. Good value food.
🐾 🏵 🌙 🖼 ♣ P ⊁

Cutnall Green

New Inn

Kidderminster Road (A442)
☎ (01299) 851202
12–2.30, 5.30 (6 Sat)–11
Banks's Mild; Marston's Bitter, Pedigree H
Small and friendly village local. Reasonably-priced lunchtime 'lite bites', plus vegetarian meals are available, and Marston's Head Brewer's Choice is stocked.
🏨 🏵 🖼 🌙 P

Droitwich Spa

Old Cock

Friar Street (off High St)
☎ (01905) 774233
11–3, 5.30–11
Marston's Bitter, Pedigree, Owd Rodger H
Superb, 17th-century inn, popular with theatre-goers. A central bar serves six separate 'rooms' and there's also a restaurant, a function room and a prize-winning patio garden. An outlet for the Marston's Head Brewer's Choice range. Wheelchair access is at the rear.
🏵 🌙 🖼 ᵬ ≋

Elcocks Brook

Brook Inn

Sillins Lane (off Windmill Drive, near Redditch)
☎ (01527) 543209
12–2.30, 5–11; 12–11 Sat
Banks's Mild; Marston's Bitter, Pedigree H
Popular country pub with a spacious single bar. Warm and comfortable, it has a friendly atmosphere. Look out for special curry and live music eves. 🏨 🏵 🌙 P

Eldersfield

Greyhound

Lime Street ☎ (01452) 840381
11.30–11
Butcombe Bitter; Wadworth 6X; guest beers G
Traditionally furnished country pub, with many unusual features: gravity-dispensed beers, quoits, and a garden full of animals (geese, goats, chickens, etc). Families are very welcome. Camping in the grounds (caravans OK).
🏨 🐾 🏵 A ♣ ⌂ P

Elmley Castle

Queen Elizabeth

West Side, Main Street
☎ (01386) 710209
12–3, 7–11
Marston's Bitter, Pedigree H
Visited by its namesake in 1575, this traditional village inn has remained unchanged under the present landlord for 30 years. Handy for walkers on Bredon Hill, but it can get rather smoky.
🏨 Q 🏵 🌙 A ♣

Evesham

Green Dragon

Oat Street ☎ (01386) 446337
11–3, 7–11; 11–11 Thu–Sat
Evesham Asum Ale, Asum Gold; John Smith's Bitter or **Draught Bass; guest beers** H
Large, lively town pub, complete with its own brewery.
Q 🐾 🏵 🌙 A ≋ ♣

Trumpet

Merstow Green (off southern end of High St)
☎ (01386) 446227
11–11
Draught Bass; Vaux Samson; Wadworth 6X H
Convivial town-centre local.
🏵 🌙 A ≋ ♣ ⊁

Forhill (Wythall)

Peacock

Icknield Street (2 miles from A441/Redhill road jct towards Wythall) OS054755
☎ (01564) 823232
12–3, 5–11 (12–11 summer)
Banks's Mild, Bitter; Camerons Strongarm; Marston's Pedigree; guest beer H

131

Hereford & Worcester

Country pub with oak beams throughout. No music, but bar billiards, skittles and quoits are played in the bar, which has a chatty, friendly atmosphere. ♨ Q ♿ ✿ ⓓ ⅅ ♿ ♠ ♣ P ⊁

Fownhope

Green Man Inn
On B4224 ☎ (01432) 860243
11–2.30, 6–11 (may be 11–11 in summer)
Hook Norton Best Bitter; Marston's Pedigree; Samuel Smith OBB; Whitbread Boddingtons Bitter Ⓗ
Classic, 500-year-old, black and white coaching inn, very popular with drinkers and out-of-town diners from Hereford, and enjoying a reputation for good value. Guests have fishing rights on the Wye. The longest-running *Guide* entry for the county. Ask for games.
Q ✿ ⛴ ⓓ ⅅ Ⓐ ♣ P

Fromes Hill

Wheatsheaf
On A4103 ☎ (01531) 640888
5 (11 Sat)–11
Draught Bass; Fromes Hill Buckswood Dingle, Overture, IDK Ⓗ
Enterprising, one-bar pub owned and operated by the Fromes Hill Brewery. It incorporates an Indian Balti house, and both the beer and food are gaining good reputations. The brewer is always experimenting with new brews. A comfortable pub with a racing theme.
♨ ✿ ⓓ ⅅ Ⓐ P

Great Malvern

Cross Keys
79 Belmont Road
☎ (01684) 572945
12–3, 7–11 Fri & Sat
Thwaites Craftsman; Whitbread Boddingtons Bitter; Wye Valley HPA; guest beer Ⓗ
A haven for real ale in this part of town. The new enterprising owners are only too glad to please and there is a strong involvement in local pub leagues. The street theme in the rear is worth a look, though loud music, TV and smoke are regular hazards. Children tolerated.
♨ ♿ ✿ ⇌ (Malvern Link) ♣ P

Foley Arms Hotel
Worcester Road
☎ (01684) 573397
12–3, 5.30–11
Draught Bass; guest beers Ⓗ

Popular bar in an enlarged 1810 coaching inn. Magnificent views across the Severn Valley can be enjoyed from the bar and terrace. Two imaginative guest beers are always available—one low gravity, one high.
Q ♿ ✿ ⛴ ⓓ ⅅ ⇌ ♣ P ⊁

Star Inn
59 Cowleigh Road
☎ (01684) 574280
12–4 (not Mon–Fri), 7–11
M&B Mild; S&N Theakston Best Bitter, XB Ⓗ
Friendly, three-roomer with some magnificent Victorian bar furniture. Its pool room and skittle alley are both well-used. Folk music Thu eve.
✿ ⇌ (Malvern Link) ♣ P

Hanley Castle

Three Kings
Church End (signed off B4211)
☎ (01684) 592686
11–3, 7–11
Butcombe Bitter; Thwaites Bitter; guest beers Ⓗ
Unspoilt, classic English pub, in the same family for over 80 years. Its welcoming and friendly atmosphere make it a good meeting place for many local clubs. Look out for the ancient beer engine in the lounge. CAMRA national *Country Pub of the Year* 1993. No food Sun eve.
♨ Q ♿ ✿ ⛴ ⓓ ⅅ ♣ ⅆ

Headless Cross

Gate Hangs Well
98 Evesham Road
☎ (01527) 401293
12–3, 5.30–11; 12–11 Sat
Ansells Bitter, Mild; HP&D, Entire Ⓗ
Well-kept, one-bar, main-road local with a warm, friendly atmosphere. Popular with younger drinkers and it can get lively eves. ♨ ✿ ⓓ ♣

Seven Stars
75 Birchfield Road (off A441, Evesham road)
☎ (01527) 402138
12–11
Marston's Pedigree; Ruddles Best Bitter; Webster's Yorkshire Bitter Ⓗ
Basic local: a bar area, a lounge, a games room and a snug all in a small pub. ♣ ⅆ

Hereford

Barrels
69 St Owen Street
☎ (01432) 274968
11–11
Wye Valley Hereford Bitter, HPA, Hereford Supreme, Brew 69; guest beers Ⓗ

Brash, lively and down-to-earth pub with a cult following. Home of the Wye Valley Brewery, it is the venue for a beer festival each Aug. No food, but there's always something happening in the three friendly bar areas. Popular with students towards the weekend, otherwise local banter dominates.
✿ ♨ ⛼ ⇌ ♣ ⅆ

Lancaster
1 St Martins Street
☎ (01432) 275480
11–3, 6–11
Beer range varies Ⓗ
Two-bar city, riverside pub with unpretentious decor and a loyal following of locals. It can be busy on barmy summer eves. Usually a minimum of three beers are offered with Fuller's and Wye Valley guesting regularly. Parking can be awkward. ⓓ ⅅ ♣ ⅆ

Sun Inn
71 St Owen Street
☎ (01432) 266403
11–3, 6–11
Bass Worthington BB, Draught Bass; Wye Valley Hereford Bitter Ⓗ
Small city pub, recently knocked-through, but retaining some of the character of the Hereford pubs of old. The discrete back bar was the last in Hereford to have table service (until 1992). Bulmers cider is sold from big wooden casks. Strong local following.
Q ⇌ ♣ ⅆ

Three Elms Inn
1 Canon Pyon Road
☎ (01432) 273338
11–11
Marston's Pedigree; Whitbread Boddingtons Bitter, Pompey Royal, Flowers Original; guest beers Ⓗ
Refreshing an otherwise poor area of Hereford, this large, open-plan, refurbished pub is good for families. The landlord ensures no-one is ever disappointed, with up to eight beers sold. Hereford CAMRA joint *Pub of the Year* 1993. Q ♿ ✿ ⓓ ⅅ ♿ P

Treacle Mine
83–85 St Martins Street
☎ (01432) 266022
11–4 (3.30 Tue; 12–3 Mon), 6–11; 11–11 Fri & Sat
Banks's Mild, Bitter; Greene King Abbot; Wood Wallop; guest beers Ⓗ
Single-bar pub on the south side of the river. An unorthodox mix of satellite TV, old timbers and brickwork attracts a good mix of clientele and it is always a popular

calling point on a pub
crawl. ☙

Victory

88 St Owen Street
☎ (01432) 274998
11–11
Beer range varies H
Pub with a galleon and
maritime theme, formerly the
Jolly Roger brew pub and now
the latest addition to the
successful Wye Valley stable.
Powder Monkey and Eight
Bells are house beers. A good
mix of clientele enjoys the
good atmosphere, live music
and good food. The restaurant
has a fishy flavour.
❀ ⬤ ◑ ♣ ○

Try also: **Castle Pool Hotel,**
Castle St (Free)

Inkberrow

Bull's Head

On A422 ☎ (01386) 792233
11–11
**Banks's Mild, Bitter; Draught
Bass; Stanway Stanney Bitter;
Shepherd Neame Bishops
Finger** E; **guest beers**
Large village pub opposite the
green with two distinct,
split-level drinking areas and a
dining room. Note the electric
dispense behind the dummy
handpulls. ❀ ◑ ▶ P ✄

Kidderminster

King & Castle

Severn Valley Railway Station,
Comberton Hill
☎ (01562) 747505
11–3 (4 Sat), 5 (6 Sat)–11
**Draught Bass; Batham Best
Bitter; guest beers** H
Pub forming part of the
Kidderminster terminus of the
Severn Valley Railway. There
are typically three guest beers
available and children are
welcome until 9pm. Eve meals
served Thu–Sun until 9pm.
🍴 ◑ ♿ ⇌ ♣ P

Red Man

92 Blackwell Street
☎ (01562) 67555
0–11
**Ansells Bitter; HP&D Mild,
Entire; Ind Coope Burton Ale;
Marston's Pedigree; Tetley
Bitter; guest beer** H
Pub situated just on the edge
of the town centre, within the
ring road. It consists of a
two-roomed lounge, with a
bar and pool room to the rear.
A large garden and play area
stand behind the pub.
❀ ◑ ▶ ⇌ ♣ ○ P

Station Inn

Farfield ☎ (01562) 822764
12–3.30, 6–11; 11–11 Fri

**Greenalls Davenports Bitter;
Tetley Bitter** H
Comfortable, welcoming local,
a few minutes' walk from BR
and SVR stations. The garden
is safe for children. No eve
meals Wed.
Q ❀ ◑ ▶ ⬤ ⇌ ♣ P

Kington

Olde Tavern

22 Victoria Road
☎ (01533) 231384
7.30–11; 11–2.30, 7.30–11 Sat; 12–2.30,
7–10.30 Sun
Ansells Bitter H
An outstanding relic of times
past—a must for all
connoisseurs of the old
English pub. Two small bars
complete with benches, settles
and curios are set behind an
ornate Victorian facade. Joint
Herefordshire CAMRA *Pub of
the Year* 1993. Q ⬤ ♣

Lea

Crown Inn

Gloucester Road (A40)
☎ (01989) 750407
11.30–2.30, 6–11
**Greene King Abbot;
Wadworth 6X; guest beer** H
Ex-Whitbread, two-level,
two-bar roadside village pub,
haunted by a ghost which has
not been seen recently.
🍴 Q ❀ ♣ P

Ledbury

Brewery Inn

Bye Street ☎ (01531) 634272
11–3.30, 7–11; often 11–11 Fri & Sat
**Banks's Mild; Marston's
Bitter** H
Back-street pub retaining
character despite a
refurbishment. Untouched
snug; games-oriented locals'
bar. Cold food served (not
Sun).
Q ⏚ ❀ ◑ ⇌ ♣ ○

Prince of Wales

Church Lane ☎ (01531) 632250
11–3, 7 (6 summer)–11
**Banks's Mild, Bitter;
Camerons Strongarm** H
Multi-barred, 16th-century inn
that features on numerous
calendars and chocolate boxes.
Comfortable and friendly, it
still has much interior
character. Food is only
available by prior
arrangement. Tricky parking.
◑ ⇌ ♣ ○

Leigh Sinton

Royal Oak

Malvern Road
☎ (01886) 832664
11–3, 6–11

Marston's Bitter, Pedigree H
Small, cosy, village local
with low beams and an
impressive collection of
implements and brasses.
Interesting reading
on the walls.
🍴 Q ❀ ◑ ⬤ ♣ P

Leominster

Black Horse

74 South Street
☎ (01568) 611946
11–2.30, 6–11; 11–11 Sat
**Courage Directors; Dunn
Plowman BHB, Woody's
Crown, Shire Horse Ale;
Solstice Golden Torc;
Wadworth 6X; guest beers** H
Outstanding free house, the
brewery tap for Dunn
Plowman (whose beers are
now brewed by Solstice). It has
a lively public bar, a small
lounge and a restaurant.
No eve meals Sun. Regular
changes in guest ales
make it well worth a visit.
Petanque played.
❀ ◑ ▶ ⬤ ⇌ ♣ P

Grapes Vaults

Broad Street
☎ (01568) 611404
11–2.30, 5–11
**Banks's Mild; Marston's
Bitter, Pedigree;
guest beer** H
Behind a plain facade is
concealed a superbly restored
town pub. Etched-glass and
old wooden screens divide it
into discrete drinking nooks
and corners. Well-run;
wholesome menu served until
9.30pm. The Marston's range
may vary. 🍴 Q ◑ ▶ ⇌

Letton

Swan

On A438 ☎ (01544) 327304
11–11; 11–3, 6–11 Mon & Tue
**Wye Valley HPA; guest
beers** H
Attractive and comfortable
roadside pub. Food is always
available. Swan Bitter is a
house beer (OG 1031/3.1%
ABV), brewed by Mansfield.
🍴 Q ❀ ◑ ▶ ⬤ A ♣ P

Malvern Wells

Malvern Hills Hotel

Wynd's Point
☎ (01684) 40237
11–11
**Draught Bass; Hobsons Best
Bitter; Wood Parish** H
Comfortable lounge bar in an
upmarket weekend retreat on
the ridge of the Malvern Hills.
Walkers are welcome but are
requested to remove muddy
boots. 🍴 ⏚ ❀ ⬤ ◑ ▶ P

Hereford & Worcester

Menithwood

Cross Keys

Between A443 and B4202
OS709690 ☎ (0158 470) 425
11–3, 6–11
Marston's Bitter, Pedigree; guest beer H
Comfortable pub in quiet countryside, popular with the local community and welcoming to visitors. Bulmers cider in summer.
⌂ Q ♞ ❀ ♿ ♣ ⌓ P

Offenham

Bridge

Boat Lane OS050457
☎ (01386) 446565
11–11
S&N Theakston Best Bitter, XB; Stanway Stanney Bitter; Wood Parish H
Ancient riverside pub with its own moorings, but there hasn't been a bridge here for 500 years. It enjoys a thriving local trade and extends a warm welcome to visitors. No price differential between the bars. ⌂ Q ❀ ◐ ◑ ♣ P

Ombersley

Crown & Sandy's Arms

Main Road (off A449 and A4133, S of roundabout)
☎ (01905) 620252
11–2.30, 6–11
Hook Norton Best Bitter, Old Hooky; guest beers H
Smart, olde-worlde, spacious pub, offering a good range of home-made food, including vegetarian options. It has a grill room and a main restaurant (booking advisable for both).
⌂ Q ❀ ⛟ ◐ ◑ P ⅟

Pensax

Bell

On B4202 ☎ (01299) 896677
12–3, 6.30–11
Hook Norton Best Bitter; Taylor Landlord; Wadworth 6X; guest beers H
Traditional country pub with an outdoor drinking area to the front and a garden behind. There have been some 65 different guest beers over the last year.
⌂ Q ♞ ❀ ◐ ◑ ♿ ♣ P

Pershore

Brandy Cask

25 Bridge Street
☎ (01386) 552602
11.30–2.30 (may extend summer), 7–11
Courage Best Bitter, Directors; Hull Governor; Ruddles Best Bitter; guest beer H
Unpretentious, town-centre pub and 'Ale Room Brasserie'. It stocks two regular guest ales plus a house brew, Spencer's (brewed by Wood). ❀ ◐ ◑ ♣

Millers Arms

8 Bridge Street
☎ (01386) 553864
11.30–4, 5.30–11
Hall & Woodhouse Tanglefoot; Smiles Exhibition; Wadworth IPA, Farmer's Glory, Old Timer H
Busy, town-centre pub with a good commitment to real ale. The most northerly outpost of Wadworth's chain, it is popular with young people, particularly at weekends, and can be smoky. ◐ ◑ ♣

Porchbrook

Alma Inn

Off B4202, signed to Rock
OS727707 ☎ (01229) 832430
12–2.30 (not Tue), 7–11
Banks's Mild, Bitter E
Two-bar pub on a quiet country lane. Light snacks served. The main car park is over the bridge, over a small brook. ⌂ Q ❀ ⊞ ♿ ♣ P

Risbury

Hop Pole Inn

½ mile E of village on Pencombe Road OS554549
11–3, 6–11
Wood Special G
No spirits, wine or keg beer are sold at this remote ex-farmhouse which is a must for the beer and pub lover. A small, plain, single bar with a fire, combined with the landlord's anecdotes, will not disappoint. ⌂ Q ❀ ♣ P

Romsley

Manchester Inn

On B4551, Bromsgrove Road
☎ (01562) 710242
11–3, 5–11
Draught Bass; Enville Ale H**; M&B Mild, Brew XI** H/E
This roadside pub, popular with walkers, lies adjacent to the North Worcester path. It has a public bar and a comfortable, busy lounge, with a well-priced and varied menu (not served Sun eve). The garden is popular in summer.
⌂ ❀ ◐ ◑ ⊞ ♣ P

Ross-on-Wye

Crown & Sceptre

Market Square
☎ (01989) 562765
11–3, 6–11 (11–11 summer)
Archers Best Bitter; Brakspear Bitter; Morland Old Speckled Hen; guest beers H
Medium-sized, one-bar, town-centre pub which can be busy at weekends. Refurbishment is underway. The landlord has made this *the* real ale pub in an otherwise disappointing pub town. Always one scrumpy cider is served by gravity dispense.
❀ ◐ ◑ ♣ ⌓

St Owen's Cross

New Inn

At A4137/B4521 jct
☎ (01989) 87274
12–3, 6–11
Draught Bass; Courage Directors; Hook Norton Old Hooky; Smiles Best Bitter; guest beers H
16th-century gem, covered with hanging baskets in summer. The beautiful interior boasts fine fireplaces, settles and period furnishings and strikes a good balance between good ale and food; try the doorstep sandwiches. A past Herefordshire CAMRA award-winner.
⌂ Q ❀ ⛟ ◐ ◑ ▲ ♣ P

Severn Stoke

Boar's Head

☎ (01905) 371484
11–3, 5.30–11 (may vary in summer)
Hobsons Best Bitter; Taylor Landlord; guest beers H
Extensively renovated, but very homely inn with solid pine tables and high-backed chairs. A wide variety of home-cooked food is well-priced. Jazz every Sun and various other special events throughout the year.
⌂ ❀ ◐ ◑ ▲ ♣ P

Shenstone

Plough

400 yards from A450/A448 jct
OS865735 ☎ (01562) 777340
11–3, 6.30–11
Batham Best Bitter, XXX H
Traditional, comfortably furnished country pub, dating from 1840, in a small hamlet. It is hard to find, but well worth the effort to taste Batham's at its best. A covered yard may be used by families. Good range of Weston's bottled ciders.
⌂ Q ♞ ❀ ♿ ♣ ⌓ P

Staunton on Wye

New Inn

Off A438 in village
☎ (01981) 500346
12–2.30 (not Mon), 7–11

Marston's Pedigree; S&N Theakston Best Bitter; Wadworth 6X H
Pleasant village pub with three distinctly different bars. It is good for pub food and an excellent location from which to explore the Wye valley. Games include petanque in the car park.
🍴 Q ✿ ◁ ▶ 🍴 & ♣ P

Stourport-on-Severn

Angel Hotel
14 Severnside
☎ (01299) 822661
11–11
Banks's Mild, Bitter H
Friendly, two-room local on the riverside, with BWB moorings. It was called the Virgins until Victorian times.
🍴 ⚲ ✿ 🛏 ◁ ▶ 🍴 ♣ ○ P

Holly Bush Inn
53–54 Mitton Street (200 yds from canal bridge on High St)
☎ (01299) 822569
12–3, 6.30–11 (11–11 summer)
S&N Theakston Best Bitter, XB, Old Peculier (summer) H
Friendly local, recently refurbished. One main bar is split into three and features a 50s and 60s jukebox.
⚲ ✿ ◁ ▶ ♣

Try also: **Tontine Inn**, Severnside (Banks's)

Tenbury Wells

Ship Inn
65 Teme Street
☎ (01584) 810269
11–2.30, 7–11
Ansells Bitter; guest beer H
Well-to-do, market town pub with a comfortable lounge and restaurant. A bar in an outbuilding is open at weekends only. Large garden.
🍴 ✿ 🛏 ◁ ▶ & ♣

Uphampton

Fruiterer's Arms
Uphampton Lane (N of Ombersley; off A449 at the Reindeer pub) OS839649
☎ (01905) 620305
12.30–2.30 (3 Sat), 7–11
Cannon Royall Arrowhead, Buckshot, Millward's Musket Mild; Donnington BB; John Smith's Bitter H
Rural pub with a plain bar and cosy, quiet lounge. The Cannon Royall Brewery is located at the rear of the pub—its beer range may vary. The landlords own the adjacent mobile home site (caravans allowed). No food

Sun. Weston's Old Rosie cider.
🍴 Q ✿ ◁ ▶ 🍴 ♣ ▲ ○ P

West Malvern

Brewer's Arms
Lower Dingle (signed off B4232) ☎ (01684) 568147
12–3, 7 (6 summer Sat)–11
Bateman Mild; Marston's Bitter, Pedigree H
Housed in a 16th-century shell, this pub stands as a shining example of sympathetic refurbishment, after a fire. It has a strong community feel, but visitors, families, and Malvern Hills walkers are all warmly welcomed. Folk music Tue eve. Marston's Head Brewer's Choice is available.
🍴 Q ✿ ◁ ▶ ♣ ○

Whitney-on-Wye

Rhydspence Inn
On A438; 1½ miles W of village ☎ (01497) 831262
11–2.30, 7–11
Draught Bass; Hook Norton Best Bitter; Robinson's Best Bitter H
Famous, historic, black and white inn, noted mainly for food but retaining a genuine public bar. Dunkerton's cider.
🍴 Q ✿ 🛏 ◁ ▶ 🍴 ♣ ○ P

Woolhope

Crown Inn
☎ (01432) 860468
12–2.30, 6.30 (7 winter Mon–Thu)–11
Hook Norton Best Bitter; Smiles Best Bitter; Tetley Bitter H
Relaxing rural inn, very busy at weekends and always popular with diners. It enjoys a county-wide reputation for its food but an area is set aside for drinking at leisure.
🍴 Q ✿ ◁ ▶ & ○ P

Worcester

Berkeley Arms
School Road, St Johns (100 yds off Bransford Rd, A4103)
☎ (01905) 421427
11–3, 6–11
Banks's Hanson's Mild, Bitter E
Friendly town local drawing a good mix of customers—one of the very few outlets for Hanson's in the area.
⚲ ✿ ♣ P

Cardinal's Hat
Friar Street ☎ (01905) 21890
11–11
Jolly Roger Ale, Shipwrecked, Flagship; guest beers H

Historic pub, claiming to be Worcester's oldest. Incongruously situated opposite a multi-storey car park, it comprises three contrasting drinking areas. The choice of food has recently improved but guest ales are expensive for the area.
✿ ◁ ▶ ⇌ (Foregate St) ♣ ○

Crown & Anchor
Hylton Road
☎ (01905) 421481
12–11
Banks's Mild; Marston's Bitter, Pedigree H
Simple pub with a new extension and a skittle alley. Popular with students.
⚲ ✿ ♣ ○

Lamb & Flag
30 The Tything
☎ (01905) 26894
10.30–2.30, 5.30 (6 Sat)–11; 12–2, 7–10.30 Sun
Marston's Bitter, Pedigree H
Often crowded, two-roomer, locally famed for its draught Guinness (keg). A friendly atmosphere adds to the experience although it can get smoky.
✿ ⇌ (Foregate St) ♣

Toad & Tulip
53 Lowesmoor
☎ (01905) 26876
12–11
Jolly Roger Ale, Shipwrecked; guest beers H
Basic, city-centre ale house, generally friendly, but crowded at weekends. It stocks up to four guest beers—one is usually Hobsons' from oak casks. Norbury's Perry is also available. Loud music.
⇌ (Foregate St/Shrub Hill) ♣ ○

Virgin Tavern
Tolladine Road
☎ (01905) 23988
11–3, 5.30–11
Marston's Bitter, Pedigree H
Well-run, modern pub out of the city centre, near a new housing estate. Good, simple pub food is served (not on Sun eve). ✿ ◁ ▶ ♣ P

Wheatsheaf Inn
Henwick Road (A443, out of the city) ☎ (01905) 423077
12–3, 6–11 (may vary)
Banks's Mild; Marston's Bitter H
One of a dying breed, unchanged for many years. The very simple decor contrasts with the unmatched views from the patio across the Severn. The landlord's organ recitals are a must. ♣

Try also: **Swan With Two Nicks**, New St (Free)

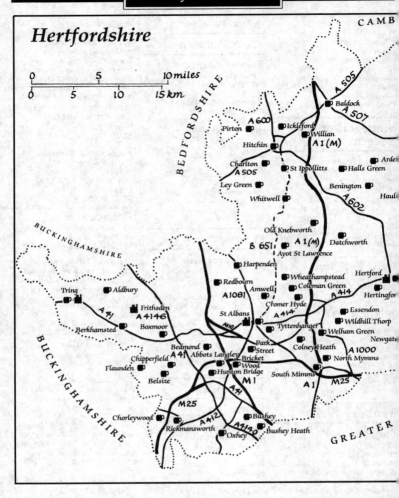

Hertfordshire

Hertfordshire

CAMB

0 — 5 — 10 miles
0 — 5 — 10 — 15 km

BEDFORDSHIRE

BUCKINGHAMSHIRE

A 505 · Baldock · A 507

Pirton · A 600 · Ickleford · Willian · A 1(M)

Hitchin

Charlton · St Ippollitts · Halls Green · Arde

A 505

Ley Green · Benington · Haul

Whitwell · A 602

Old Knebworth

B 651 · A 1(M) · Datchworth

Ayot St Lawrence

Harpenden

Redbourn · Wheathampstead · Hertford

Amwell · Coleman Green · A 414 · Hertingfor

A 1081 · Cromer Hyde · Essendon

St Albans · Tyttenhanger · Wildhill Thorp

Tring · Aldbury · M10 · Welham Green · Newgate

Frithsden · Park · Colney Heath · A 1000

A 4146 · Street · North Mymms

Berkhamsted · Boxmoor · Bricket

Bedmond · Wood

Chipperfield · Abbots Langley · Hunton Bridge

Flaunden · Belsize · M1 · South Mimms · A 1 · M25

Chorleywood · M25 · Bushey

Rickmansworth · A 412 · A 4140 · Bushey Heath

Oxhey

GREATER

 Alford Arms, *Frithsden;* **Fox & Hounds,** *Barley;*
McMullen, *Hertford;* **Philanthropist & Firkin,**
St Albans; **Tring,** *Tring*

Abbots Langley

Compasses
95 Tibbs Hill Road
☎ (01923) 262870
11–11
**Courage Best Bitter,
Directors; Ruddles County;
guest beer** H
A strong food emphasis has
not spoiled this pub, which is
still popular with locals. The
guest beer varies and has
included Tring Brewery
products. Large whisky
selection. ❀ ◑ ▶ & ♣ P

Aldbury

Greyhound
Stocks Road ☎ (01442) 851228
10.30–11
**Tetley Bitter; Tring
Ridgeway; guest beer** H
Attractive pub in a village near
Ashridge Estate (NT). The
traditional, unspoilt public bar
is dominated by a huge
fireplace. The lounge bar is
aimed towards diners with a
'bistro'-like atmosphere.
Happy hour 5–7, Mon–Fri.
🏡 ❀ 🛏 ◑ ▶ 🍴 & ♣ ⌑

Amwell

Elephant & Castle
Amwell Lane (1 mile W of
B651) OS167133
☎ (01582) 832175
11–3, 5.30–11; 11–11 Sat
**Gibbs Mew Deacon; Ind
Coope Benskins Best Bitter;
Marston's Pedigree; guest
beers** H
Delightful old pub in a quiet
setting with two bar areas at
different levels, one featuring
a 200-ft well. Two gardens,
one for families. The beer

range varies, with guests from independents.

🏚 Q ⊛ ◑ ▶ P

Ardeley

Jolly Waggoner
Off B1037, 1 mile E of Cromer
☎ (01438) 861350
12–2.30 (3 Sat & Sun; not Mon); 6.30–11
Greene King IPA G**, Abbot** H
Picturesque, 16th-century, pink-washed former cottages in a charming village setting: one recently enlarged bar, a restaurant and a large garden. Good food menu (not served Sun or Mon).
🏚 Q ⊛ ◑ ▶ P

Ayot St Lawrence

Brocket Arms
Near Shaw's Corner OS196168
☎ (01438) 820250

11–2.30, 7–11
Gibbs Mew Deacon; Greene King IPA, Abbot; Wadworth 6X; guest beers H & G
Ancient village pub in a quaint, quiet, rural setting. Excellent restaurant; good-value bar snacks.
🏚 Q ⊛ 🛏 ◑ ▶ ♣ ⌂

Baldock

White Hart
21 Hitchin Street
☎ (01462) 893247
11–11; 11–4.30, 7–11 Sat
Greene King XX Mild, IPA, Rayments Special, Abbot H
Popular, one-bar town pub displaying a large Simpson's Brewery sign. Concessions for OAPs on all real ales weekday lunchtimes. A 'pub with no grub', but customers may bring their own sandwiches.
🚆 ♣ P

Barley

Fox & Hounds
High Street ☎ (01763) 848459
12–2.30, 6–11
Barley Flame Thrower; S&N Theakston Best Bitter, XB, Old Peculier; guest beers H
Large, lively, rural village pub which has brewed since the early days of the brew pub revival. Note the unusual gallows sign spanning the road. Extensive menu of good value food, and usually at least three guest beers.
🏚 🛏 ⊛ ◑ ▶ ♿ P ✂

Bedmond

Bell Inn
High Street ☎ (01923) 262910
11–3, 5.30 (6.30 Sat)–11
Greene King IPA; Ind Coope Burton Ale; Tetley Bitter H
Cosy, friendly old pub on the main road. No food Sun.
🏚 ⊛ ◑ ♣ P

Belsize

Plough
Dunny Lane OS034008
☎ (01923) 262800
11–3, 5.30–11
Draught Bass; Greene King IPA; M&B Highgate Dark H
Friendly, out-of-the-way pub, popular with horse riders and ramblers. Steaks are a speciality (eve meals Tue–Sat).
🏚 Q ⊛ ◑ ♣ P

Benington

Lordship Arms
42 Whempstead Road (1 mile off B1037 from Stevenage via Walkern) OS308227
☎ (01438) 869665
11–3, 6–11

Fuller's ESB; McMullen AK; Young's Special; guest beers H
Recently renovated country local serving a changing range of four guest beers and a good selection of home-cooked food. Telephone memorabilia.
🏚 ⊛ ◑ ▶ ⌂ P

Berkhamsted

Boat
Gravel Path, Ravens Lane (off A41 at Baptist church, by canal bridge) ☎ (01442) 877152
11–3, 5.30–11
Fuller's Hock, Chiswick, London Pride, Mr Harry, ESB H
Large, modern canalside pub which is usually busy, but the service is excellent. Home-cooked food. Outside is an elegant patio. Sun barbecues in summer. ◑ 🚆 P

Rising Sun
George Street (off A41, by GU Canal lock 55)
☎ (01442) 864913
11–3, 6–11
Greene King IPA; Whitbread Flowers Original H
Friendly, unspoilt local, with a walled and gated, canalside patio. Small games room at the rear. Q ⊛ ◑ ▶ 🚆 ♣

Bishop's Stortford

Castle
Castle Street (off Newtown Rd) ☎ (01279) 652578
12–3, 7 (6 Fri & Sat)–11
Tetley Bitter; Tolly Cobbold Original; Whitbread Flowers Original H
Back-street local with no food, but a friendly landlord.
🏚 ⊛ 🚆 ♣ P

Three Tuns
36 London Road
☎ (01279) 767900
11–11
Greene King IPA, Rayments Special, Abbot H
Basic, down-to-earth, two-bar pub next to the station. No menu – ask for food (no frills).
⊛ ◑ ▶ ♿ 🚆 ♣ P

Boxmoor

Post Office Arms
Puller Road
☎ (01442) 61235
11–3, 5.30–11; 11–11 Fri & Sat
Fuller's London Pride, ESB H
Friendly, often busy, town local with a small public bar and a larger extended lounge. Parking can be difficult. Barbecues in summer. No food Sun. 🏚 ⊛ ◑ 🍴 🚆 ♣

Hertfordshire

Bricket Wood

Moor Mill
Smug Oak Lane (off A5183 by
M25 bridge) ☎ (01727) 875557
11–11
**Adnams Bitter; Draught Bass;
Brakspear Bitter; Courage
Directors; guest beers** H
Restored Anglo-Saxon mill
mentioned in the *Domesday
Book*. A revolving mill wheel
run by the River Ver is its
centrepiece. Ten different
beers are always available
with Millers house beer
usually on special offer. Book
for meals in the Granary
dining room (seafood specials
Tue). ♨ Q ✿ ◗ ▶ & P

Buntingford

Crown
High Street ☎ (01763) 271422
12–3, 5.30–11; 12–11 Sat
**Banks & Taylor Shefford
Bitter; Ruddles Best Bitter,
County; guest beers** H
Busy, small pub with no keg
beers. ♨ ♨ Q ☎ ✿ ◗ ▶ ♣

Bushey

Swan
25 Park Road (just off A411)
☎ (0181) 950 2256
11–11
**Ind Coope Benskins Best
Bitter, Burton Ale** H
The first *Good Beer Guide* said:
'Basic pub mostly used by
locals; friendly'. Nothing has
changed. ♨ Q ♣

Bushey Heath

Black Boy
19 Windmill Street (off A4140)
☎ (0181) 950 2230
11.30–3, 5.30–11; 12–11 Sat
**Adnams Bitter; Chiltern
Beechwood; Greene King
IPA; Ind Coope Benskins Best
Bitter, Burton Ale** H
Busy, back-street, one-bar pub,
popular with the locals.
Regular lunch trade (good
value meals). Real cider
occasionally. ✿ ◗ ▶ P

Charlton

Windmill
Charlton Road
☎ (01462) 432096
10.30–2.30 (3.30 Sat), 5.30–11
**Adnams Broadside; Wells
Eagle, Bombardier; guest
beer** H
Attractive, small country pub
in a quiet hamlet near Hitchin.
The garden runs down to the
River Hiz. Good quality,
home-cooked food.
Q ✿ ◗ ▶ ♣ P

Cheshunt

Maltsters
177 Windmill Lane (near
station) ☎ (01992) 631369
11–2.30, 5–11
**Courage Directors; McMullen
AK, Country; guest beer** H
Fairly modern McMullen pub,
with a popular and friendly
public bar. Working clothes
discouraged in the lounge. The
guest beer may be a
McMullen's seasonal brew.
✿ ⊟ ⇄ ♣ P

Chipperfield

Royal Oak
The Street ☎ (01923) 266537
12–3, 6 (6.30 Sat)–11
**Bass Worthington BB,
Draught Bass; M&B Highgate
Dark; Marston's Pedigree** H
Smart, tidy pub with a warm
welcome. No food Sun; eve
meals only by arrangement.
♨ Q ◗ & ♣ P

Chorleywood

Black Horse
Dog Kennel Lane (off A404, W
of M25 jct 18)
☎ (01923) 282252
11–11
**Adnams Bitter; Greenalls
Bitter, Original; Wadworth
6X; guest beer** H
Deceptively large pub on the
edge of the common: dogs
welcome. Occasional folk
music; home-made food (not
served Sun eve). ♨ ✿ ◗ ▶ P

Stag
Long Lane, Heronsgate (just
off M25 jct 17)
☎ (01923) 282090
11–2.30, 5.30–11
**Fuller's London Pride;
McMullen AK, Country;
guest beer** H
Smart, popular pub offering
good food. The single bar has
a restaurant section (eve meals
Tue–Sat). Guest beers include
McMullen seasonal brews.
Q ✿ ◗ ▶ & P

Coleman Green

John Bunyan
Coleman Green Lane (1 mile
off B653) OS189126
☎ (01582) 832037
11–2.30 (3 Sat), 6–11
**McMullen AK, Country;
guest beer** H
Welcoming country pub off
the beaten track: one main bar
with a separate darts area.
Good fast food (not served
Sun eve). Large play area.
♨ Q ✿ ◗ ▶ & ♣ P

Colney Heath

Crooked Billet
High Street ☎ (01727) 822128
11–2.30, 5.30–11; 11–11 Sat & bank
hols
**Greene King Abbot; Hook
Norton Best Bitter; S&N
Theakston Best Bitter;
Wadworth 6X; guest beers**
(occasional) H
300-year-old, cottage-style pub
with two bars, offering good,
home-cooked food (eve meals
Thu–Sat). A children's play
area includes pony rides.
♨ ✿ ◗ ♣ P

Cromer Hyde

Crooked Chimney
On A6129 ☎ (01707) 323832
11–2.30, 5.30–11
**Ind Coope Benskins Best
Bitter, Burton Ale; Tetley
Bitter** H
Popular country pub,
renowned for its excellent
restaurant. Old, but well-
loved, it features a beamed
ceiling and a large garden.
✿ ◗ ▶ P

Datchworth

Plough
5 Datchworth Green (off B197)
☎ (01438) 813000
11.30–2.30 (3 Sat), 6–11
**Greene King XX Mild, IPA,
Abbot** H
Small, welcoming local just off
the village green: one room
with a large, central open
wood fire and a garden to the
rear. A former Simpson's
(Baldock) house built in 1840.
♨ Q ✿ ▶ ♣ P

Tilbury
1 Watton Road (off B197)
☎ (01438) 812496
11–3, 5 (6 Sat)–11
**Draught Bass; Palmers IPA;
guest beer** H
Large, friendly, two-room pub
at a crossroads, with a no-
smoking dining area and a
large garden. The nine beers
include one mild; unusual
beers are a speciality. Wide
range of home-cooked food.
✿ ◗ ▶ ⊟ ♣ ➘ P

Essendon

Candlestick
West End Lane (off B158)
☎ (01707) 261322
11–2.30, 5.30–11; 12–2.30, 7–10.30
Sun
**Draught Bass; McMullen AK,
Country; guest beer** H
Small, relaxed, authentic
country pub, not to be missed
in summer for its large garden.
Good value food (Tue–Fri).
♨ Q ✿ ◗ ▶ ⊟ ♣ P

Flaunden

Bricklayers Arms

Long Lane, Hogpits Bottom
OS017013 ☎ (01442) 833322
11–2.30 (3 summer), 6 (5.30 summer)–11
Chiltern Beechwood; Fuller's London Pride; guest beer H
Smart, food-oriented, country pub which is still 'drinker-friendly'. Five bitters and a mild always available. No meals Sun eve.
🏚 Q ❀ ◖ ▶ P

Green Dragon

OS014007 ☎ (01442) 832269
11.30–2.30, 6–11; 11.30–11 Sat
Greene King IPA; Marston's Pedigree; guest beers H
Thriving country pub on the eastern edge of the Chiltern Hills. Five ales and two ciders are always available. Although much-extended, the pub retains its original public bar and small serving hatch.
🏚 Q ❀ ◖ ▶ ⬚ ⚑ ♣ ⌂ P

Great Amwell

George IV

Cautherley Lane (between A1170 and River Lee Navigation) ☎ (01920) 870039
11–3, 6–11
Adnams Bitter; Ind Coope Benskins Best Bitter; Tetley Bitter H
Pub with an L-shaped single bar, next to an 11th-century church. No garden, but tables out front. ❀ ◖ ▶ P

Green Tye

Prince of Wales

☎ (0127 984) 2517
11–3, 6.30–11; 11–11 Sat
McMullen AK; Whitbread Boddingtons Bitter, Flowers IPA, Castle Eden Ale; guest beer H
Small country pub in a picturesque village: two rooms, mainly frequented by locals. 🏚 ❀ ◖ ♣ ♣ P

Try also: Hoops Inn, Perry Green (Free)

Halls Green

Rising Sun

Weston Road
☎ (01462) 790487
11–2.30, 6–11
Draught Bass; Courage Directors; McMullen AK, Country; guest beer H
Beautiful, well-extended one-bar pub in the depths of the country. An enormous garden offers play equipment and a summer barbecue.
🏚 Q ⛄ ❀ ◖ ▶ ♣ P

Harpenden

Gibraltar Castle

Lower Luton Road, Batford
☎ (01582) 460005
11–3, 5.30 (6 Mon–Thu in winter) –11
Fuller's Hock, Chiswick, London Pride, ESB H
A well-sited and attractive roadside establishment where the interior drips with military antiquities. A good menu includes a vegetarian choice (no food Sun).
🏚 ❀ ◖ ▶ ♣ P

Oak Tree

15 Leyton Green
☎ (01582) 763850
11–3, 5.30–11; 11–11 Fri & summer Sat
McMullen AK; Tetley Bitter; Wadworth 6X; Whitbread Boddingtons Bitter; guest beers H
Enterprising conversion to a free house, serving seven real ales. The thoughtful use of space lends distinctiveness to the different seating areas.
❀ ◖ ⚹ ⇌ ♣ P

Haultwick

Rest & Welcome

3 miles off A10, near Dane End
OS339230 ☎ (01920) 438323
12–2, 6.30–11
McMullen AK H, **Country** G; **guest beer** H
Not easy to find, but well worth the effort; a small, one-bar village pub with a warm welcome. The garden has play equipment.
🏚 Q ❀ ◖ ▶ ♣ P

Hertford

Great Eastern Tavern

29 Railway Place
☎ (01992) 583570
11.30–2.30, 6 (7 Sat)–11
Draught Bass; McMullen AK H
Friendly, two-bar local with decor on a railway theme. A regular award-winner for its floral displays. No food Sun.
❀ ◖ ⇌ (East) ♣ P

White Horse

33 Castle Street
☎ (01992) 501950
12–2.30 (3 Sat), 5.30 (7 Sat)–11
Fuller's London Pride; Greene King IPA; Hook Norton Best Bitter H; **guest beers** G & H
Once a beerhouse, this old, timber-framed building is now a real ale connoisseur's delight. Guest beers come from independent brewers far and wide. Weekday lunches.
🏚 Q ⛄ ❀ ◖ ⇌ (East/North) ♣ ⌂ ✗

Hertingfordbury

Prince of Wales

244 Hertingfordbury Road
☎ (01992) 581149
11–2.30, 5.30–11
Fuller's London Pride; McMullen AK; Marston's Pedigree; S&N Theakston XB; Wadworth 6X; guest beer H
One-bar free house, just off the A414. The patio can get very busy in summer. No food Sun eves. 🏚 ❀ ⚑ ◖ ▶ P

High Wych

Rising Sun

1 mile W of Sawbridgeworth
☎ (0127 972) 4099
11–3, 5–11
Courage Best Bitter, Directors; guest beer G
Traditional, small country pub where the 'locals' come from near and far. Local CAMRA 1994 *Pub of the Year*, celebrating 21 consecutive years in the *Guide*. The guest beers come mostly from small independents. 🏚 Q ⚹ ♣ P

Hitchin

Victoria

1 Ickleford Road
☎ (01462) 432682
12–3, 5.30–11
Greene King IPA, Abbot H
Friendly, split-level local close to the town centre and dating back to 1865. ◖ ▶ ⇌ ♣ P

Hunton Bridge

Kings Head

Bridge Road (just off A41)
☎ (01923) 262307
11–3, 5.30–11
Ind Coope Benskins Best Bitter, Burton Ale; Tetley Bitter; guest beer H
Old pub with one rambling bar. The old canal stables now house a family room and a fold-down skittle alley (summer only). The large canalside garden offers games. Good value meals (no food Sun eve).
🏚 Q ⛄ ❀ ◖ ♣ P

Ickleford

Cricketers

107 Arlesey Road (off A600)
☎ (01462) 432629
11–3, 5.30–11; 11–11 Sat
Draught Bass; Fuller's London Pride; Ruddles Best Bitter; Taylor Landlord; Wadworth 6X; guest beer H
Lively village pub which attracts custom from near and far. Usually stocks four guest beers. No lunches Sat.
🏚 ⚑ ◖ ▶ ♣ ⌂ P

Hertfordshire

Ley Green

Plough
Plough Lane OS162243
☎ (01438) 871394
11–2.30, 5.30–11; 11–11 Fri & Sat
Greene King IPA, Abbot H
Country local, overlooking rolling farmland and woods. The enormous gardens include a children's field with livestock.
🏚 Q ☎ ⊛ ⊕ ♣ P

Much Hadham

Old Crown
Hadham Cross
☎ (0127 984) 2753
11.45–2.30, 6.45–11
Draught Bass; McMullen AK H
Friendly one-bar pub. Muddy boots are not permitted in the bar. McMullen seasonal beers stocked. Eve meals Wed–Sat.
Q ⊛ ◖ ▸ ♣ P

Newgate Street

Coach & Horses
61 Newgate Street Road
☎ (01707) 872326
11–3, 5.30–11; 11–11 Sat
Draught Bass; Ind Coope ABC Best Bitter, Burton Ale; Tetley Bitter H
Attractive, Grade II-listed, 17th-century country pub whose landlord won a 1993 *Bass Supreme Cellarman* award. The beer range varies.
🏚 ☎ ⊛ ◖ ▸ P

North Mymms

Old Maypole
43 Warrengate Road, Water End (off B197)
☎ (01707) 642119
11–2.30, 5.30–11
Greene King IPA, Abbot H
16th-century, split-level pub. Supervised children are welcome in the small no-smoking room. No food Sun.
🏚 Q ☎ ⊛ ◖ P ⊬

Try also: **Woodman**, Warrengate Rd (Free)

Old Knebworth

Lytton Arms
Park Lane ☎ (01438) 812312
11–3, 5–11; 11–11 Fri & Sat
Draught Bass; Banks & Taylor Shefford Bitter; Fuller's London Pride; S&N Theakston Best Bitter; guest beers H
Large Lutyens-designed building on the edge of Knebworth Park. The 12 beers always include one mild. Bottled beers; ciders and perry; beer festivals.
🏚 Q ☎ ◖ ▸ ♣ ⊛ ▭ P

Oxhey

Victoria
Chalk Hill ☎ (01923) 227993
11–3, 5.30–11
Ind Coope Benskins Best Bitter; guest beer H
Two-bar pub on different levels: a boisterous public bar and a comfortable saloon. Interesting guest beers.
⊛ ⇌ (Bushey) ♣

Try also: **Haydon Arms**, Upper Paddock Rd (Free)

Park Street

Overdraught
86 Park Street (A5183)
☎ (01727) 874280
11–11
Marston's Bitter, Pedigree; Tetley Bitter; Wells Bombardier; guest beers H
Revitalised village local offering a warm welcome: two bar areas, plus a summer outside bar and barbecue, with children's play area. Good value, home-cooked lunches. A different guest beer every week. 🏚 ⊛ ◖ ⇌ P

Pirton

Cat & Fiddle
7 Great Green
☎ (01462) 712245
12 (4 Mon)–11
Hall & Woodhouse Tanglefoot; Morland Old Speckled Hen; Wells Eagle; Whitbread Boddingtons Bitter H
Attractive, beamed, village pub overlooking the green with a cosy and welcoming, multi-level bar. 🏚 Q ⊛ ▸ ♣

Redbourn

Hollybush
Church End (signed from bypass) ☎ (01582) 792423
11–2.30 (3 Sat), 5.30 (7 Sat)–11
Adnams Bitter; Ind Coope Benskins Best Bitter; Tetley Bitter; guest beer H
Charming 16th-century pub in a tucked away corner of the village, with a beautiful garden. Barbecues in summer. No food Sun.
🏚 Q ⊛ ◖ ♣ P

Reed

Cabinet
High Street (off A10 opp. transport café, first right, first left) ☎ (01763) 848366
12–3, 6–11
Adnams Extra; Morrells Bitter; guest beer H

Cosy, weatherboarded village pub with two bars and a large garden. Difficult to find, but worth the effort. Three guest beers, constantly changing. No food Sun; eve meals Wed–Sat.
🏚 Q ☎ ⊛ ◖ ▸ ♣ P

Rickmansworth

Fox & Hounds
183 High Street
☎ (01923) 772174
11–11
Courage Best Bitter, Directors; guest beers H
One of the few real pubs left in the area, catering for a wide variety of tastes (but not the younger element). Regularly rotating guest beers; the only outlet for Mole's (one of the guests) for miles. Sun lunches only by arrangement.
🏚 ⊛ ◖ ⊕ ⇌ ⊖ ♣ P

St Albans

Blue Anchor
145 Fishpool Street
☎ (01727) 855038
11–3, 5.30–11 (11–11 Fri & Sat in summer)
McMullen AK, Country; guest beer H
Friendly, two-bar pub, handy for Verulamium Park, the Roman museum and the watermill; generally the cheapest pub in St Albans. The guest beer alternates with McMullen Special Reserve beers. No food Sun eve.
🏚 Q ⊛ ◖ ▸ ⊕ ♣ P

Farriers Arms
35 Lower Dagnall Street (off A5183) ☎ (01727) 851025
12–2.30 (4 Sat), 5.30 (7 Sat)–11
Draught Bass; McMullen AK, Country; guest beer H
A perennial entry in the *Guide*; a lively local with many sporting activities. Parking can be difficult. ◖ ♣

Garibaldi
61 Albert Street (off Holywell Hill) ☎ (01727) 855046
11–11
Fuller's Hock, Chiswick, London Pride, ESB H
Popular pub with a central bar and different levels of drinking areas. Good value, imaginative menu (not served Sun eve).
⊛ ◖ ▸ ⇌ (Abbey) ♣ ⊬

Lower Red Lion
34–36 Fishpool Street
☎ (01727) 855669
12–3, 5.30–11
Adnams Bitter; Fuller's London Pride; Greene King IPA, Abbot; Morland Old Speckled Hen; guest beers H

17th-century inn in the conservation area, serving three guest beers from small breweries (308 sold in 1993). Beer festivals. No food Sun.
🏚 Q ❀ 🍴 ◖ P

St Ippollitts

Greyhound

London Road (B656, outside village) ☎ (01462) 440989
11–11 (11–2.30, 6–11 Sat in rugby season)
Morland Old Speckled Hen; Whitbread Boddingtons Mild, Bitter; guest beer H
Village local, catering for all ages. Home-cooked food is a speciality. 🏚 Q ❀ ◖ ▶ P

Sawbridgeworth

Gate

81 London Road (A1184)
☎ (0127 972) 2313
11.30–2.30 (3 Fri), 5.30–11; 11–11 Sat
Morland Old Speckled Hen; Whitbread Boddingtons Bitter, Castle Eden Ale, Pompey Royal; guest beer H
Dating back to 1791, a pub standing on the site of the town's Parsonage Gate. It offers a regularly changing guest beer (from all over the country), plus at least one mild and occasional ciders. No food Sun. ❀ ◖ ♣ P

South Mimms

Black Horse

Black Horse Lane
☎ (01707) 642174
11–3, 5.30–11; 11–11 Sat
Greene King IPA, Abbot H
Pub with a classic public bar plus a welcoming saloon decorated to a horsey theme. No food Sun. ❀ ◖ ♣ P

Tring

Kings Arms

King Street (near Natural History Museum)
☎ (01442) 823318
11.30–2.30 (3 Sat), 7–11
Brakspear Special; Tring Old Icknield Ale; Wadworth 6X; guest beer H
Hard to find, but impossible to miss, this excellent, back-street local offers at least five ales. It has become the unofficial brewery tap for Tring Brewery. No-smoking area lunchtime.
Q ❀ ◖ ▶ ♣ ◔ ✦

Robin Hood

1 Brook Street
☎ (01442) 824912

11.30–2.30 (11–3 Sat), 5.30–11
Fuller's Hock, Chiswick, London Pride, Mr Harry, ESB H
Smart, one-bar, street-corner pub with a friendly welcome. The interior is bedecked with breweriana.
🏚 Q ❀ ◖ ▶ ♣

Tyttenhanger

Plough

Tyttenhanger Green (off A414, via Highfield Lane)
☎ (01727) 857777
11.30–2.30 (3 Sat), 6–11; 12–2.30, 7–10.30 Sun
Fuller's London Pride, ESB; Greene King IPA; Morland Old Speckled Hen; Taylor Landlord; Tring Ridgeway H
Popular free house offering good value lunches and featuring a huge collection of bottled beers. The garden is popular in summer. No food on bank hols.
🏚 Q ❀ ◖ ◭ P

Ware

Albion

12 Crib Street (behind St Mary's church)
☎ (01920) 463599
11–11
Whitbread Boddingtons Bitter, Flowers IPA H
One oak-beamed bar in a superb 16th/17th-century, half-timbered building, with floral displays outside in summer. Two real fires in winter. A popular pub with the locals. Lunches Mon–Fri; snacks only Sat.
🏚 ◖ ◭ ⇌

New Rose & Crown

Watton Road
☎ (01920) 462572
11.30–2.30, 5–11; 11–11 Fri & Sat
Greene King XX Mild, IPA, Rayments Special, Abbot H
Popular, unpretentious, one-bar local. No food Sun.
◖ ⇌ ♣ P

Wareside

Chequers

On B1004, Ware–Much Hadham road
☎ (0192 046) 7010
12–2.30, 6–11
Adnams Bitter, Extra; Bateman XB; Brakspear Bitter; Young's Special; guest beer H
Cottage pub with a friendly village atmosphere and excellent home-made food from a varied menu. A former Herts CAMRA *Pub of the Year*. The guest beer changes regularly. Popular with ramblers.
🏚 Q 🏚 ◖ ▶ ▲ ♣ P

Welham Green

Hope & Anchor

Station Road
☎ (01707) 262935
11–2.30, 5.30–11
Courage Best Bitter, Directors; John Smith's Bitter H
Two contrasting bars in a beamed, 18th-century village local. ❀ ◖ ◭ ◬ ⇌ P

Wheathampstead

Cross Keys

Gustard Wood (off B651)
☎ (01582) 832165
11–3, 5.30–11
Courage Directors; Fuller's London Pride, ESB; Greene King IPA, Abbot; guest beers H
Good all round pub, circa 1650. No eve meals Mon. Marston's Head Brewer's Choice served.
🏚 Q ❀ ◖ ▶ ♣ P

Whitwell

Maidens Head

High Street
☎ (01438) 871392
11.30–2.30 (4 Sat), 5 (6 Sat)–11
Draught Bass; McMullen AK, Country H
Timbered pub of character, frequently in the *Guide*.
🏚 Q ❀ ◖ ▶ ◭ ♣ P

Wildhill Thorp

Woodman

Wildhill Lane (between A1000 and B158, near Essendon) OS265068
☎ (01707) 642618
11.30–2.30, 5.30–11; 12–2, 7–10.30 Sun
Greene King IPA, Abbot; McMullen AK; guest beers H
Genuine, welcoming pub which keeps prices low, and serves good, chip-free meals (no food Sun). Sky TV in the music room/snug.
Q ❀ ◖ ♣ P

Willian

Three Horseshoes

Baldock Lane (tiny lane opp. church) ☎ (01462) 685713
11–11
Greene King IPA, Abbot H
With the same landlord for 24 years, a cosy, one-roomed country pub in a pretty village: a quiet haven where machines and muzak are banned. Home-cooked lunches (not served Sun). Park wisely.
🏚 Q ◖ ♣

Humberside

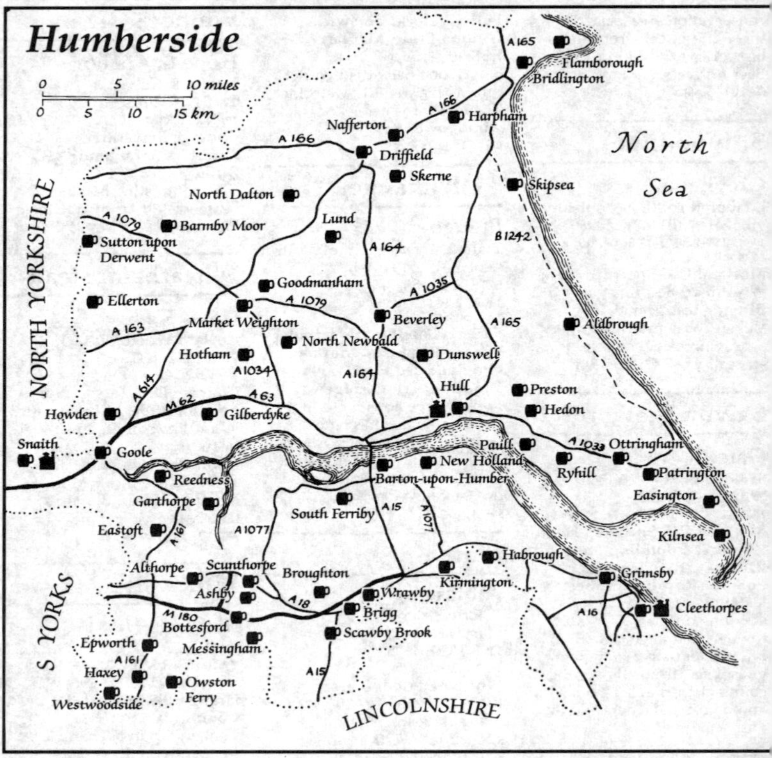

Hull, Minerva, *Hull;* **Old Mill,** *Snaith;* **Willy's,** *Cleethorpes*

Aldbrough

Elm Tree
High Street ☎ (01964) 527568
12–2.30 Thu & Fri only (Tue–Fri summer), 7–11; 12–5.30, 7–11 Sat
Bass Worthington BB, Draught Bass; Stones Best Bitter H
The locals' choice in a three-pub village. The church tower is visible from this comfortably furnished pub, where photos in the lounge show old Aldbrough, now disappeared into the sea. Occasional barbecues. ♔ ❀ ♣ P

Althorpe

Dolphin
27 Trunk Road (A18)
☎ (01724) 783469
11–3, 6–11
Vaux Samson; Wards Best Bitter H
Roadside pub with an emphasis on, and an excellent reputation for, food. Well-equipped family room.
Q ♘ ☾ ◗ ⇌ P

Ashby

Crown
209 Ashby High Street
☎ (01724) 840889
11–11
Mansfield Riding Bitter, Old Baily H
Historic old pub dating from 1909, situated in a busy shopping area. A basic drinkers' atmosphere remains following refurbishment. Live entertainment Mon and weekends. Reduced prices for Riding Bitter up to 8pm.
☾ ⊞ ♣ P

Open Hearth
Warley Road
☎ (01724) 842318
11.30–3, 7–11; 12–4, 7.30–11 Sat
Samuel Smith OBB H
Welcoming estate pub named after a type of ironmaking furnace: a smart spacious lounge and a large public bar with a good selection of games. The cheapest Sam Smith's beer in the area. No food weekends. ☾ ♣ P

Barmby Moor

Boot & Slipper Inn
☎ (01759) 303328
12–4, 7–11; 12–11 Sat
S&N Theakston Best Bitter, XB; Younger Scotch H
Friendly village pub which started life as a cobbler's shop. A comfortable lounge bar leads to a games room frequented by the younger clientele.
♘ ❀ ☾ ♿ ♣ P

Barton-upon-Humber

Volunteer Arms
13 Whitecross Street (off A1077) ☎ (01652) 632309
11–3, 6.45–11
Burtonwood Mild, Bitter, Top Hat H
Pleasant, two-roomed pub. No food Mon. Q ☾ ⇌

Beverley

Grovehill
183 Holme Church Lane (off Beckside ¾ mile E of centre)
☎ (01482) 867409
11.30–2, 7–11; 11–11 Sat
Marston's Bitter, Pedigree H
Former Moors & Robson's roadside pub, built in the 1920s and named after the Grovehill shipyard. Popular with pigeon fanciers, model enthusiasts, motorcyclists and domino players. ☼ ❀ ♣ P

Mariner's Arms
Flemingate ☎ (01482) 881241
4 (5 Thu, 12.30 Sat)–11
Wards Thorne Best Bitter H
Substantial pub near Beverley Beck and the Army Transport Museum; comfortably furnished, with two distinct drinking areas but few original features. ❀ ♣ P

Queen's Head
Wednesday Market
☎ (01482) 867363
11–3, 5–11; 11–11 Fri & Sat
Wards Thorne Best Bitter;
guest beer H
Attractive brewers' Tudor pub overlooking Beverley's smaller market place. Refurbished and extended to the rear, where families are catered for. No eve meals Sun. ◖ ▶ ≈ ♣

Rose & Crown
North Bar Without
☎ (01482) 862532
11–2.30, 5–11
Wards Thorne Best Bitter,
Best Bitter; guest beer H
Substantial brewers' Tudor pub adjacent to the historic North Bar, Westwood and racecourse. A popular eating establishment serving home-cooked food in the lounge. Comfortably furnished smoke room. Q ❀ ◖ ▶ ♣ P

Royal Standard
30 North Bar Within
☎ (01482) 882434
5 (11 Fri)–11; 11–4, 7–11 Sat
Vaux Samson; Wards Mild,
Thorne Best Bitter H
Classic, two-roomed town local with original 1920s bentwood seating in the front bar. Well-furnished lounge to the rear. Note the Darley motif in the bar window. Q ❀

White Horse Inn (Nellie's)
22 Hengate ☎ (01482) 861973
11–11
Samuel Smith OBB,
Museum H
One of Beverley's landmarks, this famous Georgian inn offers a multi-roomed interior with gas lighting, stone-flagged floors, roaring coal fires and home cooking. Folk and jazz eves upstairs. No lunches Mon.
⌨ Q ❀ ◖ ♣ P

Bottesford

Black Beauty
Keddington Road
☎ (01724) 867628
11.30 (11 Sat)–11
Mansfield Riding Mild,
Riding Bitter, Old Baily H
Popular estate pub on the fringe of town, featuring a smart bar, small wood-panelled lounge and large function room (with live music at weekends). ❀ ⌂ ♣ P

Bridlington

Hilderthorpe Hotel
Hilderthorpe Road
☎ (01262) 672205
11–11
Bass Mild, Draught Bass;
Stones Best Bitter H
Basic local popular with fishermen from the nearby harbour. A straightforward pub noted for dominoes. Good meals in summer (no lunches in winter). ⌨ ☼ ◖ ≈ ♣

New Crown
158 Quay Road
☎ (01262) 604370
11–11
Wards Best Bitter; guest
beer H
Substantial Victorian pub between the old town and the harbour. Renovated to form a large bar, with a wooden floor, and a spacious, comfortable lounge. ⌂ ◖ ≈ ♣

Old Ship Inn
90 St John's Street
☎ (01262) 670466
11–11
Wards Mild, Thorne Best
Bitter H
Thriving local by the old town, with a traditional atmosphere. Recently extended to incorporate a pool table. Facilities for children include an outdoor play area.
Q ❀ ◖ ♣

Pack Horse Inn
Market Place ☎ (01262) 675701
11–3, 7–11
Burtonwood Bitter, Top
Hat H
Listed building, thought to be 300 years old. The upper windows give an impression of three storeys, but the pub is in fact only two (a relic from Daylight Tax days). Comfortable open-plan lounge; pool room.
⌨ ❀ ◖ ♣

Brigg

Brocklesby Ox Inn
Bridge Street (A15/A18)
☎ (01652) 650292
12–3, 5.30–11; 11–11 Sat
Burtonwood Best Bitter, Top
Hat H
Smallish old pub extensively renovated, with much woodwork, stained-glass and framed pictures in evidence. The lounge contains a small dining area, and the bar a pool table. No food Mon. ⌨ ❀ ◖ ▶
⌂ ≈ (Sat service only) ♣ P

Broughton

Red Lion
High Street ☎ (01652) 652560
11–3, 6–11; 11–11 Fri & Sat
Mansfield Riding Mild,
Riding Bitter, Bitter H
Pre-war pub built on the site of earlier pubs of the same name, offering a pool table, a bowling green, dominoes and darts teams. Food not available Mon. Entertainment Sat eve. ❀ ◖ ▶ ♣ P

Cleethorpes

Crow's Nest
Balmoral Road
☎ (01472) 698867
11.30–3.30, 6.30–11
Samuel Smith OBB H
Large estate pub with a basic bar, a quiet, comfortable lounge, and a room much used for functions. The only Sam's pub for miles.
Q ☼ ❀ ⌖ ◖ ♣ P

Nottingham House
7 Seaview Street (just off sea front) ☎ (01472) 694368
12 (11 Sat)–11
Tetley Mild, Bitter H
Town drinking pub with a superb facade. Unusually for the area there are three separate rooms, including a snug. Q ⌖ ≈ ♣

Willy's Pub & Brewery
17 High Cliff Road
☎ (01472) 602145
11–11
Bateman XB; Willy's Original;
guest beers H
Popular seafront pub where the brewery can be seen from the bar. Other Willy's beers are usually available. Young staff; mixed clientele. Beer festival Nov. ❀ ◖ ▲ ≈

Driffield

Mariners Arms
47 Eastgate South (near cattle market) ☎ (01377) 253708
12–4 (6 Sat), 7–11; 12–11 Thu

Humberside

Burtonwood Mild, Bitter H
Traditional, street-corner,
two-roomed local, busy on
market day (Thu). Note the
display of beer bottles on plate
racks. ❀ ≭ ♣ P

Old Falcon
Market Place ☎ (01377) 252544
11–3, 7–11; 11–11 Thu–Sat
**Bass Worthington BB; Tetley
Bitter; guest beer** (summer) H
Market town local comprising
a wood-panelled bar area and
a well-furnished lounge with a
period fireplace. Home-made
steak and kidney pie lunches
(Thu–Sat). ◖ ≭ ♣

Dunswell

Ship Inn
Beverley Road
☎ (01482) 859160
11–11
**Hull Mild; Ind Coope Burton
Ale; John Smith's Bitter;
Tetley Bitter; guest beer** H
Welcoming pub on the old
Beverley–Hull road (A1174).
Two log-burning fires warm
the interior, part of which is
given over to a restaurant area.
Tasty home-cooked food
served 11–7. ⚌ ❀ ◖ ◗ ♣

Easington

Granby Inn
North Church Side
☎ (01964) 650294
11–11
**S&N Theakston Mild, Best
Bitter; Younger Scotch** H
Pub dating from the early
1800s but tastefully
modernised into a single,
large, L-shaped room. Pool
table in its own alcove. No
food Sun eve in winter.
❀ ⊨ ◖ ◗ ▲ ♣ P

Eastoft

River Don Tavern
Sampson Street (A161)
☎ (01724) 798225
12–3, 7–11
**John Smith's Bitter; guest
beer** H
Village pub 250 years old,
offering excellent food (not
served Tue eve) and a warm
welcome. Comprehensive
vegetarian menu. Large games
room. ⚌ Q ⊱ ❀ ◖ ◗ ♣ P

Ellerton

Boot & Shoe
Main Street ☎ (01757) 288346
6–11; 12–3, 6–11 Sat
**Old Mill Bitter; John Smith's
Bitter** H
Quaint village pub dating back
400 years and featuring an oak
tree of similar vintage. Low
and authentic beams.
Deservedly popular for food

but check opening times. A
gem! ⚌ Q ❀ ◗ ♣ P

Epworth

Red Lion Hotel
Market Place ☎ (01427) 872208
10.30–11
**Ind Coope Burton Ale; Tetley
Bitter** H
Large, well-appointed hotel
with its own restaurant,
gymnasium and nightclub. It
stands in the market place
where John Wesley preached.
⚌ ❀ ⊨ ◖ ◗ ⏸ P

Flamborough

Rose & Crown
High Street ☎ (01262) 850455
11–3, 7–11 (may extend in summer)
**Camerons Bitter; Tetley
Bitter** H
Pub where the L-shaped room
has beamed ceilings and walls
decorated with local scenes.
Comfortable atmosphere, with
the pool table tucked away
from the main bar. Meals in
summer only. Frequented by
local fishermen. ◖ ◗ ▲ ♣ P

Garthorpe

Bay Horse
Shore Road ☎ (01724) 798306
12–3, 7.30–11; 12–11 Sat
**Mansfield Riding Bitter, Old
Baily** H
Comfortable, traditional,
former John Smith's pub with
a large lounge bar and a pool
and games room. Small
entrance hall. ⚌ ◖ ◗ ♣ P

Gilberdyke

Cross Keys Inn
Main Road ☎ (01430) 440310
12–11
**John Smith's Bitter; Tetley
Bitter; Whitbread
Boddingtons Bitter; guest
beer** H
Traditional village roadside
pub still in its original form.
Strong local following from all
age groups who appreciate the
emphasis on traditional beer
and games. ⚌ ❀ ⏸ ≭ ♣ P

Goodmanham

Goodmanham Arms
Main Street ☎ (01430) 873849
12–3 (not Mon–Thu), 7–11
**Black Sheep Best Bitter; S&N
Theakston Best Bitter** H
The classic country pub: a rural
gem barely touched by the
20th century. No music or
electronic intrusions, just a
warm welcome for all. On the
Wolds Way long distance
footpath. The landlady will
open Mon–Thu lunchtimes for

groups by prior arrangement.
Wheelchair access at the rear.
⚌ Q ⊱ ❀ ⊨ ⏸ ▲ ♣ P

Goole

Old George
Market Square ☎ (01405) 763147
11–3, 7–11
**Bass Light, Worthington BB,
Draught Bass; Stones Best
Bitter** H
Small but lively town-centre
pub decorated with old coins,
banknotes, books, bottles and
small furry animals (stuffed).
Emphasis on food lunchtimes
(no meals Sun); popular with a
younger clientele after dark.
⊱ ❀ ◖ ≭ ♣ P

Woodlands
Rutland Road ☎ (01405) 762738
11–5.30, 7–11; 11–11 Sat
John Smith's Bitter H
Friendly, 1930s estate pub on
the north side of town: a very
comfortable lounge, a superb
traditional snug and a raucous
public bar. Popular with all
ages and home to many clubs.
⚌ Q ⏸ ♣ P

Grimsby

Angel
175 Freeman Street
☎ (01472) 342402
11–11
**S&N Theakston Mild;
Younger Scotch, IPA, No. 3** H
Traditional, three-roomed pub
which offers good facilities for
all. The snug is known as the
'House of Lords'. Children
allowed in at lunchtimes.
Q ⊱ ⏸ ≭ (Docks) ♣ P

Corporation
88 Freeman Street
☎ (01472) 356651
11–11
**Bass Mild, Worthington BB,
Draught Bass** H
Traditional, three-roomed pub,
very much in keeping with the
area and serving a varied mix
of customers. Wood-panelled
smoke room at the rear;
sing-alongs in the lounge some
eves. ◖ ⏸ ≭ (Docks) ♣

Hope & Anchor
148 Victoria Street
☎ (01472) 342565
11–11
**Ind Coope Burton Ale; Tetley
Mild, Bitter, Imperial; guest
beers** H
Two-roomed, town-centre pub
with a lively bar and a quieter
lounge: local CAMRA *Pub of
the Year* four of the last five
years. Beer festival Feb/Mar.
Count the pumpclips! No food
Sun. ❀ ◖ ⏸ ⏚ ≭ (Town)

Royal Oak

190 Victoria Street
☎ (01472) 354562
11–11; 11–4.30, 6.30–11 Sat
**Bass Mild, Worthington BB,
Draught Bass; Stones Best
Bitter** H
Good, basic local with a mock
Tudor facade. Folk club
alternate Fris. Close to the
National Fishing Heritage
Centre.
Q ⊞ ⇌ (Town) ♣

Spider's Web

180 Carr Lane
☎ (01472) 692065
12 (11 Sat)–11
**Courage Directors; John
Smith's Bitter, Magnet;
Wilson's Mild** ✳
Pub where a boisterous bar
contrasts with a peaceful
lounge which has paintings for
sale. The function room hosts
good quality bands. Not all the
beers may be dispensed from
one bar but are available on
request. Q ✿ ⊞ ♣ P

Swigs

21 Osborne Street
☎ (01472) 354773
11–11; 7–10.30 Sun, closed Sun lunch
**Bateman XB; Willy's Original;
guest beers** H
Town-centre pub popular with
office workers at lunchtimes
and with a varied clientele in
the eve. Other Willy's beers
are available. Three guest
beers. ◑ ♿ ⇌ (Town)

Habrough

Horse & Hounds

Station Road (B1210 opp.
church) ☎ (01469) 576940
11–11 (may close 3–7)
**McEwan 80/-; S&N Theakston
Mild, XB, Old Peculier;
Younger IPA, No. 3; guest
beer** H
Tasteful conversion of a
former farmhouse/rectory;
part of the Habrough Hotel,
but the beer prices ensure a
good local trade. The food is
much better than the usual
pub fare. Jazz Thu. 80/- and
IPA are sold separately but are
the same beer.
🏨 Q ✿ 🛏 ◑ ▶ ⊞ ⇌ ♣ P

Harpham

St Quintin Arms

Main Street ☎ (01262) 490329
7–11; 12–3, 7–11 Tue
**Courage Directors; John
Smith's Bitter** H
Community pub at the heart
of a small village just off the
A166. One bar serves two
rooms in this listed building.
Well-laid-out dining area.
🏨 ✿ 🛏 ◑ ▶ ♿ ♣ P

Haxey

Loco

31 Church Street
☎ (01427) 752879
7 (6 Fri)–11; 1.30–4, 7–11 Sat
**Ruddles Best Bitter; John
Smith's Bitter, Magnet** H
A must for railway
enthusiasts, packed with
railwayana, including a steam
engine smokebox. Converted
from the village Co-op and
fish and chip shop. Lunches
(and lunch opening) Sat and
Sun only. Q ✿ ✿ ◑ ▶ ♿ ♣

Hedon

Shakespeare Inn

9 Baxtergate ☎ (01482) 898371
11–11
**Vaux Samson, Double
Maxim, Extra Special; Wards
Mild, Thorne Best Bitter, Best
Bitter** H
Busy locals' pub also popular
with visitors, with a compact
but cosy feel and photos of old
Hedon and snuff boxes
displayed. Noted for its food
lunch and eves till 7.30 (not Sat
or Sun eve). 🏨 ◑ ▶ ♣ P

Hotham

Hotham Arms

Main Street ☎ (01430) 422939
11.30–4, 6.30–11; 11–11 Fri & Sat
**Black Sheep Best Bitter;
Tetley Bitter; Whitbread
Boddingtons Mild, Bitter** H
Dating from 1760, this pub is
very popular with visiting
diners even though the village
is off the beaten track. Used by
walkers on the Wolds Way.
No meals Mon/Tue eves.
🏨 ✿ ◑ ▶ ♿ ▲ ♣ P

Howden

Wheatsheaf

83 Hailgate ☎ (01430) 430722
11–11
John Smith's Bitter H
Traditional local close to the
minster. Welcoming
atmosphere; popular with
locals. Separate family area.
Q ✿ ✿ 🛏 ◑ ▶ ▲ ♣ P

Hull

Bay Horse

113 Wincolmlee (400 yds N of
North Bridge on W bank of
River Hull) ☎ (01482) 29227
11.30–11
**Bateman Mild, XB, XXXB,
Salem Porter, Victory;
Marston's Pedigree** H
Spectacular corner pub in an
old industrial area: Bateman's
only tied house north of the
Humber. The lofty stable bar is
warmed by a cast iron stove
and is full of Bateman's
memorabilia. The bar's
wood-panelled walls display
rugby league photos. Beware
the keg Scrumpy Jack cider on
a fake handpump. Eve meals
end 7pm. 🏨 ◑ ▶ ♣ P

Duke of Wellington

104 Peel Street (N of Spring
Bank, NW of centre)
☎ (01482) 29603
12–3 (11–5 June–Oct), 7–11
**Hull Mild; Taylor Landlord;
Tetley Bitter; guest beers** H
Back-street, re-styled,
Victorian corner local, popular
with students and locals. Often
crowded. Four, usually strong,
guest beers. ✳ ♿ ♣ P

East Riding

37 Cannon Street
☎ (01482) 29134
12–4.30 (5 Sat), 7–11
Tetley Mild, Bitter H
Small, street-corner, two-
roomed industrial pub to the
north of the city centre. The
no-nonsense bar features
rugby league memorabilia,
whilst the cosy lounge is
wood-panelled. ⊞ ♣

Grapes Inn

Sykes Street ☎ (01482) 24424
12–4, 7–11
**Camerons Strongarm; Stones
Best Bitter; Tetley Mild,
Bitter** H
Friendly local just off the
northern section of the central
orbital road, near the registry
office. Built in the 1930s, it has
two distinct areas and features
live music Fri, Sat and Mon.
Darts is popular. 🏨 ♣

New Clarence

77 Charles Street
☎ (01482) 20327
11–11
**Ind Coope Burton Ale;
Marston's Pedigree; Tetley
Mild, Bitter; guest beers** H
Tetley's first Festival Ale
House in Hull, situated off
Kingston Sq, near the New
Theatre and the original Hull
Brewery buildings. Stone
effect floor tiles, wooden
panelling and partitions give
this large, one-roomer a
traditional theme. Eve meals
till 7.30, but not Sun. ◑ ▶ ♣

Oberon

Queen Street ☎ (01482) 24886
11–3, 5.30–11
**Bass Mild, Draught Bass;
Bateman Valiant** H
Traditional, two-roomed
drinkers' pub with a collection
of nautical memorabilia: fairly
plain, but very well run.
Popular with Humber pilots
due to its location near
Corporation Pier. Q ♣

Humberside

Old Blue Bell

Market Place ☎ (01482) 24382
11–3, 7–11, 11–11 Tue, Thu, Fri & Sat
**Samuel Smith OBB,
Museum** H
Popular old town pub with its
original layout of snug,
corridor and long, narrow bar.
A courtyard connects to the
adjoining covered market.
Large collection of bells. Pool
room upstairs. ♨ Q ❀ ◐ ◗

Olde Black Boy

150 High Street
☎ (01482) 265116
11–3, 5–11
Beer range varies H
Situated in Hull's historic old
town: the first Tap & Spile
Charterhouse pub. Its history,
dating back to 1331, is
explained in the small, wood-
panelled front room. The
range of ten beers changes
daily. Hull CAMRA *Pub of the
Year* 1993. Eve meals Mon–Fri
till 7pm. ♨ Q ◐ ◗ ♣ ○

Olde White Harte

25 Silver Street
☎ (01482) 26363
11–11
**S&N Theakston XB, Old
Peculier; Younger IPA, No. 3;
guest beer** (occasional) H
16th-century courtyard pub,
originally a residence where
the Governor of Hull resolved
to deny Charles I entry to the
city. Superb woodwork, sit-in
fireplaces and stained-glass
feature. Varied lunch menu in
the bar and the upstairs dining
room. Q ❀ ◐ ♣

Royal William

Waterhouse Lane
☎ (01482) 215881
11.30–2.30 (11–3 Sat), 5.30 (6.30
Sat)–11; 7–10.30 Sun, closed Sun
lunch
**S&N Theakston Best Bitter,
XB; John Smith's Bitter;
Whitbread Boddingtons
Bitter, Castle Eden Ale,
Flowers Original** H
Hull's country pub in the
town, situated by the Princes
Quay shopping centre car
park. One L-shaped room with
an old-world atmosphere.
Meals till 8pm; summer
barbecues. Blues Mon and
Wed. ❀ ◐ ◗ ⇌ ♣

Spring Bank Tavern

29 Spring Bank
☎ (01482) 213351
11–11
**Mansfield Riding Mild,
Riding Bitter, Bitter, Old
Baily; guest beers** H
Mansfield's first cask ale
house, refurbished as a
street-corner local on the
western edge of the centre.
Can be very busy. The guest
beers (three) tend to be
expensive. No eve meals Sun;
till 7pm Mon–Thu, 6pm Sat.
◐ ◗

Kilnsea

Crown & Anchor

Main Street ☎ (01964) 650276
11–11
**Bass Mild, Draught Bass;
Tetley Bitter** H
Pub almost on Spurn Point,
facing the busy Humber
estuary. The four rooms
(including a restaurant and a
family room) house brasses,
china and household utensils.
The lounge has a Victorian
range. Popular for food.
♨ ➴ ❀ ◐ ◗ ▲ ♣ P

Kirmington

Marrowbone &
Cleaver

High Street ☎ (01652) 688335
11–3.30, 6.30–11
**Bass Worthington BB,
Draught Bass; M&B Mild** H
This traditional pub was partly
a butcher's shop in the last
century, hence its name.
Situated near Humberside
airport, a former RAF station
well featured in the lounge.
♨ Q ❀ ◐ ♣ P

Lund

Wellington Inn

The Green ☎ (01377) 217294
12–2 (not Mon; 12–3 Sat), 7–11
**Mansfield Riding Mild,
Riding Bitter, Bitter, Old
Baily** H, **Deakin's Yule
Brew** G
Pub featured in the 1954 film
Lease of Life. An inn has stood
on this site since the 13th
century. Pool league Tue, quiz
Wed, occasional entertain-
ment. Separate restaurant.
♨ ➴ ❀ ◐ ◗ ▲ ♣ P

Market Weighton

Half Moon

High Street ☎ (01430) 872247
7 (12 Fri & Sat) –11
Burtonwood Mild, Bitter H
Small market town pub with a
friendly welcome. A single
room serves as a bar and
lounge, one at either end.
Strong pool following. Popular
with all ages. ❀ & ♣ P

Messingham

Bird in the Barley

Northfield Road
☎ (01724) 762994
11.30–3 (not Mon), 5–11
**Ruddles Best Bitter, County;
John Smith's Bitter; Webster's
Yorkshire Bitter; guest beer** H
Large, one-roomed, country-
style pub noted for good food
and service. Popular with
diners lunchtime and drinkers
in the eve. Wheelchair WC.
♨ ❀ ◐ & ♣ P

Nafferton

Cross Keys

North Street ☎ (01377) 254261
11.30–3 (not Mon), 7–11
**S&N Theakston Best Bitter,
XB; John Smith's Bitter;
Younger Scotch** H
Substantial inn at the northern
end of the village, popular for
bar meals (not served Tue
eve). Separate restaurant and
games/family room.
➴ ☎ ◐ ◗ ♣

New Holland

Lincoln Castle

Barrow Road ☎ (01469) 530498
12–2, 7–11
**Bass Worthington BB; Hull
Mild; Jennings Oatmeal
Stout; Morland Old Speckled
Hen; guest beers**
(occasional) H
Pub with friendly locals in the
bar and pool room; separate
lounge. Large TV screen;
workingmen's atmosphere.
The beers may change
occasionally. ◐ ⊞ ▲ ⇌ ○ P

North Dalton

Star Inn

Water Road ☎ (01377) 217688
11–3.30, 6–11; 11–11 Sat
**John Smith's Bitter;
Whitbread Boddingtons
Bitter; guest beers** H
Friendly village local with a
restaurant (steaks a speciality).
Pleasant outdoor seating,
overlooking the pond.
♨ Q ➴ ❀ ☎ ◐ ◗ & ♣ P

North Newbald

Gnu Inn

The Green ☎ (01430) 827799
12–3 (not winter), 7–11; 12–11 Sat
**Ind Coope Burton Ale; Old
Mill Mild; Tetley Bitter;
Whitbread Castle Eden Ale;
guest beers** H
Friendly Wolds pub
overlooking the village green.
Popular with walkers and
visitors, who come to see the
horses stabled at the rear.
Strong on darts, dominoes and
football teams. No jukebox.
♨ Q ❀ ◐ ◗ & ▲ ♣ P

Ottringham

Watts Arms

Main Street ☎ (01964) 622034
7–11 (12–3, 7–11 Sat, & Wed–Fri in
summer)
Camerons Bitter; Hull Mild H
Former Darley's, former
original Hull Brewery, pub: a

bar with pool/games, etc., and a cosy, spacious, Tudor-style lounge. Regular country nights Fri. Sun lunches. ♣ P

Owston Ferry

Crooked Billet

Silver Street ☎ (01427) 728264
11–3 (not Mon, except bank hols), 7–11
Wards Thorne Best Bitter H
Friendly local on the River Trent, with its own boxing club. Weekend sing-alongs. ⌂ Q ❧ ❀ ◖ ⅃ ⅄ ♣ P

Patrington

Station Hotel

Station Road ☎ (01964) 630262
11–2.30, 5 (6.30 Sat)–11
Younger IPA, No. 3 H
Roadside pub on the western approach to the village. Its name relates to a former railway station adjacent. Three rooms: a grill room, a basic bar at the rear, and a small, friendly front lounge. Booking for meals recommended.
❀ ◖ ⅃ ⅄ P

Paull

Humber Tavern

Main Street ☎ (01482) 899347
12–3, 6.30–11; 11–11 Sat (& school summer holidays)
Bass Mild, Worthington BB; Tetley Bitter; guest beer H
Welcoming pub, dating from 1805, with a view over the Humber. The guest beer comes from national brewers. Book eve meals. ⌂ ❧ ❀ ◖ ⅃ ♣

Preston

Nag's Head

1 Sproatley Road
☎ (01482) 897517
12–3.30, 7–11 (11–4.30, 6–11 summer)
Bass Mild; Old Mill Bitter; Stones Best Bitter H
Pleasantly modernised and extended roadside pub: a large, comfortable lounge, a separate bar and a well-appointed, conservatory-type family room. Garden playground (barbecues in summer). ❧ ❀ ◖ ♣ P

Reedness

Half Moon

Main Street ☎ (01405) 704484
12–3, 7–11 (supper licence)
Marston's Pedigree; Whitbread Boddingtons Bitter, Castle Eden Ale; guest beer H
Traditional local with a caravan and campsite behind and Blacktoft Sands RSPB Reserve nearby. Whitbread collection guest beers.
⌂ ❀ ◖ ⅃ ⅄ ♣ P

Ryhill

Crooked Billet

Pitt Lane (400 yds off A1033)
☎ (01964) 622303
12–3, 7–11; 12–11 Fri & Sat
Burtonwood Bitter H
Busy village pub down a narrow lane. The lounge has a stone-floored lower level; an old box-camera collection is on display. ⌂ ◖ ♣ P

Scawby Brook

Horse & Cart

185 Scawby Road
☎ (01652) 652150
11–3, 6–11; 11–11 Sat
Marston's Pedigree; Whitbread Boddingtons Bitter, Trophy, Castle Eden Ale, Winter Royal H
Modern free house, popular with locals. Good food; friendly bar staff. Garden play area. ❀ ⌸ ◖ ⅃ ♣ P

Scunthorpe

Riveter

50 Henderson Avenue
☎ (01724) 862701
11–3, 5.30–11; 11–11 Sat
Old Mill Mild, Bitter, Bullion, Porter H
Pub converted from a workingmen's club, noisy and crowded in the eve. Large games area for pool and darts. Parking very limited. ♣ P

Skerne

Eagle

Wansford Road
☎ (01377) 252178
7–11; 12–2, 7–11 Sat
Camerons Bitter H
Classic, unspoilt village local surrounded by mature trees. Drinks are brought to your table from a Victorian cash register beer engine in the small cellar off the entrance corridor. Separate front parlour. ⌂ Q ❀ ♣ P

Skipsea

Board Inn

Back Street ☎ (01262) 468342
12–3, 7–11 (11.30 Sat supper licence)
Burtonwood Bitter, Forshaw's H
Village local dating back to the 17th century. The snug has a painted wooden bar, whilst the tap room reflects horse racing. Restaurant and children's room to the rear.
⌂ ❧ ❀ ◖ ⅃ ⅄ ▲ ♣ P

Snaith

Black Lion

9 Selby Road ☎ (01405) 860282
11–4, 7–11

John Smith's Bitter; Tetley Bitter H
The antithesis of a theme pub. Though it evolved from the stables of a former coaching inn, the welcoming landlord and loyal regulars tell different tales of the pub's history. ❀ ⊟ ◬ ⮀ (limited service) ♣ P

South Ferriby

Nelthorpe Arms Country Inn

School Lane
☎ (01652) 635235
12–3, 7–11
Tetley Mild, Bitter; guest beer H
Two-roomed, 400-year-old pub, with a reputation for good food in the lounge.
⌂ Q ❀ ⌸ ◖ ⅃ ⊟ ♣ P

Sutton upon Derwent

St Vincent Arms

Main Street
☎ (01904) 608349
11–3, 6–11
Fuller's London Pride; Mansfield Riding Bitter; Old Mill Bitter; S&N Theakston Old Peculier; Taylor Landlord; Wells Bombardier H
Traditional village inn, popular for its friendly, cosy atmosphere and excellent food. Four adventurous guest beers, keenly priced, with only lined glasses used.
⌂ Q ❧ ❀ ◖ ⅃ ▲ P

Westwoodside

Park Drain

400 yds off B1396 OS726988
☎ (01427) 752255
11–3, 5.30–11; 11–11 Sat
Mansfield Riding Bitter; John Smith's Bitter; Wilson's Mild; guest beer H
Unusual, remote, Victorian pub, built to serve the mining community of a pit that was never sunk! Comfortable lounge and excellent restaurant. Meals all day Sun.
⌂ ❀ ◖ ⅃ ⊟ ▲ ♣ P

Wrawby

Jolly Miller

Brigg Road (A15/A18)
☎ (01652) 655658
11–3, 7 (6 summer)–11
Bass Worthington BB, Draught Bass H
Small, modernised pub with a single lounge bar. Popular for meals (eves Fri–Sun only). Children's play area in the garden. ❀ ◖ ⅃ P

Isle of Wight

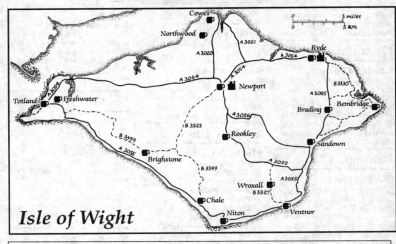

Isle of Wight

 Burts, *Newport*; **Goddard's**, *Ryde*

Bembridge

Row Barge
☎ (01983) 872874
12–11 (12–3, 6–11 winter)
Draught Bass; Burts VPA, 4X; Hall & Woodhouse Hard Tackle; Ind Coope Burton Ale; guest beers H
Lively, popular real ale and food pub, featuring a copper-covered bar and a collection of naughty postcards.
🏨 ➰ ❀ ◖ ▸

Brading

Anglers
Yarbridge (off A3055, E at traffic lights) ☎ (01983) 406212
11–11 (11–3, 7–11 winter)
Gale's Best Bitter, 5X, HSB H
Long, single-bar pub with a large garden. Its name derives from the adjacent fishing grounds. Q ❀ ◖ ▸ ⇌ ♣ P

Brighstone

Countryman
Limerstone Road (B3399, 500 yds E of village)
☎ (01983) 740616
11–3 (later summer), 6.30–11
Gibbs Mew Wiltshire; Hall & Woodhouse Badger Best Bitter; Ind Coope Burton Ale H**; guest beers**
Spacious roadside pub near downland and unspoilt beaches. The large, single bar displays a collection of rustic bygones. Function room.
🏨 Q ➰ ❀ ◖ ▸ ▲ ♣ P ✂

Try also: Sun Inn, on B3399, Hulverstone (Gale's)

Chale

Wight Mouse
Newport Road (B3399, 100 yds from A3055) ☎ (01983) 730431
11–11 (midnight restaurant)
Fuller's Chiswick; Marston's Pedigree; Wadworth 6X; Whitbread Boddingtons Bitter H
Very busy, old stone pub with an adjoining hotel, near Blackgang Chine theme park. An award-winning family pub, it has a garden play area and food is served all day. Live music every night. 365 whiskies (one for every day of the year).
🏨 🏨 ➰ ❀ ⌷ ◖ ▸ ▲ P

Cowes

Anchor
High Street ☎ (01983) 292823
11–11
Greene King Abbot; Hall & Woodhouse Badger Best Bitter, Tanglefoot; Wadworth 6X; Whitbread Boddingtons Bitter, Flowers Original; guest beers H
Ancient town-centre inn where the former stables have been converted to a games and children's room, with an occasional bar for events. Regular live groups play. Home-made food is available all day—steak & ale, and fish pies are specialities.
🏨 🏨 ➰ ❀ ◖ ▸ ♣ ♣

Woodvale
Princes Esplanade (W end)
☎ (01983) 292037
11–11

Beer range varies H
Large, friendly pub situated just off the water's edge with an unspoilt view across the Solent; the sunset can be spectacular. The constantly-changing beers come from the Whitbread portfolio. Petanque played.
➰ ❀ ◖ ▸ ♣

Freshwater

Vine
Schoolgreen Road
☎ (01983) 752959
11–3, 5.30–11
Gale's Best Bitter, 5X, HSB H
Friendly, village-centre pub, close to Tennyson's home and superb country walks.
🏨 Q ❀ 🏨 ◖ ▸ ▲ ♣ P ✂

Try also: Lord Palmerston, Golden Hill Fort (Free)

Newport

Prince of Wales
36 South Street
☎ (01983) 525026
11–11
Ushers Best Bitter, Founders H
Town-centre pub, supplying all Ushers' cask range, including seasonal beers, and a real cider (West Country), and attracting a cross-section of drinkers. Home-made food includes beer sausages made with cask ale.
🏨 Q ◖ ▸ ⌷ ♣ ⌂

Try also: Railway Medina, Sea St (Gale's)

148

Niton

Buddle

St Catherine's Road, Niton
Undercliffe (follow signs for St
Catherine's Point)
☎ (01983) 730243
11–11 (11–3, 6–11 winter)
**Whitbread Boddingtons
Bitter, Flowers IPA, Original;
guest beers** H
Ancient stone-built pub with
strong smuggling connections.
It usually offers three guest
beers, plus Hamstead
Vineyard cider. The family
room is closed in winter. Try
the seafood.
🔥 ⛄ ❀ ◐ ▲ ♣ ➳ P

Try also: White Lion, High St
(Whitbread)

Northwood

Travellers Joy

Pallance Road
☎ (01983) 298024
11–3, 6–11; 11–11 Sat
**Bateman Mild; Gibbs Mew
Bishop's Tipple; Ringwood
Old Thumper; Ruddles
County; guest beers** H
Twice winner of the local
CAMRA *Pub of the Year* award,
this pub offers nine cask ales
and a regular mild. A wide
range of ales from
independent brewers is always
available, backed up by
national brands. Well worth a
visit. ❀ ◐ ▶ ♿ ▲ ♣ ➳

Try also: Horseshoe (Gale's)

Rookley

Chequers

Off A3020 ☎ (01983) 840314
11–4, 6–11
**Courage Best Bitter,
Directors; Morland Old
Speckled Hen; John Smith's
Bitter; Wadworth 6X** H

Extremely popular, much
extended and rebuilt, ex-
Whitbread house. The accent
is very firmly on food, but it
retains a flagstone-floored
public bar. The beer is
reasonably priced. 🔥 Q ⛄
❀ ◐ ▶ ◫ ♿ ▲ ♣ P

Ryde

Castle

164 High Street (10 mins' walk
from ferry and hovercraft
terminals) ☎ (01983) 811138
11–11
Gale's BBB, 5X, HSB H
Traditional, split-level, open-
plan pub in the town centre,
with a large open fire in the
main bar and original etched
windows. 🔥 ♣

Lake Superior

59 Marlborough Road,
Elmfield (Ryde–Sandown
road, A3055)
☎ (01983) 563519
11–3, 5.30–11; 11–11 Sat
**Bass Worthington BB,
Draught Bass; Fuller's
London Pride; Goddard's
Special; guest beers** H
Converted house which has
undergone refurbishment to a
comfortable, corner-sited,
suburban local: a drinkers'
pub, with no food (except
barbecues in summer), but a
good atmosphere and
conversation. No dogs.
🔥 ⛄ ❀ ♿ ♣

Sandown

Castle

Fitzroy Street
☎ (01983) 403169
11–3, 7–11
**Morland Old Speckled Hen;
Ruddles Best Bitter, County;
John Smith's Bitter;
Wadworth 6X; guest beers** H
Handy back-street local near
the town centre: a large,

open-plan establishment with
a three-sided bar. Try the
specialist real ale sausages.
🔥 Q ⛄ ❀ ◐ ▶ ⇌ ♣

Totland

Highdown Inn

Highdown Lane (Alum Bay
old road, 2 miles E of Alum
Bay) ☎ (01983) 752450
11–11 (11–3, 7–11 winter)
**Ushers Best Bitter,
Founders** H
Superb country pub, formerly
used by smugglers, hiding on
the north side of Tennyson's
Downs. Wellies and dogs
welcome; camping in the
garden.
🔥 Q ❀ ⇌ ◐ ▲ ♣ P

Ventnor

Volunteer

30 Victoria Street
☎ (01983) 852537
11–3, 6–11; 11–11 Fri & Sat
**Burts VPA; Hall &
Woodhouse Badger Best
Bitter; Tetley Bitter** H
Former Burts town local, now
revived by new owners. Small
and friendly, it has a popular
Rings game. ♣

Try also: Spyglass, Esplanade
(Free)

Wroxall

Star

Clarence Road
☎ (01983) 854701
11–3, 7–11
**Burts Nipper, VPA; Eldridge
Pope Hardy Country;
Ringwood Best Bitter** H
Busy village pub serving a
selection of local ales and
favourites from the mainland.
It has two bars, and offers a
wide selection of food.
Q ◐ ▶ ◫ ▲ ♣ P

THE SYMBOLS

🔥	real fire	♿	easy wheelchair access
Q	quiet pub (at least one bar)	▲	camping facilities at the pub
⛄	indoor room for children		or nearby
❀	garden or other outdoor drinking	⇌	near British Rail station
	area	⊖	near underground station
⇌	accommodation	♣	pub games
◐	lunchtime meals	➳	real cider
▶	evening meals	P	pub car park
◫	public bar	✄	no-smoking room or area

Kent

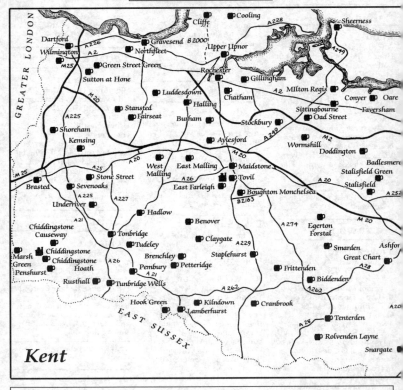

Kent

 Goacher's, *Tovil;* **Larkins,** *Chiddingstone;* **Shepherd Neame,** *Faversham*

Ashford

Beaver
Beaver Road ☎ (01233) 620264
11–3, 6–11
Shepherd Neame Master Brew Bitter; guest beers H
Extensively refurbished two years ago, this traditional local has one bar serving two rooms. Bar snacks are available (not Wed and Sun eves) and other Shepherd Neame beers are guests.
Q ❀ ◑ ≠ ♣ P

Beaver Road Off-Licence
36 Beaver Road
☎ (01233) 629904
10.30 (3 Wed)–10.30
Beer range varies G
Off-licence offering at least three beers during the week, and four at weekends, on average 20–25% cheaper than pub prices. Sample before you buy. Real cider also is available (usually Biddenden and one other). ≠ ▭

Castle
Castle Street (end of pedestrian area)
☎ (01233) 621016
11–4 (5 Fri & Sat), 7–11
Shepherd Neame Master Brew Bitter, Spitfire H
Busy town-centre pub near the WWI tank memorial. It is popular with office workers at lunchtimes (classical music while you eat) and bikers eves. Live music Sun, Wed and Fri. Beware the Scrumpy Jack on a fake handpump. Parking only for bikes.
❀ ◑ ▶ ≠ P

Hooden Horse on the Hill
Silverhill Road, Willesborough (off A20)
☎ (01233) 662226
11–2.30, 6–11
Goacher's Light; Hook Norton Old Hooky; Hop Back Summer Lightning; S&N Theakston Old Peculier; guest beers H
Formerly the Rose. This is the fourth (of four) in the Hooden

Horse Group, and features hop-decorated ceilings and candlelit tables. Two guest beers are always available, plus an extensive range of home-cooked, quality food. The large garden houses farm animals. A price premium is levied on half pints. Occasional live music.
❀ ◑ ▶ ▭ P

Aylesford

Little Gem
19 High Street
☎ (01622) 717510
11–3, 6–11; 11–11 Fri & Sat
Black Sheep Best Bitter G;
Fuller's London Pride H;
ESB G; **Harveys BB** H; **S&N Theakston Old Peculier** G;
guest beers
Claimed to be Kent's smallest pub: a former bakery, now a low-beamed, Tudor pub, with a small gallery-style upstairs drinking area. Brenchley's Best Bitter is a house beer of unspecified origin. Often very busy. ◑ ▭

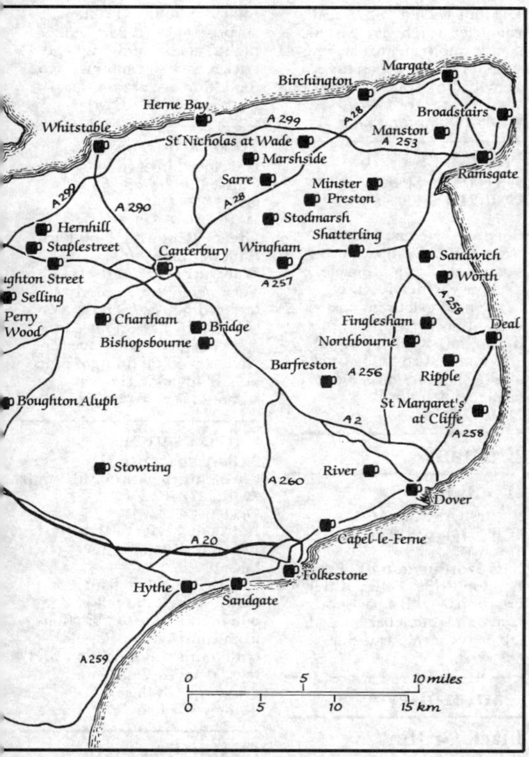

Badlesmere

Red Lion
Ashford Road (A251)
☎ (01233) 740320
11–3, 6–11; 11–11 Sat
Fuller's London Pride; Greene King XX Mild, Abbot; Shepherd Neame Master Brew Bitter; guest beers H
Village pub, dating back to the 16th century. Popular with locals and visitors, it offers two different guest ales each week and is a rare outlet for mild in the area. Look out for the gas lights in the bar and the potbellied pigs in the garden. No eve meals Tue or Wed. ♨ ◐ ◗ ♣ ⊂

Barfreston

Yew Tree Inn
Off A2, Canterbury–Dover road ☎ (01304) 831619
11–3, 6–11
Greene King XX Mild, IPA; Mauldons Black Adder H**; Otter Ale** G**; Taylor Best Bitter** H**; guest beers**
Traditional central village pub alongside the church, with a lively local clientele. About 1½ miles from Shepherdswell station. ♨ ❀ ◐ ◗ ♣ P

Benover

Woolpack Inn
Benover Road (B2162, 1 mile S of Yalding) ☎ (01892) 730356
11–2.30 (3 Sat), 6–11
Shepherd Neame Master Brew Bitter, Porter, Bishops Finger H
Attractive, comfortable, 17th-century country local where exposed beams and open fires ensure a warm welcome. Local beer-making memorabilia is displayed and generous portions of good value, home-cooked food are served (specials board daily). No food Sun eve.
♨ Q ♘ ❀ ◐ ◗ ♣ P

Biddenden

Castletons Oak
Cranbrook Road (1 mile S of village, follow signs for Chest Hospital) OS846361
☎ (01580) 291385
11–11; 11–3, 7–11 Mon
Harveys BB; guest beers H
Strangely signed pub (an old man sitting on a coffin) on a dangerous crossroads. There is a single, split-level bar, and a small dining area. Large garden for families.
♨ ❀ ◐ ◗ ▲ ⊂ P

Birchington

Seaview Hotel
Station Road ☎ (01843) 841702
11–11
Shepherd Neame Master Brew Bitter, Best Bitter, Spitfire *or* **Porter,** *or* **Bishops Finger** H
Built in 1865 to cater for travellers on the newly-built London, Chatham and Dover Railway: a one-bar pub boasting a friendly atmosphere and welcoming to all. Look for the whale's jaw bone in the garden. Eve meals in summer.
♨ ❀ ⛟ ◐ ◗ ⇌ ♣ P

Bishopsbourne

Mermaid Inn
The Street ☎ (01227) 830581
11–3, 6–11
Shepherd Neame Master Brew Bitter, Porter H
Attractive, friendly pub in a typically Kentish village, the former home of author Joseph Conrad. ♨ ❀ ◐ ♣

Boughton Street

Queens Head Inn
111 The Street
☎ (01227) 751369
11–3, 6–11; 11–11 Sat
Shepherd Neame Master Brew Bitter, Spitfire, Porter H
16th-century pub, with a lively public bar, wood-panelled saloon/dining room and a restaurant: a good place to stay if visiting Canterbury. Bat and Trap.
Q ❀ ⛟ ◐ ◗ ♿ ▲ ♣ P

Boughton Aluph

Flying Horse Inn
On A251, 5 miles N of Ashford
☎ (01233) 620914
11–11 (closed afternoons Jan–Feb)
Courage Best Bitter; Morland Old Speckled Hen; Shepherd Neame Master Brew Bitter; John Smith's Bitter; Wadworth 6X H
15th-century inn featuring open fires and oak beams, overlooking the village green (cricket in summer). An extensive range of food is available. ♨ ❀ ⛟ ◐ ◗ ♿ P

Boughton Monchelsea

Red House
Hermitage Lane (S off B2163, down Wierton Rd and East Hall Hill) OS783488
☎ (01622) 743986
12–3, 7–11; 12–11 Sat

Kent

Eldridge Pope Blackdown
Porter; Fuller's London Pride;
Greene King XX Mild, IPA,
Abbot; Hampshire Lionheart;
guest beers H
Popular country free house
with a welcoming atmosphere.
It stocks a constantly changing
selection of guest beers, a new
house beer, Knight of Wierton
(not brewed here), plus an
extensive range of speciality
and imported bottled beers.
May beer festival.
🏨 ☞ ☻ ◑ ▲ ♣ ⌂ P

Brasted

Bull Inn
High Street ☎ (01959) 562551
10.30–2.30, 5.30–11; 10.30–11 Sat
Shepherd Neame Master
Brew Bitter, Spitfire, Porter,
Bishops Finger H
Warm and friendly pub in
neo-Tudor style which caters
both for local and passing
trade in a village of many
antique shops. Very popular
for food. Bat and Trap is
played. Note: the Scrumpy
Jack handpump is fake.
☻ ◑ ◗ ♣ P

Try also: General Wolfe,
Westerham (Greene King)

Brenchley

Bull
High Street ☎ (01892) 722701
11–3, 5–11
Greene King IPA, Abbot;
Shepherd Neame Best Bitter;
guest beer H
Single-bar, Victorian inn
attracting mainly regulars, but
a very warm welcome is given
to strangers. Darts and quiz
nights are held weekly.
Brenchley has won the Best-
Kept Village in England award
and is well worth a visit.
🏨 ☻ 🚌 ◑ ◗ ♣ P

Bridge

Plough & Harrow
High Street ☎ (01227) 830455
11–3, 6–11; 11–11 Sat
Shepherd Neame Master
Brew Bitter H
Friendly, village local, good
for games. Originally a
maltings and brewery, it is
over 300 years old. 🏨 ◑ ♣ P

Broadstairs

Brown Jug
204 Ramsgate Road, Dumpton
☎ (01843) 862788
11–3, 6–11
Whitbread Fremlins Bitter;
guest beers H
Reputedly a billet for officers
during the Napoleonic Wars,

this flint-walled pub of real
character, run by two sisters,
stands out in an area lacking
decent real ale. It possesses a
homely atmosphere in the best
sense of the word. 🏨 Q ☻
🍴 ⇌ (Dumpton Pk) ♣ P

Neptune's Hall
1–3 Harbour Street
☎ (01843) 861400
11–11
Shepherd Neame Master
Brew Bitter, Spitfire, Porter H
Busy, three-bar, old-fashioned
ale house with a recently
re-opened restaurant next
door. It hosts regular dances
during folk week in Aug. A
welcome return to the Guide
after a short absence, due to a
change of landlord.
Q ☻ ◑ ⇌ ♣

Burham

Windmill
Rochester Road
☎ (01634) 861919
11–3, 6–11
Bass Worthington BB; Fuller's
London Pride; Tetley Bitter H
Free house with a back-room
restaurant and a bar billiards
table. Eve meals Thu–Sat.
◑ ◗ ♣ P

Canterbury

Black Griffin
40 St Peter's Street
☎ (01227) 455563
11–11
Greene King Abbot H / G;
Wadworth 6X; Whitbread
Boddingtons Bitter, Flowers
IPA H; guest beers H / G
City-centre pub which can be
extremely busy eves and is
popular with students.
🏨 ☻ ◑ ⅋ ⇌ (West/
East) ⌂

Canterbury Tales
12 The Friars (opp. Marlowe
Theatre) ☎ (01227) 738957
11–11
Goacher's Light; Shepherd
Neame Master Brew Bitter;
guest beers H
Smart, busy city-centre pub
and restaurant with an
adventurous guest beer policy,
taking in mini-festivals and
special promotions. Popular
with all ages, it hosts quizzes
and many theme nights. Open
all day Sun for food.
◑ ◗ ⅋ ⇌ (West/East) ⌂

King's Head
204 Wincheap (A28, Ashford
Road) ☎ (01227) 462885
11–2.30, 6.30–11; 12–2, 7–10.30 Sun
Fuller's Chiswick; Greene
King Abbot; guest beers H
Pub dating from the 15th
century. The guest beers are

rotated, but there is often a
surprise in the cellar. Quiz
night Tue; Bat and Trap and
cricket teams in summer. No
food Mon eve or Sun.
Q ☻ ◑ ◗ ⅋ ⇌ (East) ♣

New Inn
Havelock Street (near
Christchurch College)
☎ (01227) 464584
11–3 (3.30 Fri & Sat), 6–11
Greene King IPA; Hop Back
Summer Lightning;
Wadworth 6X; guest beers H
Very small pub, formerly a
terraced house, friendly both
sides of the bar, and used by
students. Beer mats cover one
wall. 20p off all draught pints
Sun. Biddenden cider in
summer. ☻ ◑ ◗ ⇌ (East) ⌂

Olive Branch
39 Burgate (opp. the
Christchurch gate of cathedral)
☎ (01227) 462170
11–11
Ind Coope Friary Meux Best
Bitter, Burton Ale; guest
beer H
Former wine merchant. For
many years it did not have a
Sun licence, due to objections
from churchgoers. Popular
with tourists at lunchtime and
regulars eves. Outdoor
drinking is in the
Buttermarket. ☻ ◑ ⇌ (East)

Capel-le-Ferne

Royal Oak
New Dover Road (B2011)
☎ (01303) 244787
11.30–3 (4 Sat), 6 (7 Sat)–11 (may vary
summer)
Shepherd Neame Master
Brew Bitter; guest beers H
Split-level, two-bar pub next to
a camp site. Games are kept
separate from the main bar
area. 🏨 ◑ ▲ ♣ P

Chartham

Cross Keys
Bolts Hill ☎ (01227) 738216
11–2.30, 7–11
Goacher's Light; John Smith's
Bitter; guest beers H
Friendly village local with
separate games and drinking
areas. 🏨 ☻ ⇌ ♣ P

Chatham

Alexandra Hotel
43 Railway Street
☎ (01634) 843959
11–3 (4 Sat), 5 (7 Sat)–11; 11–11 Fri
Shepherd Neame Master
Brew Bitter, Spitfire, Porter H
Impressive Victorian building,
stranded on a traffic island,
near the station. Quiz nights
held. ☻ ⇌ ♣

Command House

Gun Wharf, Dock Road
☎ (01634) 845910
11.30–3, 5–11; 12–2.30 (3 summer),
6–11 Sat
**Bass Charrington IPA,
Worthington BB, Draught
Bass; Fuller's London Pride;
guest beers** H
Attractive, riverside pub with
a seating area beside the
Medway. A former naval
commander's house, it has one
large bar. Food is served until
9pm; no meals Sun eve.
❀ ◖ ▶ ≉ ♣ P

Ropemakers Arms

70 New Road
☎ (01634) 402121
12–3 (not Sat), 7–11
**Goacher's Light; Greene King
Abbot; guest beers** H
Friendly haven by the busy
A2, originally used by
ropemakers from the naval
dockyards. Quiz nights on the
first Wed of each month.
Meals Mon–Fri. ◖ ≉ ♣

Chiddingstone Causeway

Little Brown Jug

On B2027 ☎ (01892) 870318
11.30–3, 6–11
Harveys BB; guest beers H
Busy, friendly, family-run pub
offering three, ever-changing,
unusual guest beers and an
excellent range of food. A
must. ᴁ Q ❀ ⊨ ◖ ▶ ੯
≉ (Penshurst) ♣ P

Chiddingstone Hoath

Rock

OS498433 ☎ (01892) 870296
11–3, 5.30–11
**Larkins Bitter; Shepherd
Neame Master Brew Bitter** H
Rural pub of 16th-century
origins, with an inglenook
housing a wood-burning
stove. The floor in the main
bar is of traditional red brick.
Hook the Bull is an amusing
game, particular to this pub.
ᴁ Q ❀ ◖ ♣ P

Claygate

White Hart

On B2162, S of Collier Street
OS714444 ☎ (01892) 730313
11–3, 6–11
**Goacher's Light; Shepherd
Neame Master Brew Bitter;
Wadworth 6X** H
Friendly local: a comfortable,
two-bar house set in open
countryside of orchards and
hop gardens. Good value bar
snacks, plus a restaurant.
ᴁ ⊨ ◖ ▶ ੯ ♠ ♣ ⭗ P

Cliffe

Victoria Inn

Church Street
☎ (01634) 220356
11–4, 7–11; 11–11 Fri & Sat
**Shepherd Neame Master
Brew Bitter** H
Jovial local, at the village
centre, hosting traditional folk
nights and boasting an
unusual farmyard of animals
next to the garden. Beware the
keg Scrumpy Jack on a fake
handpump. ᴁ ❀ ♣ P

Conyer

Brunswick Arms

The Street ☎ (01795) 521569
12–2.30 (not Mon; 12–3 Sat), 7–11
**Chiltern Beechwood; Courage
Best Bitter; Hardys &
Hansons Best Mild; guest
beers** H
Friendly, end-of-terrace pub in
a quiet hamlet, near a creek.
Skittle alley. ᴁ ❀ ◖ ▶ ♣ P

Cooling

Horseshoe & Castle

Main Road ☎ (01634) 221961
11.30–3, 7–11
Beer range varies H
Nestled in the sleepy village of
Cooling, with its Dickensian
connections, this pub, with a
reputedly haunted cellar,
offers a varying choice of beers
on three handpumps. Good
meals, but no food Tue.
ᴁ ❀ ◖ ▶ ♣ ⭗ P ⭍

Cranbrook

Prince of Wales

High Street ☎ (01580) 713058
11.30–2.30 (11–3 Sat), 6.30–11
**Harveys BB; Ind Coope
Burton Ale; Shepherd Neame
Bishops Finger; guest beers** H
Vibrant town-centre free house
with two bars; one has a
jukebox, pool, etc.; the other is
split-level and simply
furnished. Both can get busy.
ᴁ ♋ ❀ ◖ ▶

Dartford

Tiger

28 St Albans Road (off East
Hill) ☎ (01322) 293688
11–11
**Courage Best Bitter; Everards
Beacon; Shepherd Neame
Master Brew Bitter; John
Smith's Bitter** H
A bit of a sporty pub, fielding
darts, pool and Sun football
teams. A long, narrow bar,
with a 'quiet end' where the
old snug used to be, it is very
much a local in the eves and
weekends. Lunches Mon–Fri.
❀ ◖ ≉ ♣

Wat Tyler

80 High Street
☎ (01322) 272546
10–11
**Courage Best Bitter; S&N
Theakston Old Peculier;
Young's Special; guest beer** H
Historic, 14th-century, town-
centre free house with a warm,
friendly, conversational
atmosphere. Five real ales
include a house bitter. Live
folk/jazz some eves and Sun
lunchtime. Q ◖ ▶ ≉ ⭗

Deal

Alma Hotel

126 West Street
☎ (01304) 360244
11–3, 7–11
**Courage Directors; Ridleys
IPA; guest beers** H
Cosy pub with a horseshoe-
shaped bar displaying naval
memorabilia. A selection of
mustards is sold. ≉ ♣

King's Head

9 Beach Street
☎ (01304) 368194
11–3, 6–11; 11–11 Sat
**Shepherd Neame Master
Brew Bitter; Webster's
Yorkshire Bitter; guest
beers** H
Lively pub near the seafront,
attracting a young clientele.
❀ ⊨ ≉ P

Saracen's Head

1 Alfred Square
☎ (01304) 381650
11–3 (4 Fri), 6 (6.30 Fri)–11; 11–11 Sat
**Shepherd Neame Master
Brew Bitter, Spitfire** H
Large, single-bar, corner pub
in an historic part of the old
town. Other Shepherd Neame
beers are sometimes stocked.
ᴁ ◖ ▶ ≉

Ship Inn

141 Middle Street
☎ (01304) 372222
11–11
**Bass Charrington IPA,
Draught Bass; Greene King
Abbot; Shepherd Neame
Master Brew Bitter; guest
beers** H
Cosy pub in an old part of
town near the seafront. Royal
Navy prints and memorabilia
are displayed in the front bar.
Live music includes a pub
piano. ᴁ ◖ ▶ ⊟ ≉

Doddington

Chequers

The Street ☎ (0179 586) 269
11–4, 7–11; 11–11 Fri & Sat
Shepherd Neame Master

Kent

Brew Bitter, Spitfire, Bishops Finger H
Former coaching inn, full of history and character, now a traditional village local with two contrasting bars, host to two friendly ghosts as well as the Kent Vintage Motorcycle and Norton Motorbike clubs. Live folk music on the second Sun in the month. ⚫ ⚫ ◖ ◆ P

Dover

Blakes
52 Castle Street
☎ (01304) 202194
11–3, 7–11; closed Sun
Draught Bass; Shepherd Neame Master Brew Bitter; guest beers H
Popular town-centre wine bar noted for its food. Two bars attract a smart clientele (busy at lunchtime with office staff).
Q ⚫ ◖ ◗ ⇌ (Priory)

Boar's Head
46–48 Eaton Road
☎ (01304) 204490
11–3, 6–11; 11–11 Sat
Greene King IPA, Rayments Special, Abbot; guest beers H
Busy local in a residential area: a former Whitbread house offering a regularly changing selection of beers, plus occasional beer festivals and live music. Skittle alley.
⚫ ⚫ ◖ ⇌ (Priory) ◆

Crown & Sceptre
25 Elms Vale Road
☎ (01304) 201971
11.30–3 (4 Sat), 7–11; 11.30–11 Fri
Shepherd Neame Master Brew Bitter, Spitfire H
Two-bar local in a residential area. The walls are adorned with an impressive collection of ship prints.
⚫ ⇌ (Priory) ◆

Old Endeavour
124 London Road
☎ (01304) 204417
11–11
Shepherd Neame Master Brew Bitter H
Lively town pub, staging regular live music. It backs on to the River Dour, and has a large games/meeting room.
⚫ ◆

East Farleigh

Victory
Farleigh Lane
☎ (01622) 726591
11–11
Goacher's Mild, Dark; Tetley Bitter; guest beer (summer) H
There's been a recent improvement in seating inside, but it's still best to sit in the

garden on sunny afternoons here, watching the boats on the Medway.
⚫ ◖ ◗ ▲ ⇌ ◆ P

East Malling

Rising Sun
125 Mill Street
☎ (01732) 843284
12–11
Goacher's Light; Harveys BB; Shepherd Neame Master Brew Bitter, Spitfire H
Family-run pub which has earned a reputation for the best prices around. Good value food and a ready welcome make it a regular haunt of locals and aficionados alike. ⚫ ◖ ⇌ ◆

Egerton Forstal

Queen's Arms
OS893464 ☎ (01233) 756386
11–3, 6–11
Adnams Bitter; Draught Bass; Harveys BB; Ridleys Mild; Thompson's Best Bitter H
A warm welcome awaits you in this 150-year-old, two-bar, timbered ceiling pub. Jazz is played Sun lunch; no meals Tue. ⚫ Q ⚫ ◖ ◗ ◆ ◗ P

Fairseat   •

Vigo
Gravesend Road (A227, 1 mile N off A20/M20)
☎ (01732) 822547
12–2.30 (not Mon; 12–3 Sat), 6–11
Harveys XX Mild, BB; Young's Bitter, Special; guest beers H
There's always at least one Goacher's ale available, and very often two milds at this very old drovers' inn, named after a sea battle. A drinkers' haunt, it offers no frills or distractions except the Dadlums table (a Kentish form of table skittles).
⚫ Q ◆ P ✂

Faversham

Crown & Anchor
41 The Mall ☎ (01795) 532812
10.30–3 (4 Sat), 5.30 (6 Sat)–11
Shepherd Neame Master Brew Bitter H
Unspoilt, friendly pub whose engaging Hungarian landlord is justifiably proud of his good quality food (try the goulash); snacks include Spanish Tapas. No meals Sun.
⚫ ⚫ ◖ ◗ ⇌ ◆

Elephant Inn
31 The Mall ☎ (01795) 590157
11.30–2.30, 5.30–11; 11–11 Sat and summer
Greene King XX Mild, IPA,

Rayments Special, Abbot H; guest beers G
Former Fremlins' pub which has sold more than 500 different beers since reopening in 1992, including 43 different real milds in the last year. Famous for its regular beer festivals, it is a real 'Tardis' of delights. ⚫ ⚫ ◖ ◗ ⇌ ◆

Finglesham

Crown
The Street ☎ (01304) 612555
11–3, 6–11
Marston's Pedigree; Shepherd Neame Master Brew Bitter; Webster's Yorkshire Bitter; guest beers H
Popular village local with a restaurant; friendly and welcoming. ⚫ ◖ ◗ P

Folkestone

Clifton Hotel
Clifton Gardens
☎ (01303) 851231
10.30–3, 5.45–11
Draught Bass; Courage Directors H
Popular hotel on the Leas with views across the English Channel; a long-standing Mecca for Bass drinkers.
Q ⚫ ◖ ◗ ⇌ (Central)

Harveys Wine Bar
10 Langhorne Gardens
☎ (01303) 257233
11.30–11
Bass Worthington BB, Draught Bass; Ridleys IPA; guest beers H
Real ale/wine bar, built in a hotel cellar, with lots of nooks and crannies, convenient for Leas Cliff Hall next door. Beware the Addlestones cider (pressurised). ◖ ◗ ⇌ (Central)

Richmond Tavern
1 Margaret Street
☎ (01303) 254857
11–3 (2.30 Mon & Thu; 4 Sat), 6 (7 Sat)–11
Shepherd Neame Master Brew Bitter H
Thriving street-corner local, often crowded. It holds regular fund-raising activities in aid of Guide Dogs for the Blind. ⚫ ⇌ (Harbour) ◆

Frittenden

Knoxbridge Inn
Cranbrook Road (A229)
☎ (01580) 891298
12 (6 Mon)–11
Fuller's London Pride; Harveys Pale Ale; Shepherd Neame Master Brew Bitter; guest beers H
Enterprising and popular roadhouse where two areas

are separated by a long bar. One end is like a public bar with games, etc., the other, with a small dining area, is like a saloon. Occasional live music, barbecues and mini-beer festivals. Families are welcome. Eve meals Wed–Sun.
🏠 ❀ ◗ ▶ ♿ ▲ ♣ P

Gillingham

Barge
63 Layfield Road
☎ (01634) 850485
12–3, 7–11; 12–11 Sat
Greene King IPA; Wadworth 6X; guest beers H
Pub whose quiet atmosphere is enhanced by panoramic views of the Medway and authentic naval artefacts which hang in the bar. Occasional cockney sing-alongs and live bands. ❀ ◗ ▶ ♣

Cannon
15 Garden Street, Brompton
☎ (01634) 841006
11–11
John Smith's Bitter; guest beer H
Refurbished, two-bar local which promotes sports teams. It has a new play area in the garden, and still features the original Truman tiled frontage.
❀ ◗ ▶ ♣

King George V
1 Prospect Row, Brompton
☎ (01634) 842418
11–3, 6–11
Draught Bass; guest beers H
Quiet, friendly, one-bar pub which displays its strong naval links with crests and models. Good value bed and breakfast is available, plus a fine selection of malt whiskies. No food Sun. ❀ 🏠 ◗

Roseneath
79 Arden Street
☎ (01634) 852553
11.30–11
Beer range varies H
Very busy thriving local which boasts an annual charity real ale festival. Snakehound Ale is named after the pub's dog's breed and is brewed by Goacher's. The large garden is ideal for summer drinking (climbing frame for children). Six handpumps. ❀ ◗ ▶ ♣

Will Adams
73 Saxton Street
☎ (01634) 575902
11–3, 7–11; 11–11 Sat
John Smith's Bitter; Whitbread Boddingtons Bitter; guest beers H
Single bar with a large games area in a keen, sporty pub; sponsor of the local professional football club.

Good value food. Friendly.
❀ ◗ ▶ ➤ ♣

Gravesend

Jolly Drayman
1 Love Lane, Wellington Street (off A226) ☎ (01474) 352355
11–2.30, 5.30–11; 12–3, 7–11 Sat
Bass Charrington IPA, Draught Bass; Fuller's London Pride; Young's Bitter; guest beer H
Friendly, low-ceilinged pub in the offices of a former brewery, near the town centre. It stocks an impressive range of guest beers and has appeared in every edition of the *Guide*. Bar snacks available.
❀ ➤ ♣ P

Prince Albert
26 Wrotham Road (near station) ☎ (01474) 352432
11–11
Shepherd Neame Master Brew Bitter, Best Bitter, Spitfire, Porter, Bishops Finger H
Classic two-bar local, with a very friendly atmosphere. The landlord has worked very hard to bring it up to the *Guide*'s standard. Not to be missed. 🏠 ❀ ➤ ♣ P

Somerset Arms
10 Darnley Road (one-way system) ☎ (01474) 533837
11–3.30, 5–11 (midnight Thu–Sat)
Beer range varies H
Just across the road from the station: a pub holding discos Thu–Sun eves, and a Real Ale Club Mon–Thu (5–7.30) with real ale at reduced prices. Eve meals Mon–Thu; no food Sun.
🏠 ◗ ▶ ➤ ♣

Windmill Tavern
45 Shrubbery Road, Windmill Hill ☎ (01474) 352242
11–11
Harveys BB; Ruddles Best Bitter; Wadworth 6X; Webster's Yorkshire Bitter H
A country pub in the town, with a prize-winning garden (barbecues in summer). The no-smoking area is available at lunchtime in the saloon bar. Eve meals only available to order. ❀ ◗ ▶ 🍴 ➤ ♣ P ✗

Great Chart

Hooden Horse
The Street ☎ (01233) 625583
12–2.30, 6–11
Goacher's Light; Hook Norton Old Hooky; Hop Back Summer Lightning; S&N Theakston Old Peculier H; **guest beers**
Formerly the Black Dog, a pub featuring tiled and timbered

floors, a hop-strewn ceiling and candlelit tables. Two guests are always available, and an extensive range of home-cooked, quality food is served. Live music weekly. The first pub of four in the Hooden Horse Group. A price premium is levied on half pints. ❀ ◗ ▶ ♣ ⌂

Swan
The Street ☎ (01233) 632250
11–11
Fuller's London Pride H; **Morland Old Speckled Hen** G
Pub located in a now bypassed village with a notable Norman church. Completely refurbished in 1992, it offers a good blackboard menu. Four-pint jugs are offered at a discount. ❀ ◗ ▶ P

Green Street Green

Ship
On B260 ☎ (01474) 702279
11–2.30, 6–11
Banks & Taylor Shefford Mild; Courage Best Bitter; Wadworth 6X; guest beers H
Popular, 17th-century roadhouse serving excellent value lunches. Eve snacks are supplemented by regular gourmet and speciality nights. Families are welcome in the converted stables.
🏠 ♿ ❀ ◗ ♿ ♣ P

Hadlow

Fiddling Monkey
Maidstone Road
☎ (01732) 850267
11–2.30, 6–11; 11–11 Fri & Sat
Fuller's London Pride; Larkins Bitter; Whitbread Boddingtons Bitter; Young's Special H
Large, one-bar pub, popular with the village locals but welcoming to visitors. No food Sun. 🏠 ❀ ◗ ♿ ♣ P

Halling

Homeward Bound
High Street ☎ (01634) 240743
12–3, 7–11
Shepherd Neame Master Brew Bitter, Porter H
Friendly, relaxed pub at the village centre, renowned for its charity exploits. No food Sun.
🏠 ❀ ◗ ➤ ♣ P

Try also: White Hart, Cuxton (Shepherd Neame)

Herne Bay

Share & Coulter
Thornden Wood Road, West End (off A299)
☎ (01227) 374877
11–3, 6–11

Kent

Shepherd Neame Master Brew Bitter, Bishops Finger H
16th-century listed building, boasting a low, timbered ceiling and quarry-tiled floors. Children are accepted in the games room. Camping in the pub grounds. No food Sun; occasional barbecues.
🏚 ✿ ◖ ▲ ♣ P

Hernhill

Red Lion

Crockham Lane
☎ (01227) 751207
11–3, 6–11; 11–11 Sat
Fuller's London Pride; Morland Old Speckled Hen; S&N Theakston Old Peculier; Shepherd Neame Master Brew Bitter; Whitbread Boddingtons Bitter; guest beers H
14th-century inn on the village green: one bar and a restaurant upstairs. Beer festivals are held, featuring mild. Beware the keg cider on a fake handpump.
Q ✿ ◖ ♣ P

Hook Green

Elephant's Head

Furnace Lane (B2169, Lamberhurst–Bells Yew Green road) OS655358
☎ (01892) 890279
10–3, 5.30–11; 10–11 Fri & Sat (12–3, 6–11 winter)
Harveys XX Mild, Pale Ale, BB, Old Ale, Armada H
Situated on the Kent/Sussex border, this beamed pub is rare in selling the complete range of Harveys beers, including all the seasonal brews. The large south-facing gardens are ideal for a summer drink with the family. No eve meals Sun/Mon in winter. 🏚 Q ✿ ◖ ▶ P

Hythe

Duke's Head

9 Dymchurch Road
☎ (01303) 266239
11–11
Draught Bass; Greene King IPA, Abbot; Tetley Bitter G
Pleasant pub between Hythe Green and the new canal bridge. Good food in large portions is served at lunchtime. Games include darts, pool and shove-ha'penny; quiz nights.
🏚 Q ✿ ◖ P

Kemsing

Rising Sun

Cotmans Ash Lane, Woodlands OS563599
☎ (01959) 522683
11–3, 6–11

Morland Old Speckled Hen; Whitbread Boddingtons Mild, Fremlins Bitter, Flowers Original; guest beers H
Pub whose main bar area is a converted hunting lodge, offering a step back in time. An ideal country pub for the family in summer, with its lovely outdoor area. Hikers are always welcome.
🏚 Q ⭐ ✿ ◖ ▶ ▲ ♣ ⌂ P

Kilndown

Globe & Rainbow

SW of Lamberhurst, off A21
OS700253 ☎ (01892) 890283
11–2.30, 6–11
Harveys BB; Whitbread Fremlins Bitter, Flowers IPA, Original; Young's Special H
Traditional pub with a large bar area and extensive landscaped gardens. Specialities include malt whiskies and excellent, home-cooked food (bar snacks and a restaurant). A full-length skittle alley is available for hire. 🏚 Q ✿ 🛏 ◖ ▶ ♣ P

Lamberhurst

Chequers

The Broadway (A21)
☎ (01892) 890260
11–3, 5–11
Shepherd Neame Master Brew Bitter, Spitfire H
Large period pub on the banks of the River Teise. A public and a saloon cater for the young and old, and it is used by many village clubs.
🏚 Q ✿ ◖ ▶ 🍴 ♣ P

Luddesdown

Cock Inn

Henley Street OS664672
☎ (01474) 814208
12–2.30, 5–11; 12–11 Sat
Adnams Bitter; guest beers H
Isolated, attractive, two-bar free house which can be reached by public footpath from Sole Street station (1 mile). You won't regret it—this is a pub for the connoisseur, offering a changing range of at least eight real ales, including a mild. No food Sun. Eve meals end at 8pm.
🏚 Q ✿ ◖ ▶ ⌂ P

Maidstone

Greyhound

77 Wheeler Street
☎ (01622) 754032
11–3.30, 6–11
Shepherd Neame Master Brew Bitter H
There's always a friendly welcome at this traditional

street-corner pub near Maidstone prison. A second Shepherd Neame cask ale is stocked. Jazz bands Sun lunch. A regular *Guide* entry.
Q ✿ ◖ ⇌ (East) ♣ P

Hare & Hounds

45–47 Lower Boxley Road
(A229) ☎ (01622) 678388
11–3 (4 Sat), 5.30 (7 Sat)–11
Marston's Pedigree; Wadworth 6X; Whitbread Flowers IPA H
Popular and often very busy, L-shaped pub, with a patio drinking area where barbecues may be held. Eve meals finish at 7pm. ✿ ◖ ▶ ⇌ (East)

Hogshead

Earl Street
☎ (01622) 758516
11–11
Wadworth 6X; Whitbread Boddingtons Bitter, Flowers Original; guest beers H / G
Whitbread ale house-style pub, bringing a welcome choice of beers to the town centre, with up to five guests. No food Sun.
🏚 ✿ ◖ & ⇌ (East) ♣

Pilot

23–25 Upper Stone Street
(A229, S of centre)
☎ (01622) 691162
11–3, 6 (7 Sat)–11
Harveys XX Mild, BB, Old, Armada H
Consistently reliable real ale outlet on the busy main road out of town; the only Harveys outlet in the area (the seasonal ales are also sold), a Grade II-listed building on three levels. Excellent value food (no meals Sun lunch).
🏚 ✿ ◖ ▶ ♣

Wheelers Arms

1 Perry Street (off Sandling road, A229, N of centre)
☎ (01622) 752229
12–3, 6–11; 11–11 Sat
Shepherd Neame Master Brew Bitter, Spitfire, Porter H
Back-street pub with many attractions, including occasional live music, food theme nights, and quiz, bar billiards and darts teams. Friendly bar staff.
✿ ◖ ⇌ (East) ♣

Manston

Jolly Farmer

High Street ☎ (01843) 823208
10.30–3 (3.30 Fri), 5.30–11; 10.30–11 Sat
Marston's Pedigree; Morland Old Speckled Hen; Whitbread Boddingtons Bitter, Fremlins Bitter, Flowers Original; guest beers H / G

Close to RAF Manston and Kent international airport, this village pub has Battle of Britain connections. It's worth a visit to see the hi-tech tilting mechanism which allows the optimum use of gravity dispense. 🏚 ✤ ◖ ▲ P

Margate

Princess of Wales
22 Tivoli Road
☎ (01843) 223944
11–3, 6–11; 11–11 Sat
Shepherd Neame Master Brew Bitter Ⓗ
Unspoilt, two-bar, corner beer house—a good example of the type of local becoming rarer by the year. Bar snacks.
✤ ◖ ⬱ ♣

Quart in a Pint Pot
28–30 Charlotte Square
☎ (01843) 223672
11.30–2.30, 5.30–11; 11–11 Sat
Draught Bass; guest beers Ⓗ
Pub well worth the walk up the High Street from the busy seafront. Look out for the pepperpot folly on the roof. Inside is a cosy, expanded, back-street pub with an intriguing and good value beer range which changes regularly. Summer barbecues.
✤ ◖ ▶ ⬱ ♣ P

Spread Eagle
25 Victoria Road
☎ (01843) 293396
11.30–3, 5.30–11; 11–11 Fri & Sat
Fuller's London Pride; Greene King IPA; Young's Special; guest beers Ⓗ
A Victorian frontage to Georgian premises leads you into an old reliable amongst Thanet pubs, with a busy but welcoming atmosphere. No food Sun. ✤ ◖ ⬱ ♣

Marsh Green

Wheatsheaf
On B2028 ☎ (01732) 864091
11–3, 5.30–11; 11–11 Sat
Adnams Bitter; Fuller's London Pride; Harveys BB; Whitbread Boddingtons Bitter; guest beers Ⓗ
A popular spot; much enlarged from a former modest roadside pub. The bar comprises five areas, plus a rear conservatory. Wheelchair WC. 🏚 ✤ ◖ ▶ & ♣ ⌂ P ⊁

Marshside

Gate Inn
Off A28 at Upstreet, towards Chislet ☎ (01227) 860496
11–2.30 (3 Sat), 6–11
Shepherd Neame Master

Brew Bitter, Spitfire, Porter, Bishops Finger Ⓖ
Splendid country pub with ducks, apple trees, quizzes, and rugby and cricket teams. There's a regular pub pianist, plus jazz and folk eves. A beer festival is held in Aug. Mummers perform at Christmas. No-smoking area on weekday lunchtimes only.
🏚 Q ⬱ ✤ ◖ ▶ & ▲ ♣ P ⊁

Milton Regis

Three Hats
High Street ☎ (01795) 425016
10–3, 5.30–11; 10–11 Sat
John Smith's Bitter; Young's Special Ⓗ
16th-century pub at the village centre: the nearest real ale pub to the Sittingbourne and Kemsley Light Railway station. ✤ ♣

Minster (Thanet)

Saddler
7 Monkton Road
☎ (01843) 821331
10.30–2.30, 6–11; 11–11 Sat
Shepherd Neame Master Brew Bitter, Spitfire, Porter *or* **Bishops Finger** Ⓗ
This two-bar pub is very much the village local, but extends a warm welcome to casual visitors. It dates back to Victorian times when a saddler occupied the cottage next door. A mainstay of Bat and Trap leagues.
Q ✤ ◖ ▲ ⬱ ♣

Northbourne

Hare & Hounds
The Street ☎ (01304) 365429
10.30–3, 6–11
Draught Bass; Shepherd Neame Master Brew Bitter; guest beers Ⓗ
Busy, country pub in a rural village, popular for food. Normally two or three guest beers are stocked. ✤ ◖ ▶ P

Northfleet

Six Bells
Old Perry Street
☎ (01474) 567309
11–3 (4 Sat), 5.30 (6 Sat)–11
Courage Best Bitter, Directors; Wadworth 6X Ⓗ
Popular 'country' pub and restaurant in the town. Large garden. ✤ ◖ ▶ & P

Oad Street

Plough & Harrow
Opp. Craft Centre
☎ (01795) 843351
11–11

Greene King IPA, Abbot; Shepherd Neame Master Brew Bitter; guest beers Ⓗ
Pub enjoying its second consecutive year as CAMRA Swale *Pub of the Year*, not surprisingly with the range and quality on offer. Seven guest beers include a mild in summer. Popular with locals and visitors alike. Eve meals Wed–Sat; Occasional cider in summer.
🏚 ⬱ ✤ ◖ ▶ ⌂ P

Oare

Three Mariners
2 Church Road
☎ (01795) 533633
11.30–3.30, 6–11; 10.30–11 Sat
Shepherd Neame Master Brew Bitter, Spitfire, Porter, Bishops Finger Ⓗ
Situated at the village centre, this extensive public house's decor reflects its nautical associations with the nearby creek. The garden boasts an aviary and fishpond.
🏚 ⬱ ✤ ◖ ▶ ♣ P

Pembury

Black Horse
High Street
☎ (01892) 822141
11–11
Harveys BB, Old; Wadworth 6X; Young's Special Ⓗ
Warm, friendly terraced tavern with a dining area (Sun carvery). The house beer may be a national brand renamed. No meals Sun eve.
🏚 Q ✤ ◖ ▶ ♣

Penshurst

Spotted Dog
Smarts Hill (2 miles S of village) ☎ (01892) 870253
11.30–3, 6–10.30
King & Barnes Sussex; Wadworth 6X; guest beers Ⓗ
An excellent view from the garden is a bonus at this friendly pub with lots of oak beams. The house beer, Old Spotty, is Benskins Best Bitter.
🏚 Q ✤ ◖ ▲ P

Perry Wood

Rose & Crown
☎ (01227) 752214
12–2.30 (3 Sat), 7–11; closed Mon
Ind Coope Burton Ale; S&N Theakston Best Bitter; Shepherd Neame Master Brew Bitter; guest beers Ⓗ
16th-century free house with very accommodating staff, especially to families; set in woodland with plenty of walks. Live music Tue eve.
🏚 Q ◖ ▶ ♣ P ⊁

157

Kent

Petteridge

Hopbine Inn
Petteridge Lane (½ mile E of Matfield) OS668413
☎ (01892) 722561
12 (11 Sat)–2.30, 6–11
King & Barnes Mild, Sussex, Broadwood, Festive H
Picturesque pub holding the full range of King & Barnes beers and hosting regular, well-attended folk music nights. No food Wed eve.
🏠 ✿ ◖ ▶ P

Preston

Half Moon & Seven Stars
Dover Road ☎ (01227) 722296
11–11
Fuller's London Pride; Shepherd Neame Master Brew Bitter H
Village pub, nicely converted to one rambling bar. Live music is performed regularly. Note the outside mural of a customs officer coastwatching.
🏠 ✿ ◖ ▶ ♣ P

Ramsgate

Artillery Arms
36 Westcliffe Road
☎ (01843) 853282
11–11
Wells Bombardier; guest beers H
Said to have been a brothel in Victorian times, this corner local offers a good range of beers, if a little more predictably than of old. Lively atmosphere. ≈ ♣

Churchill Tavern
19–22 The Paragon
☎ (01843) 587862
11–11
Draught Bass; Courage Directors; Fuller's London Pride; Ringwood Old Thumper; S&N Theakston Old Peculier; Taylor Landlord; guest beers H
Beautifully restored pub overlooking the harbour. Rebuilt from old timbers and church pews, it offers nine real ales—more during its frequent beer festivals. Folk club Sun; jazz Wed. Good value restaurant.
🏠 Q ◖ ▶ ▲ ≈ ♣

Try also: Elms, Richmond Rd; **Wheatsheaf,** High St, St Lawrence (both Free)

Ripple

Plough
Church Lane (off A258 at Ringwould) ☎ (01304) 360209
11–3, 6–11 (may vary)

Draught Bass; Ind Coope Burton Ale; Shepherd Neame Master Brew Bitter; guest beers H
Popular, 16th-century rural local with a restaurant upstairs. It holds occasional beer festivals, and stocks a range of country wines. Note the unusual chain firescreen. Camping by arrangement.
🏠 ⛺ ◖ ▲ ♣ P

River

Royal Oak
36 Lower Road (off A256)
☎ (01304) 822073
11–11 (may close afternoons)
Shepherd Neame Master Brew Bitter H
Open-plan pub, created from an original flint building and its next door cottage, set in an attractive residential area. Other Shepherd Neame beers are sometimes stocked.
◖ ≈ (Kearsney) ♣ P

Rochester

Coopers Arms
10 St Margarets Street
☎ (01634) 404298
11–2.30, 5.30 (5 Fri)–11; 11–11 Sat
Courage Best Bitter, Directors; John Smith's Bitter H
Two-bar beamed pub near the castle and cathedral, full of reminders of Rochester's history. Well-furnished (spot the piano), it is supposedly haunted, but cosy and inviting. 🏠 ✿ ◖ ≈ P

Granville Arms
83 Maidstone Road
☎ (01634) 845243
11–11
Greene King XX Mild, IPA, Abbot H
An unusual layout in an inviting, comfortable pub with a small, square bar. A rare regular outlet for real mild, it may offer Greene King Winter Warmer at Christmastime.
🏠 ✿ ≈ P

Greyhound
68 Rochester Avenue
☎ (01634) 844120
10–3, 6–11; 10–11 Sat
Shepherd Neame Master Brew Bitter H
Late-Victorian terraced local where the public bar is basic, but the saloon has a real coal range and chaises-longues. Quiet and relaxing atmosphere. Parking can be difficult. No food Sun.
🏠 ✿ ◖ ≈ ♣

Man of Kent
6–8 John Street
☎ (01634) 818771
12–11

Beer range varies H
Lovely Style and Winch-fronted pub which offers Goacher's ales as its main beers, along with lots of guests. It is friendly and small, but beware the fake Scrumpy Jack handpump. Chess table available. 🏠 ✿ ≈ ♣

Ship Inn
347 High Street
☎ (01634) 844264
11–11
Courage Best Bitter; guest beers H
Busy, two-bar pub with two regularly changing guest beers. It hosts frequent live music, and modern jazz Sun lunch, and is the former Arkcoll's Lion Brewery tap (the old brewery buildings can be seen in an alley nearby). No food Sun. ✿ ◖ ≈

Star Inn
Star Hill ☎ (01634) 826811
11–11
Beer range varies H
Busy, town-centre pub serving good value lunches. It can be busy Sat nights. No food on winter weekends. ◖ ≈

Who'd Ha Thot It
9 Baker Street
☎ (01634) 828021
11–3, 5.30–11; 11–11 Fri & Sat
Beer range varies H
Good real ale drinkers' free house, tucked away. Very cosy, with a small back bar, it is a rare outlet for real cider. Well worth finding; no food weekends. 🏠 ◖ ⌂

Rolvenden Layne

Another Hooden Horse
26 Maytham Road (main road, 2 miles S of Rolvenden village)
☎ (01580) 241837
11.30–3 (not Mon), 6.30–11
Goacher's Light; Hook Norton Old Hooky; Hop Back Summer Lightning; S&N Theakston Old Peculier; guest beers H
Candlelit, open-beamed, hop-strewn bar, with an intimate meeting room featuring pew seats and stuffed ducks. Biddenden cider is always available and food is served until half an hour before closing time. Price premium on half pints.
◖ ▶ ⊟ ♣ ⌂ P ⅟

Rusthall

Toad Rock Retreat
1 Upper Street (off A264 1 mile W of Tunbridge Wells)
☎ (01892) 520818
11–3, 6–11; 11–11 Sat

Adnams Bitter; Harveys BB;
Whitbread Boddingtons Mild,
Bitter, Fremlins Bitter н;
guest beers G
Warm and friendly, 16th-
century pub, lying opposite
the local landmark 'Toad
Rock'. It boasts three open
fires and offers a
comprehensive food menu
daily, including four
vegetarian dishes. Nine cask
ales. ♨ Q ❀ ◖ ▷ ⊞ ♣ P

St Margaret's at Cliffe

Hope Inn

High Street ☎ (01304) 852444
10.30–11
Shepherd Neame Master
Brew Bitter н
18th-century village pub,
well-modernised and
attracting local and tourist
trade. ♨ ❀ ◖ ▷ ▲ ♣ P

St Nicholas at Wade

Bell

The Street (400 yds from A28/
A299 jct) ☎ (01843) 847250
11–2.30 (3 Sat), 6.30–11
Draught Bass; Hancock's HB;
M&B Highgate Dark;
Whitbread Fremlins Bitter,
Flowers IPA н
Country pub, dating from
Tudor times, with a post-war
extension to the rear. The large
number of small rooms helps
preserve an intimate
atmosphere (especially
suitable for families). The only
regular handpumped mild
outlet in Thanet, it is well
worth seeking out.
♨ ❀ ◖ ▷ ▲ ♣ P

Sandgate

Ship

High Street ☎ (01303) 248525
11–3, 6 (4 Sat)–11
Draught Bass; Courage
Directors G; Greene King
IPA н, Abbot; S&N
Theakston Old Peculier G;
Wadworth 6X н
Normally stocking nine beers,
most on gravity, this pub
backs on to the seafront and
has two bars; the rear one has
miniature keg beer fonts
hidden behind the bar. Q ◖ ▷

Sandwich

Greyhound

10 New Street
☎ (01304) 612675
10–3, 7–11
Courage Best Bitter,
Directors; guest beers
(occasional) н
Large, wood-panelled pub

near the market. Games room.
❀ ≋ ♣

King's Arms

Strand Street ☎ (01304) 617330
11–3, 6–11
Marston's Pedigree;
Wadworth 6X; Young's Bitter;
guest beer н
Large, recently refurbished
town pub. Country wines are
available. ♨ ▲ ≋ ♣

Sarre

Crown Inn

Ramsgate Road (A28)
☎ (01843) 847808
11–11
Shepherd Neame Master
Brew Bitter, Spitfire
(summer), Porter н
Known as the Cherry Brandy
House, and dating from 1500,
this pub was patronised by
Dickens, Kipling and others.
Sympathetically modernised
from an ale house to an inn, it
makes a good starting point
for a tour of Thanet.
❀ ⌂ ◖ ▷ ♿ ▲ P

Selling

Sondes Arms

Station Road ☎ (01227) 752246
11–4.30, 7–11 (11–11 summer Sat)
Shepherd Neame Master
Brew Bitter н
Named after a local member of
the gentry: a friendly, country
pub with a horseshoe bar, an
adjoining games room, and a
dining area. The large, safe
children's garden is full of
livestock. No food Sun eve.
♨ ❀ ◖ ▷ ≋ ♣ P

Sevenoaks

Halfway House

London Road
☎ (01732) 457108
11–2.30 (3 Fri & Sat), 6 (7 Sat)–11
Greene King XX Mild, IPA,
Rayments Special, Abbot н
Warm, friendly pub, part of
which dates from the 16th
century; the upper area is used
as a restaurant. Active quiz
team. No food Sun eves.
♨ ❀ ◖ ▷ ♿ ≋ ♣ P

Shatterling

Green Man

Pedding Hill (A257, Ash–
Wingham road)
☎ (01304) 812525
11.15–2.30 (3 Sat), 6.30–11; closed
Sun eve in winter
Draught Bass; Shepherd
Neame Master Brew Bitter;
Young's Bitter н
Isolated pub in a very
attractive rural setting,
drawing local and passing
trade. Bat and Trap played.
❀ ⌂ ◖ ▷ ▲ ♣ P

Sheerness

Man of Kent

40 Clyde Street
☎ (01795) 664106
11–5, 7–11
Shepherd Neame Spitfire or
Bishops Finger, Porter н
Cosy, back-street, terraced
local, featuring impromptu
quizzes and games. Families
welcomed. ❀ ≋ ♣

Red Lion

61 High Street, Bluetown
☎ (01795) 663165
12–3, 6 (8 Sat)–11; 12–2.30, 8–10.30
Sun
Greene King Abbot; guest
beers н
Unspoilt, quiet pub in a newly
restored area of the old
dockyards; the last surviving
original pub in the area. Food
is available Mon–Fri. Red Lion
house beer is brewed by
Greene King. Q ◖ ≋ ♣

Shoreham

Crown

High Street ☎ (01959) 522903
11–3, 6.30–11
Greene King XX Mild, IPA,
Rayments Special, Abbot н
Ideal pub set on the edge of a
quiet village, with a pleasant,
friendly atmosphere.
♨ Q ❀ ◖ ▷ ≋ ♣ P

Sittingbourne

Ship Inn

22 East Street
☎ (01795) 425087
11–3 (4 Fri & Sat), 6–11
Courage Best Bitter; John
Smith's Bitter; guest beer н
Friendly, two-bar, town-centre
pub with a strong local
following. The guest beer is
sold at a very attractive price,
but beware the keg Scrumpy
Jack on a fake handpump.
♿ ◖ ≋ P

Smarden

Bell

Bell Lane (1 mile from centre,
on Headcorn road) OS870470
☎ (01233) 770283
11.30–2.30 (3 Sat), 6–11
Fuller's London Pride;
Goacher's Light; Harveys Pale
Ale; Ringwood Old Thumper;
Shepherd Neame Master
Brew Bitter; Whitbread
Flowers Original н
Large, 15th-century country
pub with four bars, including
a family room and a no-
smoking bar (mainly used for
meals). A collectors' car rally is
held on the second Sun lunchtime of each month. ♨ Q
♿ ❀ ⌂ ◖ ▷ ▲ ♣ ⌂ P ⚥

159

Kent

Snargate

Red Lion
On B2080 ☎ (01797) 344648
11–3, 7–11
Adnams Bitter; Bateman XB; Harveys Old; guest beer G
One of the few unspoilt pubs left in Kent; 11 consecutive years in the *Guide*: a basic, one-bar, three-roomed, pub set in the Romney Marsh countryside. Note the rare marble-topped bar, bare floorboards and quarry tiles. The atmosphere is warm and friendly. ♒ Q ☜ ✿ ♣ ♙

Stalisfield

Bowl Inn
Egghill Road, Charing (signed from A20 & A2 to Stalisfield Green) ☎ (01233) 712256
12–3 (not winter Tue or Thu), 6–11; 12–11 Fri & Sat
King & Barnes Sussex; guest beers H
Classic, 16th-century free house with an inglenook, set in beautiful, remote countryside. Up to three guest beers. ♒ Q ✿ ♣ P

Stalisfield Green

Plough
Signed from A2, 7 miles S of Faversham ☎ (01795) 890256
12–3, 7–11 (closed Mon, except bank hol lunch)
Adnams Extra; Shepherd Neame Master Brew Bitter; guest beer (occasional) H
Classic, 15th-century, two-bar free house set in splendid countryside. It is noted for good food (fish is a speciality, and booking is advisable). Shut the Box and shove-ha'penny are played. Children and caravans welcome.
♒ Q ✿ ◑ ▶ ▲ ♣ P

Stansted

Black Horse
Tumbleber Road (1 mile from A20, top of Wrotham Hill)
☎ (01732) 822355
11–2.30, 6 (7 winter)–11
Beer range varies H
Pub acting as a post office, as well as the centre of village life. Four or five beers are stocked at any time. Walkers welcome; as the hub of a network of paths, it makes a good lunch stop. Three outdoor drinking areas. Caravan site a half-mile away.
♒ ☜ ✿ ◑ ▲ ♣ ⌂ P

Staplehurst

Lord Raglan
Chart Hill Road, Rabbits Cross (½ mile N of A229) OS786472

☎ (01622) 843747
11–3, 6–11
Brakspear Special; Harveys BB; Whitbread Fremlins Bitter; guest beer H
Traditional, beamed pub, adorned with hops. Good food is available at all sessions. The guest beer is usually a strong ale. Conversation rules.
♒ Q ✿ ◑ ▶ ♣ P

Staplestreet

Three Horseshoes
☎ (01227) 750842
11–3 (4.30 Sat), 6–11; 11–11 Thu & Fri
Shepherd Neame Master Brew Bitter, Porter G
Pub displaying unspoilt Kentish architecture and a list of landlords dating back to 1690. Note the collection of stone bottles. Good for games.
♒ Q ✿ ◑ ▲ ♣ P

Stockbury

Harrow
Hill Green Road (signed off A249) ☎ (01795) 842546
11–2.30, 6–11 Mon–Sat; 12–2.30, 7–10.30 Sun
Shepherd Neame Master Brew Bitter; guest beer H
Friendly, country local in an attractive village setting. The single bar focuses on freshly prepared, well-priced meals. The pub frontage displays scenes of the village in each of the four seasons. No meals Sun eve. ♒ ✿ ◑ ▶ ⌂ P

Stodmarsh

Red Lion
☎ (01227) 721339
11–3, 7–11
Beer range varies H
Unpretentious, three-bar pub near a bird sanctuary. The village boasts an interesting church with a wooden tower but has no public transport, except the postbus. However, the three and a half-mile walk from Sturry station is very pleasant. ♒ ✿ ◑ ▶ ♣ ⌂ P

Stone Street

Padwell Arms
S of A25, Seal–Ightham road OS569551 ☎ (01732) 761532
12–3, 6–11
Hall & Woodhouse Badger Best Bitter, Tanglefoot; Hook Norton Old Hooky; Young's Bitter; guest beers H
Friendly and welcoming old pub, set at the heart of the Garden of England, popular with the locals. All-weather barbecue Sat and Sun eves from June to Sept. Kent CAMRA *Pub of the Year* 1994.
♒ ✿ ◑ ▲ ♣ ⌂ P

Stowting

Tiger Inn
On North Downs Way, 3 miles W of B2068 OS121414
☎ (01303) 862130
12–3, 7–11 (may be 12–11 summer Sat)
Everards Tiger; Ind Coope Burton Ale; Tetley Bitter; Wadworth 6X H
Note the imposing Mackeson Hythe Ales frontage on this pleasant country pub which is popular for home-cooked food (served in the bar and restaurant). Live jazz Mon eve. ♒ ✿ ◑ ▶ P

Sutton at Hone

Ship
218 Main Road
☎ (01322) 863387
11–3, 5–11; 11–11 Sat
Courage Best Bitter; guest beers H
Spacious, two-bar village pub, serving two guest ales. ♒ ✿ ◑ ⇌ (Farningham Rd) ♣ P

Tenterden

White Lion Hotel
High Street ☎ (01580) 765077
11–11
Draught Bass; Harveys BB, Old H
350-year-old coaching inn, opposite Kent & East Sussex Steam Railway.
♒ ✿ ⇌ ◑ ▶ P

Tonbridge

Royal Oak
Lower Haysden Lane (W off A26 at Shell roundabout, follow signs to Lower Haysden) OS569457
☎ (01732) 350208
11–11
Adnams Bitter; guest beers H
Friendly, well-frequented pub with a helpful beer guide on a blackboard, and one beer always on special offer. Live music in one bar; an annual beer festival is held in the field opposite in July.
♒ Q ◑ ▲ ♣ P

Stag's Head
9 Stafford Road
☎ (01732) 352017
11–3, 6–11; 11–11 Thu–Sat
Butcombe Bitter; Taylor Best Bitter; Whitbread Boddingtons Bitter, Flowers IPA H
Single-bar, back-street pub, behind Tonbridge Castle. A pool table and other games are available. Note the interesting array of clocks. Some loud music. ✿ P

Tovil

Royal Paper Mill
39 Tovil Hill ☎ (01622) 752095
11–3, 7–11
Goacher's Mild, Light, Dark, Porter *or* **Old 1066 Ale; guest beer** H
Goacher's first tied house, a very friendly local. Photos of nearby papermill workers, performing traditional tasks, adorn the walls. ♨ ✿ ♣

Tudeley

George & Dragon
Five Oak Green Road (B2161, W of Five Oak Green)
OS635448 ☎ (01892) 832521
11–3, 6–11
Greene King IPA, Rayments Special, Abbot H
A smallish saloon bar, plus a larger, more spartan public bar with a bar billiards table. A restaurant offers good home-cooked food. The pub stands in the middle of the hop gardens of Kent. No food Mon eve. ♨ ✿ ◖ ▶ ♣ P

Tunbridge Wells

Crystal Palace
69 Camden Road
☎ (01892) 548412
11–3 (4 Sat), 7–11
Harveys Mild, Pale Ale, BB, Old, Armada (summer) H
The only Harveys tied house within Tunbridge Wells, this Victorian pub is popular with office workers at lunchtime and with regulars for games in the eve. No food Sun. ✿ ◖ ♣

Underriver

White Rock
Carters Hill ☎ (01732) 833112
12–3, 6–11
Harveys BB; Marston's Pedigree; guest beer H
Attractive pub, the only one in this small village. It has a pleasant saloon bar and a games-oriented public. The gardens house dovecotes.
♨ Q ✿ ◖ ▶ ♣ P

Upper Upnor

Tudor Rose
High Street ☎ (01634) 715305
12–3, 7–11
Young's Bitter, Special; guest beers H
Friendly, multi-roomed pub, near Upnor Castle and the

River Medway. Use the village car parks. Eve meals until 9pm; no food Sun.
♨ ⛵ ☀ ◖ ▶ ♣

West Malling

Joiners Arms
High Street ☎ (01732) 840723
11–3, 5–11; 11–11 Fri & Sat
Shepherd Neame Master Brew Bitter H
Two-bar pub in a picturesque small town, featuring a large open fire in the saloon. Other Shepherd Neame beers may be stocked. No food Sun.
♨ ✿ ◖ ⇌ ♣

Whitstable

Alberres
Sea Street ☎ (01227) 273400
11.30–4, 7–11; 11.30–11 Fri & Sat
Ind Coope Burton Ale; Tetley Bitter; guest beer H
Once a Tomson & Wotton house—see the etched windows: a small, comfortable corner pub, near the beach. Note the sign showing the former sea level! ⇌ ♣

Coach & Horses
Oxford Street
☎ (01227) 264732
11–11
Shepherd Neame Master Brew Bitter, Spitfire (summer), **Porter** H
Smart high street local with a separate eating area.
✿ ◖ ⇌ ♣

Noah's Ark
Canterbury Road
☎ (01227) 272332
11–3, 6–11
Shepherd Neame Master Brew Bitter H
Basic, two-bar pub run by the town's longest-serving landlord. ✿ ⇌

Tankerton Arms
Tower Hill (Tankerton seafront) ☎ (01227) 272024
12–11
Fuller's London Pride; Shepherd Neame Master Brew Bitter; guest beers H
Enjoy the views of Tankerton Slopes and the Thames estuary at this pub, and note the elegant bar-back and carvings.
♨ ⛵ ✿ ◖ ▶

Wilmington

Plough
65 High Road (B258, 1¼ miles S of Dartford)

☎ (01322) 224027
10–2.30, 5–11; 10–11 Fri; 11–3.30, 6–11 Sat
Courage Best Bitter, Directors; Webster's Green Label; Young's Bitter; guest beer H
Welcoming, friendly local where the bar is decorated with china, brass and copperware. An excellent pub for families; the large garden has rabbits, ducks, an aviary, swings and a climbing frame. No food Sun.
♨ ◖ ♣ P

Wingham

Dog Inn
Canterbury Road
☎ (01227) 720339
11–3, 6–11
Shepherd Neame Master Brew Bitter; guest beers H
Historic village pub, established in the reign of King John. During the 13th century it housed the local assizes. Later, mail was sorted here before the post office was established.
♨ ✿ ⇌ ◖ ▶ ⬠ P

Wormshill

Blacksmiths Arms
The Street (4 miles from Sittingbourne near the B2163)
☎ (0162 784) 386
12–3, 6–11
Fuller's London Pride; Greene King IPA; Shepherd Neame Master Brew Bitter; guest beer H
Welcoming, traditional country pub without loud jukeboxes or fruit machines. Note the Watney's Red Barrel sign. Good quality meals (no food Tue or Sun eves).
♨ Q ✿ ◖ ▶ ▲ ♣ P

Worth

St Crispin
The Street ☎ (01304) 612081
11–2.30, 6–11
Gale's HSB; Marston's Pedigree; Shepherd Neame Master Brew Bitter; Whitbread Boddingtons Mild H; **guest beers** G
Popular old village local that has been carefully refurbished and extended. It is noted locally for food (book the restaurant). A varied range of guest ales is always available.
♨ Q ✿ ◖ ▶ ♣ P

Try also: Blue Pigeons, The Street (Free)

Protect your pleasure — Join CAMRA (see page 528)

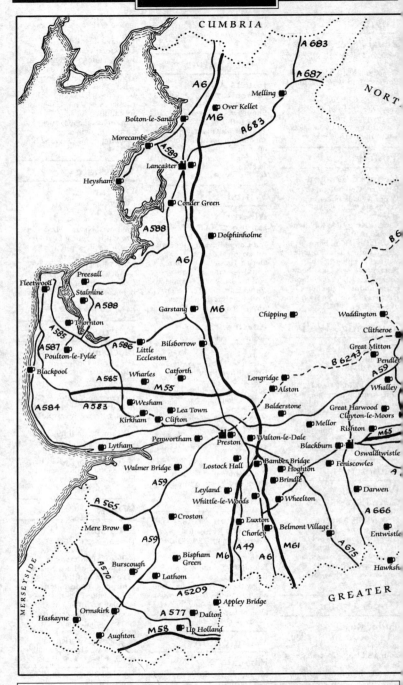

Little Avenham, *Preston;* **Mitchell's**, *Lancaster;*
Moorhouse's, *Burnley;* **Porter**, *Haslingden;*
Thwaites, *Blackburn*

Accrington

Abbey
46 Bank Street
☎ (01254) 235727
12–3.30, 7–11
**John Smith's Bitter; guest
beers** (occasional) H
Pub which has resisted
modernisation and retains its
friendly atmosphere. Families
are welcome lunchtimes.
☼ ◑ ⇌ ♣ P

George
185 Blackburn Road
☎ (01254) 383441
12–11 (meals licence Sun)
Beer range varies H
Open-plan, friendly local near
the college, with a bistro and a
conservatory. Seven, changing
beers.
☼ ⇆ ◑ ⇌ ♣

Alston

White Bull
257 Preston Road
☎ (01772) 784151
12–3, 7–11 (12–11 summer)
Thwaites Best Mild, Bitter H
Deceptively large pub between
Preston and Longridge, with a
semi-open-plan interior. Eve
meals end at 8.30; no eve
meals Mon/Tue in winter.
⇆ ☼ ◑ ▶ ♣ P

Appley Bridge

Wheatsheaf
287 Miles Lane (B5375)
☎ (01257) 252302
12–3.30, 5.30–11; 12–11 Fri & Sat
Greenalls Mild, Bitter H
Immensely popular,
comfortable pub in a semi-
rural area, awash with mugs
and water jugs. Excellent value
food (pizzas only eves).
☼ ◑ ▶ ⊞ ⇌ ♣ P

Aughton

Dog & Gun
223 Long Lane (off A59)
☎ (01695) 423303
5–11; 12–2, 7–10.30 Sun
**Burtonwood Mild, Bitter,
Forshaw's** H
Excellent, well-run, village
local: a pub for a quiet pint
and a good conversation. A
central bar serves two lounges.
Bowling green. ⇆ Q ☼
⇌ (Aughton Pk) ♣ P

Royal Oak
134 Liverpool Road (A59)
☎ (01695) 422121
11.30–3.30, 5–11
**Ind Coope Burton Ale; Tetley
Walker Mild, Bitter** H
Attractive and popular local
where comfortable drinking
areas surround a central bar. A

varied lunch menu offers good
daily specials. The original
stained-glass windows are
well-preserved. ⇆ ☼ ◑ ♿
⇌ (Aughton Pk) ♣ P

Balderstone

Myerscough
Myerscough Smithy Road
(A59) ☎ (01254) 812222
11.30–3, 5.30–11
**Robinson's Hatters Mild, Best
Bitter, Old Tom** (winter) H
Pleasant country pub which
relies on passing trade. It has a
cosy, wood-panelled lounge,
and another small room.
Opposite the British Aerospace
factory, with its preserved
aircraft. No meals Sun eve;
other eves till 8.30.
⇆ Q ⛬ ☼ ◑ ▶ P

Bamber Bridge

Olde Original Withy
Trees
157 Station Road
☎ (01772) 30396
11–11
Burtonwood Bitter H
Converted 17th-century
farmhouse, reputedly the
oldest building in the village.
New vault. Lunches are
planned. Q ⛬ ⇌ ♣ P

Barrowford

Old Bridge Inn
146 Gisburn Road
☎ (01282) 613983
3 (2 Fri)–11; 11–4, 7–11 Sat
**Robinson's Hartleys XB, Best
Bitter** H
Semi-open-plan pub, retaining
its traditional values,
and Hartley & Bell windows.
A sociable local.
⇆ ☼ ♿ ♣ P

Belmont Village

Black Dog
2 Church Street
☎ (0120 481) 218
12–4 (3 Tue & Wed), 7–11
Holt Mild, Bitter H
Popular moorland village pub
on the old Preston–Bolton
road. Occasionally, live
orchestras play here; no
jukebox. It is the only Holt pub
in Lancashire. No food Mon.
⇆ Q ⛬ ☼ ⇆ ◑ ▶ ♣ P

Bilsborrow

White Bull
Garstang Road (A6)
☎ (01995) 640324
11–11
**S&N Matthew Brown Mild,
Theakston Best Bitter** H
Pleasant, quiet, Lancaster
Canalside pub, friendly and
unspoilt. ⇆ Q P

Lancashire

Bispham Green

Eagle & Child
Malt Kiln Lane (off B5246)
☎ (01257) 462297
11.30–3, 5.30–11 (11.30–11 May–Sept)
Coach House Gunpowder Mild; Marston's Pedigree; S&N Theakston Best Bitter; Whitbread Boddingtons Bitter; guest beers H
Ex-Whitbread house, imaginatively renovated, and now a vibrant village local, rapidly gaining a good reputation for food. Bowling green. ▲ Q ♣ ✿ ◑ ♣ P

Blackburn

Florence Hotel
149 Moss Street
☎ (01254) 53100
11–2, 7–11; 11–11 Fri & Sat
Thwaites Best Mild, Bitter, Craftsman H
Attractive, large pub recently refurbished to give a games area, a concert area and a semi-open-plan bar. Very popular at weekends. A Thwaites' *Best Beer Garden* award-winner. ✿ ◑ ▶ & ♣

Globe Inn
2 Higher Eanam
☎ (01254) 671789
12–3 (not Tue or Wed), 7–12
Thwaites Best Mild, Bitter, Craftsman H
Splendid, friendly, multi-roomed corner pub revitalised by its present landlord. The windows, woodwork and furnishings have been restored.
Q ♣ ⬚ ≠ ♣ ✂

Navigation Inn
Canal Street, Mill Hill
☎ (01254) 53230
10.30–11
Thwaites Best Mild, Bitter H
Very well-patronised local in a niche alongside the canal, selling consistently cheap beer. ✿ ⬚ ≠ (Mill Hill) ♣ P

Wellington Inn
362 Livesey Branch Road
☎ (01254) 201436
2 (12 Sat)–11
Whitbread Boddingtons Bitter, Flowers IPA, Winter Royal or **Morland Old Speckled Hen** H
Much improved corner pub, handy for visitors to Ewood Park. A 'fun' pub in the true sense.
▲ ✿ ⬚ ≠ (Mill Hill) ♣

Black Lane Ends

Hare & Hounds
Skipton Old Road
☎ (01282) 863070
12–3 (not Tue or Thu), 7–11

Taylor Mild, Best Bitter H
Cosy, friendly pub, high in the Pennines, serving good value, home-cooked food. Children are welcome. Camping by prior arrangement.
▲ Q ✿ ◑ & ▲ ♣ P

Blacko

Cross Gaits
Beverley Road (A682)
☎ (01282) 616312
12–3 (not Mon–Wed), 5.30 (6 Sat)–11
Burtonwood Mild, Bitter, Top Hat H
Country pub catering for families, with a children's play area in the garden.
▲ Q ♣ ◑ ▶ ♣ P

Blackpool

Bispham Hotel
Red Bank Road (A584)
☎ (01253) 351752
11–3 (4 Sat), 6 (7 Sat)–11
Samuel Smith OBB H
Traditional, 1930s pub, popular with locals and holidaymakers alike. Live entertainment Thu–Sat eves; thriving social club. Good food. ◑ ♣ P

Counting House
10 Talbot Square (opp. North Pier) ☎ (01253) 290979
10.30–11
Cains Bitter; Whitbread Boddingtons Bitter; guest beers H
Converted from a former bank, this popular pub is very busy at weekends. Food until 7.15pm daily, and all day Sun. The family room closes at 8pm.
▲ ♣ ◑ ▶ & ≠ (North)

Empress Hotel
59 Exchange Street, off Dickson Rd ☎ (01253) 751347
11–11 (1am Fri & Sat in summer)
Thwaites Best Mild, Bitter H
Large, Victorian, old-fashioned, basic hotel with a large games room and a snooker table. Lancashire's only ever-present *Guide* entry.
♣ ⬚ & ≠ (North) ♣

Hogshead Ale House
139 Church Street
☎ (01253) 26582
11–11
Marston's Pedigree; Whitbread Boddingtons Bitter, Trophy, Castle Eden Ale H**; guest beers** H / G
Basic, popular Whitbread ale house, full of Blackpool FC memorabilia. Close to the Winter Gardens complex, it is often crowded. Wholesome food. Up to 13 guest beers are offered. Difficult parking.
▲ ◑ ≠ (North) ♣

Mount Pleasant Inn
103 High Street
☎ (01253) 293335
11–11
S&N Theakston Mild, Best Bitter, XB; guest beer H
Small, street-corner local in a tight-knit community, serving locals and holidaymakers alike. Children are welcome at lunchtime. Sky TV. Snacks lunchtime.
✿ ⬚ ≠ (North) ♣

Pump & Truncheon
13 Bonny Street (behind Promenade) ☎ (01253) 21869
11–11
Wadworth 6X; Whitbread Boddingtons Mild, Bitter H**; guest beers** H / G
An oasis near the central pier, where tourists are treated as locals. Varying range of beers (200 in its first year). Free snacks Sun eves.
▲ ◑ ♣

Raikes Hall Hotel
Liverpool Road
☎ (01253) 294372
11 (10.30 summer)–11
Bass Mild, Worthington BB, Draught Bass; Stones Best Bitter; guest beer H
Built in 1750 as part of the Raikes Hall estate, this was once a Catholic convent and is now one of Blackpool's finest pubs, with a popular games room and a resident jazz club. Meals until 7.30. Children welcome. Short mat bowls played.
✿ ◑ ▶ ⬚ & ♣ P

Ramsden Arms Hotel
204 Talbot Road (100 yds E of station)
☎ (01253) 23215
10.30–11
Cains Bitter; Fuller's London Pride; Hydes' Anvil Bitter; Ind Coope Burton Ale; Jennings Bitter; Whitbread Boddingtons Bitter; guest beers H
Refurbished in keeping with its traditional atmosphere, this large, friendly pub was the local CAMRA *Pub of the Year* 1993. ⬚ ◑ ≠ (North) ♣ P

Welcome
Vicarage Lane (off A583)
☎ (01253) 765372
11–11
Burtonwood Mild, Bitter, Forshaw's H
Large, modern pub on the outskirts of town. A cosy, intimate lounge contrasts with a large vault (snooker). The award-winning garden has a safe play area. The restaurant is open all day Sun. A former local CAMRA *Pub of the Year*. ♣ ✿ ◑ ▶ ⬚ & ▲ ♣ P

Bolton-le-Sands

Blue Anchor
Main Road ☎ (01524) 823423
11–11
Mitchell's Best Bitter, ESB H
Robust, friendly local at the heart of a large village, with a games room, a restaurant and a snug. Parking is difficult.
🏠 ❀ 🛏 ◑ ♣ ✕

Brierfield

Waggon & Horses
Colne Road ☎ (01282) 613962
11.30–2.30, 5–11; 11.30–11 Sat
Thwaites Mild, Best Bitter H
Winner of numerous CAMRA awards, including *Best Refurbished Pub* 1983. Three of the rooms feature real fires along with various antiques. Of particular note is the Italian marble fireplace in the library room.
🏠 Q ♿ ❀ ◑ ◗ ♿ ⇌ ♣ P

Brindle

Cavendish Arms
Sandy Lane (B5256)
☎ (01254) 852912
11–3, 5.30–11
Burtonwood Mild, Bitter H
Outstanding traditional village pub with stained-glass and wood carving. Children are welcome at mealtimes. The public bar is separate from the dining area.
🏠 Q ♿ ❀ ◑ ◗ 🛆 ♣ P

Burnley

Mechanics (Shuttle Bar)
Manchester Road
☎ (01282) 30005
11–3, 5.30–11
Moorhouse's Pendle Witches Brew; John Smith's Bitter; Thwaites Bitter, Craftsman; guest beers H
Part of a Council-run arts centre, adjacent to the town hall, in a Grade II-listed building. Real ale is only available in the popular downstairs bar. Guest beers from micro-breweries.
◑ 🛆 ⇌ (Manchester Rd)

Sparrow Hawk Hotel
Church Street
☎ (01282) 421551
11–3, 6–11; 11–11 Sat
Moorhouse's Premier; S&N Theakston Best Bitter, XB; John Smith's Bitter; guest beer H
Excellent, well-run hotel bar. Even the 1970s 'Tudor' decor helps to create a comfortable, relaxed atmosphere. A games room caters for pool players.
🛏 ◑ ◗ ⇌ (Central) ♣

Tim Bobbin
319 Padiham Road (near M65 jct 10) ☎ (01282) 424165
11–11; 11–3, 5.30–11 Tue–Thu
Samuel Smith OBB H
Large, popular, main-road pub with a games room.
❀ ◑ ◗ ♿ ⇌ (Barracks) ♣ P

Burscough

Martin Inn
Martin Lane (off A570/B5242)
☎ (01704) 895788
11.30–3, 5.30–11
Greenalls Original; Ind Coope Burton Ale; Tetley Walker Dark Mild, Walker Bitter, Tetley Bitter H
Remote, welcoming inn, near Martin Mere Wildfowl Trust, featuring a large stone-floored bar area. Good choice of food.
🏠 ❀ 🛏 ◑ ◗ ▲ P

Catforth

Running Pump
Catforth Road (off B5269)
☎ (01772) 690265
11.30–3.30 (not Mon), 6–11
Robinson's Hatters Mild, Bitter H, Old Tom G
Charming country pub of great character, serving excellent, home-cooked Sun lunches. One of the oldest in the area.
🏠 Q ♿ ◑ ♣ P

Chipping

Sun Inn
Windy Street ☎ (01995) 61206
11–4, 6–11; 11–11 Sat
Whitbread Boddingtons Mild, Bitter H
Deservedly popular, stone pub in a picturesque village, the centre of the Lancashire cheese-making industry. Pie and peas are a speciality. Ring the Bull.
Q ♿ ❀ ▲ ♣

Chorley

Malt'n'Hops
50–52 Friday Street
☎ (01257) 260967
12–11
Taylor Landlord; Whitbread Boddingtons Bitter; Wilson's Mild, Webster's Yorkshire Bitter; guest beers H
Former grocer's shop with an excellent view of the Manchester–Blackpool railway line. A warm welcome is assured in the single bar. Unusual exterior design.
⇌

Railway
20–22 Steeley Lane
☎ (01257) 266962
12–11
Draught Bass; S&N Matthew Brown Mild, Theakston Best Bitter; Stones Best Bitter; guest beers H
Lively local decorated in mock Edwardian style: a single bar with alcoves and a collection of model cars.
🏠 ❀ ⇌ ♣

Shepherds Arms
38 Eaves Lane (opp. bus garage) ☎ (01257) 275659
11.30–11
S&N Matthew Brown Mild, Bitter, Theakston Best Bitter; guest beer H
Friendly local, consisting of a lounge, a front room, a cosy, part-enclosed snug and a rear vault, close to Leeds and Liverpool Canal Bridge 66. Guest beers come from the S&N list. ♣

Tut'n'Shive
Market Street (A6)
☎ (01257) 262858
11–11
Whitbread Boddingtons Bitter; guest beers H
Formerly the Royal Oak; Chesters' name (the original owners) can still be seen on the exterior tilework. The inside has been transformed to the usual Whitbread style and there is a quiet downstairs bar. Six regular guests. ◑ ⇌

Clayton-le-Moors

Wellington Hotel
Barns Square
☎ (01254) 235762
2 (12 Sat)–11
Thwaites Best Mild, Bitter H
Large, multi-roomed local, semi-open-plan, with a tap room. ♣

Clifton

Windmill Tavern
Station Road (off A583, near BNFL) ☎ (01772) 687203
11–3, 6.30–11 (11–11 summer Sat)
Mitchell's Best Bitter, ESB; guest beers H
Pub dating from 1700, based on a windmill. The large lounge was once the grain store. The games room is part of the old mill and has food, and there is a children's farm and play area. Two guest beers; good value food.
🏠 ♿ ❀ ◑ ◗ ♿ ⇌ (Salwick) ♣ P

Clitheroe

New Inn
Parsons Lane ☎ (01200) 23312
11–11
Black Sheep Best Bitter; Dent Ramsbottom; Moorhouse's Premier H
Small, friendly, Whitbread drinkers' pub opposite the castle. Folk on Fri; jam sessions Sun.
🏠 Q ♿ ❀ ◑ ◗ ▲ ⇌ ♣

Lancashire

Colne

Commercial
Skipton Road ☎ (01282) 867651
11–3.30 (5 Fri & Sat), 7–11
Thwaites Best Mild, Bitter H
Lively, town-centre local offering a games room, plus Sky TV in the bar. Note the original Grimshaw Brewery windows. ≠ ♣

Conder Green

Stork
On A588 ☎ (01524) 751234
11–11
Tetley Walker Bitter; Whitbread Boddingtons Bitter; guest beers H
This long building has a large restaurant, a plush lounge bar, a snug (children welcome) and a pool room, and boasts much panelling and exposed beams. Two guest beers from the Whitbread list. Handy for the Lune Estuary path. Meals all day Sun. ♔ ☺ ❀ 🛏 ◖ ◗ ♣

Croston

Black Horse
Westhead Road
☎ (01772) 600338
11.30–11
Banks's Mild, Bitter; Camerons Strongarm; Holt Bitter; guest beers H
Excellent, large village pub with restaurant and bowling green. A true free house, it offers over 300 different beers each year, plus regular beer festivals. Meals extension Sun afternoon. ♔ Q 🐎 ☺ ❀ ◖ ◗ ♿ ▲ ≠ ♣ P 🚭

Crown Hotel
Station Road ☎ (01772) 600380
11.30–3 (2.30 Mon & Tue), 5.30 (6 Sat)–11
Tetley Walker Mild, Bitter; Thwaites Best Mild, Bitter, Craftsman; guest beer H
Friendly, welcoming village pub: a central bar serves two drinking areas. No food Sun. ♔ Q 🐎 ☺ ❀ ◖ ▲ ≠ ♣ P

Dalton

Beacon
Beacon Lane OS501077
☎ (01695) 632607
11–11
Burtonwood Bitter; S&N Theakston Mild, Best Bitter, XB, Old Peculier; guest beers H
Pub situated next to Ashurst Beacon and the municipal golf course and country park. The food is excellent and well-priced, and there's an adventurous guest beer policy. Ideal for walkers; extensive views. Q ◖ ◗ P

Darwen

Golden Cup
610 Blackburn Road
☎ (01254) 702337
11.30–3, 5.30–11
Thwaites Best Mild, Bitter, Craftsman H
The oldest pub in town: three small, cosy rooms with low ceilings and an attractive, cobbled forecourt. Good value lunches. ♔ Q ❀ ◖ ♿ P

Greenfield
Lower Barn Street
☎ (01254) 703945
12–3, 5.30–11; 12–11 Fri & Sat
Taylor Landlord; Whitbread Boddingtons Mild, Bitter; guest beers H
Open-plan pub, off the beaten track, next to the railway line. Nice and friendly, it serves good value food (all day licence Sun). Guest beers change regularly. Q ❀ ◖ ◗

Sunnyhurst Hotel
Tockholes Road
☎ (01254) 873035
12–3 (extends in summer), 7–11; 12–11 Sat
Thwaites Best Mild, Bitter H
Small, three-roomer with a homely atmosphere and a large selection of malt whiskies. Close to Darwen Moors. Q ❀ ♣

Dolphinholme

Fleece
½ mile W of village
☎ (01524) 791233
12–3, 7–11
Mitchell's Best Bitter, ESB, Winter Warmer H
Former farmhouse on a crossroads. A cosy, oak-beamed bar leads to a small games/family room and a dining room. Good quality food (no meals Sun eve or Mon). ♔ ☺ ❀ ◖ ◗ ♣ 🍎 P

Entwistle

Strawbury Duck
Overshaws Road (signed on the Edgworth–Darwen Roman road) OS727178
☎ (01204) 852013
12–3 (not Mon), 7–11; 12–11 Sat
Marston's Pedigree; Morland Old Speckled Hen; Taylor Best Bitter, Landlord; Whitbread Boddingtons Bitter; guest beers H
Old, isolated, but busy, country pub, next to the station: a good base for walks in hill country. Try the authentic Indian cuisine. Children are welcome until 8.30pm. Three guest beers. ♔ ☺ ❀ 🛏 ◖ ◗ ≠ ♣ P 🚭

Euxton

Euxton Mills
Wigan Road (A49/A581 jct)
☎ (01257) 264002
11.30–3, 5.30 (6.15 Sat)–11
Burtonwood Mild, Bitter, Forshaw's H
Cosy, comfortable pub with two lounge/dining areas and a small front vault. Children are allowed in the rear room for the excellent meals.
❀ ◖ ◗ ⊟ ♣ P

Fence-in-Pendle

Harpers Inn
Harpers Lane (near A6068/B6248 jct) ☎ (01282) 616249
11.30–3, 7–11
S&N Theakston Best Bitter, Old Peculier; Thwaites Best Mild, Bitter, Craftsman H
Attractive, rural pub with a good value restaurant and bar meals (all day Sun). Families welcome. Q ❀ ◖ ◗ P

Feniscowles

Fieldens Arms
673 Preston Old Road (A674/A6062 jct) ☎ (01254) 208045
4 (12 Fri & Sat)–11
Cains Bitter; Whitbread Chester's Best Mild, Higsons Mild, Boddingtons Bitter, Flowers IPA; guest beers H
Pub with a number of small drinking areas plus a pool area. Live entertainment Thu eves. Up to eight ales.
❀ ≠ (Pleasington) ♣ P

Fleetwood

Kings Arms
105 Lord Street
☎ (01253) 874837
11–11
S&N Theakston Best Bitter; Whitbread Boddingtons Bitter; guest beers H
Recently modernised, Victorian town-centre pub, enjoying a good local trade. English cuisine is served in the new restaurant. Family room open lunchtimes. ☺ ◖ ◗

North Euston Hotel
The Esplanade
☎ (01253) 876525
11–3.30, 6–11; 11–11 Sat
Draught Bass; Ruddles Best Bitter, County; Webster's Yorkshire Bitter, Wilson's Mild, Bitter; guest beers H
Large, Victorian stone-fronted building with impressive views, close to the pier, and bus and tram termini. Large,

spacious and elegant public rooms. ⌂ ⊞ ◖ & P

Queens Hotel

Poulton Road (beach road jct)
☎ (01253) 876740
12–11
Thwaites Best Mild, Bitter H
Busy, friendly pub where a central bar serves several alcoves plus games rooms for snooker, pool and darts. It can get busy Fri and Sat. ❀ P

Wyre Lounge Bar

Marine Hall, The Esplanade
☎ (01253) 771141
11–3.30, 7–11
Courage Directors; Moorhouse's Premier, Pendle Witches Brew; guest beer H
Popular part of the Marine Hall complex, twice a local CAMRA *Pub of the Year*. An excellent choice of guest beers can be sampled in comfortable surroundings. Q ❀ & P

Garstang

Royal Oak

Market Place ☎ (01995) 603318
11–11
Robinson's Hatters Mild, Hartleys XB, Best Bitter H
Some parts date from a 1480 farmhouse but this is mostly a 1670 coaching inn. Renovations in 1993 retained intimate drinking areas. Meals extension till 4pm Sun.
⌂ ❀ ⊞ ◖ ♣ P

Great Harwood

Merrie England

56 St Huberts Road
☎ (01254) 888358
12–3, 7–11; 12–11 Fri & Sat
Marston's Pedigree; Whitbread Boddingtons Mild, Bitter; guest beers H
Friendly local in a residential area: a lively vault and a comfortable lounge, popular with all types. Weekend entertainment. ◖ ▲ ♣

Royal Hotel

Station Road ☎ (01254) 883541
12–1.30 (3 Sat; not Mon & Tue), 7–11
Thwaites Bitter; guest beers H
Cosy, open-plan pub, free from loud music. It offers four guest beers plus a wide selection of continental bottles. A CAMRA regional *Pub of the Year*. Q ❀ ⊞ ◖ ▲ ♣

Great Mitton

Owd Ned's River View Tavern

Mitton Hall OS718385
☎ (0125 486) 544
11–11
Jennings Cumberland Ale; Marston's Pedigree;

Whitbread Boddingtons Mild, Bitter, Flowers Original; guest beer H
Overlooking the River Ribble in picturesque countryside, this pub places an emphasis on food and provides good facilities for children, including highchairs. Open 7.30am for breakfast.
⌖ Q ⌂ ❀ ⊞ ◖ ◗ & ♣ P

Haskayne

Ship Inn

6 Rosemary Lane (300 yds from A567) ☎ (0170 48) 40572
11–3, 6–11
Tetley Walker Mild, Bitter H
Canalside pub in rural surroundings. The garden is for adults only but there's a children's playground next to the pub. ⌂ ❀ ◖ ◗ P

Hawkshaw

Red Lion

91 Ramsbottom Road (A676, Bolton road) ☎ (01204) 852539
12–3 (may vary), 6–11
Taylor Golden Best, Best Bitter, Landlord; guest beers H
Set in a picturesque area, a pub just in Lancashire with its car park in Gtr Manchester. Completely rebuilt in 1990, it has a single, comfortable bar plus a restaurant. ⊞ ◖ ◗ P

Heysham

Royal

7 Main Street
11–3, 5.45–11; 11–11 Thu–Sat
Mitchell's Best Bitter H
Old, four-roomed, low-ceilinged pub, near St Patrick's chapel and rock-hewn graves. Busy local trade, and packed with holidaymakers in summer. Children are admitted to the games room until 7.30. ⌖ ❀ ◖ ⌓ ♣ P

Hoghton

Black Horse

Gregson Lane (off A675)
☎ (01254) 852541
11.30–11
Marston's Pedigree; S&N Matthew Brown Mild, Bitter, Theakston Best Bitter, XB H
Large, friendly, open-plan village pub with a games area.
❀ ◖ ♣ P

Royal Oak

Riley Green (A675/A6061)
☎ (01254) 201445
11–3, 5.30–11
Thwaites Best Mild, Bitter H
Old, low-ceilinged pub formed from a row of cottages: several cosy drinking areas, popular for food. ⌖ Q ◖ ◗ & P

Kirkham

Queens Arms

7 Poulton Street (opp. market place) ☎ (01772) 686705
12 (11.30 Thu–Sat)–11
S&N Theakston Mild, Best Bitter, XB, Old Peculier; guest beer H
Excellent, well-run, lively, town-centre local, full of character. Children are welcome in a designated area, and it also has an excellent garden and a pool room. Wheelchair WC. Barbecues in summer. ❀ & ♣

Lancaster

Bowerham

Bowerham Road
☎ (01524) 65050
11–5, 6–11
Mitchell's Best Bitter, Lancaster Bomber; guest beer H
Large, turn-of-the-century, suburban pub with several rooms: the nearest pub to the leisure park and Williamson Park (½ mile), but the trade is mostly local. Bowling green.
❀ ⌓ ♣

Fat Scot

2 Gage Street (near Dalton Sq)
☎ (01524) 63438
11–11
Mitchell's Best Bitter, Lancaster Bomber H
Small, dark pub with heavy metal on the jukebox and Gothic fantasy murals.
⇌ ♣

George & Dragon

24 St George's Quay
☎ (01524) 844739
11–11
Vaux Bitter; Wards Thorne Best Bitter, Best Bitter H
Narrow, single-bar pub decorated in modern, uncarpeted style, with nautical prints (close to the Maritime Museum). ❀ ◖ ⇌ P

John O'Gaunt

55 Market Street
☎ (01524) 65356
11.30–3, 6–11; 11–11 Fri; 11–5, 7–11 Sat
Cains Bitter; Ind Coope Burton Ale; Jennings Bitter; Tetley Walker Dark Mild, Bitter; Whitbread Boddingtons Bitter; guest beer H
Pub with a handsome original frontage: it probably sells more gallons per square foot than any other Lancaster pub. Regular live music. Don't miss the garden. No food Sun; eve meals Fri.
❀ ◖ ⇌

Lancashire

Priory

36 Cable Street (near bus
station) ☎ (01524) 32606
11–11 (may close afternoons)
**Mitchell's Best Bitter, ESB;
guest beer** H
Mitchell's original guest beer
pub. The decor is
unprepossessing but attracts
huge numbers of students as
well as ale connoisseurs.
Weston's Old Rosie cider
(and perry in summer). ⇌ ♨

Royal

Thurnham Street
☎ (01524) 65007
11.30–3, 7–11
**Thwaites Best Mild, Bitter,
Craftsman** H
Pub knocked through in 1992
to make a single large bar with
lots of corners. Trade comes
from the nearby Town Hall.
Quiz Wed; live music summer
Sun. ❀ ◑ ⇌ P

Stonewell

8–10 Church Street
☎ (01524) 388474
12–3, 7 (6 Fri)–11; 11.30–11 Sat
Thwaites Bitter, Craftsman H
Single bar with stone floors
and drinking alcoves; note the
Y&J etched windows. Students
get a discount on bitter.
No food Mon.
◑ ▶ ⇌ ♣

Lathom

Briars Hall

Briars Lane (A5209, look for
signs) ☎ (01704) 892368
11.30–3, 6.30–11; 12.30–3, 7–10.30
Sun
**Ruddles Best Bitter; Tetley
Walker Mild, Bitter; guest
beers** H
18th-century manor house, set
in three acres of gardens; now
a hotel with a large restaurant.
A very comfortable lounge is
run as a pub and attracts a
good local following. The
superb decor features antique
furniture. Great value lunches.
Q ❀ ⛴ ◑ ▶ P

Ship Inn

Wheat Lane (off A5209, near
Burscough, over canal swing
bridge) OS452115
☎ (01704) 893117
12–3, 5.30 (7 Sat)–11
**Moorhouse's Pendle Witches
Brew; S&N Theakston Mild,
Best Bitter, XB; guest beers** H
Regional CAMRA *Pub of the
Year* 1994: an excellent and
popular, canalside free house
with nine handpumps and five
ever-changing guest beers.
Locally known as the 'Blood
Tub'. Good value lunches (not
served Sun).
Q ⛵ ❀ ◑ ♣ P

Lea Town

Smiths Arms

Lea Lane (opp. BNFL E gate)
☎ (01772) 726906
11.30–3, 7–11
Thwaites Best Mild, Bitter H
Excellent, friendly traditional
pub, often overlooked in
favour of more food-oriented
outlets. A small bar serves a
comfortable drinking area
with separate quiet and games
rooms. ⌨ Q ❀ ◑ ▶ P

Leyland

Dunkirk Hall

Dunkirk Lane
☎ (01772) 422102
11–3, 5–11; 11–11 Fri & Sat
**Courage Directors; John
Smith's Bitter; Whitbread
Boddingtons Bitter** H
17th-century converted
farmhouse, now a listed
building. Flag floors, wood-
panelled walls and oak beams
feature. ❀ ◑ ▶ P

Eagle & Child

30 Church Road
☎ (01772) 433531
11.45–11
**Burtonwood Bitter,
Forshaw's** H
Popular pub, near the market.
A long layout gives several
drinking areas. The outdoor
drinking area includes an
aviary and a children's play
area. Quiz Tue. ❀ ◑ ⇌ ♣ P

Gables

Hough Lane ☎ (01772) 422032
11–3, 7–11
Greenalls Bitter, Original H
Handsome, red-brick house in
the centre of town, handy for
the Commercial Vehicle
Museum. ◑ ⊞ ⇌ ♣ P

Little Eccleston

Cartford Country Inn
& Hotel

Cartford Lane (by toll bridge)
☎ (01995) 670166
11.30–3, 7 (6.30 summer)–11
**Whitbread Boddingtons
Bitter; guest beers** H
Delightfully-situated free
house by the River Wyre
(fishing rights). An extensive
bar menu offers daily specials
and a children's menu. Four
guest beers, regularly changed.
⌨ Q ⛵ ❀ ⛴ ◑ ⅊ ♣ P

Longridge

Forest Arms

Derby Road ☎ (01772) 782610
12–3 (2 Tue; not Wed), 7 (5.30
Mon)–11; 12–11 Fri & Sat
Whitbread Boddingtons

Bitter; guest beers H
Three-roomed traditional
local, close to the town centre,
home to sports teams and a
fell-walking society. ♣

Old Oak

111 Preston Road (B6243)
☎ (01772) 783648
11–3, 5–11; 11–11 Sat
**S&N Theakston Mild, Best
Bitter; Thwaites Best Mild** *or*
Bitter H
Stone-built pub at the entrance
to the town: a single L-shaped
room with settles. ⌨ ◑ ♣ P

Towneley Arms

41 Berry Lane
☎ (01772) 782219
11–3.30, 6–11
Tetley Walker Mild, Bitter H
Town-centre pub whose
landlord is leaving in June
1995 after 30 years. No
children under 14. ⌨ ♣ P

Lostock Hall

Pleasant Retreat

Watkin Lane (A582)
☎ (01772) 35616
11–11
**Cains Bitter; S&N Theakston
Best Bitter; Whitbread
Boddingtons Bitter** H
Prominent pub next to Tardy
Gate shopping centre, with
two busy rooms. The Cains
may be replaced by a guest.
No food Sun lunch.
◑ ⇌ ♣

Victoria

Watkin Lane (A582)
☎ (01772) 35338
11–3, 6–11; 11–11 Sat
**Ruddles Best Bitter; John
Smith's Bitter** H
Large pub, set back from the
main road. The plush lounge
features music hall posters.
The spacious public bar area is
popular for games. No lunches
Sun. ◑ ⊞ ⇌ ♣ P

Lytham

Hole in One

Forest Drive (off B5261)
☎ (01253) 730598
11–3, 6–11; 11–11 Sat
Thwaites Bitter H
Busy, friendly, modern local,
by Fairhaven Golf Course. It
has a large games room and
runs popular quiz nights.
Good home-made food
includes daily specials and
Sun roasts. Children most
welcome. Wheelchair WC.
Q ❀ ◑ ⊞ ♣ P

Queens

Central Beach
☎ (01253) 737316
11–3.30, 5–11 (11–11 summer)
**S&N Theakston Best Bitter,
XB; guest beer** H

Characterful, authentic Victorian pub, in the town centre, overlooking the green and estuary. Good reputation for food (often busy).
🍴 ♿ ⊭ ◑ ▶ ⊟ ⅋ ⇌ ♣ P

Taps

Henry Street (off Lytham Sq)
☎ (01253) 736226
11–11
Burtonwood Top Hat; Cains Bitter; Marston's Pedigree; Moorhouse's Pendle Witches Brew; Whitbread Boddingtons Bitter; guest beers H
Warm, friendly, basic ale house, serving a wide choice of guest beers. The landlord has won awards. It is often crowded (difficult parking), but worth a visit. Wheelchair WC. 🍴 ♿ ◑ ⅋ ♿ ⇌

Melling

Melling Hall

☎ (01524) 221298
12–2.30 (not Wed); 6–11; 12–2, 7–10.30 Sun
Taylor Landlord; Tetley Walker Bitter; Whitbread Boddingtons Bitter H
17th-century manor house converted in the 1940s to a hotel, with a friendly locals' bar. Garden play area.
🍴 ♿ ⊭ ◑ ▶ ⊟ ♣ P

Mellor

Traders Arms

Mellor Lane ☎ (01254) 812478
12–3, 7–11
Thwaites Best Mild, Bitter, Craftsman H
Cosy, friendly pub with a games (tap) room. It is very popular with locals and staff from the nearby BAe plant. Extremely good food at good prices (no eve meals Mon or Tue). ♿ ◑ ▶ ⅋ ♣ P

Mere Brow

Legh Arms

The Gravel (off A565)
☎ (01772) 812225
11.30–3, 5–11; 11.30–11 Sat
Tetley Walker Bitter; Whitbread Higsons Mild, Boddingtons Bitter, Higsons Bitter; guest beer H
Friendly, smart and cosy village local with a good guest beer policy. Just off the main road, it attracts passing trade and locals. Try the roast lunches. Q ♿ ◑ ⊟ ⅋ ♣ P

Mereclough

Kettledrum Inn

302 Red Lees Road
☎ (01282) 424591

11–3, 5.30–11
Courage Directors; S&N Theakston Best Bitter, XB; John Smith's Bitter H
Very popular, attractive inn on the outskirts of Burnley. The bar area features much brass and pottery. The gas-lit upstairs restaurant is worth booking; children welcome.
🍴 Q ♿ ◑ ▶ ⅋ ♣ P

Morecambe

New Inn

2 Poulton Square
☎ (01524) 831120
11–11
John Smith's Bitter; Whitbread Boddingtons Mild, Bitter; guest beer H
Down-to-earth pub at the centre of the old village of Poulton-le-Sands. Smartly renovated in 1991, it retains its former layout of two small bars and a games room. Outside drinking is on the street. The guest beer is from Whitbread. Q ♣ ♣

Owls Nest

Elms Road (off B5275)
☎ (01524) 411501 (ext. 504)
11–11
Mitchell's Best Bitter, Lancaster Bomber, ESB; guest beer H
Small, classically-designed building, the lodge to the adjacent Elms Hotel when that was a private house. Opened in 1991 as an open-plan bar, it caters mainly for locals.
♿ ◑ ⇌ (Bare Lane) ♣ P

Pier

285 Marine Road
☎ (01524) 417928
11–5, 7–11
S&N Matthew Brown Mild, Bitter, Theakston Best Bitter, XB, Old Peculier H
A proper pub and not just a seafront bar, retaining two distinct bar rooms. Lunches in summer, except Sun.
♿ ◑ ⊟ ♣

Ormskirk

Greyhound

100 Aughton Street
☎ (01695) 576701
11–11
Tetley Walker Mild, Bitter, Winter Warmer H
Characterful, market town local with a traditional public bar, a snug, a large lounge with nooks and crannies, plus a games room. The central bar has a corridor serving hatch.
🍴 Q ⊟ ♣

Kicking Donkey

Narrow Moss Lane (1 mile from centre, 1st right after A59/A570 jct)

☎ (01695) 572657
11.30–3, 5.30–11
Ind Coope Burton Ale; Walker Mild, Best Bitter, Winter Warmer H
Attractive rural pub with an L-shaped bar, serving a spacious lounge and a dining area (eve meals finish at 7.30).
🍴 Q ♿ ◑ ▶ P

Prince Albert

109 Wigan Road, Westhead
☎ (01695) 573656
12–3 (5 Sat), 5 (7 Sat)–11
Tetley Walker Dark Mild, Bitter; guest beers H
A Tetley *Golden Huntsman* award-winner, going from strength to strength, this comfortable, friendly village pub enjoys good local support. The meals are good value.
🍴 Q ♿ ◑ A ♣ P

Yew Tree

Grimshaw Lane
☎ (01695) 573381
12–3.30, 5–11.30
Cains Bitter; guest beers H
Modern pub with a spacious lounge, a well-patronised public bar and a genuine snug. Serious dominoes and darts are played. Good value food (not served Sun). Worth the short walk from the centre.
Q ◑ ⊟ ⇌ ♣ P

Oswaldtwistle

Royal Oak Inn

334 Union Road
☎ (01254) 236367
12–4 (4.30 Sat), 7–11
Thwaites Best Mild, Bitter H
Open-plan pub with a small games area. ⇌ (Church & Oswaldtwistle) ♣

Over Kellet

Eagle's Head

Nether Kellet Road
☎ (01524) 732457
12–3, 7–11
Mitchell's Best Bitter H
The original, 17th-century village inn here now forms a dining/children's room and an adjacent snug. Today's main bar area was converted from a barn in the 1970s, leaving the roof timbers and stone walls exposed.
🍴 ♿ ◑ ♣ P

Padiham

Alma Inn

36 Alma Street
☎ (01282) 772894
12–3, 7–11; 12–11 Sat
Tetley Walker Bitter; Webster's Green Label, Yorkshire Bitter H
Traditional local: a small lounge and a games room with a hatch to the bar. ◑ ▶ ⅋ ♣

Lancashire

Hand & Shuttle

1 Eccleshill Street (opp. post office) ☎ (01282) 771795
11.30–4, 6–11
Thwaites Best Mild, Bitter H
Recently refurbished, town-centre pub, retaining the character of a local. ♣ P

Pendleton

Swan With Two Necks

Off A59 ☎ (01200) 23112
12–3 (not Mon), 7–11
**Bass Worthington BB;
Marston's Pedigree; Tetley
Walker Bitter** H
Small pub, incorporating the village post office.
🛏 Q ☎ ❀ ◑ ◗ ♣ P

Penwortham

St Teresa's Parish Centre

Queensway ☎ (01772) 743523
7–11; 12–4, 7–11 Sat
**Burtonwood Mild, Bitter,
Forshaw's; Ind Coope Burton
Ale; Tetley Walker Mild,
Bitter; guest beers** H
Thriving, three-bar Catholic club in a residential area: a comfortable lounge, a games room and a concert room. Two weekly guest beers. A former CAMRA *Club of the Year* award-winner. Entry restrictions: CAMRA members anytime; others six times per year (25p). ☎ ❀ ◬ P

Poulton-le-Fylde

Thatched House

Ball Street
11–11
**Whitbread Boddingtons
Bitter; guest beer** H
Popular, village pub, busy at weekends, but the service is good. The guest beer changes every few days. No music or pool table: a 'proper' pub with a public bar. 🛏 Q ◬ ⇌

Preesall

Saracens Head

200 Park Lane (B5377)
☎ (01253) 810346
12–3, 5.30–11
Thwaites Best Mild, Bitter H
Very busy village pub with a well-deserved reputation for good value food (open all day Sun for meals). Look for the old head which guards the car park. ❀ ◑ ◗ ♠ ♣ P

Preston

Black Horse

166 Friargate
11–11; 11–4, 7.30–11 Sat; 7–10.30 Sun, closed Sun lunch

**Robinson's Hatters Mild,
Hartleys XB, Best Bitter, Old
Tom** H
Superb, thriving town-centre pub in a pedestrianised area; a Grade II-listed building with side rooms, an upstairs 1920s-style bar, and an unusual, curved, tiled main bar. Wood panelling, stained-glass and a mosaic floor all feature. Q ◑ ⇌

Church Street Tavern

40–42 Church Street
☎ (01772) 253913
11–3, 7–11
Vaux Samson; guest beers H
18th-century inn, recently refurbished, with a warm, friendly atmosphere. It offers good value lunches (not served Sun), and a changing guest beer list. ◑ ◬ ⇌ ♣

Gastons

30 Avenham Street
☎ (01772) 251380
12–3, 6–11
**Little Avenham Arkwright
Ale, Pickled Priest, Clog
Dancer, Torchlight,
Pierrepoints Last Drop; guest
beers** H
Multi-level, two-bar free house which started brewing in 1992, the first brewery in Preston since 1968. The upper bar is popular with young people; downstairs is quieter. Up to six guest beers. Lunches Mon–Sat; eve meals Sun–Thu. Family room open Sun.
☎ ◑ ◗ ⇌ ♣ ○

Lamb & Packet

91a Friargate ☎ (01772) 251857
11.30–11; 11.30–3, 6.30–11 Sat
**Thwaites Best Mild, Bitter,
Craftsman** H
Busy, one-roomed pub near Preston University. At lunchtimes, the good value food attracts a mix of students and office workers, but the students take over eves. Meals served all day (until 7pm) weekdays. ◑ ◗ ⇌

Mitre Tavern

90–91 Moor Lane
☎ (01772) 251918
12–2.30, 5.30–11; 12–11 Wed–Sat
**Vaux Samson; Wards Best
Bitter; guest beers** H
Friendly pub, just out of the town centre: a comfortable lounge and a good vault with pool and darts. Guest beers come from Vaux. ◑ ◬ ♣ P

New Britannia

6 Heatley Street
☎ (01772) 253424
11–3 (4 Fri & Sat), 6–11
**Marston's Pedigree;
Whitbread Trophy, Castle
Eden Ale, Flowers Original;
guest beer** H

Small, one-bar pub near the university and town centre, often crowded at weekends. Lunches Mon–Fri. Guest beers from Whitbread.
❀ ◑ ◬ ⇌ ○

New Welcome

15–17 Cambridge Walk
(½ mile from centre)
☎ (01772) 253933
12–3 (4 Sat), 7–11
Thwaites Best Mild, Bitter H
A warm welcome in a friendly local where a central bar serves three areas. 🛏 ♣ P

Old Black Bull

35 Friargate ☎ (01772) 254402
10.30–11
**Whitbread Boddingtons
Bitter; guest beers** H
Pub with a large lounge and a small vault on the street front, offering 20–25 guest beers a week. Popular with all, it holds beer festivals in the autumn. A local CAMRA award-winner for the last two years. Good value food, Mon–Fri. ❀ ◑ ⊞ ⇌ ♣ ○

Olde Blue Bell

114 Church Street
☎ (01772) 251280
11–3 (4 Sat), 6 (7 Sat)–11
Samuel Smith OBB H
A country pub in the town. This warm, intimate pub is the oldest in Preston, and is good for conversation. Quiz Tue. Good value food (not served Sun). 🛏 ❀ ◑ ⇌ P

Real Ale Shop

47 Lovat Road
☎ (01772) 201591
11–2, 5–10; 12–2, 7–10 Sun
**Fuller's London Pride;
Moorhouse's Pendle Witches
Brew** H; **guest beers** H / G
Busy off-licence selling an ever-changing range of ales, continental beers, fruit wines and home brewing supplies. ○

Sumners

Watling Street Road, Fulwood
(B6241) ☎ (01772) 705626
11.30 (11 Sat in football season)–11
**S&N Theakston Best Bitter;
Whitbread Boddingtons Mild,
Bitter** H
Large, modern pub, handy for the football ground. It has a large lounge, a games room and a small snug, and can get very busy. No food Sun. No-smoking area at lunchtime.
Q ❀ ◑ ⊞ ◬ ♣ P ⊁

Rishton

Rishton Arms

Station Road ☎ (01254) 886396
7 (11 Sat)–11
**Thwaites Best Mild, Bitter,
Craftsman** H

Pleasant, two-roomed pub, handy for the cricket ground. Note the grandfather clock in the lounge and the limited opening times. ⇌ ♣ P

Salterforth

Anchor Inn
Salterforth Lane (50 yds off B6383) ☎ (01282) 813186
12–11
Bass Mild, Special, Worthington BB, Draught Bass H
Listed building dating back to 1655, and raised in 1788 due to the construction of the Leeds–Liverpool Canal. Stalactites and stalagmites can be seen in the cellar. Busy in summer; children welcome.
🏚 Q ❀ ◑ ▶ ₲ ♣ ♣ P

Stalmine

Seven Stars
Hallgate Lane (A588)
☎ (01253) 700207
11.30 (1.30 Tue)–3, 7 (6.30 Thu–Sat)–11
Greenalls Bitter, Original H
Very popular, 16th-century, roadside pub, next to the church. The bar displays old photos of the pub; the lounge has brasses and a real fire. Resident organist Sun. Excellent B&B; no food Tue.
🏚 Q ⏰ ❀ ◁ ◑ ▶ ♣ ♣ P

Thornton

Burn Naze
Gamble Road
☎ (01253) 852954
11–11
Moorhouse's Premier; Tetley Walker Dark Mild, Bitter H
Late-Victorian pub of character, popular with the locals, with one of the few public bars left in the area. Next to ICI. ◑ ▶ ♣ P

Up Holland

White Lion
Off A577 ☎ (01695) 622727
12–3, 7.30 (7 Fri & Sat)–11
Tetley Walker Bitter; guest beer H
Picturesque village pub, opposite the church. Up Holland's oldest inn, it probably originated as a monks' brewhouse.
🏚 Q ◑ ♣ P

Waddington

Buck Inn (Lower Buck)
Church Road (200 yds off B6478) ☎ (01200) 28705
11–3, 6–11; 11–11 Thu–Sat

Bass Worthington BB, Draught Bass; Taylor Best Bitter; guest beer H
Unaltered Dickensian pub in a Grade I-listed building. A good village local. 🏚 Q ⏰ ❀ ⌂ ◑ ▶ ₲ ♣ ♣ P

Walmer Bridge

Longton Arms
2 Liverpool Old Road
☎ (01772) 612335
2 (12 Sat)–11 (12–midnight bank hols)
Greenalls Mild, Bitter H
Small, end-of-terrace village local with a lounge and a tiny public bar at the front. Note the hand-painted wildfowl frieze. 🏚 Q ❀ ◑ ▦ ♣ P

Walton-le-Dale

Victoria
97 Higher Walton Road (A675)
☎ (01772) 204420
11–11
Whitbread Boddingtons Bitter; guest beers H
Victorian local where a central bar serves a lounge and a vault. 🏚 ❀ ◑ ▦ P

Yew Tree
100 Victoria Road (A6/A675 jct) ☎ (01772) 555103
11.30–3, 6–11
Whitbread Boddingtons Bitter; guest beers H
Large, roadside pub with an emphasis on meals, but enjoying a local following for three guest beers. ❀ ◑ ▶ ₲ P

Waterfoot

Jolly Sailor
Booth Road, Booth Place (off B6238) ☎ (01706) 214863
11–3, 5.30–11; 11–11 Fri & Sat
S&N Theakston Best Bitter; Taylor Landlord; Whitbread Boddingtons Mild, Bitter, Flowers IPA H
Pub with a tastefully decorated lounge and a dining room (children welcome for meals). No lunches Mon or Tue. ❀ ⌂ ◑ ♣

Railway
390 Bacup Road
☎ (01706) 213347
11–11
John Smith's Bitter; Webster's Yorkshire Bitter, Wilson's Mild H
Nestling on the bank of the River Irwell, this cosy pub is a one-roomed local with a central bar. The railway itself is long gone. ❀ ♣

Wesham

Stanley Arms
8 Garstang Road South
☎ (01772) 685254

11–3 (5 Thu–Sat), 7–11
S&N Theakston Best Bitter, XB; guest beer H
Old-fashioned, small, friendly, street- corner local, run by an award-winning landlady.
Q ◑ ◁ ₲ ⇌ (Kirkham & Wesham) ♣ ½

Whalley

Swan
62 King Street
☎ (01254) 822195
11–11
John Smith's Bitter; Thwaites Bitter; Whitbread Boddingtons Bitter; guest beers H
Rural pub in the heart of the Ribble Valley, a former coach house from the 17th century. Three guest beers.
Q ⏰ ❀ ⌂ ◑ ▶ ₲ ♣ P

Wharles

Eagle & Child
Church Road OS448356
☎ (01772) 690312
7–11; 12–3, 7–11 Sat & bank hols
Whitbread Boddingtons Bitter; guest beers H
Rural, thatched, free house. The collection of farm implements, unspoilt decor and carved wooden-backed chairs make this a quiet pub not to be missed. 🏚 Q ❀ P

Wheelton

Red Lion
196 Blackburn Road, Lower Wheelton (off A674)
☎ (01254) 830378
12–3, 6–11; 12–11 Sat
Coach House Coachman's; S&N Theakston Mild, Best Bitter; Whitbread Boddingtons Bitter; guest beers H
A recent convert to cask beer, this former Matthew Brown pub has a split-level interior with a comfortable bar and a games room. A short walk from Johnson's Hillock (Top Lock) on the Leeds–Liverpool Canal. 🏚 ❀ ◑ ▶ ♣ P

Whittle-le-Woods

Royal Oak
216 Chorley Old Road
☎ (01254) 76485
2.30–11
Marston's Pedigree; S&N Matthew Brown Mild, Bitter, Theakston Best Bitter; guest beer H
Small, neat, terraced local, with a compact front room and a games room. Full of atmosphere and character; a real local. Note the Nuttalls windows. 🏚 Q ❀ ₲ ♣

Leicestershire

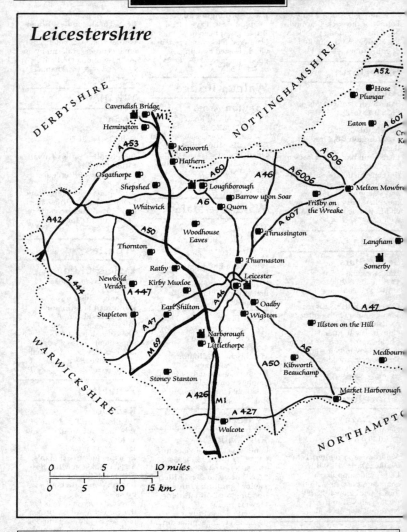

Everards, Narborough; Featherstone, Hoskins, Hoskins & Oldfield, Leicester; Oakham, Oakham; Parish, Somerby; Phantom & Firkin, Loughborough; Ruddles, Langham; Shardlow, Cavendish Bridge

Barrow upon Soar

Riverside
14 Bridge Street
☎ (01509) 412260
11–2.30 (11.30–3 Sat), 7–11
Courage Directors; Ruddles County; John Smith's Bitter H
Riverside pub with moorings, and a large outside drinking area fronting the river. Quiz night Thu. ❀ ◑ ▶ & ▲ P

Cavendish Bridge

Old Crown
Off A6 ☎ (01332) 792392
11–3, 5–11
Draught Bass; Marston's Pedigree; guest beers H
Riverside pub with extensive decorations to every beam and shelf in sight. Dated advertisements, ceramic jugs, copper kettles, armour, etc.

add much to the conversation. Extensive lunchtime menu.
Q ❀ ◑ & P

Croxton Kerrial

Peacock Inn
1 School Lane (A607)
11.30–2.30, 6.45–11
Morland Old Speckled Hen; Wadworth 6X; Whitbread Boddingtons Bitter; guest beers H

Eaton

Castle Inn

33 Vicarage Lane
☎ (01476) 870949
12–3, 7–11; 12–3 Sun, closed Sun eve
Mansfield Old Baily H
Friendly, out of the way pub
with large grounds for
camping (caravans allowed).
Welcoming to locals and
visitors alike—whatever the
size of the party. Table and
long alley skittles.
🏰 ◖ ▶ & ▲ ♣ P

Essendine

Essendine Hotel

On A6121 ☎ (01780) 63048
12–2.30, 6–11
Vaux Double Maxim H
19th-century, brick-built,
non-residential pub,
unchanged since the 1960s,
with three rooms to satisfy the
locals. Good value beer and
four-star petrol sold (from the
car park pumps). A local
version of shove-halfpenny is
played. Q ❀ ⊕ ♣ P

Frisby on the Wreake

Bell Inn

Main Street ☎ (01664) 434237
12–2.30, 6–11; 12–2.30, 7–10.30 Sun
**Ansells Bitter; Draught Bass;
Bateman Mild, XXXB;
Marston's Pedigree; Tetley
Bitter; guest beers** H
Large village local with a
friendly atmosphere. It dates
back to 1759 but has been
extended at the rear. Popular
with diners and the farming
community. Lunches end at
1.30. 🏰 ☕ ❀ ◖ ▶ ♣ P

Hathern

Dew Drop

49 Loughborough Road
☎ (01509) 842438
7–11; 1–2.30, 7–11 Fri & Sat
**Hardys & Hansons Best Mild,
Best Bitter** H
Small, traditional pub with
limited opening hours. Small
lounge; large selection of malt
whiskies. Tiny car park.
🏰 Q ♣ P

Three Crowns

Wide Lane ☎ (01509) 842233
12–2.30, 5.30–11 (11–11 winter Sat)
**Bass Worthington BB,
Draught Bass; M&B Mild,
Highgate Dark** H
Lively village local with three
separate drinking areas. Home
of village sports teams. Skittle
alley. 🏰 ❀ ♣ P

Hemington

Jolly Sailor

Main Street ☎ (01332) 810448
11–11
**Draught Bass; M&B Mild;
Marston's Pedigree; guest
beers** H
Popular village local close to
East Midlands airport.
🏰 ❀ & ♣ ♠ ♡ P

Hose

Black Horse

Bolton Lane ☎ (01949) 60336
12–2.30, 6.30 (7 Sat)–11
**Home Mild, Bitter; John
Smith's Bitter; guest beers** H
Excellent example of a mid-
Victorian village pub: an
authentic 1930s tap room plus
a cosy snug and lounge/
dining room. Food is
imaginative (traditional and
international menu). Book for
meals eves and Sun lunchtime.
🏰 Q ☕ ❀ ◖ ▶ ⊕ & ♣ P

Illston on the Hill

Fox & Goose

Main Street ☎ (0116) 2596340
12–2, 7–11; 12–2, 7–10.30 Sun
**Everards Beacon, Tiger, Old
Original, Daredevil; guest
beer** H
Basic, two-roomed country
local, totally unspoilt, friendly
and relaxed. Local mementoes
include three CAMRA awards
collected over the years. Well
worth finding. The guest beer
is supplied by Everards.
🏰 Q ❀

Kegworth

Britannia Inn

37 London Road (A6)
☎ (01509) 672212
11–3, 6–11
**Hardys & Hansons Best
Bitter** H
Typical roadside inn on the
edge of the village.
❀ ◖ ▶ & ▲ ♣ P

Red Lion

High Street ☎ (01509) 672466
11–3, 5–11
**Draught Bass; M&B Mild;
Marston's Pedigree; S&N
Theakston Best Bitter;
Whitbread Boddingtons
Bitter; guest beer** H
Three-roomed thriving village
local offering good value for
the area. Private room for hire.
HQ of various village societies.
Near Donington race track and
East Midlands airport. Book
camping in advance. Children
welcome till 8.30pm.
🏰 Q ☕ ❀ ◖ & ▲ ♣ P

300-year-old inn, warm and
comfortable: basically one bar
sectioned for regulars and
diners. Excellent range of
guest beers with six always
available. Good home-cooked
food. Interesting aviary in the
garden; skittle alley.
🏰 Q ☕ ❀ ◖ ▶ & ♣ P

Earl Shilton

Red Lion

High Street (A47)
☎ (01455) 840829
11–2.30 (3 Sat), 5.30 (6 Sat)–11
Draught Bass; M&B Mild H
Basic beer drinkers' pub which
still has three separate rooms,
with one central bar. No food
at all. ❀ ⊕ P

Leicestershire

Kibworth Beauchamp

Coach & Horses
2 Leicester Road (A6)
☎ (0116) 2792247
11.30–2.30, 5–11; 11–11 Sat
Ansells Bitter; Mild; Draught Bass; Tetley Bitter Ⓗ
Warm, cosy old coaching inn on the main A6, with coin-filled beams and horse brasses. Popular with locals and passing custom. Traditional home-cooked food (no meals Sun eve). 🍴 ◖ ▶ P

Kirby Muxloe

Royal Oak
Main Street ☎ (0116) 2393166
11–2.30, 6–11
Adnams Bitter; Everards Mild, Beacon, Tiger, Old Original; guest beers Ⓗ
Pub where a modern exterior conceals a comfortable, traditionally-styled lounge and a restaurant, popular for business lunches. Basically a locals' pub and formerly called the Spanish Blade. The guest beer is from Everards Old English Ale Club. ✿ ◖ ▶ P

Langham

Black Horse
12 Church Street
☎ (01572) 722954
11–11
Draught Bass; Marston's Pedigree; Tetley Bitter Ⓗ
Food-oriented pub (meals all day Sun), with a large lounge split between diners and drinkers. Attractive garden.
✿ ◖ ▶ & ♠ ⬥ P ✗

Leicester

Black Horse
1 Foxton Street, Braunstone Gate ☎ (0116) 2540030
12–2.30 (3 Thu–Sat), 5.30 (6 Sat)–11
Everards Beacon, Tiger, Old Original; Ridleys IPA; guest beers Ⓗ
120-year-old drinkers' pub, close to the city centre and popular with students. Friendly atmosphere, untouched by refurbishment. The guest beer comes from Everards Old English Ale Club. ✿ ♣

Bowlturners Arms
156 Belgrave Gate
☎ (0116) 2532081
12–3 (4 Fri; 11–4 Sat), 6–11
Greenalls Shipstone's Mild, Shipstone's Bitter Ⓗ
Basic, two-roomed, city-centre, beer-drinkers' pub; small but popular with regulars.

Clarendon
West Avenue, Clarendon Park (500 yds from A6)
☎ (0116) 2707530
11.30–11
Draught Bass; M&B Mild; guest beer Ⓗ
Pleasant, two-roomed corner pub in a terraced residential area. Popular with students in the eve. No food.

Fuzzock & Firkin
203 Welford Road (A50)
☎ (0116) 2708141
11.30–2.30, 5–11; 11–11 Fri & Sat
Firkin Dogbolter; Tetley Bitter; guest beer Ⓗ
Formerly the Stork's Head, now fully refurbished, with beer supplied by the Phantom & Firkin in Loughborough. Basic wooden floor and furniture; occasional live music. Popular with the young in the eve, but for all ages during the day. Eve meals till 7pm. A house bitter is also on sale. ✿ ◖ ▶ & P

Hat & Beaver
60 Highcross Street (near Shires shopping mall)
☎ (0116) 2622157
11–3, 6–11
Hardys & Hansons Best Mild, Best Bitter, Kimberley Classic Ⓔ
Basic, two-roomed locals' pub, formerly a Bass house. Relaxed atmosphere; TV in the bar. Well-filled cobs are usually available. ✿ ⊞ ♣

Northbridge Tavern
1 Frog Island (A50)
☎ (0116) 2512508
11–11
Hoskins & Oldfield HOB Bitter; Marston's Pedigree; Tetley Bitter; Whitbread Boddingtons Bitter; guest beers Ⓗ
Former Leicester Brewing & Maltings house, the city's only canalside pub. Pleasant decor with wood-panelled walls. Busy at lunchtimes with meals, but food is served all day. Usually two guest beers. Function room. ⛵ ◖ ♣ P

Rainbow & Dove
185 Charles Street
☎ (0116) 2555916
11.30–3, 5.30–11; 11.30–11 Fri & Sat
Banks's Mild, Bitter; Camerons Strongarm; Marston's Pedigree; guest beers Ⓗ
One-roomed, town-centre beer drinkers' pub where a map of England made from brass shive holders adorns the end wall. Formerly an Ansells pub, then Hoskins, until 1992. Opposite the main police station. ✿ ◖ ⇌ (London Rd)

Salmon
19 Butts Close Lane
☎ (0116) 2532301
11–11
Banks's Mild, Bitter Ⓔ
Small pub, fully refurbished in typical Banks's style: one U-shaped room serving a varied clientele. Close to St Margaret's bus station and the Shires shopping centre. ✿ ◖

Tudor
100 Tudor Road
☎ (0116) 2620087
11–2.30 (3 Sat), 6–11
Everards Mild, Beacon, Tiger, Old Original Ⓗ
Corner pub in a terraced area, with a Victorian exterior. It still has two rooms, as well as a games room upstairs. ✿ ♣

Victoria Jubilee
112 Leire Street (off Melton road, A46) ☎ (0116) 2663599
11–2.30 (3.30 Sat), 6–11
Marston's Bitter, Pedigree Ⓗ
Friendly, two-roomed local in a terraced area. Originally called the Full Moon, until Queen Victoria's jubilee in 1887. ✿ ⊞ ♣

Wilkie's
29 Market Street
☎ (0116) 2556877
12–11; closed Sun
Whitbread Boddingtons Bitter; guest beers Ⓗ
Lively German-styled bar popular with younger drinkers. Large selection of imported bottled beers and continental food. Access also from Pocklingtons Walk. ◖ ⌂

Littlethorpe

Plough
Station Road ☎ (0116) 2862383
11–2.30 (3 Sat), 6–11
Everards Mild, Beacon, Tiger, Old Original; guest beers Ⓗ
Friendly, thatched village local with an unspoilt, cosy interior. Long alley skittles by arrangement. Guest beers from Everards Club.
✿ ◖ ▶ ⇌ (Narborough) ♣

Loughborough

Beacon
Beacon Road (off Epinal Way, ring road) ☎ (01509) 214360
12–3, 6.30–11
Home Mild, Bitter; S&N Theakston XB; guest beer Ⓗ
1960s local, a mile from the town centre. The large lounge provides a meeting place for local clubs and societies; pool, darts and pinball in the bar; skittle alley downstairs. Live entertainment at weekends.
✿ ⊞ ♣ P

Gate Inn

99 Meadow Lane
☎ (01509) 263779
11.30–2.30 (3 Fri & Sat), 6–11
Banks's Mild; Marston's Pedigree H
Small, three-roomed, traditional local. Barbecues in the garden in summer. Eve meals by prior arrangement.
🏠 ❀ ◗ ≒ ♣ P

Greyhound

69 Nottingham Road
☎ (01509) 216080
12–2, 5.30–11; 11–11 Fri & Sat
Marston's Bitter, Pedigree H
Former coaching inn, now a lively pub, popular at night for pool and darts. The function room was formerly a pavilion for one of the largest sports grounds in Europe, and is now a meeting room for live music groups. Marston's Head Brewer's Choice is also sold.
❀ 🛏 ≒ ♣ P

Royal Oak

70 Leicester Road
☎ (01509) 263860
11–3, 7–11
Burtonwood Mild, Bitter, Forshaw's, Top Hat H
Large, two-roomed pub on the main road. Collection of naval artefacts in the lounge; basic bar. Very welcoming atmosphere and a genial host.
🏠 ❀ ♣ P

Swan in the Rushes

21 The Rushes (A6)
☎ (01509) 217014
11–2.30 (3.30 Sat), 5 (6.30 Sat)–11
Archers Golden; Marston's Pedigree; Whitbread Boddingtons Bitter; guest beers H
Popular town pub catering for students, locals and business people alike. Good range of ever-changing guest beers and real cider. Food is reasonably priced and imaginative. Live music during the week.
🏠 Q ◗ ◗ 🍺 ♿ ↺ P

Tap & Mallet

36 Nottingham Road
☎ (01509) 210028
12–2, 5.30–11; 11–11 Fri & Sat
Bateman Mild; S&N Theakston Best Bitter, XB; Taylor Landlord; guest beers H
Recently refurbished, ex-S&N pub, now a popular free house. Large garden to the rear, with children's play equipment and a pets corner.
🏠 ❀ 🛏 ≒ ♣ ↺

Windmill Inn

Sparrow Hill ☎ (01509) 264071
11–2.30 (3 Sat), 5–11
Banks's Mild; Marston's Bitter, Pedigree H
Three-roomed pub near the town centre which has retained its character due to sympathetic refurbishment. Spanish food is a speciality in this, the oldest pub in town (eve meals if booked). Marston's Head Brewer's Choice is regularly available.
🏠 ❀ ◗ ▶ ≒ ♣ P ✕

Manton

Horse & Jockey

2 St Mary's Road
☎ (01572) 851335
11–2.30, 7–11
Mansfield Riding Bitter, Old Baily H
A rarity near Rutland Water: a 250-year-old, unspoilt village local. It caters for passing cycle trade with puncture repair kits on sale. Pasta dishes feature.
🏠 Q 🛏 ◗ ▶ ♣

Market Harborough

Red Cow

58–59 High Street (old A6)
☎ (01858) 463637
11–3 (4 Sat), 6 (7 Sat)–11
Marston's Bitter, Pedigree H
Traditional, one-roomed beer drinkers' pub with limited food service. Popular for darts, dominoes and cribbage. ♣

Medbourne

Nevil Arms

12 Waterfall Way
☎ (0185 883) 288
12–3, 6–11
Adnams Bitter; Ruddles Best Bitter, County; guest beer H
Pub built in 1876 as a coaching inn on the village green, next to an attractive stream. A popular weekend venue for families. Unusual pub games are available by arrangement for parties.
🏠 ⛵ ❀ 🛏 ◗ ▶ ♣ P

Melton Mowbray

Boat

57 Burton Street (opp. station)
☎ (01664) 60518
12–2, 7–11
Burtonwood Bitter, Forshaw's, Top Hat H
Old-style pub with many original features, including a brass footrail. A cosy, honest boozer. 🏠 ❀ ≒ ♣

Newbold Verdon

Jubilee

Main Street ☎ (01455) 822698
11–2.30 (not Wed), 6 (5.30 Thu–Sat)–11; 12–2, 7–10.30 Sun
Banks's Mild; Marston's Bitter, Pedigree H
Friendly, two roomed village local, cosy and unspoilt.
🏠 ❀ ♣ P

Oadby

Cow & Plough

Stoughton Farm Park, Gartree Road (signed from A6)
☎ (0116) 2720852
5 (7 Sun)–9
Hoskins & Oldfield Mild, HOB Bitter; guest beer H
Old converted barn, part of the Farmworld Leisure Park during the day: an atmospheric pub adorned in breweriana with a genuine Victorian bar. Always three, changing guest beers, mainly from independent breweries.
Q ❀ ♿ ↺ P

Oakham

Wheatsheaf

2–4 Northgate
☎ (01572) 723458
11.30 (11 Sat)–2.30, 6–11
Adnams Bitter; Everards Beacon, Tiger H
17th-century, two-roomed pub near the church. No-smoking area lunchtimes only; no food Sun. 🏠 Q ❀ ◗ 🍺 ≒ ✕

White Lion Hotel

30 Melton Road
☎ (01572) 72844
11–2.30, 6–11
Draught Bass; Jennings Mild, Bitter; Ruddles Best Bitter H
Popular, split-level pub, a Grade II-listed building, reopened in 1989 after closure in 1978. Collection of ties on display. 🏠 🛏 ◗ ▶ ≒ ♣ P

Osgathorpe

Royal Oak

Main Street ☎ (01530) 222443
7–11; 12–3, 7–11 Sat
M&B Mild; Marston's Pedigree H
Friendly local in a farming community. Horse brasses add to the decor. Note: closed lunchtime Mon–Fri.
🏠 Q ⛵ ❀ 🛏 ▲ ♣ P

Plungar

Belvoir Inn

Granby Lane ☎ (01949) 60589
12–11
Draught Bass; Bateman XB; Courage Directors; S&N Theakston XB; John Smith's Bitter H
Pleasant, tastefully decorated rural pub, in an isolated Vale of Belvoir village. Additional beers are sometimes available.
🏠 Q ⛵ ❀ 🛏 ◗ ▶ P

Leicestershire

Quorn

Apple Tree
2 Stoop Lane ☎ (01509) 412296
12–2 (11.30–3 Sat), 7–11
Draught Bass; M&B Mild H
Traditional locals' pub with
two rooms, both small and
with their own separate
entrances. Can be very busy.
🏠 ❀ 🍴 ♣ P

Blacksmith's Arms
29 Meeting Street
☎ (01509) 412751
12–2, 5.30–11
Marston's Pedigree H
Old, beamed pub with a tiny
lounge, a comfortable bar and
a well-appointed rear room for
families. The Great Central
Railway passes through
Quorn; the station is a mile
away. 🏠 Q ❦ ❀ 🍴 ♣ P

Ratby

Plough Inn
6 Burroughs Road
☎ (0116) 2392103
11.30–3, 5.45 (6 Sat)–11
**Banks's Mild; Marston's
Bitter, Pedigree** H
Large, recently refurbished
pub, still a regulars' haunt but
popular with diners.
🏠 ❦ ❀ ◖ ▶ ♣ P

Sewstern

Blue Dog Inn
Main Street ☎ (01476) 860097
12.30 (12 Sat)–3, 6–11
**Whitbread Boddingtons
Bitter, Castle Eden Ale,
Flowers Original; guest beers**
(weekends) H
Built in the 1640s, a friendly
pub near the Viking Way and
Isaac Newton's birthplace
(Woolsthorpe Manor). The
pub was used as a hospital in
Cromwell's time.
🏠 Q ❀ ◖ ▶ ♣ P

Shepshed

Lifeguardsman
55 Brook Street
☎ (01509) 503882
12–3, 7.30–11; 11–11 Sat
**Banks's Mild; Marston's
Pedigree** H
Traditional, two-roomed pub.
♣ P

Richmond Arms
Forest Street ☎ (01509) 503309
12–2.30, 7–11
**Draught Bass; M&B Mild;
guest beer** H
Hospitable local with a
sporting emphasis. Recent
improvements have not
altered the character. ❀ ♿ ♣

Stapleton

Nag's Head
Main Street ☎ (01455) 845056
11–2.30 (11.30–3 Sat), 5.30–11
Marston's Bitter, Pedigree H
Typical country pub, popular
with both regulars and passing
trade. Lunches Mon–Sat; eve
meals Wed–Sat. ❀ ◖ ▶ P

Stoney Stanton

Francis Arms
Huncote Road
☎ (01455) 272034
11–2, 5.30–11
**Banks's Mild; Marston's
Bitter, Pedigree** H
Basic, village beer drinkers'
pub with a collection of rifles
on the ceiling. Two separate
rooms. No food. 🏠 🍴 ♣

Thornton

Bricklayer's Arms
Main Street ☎ (01530) 230808
12–3, 7 (6 summer)–11
**Everards Mild, Beacon, Tiger,
Old Original, Daredevil;
guest beers** H
Old, traditional village local,
part of which dates from the
16th century: a basic stone
floor bar area and a cosy
lounge, overlooking trout
fisheries. Unspoilt and worth
finding. 🏠 Q ❦ ◖ ▶ P

Thrussington

Blue Lion
5 Rearsby Road
☎ (01664) 424266
12–3, 6–11
Marston's Bitter, Pedigree H
Large village pub where the
landlord has historic
connections with the pub and
its previous owners, Sileby
Brewery. Welcoming
atmosphere; bizarre collection
of teapots on the shelves,
amongst agricultural artefacts.
Q ❀ ◖ ▶ ♿ ▲ ♣ P

Thurmaston

Unicorn & Star
796 Melton Road (old main
road) ☎ (0116) 2692849
11–3, 6–11
**Greenalls Shipstone's Mild,
Shipstone's Bitter** H
Basic beer drinkers' bar with
no frills and a comfortable
lounge. Known as the Top
House. 🏠 ❀ 🍴 ♣ P

Walcote

Black Horse
Main Street ☎ (01455) 552684
12–2.30 (not Mon or Tue), 7 (6.30 Fri &
Sat)–11; 12–2.30, 7–10.30 Sun

**Hook Norton Old Hooky;
Taylor Landlord; guest
beers** H
Popular free house famous for
its continental bottled beers
and Thai food. A house beer is
brewed by Judges.
🏠 Q ❦ ❀ ◖ ▶ ⊖ P

Whitwick

Three Horseshoes
11 Leicester Road
☎ (01530) 837311
11–3, 6.30–11
Draught Bass; M&B Mild H
Traditional, two-roomed pub
with a welcoming public bar.
🏠 Q ❀ 🍴 ♿ ♣

Wigston

Horse & Trumpet
Bull Head Street (A50)
☎ (0116) 2886290
11–2.30, 5 (6 Sat)–11; 12–2.30, 7–10.30
Sun
**Everards Beacon, Tiger, Old
Original; guest beers** H
Old coaching inn with a
modernised lounge bar.
Popular for business lunches,
and with younger drinkers in
the eve. Long alley and table
skittles. Guest beers from
Everards Ale Club. No food
Sat. ❀ ◖ ♿ ♣ P

Meadowbank
Kelmarsh Avenue (300 yds
from A50) ☎ (0116) 2811926
11–2.30, 6–11; 11.30–3, 5.30–11 Sat
Banks's Mild, Bitter E;
Marston's Pedigree H
Modern estate pub with a
basic bar and a comfortable
lounge. ❀ ◖ 🍴 ♿ ♣ P

Wing

Cuckoo
3 Top Street ☎ (01572) 85340
11.30–3, 6.30–11
**Draught Bass; Marston's
Pedigree; guest beers** H
Whitewashed, thatched village
local, with a friendly
atmosphere. Beer festival and
steam rally in summer.
🏠 ❀ ◖ ▲ ♣ ⊖ P

Woodhouse Eaves

Wheatsheaf
Brandhill (up hill, Leicester
side of the village)
☎ (01509) 890320
12–3 (2.30 winter), 6 (7 winter)–11
**Draught Bass; Marston's
Pedigree; Ruddles County;
Taylor Landlord; guest
beers** H
Smart country pub serving
good food in the bar and
separate restaurant. Fruit wine
is always featured. Cricket
artefacts. 🏠 ❀ 🛏 ♿ ♣ P

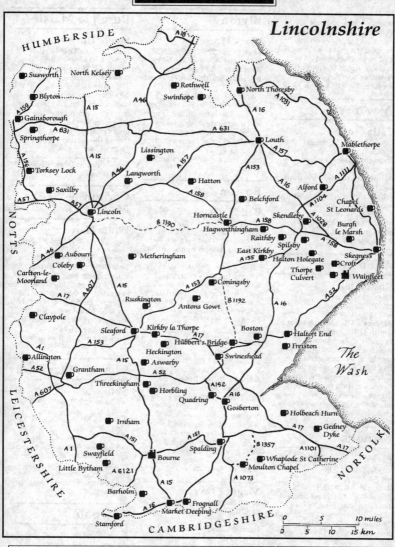

Lincolnshire

 Bateman, *Wainfleet;* **Lincolnshire Steam,** *Bourne*

Alford

Half Moon
West Street ☎ (01507) 463477
10–11 (1am Fri & Sat)
**Bass Worthington BB,
Draught Bass; Vaux Samson;
guest beers** H
A warm welcome from the
enterprising owners and
diverse patrons in this ever-
expanding pub/restaurant,
situated in a popular craft-
oriented market town that is
an ideal base for exploring the
Wolds, Tennyson country and
nearby coastal resorts.
❀ ◑ ⊟ ♣ P

Allington

Welby Arms
The Green ☎ (01400) 81361
12–2.30 (3 Sat), 5.30 (6.30 Sat)–11
**Draught Bass; Greene King
Abbot; Oak Wobbly Bob;
John Smith's Bitter; Taylor
Landlord; guest beers** H
A perfect traditional village
inn, featuring a separate
dining area (including a
no-smoking room), but
retaining a genuine
commitment to real ale.
Different guest beers are
available each week. Well
worth seeking out.
🏨 Q ❀ ◑ & P

Antons Gowt

Oak Tree Inn
Frith Bank (left at Cowbridge
off B1183) ☎ (01205) 360369
11–3, 7 (6.30 Sat)–11
**Bateman XB; Marston's
Pedigree; Tetley Bitter** H

177

Lincolnshire

Mainly food-oriented pub situated close to the River Witham. The large restaurant offers an extensive menu, including a good choice of fish and vegetarian meals. The caravan site at the rear offers space for tourers, and caravans for hire. ⚲ ❀ ◖ ⅃ ♿ ▲ ♣ P

Aswarby

Tally Ho
On A15 ☎ (01529) 5205
12–3, 6–11
Draught Bass; Bateman XB; guest beers H
Attractive roadside inn built in local stone, part of a local estate: a meeting place for the local hunt and the farming fraternity, with a welcoming atmosphere. A long-standing entry in this guide.
🛏 ❀ 🚪 ◖ ▶ P

Aubourn

Royal Oak
Royal Oak Lane
☎ (01522) 788291
12–2.30, 7–11; 12–2.30, 7–10.30 Sun
Bateman XB, XXXB; Samuel Smith OBB; guest beers H
Friendly village local, well worth seeking out (watch out for the one-way system). The mock Tudor beams in the lounge are adorned with horse brasses and there's also an impressive collection of pump clips. Always two guest beers available. 🛏 ❀ ◖ ▶ ♣ P

Barholm

Five Horseshoes
☎ (01778) 560238
6 (5 Fri)–11; 12–2.30, 6–11 Sat
Bateman XB, XXXB; S&N Theakston XB; guest beers H
This fine, stone-built pub draws in customers because of its quiet hamlet setting and consistent beers. Guest beers mainly at weekends.
🛏 ⚲ ❀ P

Belchford

Blue Bell
Main Street ☎ (01507) 533602
11–3, 7–11
Ind Coope Burton Ale; guest beers H
Situated in the heart of the Wolds, on the Viking Way, a pub where walkers are welcome. Amazing array of old farm implements. Always two guest beers. A worthy member of the Ind Coope Cellarmanship Guild.
🛏 Q ❀ ◖ ▶ ▲ ♣ P

Blyton

Black Horse
High Street ☎ (01427) 628277
11.45–3 (not Mon in winter), 5–11
Bass Special, Worthington BB; John Smith's Bitter; guest beer H
Cosy village local on the main Gainsborough to Scunthorpe road: a small bar-cum-lounge and a separate dining room (families made welcome). Small garden at the rear with a children's play area. Two guest beers may be available in summer. 🛏 ❀ ◖ ▶ ♣ P

Boston

Ball House
Wainfleet Road (A52, 1 mile from Boston) ☎ (01205) 364478
11–3, 6.30–11; 11–11 Sat & summer
Draught Bass; Bateman Mild, XB H
Mock Tudor pub, with a large, roaring fire in winter, which always affords a welcome. The home-cooked food (with daily specials) is popular and has a deserved reputation.
🛏 ❀ ◖ ▶ ♿ ▲ ♣ P

Eagle
144 West Street
☎ (01205) 361116
11–3, 6 (5 Thu & Fri)–11; 11–11 Sat
Adnams Bitter, Broadside; Marston's Pedigree; Taylor Landlord; guest beers H
Busy town pub, near the rail and bus stations, with a cosmopolitan clientele. Live music some weekends. A regular meeting place for the local folk club. A guest beer is often sold at a promotional price. 🛏 ❀ ◖ ⚲ ♣ ☺

Magnet Tavern
South Square
☎ (01205) 369186
11–3, 6–11; 11–11 Sat
Draught Bass; Stones Best Bitter; Taylor Landlord; guest beers H
Comfortable, riverside pub close to Blackfriars Theatre and Arts Centre and the Guildhall.
🛏 🚪 ◖ ▶ 🍴 ⚲ ♣

Ship Tavern
Custom House Lane
☎ (01205) 358156
11–3, 6–11
Draught Bass; Bateman XB; Whitbread Boddingtons Bitter H
Tucked away behind the former customs house, this ancient town pub has been tastefully refurbished and re-opened after years in the wilderness. ◖ ♣

Burgh le Marsh

Fleece Inn
Market Place ☎ (01754) 810215
10.30–2.30 (3 summer), 6–11
Hardys & Hansons Best Bitter E
The impressive frontage of this 400-year-old coaching inn commands a central position in this former market town, which, in Roman times, guarded the seacoast. Park free in the market place.
Q ⚲ ❀ 🚪 ◖ ▶ ▲

Try also: **Red Lion**, Storeys Lane (Free)

Carlton-le-Moorland

White Hart
High Street ☎ (01522) 788863
11–3, 7–11
Courage Directors; Ruddles Best Bitter; John Smith's Bitter; guest beer H
Lively, old pub, tastefully extended, in the centre of the village. The door is round the back. Note the collection of brewery symbols/coats of arms by the kitchen door. Book to camp in the garden.
🛏 ❀ ◖ ▶ ♿ ▲ ♣

Chapel St Leonards

Ship
Sea Lane ☎ (01754) 72975
11–3, 7–11
Bateman Mild (summer), XB, Valiant H
Situated on the outskirts of the village, this pub features open fires, brassware and a large garden and play area. Coarse fishing available. Keen supporters of Guide Dogs for the Blind. 🛏 ❀ ▲ ♣ P

Claypole

Five Bells
Main Street ☎ (01636) 626561
12–3, 7–11
Bateman XB; Wards Best Bitter; guest beers H
Plainly refurbished village inn with an excellent atmosphere. Good value, home-cooked food (not served Tue). Up to four guest beers at any time.
🛏 Q ❀ 🚪 ◖ ▶ ♿ ♣ P

Woolpack
Main Street ☎ (01636) 626274
12–11
Marston's Bitter, Pedigree; guest beers H
Cosy, low-ceilinged local with nooks and crannies. At least two guest beers.
🛏 Q ❀ ◖ ▶ ♣ P

Coleby

Tempest
Hill Rise ☎ (01522) 810287
11.30–2.30, 6.30–11
**Bateman XB; Marston's
Pedigree; Webster's Yorkshire
Bitter** H; guest beer
Popular village local with fine
country views and excellent
food. The scene of many crazy
stunts and pranks. Growing
collection of pump clips from
the frequent guest beers.
✿ ◖ ▶ & ♣ P

Coningsby

Ratty's
High Street ☎ (01526) 344609
12–3, 7–11
**Courage Directors; Whitbread
Boddingtons Bitter; guest
beers** H
On the banks of the River
Bain, overlooked by the
church with its one-handed
clock and the grave of the
legendary Tom Thumb, this
former restaurant is ideally
situated for a visit to the RAF
Battle of Britain Memorial
Flight. Q ✿ ◖ ▶ & ▲ P

Try also: Leagate Inn, Leagate
Rd (Free)

Croft

Old Chequers Inn
Lymn Bank OS503611
☎ (01754) 880320
12–3, 7–11
Bateman Mild, XB H
Small, rural watering-hole
reputed to be the oldest pub in
Lincolnshire; well off the
beaten track. Sit by the roaring
open fire in the snug bar, or sit
outside and watch the world
idle by. No food Mon.
🏚 Q ✿ ◖ ▶ & ♣ P

East Kirkby

Red Lion
☎ (01790) 763406
11–3, 7–11
**Bateman XB; John Smith's
Bitter; guest beers** H
An extensive breweriana
collection adorns every
available space within and
without this popular rural pub
which maintains links with
aircrews once stationed at the
nearby wartime airfield (now
an impressive air museum).
🏚 Q ⋟ ✿ ◖ ▶ & ▲ ♣ P

Freiston

King's Head
Church Road
☎ (01205) 760368
11–2.30, 7–11; 11–11 Sat
Bateman Mild, XB, Valiant H

15th-century, traditional
country pub, with a separate
'Lancaster' restaurant. A
frequent winner of Bateman's
award for floral displays.
Featured in *The Beer Hunter* TV
series. 🏚 Q ✿ ◖ ▶ ♣ P

Frognall

Goat
155 Spalding Road
☎ (01778) 347629
11–2.30, 6–11
**Adnams Bitter; Draught Bass;
Morland Old Speckled
Hen** H; guest beers G
Set back from the main road,
this well-run establishment
boasts guest beers from the
smaller independents (three in
winter, augmented by gravity
dispense beers straight from
the cellar in summer).
🏚 ⋟ ✿ ◖ ▶ ▲ P

Gainsborough

Plough
37 Church Street
☎ (01427) 613696
11–3, 7–11
**Bass Mild, Worthington BB;
Stones Best Bitter** H
Basic town-centre pub with a
loyal following, a true local. It
stays open late on market day
lunchtimes (Tue and Sat).
🏚 ✿ ⇌ ♣ P

Gedney Dyke

Chequers
☎ (01406) 362666
11–3, 7–11
**Adnams Bitter; Draught Bass;
Bateman XXXB; Greene King
Abbot; Morland Old
Speckled Hen** H
Comfortable country pub with
an adjoining restaurant, well
worth seeking out, especially if
hungry as well as thirsty: an
attractive building in a quiet
village setting, dating back to
circa 1795. 🏚 ✿ ◖ ▶ ♣ P

Gosberton

Bell
High Street ☎ (01775) 840186
11–3, 6–11
**Ansells Bitter; Ind Coope
Burton Ale; guest beers** H
Grade II-listed building dating
from 1671, with wood-
panelled interior walls and a
pleasant, friendly atmosphere.
🏚 Q ✿ 🛏 ◖ ▶ 🍺 P

Grantham

Beehive Inn
10–11 Castlegate
☎ (01476) 67794
11.30–3, 7–11

**Adnams Broadside;
Whitbread Boddingtons
Bitter; guest beers** H
Renowned for being the only
pub in England with a living
pub sign. Friendly and
popular with young people.
✿ ◖ ⇌ ♣

Blue Bull
64 Westgate ☎ (01476) 70929
11–3 (4 Sat), 7 (6.30 Sat)–11
**Gale's Best Bitter; Marston's
Pedigree; North Yorkshire
Best Bitter; Whitbread
Boddingtons Bitter; guest
beers** H
Pub built about 1850. Both
main bar areas are clean and
comfortable; small, separate
restaurant and meeting room.
Interesting display of
Victoriana; welcoming
atmosphere. Good home-
cooked food, wide range of
guest beers and an occasional
cider. Q ◖ ▶ ⇌ ♣ ⌂ P

Chequers Inn
25 Market Place
☎ (01476) 76383
5–11; 12–3, 5–11 Thu; 12–11 Fri; 11–4,
7–11 Sat
**S&N Theakston Best Bitter,
XB, Old Peculier; Younger
IPA, No. 3; Young's Special;
guest beers** H
Local CAMRA *Pub of the Year*
1993, serving at least six guest
beers per week. Children
allowed in the back room.
◖ ⇌ ♣

Odd House
4 Fletcher Street
☎ (01476) 65293
11–11
**Bateman XXXB; Courage
Directors; Ruddles Best
Bitter; John Smith's Bitter;
guest beers** (occasional) H
There's always a welcome in
this terrace row pub, popular
with all ages and close to the
station. 🏚 Q ✿ ◖ ⇌ ♣

White Lion
53 Bridge End Road
☎ (01476) 62084
11–11
**Courage Directors; Everards
Daredevil; John Smith's
Bitter; guest beer** H
Popular town pub which
caters for all ages. Games-
oriented bar; quiet lounge.
🏚 Q ✿ 🛏 ◖ 🍺 & ⇌

Try also: Manners Arms,
London Rd (Everards)

Hagworthingham

George & Dragon
Main Road ☎ (01507) 588255
11.30–2.30, 7–11 (closed Mon in
winter)
**Courage Directors; John
Smith's Bitter; guest beers** H

Lincolnshire

Large, comfortable village pub in the middle of Tennyson country, on the Twenty Ramblers Trail. Bar food not available Mon.
⌘ ⍥ ◖ ▷ & ♿ ♣ P

Haltoft End

Castle Inn
Wainfleet Road
☎ (01205) 760393
11–3, 7–11
Bateman Mild, XB, Valiant H
Typical, friendly local with a balanced mix of clientele. A keen darts and domino pub, also holding occasional clay pigeon shoots in aid of local charities. Excellent adventure playground for children. Reputedly haunted.
⌘ ⍥ ⌂ ◖ ♣ P

Halton Holegate

Bell
Firsby Road ☎ (01790) 53242
11–3, 7–11
Draught Bass; Bateman XB; Mansfield Riding Bitter; guest beers (occasional) H
Connections with the past include a pub sign depicting a Lancaster bomber from a nearby wartime airfield, and a railway sleeper as a mantlepiece, within this unpretentious, hospitable inn.
⌘ Q ⍥ ◖ ▷ ♣ P

Hatton

Midge Inn
Main Road ☎ (01507) 578348
11–3, 7–11
Draught Bass; Stones Best Bitter; guest beers H
Pleasant pub on the Lincoln to Skegness road, offering good value home-cooked food in a pleasant atmosphere. No eve meals winter Mon.
⌘ Q ⍩ ⍥ ◖ ▷ ♣ P

Heckington

Nag's Head
High Street ☎ (01529) 60218
11–3, 5–11
Vaux Double Maxim; Wards Best Bitter H
17th-century, oak-beamed pub with a friendly welcome. The emphasis is on catering, with many home-made dishes.
Q ⍥ ⌂ ◖ ▷ & ♿ ⇌ ♣ P

Try also: Royal Oak, Boston Rd (Tetley)

Holbeach Hurn

Rose & Crown
Marsh Road ☎ (01406) 26085
11–11
Elgood's Cambridge Bitter H

Friendly rural pub with a mixed clientele. Set in six acres and ideal for picnics and barbecues (barbecues provided, bring your own food). ⍥ ◖ ▷ ♿ P

Horbling

Plough
Spring Lane ☎ (01529) 240263
11–2.30, 5.30–11
Whitbread Boddingtons Bitter, Castle Eden Ale; guest beer H
Grade I-listed, multi-roomed, traditional pub owned by the parish. The small snug holds only eight persons. A different guest beer each week.
⌘ Q ⍩ ⍥ ◖ ▷ ♣ P

Horncastle

King's Head (Thatch)
Bullring ☎ (01507) 523360
11–3 (4 Sat), 7–11
Bateman Mild, XB, Valiant, Salem Porter; John Smith's Bitter H
Cosy, diminutive pub which, with its award-winning outdoor floral display, affords a warm welcome. Known locally as the Thatch and once popular with petty thieves during the town's fairs and market-days because of the ease of escape through the back door. ⌘ Q ◖ ▷

Red Lion
1 Bullring ☎ (01507) 523338
11–3, 7–11
Greenalls Shipstone's Mild, Bitter; Tetley Bitter H
Pleasant pub with a friendly welcome: a regular meeting place for local clubs and societies. It also supports a flourishing theatre in the converted stables.
⌘ Q ⍩ ⌂ ◖ & ♣ P

Hubbert's Bridge

Wheatsheaf
Station Road ☎ (01205) 290347
11–3, 6–11
Vaux Samson; Wards Thorne Best Bitter H
Family-run, bankside pub, ideal for fishing and near good golfing facilities. Excellent quality food is served in both the bar and restaurant.
⌘ ⍥ ⌂ ◖ ▷ ♿ ⇌ ♣ P

Irnham

Griffin Inn
Bulby Road (N off A151 via Corby Glen) ☎ (01476) 550201
12–2.30 (not Mon–Fri in winter; 12–3 Sat), 7–11
S&N Theakston Old Peculier; Younger IPA; guest beers H

400-year-old, stone pub in an even older village. The public bar is dominated by a pool table and young people; the quiet and comfortable, split-level lounge features a through-the-wall real fire. Good value food. Summer beer festival in the garden.
⌘ Q ⍥ ⌂ ◖ ▷ ♣ P

Kirkby la Thorpe

Queen's Head
Church Street
☎ (01529) 305743
11.30–3, 6.30–11
Draught Bass E
Large pub just off the Sleaford by-pass. Food oriented, with a good cold carvery. ⍥ ◖ ▷

Langworth

New Station
Main Road ☎ (01522) 750475
11–3, 7–11
Courage Directors; John Smith's Bitter H
Large, modern roadside pub, much extended. The landlord's fish and chips are known far and wide.
⌘ ⍥ ◖ ▷ ⌖ & ♣ P

Lincoln

Dog & Bone
10 John Street
☎ (01522) 522403
12–3, 7–11
Draught Bass; Bateman XB, Valiant, XXXB, Salem Porter; guest beer H
Friendly, one-roomed pub, once known as the Gay Dog, boasting an array of old relics and antiques with a touch of humour. Popular with students. Occasional pub fun nights and Sun quiz nights. Always at least one guest beer.
⌘ ⍥ & ⇌ ♣ P

Golden Eagle
21 High Street
☎ (01522) 521058
11–3, 5.30–11; 11–11 Sat
Adnams Mild, Extra; Bateman XB; Gale's Best Bitter; guest beers H
Traditional, friendly pub at the southern end of the high street; the second pub in Lincoln to be run by the Small Beer agency. The quiet front bar is decorated with old Lincoln memorabilia. Changing selection of guest beers. Q ⍩ ⍥ ◖ ⌖ ♣ ⌣ P

Jolly Brewer
26 Broadgate ☎ (01522) 528583
11–11
Draught Bass; Everards Tiger; S&N Theakston XB; Younger Scotch, No. 3; guest beers H

Very popular, city-centre pub attracting a wide range of customers. Previously known as the Unity.
🏠 ⊛ ◑ ⅙ ≥ ♣ ⚲ P

Peacock Inn
23 Wragby Road
☎ (01522) 524703
11.30–2.30, 5–11; 11–11 Fri & Sat
Hardys & Hansons Best Mild, Best Bitter, Kimberley Classic H
Friendly local within easy walking distance of the tourist area and city centre. No food Sun. 🏠 ⊛ ◑ ♣ P

Portland Arms
50 Portland Street
☎ (01522) 513912
11–11
Draught Bass; Courage Directors; John Smith's Bitter, Magnet; Wilson's Mild; guest beers H
Simple, clean town pub with absolutely no ties. Five guest beers from near, far and wide served in a lively tap room (with a pool table and the usual pub games), and a cosy, quiet best room. Friendly atmosphere. ⊛ ⊟ ≥ ♣ P

Queen in the West
12–14 Moor Street
☎ (01522) 526169
11.30–3, 5.30–11; 11.30–11 Fri & Sat
Bateman XB; S&N Theakston Old Peculier; John Smith's Bitter; Taylor Landlord; Wells Bombardier; guest beers H
Popular back-street local, which has been in this guide for many years. Additional beers are regularly available. Two contrasting drinking areas complement each other and are busy lunchtimes with local factory workers. ◑

Sippers
26 Melville Street
☎ (01522) 527612
11–3, 5 (4 Fri, 7 Sat)–11; 7–10.30 Sun, closed Sun lunch
Courage Directors; Marston's Pedigree; Ruddles County; Shepherd Neame Spitfire; John Smith's Bitter; Wilson's Mild; guest beers H
Popular and comfortable, street-corner pub near the station, with a large display of seafaring memorabilia. Always a welcome and a wide range of guest beers. ◑ ▶ ≥ ♣

Small Beer Off-Licence
91 Newland Street West, just off A57 ☎ (01522) 528628
10.30–10.30
Bateman XXXB; Everards Beacon; Taylor Landlord; guest beer H
Well-established off-licence with a wide range of draught

guest beers as well as foreign and British bottled beers. ⚲

Strugglers
83 Westgate ☎ (01522) 524702
11–3, 5.30–11; 11–11 Fri & Sat
Bass Worthington BB, Draught Bass H
Busy, basic and bursting with people, this little gem has graced the *Guide* for over 20 years. The mild has been replaced with Worthington but there is talk of a guest beer to compensate. Q ⊛ ♣

Tap & Spile
21 Hungate ☎ (01522) 534015
11–11
Draught Bass; Cropton King Billy; Marston's Pedigree; Mitchell's ESB; Nethergate Bitter; Ruddles Best Bitter; guest beers H
Pleasantly renovated addition to the Tap & Spile chain, well situated between uphill and downhill Lincoln. Warm welcome; superb range of guest beers. Eve meals on request. Q ◑ ⅙ ≥ ♣ ⚲ ✂

Victoria
6 Union Road (by west gate of castle) ☎ (01522) 536048
11–11
Adnams Extra; Bateman XB; Everards Old Original; Taylor Landlord; guest beers H
The city's most celebrated on-going beer exhibition. The five guest beers include a mild, more are added on special feature nights and there are June and Xmas mini-festivals. Good home-cooking at lunchtime. The upstairs restaurant is used for Sun lunches. Q ⊛ ◑ ♣ ⚲

Lissington

White Hart
☎ (01673) 885205
11–2.30 (not Mon), 7–11; 12–2.30, 7–10.30 Sun
Bass Worthington BB, Draught Bass H
Cosy village inn offering excellent food and occasional speciality eves. A centre for sports in and out of the pub. Guest Scotch policy.
🏠 Q ⊛ ◑ ▶ ⊟ ⅙ ♣ P

Little Bytham

Willoughby Arms
Station Road (B1176)
☎ (01780) 410276
12–3 (not Mon-Fri), 6–11
Ruddles County; guest beers H
Cosy and welcoming village pub with splendid views over rolling fields from the back room bar. Two guest beers. Good home-cooking every eve. 🏠 Q ⊛ ▶ ⅙ ♣ P

Louth

Masons Arms
Cornmarket ☎ (01507) 609525
11–11 (supper licence)
Draught Bass; Bateman Mild, XB, Valiant, XXXB; Salem Porter; Marston's Pedigree H
Old posting or coaching inn from the 18th century, splendidly restored and providing all the facilities of a small country hotel. Excellent, home-made fare through the day. Q ⊛ ⇦ ◑ ♣ ♣

Olde Whyte Swanne
45 Eastgate ☎ (01507) 601312
11–3, 7–11; 11–11 Sat
Bass Worthington BB, Draught Bass; M&B Highgate Dark; Stones Best Bitter H
Built in 1612, the oldest pub in Louth, with a magnificent public bar at the front and a modern lounge at the rear. The cellars are reputedly haunted. Next to a public car park (free at nights and on Sun). No food Sun. 🏠 ◑ ⊟ ♣

Woodman Inn
134 Eastgate ☎ (01507) 602100
11–3 (4 Fri), 7–11; 11–11 Sat
John Smith's Bitter; guest beers H
Comfortable, good value, one-room pub. No food weekends. 🏠 ⊛ ◑ ♣

Woolpack
14 Riverhead Road (1 mile E of centre, at riverhead of old canal) ☎ (01507) 606568
11–3 (not Mon), 7–11
Bateman Mild, XB, Valiant or XXXB; Marston's Pedigree H
Former 19th-century wool merchant's house, now a friendly local with three rooms to suit all tastes. The short walk out of town is well rewarded. 🏠 Q ⊟ ♣ P

Mablethorpe

Montalt Arms
George St ☎ (01507) 472794
11.30–3, 7–11
Draught Bass; Bateman XB; Stones Best Bitter; guest beer H
Pub named after a local medieval knight killed in a duel. The friendly, L-shaped lounge bar has photos of bygone Mablethorpe and an adjoining, well-appointed restaurant. A haven from the seafront bustle. No meals winter Mons. ⊛ ◑ ▶

Market Deeping

Vine
19 Church Street
☎ (01778) 342387
11–3, 5.30–11

Lincolnshire

Wells Eagle, Bombardier;
guest beers H
Former 1870s prep school,
now a friendly local with a
small lounge and a larger,
busy bar. The many social
nights include quizzes and
barn dances; active charity
fund-raising. Ask to see the
model train set.
🏠 Q ❀ ☕ ♣ P

Try also: Waterton Arms,
Deeping St James (Free)

Metheringham

Londesborough Arms
Middle Street
☎ (01526) 320637
11–2.30 (4 Sat), 6.30 (7 Sat)–11
Bateman XB, Valiant H
Slightly unusual-looking pub
from the outside, but a nice
example of a traditional
Bateman's village pub inside.
XXXB may also be sold.
🔥 ❀ ❄ ♣ P

Moulton Chapel

Wheatsheaf
4 Fengate ☎ (01406) 380525
11–3 (not Wed), 7–11
Draught Bass; Elgood's
Cambridge Bitter; Greene
King IPA H
Friendly, two-roomed pub in
an out-of-the-way Fenland
village. The public bar boasts a
splendid range and a
collection of 'pig-eriana'; the
lounge is built on the site of
Bradford's brewery (closed
1928). Beware—the Scrumpy
Jack handpump dispenses keg
cider. Eve meals and camping
by arrangement.
🏠 ❀ ☕ ▶ 🏠 ☖ ♣ P

North Kelsey

Royal Oak
High Street ☎ (01652) 678544
12–3, 7–11
Draught Bass; Stones Best
Bitter; Vaux Samson; Wards
Best Bitter H
Fine, old village pub with a
friendly atmosphere. The
lounge bar has two fires;
there's also a games room and
a snug. Trivia quiz Tue night;
music quiz Sat. Popular for
meals (not served Mon).
🏠 ❀ ☕ ▶ ♣ P

Try also: Queen's Head,
North Kelsey Moor (Free)

North Thoresby

New Inn
Station Road (B1201)
☎ (01472) 840270
11.30–3, 6–11; 11.30–11 Sat

Bass Mild, Draught Bass;
Stones Best Bitter; guest
beers H
Comfortable village pub,
popular with locals and with a
strong games following. At
least two beer festivals each
year. 🏠 Q ❀ ♣ P

Quadring

White Hart
7 Town Drove
☎ (01775) 821135
11–3 (not Mon), 6.45–11
Bateman Mild, XB, XXXB H
Comfortable and popular
village local with a welcoming
atmosphere, catering for all
ages. At one time, the back of
the pub was a bakery.
Challenge the pub's dog to a
beermat-flipping contest!
Wheelchair access is via the
car park. 🔥 ❀ ☕ ♣ P

Raithby

Red Lion
Main Street ☎ (01790) 53727
11–3 (not Mon–Fri), 7–11
Home Bitter; S&N Theakston
XB H
Inviting and friendly pub
situated in an attractive Wolds
village, where excellent cuisine
complements the fine
cellarmanship (intimate
restaurant: eve meals Wed–Sat
only). Freshly-made pizzas
also served. Comfortable
accommodation.
🔥 Q ❀ 🏠 ☕ ▶ ♣ P

Rothwell

Nickerson Arms
Hillrise (off A46)
☎ (01472) 371300
12–2, 5 (6 Sat)–11
Beer range varies H & G
Pub offering up to ten real
ales, plus Belgian classics
(including Liefmans Kriek and
bottled Trappist brews), and
excellent food: a formula to
suit all tastes. Converted from
a former blacksmith's and
adjoining pub, in a lovely
Wolds village.
🔥 Q ❀ ☕ ▶ 👃 P

Ruskington

Black Bull
Rectory Road
☎ (01526) 832270
11.30–2.30 (3 Fri & Sat), 6.30–11
Bateman XB H
Comfortable local in a thriving
village. Part of the bar used to
be stables. Interesting
sculptures above the front
door. Lunches served Wed–
Sun, eve meals Wed–Sat.
❀ 🏠 ☕ ▶ ☖ ❄ ♣ P

Saxilby

Ship
Bridge Street ☎ (01522) 702259
11.30–2.30 (3 Fri & Sat), 7–11
Ruddles Best Bitter; John
Smith's Bitter H
Plain pub in a pleasant village,
popular with sportsmen and
canal boaters. Reasonably
priced, simple food (eve meals
to order). Caravans allowed in
the car park overnight by prior
arrangement.
❀ ☕ ▶ 🚶 ❄ ♣ P

Skegness

Vine
Vine Road, Seacroft (1 mile S
of centre, off Drummond Rd)
☎ (01754) 763018
11–11
Draught Bass; Bateman XB,
Valiant, XXXB, Salem
Porter H
An oasis of peace and calm in
a secluded wooded setting,
away from the hurly burly of
the resort. Leafy gardens in
summer; roaring fires in
winter.
🔥 ❀ 🏠 ☕ ▶ 🚶 ☖ ♣ P

Skendleby

Blacksmith's Arms
Main Road ☎ (0175 485) 662
11–3, 6–midnight
Bateman XB, XXXB H
Pub where a cosy bar has an
open view of the cellar and the
large restaurant houses a well
dating back to 1650.
🔥 Q ❀ 🏠 ☕ ▶ ☖ ☗ P

Sleaford

Nag's Head
64 Southgate ☎ (01529) 413918
11–3, 7–11; 11–11 Fri & Sat
Draught Bass; Bateman XB,
XXXB H
Friendly, no-frills town pub
serving good value food.
🔥 ☕ ❄ ♣ P

Rose & Crown
4 Watergate ☎ (01529) 303350
11–2.30 (3 Fri & Sat), 7–11
Mansfield Riding Bitter,
Bitter, Old Baily H
Popular, town-centre local
with friendly staff and strong
pub games teams (games area
on a lower level to the bar).
Weekday lunches. Small car
park. ❀ ☕ ❄ ♣ P

Spalding

Lincolnshire Poacher
11 Double Street
☎ (01775) 766490
11–3, 5–11

S&N Theakston Best Bitter, XB, Old Peculier; guest beers H
Busy and lively pub with a pleasant riverside frontage which always serves at least four guest beers. The enterprising landlord has created a cosmopolitan atmosphere. ⌾ ⌂ ⬦ ◗ ⅃ ⩔

Olde White Horse

Churchgate
☎ (01775) 766740
11.30–3 (4 Sat), 7–11
Samuel Smith OBB, Museum H
Imposing, 14th-century, thatched building on the riverside, reputedly visited by Hereward the Wake. Recently refurbished with oak beams, a stone-flagged floor and three large fireplaces. Quiz night Mon. ⌂ Q ⌾ ◗ ◗ ♣ P

Spilsby

Nelson Butt

10 Market Street
☎ (01790) 52258
10.30–3, 7–11; 12–2, 7–10.30 Sun
Draught Bass; Bateman XB H
Basic, no-frills, small market town pub with a friendly welcome. Park in the market place. Q ♣

Springthorpe

New Inn

Hill Road ☎ (01427) 83254
11–3, 7–11
Bateman Valiant; Marston's Pedigree H
Excellent village local with a basic bar and a comfortable lounge, specialising in real food. Expect a song from your genial host! ⌂ Q ◗ ♣ P

Stamford

Dolphin

East Street (400 yds from police station, towards Ryhall)
☎ (01780) 55494
11–3, 5.30–11
Wells Eagle, Bombardier; guest beers H
18th-century building split into small rooms, a popular locals' pub featuring a unique collection of old Stamford prints. Beer festival held in July (25 beers).
Q ⌾ ⌂ ◗ ◗ ⅄ ♣ P

St Peter's Inn

St Peter's Street
☎ (01780) 63298
12–2.30, 5.30–11; 11–11 Fri & Sat
Marston's Bitter, Pedigree; guest beers H / G

Local CAMRA 1993 *Pub of the Year*. Head for the downstairs 'Cloisters' bar for gravity dispense guest beers or drink upstairs in the more intimate lounge bar. Eve meals served Thu–Sat, lunches Tue–Sun.
⌾ ◗ ⅃ ♣

Try also: Black Bull, Stamford Walk (Free); **White Swan**, Scotgate (Bateman)

Susworth

Jenny Wren

Main Street ☎ (01724) 783441
12–3, 6.30–11 (midnight supper licence)
John Smith's Bitter; Tetley Bitter; Webster's Yorkshire Bitter; guest beer H
Superbly appointed, 18th-century country pub, located close to the River Trent. The large ground floor drinking area has many nooks and crannies; restaurant facilities upstairs (reputation for fine food). Variety of guest beers. Wheelchair WC available.
⌂ ⌾ ⌂ ◗ ◗ ⅄ ♣ P

Swayfield

Royal Oak

High Street ☎ (01476) 550247
11–2.30, 6–11
Draught Bass; guest beers H
Excellent, old village pub with a good atmosphere, serving one regular brew and two guest beers. Value for money food. ⌂ ⌾ ⌂ ◗ ◗ ⅄ ♣ P

Swineshead

Wheatsheaf Hotel

Market Place ☎ (01205) 820349
12–2.30, 6–11; 12–11 Sat
Draught Bass; Bateman XB; Tetley Bitter H
Traditional village pub with a good selection of bar and restaurant meals. Trad jazz live on alternate Thus; strong football ties. Bar food not available Tue or Sun.
⌂ Q ⌾ ⌂ ◗ ◗ ⅃ ⅄ ♣ P

Swinhope

Click'em Inn

On B1203, 3 miles from Binbrook ☎ (01472) 398253
11–2.30 (3 Sat; not Mon), 7–11
Bateman Mild; Morland Speckled Hen; S&N Theakston XB, Old Peculier H**; guest beers**
This isolated but popular Wolds pub is a genuine free house, well worth the find. Its name derives from the click of the gate to the opposite field, into which farmers drove flocks whilst drinking at the pub. ⌂ Q ⌾ ◗ ◗ ♣ P

Thorpe Culvert

Three Tuns

Culvert Road
☎ (01754) 880495
Tetley Bitter; Vaux Samson H
250-year-old riverside pub with a large garden, handy for fishing. Regularly lit with old gas lamps to enhance the atmosphere. Steaks (36oz) and Irish cuisine served.
⌂ Q ⌾ ◗ ◗ ⅄ ⅃ ♣ P

Threekingham

Threekingham Inn

Salters Way (off A52)
☎ (01529) 240249
11–11
Bass Worthington BB, Draught Bass; Stones Best Bitter H
Welcoming, 17th-century coaching inn. Its interesting collection of handpumps includes an original swan neck pump. Recently opened dining room. ⅀ ⌾ ⌾ ◗ ⅄ ♣ P

Torksey Lock

White Swan

Newark Road
☎ (01427) 71653
11–3, 6.30–11
Bass Mild, Special, Draught Bass; Stones Best Bitter H
Pub pleasantly set close to a picturesque lock, very popular with holidaymakers from a nearby caravan site.
Q ⌾ ◗ ⅂ ⅄ ♣ P

Wainfleet

Red Lion

High Street ☎ (01754) 880301
11–3, 7–11
Bateman Mild, XB, Valiant H
A waddle of ducks round the fireplace, cats curled up on the rug and Sam, the dog, with a little help from the landlord and landlady, all help to make this a warm, welcoming pub. Campers can awake to the sight and aroma of Bateman's brewery. ⌂ ⌾ ⌾ ◗ ◗ ⅂ ⅄ ⩔ ♣ P

Whaplode St Catherine

Blue Bell

Cranesgate ☎ (01406) 540300
7–11; 12–4, 7–11 Sat
Bateman XB; Vaux Samson; guest beers H
Lively village local with an enthusiastic landlord. Built in the 17th century and in the same ownership for over 25 years. ⌂ ⌾ ⅄ ♣ P

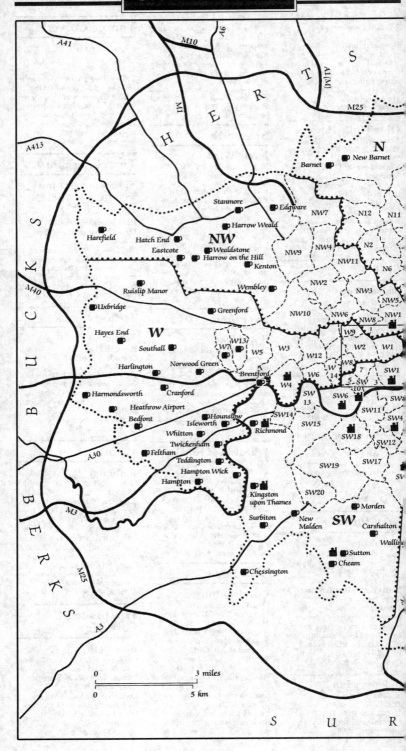

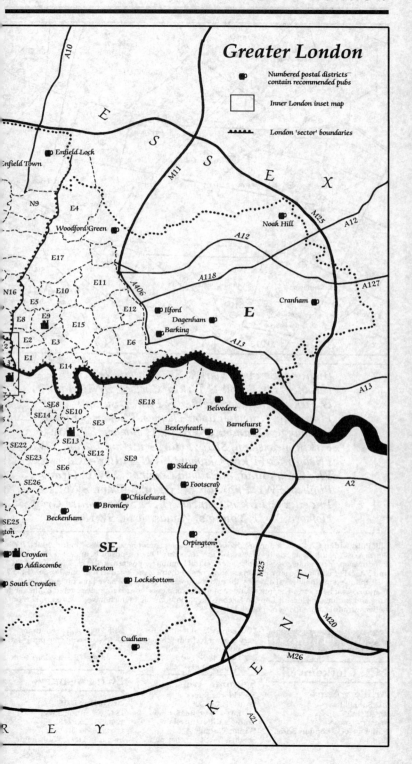

Greater London

Numbered postal districts contain recommended pubs

Inner London inset map

London 'sector' boundaries

E S S E X

A10

M11

M25

A12

Enfield Lock

Enfield Town

N9

E4

Woodford Green

E17

N16

E10

E11

E5

E8

E9

E15

E2

E3

E1

E14

A406

E12

E6

Ilford

Dagenham

Barking

A118

A12

Noak Hill

Cranham

E

A127

A13

SE8

SE14

SE10

SE3

SE18

Belvedere

Barnehurst

Bexleyheath

SE22

SE13

SE23

SE12

SE9

SE6

SE26

Sidcup

Footscray

Chislehurst

A2

A13

SE25

Beckenham

Bromley

Croydon

Addiscombe

South Croydon

Keston

Locksbottom

Orpington

SE

Cudham

K E N T

M25

M20

M26

A21

S U R R E Y

185

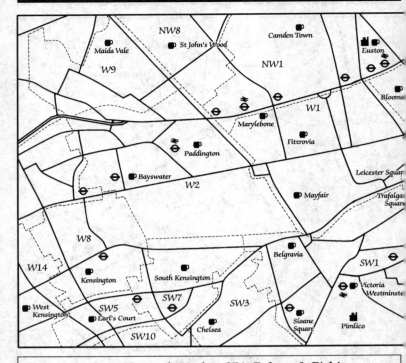

Bishops, Borough Market, SE1; **Falcon & Firkin,** Hackney, E9; **Ferret & Firkin,** Chelsea, SW10; **Fiddler & Firkin,** Croydon; **Fielder & Firkin,** Sutton; **Flamingo,** Kingston upon Thames; **Flicker & Firkin,** Richmond; **Flounder & Firkin,** Holloway, N7; **Fox & Firkin,** Lewisham, SE13; **Friar & Firkin,** Euston, NW1; **Friesian & Firkin,** Clapham, SW4; **Fuller's,** Chiswick, W4; **Greyhound,** Streatham Common, SW16; **Orange,** Pimlico, SW1; **Pharoah & Firkin,** Fulham, SW6; **Phoenix & Firkin,** Camberwell, SE5; **Yorkshire Grey,** Holborn, WC1; **Young's,** Wandsworth, SW18

NB: Pubs within Greater London are divided into seven geographical sectors: Central, East, North, North-West, South-East, South-West and West, reflecting London postal boundaries (see Greater London map on previous pages). Look under Central London for postal districts EC1 to EC4, and WC1 and WC2. For each of the surrounding sectors, postal districts are listed in numerical order (E1, E2, etc.), followed in alphabetical order by the outlying areas which do not have London postal numbers (Barking, Cranham, etc.). The Inner London map, above, shows the area roughly covered by the Circle Line and outlines regions of London (Bloomsbury, Holborn, etc.) which have featured pubs. Some regions straddle more than one postal district.

Central London

EC1: Clerkenwell

Artillery Arms
102 Bunhill Row
☎ (0171) 253 4683
11–11; 11–3, 7–11 Sat
Fuller's Hock, London Pride, ESB Ⓗ

Tiny corner local that can be very busy; a welcome change from the usual city pub.
Ⓓ ▶ ⇌ (Old Street)
⊖ (Moorgate) ♣

Sekforde Arms
34 Sekforde Street
☎ (0171) 253 3251
11–11; 12–3 Sun, closed Sun eve
Young's Bitter, Special, Winter Warmer Ⓗ
Small, attractive corner pub

with an upstairs restaurant. Diners are welcome until 4pm Sun.
Ⓠ Ⓓ ▶ ⇌ (Farringdon) ⊖ ♣

EC1: Finsbury

Sutton Arms
15 Great Sutton Street
☎ (0171) 253 2462
11–11 (4 Sat); closed Sun
Everards Tiger; Wells Eagle;

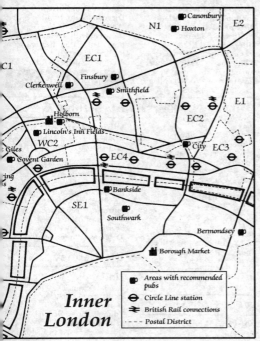

Inner London

Areas with recommended pubs
⊖ Circle Line station
⇌ British Rail connections
- - - Postal District

Whitbread Boddingtons Bitter, Flowers Original; guest beers Ⱨ
Bustling side-street pub where the beer range may vary.
◖ ⇌ (Barbican) ⊖

EC1: Holborn

Melton Mowbray
18 Holborn ☎ (0171) 405 7077
11–11; closed Sat & Sun
Fuller's Hock, Chiswick, London Pride, ESB Ⱨ
Part of the Fuller's Ale & Pie chain, this pub was converted from a shop in 1993, but looks as though it has been a pub for hundreds of years.
Q ◖ ▶ & ⇌ (Farringdon)
⊖ (Chancery Lane)

EC1: Smithfield

Bishops Finger
9–10 West Smithfield
☎ (0171) 248 2341
11–11 (3 Sat); closed Sun
Shepherd Neame Master Brew Bitter, Best Bitter, Spitfire, Porter, Bishops Finger; guest beer Ⱨ
Popular, small, single-bar pub.
◖ ⇌ (Farringdon) ⊖ ♣

EC2: City

Fleetwood
36 Wilson Street
☎ (0171) 247 2242
11–9.30 (3 Sat); closed Sun
Fuller's Hock, Chiswick, London Pride, Mr Harry, ESB Ⱨ
Modern pub within the Broadgate development. A busy, city venue with quick service from friendly staff, it is possibly the best city pub for food; free bar snacks most eves. Note: the Scrumpy Jack cider is keg.
❀ ◖ ▶ ⇌ (Liverpool St)
⊖ (Moorgate)

EC3: City

East India Arms
67 Fenchurch Street
☎ (0171) 480 6562
11–9; closed Sat & Sun
Young's Bitter, Special, Winter Warmer Ⱨ
The first Young's pub in the city since WWII, always busy and friendly. Basic, but note the unusual handpumps.
Q ⇌ (Fenchurch St)
⊖ (Tower Hill/Aldgate)

Swan
Ship Tavern Passage, 77–80 Gracechurch Street
☎ (0171) 283 7712
11–9; closed Sat & Sun
Fuller's Hock, Chiswick, London Pride, ESB Ⱨ
Unique, traditional bar at ground level, with a larger bar upstairs. Q ⇌ (Bank)
⊖ (Monument)

Three Lords
27 Minories
11–11 (may close earlier); closed Sat & Sun
Young's Bitter, Special, Winter Warmer Ⱨ
Pub whose name appears to commemorate the Jacobite Rebellion in 1745.
Q ⇌ (Fenchurch St)
⊖ (Aldgate) ✄

Wine Lodge
145 Fenchurch Street
☎ (0171) 626 0918
11–7.30 (10 downstairs)
Young's Bitter, Special, Winter Warmer Ⱨ
Basic pub with wooden floors, which was privately-owned until taken over by Young's. The no-smoking area is closed eves. Q & ⇌ (Fenchurch St)
⊖ (Bank) ✄

EC4: City

Banker
Cousin Lane
☎ (0171) 283 5206
11–9; closed Sat & Sun
Fuller's Hock, Chiswick, London Pride, ESB Ⱨ
Pub built in an archway under Cannon Street station, with views of the Thames from the raised drinking area and patio. Eve meals on request.
❀ ◖ ▶ & ⇌ (Cannon St) ⊖

City Retreat
74 Shoe Lane
☎ (0171) 353 7904
11–9 (may vary); 11–11 Fri; closed Sat & Sun
Young's Bitter, Special Ⱨ, **Winter Warmer** Ꮐ
Small, cosy, single bar, which, despite its location at the foot of an office block, is developing a local character.
◖ ⇌ (Farringdon/Blackfriars)
⊖ ♣

WC1: Bloomsbury

Calthorpe Arms
252 Gray's Inn Road
☎ (0171) 278 4732
11–3, 5.30–11; 11–11 Thu–Sat
Young's Bitter, Special, Winter Warmer Ⱨ
Relaxed, welcoming local near the ITN building. The upstairs dining room is open lunchtimes; eve meals on request.
Q ❀ ◖ & ⇌ (King's Cross)
⊖ (Russell Sq)

Pakenham Arms
1 Pakenham Street
☎ (0171) 837 6933
11–3, 5–11
Brakspear Special; Exmoor Gold; Whitbread Flowers Original; guest beers Ⱨ
Refurbished, two-bar, corner pub with an unusual range of

Greater London

games. No lunches winter weekends. ⚬ ⬤ ≠ (King's Cross) ⊖ (Russell Sq) ♣

Queens Head
66 Acton Street
☎ (0171) 837 4491
Draught Bass; Fuller's London Pride; Hook Norton Best Bitter; Stones Best Bitter H
Pleasant pub featuring wooden floors and tiled walls. Cider in summer.
⬤ ≠ (King's Cross) ⊖ ♣ ⬭

WC1: Holborn

Cittie of Yorke
22 High Holborn
☎ (0171) 242 7670
11.30–11; 11.30–3, 5.30–11 Sat; closed Sun
Samuel Smith OBB, Museum H
Distinctive, Gothic building on the site of a 15th-century inn and coffee house. The baronial hall at the rear boasts huge vats, screened compartments and an unusual triangular stove. There is also a comfortable panelled front bar, plus a cellar bar. ⬛ Q ⚬ ⬤ ⬥ ≠ (Farringdon) ⊖ (Chancery Lane) ♣

Three Cups
Sandland Street
☎ (0171) 831 4302
11–11; closed Sat & Sun except in summer
Young's Bitter, Special, Porter, Winter Warmer H
Busy, back-street, ex-Finch's house catering for office trade.
Q ⚬ ⬤ ⊖

WC2: Charing Cross

Marquis of Granby
51 Chandos Place
☎ (0171) 836 7657
11–11
Adnams Bitter; Ind Coope Burton Ale; Tetley Bitter H
Friendly pub near St Martin-in-the-Fields ⬤ ⬥ ≠ ⊖

WC2: Covent Garden

Freemasons Arms
81–82 Long Acre
☎ (0171) 836 3115
11–11
Greene King IPA, Rayments Special, Abbot H
Large, comfortable pub with an upstairs bar, often crowded and noisy. The Football Association was founded here.
⬤ ⊖

Hogshead Ale House
21 Drury Lane
11–11

Brakspear Bitter; Fuller's London Pride H; Morland Old Speckled Hen G; Whitbread Boddingtons Bitter H; guest beers G
Formerly the Sun, now a Whitbread-owned free house. Some beers are served by gravity from a cooled stillage; up to four guest beers. ⬤ ⬥ ⊖

Marquess of Anglesey
Bow Street ☎ (0171) 240 3216
11–11
Young's Bitter, Special, Winter Warmer H
Busy, corner pub handy for Covent Garden Plaza.
⬤ ⬥ ≠ (Charing Cross) ⊖ (Covent Garden)

Roundhouse
1 Garrick Street
☎ (0171) 836 9838
11–11
S&N Theakston Best Bitter; Old Peculier; Wadworth 6X; Younger IPA; guest beer H
Wedge-shaped pub. One of S&N's T&J Bernard chain, it also sells Trappist bottled beers. ⬤ ⬥ ⊖ ⬭

WC2: Holborn

Newton Arms
31 Newton Street
11–11; 11–3, 7–11 Sat; closed Sun
Greene King IPA; Ind Coope Burton Ale; Taylor Walker Best Bitter; Tetley Bitter H
Pleasant corner pub in a 1960s office block. No meals Fri eve.
⬤ ⬥ ⊖ ♣

WC2: Leicester Square

Moon Under Water
28 Leicester Square
11–11
Courage Directors; S&N Theakston XB; Wadworth 6X; Younger Scotch; guest beer H
Typical Wetherspoon pub, converted from shop premises, next to the Odeon cinema. Very reasonably priced for the area. Q ⬤ ⬥ ⊖ ⤸

WC2: Lincoln's Inn Fields

Seven Stars
53 Carey Street
11–11 (may close earlier); closed Sat & Sun
Courage Best Bitter, Directors H
Small, busy pub behind the law courts, much used by the legal profession. ⬤

WC2: St Giles

Angel
61 St Giles High Street
12–11; 12–3.30, 6–11 Sat; closed Sun

Courage Best Bitter, Directors; John Smith's Bitter; Wadworth 6X H
Old, reputedly-haunted pub near Centrepoint; handy for the Oxford St shops.
⬤ ⊖ (Tottenham Ct Rd)

East London

E1: Bethnal Green

White Hart
1 Mile End Road, Whitechapel
☎ (0181) 790 2894
11–11
Draught Bass; Freetraders Twelve Bore; Greene King Abbot; guest beers H
Basic boozers' pub with a superb glass partition and mirrors. A true East End local. Very reasonable prices. The beer range may change.
⬛ ≠ ⊖ (Whitechapel)

E1: Stepney

Hollands
Brayford Square
☎ (0171) 790 3057
11–11
Young's Bitter, Special, Winter Warmer H
A treasure house of Victoriana, breweriana and press cuttings, Grade II-listed for its original interior, with boarded ceiling, pine panelling and glasswork.
⬤ ≠ (Limehouse) ⊖ (Whitechapel/Shadwell)

E1: Whitechapel

Lord Rodney's Head
285 Whitechapel Road
11–11
Banks & Taylor Shefford Mild, Bitter, SOS, SOD, 2XS H
Long, narrow bar with dozens of clocks. Live music. ⊖ ♣

E2: Bethnal Green

Camden's Head
456 Bethnal Green Road
11–11
Courage Directors; S&N Theakston Best Bitter, XB; Wadworth 6X; Younger Scotch; guest beers H
An oasis of calm and quality in a desert of mediocrity.
Q ⚬ ⬤ ⬥ ≠ ⊖ ⤸

E2: Hackney

Owl & Pussycat
34 Redchurch Street
☎ (0171) 739 2808
11–11 (midnight Fri & Sat)
Arkell's 3B; Courage Directors; Fuller's London Pride; Shepherd Neame Spitfire; Taylor Landlord H

Popular free house offering varying beers in a convivial atmosphere. Grade II-listed, it has an upstairs restaurant. Music Fri and Sat night, mostly jazz.
⊛ ⬥ ⇌ (Liverpool St) ♣

E3: Bow

Unicorn
27 Vivian Road
11–11
Fuller's Hock, London Pride H, Mr Harry G; Whitbread Boddingtons Bitter, Flowers Original H
Friendly, East End, back-street local. No food Sun. ⊛ ⬥ ⬥

E4: Chingford

Royal Oak
219 Kings Head Hill
☎ (0181) 529 1492
11–3, 5.30–11; 11–11 Sat
Draught Bass; Courage Directors; McMullen AK, Country H
Large house at the bottom of the hill—a very welcoming public bar and a superb lounge with an accent on food.
Q ⊛ ⬥ ▶ ⬥ P

E5: Clapton

Anchor & Hope
15 High Hill Ferry
☎ (0181) 806 1730
11–11
Fuller's London Pride, ESB H
Small, popular riverside pub (one bar) unchanged for many years. The landlord has notched up 40 years. ⊛ ♣

Prince of Wales
Lea Bridge Road
☎ (0181) 533 3463
11.30–11
Young's Bitter, Special, Winter Warmer H
Large, attractive riverside pub with two wood-panelled bars.
⊛ ⬥ ▶ ⬥ ♣ P

E6: East Ham

Miller's Well
419–421 Barking Road (opp. town hall) ☎ (0181) 471 8404
11–11
Courage Directors; S&N Theakston Best Bitter, XB; Wadworth 6X; Younger Scotch; guest beer H
Well-kept beer and a friendly welcome have earned this pub a loyal following since becoming a Wetherspoon house. Q ⬥ ⊖ ⬦

E8: Hackney

Lady Diana
95 Forest Road
☎ (0171) 254 3439

11.30–3.30, 5–11
Fuller's Chiswick, London Pride; Greene King Abbot; Whitbread Boddingtons Bitter; guest beers (occasional)
Friendly local, comfortably furnished. Pizzas feature on the menu. ⊛ ⬥ ▶ ⇌ ♣

E9: Hackney

Falcon & Firkin
360 Victoria Park Road
11–3, 5.30–11; 11–11 Sat
Firkin Mild G, Falcon Bitter, Hackney Bitter, Dogbolter H; guest beer G
One of the Firkin chain's main breweries, drawing a lively, loud clientele. Pleasant in summer, with a large outside area. ⬥ ⊛ ⬥ ⬥
⇌ (Hackney Wick) ♣ P

E9: Victoria Park

Royal Standard
84 Victoria Park Road
☎ (0181) 985 3224
12–11
Adnams Extra; Courage Best Bitter, Directors; Marston's Pedigree; guest beers H
Two-bar local. Imperial Russian Stout is also sold.
⬥ ♣

E10: Leyton

Drum
557 Lea Bridge Road
11–11
Courage Directors; Greene King Abbot; Hop Back Special; Morland Old Speckled Hen; S&N Theakston Best Bitter, XB H
A typical Wetherspoon house and a friendly local. Q ⊛ ⬥ ⬥
⇌ (Walthamstow Central) ⊖

Hollybush
32 Grange Road
11.30–3, 5.30–11
Greene King IPA, Abbot H
Modernised interior in a Victorian exterior—an essential call for anyone visiting Leyton Orient FC.
⊛ ⇌ ⊖ ♣

E11: Leytonstone

Birkbeck Tavern
45 Langthorne Road
☎ (0181) 539 2584
11–11
Draught Bass; Nethergate Bitter; Tetley Bitter; guest beers H
Everyone deserves a local like this: a sympathetic restoration complements its friendly atmosphere. Excellent range of beers (regularly changed).
⊛ ⬥ ⊖ (Leyton) ♣

Woodhouse Tavern
119 Harrow Road
11–3, 5–11; 11–11 Fri & Sat
Whitbread Flowers Original; guest beers H
Refurbished pub with a new no-smoking extension: a friendly, traditional, East End pub. Sun roasts. ⚌ Q ⬥
⊛ ⬥ ⬥ ⇌ (Midland) ♣ ⬦

E11: Wanstead

George
High Street ☎ (0181) 989 2921
11–11
Courage Directors; Morland Old Speckled Hen; S&N Theakston Best Bitter, XB; Wadworth 6X; Younger Scotch; guest beers H
Grandiose corner pub, popular with all ages. One or two guest beers are changed several times a week. Occasional beer festivals. Pictures of old Wanstead, and photos of famous Georges add to the decor. Q ⊛ ⬥ ▶ ⊖ P ⬦

E12: Manor Park

Blakesley Arms
53 Station Road
☎ (0181) 478 6023
11–11
Draught Bass; Hancock's HB; Wadworth 6X H
Large, friendly pub with old posters and maps on the wall. Shove-ha'penny is played in the saloon; small public bar.
Q ⊛ ⬥ ⇌ ♣

E14: Isle of Dogs

Cat & Canary
Fishermans Walk, Canary Wharf
☎ (0171) 512 9187
11–9; 12–3 Sat & Sun, closed Sat & Sun eves
Fuller's Hock, Chiswick, London Pride, ESB H
Although this pub is situated in the office complex of Canary Wharf, it has a real traditional atmosphere. The interior decor was rescued from a church in France. No meals at weekends. Q ⊛ ⬥
⊖ (DLR Canary Wharf) ♣

E14: Stepney

Queens Head
8 Flamborough Street
11–2.30, 5.30 (7.30 Sat)–11
Young's Bitter, Special, Winter Warmer H
Friendly local in a conservation area, comprising three drinking areas. Note the London 'Fives' dartboard. Lunches served Mon–Fri.
⬥ ⇌ (Limehouse) ⊖ ♣

E15: Stratford

Goldengrove
146–148 The Grove
☎ (0181) 519 0750
11–11
Courage Directors; S&N Theakston Best Bitter, XB; Wadworth 6X; Younger Scotch; guest beers H
Split-level pub, expertly converted from former shop premises and decorated with photos of local industries.
Q ❀ ◖ ◗ ♿ ⇌ ⊖ ⌓ P ⚟

E17: Walthamstow

Copper Mill
Coppermill Lane
11–11
Eldridge Pope Hardy Country; Fuller's London Pride, ESB; Greene King IPA; Marston's Pedigree; Tetley Bitter H
Small pub appealing to all ages, converted from an off-licence.
❀ ⇌ (St James St)
⊖ (Blackhorse Rd)

Grove Tavern
74 Grove Road
☎ (0181) 509 0230
11–11
Bass Charrington IPA, Draught Bass; Brakspear Bitter; Marston's Pedigree; Tetley Bitter H
Good, olde-worlde, family house due for renovation. Note the old screens above the bar.
Q ❀ ◖ ⇌ (Central) ⊖

Barking

Britannia
1 Church Road (near A123)
☎ (0181) 594 1305
11–3, 5–11; 11–11 Sat
Young's Bitter, Special, Winter Warmer H
Large, comfortable and friendly: the only Young's tied house in 'Greater Essex' offers a warm, plush saloon bar and a more basic public bar with pool and darts. Home-cooked, good value food (not served Sun). Q ❀ ◖ ⊞ ⇌ ⊖ ♣ P

Cranham

Thatched House
348 St Mary's Lane (B187)
☎ (01708) 228080
11–3 (3.30 Fri, 4 Sat), 5.30 (6 Sat)–11
Bass Charrington IPA, Draught Bass; guest beer H
Friendly local with a varied clientele. Children's room with toilets. Eve meals at weekends.
🚼 ❀ ◖ ◗ P

Dagenham

Eastbrook Hotel
Dagenham Road (A1112)
☎ (0181) 592 1873
11–3 (4 Sat), 5 (6 Sat)–11
Draught Bass; Courage Best Bitter; Fuller's ESB; Webster's Green Label; guest beer (occasional) H
Unspoilt, roomy, comfortable pub with wood panelling, plus a large public bar and a restaurant area (no food Sun).
Q ❀ 🛏 ◖ ⊞ ♿
⊖ (East) ♣ P

Ilford

Prince of Wales
63 Green Lane (A1083)
☎ (0181) 478 1326
11–3, 5.30–11; 11–11 Fri & Sat
Ind Coope Burton Ale; Tetley Bitter H
Pleasant pub on the eastern fringe of Ilford. It has distinct drinking areas—used by office workers lunchtimes and locals eves. The split-level garden is the best in the area. Lunches weekdays. ❀ ◖ ⊞ ♣ P

Rose & Crown
16 Ilford Hill (A118)
☎ (0181) 478 7104
11–11
Ind Coope Burton Ale; Tetley Bitter; guest beers H
Comfortable and friendly town pub with one large bar. At least two guest beers. No food Sun. ◖ ⇌ ⌓

Noak Hill

Bear
Noak Hill Road
11–3.30, 5.30–11; 11–11 Fri & Sat
Draught Bass; Fuller's London Pride; Hancock's HB; Wadworth 6X H
Large, comfortable pub. The large garden has children's playthings. The beer range may vary; occasional festivals. No food Sun; eve meals Mon–Thu. 🚼 ❀ ◖ ◗ ♿ P

Woodford Green

Cricketers
299–301 High Road (A11)
☎ (0181) 504 2734
11–3 (4 Sat), 5.30–11
Draught Bass; McMullen AK, Country, Stronghart H
Friendly pub with two distinct bars—a basic public and a comfortable saloon. McMullen Special Reserve beers. No food Sun. Q ◖ ⊞ ♣ P

Travellers Friend
496–498 High Road (A104)
☎ (0181) 504 2435
11–11
Courage Best Bitter, Directors; Ridleys IPA, ESX; Wadworth 6X H
Superb little drinkers' pub with panelled walls and snob screens. Warm and friendly, it has a good atmosphere. The beer range may vary. No food Sun. Q ❀ ◖ ♿ P

North London

N1: Canonbury

Earl of Radnor
106 Mildmay Grove
☎ (0171) 241 0318
11–11
Fuller's London Pride, ESB H
Lovingly restored Victorian pub offering good, home-cooked food (not served Sat). No fruit machines or jukebox, but occasional taped music. An all too rare Fuller's house for this side of town.
❀ ◖ ♿ ⇌ ♣

Marquess Tavern
32 Canonbury Street
☎ (0171) 354 2975
11–11
Young's Bitter, Porter (summer), **Special, Winter Warmer** H
Excellent pub in a fine Georgian building. The single bar, with distinct saloon and public areas, is traditional and comfortable.
♨ Q ❀ ◖ ◗ ⇌ (Essex Rd/ Highbury) ⊖ ♣

N1: Hoxton

George & Vulture
63 Pitfield Street
☎ (0171) 607 9207
11–3 (4 Sat), 5 (7 Sat)–11
Fuller's Hock, London Pride, ESB H
Quiet, twin-bar pub, like a country pub in town. Do not be deterred by the surroundings.
Q ◖ ◗ ⇌ (Old St) ⊖

Prince Arthur
49 Brunswick Place, Charles Square ☎ (0171) 253 3187
11–11; 11–5, 8–11 Sat; 12–2.30, 8.30–10.30 Sun
Shepherd Neame Master Brew Bitter, Spitfire H
Single-bar local over 300 years old. Cider in summer.
Q ❀ ◖ ⇌ (Old St) ⊖

Wenlock Arms
26 Wenlock Road
☎ (0171) 608 3426
11–11
Crouch Vale Best Bitter; Ind Coope Burton Ale; Ridleys Witchfinder; Tetley Bitter; guest beers H
Small local offering six ales, including four ever-changing

guest beers, served in oversized glasses. A well-preserved single bar by the former Wenlock Brewery.
♛ Q ⇌ (Old St) ⌂

N1: Islington

Crown
116 Cloudesley Road
☎ (0171) 837 7107
11–11
Fuller's Hock, Chiswick, London Pride, ESB H
A 19th-century building with lots of wood panelling, mirrors and etched-glass, divided into distinct areas.
♛ ❀ ◐ ◗ ♿ ⊖ (Angel) ♣

N2: East Finchley

Welch's Ale House
130 High Road
☎ (0181) 444 7444
11–3, 5.30–11; 11–11 Sat
Fuller's London Pride; Greene King Abbot; Ruddles County; Wadworth 6X; Webster's Yorkshire Bitter; guest beers H
One of the earlier shop conversions. Twelve handpumps dispense five guest beers. Country wines are also available. ◐ ⊖ ♣ ⌂

N6: Highgate

Bull
North Hill ☎ (0181) 340 4412
12–11
Adnams Bitter; Ind Coope Burton Ale; Taylor Walker Bitter; Tetley Bitter; guest beer H
One of the oldest pubs in Highgate village, retaining its original atmosphere though altered over the years.
♛ Q ❀ ◐ ◗ ♿ ⊖ ♣ P

Red Lion & Sun
25 North Road
☎ (0181) 340 1780
12–4, 6–11; 11–11 Fri & Sat
Draught Bass; Greene King IPA, Rayments Special (occasional), **Abbot** H
Wood-panelled, 1920s mock Tudor local, set back behind a pleasant, tree-lined courtyard. Greene King took over in 1993.
Q ❀ ♿ ⊖ ♣ P

N7: Holloway

Admiral Mann
9 Hargrave Place
☎ (0171) 485 4739
11–3 (4 Sat), 6 (7 Sat)–11; 11–11 Fri
McMullen AK, Country, Stronghart *or* guest beer H
Unobtrusively located, two-bar pub, more typical of McMullen than N London. Mostly local trade.
❀ ◐ ◗ ♿ ⇌ (Camden Rd) ♣

N8: Crouch End

Railway
23 Crouch End Hill
☎ (0181) 340 3875
12–11
Draught Bass; Hancock's HB; guest beers H
Two-bar pub, offering at least three guest ales a week, plus occasional mini-beer festivals. It also boasts its own golf driving range. ♛ Q ❀ ⊞ ♿
⊖ (Finsbury Pk) ♣ ⌂

N9: Lower Edmonton

Lamb
52–54 Church Street
☎ (0181) 887 0128
11–11
Courage Directors; Morland Old Speckled Hen; S&N Theakston Best Bitter, XB, Younger No. 3; guest beers H
A haven of peace and civility in an area better known for over-loud jukeboxes. Wheelchair WC. Q ◐ ◗ ♿ ⛺
⇌ (Edmonton Green) ⌂ ⚟

N11: New Southgate

Banker's Draft
36–38 Friern Barnet Road
☎ (0181) 361 7115
11–11
Courage Directors; Morland Old Speckled Hen; S&N Theakston Best Bitter, XB; guest beers H
Former bank yielding more interest as a pub, with three guest beers a week. Q ◐ ◗ ♿
⇌ ⊖ (Arnos Grove) ⌂ ⚟

N12: North Finchley

Tally Ho
749 High Road
☎ (0181) 445 4390
11–11
Courage Directors; Greene King Abbot; S&N Theakston Best Bitter, XB; guest beer H
Imposing landmark pub, renovated in Wetherspoon style and due for enlargement. Photos of old Finchley decorate the walls. The upstairs bar is no-smoking.
Q ◐ ◗ ⊖ (Woodside Pk)
♣ ⌂ ⚟

N16: Stoke Newington

Rochester Castle
145 Stoke Newington High Street ☎ (0171) 249 6016
11–11
Courage Directors; Greene King Abbot; S&N Theakston Best Bitter, XB; Wadworth 6X; Younger Scotch; guest beer H
Very large, single-bar pub with a conservatory and a garden. Q ❀ ◐ ◗ ⇌ ⌂ ⚟

Shakespeare
57 Allen Road
☎ (0171) 254 4190
12–2.30, 5–11; 12–11 Sat
Adnams Extra; Fuller's Hock, London Pride; Greene King Abbot; Taylor Landlord; Whitbread Boddingtons Bitter H
Victorian pub with French posters and Shakespearean paintings. It draws a young, friendly clientele with a bluesy jukebox and a large selection of foreign beers. ❀ ⇌ ♣

N21: Winchmore Hill

Dog & Duck
76 Hoppers Road
☎ (0181) 886 1987
12–11
Morland Old Speckled Hen; Whitbread Boddingtons Bitter, Strong Country, Flowers Original H
Welcoming local known as the Woof & Kwak. The beer range may vary. ♛ ❀ ⇌ (Palmers Green) ♣

Green Dragon
889 Green Lanes
☎ (0181) 360 3725
11–11
Courage Best Bitter, Directors; Wadworth 6X H
Former CAMRA London *Pub of the Year*, comprising two large, wood-panelled bars, and a pool room. Under-21s may not be admitted. No food Sun.
Q ❀ ◐ ⊞ ⇌ ♣ P

Orange Tree
18 Highfield Road
☎ (0181) 360 4853
11–11
Adnams Bitter; Greene King IPA; Tetley Bitter; guest beer H
Down-to-earth, back-street, local offering a changing guest beer. Under-21s may not be admitted. Eve meals finish at 7pm. ❀ ◐ ◗ ⇌ ♣

N22: Wood Green

Starting Gate
Station Road
☎ (0181) 889 9789
12–11
Ind Coope Burton Ale; Marston's Pedigree; Tetley Bitter; Wadworth 6X; Young's Bitter; guest beer H
Fine Victorian pub near

Greater London

Alexandra Park and Palace. Recently refurbished, the mirrors and etched-glass add to the welcoming atmosphere. 🏠 Q ❀ ◑ ⇌ (Alexandra Palace) ⊖ (Wood Green) ♣

Barnet

Black Horse

Wood Street ☎ (0181) 449 6438
11–11
Ansells Mild; Ind Coope ABC Best Bitter, Burton Ale; Marston's Pedigree; Tetley Bitter; guest beers H
Attractive, one-bar pub on a busy street corner. The guest beers may include a mild. No food Sun.
❀ ◑ ⊖ (High Barnet) ♣

Moon Under Water

148 High Street
☎ (0181) 441 9476
11–11
Courage Directors; Greene King IPA, Abbot; Morland Old Speckled Hen; S&N Theakston XB; guest beers H
Pub whose narrow, street frontage opens into a long, narrow bar, which leads to an expanded rear area. Q ❀ ◑ ⊖ (High Barnet) ⌂ ⊬

Old Mitre

58 High Street
☎ (0181) 449 6582
11–11; 11–3, 7–11 Sat
Ind Coope Benskins Best Bitter, Burton Ale; Tetley Bitter; guest beer H
Traditional coaching inn, now themed as an ale house. It is an oasis of tranquillity compared with some of its neighbours. No food Sun.
Q ◑ ⊖ (High Barnet) ♣ P

Enfield Lock

Greyhound

425 Ordnance Road
☎ (01992) 764612
11–2.30 (3 Fri & Sat), 6.30 (7 Sat)–11
McMullen AK, Country, Stronghart H
Unspoilt, two-bar oasis on the River Lea Navigation opposite the former Royal Small Arms factory. The bars have been transposed in a recent refurbishment. McMullen's Special Reserve beers.
🏠 Q ❀ ◑ ▶ ⇌ ♣ P

Enfield Town

Cricketers

17–19 Chase Side Place
☎ (0181) 363 5218
11–3, 5.30–11; 11–11 Sat
Courage Directors; McMullen AK, Country, Stronghart H
Tucked-away pub, close to the historic Gentleman's Row. Bar billiards is played in the

unspoilt public bar. The saloon has a part set aside for lunches and eve meals (book). ❀ ◑ ▶ 🍴 ⇌ (Enfield Chase) ♣ P ⊬

Moon Under Water

115–117 Chase Side
☎ (0181) 366 9855
11–11
Courage Directors; Greene King IPA, Abbot; S&N Theakston Best Bitter, XB; guest beers H
Large, rambling bar, serving several distinct drinking areas. A large cart occupies prime floor space. Very busy at weekends. Q ❀ ◑ ▶ ⇌ (Enfield Chase) ⌂ P ⊬

Old Wheatsheaf

3 Windmill Hill
☎ (0181) 363 0516
11–3, 5–11; 11–11 Fri & Sat
Adnams Bitter; Ind Coope Burton Ale; Taylor Walker Best Bitter; Tetley Bitter; guest beer H
Fine Edwardian, two-bar pub, near the town centre. A former London CAMRA *Pub of the Year*, it continues to maintain high standards. Gym at the rear. No food Sun.
❀ ◑ ⇌ (Enfield Chase) ♣ P

New Barnet

Hadley Hotel

113 Hadley Road
☎ (0181) 449 0161
11–11
Fuller's London Pride; Ruddles County; Webster's Yorkshire Bitter H
Not at all what one expects to find in leafy suburbia: a single bar with three drinking areas. Pub accommodation is rare in this part of London. No food Sun. ❀ 🏠 ◑ ▶ ♣ P

Railway Bell

13 East Barnet Road
☎ (0181) 449 1369
11–11
Courage Directors; Greene King IPA, Abbot; S&N Theakston XB; guest beer H
Large, one-bar pub, visible from King's Cross main line. Local CAMRA *Pub of the Year* twice in the last three years.
Q ❀ ◑ ▶ ⇌ ⊖ P ⊬

NW1: Camden Town

Spread Eagle

141 Albert Street, Parkway
☎ (0171) 267 1410
11–3, 5–11; 11–11 Fri & Sat

Young's Bitter, Porter, Special, Winter Warmer H
Built in 1858, this multi-roomed pub has expanded over the years to take in two adjoining premises. It attracts a friendly, local trade plus visitors to the market.
Q ❀ ◑ ▶ ⇌ (Camden Rd) ⊖ (Camden Town)

NW1: Euston

Neptune

51 Werrington Street
☎ (0171) 380 1390
11–11
Wells Eagle, Bombardier; guest beer H
Comfortable, single-bar, corner pub. Bar snacks are available. It featured on TV's *The Real McCoy*. & ⇌ (Euston) ⊖ ♣

NW1: Marylebone

Perseverance

Shroton Street
11–3, 5–11
Draught Bass; Fuller's London Pride H
Two-bar pub, nicely decorated and a cut above most pubs in the area. Q ◑ ⇌ ⊖

NW2: Cricklewood

Beaten Docket

50–56 Cricklewood Broadway
☎ (0181) 450 2972
11–11
Courage Directors; Greene King IPA, Abbot; S&N Theakston XB; Younger Scotch; guest beers H
Large pub, a typical Wetherspoon house, in an Irish district which is not noted for real ale. Very popular, particularly eves and weekends, it offers up to three guest beers a week. Q ❀ ◑ ▶ & ⇌ ⊖ (Kilburn) ⊬

NW3: Belsize Park

Washington

50 Englands Lane
☎ (0171) 722 6118
11–11
Ind Coope Burton Ale; Marston's Pedigree; Tetley Bitter; Young's Bitter; guest beer H
Well-preserved, Victorian corner pub built in 1865. The spacious single bar boasts ornate mirrors and woodwork. Very popular with locals; sport oriented. ◑ & ⊖ ♣

NW3: Hampstead

Duke of Hamilton

New End ☎ (0171) 794 0258
11–11

Draught Bass; Fuller's Hock, London Pride; guest beer H
Friendly Victorian, traditional house popular with rugby and cricket fans. Cellar bar for functions. ❀ ◖ ▶ ⊖

Flask
14 Flask Walk
☎ (0171) 435 4580
11–11
Young's Bitter, Porter, Special, Winter Warmer H
Friendly, historic local with high Edwardian windows. A conservatory provides eating space (eve meals Thu–Sat). Very pleasant on sunny days.
Q ◖ ▶ ⊟ ♿ ⊖ ♣

Holly Bush
22 Holly Mount
☎ (0171) 435 2892
11–3 (4 Sat), 5.30 (6 Sat)–11
Ind Coope Benskins Best Bitter, Burton Ale; Tetley Bitter H
Pleasant, back-street, gas-lit pub full of breweriana.
🏭 ⌂ ❀ ◖ ▶ ⊖ ♣

Horse & Groom
68 Heath Street
☎ (0171) 435 3140
11–11
Young's Bitter, Porter, Special, Winter Warmer H
Pub displaying military prints in its saloon bar. ◖ ⊖ ♣

Magdala
South Hill ☎ (0171) 435 2503
11–11
Draught Bass; Fuller's London Pride; Morland Old Speckled Hen; guest beers H
Traditional Victorian, tiled pub. ◖ ▶
≋ (Hampstead Heath) ⊖

Spaniards Inn
Spaniards Road
☎ (0181) 455 3276
11–11
Adnams Bitter; Bass Charrington IPA; Fuller's London Pride; M&B Highgate Dark; guest beers H
Fine classic roadhouse on Hampstead Heath, near Kenwood House. It has many historic connections, not least with Dick Turpin.
🏭 Q ⌂ ❀ ◖ ▶ ♿ P ✂

NW4: Hendon

Chequers
20 Church End
☎ (0181) 203 5658
11–11
Courage Best Bitter, Directors H
An island bar serves two distinct drinking areas in this popular local near Church House Museum.
❀ ◖ ▶ ♿ ⊖ ♣ P

NW5: Kentish Town

Pineapple
51 Leverton Street
☎ (0171) 485 6422
12 (11 Sat)–11
Brakspear Bitter; Marston's Pedigree; Whitbread Boddingtons Bitter H
Cosy, friendly back-street local with a passionate following. Local artists' paintings are for sale. The famous brewery mirrors remain after redecoration. ≋ ⊖ ♣ ♠

NW6: Kilburn

Queen's Arms
1 Kilburn High Road
☎ (0171) 624 5735
11–11
Young's Bitter, Special, Winter Warmer H
Pub built in 1958 after the original was destroyed in WWII. Separated into different areas with lots of wood panelling, it boasts framed prints, and an unusual roof garden. 🏭 Q ❀ ◖ ▶ ⊟
≋ ⊖ (Queens Pk) ♣ P

NW7: Mill Hill

Rising Sun
137 Marsh Lane
☎ (0181) 959 3755
12 (11 Sat)–3, 5.30–11
Ind Coope Burton Ale; Tetley Bitter; Young's Bitter; guest beer H
Unspoilt, Taylor Walker Heritage Inn in a rural setting with a tiny bar and an unusual raised snug. Popular with families (children welcome until 9pm). An additional lounge opens at busy times. No eve meals Sun or Mon.
Q ⌂ ❀ ◖ ▶ ♣ P

NW8: St John's Wood

Clifton Hotel
96 Clifton Hill
☎ (0171) 624 5233
11–11
Adnams Bitter; Ind Coope Burton Ale; Nicholson's Best Bitter; Tetley Bitter H
Victorian villa, split into three areas with a conservatory dining area. Upmarket and expensive for the area. No food Sun eve. 🏭 Q ❀ ◖ ▶ ✂

New Inn
Allitsen Road
☎ (0171) 722 0726
11–11
Greene King IPA, Rayments Special, Abbot H

Traditionally renovated, one-bar pub in a side road, quiet and friendly. Good value bar meals at all times in the dining area. Q ◖ ▶ ⊖

Princess Royal
11 Circus Road
☎ (0171) 483 1284
11–11
Bass Worthington BB; guest beer H
One-bar, basic London tavern, with a good wine list.
❀ ◖ ⊖

NW9: Kingsbury

JJ Moon's
553 Kingsbury Road
☎ (0181) 204 9675
11–11
Courage Directors; Greene King Abbot; Morland Old Speckled Hen; S&N Theakston Best Bitter, XB; Younger Scotch; guest beers H
Former shop, now a small, busy Wetherspoon local, with a long, narrow bar. The menu includes good value Sun roasts. Q ◖ ▶ ⊖ ⌂ ✂

NW9: Neasden

Outside Inn
314 Neasden Lane
☎ (0181) 452 3140
11–11
Courage Directors; Greene King IPA; Morland Old Speckled Hen; S&N Theakston Best Bitter, XB; Younger Scotch; guest beers H
Wood-panelled, ex-Woolworth store, large, comfortable and a rare outlet for real ale in the area. Occasional beer festivals.
Q ❀ ◖ ▶ ⊖ ✂

NW10: Harlesden

Coliseum
2 Manor Park Road
☎ (0181) 961 6570
11–11
Courage Directors; S&N Theakston Best Bitter, XB; Wadworth 6X; Younger Scotch; guest beers H
Former cinema, now part of the Wetherspoon chain and a welcome addition to the area. Note the large mural of Gary Cooper and Merle Oberon, plus the film posters.
Q ❀ ◖ ▶
♿ ≋ (Willesden Jct) ⊖ ✂

Grand Junction Arms
Acton Lane
☎ (0181) 965 5670
11–11
Young's Bitter, Special, Winter Warmer H

Greater London

Large, comfortable, three-bar pub with moorings on the Grand Union Canal. The garden offers children's play equipment, and barbecues in summer. Good value food, served all day (no meals Sun). Not all bars may be open.
Q ❀ ◑ ▶ ⊟ ᕁ ⇌ ⊖ ♣ P

NW11: Golders Green

White Swan

243 Golders Green Road
☎ (0181) 458 2036
11–11
Ind Coope Burton Ale; Tetley Bitter; Young's Bitter H
Lively local in an under-pubbed area, featuring an attractive garden. Good food. ❀ ◑ ▶
⊖ (Brent Cross) ♣

Eastcote

Case Is Altered

High Road
☎ (0181) 866 0476
11–3, 5.30–11; 11–11 Sat
Ind Coope Benskins Best Bitter, Burton Ale; Tetley Bitter; Young's Special; guest beer H
Grade I-listed ex-farmhouse with a stone flagged floor in the 'old' public bar, which used to be the stables. The restaurant in the barn behind is popular.
🏚 Q ❀ ◑ ▶ ♣ P

Edgware

Change of Hart

21 High Street
☎ (0181) 952 0039
11–11
Adnams Bitter; Ind Coope Burton Ale; Marston's Pedigree; Tetley Bitter; Wadworth 6X; guest beer H
Formerly the White Hart, and once a coaching inn where Dick Turpin reputedly stayed. A one-bar pub, it retains separate drinking areas. The food is very reasonably priced. Hart Bitter is brewed at the Falcon & Firkin. Wheelchair WC. Q ❀ ◑ ▶ ᕁ ⊖ P

Harefield

Breakspear Arms

Breakspear Road South
☎ (01895) 632239
11–11
Morland Bitter, Old Masters, Old Speckled Hen H
Very modern, chalet-style pub with an indoor children's room (no-smoking) and a well-equipped outdoor play area. Open Sun afternoon for meals. ⅏ ❀ ◑ ▶ ᕁ P

Plough

Hillend Road
☎ (01895) 822129
11–3, 5.30–11
Brakspear Bitter; Fuller's London Pride; Ringwood Best Bitter; Taylor Landlord; Thwaites Craftsman; Wadworth 6X; guest beer H
Excellent, one-bar free house near the hospital; very busy in summer. Good value food (not available Sun). ❀ ◑ P

White Horse

Church Hill
☎ (01895) 822144
11–3 (4 Sat), 6–11
Cains Bitter; Greenalls Bitter, Shipstone's Bitter, Original; Tetley Bitter; Wadworth 6X H
Excellent, lively, traditional local on the south side of the village, a Grade II-listed building from the 17th century.
🏚 Q ❀ ◑ ▶ ♣ P ✂

Harrow on the Hill

Castle

30 West Street
☎ (0181) 422 3155
11–11
Fuller's Hock, London Pride, ESB H
Friendly, well-run pub with a welcoming atmosphere. It has a small public bar and a large lounge at the rear. Q ❀ ◑
⊟ ⇌ ⊖ (S Harrow) ♣

Harrow Weald

Seven Balls

749 Kenton Lane
☎ (0181) 954 0261
11.30–3, 5.30 (6 Sat)–11
Eldridge Pope Hardy Country or Royal Oak; Ind Coope ABC Best Bitter, Benskins Best Bitter; Tetley Bitter; guest beers H
250-year-old pub, losing no appeal after refurbishment. Occasional beer festivals. No food Sun eve. ◑ ▶ ♣ P ✂

Hatch End

Moon & Sixpence

250 Uxbridge Road
☎ (0181) 420 1074
11–11
Courage Directors; Greene King IPA, Abbot; S&N Theakston XB; Younger Scotch; guest beer (weekends) H
A good conversion of a former bank. It can get crowded, but is a welcome change in an area dominated by Carlsberg-Tetley pubs. Occasional beer festivals; pleasant garden.
Q ❀ ◑ ▶ ᕁ ⇌ ⏚ ✂

Kenton

New Moon

25–26 Kenton Park Parade
☎ (0181) 909 1103
11–11
Courage Directors; Greene King IPA, Abbot; S&N Theakston XB; Younger Scotch; guest beer H
Easily Kenton's best pub, where guest beers are often chosen by customers. Occasional beer festivals.
Q ❀ ◑ ▶ ⇌ ⊖ ✂

Stanmore

Vine

154 Stanmore Hill
☎ (0181) 954 4676
11–3, 5–11
Ind Coope Benskins Best Bitter, Burton Ale; Tetley Bitter; guest beers H
Old coaching inn, recently refurbished but retaining separate drinking areas. Part of the original bar can be seen in the rear room. Bar billiards played. ⅏ ❀ ◑ ▶ ♣ P

Wealdstone

Royal Oak

60 Peel Road
☎ (0181) 427 3122
11–11
Ind Coope Burton Ale; Tetley Bitter; guest beer H
Imposing pub built in 1932, with a pleasant conservatory. The lounge is split into drinking areas; separate public bar. Oak Bitter is brewed by the Falcon & Firkin brew pub.
Q ⅏ ❀ ◑ ᕁ ⇌ (Harrow & Wealdstone) ⊖ ♣ P

Sarsen Stone

High Street ☎ (0181) 853 8633
11–11
Courage Directors; Greene King IPA, Abbot; S&N Theakston XB; Younger Scotch; guest beers H
Popular High Street boozer, with an individual atmosphere. Occasional beer festivals; the guest beer is available mainly at weekends.
Q ◑ ▶ ⇌ (Harrow & Wealdstone) ⊖ ⏚ ✂

Wembley

JJ Moon's

397 High Road
☎ (0181) 903 4923
11–11
Courage Directors; Greene King IPA, Abbot; S&N Theakston XB; Younger Scotch; guest beer H
Cavernous pub, popular with local office workers and handy

for Wembley Stadium. It offers
occasional beer festivals, plus
a guest beer (mainly at
weekends). Q ◖ ▮ ⅃
≢ (Central) ⊖ ⌂ ⅍

South-East London

SE1: Bankside

Founders Arms
52 Hopton Street
☎ (0171) 928 1899
11–11
**Young's Bitter, Special,
Winter Warmer** H
Modern pub with a riverside
terrace and extensive views of
the City of London. Popular
with business people; separate
restaurant. Q ❀ ◖ ▮
⅃ ≢ (Blackfriars) ⊖

SE1: Bermondsey

Ship Aground
33 Wolsey Street, Dockhead
☎ (0171) 237 3314
11–11
**Courage Best Bitter,
Directors** H
Friendly, back-street local,
next to Dockhead, alias
'Blackwall' fire station from
TV's *London's Burning*. ◖ ⅃

SE1: Southwark

Abbey
94 Webber Street
☎ (0171) 928 4480
11–11
**Shepherd Neame Spitfire;
guest beers** (occasional) H
Friendly, back-street free
house. ◖ ≢ (Blackfriars)
⊖ (Borough) ♣

Lord Clyde
27 Clenham Street
☎ (0171) 407 3397
11–11; 11–4, 7–11 Sat
**Courage Directors; Ruddles
Best Bitter; Webster's
Yorkshire Bitter; Young's
Bitter; guest beer** H
Traditional, welcoming house,
in the same family for 36
years. The Truman's tiled
frontage is untouched.
◖ ≢ (London Bridge)
⊖ (Borough) ♣

Prince William Henry
217 Blackfriars Road
☎ (0171) 928 2474
11–11; 12–3, 7–11 Sat
**Young's Bitter, Special,
Winter Warmer** H
Cosy, modern pub with an
outside drinking area, named
after King Henry IV. It is
frequented by musicians from
the South Bank concert halls.
❀ ◖ ▮ ≢ (Waterloo) ⊖

Ship
68 Borough Road
☎ (0171) 403 7059
11–11
**Fuller's Hock, Chiswick,
London Pride, Mr Harry,
ESB** H
Friendly pub on a busy
junction. Its one long bar can
get very crowded eves, as it is
popular with office workers.
❀ ◖ ▮ ≢ (London Bridge)
⊖ (Borough)

SE3: Blackheath

Bitter Experience
129 Lee Road
☎ (0181) 852 8819
11 (10 Sat)–9.30; 12–2, 7–9 Sun
Beer range varies G
Enterprising off-licence with
an ever-changing range of real
ales, plus a wide selection of
bottled beers and ciders. ⌂

Hare & Billet
Alehouse
1a Eliot Cottages, Hare &
Billet Road
☎ (0181) 852 2352
11–11
**Brakspear Bitter; Fuller's
London Pride; Marston's
Pedigree** H; **guest beers** G
Theme pub, with bare boards;
friendly and sometimes very
busy. A top up is never
refused. It also sells Whitbread
cask beers. The heath provides
an expansive garden.
❀ ◖ ≢

SE5: Camberwell

Duke of Clarence
181 Camberwell Road
☎ (0171) 703 4007
11–11
**Greene King IPA, Abbot;
M&B Highgate Dark** H
A rare treat for the area. The
narrow unassuming frontage
belies the character and size of
this staunch family local. The
public bar fronts the main
road and the comfortable
saloon is at the rear, with a
cosy snug in-between.
◖ ≢ (Denmark Hill) ♣

Fox on the Hill
149 Denmark Hill
☎ (0171) 738 4756
11–11
**Courage Directors; S&N
Theakston Best Bitter, XB;
Wadworth 6X; Younger
Scotch** H
Very large pub, atop Denmark
Hill, with commanding views.
It has typical Wetherspoon
decor, but on a grand scale,
with many quiet alcoves and a
restaurant/no-smoking area.
The bar boasts 18
handpumps.
❀ ◖ ▮ ≢ ⌂ P ⅍

Hermit's Cave
28 Camberwell Church Street
☎ (0171) 703 3188
11–11
**Morland Old Speckled
Hen** H; **guest beers** G
Pub recently themed as a
Hogshead Ale House, but
retaining the excellent etched
window panels. An extensive
range of ever-changing high
gravity guest beers is sold
from a stillage behind the bar.
It also sells Whitbread cask
ales. ◖ ▮ ≢ (Denmark Hill)

SE6: Catford

Rutland Arms
55 Perry Hill
11–3, 5.30–11; 11–11 Fri & Sat
**Adnams Extra; Draught Bass;
Fuller's London Pride; Greene
King Abbot; Young's Bitter;
guest beers** H
Popular free house hosting
good live jazz most eves. The
large, open-plan interior
features plain, comfortable
seating and decor. ❀ ◖ ≢ ♣

Tiger's Head
350 Bromley Road
☎ (0181) 698 8645
11–11
**Courage Directors; S&N
Theakston Best Bitter, XB;
Wadworth 6X; Younger
Scotch; guest beer** H
Large, popular, Wetherspoon
pub staging occasional beer
festivals and promotions. No
food Sun eves. Q ❀ ◖ ▮ ⅃
≢ (Bellingham) ♣ ⌂ P ⅍

SE8: Deptford

Crystal Palace Tavern
105 Tanner's Hill
☎ (0181) 692 1536
11–midnight (1am Fri & Sat)
**Marston's Pedigree; Morland
Old Speckled Hen; Wadworth
6X; guest beers** H
Family pub. Live groups; very
varied guest beer and cider
range. ❀ ≢ (St Johns/New
Cross) ⊖ ⌂

Dog & Bell
116 Prince Street
☎ (0181) 692 5664
11–11
**Fuller's London Pride, ESB;
guest beers** H
Genuine, friendly back-street
local, worth seeking out for its
wide range of malt whiskies
and guest beers from small
independents. 1993 SE London
CAMRA *Pub of the Year*.
Q ❀ ◖ ▮ ≢ ♣

SE9: Eltham

Banker's Draft
80 High Street
☎ (0181) 294 2578
11–11

195

Courage Directors; S&N Theakston Best Bitter, XB; Wadworth 6X; Younger Scotch; guest beers H
Recently opened pub in a former bank premises, one of Wetherspoon's smallest outlets. Photos of Frankie Howerd, Eltham's famous son.
Q ⊛ ◖ ▶ ≉ ⏚ ⚲

Porcupine
24 Mottingham Road
☎ (0181) 857 6901
10.30–3 (4 Sat), 5.30 (6 Sat)–11
Courage Best Bitter, Directors; John Smith's Bitter H
Pub with a 1930s mock Tudor interior. Its large garden, with an aviary and small zoo, attracts families. ⚲ ⊛ ◖ ⅋
≉ (Mottingham) ♣ P

SE10: Greenwich

Ashburnham Arms
25 Ashburnham Grove
☎ (0181) 692 2007
12–3, 6–11
Shepherd Neame Master Brew Bitter, Best Bitter, Spitfire, Bishops Finger, Porter H
Thriving local, popular with all ages, where the small back room displays work by local artists. A wide range of pasta dishes is available Tue, Fri and Sat. The recently opened garden is popular. Oversized glasses. ⊛ ◖ ≉ ♣ P

Coach & Horses
13 Greenwich Market
☎ (0181) 293 9273
11–11
Adnams Bitter; Ind Coope Burton Ale; Tetley Bitter; Young's Special; guest beer H
Pub located in Greenwich Market with an outside seating area. Lunches daily, families welcome. The guest beer changes every two weeks.
⊛ ◖ ≉

Hardy's Free House
92 Trafalgar Road
☎ (0181) 858 5292
11–11
Eldridge Pope Hardy Country, Royal Oak; Marston's Pedigree; guest beer G
Popular, ex-Young's pub, with casks on a cooling rack behind the bar. Lunches Mon–Fri.
⊛ ◖ ≉ (Maze Hill)

McGowan's Free House
56 Royal Hill
☎ (0181) 692 6147
11–11
Fuller's London Pride; Greene King Abbot; Young's Bitter; guest beer H

Free house decorated with a hunting theme—the pub was previously the Fox & Hounds. The guest beer changes weekly. Children are allowed in the dining area. ⊛ ◖ ▶ ≉

Vanbrugh Tavern
91 Colomb Street
☎ (0181) 305 1007
11–3 (12–4 Sat), 5.30 (7 Sat)–11
Bass Charrington IPA, Draught Bass H
Popular local in a back street near the hospital. Home-cooked food (eve meals till 8.30pm).
⊛ ◖ ▶ ≉ (Maze Hill)

SE12: Lee

Crown
117 Burnt Ash Hill
☎ (0181) 857 6607
11–11
Young's Bitter, Special, Winter Warmer H
Large, comfortable pub in a residential area, with a village-type atmosphere in its compact public bar. No food Sun. Q ◖ ≉ P

SE14: New Cross

Rose Inn
272 New Cross Road
☎ (0181) 692 3193
11–4, 5.30 (7 Sat)–11
Courage Best Bitter, Directors; Young's Special H
A warm and friendly welcome is assured in this busy pub opposite New Cross Gate station. The cosy interior has screens dividing the bar into small alcoves. ⊛ ◖ ≉ ⊖

SE17: Walworth

Crown
115–117 Brandon Street
☎ (0171) 703 3580
11–11
Draught Bass; Fuller's London Pride; Young's Special H
Friendly, Victorian local with a restored Wenlock facade, near East St Market, birthplace of Charlie Chaplin. ⊛
≉ (Elephant & Castle) ⊖ ♣

SE18: Woolwich

Bull
151 Shooters Hill Road (A207)
☎ (0181) 856 0691
11–3, 5.15 (7 Sat)–11
Courage Best Bitter, Directors H
Grade II-listed building, built in 1881 to replace the original Bull, which dated back to the early 1700s. It stands near the top of Shooters Hill, the Roman road from London to

Dover. No food Sun.
Q ⊛ ◖ ⊞ ⅋

Prince Albert (Rose's)
49 Hare Street
☎ (0181) 854 1538
11–11
Greene King Abbot; Shepherd Neame Master Brew Bitter, Porter; guest beers H
Welcoming, town-centre pub, home to plenty of sporting teams. Up to 12 guest beers a week.
◖ ▶ ≉ (Arsenal) ♣

Red Lion
6 Red Lion Place
☎ (0181) 856 0333
11–11
Courage Best Bitter, Directors H
Ex-Beasley's pub on Shooters Hill, with highwayman connections. The jukebox is sometimes loud. ⊛ ◖ P

SE22: East Dulwich

Clockhouse
196a Peckham Rye Common
☎ (0181) 693 2901
11–11
Young's Bitter, Special, Winter Warmer H
Comfortable pub, facing Peckham Rye. Note the collections of clocks and old beer bottle labels in the raised drinking area. A frequent winner of the London *Pubs in Bloom* competition. ⊛ ◖

Crystal Palace Tavern
193 Crystal Palace Road
☎ (0181) 693 4968
12–11
Ind Coope Burton Ale; Taylor Walker Best Bitter; Tetley Bitter; Young's Bitter; guest beer H
Popular local with interesting architecture, including etched-glass panels. Note the pictures of the Crystal Palace exhibition in the saloon. Food is served 12–4 weekdays. Q ◖

SE23: Forest Hill

Bird in Hand
35 Dartmouth Road
☎ (0181) 699 7417
11–11
Greene King IPA, Abbot; S&N Theakston XB; Younger Scotch; guest beer H
Quiet Wetherspoon pub offering a friendly welcome and reasonably priced food (until 10pm). Q ◖ ▶ ≉ ⏚ ⅋

Railway Telegraph
112 Stanstead Road (A205)
☎ (0181) 699 6644
11–3, 5.30–11; 11–11 Fri & Sat

Shepherd Neame Master
Brew Bitter, Best Bitter,
Spitfire, Bishops Finger,
Porter H
Large, popular pub on the
South Circular. Railway
memorabilia features.
⊠ ⊛ ◖ ⬍ ⮡ ✦

SE25: South Norwood

Alliance
91 High Street (A213)
☎ (0181) 653 3604
11–11
Courage Best Bitter,
Directors; Marston's Pedigree;
Morland Old Speckled Hen;
Wadworth 6X; guest beer H
Popular, one-bar corner local.
One quickly changing guest
beer, normally from a small
brewery, is usually on offer
and Imperial Russian Stout is
stocked. The family room is
open weekends. No food
Sun.
⊠ ⊛ ◖ ⮡ (Norwood Jct)

Port Manor
1 Portland Road (A215)
☎ (0181) 655 1308
11–11
Fuller's London Pride; Greene
King Abbot; Young's Special;
guest beers H
Lively, friendly, open-plan,
one-bar pub, popular with all
ages. It always offers six beers
at reasonable prices. No
food Sun; family room
weekends.
⊠ ⊛ ◖ ⮡ (Norwood Jct)

SE26: Dulwich

Dulwich Wood House
39 Sydenham Hill
☎ (0181) 693 5666
11–11
Young's Bitter, Porter or
Winter Warmer, Special H
Large, multi-roomed pub,
popular with families; the
garden has play equipment.
Strong sporting following. No
lunches Sun. Q ⊛ ⮡ (Sydenham Hill) ✦ P

SE26: Sydenham

Bricklayers Arms
189 Dartmouth Road
☎ (0181) 699 1260
11–11
Young's Bitter, Special,
Winter Warmer H
Pub rebuilt in 1924, where an
imposing corner frontage
encloses a public bar, with a
larger, multi-roomed saloon at
the rear, including a purpose-
built children's area. No
food weekdays.
Q ⊠ ⊛ ◖ ⮡

SE27: West Norwood

Hope
49 Norwood High Street
☎ (0181) 670 2035
11–11
Young's Bitter, Special,
Winter Warmer H
Small, friendly, one-bar local
with a five-pump bar engine
on the central bar. Note the
pictures of ships. Regular
fundraising events. Lunches
Mon–Fri. Q ⊛ ◖ ⮡

Addiscombe

Claret Free House
5a Bingham Corner, Lower
Addiscombe Road (A222)
☎ (0181) 656 7452
11.30–11
Eldridge Pope Dorchester,
Royal Oak; Palmers IPA;
guest beers H
Cosy, shopping parade bar.
The guest beers are changed
monthly. Lunches Mon–Fri.
◖ ♿ ⮡

Barnehurst

Red Barn
Barnehurst Road
☎ (01322) 332361
11–3, 6–11
Bass Charrington IPA;
Fuller's London Pride; Greene
King IPA; Hancock's HB;
guest beers H
A former *Guide*-listed pub,
back where it belongs. Three
bars at ground level while
another bar downstairs is used
for functions. A plaque claims
this pub to be the birthplace of
British trad jazz. ⊛ ⮡ ✦

Beckenham

Coach & Horses
Burnhill Road (off A222)
☎ (0181) 650 9142
11–3, 5.30–11
Courage Best Bitter,
Directors H
Small, friendly pub, just off the
high street. The locals have
raised over £10,000 for
charities. Unspoilt and a must.
Over-21s only; no food Sun.
Q ⊛ ◖ ♿ ⮡ (Beckenham Jct)
✦ P

Jolly Woodman
9 Chancery Lane (off A222)
☎ (0181) 650 3664
11–11
Bass Charrington IPA,
Draught Bass; guest beer H
Invariably busy, side-street
local with a village
atmosphere. Plenty of sporting
teams; occasional live music.
⊛ ◖ ⮡ (Beckenham Jct) ✦

Belvedere

Royal Standard
39 Nuxley Road
☎ (01322) 432774
11–11
Bass Worthington BB,
Draught Bass; Fuller's
London Pride; Greene King
IPA; guest beers H
Patriotic pub with a nautical
theme. ⊠ ⊛ ◖ P

Bexleyheath

Robin Hood & Little John
78 Lion Road
☎ (0181) 303 1128
11–3, 6–11; 12–2.30, 7–10.30 Sun
Courage Best Bitter,
Directors; Ruddles County;
John Smith's Bitter;
Wadworth 6X; guest beer H
Friendly Grade II-listed
building, dated early 1800. The
tables are made from sewing
machine treadles. Home-made
meals and bar snacks (not
Sun). ⊠ ⊛ ◖ ✦

Royal Oak (Polly Clean Stairs)
Mount Road
☎ (0181) 303 4454
11.30–3, 6–11
Courage Best Bitter; Ruddles
County; Wadworth 6X H
Excellent, historic hostelry; if
only more pubs were like this.
Snacks Mon–Sat lunchtimes.
Q ⊛ ✦ P

Bromley

Anglesey Arms
90 Palace Road
☎ (0181) 460 1985
11–3, 5–11
Courage Best Bitter; Fuller's
London Pride; Young's
Bitter H
One-bar, back-street local,
with a piano-player Sat eve.
Lunches Mon–Fri.
⊛ ◖ ⮡ (North) ✦

Bitter End
139 Masons Hill
☎ (0181) 466 6083
12–3 (not Mon), 5–10 (9 Mon); 11–10
Sat; 12–2, 5–9 Sun
Adnams Broadside; Brains
SA; Fuller's ESB; King &
Barnes Festive; Whitbread
Flowers Original G
Enterprising off-licence with
an ever-changing range of real
ales and often up to nine beers
at weekends. Bottled beers and
ciders stocked. ⮡ (South) ⌂

Chislehurst

Rambler's Rest
Mill Place (off A222)
☎ (0181) 467 1734
11–3, 5–11

Adnams Bitter; Courage Best Bitter, Directors; Marston's Pedigree; Wadworth 6X H
Split-level bar where the upper level is normally pleasantly bustling. At the edge of the common, it is ideally set for commuters, after the trek uphill from the station. No food Sun. Q ❀ ◖ ≹ P

Croydon

Arkwright's Wheel
151 North End
☎ (0181) 649 8638
11–11; closed Sun eve
Ind Coope Burton Ale; Marston's Pedigree; Tetley Bitter; Young's Bitter; guest beers H
Reincarnation of the former Railway Bell as a Victorian-style ale house; London's third 'Wheel'. Arkwright's Ale is a keenly-priced house beer. No food Sun. Q ◖ ◗ ≹ (West)

Builder's Arms
65 Leslie Park Road (off A222)
11.30–3, 5 (6.30 Sat)–11; 11.30–11 Fri
Fuller's Hock, Chiswick, London Pride, ESB H
Old, back-street local, extended in Victorian times. Two rather small and crowded bars are due for refurbishment. Excellent garden and good value food (eve meals Mon–Thu until 8.30). Q ❀ ◖ ◗ ≹ (East)

Crown
90 Stanley Road (between A23 & A235) ☎ (0181) 684 4952
11–11
Ruddles County; Webster's Yorkshire Bitter H
Excellent, street-corner local with a collection of plates in the single large bar. Two dartboards and a large range of board games (ask). Live music Sat night. ◖ ♣

Dog & Bull
24 Surrey Street
☎ (0181) 688 3664
11–11
Young's Bitter, Special, Winter Warmer H
18th-century, Grade II-listed building in the street market. Recent works have extended the bar, provided a food servery, and equipped the yard for outdoor drinking; all this without loss of character! CAMRA Greater London *Pub of the Year* 1994. Meals Mon–Fri.
Q ❀ ◖ ◗ ≹ (East/West) ♣

Porter & Sorter
Station Road (off A222)
☎ (0181) 688 4296
11–11; 11–3, 7–11 Sat; 12–3 Sun (closed eves Sun & bank hols)
Courage Best Bitter, Directors; Marston's Pedigree; Ruddles County; Wadworth 6X; Young's Special; guest beers (occasional) H
Small survivor of old Croydon; modernised without the loss of character. Its decor follows a railway theme. Popular with local workers at lunchtime and commuters eves. Food 12–6 Mon–Fri.
❀ ◖ ≹ (East) ♣ P

Princess Royal
22 Longley Road (off A213)
☎ (0181) 684 4056
11–11
Greene King XX Mild, IPA, Rayments Special, Abbot H
Small, friendly pub with a cosy atmosphere. The mild is a rare but welcome sight in Croydon.
⛫ ◖ ◗ ≹ (West) ♣

Royal Standard
1 Sheldon Street
☎ (0181) 688 9749
11.30–3, 5–11; 11–11 Fri & Sat
Fuller's Hock, London Pride, Mr Harry, ESB H
Busy, two-bar, L-shaped pub behind a multi-storey car park, under the flyover. Note the etched windows and large whiskey mirror in the back bar. Large garden across the road. Q ❀ ≹ (East)

Cudham

Blacksmith's Arms
Cudham Lane
☎ (0195 95) 72678
11–2.30 (3 Sat), 6–11
Courage Best Bitter, Directors; King & Barnes Sussex; Wadworth 6X H
Popular village local retaining its olde worlde charm. Barbecues summer weekends. Near the start of the Cudham Circular Walk. No food Mon eve. ⛫ Q ❀ ◖ ◗ ♣ P

Footscray

Seven Stars
High Street ☎ (0181) 300 2057
11.30–3.30, 5–11
Bass Charrington IPA, Draught Bass; Fuller's London Pride, ESB; Greene King IPA; Young's Bitter H
16th-century pub retaining many original features and offering a wide range of guest beers. ❀ ◖ ♣

Keston

Greyhound
Commonside (off B265)
☎ (01689) 856338
11–11
Courage Best Bitter, Directors; Ruddles County H
Pub opposite Keston Common, formerly a Style & Winch house. Live music at weekends. The beer prices reflect the area's affluence.
❀ ◖ ◗ P

Locksbottom

Olde Whyte Lyon
Farnborough Common (A21/A232 jct) ☎ (01689) 852631
11–3, 5.30 (6 Sat)–11
Courage Best Bitter; Greene King IPA; S&N Theakston Old Peculier; Shepherd Neame Master Brew Bitter; Wadworth 6X; guest beer H
17th-century coaching inn, with two large fireplaces. While the interior has been tastefully modernised, the exterior is magnificent. Book for eve meals. ⛫ Q ❀ ◖ ◗ P

Orpington

Cricketers
93 Chislehurst Road (off A208)
☎ (01689) 820164
11–3, 5–11; 11–11 Sat
Courage Best Bitter, Directors; guest beers H
Comfortable, one-bar pub by Broomhill Common offering ever-changing guest beers. Good range of food in the dining area. ♉ ❀ ◖ ◗ ♣ P

Sidcup

Alma
Alma Road
11–2.30, 5.30 (7 Sat)–11
Courage Best Bitter; Young's Bitter, Special H
Deservedly popular, back-street local, retaining some of its Victorian-style interior.
❀ ♿ ≹ ♣

Bitter Experience
3 Elm Parade, Main Road
☎ (0181) 309 5597
11–2, 6–9; 10.30–9.30 Thu–Sat; 7–9 Sun
Beer range varies G
Now the only real ale off-licence in the Borough, since the closure of the Bexleyheath shop.

South Croydon

Rail View
188 Selsdon Road (B275)
☎ (0181) 688 2315
11–3, 5–11; 11–11 Fri; 12–11 Sat
Bass Charrington IPA, Draught Bass; Fuller's London Pride H
Popular local with a lively public bar and a comfortable lounge, decorated on a railway theme. ❀ ◖ ⊞ ♿ ≹ ♣ P

Stag & Hounds
26 Selsdon Road
☎ (0181) 688 2885
11–11
Bass Worthington BB; Fuller's London Pride; Harveys BB Ⱨ
Pub with a square-shaped bar, adorned with paintings and photos, and busy at weekends with the football/rugby fraternity. Lunches Mon–Fri.
✿ ◖ ⇌ P

Thornton Heath

Horseshoe
745 London Road (A23/A235 jct) ☎ (0181) 684 1956
11–11
Courage Best Bitter, Directors Ⱨ
Welcoming, two-bar pub where pool and darts are played. The public bar can be loud, while the saloon is comfortable. The seating area at the rear is usually quiet. Weekday lunches. ◖ P

Wallington

Whispering Moon
25 Ross Parade, Woodcote Road (A237)
☎ (0181) 647 7020
11–11
Courage Directors; Greene King IPA; S&N Theakston Best Bitter, XB; Younger Scotch; guest beers Ⱨ
Another Wetherspoon conversion, this one from a former cinema. Local history is shown in photos. It appeals to all ages and is crowded at weekends. Guest beers are usually from the new small brewers. Q ◖ ◗ & ⇌ ⌂ ⊭

South-West London

SW1: Belgravia

Star Tavern
6 Belgrave Mews West
☎ (0171) 234 2806
11–3, 5–11; 11.30–11 Fri; 11.30–3, 7–11 Sat
Fuller's Chiswick, London Pride, ESB Ⱨ
Unchanging and unspoilt; in every edition of the *Guide*.
🏠 Q ◖ ⊖ (Hyde Pk Crnr)

Turks Head
10 Motcomb Street
11–11
Bass Worthington BB, Draught Bass; Fuller's London Pride; Greene King IPA Ⱨ
Pleasant pub, near Knightsbridge and the shops. Recently extensively rebuilt, but not altered internally.
◖ ◗ ⊖ (Hyde Pk Crnr)

SW1: Sloane Square

Fox & Hounds
29 Passmore Street
11–3, 5.30–11; 12–2, 7–10.30 Sun
Bass Charrington IPA, Draught Bass; Greene King IPA Ⱨ
Small, unspoilt friendly local which has a beer and wine licence only. It has featured in every edition of the *Guide*, with the same landlady.
◖ ⊖ (Sloane Sq)

SW1: Trafalgar Square

Old Shades
37 Whitehall
11–11
Bass Worthington BB, Draught Bass; Fuller's London Pride; Stones Best Bitter Ⱨ
Long, narrow, wood-panelled pub which opens out into a lounge at the rear. In common with pubs in this area, its licence is granted by Buckingham Palace.
🏠 ◖ ◗ ⇌ (Charing Cross) ⊖

SW1: Victoria

Wetherspoon's
Victoria Island, Victoria Station
11–11
Courage Directors; S&N Theakston Best Bitter, XB; Younger Scotch; guest beer Ⱨ
Untypical Wetherspoon's free house on the new Victoria development above WH Smith. Not everyone's idea of a cosy pub, but handy for trainspotters. Q ◖ ◗ ⇌ ⊖

SW1: Westminster

Buckingham Arms
62 Petty France
☎ (0171) 222 3386
11–11; 11–3, 5.30–11 Sat
Young's Bitter, Special, Winter Warmer Ⱨ
Popular pub, near the Passport Office, with a corridor drinking area behind the bar. Featured in every edition of the *Guide*. ◖ ◗ ⇌ (Victoria) ⊖ (St James's Pk)

Cardinal
23 Francis Street
11–11; 11–3, 8–11 Sat
Bass Worthington BB, Draught Bass; Fuller's London Pride Ⱨ
Large, ex-Finch's house with a wine and food bar at the rear, plus a restaurant upstairs. Occasional beer festivals.
◖ ⇌ (Victoria) ⊖

Morpeth Arms
58 Millbank ☎ (0171) 834 6442
11–11
Young's Bitter, Special, Winter Warmer Ⱨ
Pleasant corner pub, overlooking the Thames at Vauxhall Bridge and handy for the Tate Gallery.
◖ ◗ ⇌ (Vauxhall) ⊖ (Pimlico)

Paviours Arms
Page Street
11–11; 12–5 Sat; 12–3 Sun (closed Sat/Sun eves)
Fuller's Hock, Chiswick, London Pride, Mr Harry, ESB Ⱨ
Three-bar, Art Deco pub. Traditional and Thai food is available and it opens for breakfast 9–11. Only the Thames Bar is open at weekends (when no food is served).
◖ ◗ ⊞ ⇌ (Victoria) ⊖

Royal Oak
2 Regency Street
11–11; 11–3, 8–11 Sun
Young's Bitter, Porter, Special, Winter Warmer Ⱨ
Small corner pub, handy for the Horticultural Halls. ◖

Westminster Arms
9 Storeys Gate
11–11
Draught Bass; Brakspear Bitter; Everards Tiger; Wadworth 6X; Young's Bitter; guest beer Ⱨ
Pleasant haven close to Westminster and the Houses of Parliament. Wine bar on the lower floor.
◖ ⊖ (St James's Pk)

SW2: Brixton

Hope & Anchor
123 Acre Lane
☎ (0171) 274 1787
11–11
Young's Bitter, Special, Winter Warmer Ⱨ
One-bar pub with a friendly clientele. The large garden has a children's play area and boules. Good quality, home-cooked food. Local CAMRA *Pub of the Year* 1993. Family room only open Sun in winter.
🏠 Q ⚲ ✿ ◖ & ⇌ ⊖ ♣

SW3: Chelsea

Coopers Arms
87 Flood Street
11–11
Young's Bitter, Porter, Special Ⱨ
Busy, café-bar style pub with an extensive menu. ◖ ◗

Princess of Wales
145 Dovehouse Street
☎ (0171) 351 5502

199

Greater London

11–11
**Courage Best Bitter,
Directors; Wadworth 6X** H
Small, quiet pub behind the
Royal Marsden Hospital. ⊄ ⅃

Rose
86 Fulham Road
☎ (0171) 589 6672
11–11
**Fuller's Chiswick, London
Pride, ESB** H
Ornate pub with original
wood and tilework. ⊄ ▶

Surprise
6 Christchurch Terrace
11–11
**Bass Worthington BB,
Draught Bass; Fuller's
London Pride; M&B Brew
XI** H
Popular, back-street pub; one
bar but with two distinct
areas. Note the frieze around
the top of the bar. ⊄ ⅃

SW4: Clapham

Manor Arms
128 Clapham Manor Street
☎ (0171) 622 2894
11–11
**Brakspear Bitter; Marston's
Pedigree; Morland Old
Speckled Hen; Whitbread
Boddingtons Bitter; guest
beer**
Small, friendly, back-street
pub. It serves good value food
(Sun roast to order), and
regular barbecues in summer.
❀ ⊄ ⇌ (High St)
⊖ (North/Common) ♣

SW5: Earl's Court

Blackbird
209 Earl's Court Road
☎ (0171) 835 1855
11–11
**Fuller's Hock, Chiswick,
London Pride, ESB** H
Fuller's Ale & Pie House,
created in former premises of
the Midland Bank. Furnished
to a very high standard, it
stands opposite Earl's Court
station. ⊄ ▶ ⊖

SW6: Fulham

Jolly Brewer
308 North End Road
11–11
**Courage Best Bitter; Ruddles
County; Webster's Yorkshire
Bitter** H
Busy, popular street-market
pub. ⊄ ⌸ ⅃ ⊖ (Broadway)

White Horse
1 Parsons Green
☎ (0171) 736 2115
11–3, 5 (7 Sat)–11
**Adnams Extra; Bass
Worthington BB, Draught**
Bass; M&B Highgate Dark;
guest beer H
Large, busy, upmarket pub
facing Parsons Green, with an
outdoor terrace in front. Many
guest beers and several beer
festivals and promotions every
year. ⊄ ▶ ⊖ (Parsons Green)

SW7: South
Kensington

Anglesea Arms
15 Selwood Terrace
11–3, 5.30–11
**Adnams Bitter; Brakspear
Special; Greene King Abbot;
Young's Special; guest beer** H
Extremely busy and lively
pub, in every edition of this
guide. ⊄ ▶

SW8: Battersea

Old Red House
133 Battersea Park Road
(A3205) ☎ (0171) 622 1664
11–11
**Adnams Bitter; Courage Best
Bitter, Directors; Wadworth
6X; Wells Bombardier;
Young's Bitter** H
Pub with a good family
atmosphere; music at
weekends. Office workers and
staff from the Dogs Home are
regulars. Summer barbecues.
❀ ⊄ ⇌ (Battersea Pk) ♣ P

SW8: South
Lambeth

Royal Albert Ale
House
43 St Stephen's Terrace
☎ (0171) 735 3789
11–11; 12–3, 7.30–10.30 Sun
**Whitbread Boddingtons
Bitter; guest beers** H
Large community estate pub.
The front has TV (Mon night
soccer); the back is quiet and
furnished like a library. It has
a pool hall (upstairs), skittles
and a large garden. Beer
festivals. ❀ ⊄ ⇌ (Vauxhall)
⊖ (Stockwell) ♣ ⌂

SW8: Stockwell

Priory Arms
83 Lansdowne Way
☎ (0171) 622 1884
11–11
**Young's Bitter, Special; guest
beers** H
Friendly, popular local,
CAMRA SW London *Pub of the
Year* 1992. It has a good range
of games and frequently
changed guest beers.
⊄ ⊖ ♣ ⌂

Surprise
16 Southville
☎ (0171) 622 4623

11–11
**Young's Bitter, Special,
Winter Warmer** H
Small pub on a street which is
now a park. The friendly
clientele includes students.
Note the framed caricatures of
regulars in the back room.
Home-cooked food at good
prices, Mon–Fri (eves finish
early). ⛽ Q ❀ ⊄ ▶ ⅃ ⊖ ♣

SW8: Vauxhall

Roebuck
84 Ashmole Street
☎ (0171) 820 9793
11–11
**Bass Worthington BB,
Draught Bass; guest beer** H
Very good-looking pub inside
and out, with velour and high
leather chairs, soft low lighting
and air conditioning. The
clientele is mainly local.
Barbecues summer nights;
book eve meals. ⊱ ❀ ⊄ ▶
⅃ ⇌ ⊖ (Oval) ♣ ⌂ P ⌿

SW10: West
Brompton

Chelsea Ram
32 Burnaby Street
☎ (0171) 351 4008
11–3, 5.30–11; 11–11 Fri
**Young's Bitter, Special,
Winter Warmer** H
Comfortable pub near Lots Rd
Power Station and handy for
Chelsea Wharf. No jukebox or
piped music. Q ⊄

Fox & Pheasant
1 Billing Road
☎ (0171) 352 2943
12–3, 5.30–11
**Draught Bass; Greene King
IPA, Rayments Special,
Abbot** H
Small, two-bar local in a
private road off Fulham Rd,
near Chelsea football ground.
It was acquired by Greene
King from Bass in 1993.
Parking is very difficult.
❀ ⊄

SW11: Battersea

Beehive
197 St John's Hill
☎ (0171) 228 3253
11–11
**Fuller's Chiswick, London
Pride, ESB** H
Small, unpretentious, one-bar
pub, twice CAMRA SW
London *Pub of the Year*;
recently redecorated.
❀ ⊄ ⅃ ⇌ (Clapham Jct)

Castle
115 Battersea High Street
☎ (0171) 228 8181
11–11

Young's Bitter, Special, Winter Warmer H
Very smart and friendly pub where a big open fireplace features a 19th-century spit-roast. Food is available at all times. 🏃 Q ❀ ◖ ◗ ⅋ ⟠ (Clapham Jct) ♣ P

SW12: Balham

Grove Hotel
39 Oldridge Road
☎ (0181) 673 6531
11–11
Young's Bitter, Special H
Large, well-decorated Victorian house. Much under-used, it is pleasant for an uninterrupted pint and a chat. Quiet jukebox in the saloon bar; darts and bar billiards in the public. Lunches 11–3, Mon–Fri. ❀ ◖ ⊖ (Clapham S) ♣

Nightingale
97 Nightingale Lane
☎ (0181) 673 1637
11–3, 5.30–11; 11–11 Fri & Sat
Young's Bitter, Special, Winter Warmer H
Bustling, friendly pub, superbly managed: local CAMRA *Pub of the Year* 1991, and a massive fundraiser for local charities through its famous annual walk. No meals Sun eve. It can be very busy Fri eve. Q ⅘ ❀ ◖ ◗ ⅛ ⊖ (Clapham S) ♣

SW13: Barnes

Coach & Horses
27 Barnes High Street (A3003)
☎ (0181) 876 2695
11–11
Young's Bitter, Special, Winter Warmer H
Very cosy, welcoming, conversational, one-bar local with a huge log fire. It has a garden play area, plus a 'Paddock Room' for children, functions and barbecues. 🏃 Q ⅘ ❀ ◖ ◗

Red Lion
2 Castelnau (A306)
☎ (0181) 748 2984
11–11
Fuller's Hock, Chiswick, London Pride, ESB H
Large, Georgian-fronted pub, extended over the years, close to Barnes Common and pond, which creates a village atmosphere. A wide selection of meals is always available; summer barbecues in the large garden. 🏃 ❀ ◖ ◗ ⟠ ♣ P

SW14: Mortlake

Hare & Hounds
216 Upper Richmond Road, East Sheen ☎ (0181) 876 4304
11–11

Young's Bitter, Special, Winter Warmer H
Comfortable and roomy pub. The oak-panelled lounge has a pleasant atmosphere. Part of the bar is set aside for snooker, whilst a large, walled garden provides a children's play area and barbecues. Wide variety of good value food. 🏃 Q ❀ ◖ ◗ ⅋ ⟠

SW15: Putney

Fox & Hounds
167 Upper Richmond Road
☎ (0181) 788 1912
11–11
Fuller's London Pride; Wadworth 6X; Whitbread Boddingtons Bitter, Flowers Original H**; guest beers** H / G
Comfortable, spacious, one-bar pub with two open-plan rooms forming an L-shape. Busy, with a younger clientele, it stages occasional beer festivals. Eve meals finish at 7pm (not served Sun). ❀ ◖ ◗ ⅛ ⟠ ⊖ (East) ♣

SW15: Streatham

White Lion
232–236 Streatham High Road
☎ (0181) 769 4508
11–11
Ruddles County; Webster's Yorkshire Bitter; guest beers H
Basic, main-road boozer with thoughtful staff. Parking is difficult. ⅘ ◖ ◗ ⟠ ♣ ⟲

SW17: Earlsfield

Leather Bottle
538 Garratt Lane
☎ (0181) 946 2309
11–11
Young's Bitter, Special, Winter Warmer H
Two-bar pub: a large lounge bar with a warm atmosphere, and a lively public bar. Parts date from 1650. Barbecues in the large garden.
🏃 Q ⅘ ❀ ◖ ◗ ⅋ ⅛ ⟠ ♣ P

SW17: Tooting

Castle
38 Tooting High Street
☎ (0181) 672 7018
11–3, 6–11
Young's Bitter, Special, Winter Warmer H
Large, one-bar pub featuring light wood panelling and various drinking areas. Good atmosphere. Q ❀ ◖ ⅛
⟠ ⊖ (Broadway) ♣ P

JJ Moon's
56a High Street
☎ (0181) 672 4726
11–3, 6–11

Courage Directors; Greene King IPA, Abbot; Morland Old Speckled Hen; S&N Theakston XB; Younger Scotch; guest beers H
Former fast food shop and, before that, a public baths: a long and narrow pub, featuring wood panelling and ethnic art. Lively at the front, but quieter in the back.
Q ◖ ◗ ⟠ ⊖ ⟲ ⅛

SW17: Wandsworth Common

Hope
1 Bellevue Road
☎ (0181) 672 8717
11–11
Adnams Bitter; Ind Coope Burton Ale; Marston's Pedigree; Taylor Walker Best Bitter; guest beers H
Smallish, Victorian house, with an island bar, much improved. Local and passing trade creates an amiable atmosphere. Good pub food menu, including Sun lunches.
❀ ◖ ⟠ ♣

SW18: Earlsfield

Country House
2–4 Groton Road
☎ (0181) 874 2715
12–11
Courage Best Bitter, Directors; John Smith's Bitter; Young's Bitter H
Very local, friendly pub, countryfied for the area. It raises lots of money for charity. ◖ ◗ ⟠ ♣

SW18: Wandsworth

Brewery Tap
68 Wandsworth High Street
☎ (0181) 870 2894
11–3, 5.30–11
Young's Bitter, Special, Winter Warmer H
Pub of great splendour, retaining its public bar. The food is home-made with vegetarian options. 🏃 Q ◖ ⅋ ⟠ (Town)

County Arms
345 Trinity Road
☎ (0181) 874 8532
11–11
Young's Bitter, Special, Winter Warmer H
Traditional, main-road pub, sensitively renovated. The public area remains, but is incorporated into the large, rambling saloon and lounge bars. Ideal for prison visitors and footballers. No food Sun. Parking is difficult.
🏃 Q ❀ ◖ ◗ ♣ ⅛

Greater London

Old Sergeant

104 Garrett Lane
☎ (0181) 874 4099
11–3, 5–11; 11–11 Mon, Fri & Sat
Young's Bitter, Special, Winter Warmer H
Two-bar house with many pictures and copper objects on the walls; TV in the lounge bar. A quiet and welcoming pub.
Q ◑ ♣

SW19: Merton

Princess Royal

25 Abbey Road
☎ (0181) 542 3273
11–3, 5.30–11
Courage Best Bitter, Directors; Fuller's London Pride; Wadworth 6X H
Compact, unpretentious 200-year-old corner house with two bars, good food and a welcoming atmosphere: a gem. Q ✿ ◑ ▶
⊖ (S Wimbledon) ♣

SW19: Wimbledon

Dog & Fox

24 High Street
☎ (0181) 946 6565
11–11
Young's Bitter, Special, Winter Warmer H
Large pub in the trendy village, now refurbished. Popular function room. Parking is very difficult.
▨ Q ✿ ◑ ▶ ⇌ ⊕ ♣ ⊬

Hand in Hand

6 Crooked Billet
☎ (0181) 946 5720
11–11
Young's Bitter, Special, Winter Warmer H
Larger pub, which a horseshoe bar divides into public bar and saloon areas; a bakehouse and beerhouse until 1974. Packed in summer; outside drinking on the Common. No eve meals in winter.
▨ Q ⊱ ✿ ◑ ▶ ఉ ♣

SW20: Raynes Park

Cavern

100 Coombe Lane
☎ (0181) 944 8211
11–11
Fuller's London Pride; S&N Theakston XB; Whitbread Boddingtons Bitter; Young's Bitter, Special H
One-room pub by a busy road, featuring a Beatles/1960s rock'n'roll theme; good jukebox. A red telephone box adds to the decor. Good atmosphere: a welcome addition to SW20.
✿ ◑ ⇌

Carshalton

Fox & Hounds

41 High Street (A232)
☎ (0181) 773 3468
12–11; 12–4, 7–11 Sat
Ind Coope Friary Meux Best Bitter, Burton Ale; Tetley Bitter; guest beers H
Large, one-bar, main-road town pub with live jazz Wed and Sun eves. Friendly atmosphere. ✿ ◑ ఉ ⇌ P

Racehorse

17 West Street (off A232)
☎ (0181) 647 6818
11–11
Courage Best Bitter, Directors; King & Barnes Sussex; guest beers H
Smart, two-bar pub with a formal eating area in the lounge (excellent menu). Good bar meals, too. The enterprising tenant also leases the Windsor Castle. At least two guest beers every week; no food Sun eve.
Q ✿ ◑ ▶ ఉ ⇌ ♣ P

Railway Tavern

47 North Street (off A232)
☎ (0181) 669 8016
12–11
Fuller's Chiswick, London Pride, ESB H
Small, street-corner local with ornate windows, mirrors and railwayana. A home for many teams, from marbles to morris dancing. It may close afternoons; knock twice on the door! Crusty bread sandwiches served (except Sun). ⇌ ♣

Windsor Castle

378 Carshalton Road
☎ (0181) 773 3596
11–3, 5–11
Bass Worthington BB, Draught Bass; Fuller's London Pride; guest beers H
Large, one-bar pub at the main crossroads. It stocks a good range of guest beers, and offers excellent food in the restaurant or bar. No meals Sun eve. ✿ ◑ ▶ ఉ ⇌ ♣ P

Cheam

Railway

32 Station Way (off A217/A213) ☎ (0181) 642 7416
11–11
Courage Best Bitter, Directors; guest beer H
Detached, 19th-century building housing a comfortable single bar with 'Lords' and 'Commons' ends. Very much a local, its emphasis is on beer and conversation. No food Sun.
Q ◑ ▶ ⇌ ♣

Chessington

North Star

271 Hook Road, Hook (A243)
☎ (0181) 397 4227
12 (11 Sat)–11
Bass Charrington IPA, Draught Bass; M&B Highgate Dark, Highgate Old H
A long-established mild outlet which may also stock guest beers (from the Bass range). No food at weekends.
Q ✿ ◑ ♣ P

Kingston upon Thames

Boaters Inn

Canbury Gardens, Lower Ham Road ☎ (0181) 541 4672
11–3, 5–11; 11–11 Fri, Sat & summer
Draught Bass; Brakspear Bitter; Everards Tiger; Gale's Best Bitter; John Smith's Bitter H
Attractive, modern pub in Thames-side gardens, with its own moorings. It gets crowded in summer. Jazz Sun eve. *Three Men in a Boat* was set near here. ✿ ◑

Bricklayers Arms

53 Hawks Road (off A2043)
☎ (0181) 546 0393
11–11
Morland Bitter, Old Masters, Old Speckled Hen H
Excellent food in a genuinely welcoming local. Eve meals until 8pm (6pm Sat; no eve meals Sun). ⊱ ✿ ◑ ▶ ♣

Canbury Arms

49 Canbury Park Road
☎ (0181) 546 1822
11–11
Courage Best Bitter, Directors; John Smith's Bitter; guest beers H
Pub where good value meals are a lunchtime attraction. The dining area is in the 'Library' at the rear. Constantly changing (some unusual) guest beers. No meals Sun eve.
✿ ◑ ▶ ఉ ⇌ ♣ P

Cocoanut

16 Mill Street
☎ (0181) 546 3978
11–3, 5.30–11; 11–11 Sat
Fuller's Hock, Chiswick, London Pride, ESB H
Part of the local community, where a warm welcome is assured. CAMRA Greater London *Pub of the Year* 1992. Families welcome. Good food (no meals Sun). ✿ ◑ ♣ P

Kelly Arms

2 Glenthorne Road
☎ (0181) 546 8450
12–11; 12–3.30, 5.30–11 Mon

Courage Best Bitter, Directors; Marston's Pedigree; guest beer H
Locals' pub hidden in the back streets and dating from 1888, when there were five rooms. Occasional mini-beer festivals. No food Sun. ❀ ◖ ♣ ◠

Park Tavern
19 New Road
11–11
Brakspear Special; Whitbread Boddingtons Bitter; Young's Bitter, Special; guest beer H
Welcoming local, near the Kingston Gate of Richmond Park. Parking is difficult.
♨ ❀ ♣

Wych Elm
Elm Road ☎ (0181) 546 3271
11–3, 5–11; 11–11 Sat
Fuller's Hock, Chiswick, London Pride, Mr Harry, ESB H
Friendly pub, with a large regular following. Attractive garden. No food Sun; snacks only Sat. ❀ ◖ ⊟ ♣

Morden

Beverley
Lower Morden Lane (B279)
☎ (0181) 337 3071
11–3, 6–11
Ruddles Best Bitter, County; Webster's Yorkshire Bitter H
Comfortable saloon with an added conservatory, which doubles as the children's room, and a good, basic, public bar. Named after the local brook. ⛟ ❀ ◖ ▶ ♣ P

New Malden

Royal Oak
90 Coombe Road (B283)
☎ (0181) 942 0837
11–11
Ind Coope Benskins Best Bitter, Burton Ale; Tetley Bitter; Young's Bitter; guest beer H
Refurbished, large corner local. Quiz Tue; comedy Mon. No food Sun eve.
❀ ◖ ▶ ⊟ ≢ ♣ P ⍭

Richmond

Orange Tree
45 Kew Road
☎ (0181) 940 0944
11–11
Young's Bitter, Special, Winter Warmer H
Fine, popular pub in a large Victorian building with a fringe theatre upstairs and a bistro/wine bar downstairs. Good variety of meals; food is served from a counter in the lounge (no food Sun eve). Live jazz in the wine bar Wed eve.
♨ Q ❀ ◖ ▶ ≢ ⊖

Prince's Head
The Green ☎ (0181) 940 1572
11–11
Fuller's Chiswick, London Pride, ESB H
Attractive pub, established circa 1740. The lounge bar, in traditional style, is enhanced with prints of old Richmond. Try the good bar food, then enjoy a stroll around Richmond Green.
❀ ◖ ▶ ≢ ⊖

Triple Crown
15 Kew Foot Road
☎ (0181) 940 3805
11–11
Draught Bass; Bateman XXXB; Courage Best Bitter; Hook Norton Old Hooky H
Pub just outside the town centre; one of the few unspoilt hostelries left in this area, offering a constantly changing range of beers. ◖ ≢ ⊖ ⊖

White Cross Hotel
Water Lane ☎ (0181) 940 6844
11–11
Young's Bitter, Special, Winter Warmer H
Extremely popular, Thames-side pub in a splendid, picturesque setting, offering excellent bar food and service. The riverside terrace bar is open in summer. Local CAMRA *Pub of the Year* 1992.
♨ Q ❀ ◖ ▶ ≢ ⊖

Surbiton

Waggon & Horses
1 Surbiton Hill Road (A240)
11–2.30, 5–11; 11–11 Fri & Sat
Young's Bitter, Special, Winter Warmer H
The landlord celebrated his 27th year here in 1994, with £100,000 collected for charity during that period. Local CAMRA *Pub of the Year* 1993. Summer barbecues are held; no food weekends.
Q ❀ ◖ ⊟ ♣

Sutton

New Town
7 Lind Road (off A232)
☎ (0181) 642 0567
11–3, 5–11; 11–11 Sat
Young's Bitter, Special, Winter Warmer H
Popular, friendly, street-corner pub where the public bar has an adjoining games room and there is a contrasting, three-level saloon. No food Sun eve.
Q ❀ ◖ ▶ ⊟ ≢ ♣

Windsor Castle
13 Greyhound Road (off A232)
☎ (0181) 643 2574
11.30–3, 5–11; 11.30–11 Sat
Fuller's Hock, London Pride, ESB H

This popular local is known locally as the Little Windsor, to differentiate it from the Windsor Castle in Carshalton. The smart single bar is one of the smallest in the area. Meals Mon–Fri. ❀ ◖ ▶ ≢

West London

W1: Fitzrovia

Bricklayers Arms
31 Gresse Street
11–11
Samuel Smith OBB, Museum H
Small, pleasant, two-floor pub, a previous winner of CAMRA's *Pub Refurbishment* award.
◖ ▶ ⊖ (Tottenham Ct Rd)

Duke of York
47 Rathbone Street
11–11
Draught Bass; Greene King IPA, Rayments Special, Abbot H
Locals' pub at the end of a pedestrian street; a Greene King acquisition from Bass.
◖ ▶ ⊖ (Goodge St)

King & Queen
1 Foley Street
☎ (0171) 636 5619
11–11; 11–3, 7–11 Sat
Adnams Extra; Ruddles Best Bitter, County H
Friendly, red-brick pub in Gothic style, near Middlesex Hospital.
◖ ▶ ⊖ (Goodge St)

W1: Marylebone

Beehive
7 Homer Street
11–3, 5.30 (7 Sat)–11; 11–11 Fri
Brakspear Bitter; Whitbread Boddingtons Bitter, Wethered Bitter H
Small, neat back-street pub with local trade. ◖ ≢ ⊖

Golden Eagle
59 Marylebone Lane
11–11; 11–3, 5.30–11 Sat
Adnams Bitter; Brakspear Bitter; Marston's Pedigree; guest beer H
Tiny corner pub, with live piano at weekends. It serves a variety of sausages. ◖ ▶

Turners Arms
26 Crawford Street
11–11
Shepherd Neame Master Brew Bitter, Spitfire, Bishops Finger H
Pub owned by an unusual brewer for this area, displaying antique weapons in the bar. ◖ ▶ ≢ ⊖

Greater London

Wargrave Arms
40 Brendon Street
☎ (0171) 723 0559
11–11; 11–3, 7–11 Sat
**Young's Bitter, Porter,
Special, Winter Warmer** H
Narrow corner pub, one of the
Finch's pubs taken over by
Young's.
◗ ▶ ≠ (Paddington)
⊖ (Edgware Rd)

Worcester Arms
89 George Street
11–11; 11–3, 5.30–11 Sat
**Draught Bass; Brakspear
Bitter; S&N Theakston XB; guest
beer** H
Small, friendly pub with an
Alton Brewery mirror. The
beer range varies. ◗

W1: Mayfair

Guinea
30 Bruton Place
☎ (0171) 409 1728
11–11; 11–3, 7–11 Sat; closed Sun
**Young's Bitter, Porter,
Special, Winter Warmer** H
Small, intimate mews pub
with an exclusive restaurant at
the rear. The manager has won
awards for pub food. No
lunches Sat. There has been a
pub on this site since 1423.
Q ◗ ▶ ⊖ (Green Pk)

Windmill
6 Mill Street ☎ (0171) 491 8050
11–11 (3 Sat); closed Sun
**Young's Bitter, Porter,
Special, Winter Warmer** H
Split-level pub, giving the
effect of two separate bars.
Restaurant on the first floor.
◗ ▶ ⊖ (Oxford Circus)

W2: Bayswater

Archery Tavern
4 Bathurst Street
11–11
**Hall & Woodhouse Badger
Best Bitter, Hard Tackle,
Tanglefoot; Wadworth 6X;
guest beers** H
Wood-panelled pub, acquired
by Hall & Woodhouse and
usually offering a beer from
the Gribble brew pub at
Oving. Working stable next
door. ◗ ⊖ (Lancaster Gate)

Leinster Arms
17 Leinster Terrace
☎ (0171) 723 5757
11–11
**Ind Coope Burton Ale;
Nicholson's Best Bitter;
Tetley Bitter** H
Warmly decorated, friendly
pub in a tourist area. The
licensee won the 1994
Grandmaster Cellarman award
for her Burton Ale. A gem in
an area dominated by hotels.
Q ❀ ◗ ▶ ⊖ (Lancaster Gate)

Victoria
10a Strathearn Place
11–11
**Fuller's Chiswick, London
Pride, ESB** H
Victorian pub with much
original woodwork. Queen
Victoria is alleged to have
rested here on the way to open
Paddington station.
◗ ▶ ⊖ (Paddington)

W2: Paddington

Clutterbucks
329 Edgware Road
☎ (0171) 723 3899
11–11
**Adnams Bitter; Marston's
Pedigree; Tetley Bitter; guest
beers** H
Traditional-style ale house
with bare floorboards and pew
seating. It offers doorstep
sandwiches and baps, plus
three guest ales which change
every six weeks; Clutterbucks
is Friary Meux Best Bitter.
Q ❀ ≠ (Marylebone)
⊖ (Edgware Rd)

White Hart
31 Brook Mews North
☎ (0171) 402 4417
12–11
**Courage Best Bitter,
Directors; Wadworth 6X** H
Friendly pub at the end of a
mews; a former Reffell's of
Bexley house. ◗ ≠ ⊕ ♣

W3: Acton

Castle
140 Victoria Road
☎ (0181) 992 2027
11–11
**Fuller's Hock, Chiswick,
London Pride, ESB** H
An oasis. The very comfortable
lounge is adorned with
memorabilia of the BBC Radio
era and there are still links
with the BBC as rehearsal
studios are nearby. It can get
busy lunchtimes, but is ideal
for a quiet eve drink.
❀ ◗ ▶ ⊞ ⊖ (North) ♣ P

George & Dragon
183 High Street
☎ (0181) 992 1932
11–11
**Courage Directors; Fuller's
London Pride** H
The oldest pub in Acton, this
former coaching inn retains
the look and atmosphere of its
origins. The main bar is cosy
and welcoming; another bar
opens weekends for live music
(no real ale). No food Sun eve.
❀ ◗ ▶ ≠ (Central)

Red Lion & Pineapple
281 High Street
☎ (0181) 992 0465
11–11

Courage Directors; S&N
Theakston Best Bitter, XB;
Wadworth 6X; Younger
Scotch; guest beers H
Recently converted Fuller's
house which now has a large
island bar. There is little
evidence of its history as two
pubs, since being refurbished
in Wetherspoon's style.
Q ❀ ◗ ▶ ☖ ⊖ (Town) ⌂ ✄

W4: Chiswick

George IV
184 Chiswick High Road
☎ (0181) 994 4624
11–11
**Fuller's Hock, London Pride,
ESB** H
Large, two-bar pub where the
lounge is broken up by
intimate alcoves.
❀ ◗ ▶ ⊞ ⊖ (Turnham Green)

JJ Moon's
80–82 Chiswick High Road
☎ (0181) 742 7263
11–11
**Courage Directors; Morland
Old Speckled Hen; S&N
Theakston XB; Wadworth 6X;
Younger Scotch; guest beer** H
Wetherspoon pub in an
ex-betting shop: a welcome
addition to a sparsely pubbed
area. Wheelchair WC.
Q ◗ ▶ ☖ ⊖ (Stamford Brook)

Windmill
214 Chiswick High Road
11–11
**Fuller's Hock, Chiswick,
London Pride, ESB** H
Popular local with a large
outside drinking area in front.
The interior is decorated in
'Swiss chalet' style.
◗ ▶ ⊖ (Turnham Green)

W5: Ealing

Fox & Goose
Hanger Lane
☎ (0181) 997 2441
11.30–11
**Fuller's Hock, Chiswick,
London Pride, ESB** H
The very small public bar,
large saloon and pleasant
garden here all offer a
welcome refuge from the
infamous Hanger Lane
gyratory system. Live jazz Tue
eve. Q ❀ ◗ ▶ ⊞ ⊖ ♣ P

Red Lion
13 St Mary's Road
☎ (0181) 567 2541
11–11
**Fuller's Chiswick, London
Pride, ESB** H
Also known as Stage 6, due to
its proximity to the Ealing film
studios, this gem of a pub has
its walls lined with photos
from films and TV. Try the

award-winning garden.
Q ❀ ⇌ (Broadway)
⊖ (South) ♣

Rose & Crown

Church Place, St Mary's Road
☎ (0181) 567 2811
11–11
**Fuller's Hock, Chiswick,
London Pride, ESB** H
Popular local with a genuine
public bar and a large saloon,
which includes a 'greenhouse'
annexe. Tucked away behind
St Mary's church.
❀ ◖ ▶ ⊕ ⅄ ⊖ (South)

Wheatsheaf

41 Haven Lane
☎ (0181) 997 5240
11–11
**Fuller's Hock, Chiswick,
London Pride, ESB** H
Pub which actually gained a
small public bar during a
recent refurbishment. The
saloon is quite large, with
much wood in evidence.
Q ⌣ ❀ ◖ ▶
⇌ (Broadway) ⊖ ♣

W6: Hammersmith

Cross Keys

57 Black Lion Lane
☎ (0181) 748 3541
11–11
**Fuller's Chiswick, London
Pride, ESB** H
Popular pub between King St
and the Thames, extensively
refurbished. ❀ ◖ ▶

Dove

19 Upper Mall
11–11
**Fuller's Chiswick, London
Pride, ESB** H
Historic, 17th-century
riverside pub, originally the
Dove Coffee House. It has
been listed in the *Guinness
Book of Records* as having the
smallest public bar. *Rule
Britannia* was composed
upstairs. ❀ ◖ ▶ ⊕ ⊖

Salutation

154 King Street
11–11
**Fuller's Chiswick, London
Pride, ESB** H
Large busy pub in
Hammersmith's shopping
street, with a tiled frontage.
❀ ◖ ▶ ⊕ ⊖ (Ravenscourt Pk)

Thatched House

115 Dalling Road
☎ (0181) 748 6174
11–11
**Young's Bitter, Porter,
Special, Winter Warmer** H
Popular pub close to
Brackenbury village.
Barbecues in summer.
⌂ ◖ ▶ ⊖ (Ravenscourt Pk)

W7: Hanwell

White Hart

324 Greenford Avenue
☎ (0181) 578 1708
11–11
Fuller's London Pride, ESB H
Corner pub, featuring three
bars, an off-licence and a quiet
'private' bar. Antique
handpumps adorn the saloon
wall. ⌂ Q ⊕
⇌ (Castle Bar Pk) ♣ P

W8: Kensington

Britannia

1 Allen Street
☎ (0171) 937 1864
11–11
**Young's Bitter, Porter,
Special, Winter Warmer** H
Busy, wood-panelled pub
close to shops. The split-level
lounge has two bars and a
conservatory, which serves as
a no-smoking area at
lunchtime. Small public bar.
Q ◖ ▶ ⊕ ⊖ (High St) ⅄

Churchill Arms

119 Kensington Church Street
☎ (0171) 727 4242
11–11
**Fuller's Chiswick, London
Pride, ESB** H
Extremely busy pub with a
large collection of bric-a-brac.
⌣ ◖ ▶ ⊖ (Notting Hill Gate)

Windsor Castle

114 Campden Hill Road
☎ (0171) 727 8491
11–11
**Adnams Extra; Draught Bass;
Young's Bitter; guest beer** H
Cosy, wood-panelled pub with
three bars, also a garden bar
open in good weather. Food
all day; Sun lunches served
until 4pm. Q ❀ ◖ ▶
⊖ (Notting Hill Gate)

W9: Maida Vale

Warrington Hotel

93 Warrington Crescent
☎ (0171) 286 2929
11–11
**Fuller's London Pride, ESB;
Ruddles County; Young's
Special; guest beer**
(occasional) H
Large, ornate Victorian 'Gin
Palace' with florid decor and a
semi-circular marble bar top.
Thai restaurant upstairs (eves).
◖ ▶ ⊕ ⊖ (Warwick Ave)

Warwick Castle

6 Warwick Place
11–11
**Bass Worthington BB,
Draught Bass; Fuller's
London Pride; Wadworth 6X;
guest beer** H

Pleasant pub near Regent's
Canal Paddington Basin. Note
the Victorian print of
Paddington station.
⌂ ◖ ⊖ (Warwick Ave)

W12: Shepherd's Bush

Crown & Sceptre

57 Melina Road
☎ (0181) 743 6414
11–11
Fuller's London Pride, ESB H
Popular back-street pub in a
real ale desert. May close Sat
afternoons if QPR are at home.
◖ ⊕

Moon on the Green

172–174 Uxbridge Road
☎ (0181) 749 5709
11–11
**Courage Directors; Greene
King IPA; S&N Theakston
Best Bitter, XB; Younger
Scotch; guest beer** H
Typical Wetherspoon pub
which seems to have settled
into the area. Q ◖ ▶ ⊖

W13: West Ealing

Kent

2 Scotch Common
☎ (0181) 997 5911
11–11
**Fuller's Hock, London Pride,
ESB** H
Large, slightly upmarket
house in a residential area,
with a huge garden. A small
public bar has been retained
while the split-level saloon
takes up most of the area.
Q ⌣ ❀ ◖ ⅄
⇌ (Castlebar Halt) ♣ P

W14: West Kensington

Seven Stars

253 North End Road
11–11
**Fuller's Hock, London Pride,
ESB** H
Large, two-bar pub, rebuilt in
1938 and decorated in Art
Deco style. ❀ ◖ ⊕ ⊖

Warwick Arms

160 Warwick Road
☎ (0171) 603 3560
11–11
**Fuller's Hock, Chiswick,
London Pride, Mr Harry,
ESB** H
Traditional pub, built in 1830,
popular with office workers
lunchtime and locals in the
eve. Note the Wedgwood
pump handles. Handy for the
exhibition halls. No food Sun
eve. Q ◖ ▶ ⇌ (Olympia)
⊖ (Earl's Ct) ♣

Greater London

Bedfont

Beehive
333 Staines Road
☎ (0181) 890 8086
11–11
Fuller's London Pride, ESB H
Excellent pub with a friendly atmosphere, an attractive lounge and a well-kept garden. It offers good value meals from a Thai and traditional menu (not served Sat lunch or Sun); barbecues in summer. ⌖ ◖ ❱ P

Brentford

Globe
104 Windmill Road
☎ (0181) 560 8932
11–11
Fuller's Hock, Chiswick, London Pride, ESB H
One-bar pub with an attractive garden. Note the old photos of local landmarks. Trad jazz Mon and Wed eves; no food Sun eve. ⌖ ◖ ◗ ଐ ⇌ ♣

Cranford

Queen's Head
123 High Street
☎ (0181) 897 0722
11–11
Fuller's Hock, Chiswick, London Pride, ESB H
Tudor-style pub with one bar, but two distinct drinking areas. A lounge to one side is used for dining (home-cooked food; not served weekend eves). Award-winning garden. ⌂ Q ⌣ ⌖ ◖ ❱ ♣ P

Feltham

General Roy
Poplar Way ☎ (0181) 893 2977
11–11
Bass Worthington BB, Draught Bass; Fuller's London Pride; guest beers H
Fine new pub named after General William Roy, the 18th-century mapmaker whose work locally led to the founding of the Ordnance Survey. A spacious lounge, traditionally furnished, has a good atmosphere. Wide choice of good meals (not served Sun eve). ⌖ ◖ ❱ ଐ ⇌ P

Greenford

Black Horse
425 Oldfield Lane
☎ (0181) 578 1384
11–11
Fuller's Chiswick, London Pride, ESB H
On the Paddington arm of the Grand Union Canal: a busy

and friendly pub with moorings. The large garden has a children's play area.
Q ⌖ ◖ ଐ ⇌ ❂ ♣ P

Hampton

White Hart
70 High Street
☎ (0181) 979 5352
11–3, 5.30–11; 11–11 Fri & Sat
Brakspear Special; Brewery on Sea Black Rock; Greene King Abbot; Whitbread Boddingtons Bitter, Castle Eden Ale, Flowers Original H
Genuinely free house with eight handpumps serving a regularly changing selection of beers, in a comfortable, friendly atmosphere. ⌂ Q ◖

Hampton Wick

White Hart
High Street ☎ (0181) 977 1786
11–3, 5.30–11; 11–11 Thu–Sat
Fuller's Hock, London Pride, ESB H
Large, mock Tudor pub at the foot of Kingston Bridge. The comfortable atmosphere is enhanced by the real fire and excellent, good value food (Mon–Fri). ⌂ ⌖ ◖ ⇌ P

Harlington

White Hart
158 High Street
☎ (0181) 759 9608
11–11
Fuller's Hock, Chiswick, London Pride, ESB H
Pleasant, one-bar pub and restaurant, subtly-lit.
⌖ ◖ ❱ P

Harmondsworth

Crown
High Street ☎ (0181) 759 1007
11–11
Brakspear Bitter; Courage Best Bitter, Directors; Marston's Pedigree H
Despite its proximity to Heathrow Airport, this is still a true village local, convivial, characterful and occasionally lively. Local newspapers and enamel signs feature.
⌂ ⌖ ◖ ❱ ♣

Hayes End

Angel
697 Uxbridge Road
☎ (0181) 573 0175
11–3 (4 Sat), 5.30–11
Fuller's Hock, London Pride, ESB H
Traditional pub with three separate bar areas: public, saloon and lounge. Music Fri and Sat nights in the lounge; the public bar is popular for darts. Q ⌖ ◖ ⌷ ❱ ♣ P

Heathrow Airport

Tap & Spile
Upper Concourse, Terminal 1
☎ (0181) 897 3696
11–11
Marston's Pedigree; guest beers H
Busy airport bar providing a large choice of beers for the thirsty traveller, most of which change regularly and include Marston's Head Brewer's Choice beers. It opens at 9am for continental breakfasts.
Q ❱ ⌖ ⌅ ⌦

Hounslow

Cross Lances
236 Hanworth Road (A314)
☎ (0181) 570 4174
11–11
Fuller's London Pride, ESB H
Early Victorian, traditional local with a popular public bar. The saloon has a large welcoming fire. Wholesome meals (not served Sun).
⌂ ⌖ ◖ ⌷ ⇌ P

Earl Russell
274 Hanworth Road (A314)
☎ (0181) 570 1560
11–11
Fuller's Hock, Chiswick, London Pride, ESB H
Traditional, Victorian local with a comfortable saloon bar. Lunches Mon–Fri.
⌖ ◖ ⌷ ⇌ ❂ (Central) P

Jolly Farmer
177 Lampton Road
☎ (0181) 570 1276
11–11
Courage Best Bitter, Directors; Wadworth 6X H
Popular, cosy local. The friendly licensees offer very good weekday lunches.
⌖ ◖ ⌷ ❂ (Central) ♣ P

Moon Under Water
84–86 Staines Road
☎ (0181) 572 7506
11–11
Courage Directors; Greene King IPA, Abbot; S&N Theakston XB; Wadworth 6X; Younger Scotch H
Very popular Wetherspoon pub with a strong commitment to customer service. Good value food at all hours; occasional beer festivals.
Q ⌖ ◖ ❱
⇌ ❂ (Central) ⌦

Isleworth

Bridge Inn
457 London Road
☎ (0181) 568 0088
11–11
Courage Best Bitter; Marston's Pedigree; John Smith's Bitter H

Friendly pub, near Isleworth station. Originally built in the 1870s and called the Iron Bridge, it has recently been refurbished, incorporating an excellent Thai restaurant. No food Sun. ⨝ ◖ ▶ ⇌

Castle
18 Upper Square, Old Isleworth ☎ (0181) 560 3614
11–11
Young's Bitter, Special, Winter Warmer Ⓗ
Friendly, popular pub in Old Isleworth, close to the Thames. Try the good value Sun roast. ⨝ ⌁ ⍟ ◖ ⊞ P

County Arms
2 Hall Road ☎ (0181) 560 3971
12–11
Brakspear Bitter; Exmoor Beast; Morland Old Speckled Hen; Ringwood Fortyniner; Wadworth 6X; Webster's Yorkshire Bitter Ⓗ
Former Watney pub, now free of a tie, offering an excellent and constantly changing range of beers. Live music five nights a week (mainly Blues). The County Bar retains a 1930s atmosphere. Summer barbecues. Children welcome until 8pm. ⨝ Q ⌁ ⍟ ◖ ⊞ ⇌ (Hounslow) ♣ ⌂ P

Town Wharf
Swan Street, Lower Square, Old Isleworth (off A300)
☎ (0181) 847 2287
11–3, 5.30–11 (11–11 summer)
Samuel Smith OBB, Museum Ⓗ
Riverside pub on the old wharf, with a comfortable upstairs lounge and terrace overlooking the Thames. The downstairs bar has a tiled floor and glazed-wood partitions. Q ⌁ ⍟ ◖ ⊞ ♣ P

Norwood Green

Plough
Tentelow Lane
☎ (0181) 574 1945
11–11
Fuller's Chiswick, London Pride, ESB Ⓗ
Fuller's oldest inn, which can trace its roots back to 1349. In a village setting, facing the church, this pub is popular with locals, sports clubs and the car-borne trade alike. Weekday lunches; free snacks at weekends. ⨝ Q ⍟ ◖ ♣ P

Ruislip Manor

JJ Moon's
12 Victoria Road
☎ (0181) 622373
11–11
Courage Directors; Greene King IPA, Abbot; S&N Theakston XB; Younger

Scotch; guest beer Ⓗ
Traditional-style, mock Victorian ale house, converted from an old Woolworth's store. Very popular with all ages. Q ⍟ ◖ ▶ ⚓ ⊖ ⌂ ⌁

Southall

Hambrough Tavern
The Broadway
☎ (0181) 813 9522
11–11
Beer range varies Ⓗ
Two-bar pub on the east bank of the Grand Union Canal, rebuilt in 1982 after the original burnt down. A changing range of beers, mostly from independent breweries, is served from three handpumps. ⍟ ◖ ♣ P

Teddington

Builders Arms
38 Field Lane
☎ (0181) 977 4710
11–3, 5.30–11; 11–11 Sat & summer
Brakspear Bitter; Courage Best Bitter, Directors; King & Barnes Sussex; Marston's Pedigree Ⓗ
Cosy, two-roomed local, recently refurbished, with a friendly atmosphere, and always something going on. ⍟ ◖ ⊞ ⇌ ♣

Hogarth
58 Broad Street
☎ (0181) 977 3846
11–11
Fuller's Hock, Chiswick, London Pride, ESB Ⓗ
Busy, town-centre pub, formerly the Britannia. Impending structural additions will include a no-smoking food area. ◖ ▶ ⇌

Queen Dowager
49 North Lane
☎ (0181) 977 2583
11–3, 5.30–11; 11–11 Fri & Sat
Young's Bitter, Special, Winter Warmer Ⓗ
Small, comfortable local off the main street, with an excellent garden. It was named after Queen Adelaide, the widow of William IV. Local CAMRA *Pub of the Year* 1993. No food Sun. Q ⍟ ◖ ⊞ ⇌ ♣

Twickenham

Albany
Station Yard
☎ (0181) 892 1554
11–3, 5.30–11; 11–11 Fri & Sat
Bass Worthington BB, Draught Bass; Young's Bitter, Special; guest beers Ⓗ
Large, town pub, popular with all ages, and rugby fans. It offers pool, snooker, and cable TV for sports; a dining area in the bar serves recommended

food, Mon–Fri (eves on request). Occasional beer festivals. ⌁ ◖ ▶ ⇌ ♣ P

Eel Pie
9 Church Street (off A305)
☎ (0181) 891 1717
11–11
Hall & Woodhouse Badger Best Bitter, Hard Tackle, Tanglefoot; Wadworth 6X; Wells Eagle Ⓗ
Smart, converted wine bar near the riverside, in the town's oldest shopping street. Traditional and continental lunches served weekdays and Sun. ◖ ⇌ ♣

Prince Albert
30 Hampton Road (A311)
☎ (0181) 894 3963
11–11
Fuller's Hock, Chiswick, London Pride, ESB Ⓗ
Friendly, Victorian local, recently given a slightly airier atmosphere by lighter wood, but otherwise unchanged. Occasional live Blues. Sun lunches a speciality. Q ⍟ ◖ ⇌ (Strawberry Hill)

Prince Blucher
124 The Green
☎ (0181) 894 1824
11–11
Fuller's Hock, Chiswick, London Pride, ESB Ⓗ
Old pub, modernised but retaining its original character in one large bar with real fires. Large floodlit garden with a children's play area. ⨝ ⍟ P

Uxbridge

Load of Hay
33 Villier Street
☎ (01895) 234676
11–3, 5.30 (7 Sat)–11
Courage Best Bitter; guest beers Ⓗ
Cosy local (near Brunel University), originally built as Elthorne Light Militia officers' mess. The small front bar opens as a restaurant Sat eve (book). An ever-changing range of guest beers make this a popular local. No food Sun/ Mon eves. ⍟ ◖ ⊖ P ⌁

Whitton

White Hart
123 Kneller Road
☎ (0181) 893 3646
11–11
Greene King IPA; Smiles Best Bitter; Wadworth 6X; Webster's Yorkshire Bitter Ⓗ
17th-century coaching inn, purchased as a free house in 1991 after closure in 1989 following a fire and sympathetically restored. Excellent food (not served Sun eve). ⍟ ◖ ▶ ⇌ ♣ P

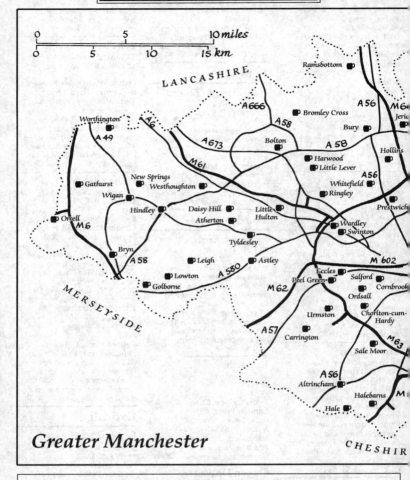

Greater Manchester

 Flea & Firkin, Hydes' Anvil, *Manchester*; Holt, *Cheetham*; Lass O'Gowrie, *Manchester*; Lees, *Middleton Junction*; Thomas McGuinness, *Rochdale*; Oak, *Heywood*; Robinson's, *Stockport*; West Coast, *Chorlton-on-Medlock*

Altrincham

Hogshead Alehouse
Old Market Place
☎ (0161) 972 7062
11–11
Beer range varies H
Once Altrincham town hall, now a recent Hogshead conversion that has worked well. It's rumoured that Bonnie Prince Charlie called in here. Live music Sun eve.
🏠 ☎ ❀ ◖ ≠ ⊖ ⊖ ⅍

Malt Shovels
68 Stamford Street
☎ (0161) 928 2053
12–3, 5–11; 12–11 Fri & Sat
Samuel Smith OBB, Museum H
Friendly town-centre pub with live jazz five nights a week. No food Sun.
❀ ◖ ≠ ⊖ ♣

Orange Tree
Old Market Place
☎ (0161) 928 2600
11–11
Courage Directors; Marston's Pedigree; Webster's Green

Label, Wilson's Bitter; guest beer H
Once the smallest pub in Altrincham, where, in 1823, a man sold his wife for 1/6d. The present building dates from 1880. Note the old photos showing local pubs now gone and the pub under restoration.
Q ☎ ◖ ≠ ⊖ ⅍

Tatton Arms
3–5 Tipping Street (near Sainsbury's) ☎ (0161) 941 2502
11–11
Whitbread Boddingtons Bitter H

208

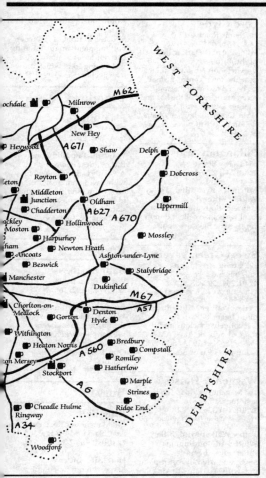

Whitbread Chester's Mild, Boddingtons Bitter; Marston's Pedigree; guest beers H
Long-established free house serving an impressive array of guest beers from five pumps. The large red brick building has three separate areas, as well as a conservatory and garden. Regular beer festivals. Folk club Mon. Occasional cider. ✿ ◖ ⇌ ♣ ☺

Witchwood

152 Old Street
☎ (0161) 344 0321
12–11
Holt Bitter; S&N Theakston Best Bitter, XB; John Smith's Bitter; Whitbread OB Bitter; guest beers H
Deservedly popular, town-centre pub, far enough out to miss the Fri/Sat night revellers. Noted concert room at the rear with a late bar. Usually three, reasonably-priced guest beers. ◖ ⇌

Astley

Cart & Horses

221 Manchester Road
☎ (01942) 870751
12–11
Holt Mild, Bitter H
Popular roadside local with a cobbled area at the front. The large, open-plan lounge gives a two-room feel. Raised no-smoking area; popular tap room. ✿ ◖ ♣ P ⤬

Atherton

Bay Horse

30 Bolton Old Road
☎ (01942) 894814
12–11
Tetley Walker Dark Mild, Bitter H
Edge-of-town, popular local where the large lounge is divided in two. There's also a standing area in front of the bar, a tap room and a separate pool room. ♨ ⊞ ⇌ ♣ P

Spinners Arms

76 Bolton Road
☎ (01942) 882498
12–3.30, 7–11; 12–11 Thu–Sat
Tetley Walker Dark Mild, Bitter; guest beers H
Good roadside local with a large cobbled car park at the front. The long, narrow lounge has a raised area at the far end; also a tap room. Note the George Shaw etched windows. Families welcome till 7pm.
⚲ ✿ ◖ ⇌ ♣ P

Beswick

Britannia

2 Rowsley Street (off A662 at Mosley pub)

Thriving two-room local where the pictures reflect the long-serving landlord's nautical background and the locals' interest in the two Manchester football clubs. No food Sun.
♨ ✿ ◖ ⊞ ⇌ ♣ P

Ancoats

Mitchel Arms

215 Everly Street
☎ (0161) 273 3097
12–3, 7–11; 12–11 Fri & Sat
Banks's Mild, Bitter E
Friendly, two-roomed estate pub. ⊞ ♣ P

Ashton-under-Lyne

Dog & Pheasant

528 Oldham Road
☎ (0161) 330 4894
12–5.30 (6 Sat), 7.30–11
Banks's Mild; Marston's Bitter, Pedigree H

Hospitable and comfortable pub close to Daisy Nook Country Park. The menu features tempting puddings.
✿ ◖ P ⤬

Oddfellows Arms

Kings Road, Hurst
☎ (0161) 330 6356
12–11
Robinson's Hatters Mild, Best Bitter, Hartleys XB, Old Tom (winter) H
In the same family for 80 years: a cosy, many-roomed local with traditional features, plus a walled garden. A recent extension is the no-smoking Tom's Bar. The reputed birthplace of the NUM. Lunches on request.
Q ♣ ⤬

Station

Warrington Street (by pass)
☎ (0161) 330 6776
11.30–11; 11.30–3, 7–11 Sat; 12–2, 7–10.30 Sun

Greater Manchester

☎ (0161) 223 1604
11–11; 11–4, 8–11 Sat
Lees GB Mild, Bitter H
Next to (but safe from) a
massive redevelopment site,
this well-kept two-roomer is a
welcome survivor of E
Manchester's sadly diminished
pub stock. The vault has darts
and often TV; the lounge is
quieter but has a pool table.
Good humour throughout.
Lunches Mon–Fri. Ⓓ ⊟ ♣

Blackley

Pleasant Inn
370 Chapel Lane (off A6104 at
Tweedle Hill Rd)
☎ (0161) 740 3391
1–11
**Robinson's Hatters Mild, Best
Bitter** H, **Old Tom** (winter) G
Small community pub in the
15th-century Crab village; a
lively sporting vault, a lounge
and a snug. Small golf society
club room. Q ❀ ⊟ ♣

Bolton

Anchor Inn
14–16 Union Buildings (off
Bradshawgate)
☎ (01204) 26467
11–11; 12–5, 7–11 Sat
**Bass Worthington BB,
Draught Bass; Stones Best
Bitter** H
Small, one-bar pub,
refurbished to a maritime
theme in the late 1980s.
Ⓓ ⇌ ♣

Bob's Smithy Inn
1448 Chorley Old Road
☎ (01204) 842622
12–3.30 (may extend), 5.30–11
**Taylor Best Bitter; Walker
Bitter; Whitbread
Boddingtons Bitter; guest
beers** H
Popular pub on the fringes of
the moors, with views of
Bolton. Named after the local
blacksmith who frequented it.
🏭 Q ❀ Ⓓ ♣ P

Clifton Arms
94 Newport Street (opp.
rail/bus interchange)
☎ (01204) 392738
11–11
**Jennings Bitter; Moorhouse's
Premier; Tetley Walker Mild,
Bitter, Walker Best Bitter** H
A popular pub, convenient for
travellers. No food Sun.
Ⓓ ⇌ ♣

Lodge Bank Tavern
264 Bridgeman Street
☎ (01204) 31946
12–11
Lees GB Mild, Bitter H
Large, brick-built Victorian
pub which stands on its own
near a park. A cheerful local.
❀ ♣ P

Lord Clyde
107 Folds Road (A676)
12–11; 12–5, 7–11 Tue, Wed & Sat
**Hydes' Anvil Dark Mild,
Light, Bitter** E
Very friendly, traditional local
near the town centre: a small,
L-shaped tap room, a small
room at the rear of the bar and
a larger lounge with a pool
table. Open all day Sat when
Bolton FC are at home.
❀ Ⓓ ♣ P

Pilkington Arms
154 Derby Street
☎ (01204) 27960
11–11
**Mitchell's Best Bitter; Tetley
Walker Bitter** H
Unpretentious and welcoming
local with an excellent domino
vault. Near the town centre.
♣

Sweet Green Tavern
127 Crook Street (opp.
rail/bus interchange)
☎ (01204) 392258
11.30–3 (3.30 Sat), 6.30–11; 11.30–11
Thu & Fri
**Tetley Walker Mild, Bitter;
guest beers** H
Deceptively spacious, multi-
roomed pub. Bolton CAMRA
Pub of the Year 1992 and 1993.
No lunches Sat or Sun.
🏭 Ⓓ ⇌ ♣ P

Waggon & Horses
160 Manchester Road (B6536,
near football ground)
☎ (01204) 32602
11–3, 7–midnight (1am Thu, 2am Fri &
Sat)
**Tetley Walker Mild, Bitter;
Whitbread Boddingtons
Bitter; guest beers** H
Smart and friendly, open-plan
pub with separate drinking,
eating and games areas,
popular at night with young
people. Note the late closing
times (entrance charge some
nights). Open for meals all day
Sun. ❀ Ⓓ ❱ ⇌ ♣ P

Bredbury

Arden Arms
Ashton Road
☎ (0161) 430 2589
11.30–3, 5.30–11; 11.30–11 Thu, Fri &
summer; 12–3.30, 6–11 Sat
**Robinson's Hatters Mild, Best
Bitter** E
One of the few traditional
Robinson's pubs left. Small
rooms contribute to the
comfortable atmosphere and
its semi-rural setting makes it
very popular summer
weekends. Q ❀ ♣ P

Horsfield Arms
Ashton Road
☎ (0161) 430 6930
11.45–11; 11.45–3, 7–11 Sat

**Robinson's Hatters Mild, Best
Bitter** E
Situated in front of Robinson's
bottling plant: an unassuming
exterior hides a comfortable,
welcoming local which draws
a loyal clientele. Q ❀ Ⓓ P

Bromley Cross

Flag Inn
50 Hardmans Lane (200 yds
from B6472) ☎ (01204) 302236
11–11
**Whitbread Boddingtons
Bitter; guest beers** H
A Whitbread cask ale house,
with a wide range of beers
always on offer. Very popular
in the eve. Named after a large
slab of stone brought from the
local quarry. Cellar viewing
area. 🏭 ❀ ♣ ○

Bryn

Bath Springs
Wigan Road (A49)
☎ (01942) 202716
11–11
**Ind Coope Burton Ale; Tetley
Walker Mild, Bitter, Walker
Best Bitter; guest beers** H
Welcoming local named after
the Bath Springs Brewery of
Ormskirk. Good value
lunches. Very smart function
room. Ⓓ ⇌ ♣

Bury

Blue Bell
840 Manchester Road (A56,
near Blackford Bridge)
☎ (0161) 766 2496
12–11
Holt Mild, Bitter H
Large, three-roomed pub with
a traditional vault, popular
with mature Man Utd
supporters. The big,
comfortable lounge is enjoyed
by friendly locals. Very
popular Sun lunchtimes. Pool
room. Q ❀ & ♣ P

Dusty Miller
87 Crostons Road (B6213/
B6214 jct) ☎ (0161) 764 1124
12–11; 12–4, 7–11 Sat
**Moorhouse's Black Cat Mild,
Premier, Pendle Witches
Brew; guest beers** H
A rare Moorhouse's tied
house, offering one room on
each side of a central bar and a
friendly welcome. The
enclosed courtyard to the rear
provides seating for sunny
days. ⌂ ❀ Ⓓ & ⊖ ♣

Old Blue Bell
2 Bell Lane (B6221/B6222 jct)
☎ (0161) 761 3674
12–11; 12–4.30, 7–11 Sat
Holt Mild, Bitter H

Extensive, multi-roomed pub acquired by Holt and nicely refurbished. Live music Thu; disco Sun. Note the splendid weather vane and the star carved in stone to symbolise the old Star Brewery.
ౘ ⊖ ♣

Tap & Spile
36 Manchester Old Road (off A56) ☎ (0161) 764 6461
12–3, 5–11; 12–11 Fri & Sat
Beer range varies ᴴ
Railway-themed pub, very popular with E Lancs Railway volunteers. Spot the previous pub name in the decor. At least six guest beers served at any one time. Food available Mon–Sat. Families welcome till 7pm. ౘ ◖ ⊖ ⊖

Carrington

Windmill Inn
Manchester Road
☎ (0161) 775 2251
11.30–11
Samuel Smith OBB, Museum (occasional) ᴴ
Low-ceilinged former coaching house, with wooden settle seating. The large garden/play area is very popular with families on summer eves and at weekends. ⊛ ◖ ⊟ ♣ P

Chadderton

Horton Arms
19 Streetbridge (B6195, almost under A627M)
☎ (0161) 624 7792
11.30–11
Lees GB Mild, Bitter ᴴ
Comfortable, modernised house retaining a number of separate drinking areas and a country pub feel. Weekday lunches. ♨ Q ౘ ⊛ ◖ ♣ P

Sun Mill Inn
505 Middleton Road (opp. town hall) ☎ (0161) 624 6232
12–3, 5 (7 Sat)–11
Whitbread OB Mild, Chester's Mild, Boddingtons Bitter, OB Bitter; guest beers ᴴ
Busy, cheerful, main road pub named after a local mill. A working pianola vies for attention with the aquarium in the lounge. Fine etched windows of the Oldham Brewery feature. Weekday lunches. ◖ ♣ P

Cheadle Hulme

Cheadle Hulme
Station Road (A5149)
☎ (0161) 485 4706
11–11; 11–3, 7–11 Sat
Holt Mild, Bitter ᴴ

An atypical Holt pub with typically low Holt prices. Despite the plush furniture and tied back curtains, it also has that unique Holt ambience. The restaurant is open Tue–Sun lunch and eve (except Sat lunch). No bar meals Sun. ⊛ ◖ ⅋ ⇌ P

Old Mill
Mill Lane (off Ladybridge Rd)
☎ (0161) 488 4090
12–3, 7–11
Ind Coope Burton Ale; Tetley Walker Bitter; guest beers ᴴ
The use of recycled materials gives an old-world feel to this modern pub, which provides extensive outside seating, semi-rural views and regular events. Lively atmosphere. Usually four guest beers; beer festivals (with over 25 beers).
⊛ ◖ ▶ ⅋ ⇌ P ⌿

Cheetham

Queens Arms
Honey Street
☎ (0161) 834 4239
12–4, 7–11; 12–11 Thu & Fri
S&N Theakston Best Bitter, XB, Old Peculier; Taylor Best Bitter, Landlord; guest beers ᴴ
Pub with a lovely example of an Empress Brewery tiled facade. Its large garden overlooks the Irk valley and the city centre. Six handpumps serve a changing range of guest beers. Fine range of continental bottled beers. Eve meals by arrangement. ♨ ⊛ ◖ ⇌ (Victoria) ⊖ ♣ ⊖

Chorlton-cum-Hardy

Beech
Beech Road ☎ (0161) 881 1180
11–11; 11–4, 7–11 Sat
Marston's Pedigree; Morland Old Speckled Hen; Taylor Best Bitter; Wadworth 6X; Whitbread Chester's Bitter, Flowers Original; guest beers ᴴ
Thriving, popular, three-room pub just off the village green. No food, no music, no gimmicks. Q ⊛ ⊟

Chorlton-on-Medlock

Kings Arms
4a Helmshore Walk (off A6 at Ardwick Green, via Cale St/ Skerry Close)
☎ (0161) 273 1053
11–11
West Coast Mild, Best Bitter, Ginger Beer, Pale Ale, Porter, Extra Special Bitter ᴴ
A West Coast Brewery tied house, offering the full range,

---

with seasonal specials. Architecturally at odds with the surrounding housing estate, the pub's lively, basic front room contrasts with the carpeted rear room.
◖ ⇌ (Piccadilly) ⊖ P

Compstall

Andrew Arms
George Street
☎ (0161) 427 2281
11–11
Robinson's Hatters Mild, Best Bitter ᴴ
Pub which pleases all who visit, offering an open fire in the comfortable lounge and a vault for TV fans and card players. ♨ ⊛ ◖ ♣ P

Cornbrook

Hope Inn
459 Chester Road (A56)
☎ (0161) 848 0038
11–4, 7–11
Hydes' Anvil Light, Bitter ᴱ
Basic, two-roomed, street-corner local in an area which once boasted a multitude of pubs and breweries. A lone handpump stands on the bar in case of powercuts! ♣

Daisy Hill

Rose Hill Tavern
321 Leigh Road (B5235)
☎ (01942) 815529
12–11
Holt Mild, Bitter ᴴ
Large, busy, ex-Tetley pub, tastefully refurbished. No food Mon–Thu eves.
⊛ ◖ ▶ ⇌ ♣ P

Delph

Royal Oak
(Th' Heights)
Broad Lane, Heights (1 mile above Denshaw Rd) OS982090
☎ (01457) 874460
7–11
Whitbread Chester's Mild, Boddingtons Bitter; guest beers ᴴ
Isolated, 250-year-old stone pub on an historic packhorse route overlooking the Tame valley: a cosy bar and three separate rooms. Good home-cooked food, Fri–Sun eves.
♨ Q ⊛ ▶ ⅋ P

Denton

Dog & Partridge
148 Ashton Road
☎ (0161) 336 3954
12.30–11
Robinson's Bitter ᴴ
Surprisingly large, multi-roomed, end-of-terrace pub

211

out of the town centre, with a mixed clientele and a friendly atmosphere. The rare ordinary bitter is strongly supported by stalwart regulars, to the exclusion of other beers.
Q 🍺 ♣

Red Lion Hotel

1 Stockport Road, Crown Point
☎ (0161) 337 8032
11–11; 11–4, 7–11 Sat
Hydes' Anvil Dark Mild, Light, Bitter E
Prominent, Victorian, red-brick local at a town-centre crossroads. Four spacious, open rooms provide a warm and friendly atmosphere. Busy at weekends. A rare outlet for Dark Mild in this area. Q ♣

Dobcross

Navigation Inn

Wool Road (A670)
☎ (01457) 872418
11.30–3, 5 (6 Sat)–11
Banks's Hanson's Mild, Bitter; Camerons Strongarm; Marston's Pedigree H
Popular stone pub built next to the Huddersfield Narrow Canal in 1806, to slake the thirst of navvies. The open-plan interior is a shrine to brass band music. No eve meals Sun. ◑ ♣ ♠ ♣ P

Dukinfield

Commercial Inn

106 Astley Street
☎ (0161) 330 1954
11–11
Tetley Walker Dark Mild, Bitter H
Well-supported, friendly local with a separate public bar and a comfortable lounge (ornate ceiling). Good age mix. Lunches on Sun only. ❀ ♣ P

Eccles

Crown & Volunteer

Liverpool Road (A57)
11–11
Holt Mild, Bitter H
Popular community pub with an attractive 1930 interior, including most of its original features. 🍺

Lamb Hotel

5 Regent Street
☎ (0161) 789 3882
11–11
Holt Mild, Bitter H
Four-roomed Edwardian pub of great character. Note the superb mahogany bar. Full-sized snooker table in the billiard room. Children welcome at lunchtime.
Q ❀ 🍺 ♠ ♣ P

Park Hotel

142 Monton Road, Monton
☎ (0161) 787 8608
11–11; 11–4.15, 7–11 Sat
Holt Mild, Bitter E
Bustling, 1960s, three-room local with a large vault, a lounge and a snug, adorned with memorabilia. Q 🍺 ♣ P

Gathurst

Gathurst Station Inn

Station Approach (off Gathurst Lane) ☎ (01257) 252690
12–3.30 (not Mon), 7–11; 12–11 Thu–Sat
Beer range varies H
Former station building, brought back to life as an excellent free house offering a wide range of beers, mainly from independent brewers. Handy for the Douglas Valley Way and the Leeds–Liverpool Canal. Meals in summer and all day Sun.
🚇 ❀ ◑ ♦ ♠ ♣ P

Golborne

Millstone Inn

52 Harvey Lane (½ mile from centre) ☎ (01942) 728031
12–4, 7–11; 12–11 Fri & Sat
Greenalls Mild, Bitter; Stones Best Bitter H
Pub on the edge of town, avoiding the more boisterous crawlers. A friendly atmosphere pervades two smart lounges, a sporting tap room and a pool area. Close to Haydock Park racecourse. No food weekends. ☎ ◑ 🍺 ♣ P

Gorton

Coach & Horses

227 Belle Vue Street (A57 near Showcase cinema)
☎ (0161) 223 0440
12–3, 6–11; 12–11 Sat & occasional weekdays
Robinson's Hatters Mild, Best Bitter, Old Tom H
Friendly, two-bar local with a warm-hearted and welcoming atmosphere. The vault bustles with darts, TV and conversation, while the lounge provides a quieter refuge. Note the attractive tilework.
🍺 ♠ (Belle Vue) ♣ P

Hare & Hounds

187 Abbey Hey Lane (off Ashton Old Road, A635)
☎ (0161) 370 1258
12–11
Whitbread Boddingtons Bitter; guest beer (weekends) H
Old-fashioned, side-street pub which sums up the traditional virtues. A lively vault houses reminders of the pub's past, while, for quieter drinking,

there's a delightful smoke room and a plusher rear lounge. ❀ 🍺 ♠ ♣

Travellers Call

521–523 Hyde Road (A57, near A6010 jct) ☎ (0161) 223 1722
11–11
Hydes' Anvil Mild, Bitter E
A postponed road scheme means this fine example of a simple, basic Manchester ale house will survive this edition—but perhaps not much longer. The heart is the front vault, busy with TV and animated conversation, but don't miss the back room (closed when quiet).
🍺 ♠ (Belle Vue) ♣

Vale Cottage

1 Croft Bank (off Kirk St, Hyde Rd, A57, by path at side of Lord Nelson)
☎ (0161) 223 2477
11.30–3, 5.30–11
Marston's Pedigree; Taylor Landlord; Webster's Yorkshire Bitter H
A tree-shaded setting, looking down to the brook, belies this attractive pub's location in a busy suburb. High standards are aimed at and achieved without a hint of snobbery. Lunches Mon–Fri, plus Sun; eve meals Mon–Fri, till 7.30. Excellent and popular.
❀ ◑ ♦ ♠ P

Waggon & Horses

738 Hyde Road (A57)
☎ (0161) 231 6262
11–11
Holt Mild, Bitter H
In an area well-served with good pubs, the Waggon offers a quality pint at Holt's usual keen prices. Linked, but clearly defined, drinking areas (one for darts and pool) offer something for everyone.
♠ (Ryder Brow) ♣ P

Hale

Railway

128 Ashley Road (opp. station)
☎ (0161) 941 5367
11–11
Robinson's Hatters Mild, Best Bitter, Hartleys XB, Old Tom (winter) H
Unspoilt, 1930s-style, multi-roomed pub, retaining plenty of wood panelling. Patio at the rear. No lunches Sun.
Q ☎ ❀ ◑ 🍺 ♠ ↔ (Altrincham) ♣

Halebarns

Unicorn

Hale Road ☎ (0161) 980 4347
11.30–3.30, 5.30–11
Hydes' Anvil Mild, Bitter E
Large, comfortably furnished roadside pub with a smart

function room. Children allowed in the restaurant lunchtime and early eve. No eve meals Sun.
Q ⋈ ◖ ▶ ⊞ ⅋ ♣ P

Harpurhey

Junction
1 Hendham Vale, Queens Road ☎ (0161) 202 5808
11–11
Holt Bitter; Lees Bitter; Whitbread Boddingtons Bitter H
Friendly, unspoilt, three-roomed free house, popular with the Irish community. It boasts an unusual curved frontage and the deepest cellar in Manchester: ask the landlord for a tour. Keen prices.
⚲ ⊞ ⊖ (Woodlands Rd) ♣

Harwood

House Without a Name
Leagate ☎ (01204) 300063
12.30 (12 Wed–Sat)–11
Holt Bitter; Whitbread Boddingtons Bitter H
Small pub in row of stone cottages dating from 1832, boasting separate lounge and public bars. Originally an unlicensed brew pub, given its unusual name by an impatient licensing magistrate. ❀

Hatherlow

Spread Eagle
On main Marple–Bredbury road ☎ (0161) 430 2846
11–11
Whitbread Boddingtons Bitter E; **guest beers** H
Beautiful old pub with a huge main room, plus a large vault and other rooms. Located in a well-to-do residential area, which is reflected in its clientele. Q ❀ ◖ ⅋ ♣ P

Heaton Mersey

Griffin
552 Didsbury Road (A5145)
☎ (0161) 432 2824
12–11
Holt Mild, Bitter H
Heavily traditional pub, given a well-executed extension in 1992. The rooms on the east side have more character and a superb mahogany bar is a feature. Sometimes very busy. Meals Mon–Fri.
Q ❀ ◖ ⋟ (Didsbury) P ⅊

Heaton Norris

Moss Rose
63 Didsbury Road (A5145)
☎ (0161) 442 9510
11.30–11; 12–4, 7–11 Sat

Hydes' Anvil Light, Bitter E
An unpromising early 1970s exterior conceals a comfortable, welcoming local with a traditional feel. Good contrast between the lounge and vault. No food Sun.
◖ ⊞ ♣ P

Nursery
Green Lane (off A6)
☎ (0161) 432 2044
11.30–3, 5.30–11; 11.30–11 Sat & bank hols
Hydes' Anvil Mild, Bitter H
Comfortable, unspoilt 1930s pub with its own bowling green, well-hidden in a pleasant suburb. Its good choice of rooms includes a lounge with fine wood panelling. Excellent bar food (set lunches only Sun).
Q ❀ ◖ ⊞ ♣ P

Heywood

Engineers Arms
11–13 Aspinall Street (just off A58) ☎ (01706) 368365
11–3, 7–11; 11–11 Fri & Sat
Samuel Smith OBB H
Friendly local just outside the town centre. Recent renovation has restored original features to the bar area. ❀ ▲ ♣ P

Hindley

Edington Arms
186 Ladies Lane
☎ (01942) 59229
12–11
Holt Mild, Bitter; Moorhouse's Black Cat Mild, Premier; Walker Best Bitter; Whitbread Boddingtons Bitter; guest beers H
Though on the edge of town, this excellent pub is always busy, due to its large range of good value beers. The origin of the house beer, Savage Head, is unknown. Children welcome early eves. ❀ ⅋ ⋟

Hollins

Hollins Bush Inn
257 Hollins Lane (off A56 at Blackford Bridge)
☎ (0161) 766 5692
12–3, 6–11; 12–11 Fri & Sat
Lees GB Mild, Bitter E
Friendly, three-roomed local, reputed to be 200 years old. Very popular with families at weekends. Good selection of bar snacks (not served Sun).
Q ❀ ⅋ ♣ P

Hollinwood

Bridgewater
197 Manchester Road (A62)
☎ (0161) 628 8464
11.30–11; 11.30–3, 7–11 Sat

Holt Mild, Bitter H
Holt's 'rebuilt' house, which is now the only Holt outlet in the locality. An open-plan lounge and an extremely busy vault.
❀ ◖ ⊞ ⅋ ♣ P

Hyde

Oddfellows
33 Ridling Lane
☎ (0161) 351 1725
12–4, 7–11; 11–11 Fri & Sat
Vaux Mild, Bitter, Samson H
Recently acquired by Vaux and given a facelift. Welcoming atmosphere; well used by locals. ⋟ (Newton)

White Lion
Market Place
☎ (0161) 368 2948
11.30–11; 11.30–3, 5–11 Tue; 11.30–4.30, 7–11 Sat
Robinson's Hatters Mild, Best Bitter E, **Old Tom** H
Friendly pub which is very busy on market days and has a nicely tiled tap room with an impressive long bar. It still retains brown glazed lions from its days as a Kay's Atlas brewery house, though the exterior and lounge have been 'Robinsonised'. Note: the Old Tom pump has no clip.
◖ ⊞ ⋟ ♣

Jericho

Famous Game Cock Inn
455 Rochdale Old Road (B6222, opp. Fairfield hospital)
☎ (0161) 764 4784
12–4, 6–11
Moorhouse's Premier; Whitbread Boddingtons Bitter; guest beers H
Modestly refurbished, old stone building, keeping its traditional lounge and three-room layout (games room). Pictures provide an insight into the pub's history. A house beer is brewed by Oak. Good food, curries a speciality.
⚲ Q ⋎ ❀ ◖ ▶ ♣ P

Leigh

Red Brick Inn
Twist Lane ☎ (01942) 671698
12–11
Hydes' Anvil Light, Bitter; Tetley Walker Mild, Bitter H
Large, impressive building formerly known as the Oddfellows. Its refurbished interior has a tap room, a clean, comfortable lounge bar, a raised lounge/games area, and a restaurant.
⋈ ◖ ▶ ⊞ ♣ P

Tamar
416 Wigan Road (1½ miles from centre) ☎ (01942) 679459
12–11

213

Greater Manchester

Holt Mild, Bitter H
Popular local, with a tiled
exterior: a tidy lounge bar with
a separate tap room. The
stained-glass in the passage
depicts the bowling green.
Function room.
🏠 🌳 ◖ ▮ ♣ P

Victoria
Kirkhall Lane
☎ (01942) 606114
12–11
**Tetley Walker Dark Mild,
Bitter** H
Sporty, end-of-terrace, multi-
roomed gem, a locals' pub
where visitors are made
welcome. Handy for Leigh
RLFC. 🏠 Q 🌳 ❦ ♣

Little Hulton

Dun Mare
277 Manchester Road West
(A6, ½ mile from M61 jct 4)
☎ (0161) 790 5235
12–4 (5.30 Sat), 7–11
Walker Mild, Best Bitter H
Refurbished, splendid
Walker's outlet. Note the 1964
price list. Q 🌳 ❦ ⅙ ♣ P

Little Lever

Horseshoe Inn
71 Lever Street (off A6053)
☎ (01204) 720811
12–4, 7–11; 12–11 Sat
Hydes' Anvil Light, Bitter E
Busy, traditional, two-roomed
pub with a lounge, a vault
and lots of sports teams.
Q ❦ ♣

Jolly Carter Hotel
168 Church Street (A6053)
☎ (01204) 71344
12–11
**Morland Old Speckled Hen;
Taylor Landlord; Whitbread
Chester's Mild, Boddingtons
Bitter; guest beers** H
Bright, friendly, welcoming
pub where a lounge and vault
are served from a central bar.
One of few pubs in the area to
offer early eve meals (except
Fri). 🌳 ◖ ▮ ♣ P

Lowton

Hare & Hounds
1 Golborne Road (Stone Cross
Lane/B5207 jct)
☎ (01942) 728387
12–11
**Tetley Walker Dark Mild,
Bitter; guest beers** H
Enlarged, open-plan pub: a
cosy, low-beamed lounge and
games room, plus a newer
lower lounge area, bright and
spacious. Outdoor children's
playground.
🏠 🌳 ◖ ▮ ❦ ♣ P

Manchester City Centre

Beerhouse
Angel Street (off Rochdale Rd,
just beyond Miller St)
☎ (0161) 839 7019
11.30–11
**Courage Directors;
Moorhouse's Pendle Witches
Brew; guest beers** H
Refurbished to increase the
serving area, this popular,
basic boozer offers bottled
continental beers to
complement the 12 changing
ales. ◖ ⇌ (Victoria) ⊖ ⌂

Castle
66 Oldham Street
☎ (0161) 236 2945
11.30–5.30, 8–11
**Robinson's Hatters Mild,
Bitter, Best Bitter, Old Tom** H
The only Robinson's pub in
the town centre: a Victorian
boozer with pleasant people
and no hint of trouble. Live
music in one of the two back
rooms Thu eve. No family
room in the eve.
Q ❧ ⇌ (Victoria/Piccadilly)
⊖ (Piccadilly Gdns) ♣

Circus Tavern
86 Portland Street (A62)
☎ (0161) 236 5818
12–4.30 (may extend), 5.30–11
Tetley Walker Bitter H
The smallest pub in the city: a
one-person bar serving a
single draught beer. No lager;
no music: a two-roomed gem
that defies progress. All the
atmosphere of a village local
in the eve.
🏠 Q ⇌ (Piccadilly)
⊖ (Piccadilly Gdns)

Crown & Anchor
Cateaton Street
☎ (0161) 834 7046
11.30–11
Holt Mild, Bitter H
Pub extended and refurbished
in the standard Holt format,
with some original Victorian
features retained.
◖ ⅙ ⇌ (Victoria) ⊖

Hare & Hounds
46 Shude Hill
☎ (0161) 832 4737
11–11
**Cains Mild, Bitter; Tetley
Walker Bitter** H
Traditional city pub, with a
front vault, a lobby, a
comfortable back room,
extensive brown and cream
tiling and etched-glass. Large
function room. Eve meals on
request. ◖ ⇌ (Victoria)
⊖ (High St) ♣

HR Fletcher's
2–10 St Mary's Street (off
Deansgate)

☎ (0161) 835 1567
11.30–11; closed Sun
**Bass Worthington BB,
Draught Bass; Fuller's
London Pride; M&B Highgate
Dark; Wadworth 6X; Young's
Special; guest beer** H
Side street pub formerly
known as the Gemstone. Good
food (eve meals until 7). Music
Wed eve. Waiter service 2–6.
◖ ▮ ⇌ (Deansgate/Victoria)
⊖ (St Peter's Sq) ♣ ⌂

Peveril of the Peak
127 Great Bridgewater Street
12–3, 5.30 (7 Sat)–11;
7–10.30 Sun, closed Sun lunch
**Courage Directors; Ruddles
Best Bitter; Webster's
Yorkshire Bitter, Wilson's
Bitter** H
Named after a famous
stagecoach, a classic pub
triangular in shape. Note the
exterior tiling and the stained-
glass and wood interior.
Popular with students and
home to Manchester's longest
serving landlady. Open Sat
lunch when Man Utd are at
home. 🏠 ⇌ (Oxford Rd)
⊖ (St Peter's Sq) ♣

Unicorn
26 Church Street
☎ (0161) 832 7938
11.30–11; 11.30–3, 5.30–11 Sat; 12–2,
7–10.30 Sun
**Bass Worthington BB,
Draught Bass; Stones Best
Bitter** H
Comfortable and cosy, multi-
roomed, 19th-century pub
with extensive oak panelling
and etched-glass.
Q ⅙ ⇌ (Victoria)
⊖ (High St)

Vine
Kennedy Street
☎ (0161) 236 3943
11.30–11; 11.30–3, 7–11 Sat; 12–3 Sun,
closed Sun eve
**Courage Directors; John
Smith's Bitter; Whitbread
Boddingtons Bitter** H
Busy pub with a listed, tiled
exterior. The bars are on three
levels, with varying music and
noise. No meals Sat or Sun.
◖ ⇌ (Oxford Rd)
⊖ (St Peter's Sq)

Walkers
37 Swan Street (A665 near
A664 jct) ☎ (0161) 834 4424
11–11; 11–3, 7–11 Sat
**Bateman XB; Fuller's London
Pride; Marston's Bitter,
Pedigree** H
Old market pub surviving
several transformations and
improved by the present
owner. Dining/select area at
the rear. Barrel ends and brass
taps adorn the front bar.
Q 🛏 ◖ ▮ ⇌ (Victoria)
⊖ (High St) ♣ P

White House

123 Great Ancoats Street
(corner of Laystall St)
☎ (0161) 228 3231
12–4 (2 Sat), 7 (7.30 Sat)–11; 11–11
Thu & Fri
Cains Bitter; Holt Bitter H
Friendly pub with a lounge
bar and a separate vault, near
the new superstore complex
and 'Village' development on
the Rochdale/Ashton Canal.
⌂ ≹ (Piccadilly) ⊖

White Lion

43 Liverpool Road, Castlefield
☎ (0161) 832 7373
11.30–11
**Morland Old Speckled Hen;
Taylor Landlord; Whitbread
Boddingtons Bitter; guest
beers** H
Pub close to moorings on the
Bridgewater Canal. Live
entertainment; good, home-
cooked food (excellent
curries). Eve meals (Mon–Thu)
end at 8; lunches served seven
days a week.
⊛ ⌂ ▶ ≹ (Deansgate)
⊖ (G Mex) P

Marple

Crown Inn

Hawk Green Road, Hawk
Green (¾ mile from Marple on
the Disley back road)
11–3, 5.30–11
**Robinson's Hatters Mild, Best
Bitter** H
Large, busy pub, mostly a
haunt of the young (live music
quite often). The food trade is
reviving. ⊛ ⌂ ▶ ♿ P

Middleton

Brunswick Hotel

122 Oldham Road (A669)
☎ (0161) 653 4543
7 (11 Fri & Sat)–11
**Coach House Gunpowder
Mild; Tetley Walker Bitter;
guest beers** H
Vibrant pub, with bikers,
punks and more conventional
types mixing easily. Loud
music in the back room
(occasionally live);
conversation (shouted at
times) in the bar. Always four
guest beers served, plus
Brunswick Bitter (brewed by
Coach House). ⊛

Crown Inn

52 Rochdale Road
☎ (0161) 643 3753
11.30–11
Lees GB Mild, Bitter E
Incredibly busy, end-of-
terrace, two-roomed local
where a large, comfortable,
brass-hung lounge
complements a small snug-
cum-darts room. ♣ P

Lancashire Fold

77 Kirkway Alkrington (½
mile off A664)
☎ (0161) 643 4198
11–11
Lees GB Mild, Bitter H
Busy and fairly modern estate
pub with separate lounge and
public bars. Eve meals
available till 8pm. ⌂ ▶ ♣ P

Tandle Hill Tavern

14 Thornham Lane, Slattocks
(unmetalled road 1 mile off
A671/A664) ☎ (01706) 345297
7–11; 12–4, 7–11 Sat
Lees Bitter H, **Moonraker**
(winter) E
Small, welcoming pub at the
heart of a small farming
community: a good stop on
walks. Informal quizzes and
snacks at weekends. A proper
country pub. ⚒ Q ♣

Milnrow

Free Trade Tavern

115 New Hey Road (B6225)
☎ (01706) 847056
12–3, 5–11
Lees GB Mild, Bitter H
Friendly pub on the edge of
town. Q ⊛ ≹ ♣ P

Waggon Inn

Butterworth Hall (off Newhey
Rd, B6225) ☎ (01706) 48313
11–11
Burtonwood Mild, Bitter H
Friendly and popular, 18th-
century village local retaining
a multi-room layout.
☼ ⊛ ▲ ≹ ♣ P

Mossley

Tollemache Arms

Manchester Road
☎ (0145 783) 2354
11.30–3, 5–11
**Robinson's Hatters Mild, Best
Bitter** H
Popular, cosy and sociable,
stone local next to the
Huddersfield Narrow Canal,
which is overlooked by the
small garden. Compact,
oak-panelled rooms, a
polished bar and conversation
feature. In the same family
since 1959. ⚒ Q ⊛ ♣ P

Moston

New Moston

57 Belgrave Road
12–4, 7–11
**Banks's Mild; Marston's
Bitter, Pedigree** H
Comfortable pub attracting a
range of ages in a residential
backwater close to Failsworth.
It retains a distinctly
traditional vault and also
offers Marston's Head

Brewer's Choice beers.
⊛ ⊟ ≹ (Failsworth—not
Sun) ♣

New Hey

Bird in the Hand
(Top Bird)

113 Huddersfield Road (A640)
☎ (01706) 847978
11.30–3, 5–11; 11.30–11 Sat
Samuel Smith OBB H
Small, friendly pub, one of the
growing number of traditional
Sam's pubs in the area. Note
the almost identically-named
pub (also Sam's) down the
road. Q ⊛ ≹ ♣ P

New Springs

Colliers Arms

Wigan Road (B5238 NE of
Wigan) ☎ (01942) 831171
1.30 (12 Sat)–5.30 (not Thu), 7.30–11
Burtonwood Mild, Bitter H
Not to be missed: one of the
few original locals in the area.
Regular toast and crumpet
nights, and occasional sing-
alongs. Near the Leeds–
Liverpool Canal. ⚒ Q ♣ P

Newton Heath

Railway

Dean Lane (off A62, Oldham
Rd) ☎ (0161) 681 8199
11–11; 11–4, 7–11 Sat
Holt Mild, Bitter E
Imposing, very popular
Victorian pub whose character
has not been diminished by a
refurbishment. Steam
locomotives feature in the
etched windows.
⊟ ≹ (Dean Lane) ♣

Oldham

Bridge Inn

Moorhey Street (just off A669)
☎ (0161) 624 8626
11–11
Lees GB Mild, Bitter E
Popular, friendly, three-
roomer with pleasant
surroundings. Busy at
weekends. Look for the
stained-glass window
depicting the pub's name.
⊛ ⊟ ♣ P

Dog & Partridge

376 Roundthorn Road (off
B6194) ☎ (0161) 624 3335
7 (11 Fri)–11; 11.30–3, 7–11 Sat
Lees GB Mild, Bitter E
Popular, detached pub in a
semi-rural setting, with low,
beamed ceilings. Comfortably
furnished. ⚒ ⊛ ♣ P

Hark to Topper

5 Bow Street
☎ (0161) 624 7950
11.30–3, 7–11; 11.30–11 Fri

Greater Manchester

Samuel Smith OBB H
Detached town-centre pub with an impressive brick exterior, dating from 1835, just off the high street. Its pleasant, open-plan interior has a central bar and etched windows. A former Rochdale & Manor brewery house, once known as the Manor Inn.
⌂ ≹ (Mumps)

Royal Oak
178 Union Street
☎ (0161) 624 1031
11–11
Robinson's Hatters Mild, Best Bitter E, **Old Tom** (winter) G
Welcoming town-centre local with a separate snug. Its impressive horseshoe bar dates from 1928 and forms the central feature. Large function room; separate pool room.
Q ⌂ ≹ (Mumps) ♣

Ordsall

Welcome
Robert Hall Street (off A5066)
☎ (0161) 872 6040
11.30–4, 7–11
Lees GB Mild, Bitter H
Immaculate pub in an area where much of the local housing is empty ready for refurbishment. The landlady is to be commended for running an excellent house under difficult circumstances. The handpumps are electrically assisted.
Q ⌐ ♣ P

Orrell

Rose & Crown Hotel
9a Church Street (left from station, 300 yds)
☎ (01695) 625569
11–11
Tetley Walker Mild, Bitter; guest beer H
Worth seeking out and handy for Orrell RUFC: a pub serving good food, with the guest beer changed regularly. The large garden has a play area.
Q ❀ ⌐ ▶ ⌐ ≹ ♣ P

Peel Green

Grapes
439 Liverpool Road (A57 ½ mile E of M63 jct 2)
☎ (0161) 789 6971
11–11; 11–4.30, 7–11 Sat
Holt Mild, Bitter H
Polished wood and etched-glass feature throughout this large, archetypal, Edwardian Holt house. Its many separate rooms include a billiards room, housing two pool tables.
❀ ≹ (Patricroft) ♣ P

Prestwich

Royal Oak
23 Whittaker Lane
☎ (0161) 773 8663
12–11; 11.30–5, 7–11 Sat
Hydes' Anvil Mild, Bitter E
Comfortable, friendly local just off the Bury Old Road, by Heaton Park metro. The only Hydes' outlet in the area, it consists of three rooms: a vault, a lounge and a news room. Q ⌐ ⊖ ♣

Ramsbottom

Royal Oak
Bridge Street ☎ (01706) 822786
12–11
Thwaites Best Mild, Bitter, Craftsman H
Friendly village-centre pub near the East Lancs Railway; renovated and extended but retaining its three rooms. Thriving pub games teams add to the atmosphere. Meals Wed–Sun lunchtimes. ⌣ ⌐ ♣

Ridge End

Romper
Ridge End Road
☎ (0161) 427 1354
12–2.30 (3 Sat), 6–11
Greenalls Mild; Ind Coope Burton Ale; Jennings Bitter; Taylor Landlord; Tetley Walker Bitter H
A longtime haunt of the Cheshire set, now giving beer the same prominence as the well-known food. Tucked on a bend, with the Dark Peak on one side, its neon sign illuminates the Cheshire Plain on the other—a setting threatened by a new road scheme. ❀ ⌐ ▶ P

Ringley

Lord Nelson
Kearsley Hall Road (off A667)
☎ (01204) 794563
12–3 (4 Sat), 7–11
Thwaites Best Mild, Bitter H
Large, multi-roomed village pub, beside Ringley Bridge. Watercolour prints adorn walls and one room is decorated with railway memorabilia. Folk nights Tue and Thu. The large garden has a children's play area.
⌂ ❀ ≹ (Kearsley) ♣ P

Ringway

Romper
Sunbank Lane (off A538, 200 yds from M56 jct 6, towards Wilmslow) ☎ (0161) 980 6806
11.30–11; 11.30–3, 5.30–11 Sat

Draught Bass; S&N Theakston Best Bitter; Whitbread Boddingtons Mild, Bitter; guest beer H
Low-ceilinged, multi-roomed country pub, now threatened by plans to extend Manchester airport. Stone floors and original fireplaces are features. The large garden can be noisy due to air traffic. No food Sun.
⌂ Q ❀ ⌐ ♣ P

Rochdale

Albert
62 Spotland Road (A608)
☎ (01706) 45666
11–11
Burtonwood Mild, Bitter H
Popular local with a good early eve atmosphere in its open-plan bar. Separate games, TV and pool rooms. Free oldies jukebox. ⌂ ♣

Cask & Feather
1 Oldham Road
☎ (01706) 711476
11–11
Thomas McGuinness Mild, Best Bitter, Special Reserve, Junction, Tommy Todd Porter; guest beers H
Distinctive, castle-style, stone-fronted pub on a main shopping street close to the town centre. Home of the Thomas McGuinness Brewing Co. (brewery trips by appointment). Well-appointed and spacious. ⌐ ≹

Healey Hotel
172 Shawclough Road (B6377)
☎ (01706) 45453
12–3, 5–11
Robinson's Hatters Mild, Best Bitter, Old Tom (winter) H
Friendly and popular pub retaining a traditional feel with separate rooms and a splendid tiled interior. Lunches served Mon–Fri; eve meals Wed and Thu only. Healey Dell nature reserve is opposite. Q ❀ ⌐

Mash Tun
Drake Street
☎ (01706) 869812
11–3, 5–11; 11–11 Fri & Sat
Beer range varies H
Up to eight beers at any one time, from the widest range of independents' beers in town. No food Sun. ⌐ ♣ ⌣

Merry Monk
234 College Road (near A6060/B6222 jct)
☎ (01706) 46919
12–11
Marston's Bitter, Pedigree; Thwaites Best Mild; guest beers H
Friendly, unpretentious local with Ring the Bull. ♣ P

Romiley

Duke of York
Stockport Road
☎ (0161) 430 2806
11.30–11
Courage Directors; John Smith's Bitter; guest beer H
Long, low, white pub of harmonious proportions. Just as pleasing inside, too, with a beamed lounge and a vault.
❀ ◖ ▸ ⇌ ♣ P

Royton

Dog & Partridge Inn
148 Middleton Road (B6195)
☎ (0161) 620 6403
11.30–11
Lees GB Mild, Bitter H
Not far from Royton centre, a thriving, popular and friendly local. Good selection of malt whiskies. Q ♣

Puckersley Inn
22 Narrowgate Brow (via Dogford Road, off A671)
☎ (0161) 624 4973
5 (4.30 Fri, 12 Sat)–11
Lees GB Mild, Bitter H
Popular, detached, stone-fronted pub on the edge of the green belt, with panoramic views. The beamed interior is artistically furnished, providing several welcoming rooms. Q ⊞ ♣ P

Sale Moor

Legh Arms
Northenden Road
(A6144/B5166 jct)
11–11
Holt Mild, Bitter E
Large, multi-roomed local whose many original features include a revolving door. An island bar serves a large and lively vault, a lounge, a snug, a lobby and a smoke room. Live music Fri–Sun nights. Bowling green. ❀ ⊞ ♣ P

Salford

Ashley Brook
517 Liverpool Street
☎ (0161) 737 0988
11.30–11; 11.30–4, 7–11 Sat
Holt Mild, Bitter H
Busy 1990 pub which has acquired an excellent community spirit. A good example of how a modern pub can be built and run. Q P

Crescent
20 Crescent (opp. Salford University) ☎ (0161) 736 5600
12–11; 7–10.30 Sat
Beer range varies H
Three-roomed public house,

popular with students. Good selection of home-cooked meals, Mon–Fri—try the curry.
🍴 ❀ ◖ ⇌ (Crescent) ⇔ P

Kings Arms
11 Bloom Street
☎ (0161) 839 4338
12–11
Cains Bitter; S&N Theakston Best Bitter; Taylor Landlord; Whitbread OB Bitter H
Popular, two-roomed Boddington Pub Co. Ale House with 11 real ales. The separate back room is used by a variety of enthusiastic parties.
◖ ⅋ ⇌ (Central) ♣ ⇔

Prince of Wales
165 Oldfield Road (A5066, between A6 and A57)
☎ (0161) 832 5716
11–3.30, 6.30 (7 Sat)–11
Lees Bitter; Whitbread Chester's Mild, Boddingtons Bitter H
Friendly free house in an area where much of the housing has been demolished: a lounge, a bar and a small snug, leading to a garden.
🍴 Q ❀ ⚭ ◖ ▸ ⅋
⇌ (Central/Crescent) ♣

Union Tavern
105 Liverpool Street
☎ (0161) 736 2885
11–11
Holt Mild, Bitter H
Welcoming local with a garden planned.
⅋ ⅋ ⇌ (Crescent) ❀ ♣ P

Shaw

Black Horse
203a Rochdale Road (B6194)
☎ (01706) 847173
2 (12 Sat)–11
Lees GB Mild, Bitter E
Stone roadside pub with a cosy, timber-framed lounge and a friendly vault. ❀ ♣ P

Blue Bell
13 Market Street
☎ (01706) 847856
11.30–11; 11–4, 7–11 Sat
Robinson's Hatters Mild, Best Bitter E, **Old Tom** (winter) H
Detached, stone, three-storey pub with mullioned windows from 1763. The top floor was originally used for weaving. Several distinct rooms/areas. No meals weekends.
⅄ ❀ ◖ ⇌ ♣ P

Stalybridge

Rose & Crown
Market Street
☎ (0161) 303 7098
11–11
Vaux Mild, Bitter, Samson, Extra Special H

Very friendly, multi-roomed pub still showing signs of refurbishment but building a strong following. ⇌ ♣ P

White House
Water Street ☎ (0161) 303 2288
11–11
Marston's Bitter, Pedigree; Mitchell's Best Bitter; guest beers H
Welcoming community pub with four rooms. At least three guest beers, a range of foreign bottled beers and over 50 whiskies. Breakfasts from 9.30am. ◖ ⇌ P

Stockport

Arden Arms
23 Millgate (off Market Place)
☎ (0161) 480 2185
11–11
Robinson's Hatters Mild, Best Bitter, Old Tom (winter) H
Classic, multi-roomed pub with an original snug. A collection of grandfather clocks, tropical fish and a fine bar add to the interest. Folk club every Sun. Well-respected and well-liked. No food Sun.
Q ❀ ⚭ ◖ ⅋ ♣ P

Armoury
Shaw Heath (off A6, along Greek St) ☎ (0161) 480 5055
11–11; 11–4, 7.30–11 Sat
Robinson's Hatters Mild, Best Bitter E
Unspoilt, multi-roomed, ex-Bell's pub. Choose from a bright lounge, a back darts room, a superb vault and a lobby. Public parking nearby. Handy for Edgeley Park.
Q ⅋ ⇌ ♣

Blossoms
Buxton Road, Heaviley
(A6/Bramhall Lane, A5102 jct)
☎ (0161) 480 2246
12–3, 5.30–11; 12–11 Fri & Sat
Robinson's Hatters Mild, Best Bitter, Old Tom H
A very warm welcome in a classic, multi-roomed local, a former Bell's house with three contrasting rooms (including a wonderful smoke room) off a central bar. A meeting place for pigeons (folk club Sat eve). Local CAMRA *Pub of the Year* 1992. Q ◖ ▸ ⅋
⇌ (Davenport) ♣ P

Boar's Head
Market Place
☎ (0161) 480 3978
11–4, 6 (7 winter)–11; closed Sun
Samuel Smith OBB, Museum H
Good, cosmopolitan atmosphere in a two-room pub on the vibrant Market Place. A corner bar serves a rambling lounge area, while quality

Greater Manchester

music can be enjoyed in the music room (late licence).
🍺 ≋

Crown Inn
154 Heaton Lane (150 yds W of A6, under viaduct)
☎ (0161) 429 0549
12–11
Beer range varies H
Popular, cosmopolitan pub with an ever-changing range of beers. Sensitively converted into an 'ale house' in early 1993, with many well-defined areas. No food Sun. Local CAMRA *Pub of the Year* 1993.
🏠 🏡 🍺 ≋ ♣ ✄

Manchester Arms
25 Wellington Road South (A6) ☎ (0161) 480 2852
11–11
Robinson's Hatters Mild, Best Bitter, Old Tom H
Basic, down-to-earth, lively and friendly pub, attracting businessmen and bikers. A corner bar serves a simple vault, a boisterous pool room and a more comfortable 'lounge'. Not for the faint-hearted! 🏠 🍺 ≋ ♣

Olde Vic
1 Chatham Street, Edgeley
☎ (0161) 480 2410
12–3, 5.30–11; 11.30–11 Fri & Sat
S&N Theakston Best Bitter; Taylor Landlord; guest beers H
The first local pub which offered guest beers—three or four are available and include brews from the more obscure micros. Small and sometimes smoky. Compact garden.
🏡 🍺 ▶ ≋ ♣

Olde Woolpack
Brinksway (A560)
☎ (0161) 429 6621
11.30–3, 7.30–11; 11.30–11 Fri
Marston's Pedigree; S&N Theakston Best Bitter; Tetley Walker Bitter; guest beers H
Thriving free house offering a guest mild as well as a guest bitter. Open-plan, but with quite distinct drinking areas, it gets crowded at weekends. Park by the large pyramid.
🏡 🍺 🛠 ≋ ♣ P

Queen's Head (Turner's Vaults)
12 Little Underbank (down steps from market)
☎ (0161) 480 1545
11.30–11; 7–10.30 Sun, closed Sun lunch
Samuel Smith OBB, Museum H
An award-winning renovation in 1990 restored this superb little pub to its former glory. Originally the tasting room for the wine vaults, it is full of

interesting features, including 28 original spirit taps on the bar, a haunted room and the world's smallest gents'!
Q 🍺 ≋ ♣ ✄

Stanley Arms
40 Newbridge Lane
☎ (0161) 480 5713
5–11; 12–3, 5–11 Fri; 12–11 Sat
Ryburn Best Bitter, Rydale Bitter, Stabbers; guest beers H
Pub of great contrasts, with four areas over split-levels. Up to 16 beers are sold at any time, including two house milds from Ryburn, and new brews from micros all over the UK. Lunches Fri and Sat; live music/DJ weekends. Can be noisy when busy. 🏡 🍺 ♣ P

Swan With Two Necks
36 Princes Street
☎ (0161) 480 2341
11–4, 6.30 (7 Fri, 7.30 Sat)–11; 12–3 Sun, closed Sun eve (closed Mon–Wed eves in winter)
Robinson's Hatters Mild, Best Bitter E
Classic, 1930s, wood-panelled gem—the real sky-lit lounge is a particular delight, although the whole pub oozes warmth and character. A welcome refuge from the Merseyway shopping precinct.
Q 🍺 ≋ ♣

Strines

Sportsman's Arms
105 Strines Road (1 mile from Marple on the New Mills road)
☎ (0161) 427 2888
11.30–3, 5.30–11
Bateman Mild; Mitchell's Best Bitter; guest beers H
Welcoming country pub with two rooms: a vault and a lounge/dining room. The guest beers change regularly.
Q 🏡 🍺 ▶ 🛠 ▲ ≋ ⌂ P

Swinton

Cricketers Arms
227 Manchester Road (A6 near A572 jct) ☎ (0161) 794 2008
11.45–11; 11.45–4, 7–11 Sat
Holt Mild, Bitter E
Thriving, two-roomed local, popular with older customers.
♣

Tyldesley

Half Moon Inn
115–117 Elliot Street
☎ (01942) 873206
11–4 (4.30 Sat), 7–11
Holt Mild, Bitter; guest beers H
Deservedly popular town pub with a large bar room and a separate pool and darts room. Good local following, of all ages. 🏡 ♣

Mort Arms
235–237 Elliot Street
☎ (01942) 883481
12–11
Holt Mild, Bitter H
Excellent town-centre local. The comfortable lounge is complete with a mahogany bar, etched-glass and wall panels; lively bright tap room.
🍺 ♣

Uppermill

Cross Keys
Off Running Hill Gate (off A670, along Church Rd)
☎ (01457) 874626
11–3, 6.30–11; 11–11 Sat & summer
Lees GB Mild, Bitter H
Attractive, 18th-century stone building overlooking Saddleworth church. The public bar has a stone-flagged floor and a Yorkshire range. The hub of many activities, including mountain rescue. Folk nights Wed.
🏠 Q 🏡 🍺 🛠 ▲ ♣ P

Urmston

Lord Nelson Hotel
41 Stretford Road
☎ (0161) 747 7685
11–11
Holt Mild, Bitter H
Popular pub built shortly after Nelson's death at Trafalgar (1805), rebuilt and extended in 1877. The first floor rear windows depict his battles. Refurbished, but retaining its multi-roomed layout.
🍺 ≋ ♣ P

Wardley

Morning Star
520 Manchester Road (A6)
☎ (0161) 794 4927
12–11
Holt Mild, Bitter H
Friendly atmosphere in a pub on the edge of town, traditionally refurbished. Live music at weekends. No meals Sun.
🏡 🍺 🍺 ≋ (Moorside) ♣ P

Westhoughton

Cross Guns
27 Bolton Road (B5235)
☎ (01942) 811124
11.30–3 (4 Sat), 7–11
Tetley Walker Mild, Walker Best Bitter H
Small, welcoming town-centre pub. 🏠 🏡 ♣

Whitefield

Coach & Horses
71 Bury Old Road (A665)
☎ (0161) 798 8897
11.30–11; 11.30–5, 7–11 Sat

Holt Mild, Bitter H
Pub built in the 1830s: a busy roadside hostelry that always extends a welcome. The Metrolink system gives good access to other nearby pubs.
Q ⊖ (Besses o' the' Barn)
♣ P

Eagle & Child
Higher Lane (A667)
☎ (0161) 766 3024
12–11
Holt Mild, Bitter H
This pub first served beer in 1802 and has been renovated over the years. Its Tudor exterior conveys the impression of a city-centre pub, however the interior is warm and welcoming. Splendid bowling green.
Q ⧖ ❀ ◁ ⌒
⊖ (Besses o' the' Barn) ♣ P

Wigan

Beer Engine
69 Poolstock Lane (B5238, off A49) ☎ (01942) 42497
12–11
Beer range varies H
Wigan CAMRA *Pub of the Year* 1993: a comfortable lounge and a large concert room, which offers a range of events. Annual beer, pie and music festival. Close to the Leeds–Liverpool Canal, with its own bowling green.
❀ ◁ ▶ ⊕ ♣ P

Bird i' th' Hand (Th' En 'Ole)
102 Gidlow Lane (off B5375)
☎ (01942) 41004
12–11
S&N Theakston Best Bitter; Tetley Walker Mild, Bitter; guest beers H
The apotheosis of the two-roomed local. Admire the Walker's mosaic and ironwork over the door.
❀ ◁ ▶ & ♣ P

Bold Hotel
161 Poolstock Lane (B5238, off A49) ☎ (01942) 41095
12–4.30, 7 (5 Sat)–11
Burtonwood Mild, Bitter H
Small, unchanged boozer on the edge of town, popular with RL fans. Collection of walking sticks. Q ⊞ ♣

Gems
15 Upper Dicconson Street (close to centre, off Northway)
☎ (01942) 826588
11–11
Holt Bitter; Tetley Walker Bitter; Walker Best Bitter; Whitbread Boddingtons Bitter; guest beers (occasional) H
Busy, one-room pub, popular for food. ❀ ◁ ⇌

Millstone
67 Wigan Lane (N of centre, near infirmary)
☎ (01942) 45999
12–4.30, 7.30–11
Thwaites Best Mild, Bitter H
Small, cosy, well-loved pub. Good, home-cooked lunches.
Q ❀ ◁ ⇌ ♣

Old Pear Tree
Frog Lane ☎ (01942) 43677
11.30–11; 11–4, 7–11 Sat
Burtonwood Mild, Bitter, Forshaw's, Top Hat H
Excellent town-centre pub near the bus station. Relaxing atmosphere in the lounge; lively vault. Good value food (no eve meals Fri).
⌂ ❀ ◁ ▶ ⊞ ♣

Orwell
Wigan Pier, Wallgate
☎ (01942) 323034
11–11
Bateman Mild; Taylor Best Bitter; Tetley Walker Bitter; Whitbread Boddingtons Bitter; guest beers H
Large, modern pub at the heart of the Wigan Pier complex. Food is available all afternoon in summer, when it is busy with the tourist trade. Eves are quieter. Children welcome.
❀ ◁ ⇌ (NW/Wallgate)

Raven
5 Wallgate (A49)
☎ (01942) 43865
11–11; 7–10.30 Sun, closed Sun lunch
Ind Coope Burton Ale; Walker Mild, Best Bitter, Winter Warmer H
Ornate Edwardian pub much improved by refurbishment. Note the mosaic floor. Busy at weekends.
❀ ◁ ⇌ (NW/Wallgate)

Seven Stars
262 Wallgate (A49, near Wigan Pier) ☎ (01942) 43126
12–5, 7–11
Thwaites Best Mild, Bitter H
Traditional pub with a large bar area. A typical Magee Marshall's turn-of-the-century pub, handy for the canal and Wigan Pier. Comfortable and friendly. ◁ ⇌ ♣ P

Springfield
46 Springfield Road (by Springfield Park)
☎ (01942) 42072
12–3, 7–11; 11–11 Sat
Walker Mild, Bitter, Winter Warmer H
Magnificently furnished Edwardian pub, with a fine use of English oak throughout its three rooms. ⊞ ♣ P

Swan & Railway
80 Wallgate (A49, opp. NW station) ☎ (01942) 495032

11–3.30, 5.30–11; 12–2.30, 7–10.30 Sun
Banks's Mild, Bitter; Bass Mild, Draught Bass; Courage Directors; John Smith's Bitter; guest beers H
Friendly pub with one of the widest selections of ales in Wigan and a collection of clocks and train memorabilia.
Q ⧖ ⋈ ◁
⇌ (NW/Wallgate)

Tudor House Hotel
New Market Street
☎ (01942) 42190
11–11
Draught Bass; M&B Highgate Dark; guest beers H
Tudor-style, town-centre pub, next to the bus station. Its varied clientele includes many students. Live music Wed; traditional Irish bands Thu. Food served till 6pm.
⌂ ❀ ⋈ ◁ ⇌ ⌒

Withington

Red Lion
Wilmslow Road (B5093)
11–11
Banks's Mild; Marston's Bitter, Pedigree, Owd Rodger H
Popular pub on a busy main road, famous for its garden and bowling green, and extended at the rear. The front lounges and bar exude character. Wide range of food lunchtimes and Mon–Thu eves.
⧖ ❀ ◁ ▶ & P

Woodford

Davenport Arms (Thief's Neck)
550 Chester Road (A5102)
☎ (0161) 439 2435
11–3.30, 5.15 (5.30 Sat)–11
Robinson's Hatters Mild, Best Bitter H, **Old Tom** E
Superb, unspoilt country pub on the edge of suburbia. Its multi-roomed layout includes a no-smoking snug where children are admitted lunchtimes. In the same family for over 60 years.
⌂ Q ⧖ ❀ ◁ ⊞ ♣ P ✗

Worthington

Crown
Platt Lane, Standish (between A5106 and A49, at the end of Bradley Lane)
☎ (01257) 421354
11–11
Beer range varies H
Not to be missed! A country pub and restaurant with antique furnishings, a wide range of beers and good value meals. ⌂ Q ◁ P

Merseyside

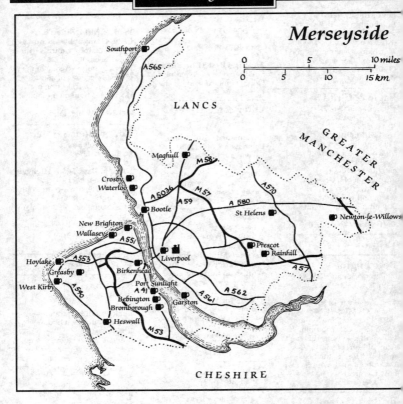

Merseyside

 Black Horse & Rainbow, Cains, Finch & Firkin, Passageway, *Liverpool*

Bebington

Cleveland Arms
31 Bebington Road, New Ferry
☎ (0151) 645 2847
11–11
Thwaites Best Mild, Bitter H
Ever-popular, open-plan local
in a pedestrian area. A
previous local CAMRA *Pub of
the Year* which has maintained
its high standards. Friendly
staff ensure a warm welcome
and a good atmosphere.
≠ ♣

Rose & Crown
57 The Village
☎ (0151) 643 1312
11.30–3, 5.30–11; 11.30–11 Fri & Sat
Thwaites Best Mild, Bitter H
Bustling, friendly, multi-room
local, popular with office
workers and shoppers at
lunchtime, and with local
residents at night. No food
Sun.
Q ⅊ ≠ ♣

Birkenhead

Crown
128 Conway Street
☎ (0151) 647 9108
12–11
**Cains Mild, Bitter, FA;
Jennings Mild, Sneck Lifter;
guest beers** H
Multi-roomed town-centre
alehouse with the biggest
choice of beers for miles. Wide
range of food: an all-day
breakfast is served. Handy for
the shops and market.
Children welcome until 6pm.
☎ ⅊ ▸ ≠ (Central/
Hamilton Sq) ♣ ⌂

Lord Napier
St Pauls Road, Rock Ferry (off
A41) ☎ (0151) 645 3659
11–11
**Cains Mild; Mansfield Old
Shilling; Whitbread
Boddingtons Bitter** H
Friendly, comfortable, two-
roomed pub with a family
atmosphere. Keen darts and
bowls teams.
⅊ ≠ (Rock Ferry) ♣

Old House at Home
30 Queen Street, Tranmere
☎ (0151) 666 1578
11–11
Banks's Mild, Bitter E
Friendly local, serving
drinkers of all ages, with
thriving darts and quiz teams.
The caring landlord seldom
misses a chance to speak to
customers.
⊛ ⅊ ≠ (Green Lane) ♣

Shrewsbury Arms
38 Claughton Firs, Oxton
☎ (0151) 652 1775
11.30–3, 5–11, 11.30–11 Sat
**Cains Mild, Bitter, FA; S&N
Theakston Best Bitter;
Whitbread Boddingtons
Bitter** H
Traditional, friendly, very
popular pub with beamed
ceilings. The new small
extension has a no-smoking

220

area. No food Sun.
Q ✿ ◖ P ✗

Bootle

Cat & Fiddle

Stanley Road
Ind Coope Burton Ale; Tetley Walker Mild, Bitter; guest beers H
Once a seedy bar in decline, this pub has now been given an expensive re-build and features lots of bare bricks, floorboards and barrels. Eight real ales, including four guests. Busy lunchtime trade.
◖ ⊖ (Bootle Strand/Oriel Rd)

Bromborough

Archers

149 Mark Rake
☎ (0151) 334 3406
11–11
Cains Bitter; Jennings Bitter; Tetley Walker Bitter H
Large, two-roomed pub attracting customers of all ages. Quiz Tue, live music Wed–Sun. ✿ ও ⇌ ♣ P

Crosby

Crows Nest

63 Victoria Road
☎ (0151) 931 3081
11.30–3, 5.30–11
Cains Bitter H
Well-established local with a bar, a snug and a lounge. The absence of a jukebox and fruit machine (thanks to the opposition of the locals) maintains the pub's lively conversational character.
Q ⊞ ⇌ (Blundellsands) P

Garston

Dealers Arms

79–81 St Mary's Road
☎ (0151) 427 5877
11.30–11
Cains Mild, Bitter H
Locals' pub with a loyal clientele. Cable TV. ⊞ ⇌ ♣

King Street Vaults

74–76 King Street
☎ (0151) 427 5850
11–11
Walker Mild, Bitter H
Friendly pub with strong sporting connections. It boasts a permanent 'happy hour' and cable TV. Wheelchair WC.
⊞ ও ♣

Swan Inn

6 James Street
☎ (0151) 427 2032
11–11
Tetley Walker Mild, Bitter H
Small, side-street pub known locally as the Duck. Cable TV.
⊞ ⇌ ♣

Greasby

Irby Mill

Mill Lane ☎ (0151) 604 0194
11.30–3, 5–11; 11.30–11 Sat
Cains Mild, Bitter; Jennings Bitter; S&N Theakston Best Bitter; Tetley Walker Bitter; guest beers H
CAMRA Wirral *Pub of the Year* 1994: an unspoilt, traditional country pub with three rooms.
Q ✿ ◖ P

Heswall

Black Horse

Village Road, Lower Heswall
☎ (0151) 342 2254
11.30–11
Bass Mild, Special, Draught Bass; guest beers H
Popular village local, appealing to all ages. Darts and dominoes in the bar; the lounge has a snug and a sunken conservatory. No food Sun. ◖ ⊞ ♣ P

Hoylake

Blue Anchor

Market Street
☎ (0151) 632 2197
11.30–11
Cains Bitter; Whitbread Boddingtons Mild, Bitter H
Recently refurbished, popular roadside pub, with friendly staff. ◖ ⊞ ও ⇌ ♣ P

Liverpool: *City Centre*

Black Horse & Rainbow

21–23 Berry Street, L1
☎ (0151) 709 5055
12–2am
Black Horse Bitter, Celebration H
Brew pub where a large, open drinking area caters for a busy late trade. The brewery is visible from the bar or the street. Regular live music. Function room. ⚰ ✿ ⇌ (Lime St) ⊖ (Central)

Brewery Tap

35 Stanhope Street, L8 (off Parliament St)
☎ (0151) 709 2129
11–11
Cains Mild, Bitter, FA; guest beers H
Inspired evocation of how pubs used to be, with original Liverpool Brewery posters and bottle labels on display. The only Cains tied house, it always has three guest beers and other Cains brews.
Q ◖ P

Carnarvon Castle

Tarleton Street, L3
12–8 (11 Wed–Sat); closed Sun
Cains Mild, Bitter H
Small, busy, one-roomed pub which caters for the drinking shopper. Collection of Dinky toys in display cabinets.
⚰ Q ⇌ (Lime St)

Everyman Bistro

Hope Street, L1
☎ (0151) 708 9545
12–midnight; closed Sun
Brakspear Bitter; Cains Bitter; Fuller's Chiswick; guest beers H
Continental-style basement bar and bistro, popular with theatre-goers. The upstairs theatre has been rescued from closure. Extensive, excellent meal range. Very busy after 11pm. Q ◖ ◗ ⌂

Flying Picket

24 Hardman Street, L1
☎ (0151) 709 3995
12–11
Cains Bitter; Coach House Coachman's; guest beers H
Pub attached to the unemployment resource centre (through the archway). Varied entertainment makes it a lively eve venue. Handy for restaurants. Wheelchair WC. ◖ ও
⇌ (Lime St) ⊖ (Central) P

Globe

17 Cases Street, L1 (opp. Central station)
11–11
Cains Mild, Bitter; guest beers H
A local in the city centre, with a tiny back lounge. Beware the sloping floor!
⇌ (Lime St) ⊖ (Central)

Grapes

60 Roscoe Street, L1 (near Chinatown) ☎ (0151) 709 8617
11–11
Cains Bitter; guest beers H
Cosy local that welcomes visitors and regulars, and hosts charity events.
✿ ⊖ (Central) ♣

Mount Vernon

1 Irvine Street, L7 (edge of centre) ☎ (0151) 709 9432
11–11
Cains Bitter; guest beers H
Refurbished, and re-opened as a 'free house'-type venture, this pub now has a good regular following, including students. There is a comfortable back room and a games room with Sky TV, a quiz Thu and regular mini-beer festivals. Frequent buses from the centre. Children welcome until 7pm. Always at least one mild sold.
⛫ ⇌ (Lime St) ♣ P

221

Merseyside

Peter Kavanagh's
2–6 Egerton Street, L8 (off Catherine St)
☎ (0151) 709 3443
11–11
Cains Bitter; Ind Coope Burton Ale; Tetley Walker Bitter H
Splendid old pub in a row of cottages. The original bar has two (usually) quiet rooms on either side, with another two rooms off. Q ◖ ▶

Pig & Whistle
12 Covent Garden, L2
☎ (0151) 236 4760
11.30–11 (may vary Mon–Wed); 12–9 Sat; closed Sun
Walker Mild, Bitter, Best Bitter; guest beer H
Small, traditional pub with a convivial atmosphere in the business area. The upstairs bar opens at lunchtime. Good value food (Mon–Fri).
◖ ⊖ (Moorfields/James St)

Poste House
23 Cumberland Street, L1
☎ (0151) 236 4130
Cains Mild, Bitter; guest beers H
Small, back-street pub in the business area. Two rooms: one up, one down, which can get very busy at lunchtime (meals weekdays). Q ◖
⇌ (Lime St) ⊖ (Moorfields)

Railway
18 Tithebarn Street, L2
☎ (0151) 236 7210
11.30–11
Cains Mild, Bitter; guest beers H
Newly refurbished, former Mellors pub opposite the remains of Exchange Station. Popular for good value lunches (not served Sun).
◖ ⇌ (Lime St) ⊖ (Moorfields)

Roscoe Head
Roscoe Street, L1 (opp. bombed out church)
☎ (0151) 709 4490
11.30 (12 Sat)–11
Ind Coope Burton Ale; Jennings Bitter; Tetley Walker Mild, Bitter H
Award-winning city-centre gem with no music or electronic invaders. A bar snug, a back lounge, and a side lounge off the main bar complete this friendly, unspoilt pub, one of the best. Meals Mon–Fri.
Q ◖ ⇌ (Lime St) ⊖ (Central)

Ship & Mitre
133 Dale Street, L2 (near Birkenhead–Mersey tunnel entrance) ☎ (0151) 236 0859
11–11; 12.30–11 Sat; closed Sun
Cains Mild, Bitter; Dyffryn Clwyd Cysur Bitter, Castell; Holt Bitter; guest beers H

Gas-lit pub, popular with students at lunchtime. It offers good value, weekday lunches, and the best range of beers in Liverpool (up to 12). *Mersey Drinker Pub of the Year* 1993. Two ciders. ◖ ⇌ (Lime St) ⊖ (Moorfields) ♣ ⟳ P

Swan
86 Wood Street, L1
☎ (0151) 709 5281
11.30–11
Marston's Pedigree; Oak Wobbly Bob; guest beers H
Back-street pub, with the bar upstairs, very busy at night. Rock jukebox; live music Mon. Up to three guest beers and good value, tasty, home-cooked lunches. ◖
⇌ (Lime St) ⊖ (Central) ⟳

United Powers
66–68 Tithebarn Street, L2
☎ (0151) 236 5205
11.30–11; closed Sun
Beer range varies H
Well-run pub in the business area, offering good value lunches. Note the impressive old station clock. Warm welcome. Trad jazz Wed eve; no food Sat. ◖
⇌ (Lime St) ⊖ (Moorfields)

White Star (Quinns)
24 Rainford Gardens, L2
☎ (0151) 236 8520
11.30–11
Bass Worthington BB, Draught Bass; Cains Bitter; guest beers H
Near to the Cavern, of Beatles fame, a pub catering for shoppers and business people, while maintaining a strong regular trade.
⇌ (Lime St) ⊖ (Moorfields)

Liverpool: *East*

Albany
40–42 Albany Road, L13
☎ (0151) 228 8597
11–11
Cains Mild, Bitter H
Recently refurbished, creating extra space and a third room, the Albany is known for the quality of its mild. Friendly staff; meals Mon–Fri. ◖ ♣

Claremont
70 Lower Breck Road, L6
☎ (0151) 263 7656
12–11
Cains Bitter; Tetley Walker Mild, Bitter H
Two-room pub, in an attractive building of architectural interest. Good value snacks (home-made soups); no food Sun. ⊞ ♣

Clock
110 High Street, L15
☎ (0151) 733 7980
2 (12 Mon & Sat)–11

Cains Bitter H
Pub close to Picton Clock, a local landmark. Much expanded from the cosy pub of the 1970s, but it retains its local feel. Wheelchair access is at the rear. Cheap beer until 7pm. ❀ ☕ ♣

Clubmoor
119 Townsend Lane, Anfield, L6 ☎ (0151) 263 4220
11–11
Cains Mild, Bitter H
Handsome, detached building comprising a bar (with Sky TV) and a large lounge. On the main road, near Everton and Liverpool FCs. ❀ ⊞

Durning Arms
149 Wavertree Road, L7
☎ (0151) 263 8747
11.30–3, 5–11; 11.30–11 Fri & Sat
Cains Bitter, FA; Tetley Walker Bitter H
Rebuilt in the 1960s: a well-used bar and a comfortable lounge. It fields a darts team, and hosts quiz nights and occasional live music.
⊞ ⇌ (Edge Hill) ♣ P

Edinburgh
4 Sandown Lane, L15
12–11
Cains Bitter; Walker Mild, Bitter H
Tiny local, hidden away from the busy Wavertree High Street. It has a separate bar, but the same prices apply throughout. Friendly welcome.

Falstaff
110 Gateacre Park Drive, L25
☎ (0151) 428 5116
11–11
Jennings Bitter; Tetley Walker Mild, Bitter H
1960s pub, refurbished. It hosts live music Sat and Sun eves, and a quiz Mon night. Cheap beer Thu; Sky TV.
♣ P

Kensington
109 Kensington, L7
☎ (0151) 263 9975
11–11
Cains Mild, Bitter H
Cosy, two-roomed gem on a main road. Well worth the trip from the city centre. Sky TV.
⚄ ⊞ ⇌ (Edge Hill) ♣

Rocket
2 Bowring Park Road, L14 (end of M62 motorway)
☎ (0151) 220 8821
11–11
Cains Bitter H
Modern pub, named after the famous pioneer loco, depicted in relief on the side of the pub. No food Sat.
❀ ◖ ☕ ⇌ (Broad Green) P

Royal Standard
Deysbrook Lane, L12
☎ (0151) 228 2777
12–11
Cains Bitter; Greenalls Mild, Bitter, Original H
Suburban pub, pleasantly modernised. The single lounge bar has alcoves. ❀ P

Wheatsheaf
186 East Prescot Road, L14 (A57) ☎ (0151) 228 5080
11.30–11
Cains Bitter; guest beer H
Hospitable, traditional pub, offering waitress service in two lounges, plus a comfortably furnished, busy bar. Q ⊞ P

Liverpool: *North*

Abbey
153 Walton Lane, L4
☎ (0151) 207 0086
11–11
Walker Mild, Bitter H
Homely, comfortable pub with an impressive facade. Regular quiz nights; handy for Everton FC. ⚫ ⊞ ♣

Bull
Dublin Street, L3
☎ (0151) 207 1422
11–11
Tetley Walker Mild, Bitter H
One-bar, popular, discernibly Irish pub, always packed at lunchtimes. Good value sandwiches and pies served. Friendly, warm and inviting: a classic. ⇌ (Sandhills)

Clock
167 Walton Road, L4
☎ (0151) 207 3594
11–11
Walker Mild, Bitter H
Busy, two-roomed, street-corner local; a truly classic Liverpool pub, run by an effervescent licensee. Well worth a visit.
⚫ ⊞ ⇌ (Kirkdale) ♣

Prince Arthur
93 Rice Lane, L9 (A59, next to Walton Hospital)
☎ (0151) 525 4508
11–11
Walker Mild, Bitter, Winter Warmer H
A former CAMRA *Pub-Preservation* award-winner which remains unspoilt. It comprises an L-shaped bar with a corridor drinking area and a comfortable lounge. A well-used pub, and always lively. ⊞ ⇌ (Rice Lane/Walton) ♣ ⇔

Sefton Arms
2 Ormskirk Road, L9
☎ (0151) 525 8787
11.30–11

Cains Mild, Bitter H
Modern pub near Aintree Racecourse. The large lounge has a jukebox, and a family area to the rear; the bar is quiet. Wheelchair WC: ask bar staff. Popular Sun market nearby. No food Sun.
Q ⏰ ❀
◑ ⊞ ♿ ⇌ (Aintree) ♣ P

Liverpool: *South*

Anglesea Arms
36 Beresford Road, L8
☎ (0151) 727 4874
11–11
Tetley Walker Mild, Bitter H
Friendly local with a lively atmosphere where two rooms lie either side of a central bar. Opposite Toxteth market and near a lively shopping area. Well worth travelling the short distance from town. ⊞ ♣

Masonic
19 Lodge Lane
☎ (0151) 734 2271
Tetley Walker Mild, Bitter H
Small, friendly, characterful local in a busy shopping street on the edge of the Toxteth area. It has a public bar, but the same, very reasonable, price is charged throughout.
⚫ ⇌ (Edge Hill)

Royal George
99 Park Road, L8
☎ (0151) 708 9277
11–11
Tetley Walker Dark Mild, Bitter; guest beers H
Popular pub, known locally as Black's, hosting regular live music and karaoke. Happy hours Mon–Thu 5–8pm. Always one changing guest beer available, the cheapest in the city. Sky TV. ◑ ♣

Willowbank
329 Smithdown Road, L15
11–11
Ind Coope Burton Ale; Walker Mild, Bitter, Winter Warmer H
Comfortable pub, popular with students in the eve. The traditional public bar caters for locals. ❀ ⊞ ♣ P

Maghull

Red House
31 Foxhouse Lane
☎ (0151) 526 1376
11–3, 5–11; 11–11 Fri & Sat
Tetley Imperial; Walker Mild, Best Bitter; Winter Warmer H
Suburban local serving good value lunches (not on Sun). Liverpool buses stop outside. Warm and friendly welcome.
❀ ◑ ⊞ ⇌ ♣ P

New Brighton

Stanley's Cask
212 Rake Lane
☎ (0151) 691 1093
11.30–11
McEwan 70/-; S&N Theakston Best Bitter, XB, Old Peculier; Younger IPA; guest beers H
Small, popular, dark pub with a TV room. Frequently changing guest beers at reasonable prices. ❀ ◑ ⇌ ♣

Newton-le-Willows

Blue Lion Hotel
High Street ☎ (01925) 225062
11–11
Walker Mild, Bitter, Best Bitter H
Pub with a large, comfortable lounge, popular with the young, and a games-oriented tap room. ❀ ◑ ⊞ ⇌ ♣ P

Old Crow Inn
248 Crow Lane East (A572, 1 mile from centre)
☎ (01925) 225337
11.30–3.30, 7–11; 12–11 Fri & Sat
Tetley Walker Mild, Dark Mild, Bitter; guest beers H
There's a good tap room following in this welcoming roadside hostelry with a large, comfortable lounge. Lunchtime snacks. ❀ ⊞ ♣ P

Port Sunlight

Bridge Inn
Bolton Road ☎ (0151) 645 8441
11.30–3, 5–11
Marston's Pedigree; Tetley Walker Bitter; guest beers H
Large, smart lounge bar attached to an hotel in the centre of this garden village. Bar snacks are served until 9.15pm, or eat in the hotel restaurant. ⌂ ◑ ⇌ ♣ P

Prescot

Clock Face
54 Derby Street
☎ (0151) 430 0701
11–11
Thwaites Bitter, Craftsman H
Attractive pub on the edge of the town centre. Relaxed, friendly, and an oasis for the quiet drinker. Good value food. Quiz Mon. Liverpool buses stop outside. ⚫ Q ◑ P

Rainhill

Commercial
Station Road (off A57)
☎ (0151) 426 6446
12–11
Cains Mild, Bitter; S&N Theakston Best Bitter; Tetley Walker Bitter H

Merseyside

Large Victorian pub, known locally as the Comic, with Joseph Jones Knotty Ash Ales windows. ✿ ⊞ ≋ ♣ P

St Helens

Brown Edge
299 Nutgrove Road
☎ (0151) 426 4156
12–11
Burtonwood Forshaw's H
Three-roomed pub, with a lively bar, a cosy lounge and a garden lounge (suitable for children), overlooking a bowling green and a play area. Book Sun lunch. ⏳ ✿ ◖
⊞ ≋ (Thatto Heath) ♣ P

Hope & Anchor
194 City Road ☎ (01744) 24199
12–11
Tetley Walker Mild, Bitter H
Well-run pub, hosting events. The disco is loud. ⊞ ⎌

Phoenix
Canal Street (off A53)
☎ (01744) 21953
11–11
Cains Bitter; S&N Theakston Best Bitter; guest beers H
Friendly alehouse, popular with students at weekends. The public bar, with its rugby league photos, is always busy and is home to a serious darts team. Happy hours; lunchtime snacks. ⊞ ≋ (Shaw St) ♣

Royal Alfred
Shaw Street ☎ (01744) 26786
11–11
Cains Bitter E
Busy, cosmopolitan, town-centre pub offering quizzes, live music and discos. Over-sized glasses are used.
⛵ ◖ ⊞ ≋ (Central) ♣ P

Turks Head
49–51 Morley Street
☎ (01744) 26949
11–11
Cains Mild, Bitter; Tetley Walker Bitter H
Interesting, half-timbered pub, unusual for the area. A true community local, it runs a Kiddies' Club. The lunches are highly recommended.
🚌 ✿ ◖ ⊞ ≋ (Central) ♣ P

Wheatsheaf
Westfield Street
☎ (01744) 37453
11–11
Tetley Walker Mild, Bitter H
Small, busy, one-room pub that caters for all tastes.
≋ (Central) ♣

Southport

Berkeley Hotel
19 Queens Road
☎ (01704) 530163
12–11

Courage Directors; Moorhouse's Black Cat Mild, Pendle Witches Brew; Ruddles Best Bitter; guest beers H
Family-run hotel near the town centre, stocking nine cask beers, including four guests, plus Berkeley Bitter, brewed by Moorhouse's. Fun quizzes Thu. Good food.
✿ 🛏 ◖ ▶ ≋ (Chapel St) P

Guest House
Union Street ☎ (01704) 537660
12–11
Draught Bass; Cains Mild, FA; Whitbread Boddingtons Bitter; guest beer H
Traditional, largely unspoiled, ex-Higsons pub of great character. Q ◖ ⌖ ≋ ♣ ⚥

Legendary Lancashire Heroes
101 Shakespeare Street
☎ (01704) 533668
12–10.30
Moorhouse's Pendle Witches Brew; Oak Best Bitter; Taylor Landlord; guest beers H
Enterprising off-licence with a changing range of real ales and foreign bottled beers.

Pageant
Ovington Drive
☎ (01704) 544629
11.30–5, 5–11; 11–11 Sat
Courage Directors; Marston's Pedigree; John Smith's Bitter; Tetley Walker Bitter; Wilson's Mild H
Spacious, split-level estate pub, used mainly by locals. Excellent range of food; quizzes. ✿ ◖ P

Upsteps
20 Upper Aughton Road (off A526) ☎ (01704) 69931
11.30–11
S&N Matthew Brown Bitter, Theakston Mild, Best Bitter, XB H
Cosy, traditional pub with a friendly licensee. The name comes from the steps up to the door. ⊞ ≋ (Birkdale) ♣

Zetland Hotel
Zetland Street
☎ (01704) 544541
11.30–11
Burtonwood Mild, Bitter, Forshaw's, Top Hat H
Well-renovated, Victorian pub with its own bowling green. Public bar prices are the same as the rest of the pub. The family room is open until 8.30pm. 🚌 ⏳ ✿ ◖ ▶ ♣ P

Wallasey

Farmers Arms
Wallasey Village
☎ (0151) 638 2110
11.30–3, 5–11; 11.30–11 Fri & Sat

Cains Bitter; S&N Theakston Best Bitter; Tetley Walker Bitter; guest beers H
Well-furnished and justifiably popular: a previous local CAMRA *Pub of the Year*, comprising a front bar, a side snug and a back lounge. Quiz nights Tue. No jukebox. No food Sun. ◖ ⊞ ≋ (Grove Rd)

Ferry
Tobin Street ☎ (0151) 639 1753
11–11
Cains Bitter, FA; Whitbread Boddingtons Bitter H
Known locally as the Eggy, a pub affording good views across the Mersey, near the ferry terminal at Seacombe. No food Sun. ⏳ ✿ ◖ ▶ ♣ P

Primrose Hotel
11 Withens Lane, Liscard
☎ (0151) 637 1340
12–11
Cains Bitter; S&N Theakston Best Bitter; guest beers H
Unmistakeable, half-timbered pub with wood-panelled walls and an ornate ceiling. ✿ ♣ P

Prince Alfred
3 Church Road, Seacombe
☎ (0151) 638 1674
11–11
Cains Bitter; Whitbread Boddingtons Mild, Bitter; guest beers H
Superb, small, community pub with a friendly atmosphere. Almost lost amidst a sea of keg pubs, it stands close to the famous Mersey ferry terminal at Seacombe. ◖ ⌖ ♣

Waterloo

Volunteer Canteen
East Street ☎ (0151) 928 6594
11–11
Cains Bitter; S&N Theakston Best Bitter H
Busy local community pub, featuring waitress service in the cosy lounge. Very busy at weekends. A Victorian building with a good atmosphere. Q ✿ ⊞ ≋ ♣

West Kirby

Hilbre Court
Banks Road ☎ (0151) 625 7811
11–11
Ind Coope Burton Ale; Jennings Bitter; Tetley Walker Dark Mild, Bitter; guest beers H
Friendly, two-roomed pub with an adjoining restaurant and a lounge extension. Try the excellent pub lunches. Close to West Kirby Promenade and Wirral Way. Q ✿ ◖ ▶ ≋ ♣ P

BEER FESTIVAL CALENDAR 1995

CAMRA beer festivals provide wonderful opportunities for sampling beers not normally found in the locality. Festivals are staffed by CAMRA members on a voluntary basis and offer a wide range of interesting real ales from breweries all over the country, plus live entertainment and much more. The major event is the Great British Beer Festival in August, where over 400 different beers can be enjoyed. For further details of this and the regional events outlined below, together with precise dates and venues, contact CAMRA on (01727) 867201, or see your local press.

JANUARY
Atherton
Exeter
York

FEBRUARY
Basingstoke
Battersea
Bradford
Dorchester
Dover
Durham
Fleetwood
Llandudno
Plymouth
Sussex
Truro

MARCH
Bristol
Camden (London Drinker)
Darlaston
Darlington
Dukeries (N Notts)
Ealing
Eastleigh
Gosport
Leeds
Rugby
Wigan

APRIL
Barnsley
Coventry
Farnham
Luton
Mansfield
Newcastle upon Tyne
Oldham
Swansea

MAY
Alloa
Barnsley
Boat of Garten
Cambridge
Camden (Cider and Perry Exhibition)

Chester
Chippenham
Cleethorpes
Colchester
Dewsbury
Dudley
Frodsham
Lincoln
Milton Keynes
Northampton
Ongar
Rhyl
Ripon
Wolverhampton
Woodchurch
Yapton

JUNE
Bury St Edmunds
Catford
Doncaster
Exeter
Grays
St Ives (Cambs)
Salisbury
Stockport

JULY
Ardingly
Canterbury
Chelmsford
Cotswolds
Derby
Grantham
Southminster
Surrey
Tameside Canals
Woodcote

AUGUST
Great Bntish Beer Festival
Peterborough
Portsmouth
Truro

SEPTEMBER
Birmingham
Burton upon Trent
Chappel
Denbigh
Durham
Feltham
Harbury
Ipswich
Letchworth
Maidstone
Newton Abbot
Northampton
Sheffield
Shrewsbury

OCTOBER
Alloa
Bath
Bedford
Bury
Cardiff
Darlington
East Lancs
Eastleigh
Edinburgh
Guernsey
Holmfirth
Keighley
Loughborough
Middlesbrough
Norwich
Nottingham
Overton
Scunthorpe
Stoke-on-Trent
Wakefield

NOVEMBER
Aberdeen
Dudley
Jersey
Mid Wales
Rochford

DECEMBER
London (Pig's Ear)

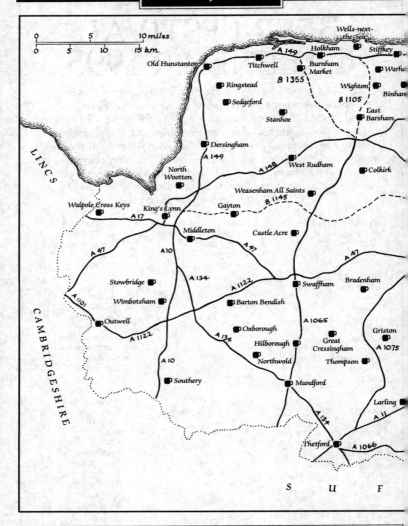

 Buffy's, *Tivetshall St Mary;* **Chalk Hill**, *Norwich;*
Reepham, *Reepham;* **Reindeer**, *Norwich;*
Woodforde's, *Woodbastwick*

Attleborough

Griffin Hotel
Church Street
☎ (01953) 452149
10.30–2.30, 5.30–11
**Adnams Mild; Brakspear
Bitter; Greene King Abbot;
Whitbread Wethered Bitter;
guest beer** H
16th-century coaching inn,
restored to display its original
features to maximum
advantage. Quality food.
Q ✿ 🏠 ◑ ▶ ▲ 🛱 ♣ P

Barton Bendish

Spread Eagle
Church Road (1 mile from
A1122) ☎ (01366) 347295
12–3, 7–11; 12–11 Sat
**Greene King IPA, Abbot;
Tolly Cobbold Mild** H
Homely, 17th-century pub in a
picturesque setting. The large
garden is perfect in summer.
Accommodation or camping
is available at exceptional
rates.
🏰 Q ☎ ✿ 🏠 ◑ ▶ 占 ▲ ♣ P

Berney Arms

Berney Arms
OS468053 ☎ (01493) 700303
11–3, 6–11; 11–11 Sat (closed
Nov–Mar)
**Courage Best Bitter,
Directors; Greene King XX
Mild, IPA, Abbot** H
Set in 26 acres of marshland,
this is a multi-roomed pub
with stone floors and high-
backed settles. Only accessible
by foot, rail, water and bicycle.
🏰 ☎ ✿ ◑ ▶ ▲ 🛱 ♣

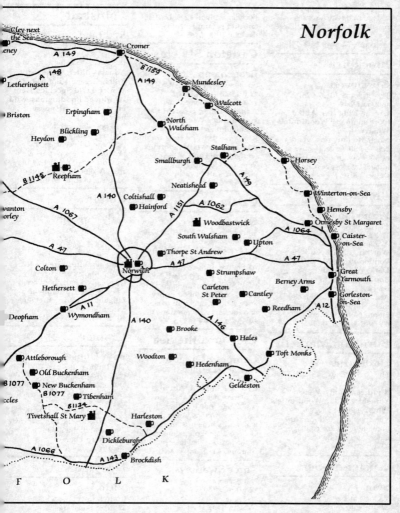

Norfolk

Binham

Chequers
Front Street ☎ (01328) 830297
11–11
**Adnams Bitter; Draught Bass;
M&B Highgate Dark;
Woodforde's Wherry,
Headcracker; guest beers** H
Popular pub, offering a wide
choice of ales; a 17th-century
inn with a comfortable
atmosphere, featuring an old
inglenook. Quiet campsite at
the back. All-day breakfasts.
🏰 Q ॐ ❀ 🛏 ◖ ▶ ▲ ♣ P

Blakeney

Manor Hotel
☎ (01263) 740376

11–2.30, 6–11
Adnams Mild, Bitter, Extra H
Relaxed and comfortable hotel
bar with upholstered settles,
situated in a picturesque
coastal village. Worthington
White Shield is available.
Q 🐾 ❀ 🛏 ◖ ▶ ▲ ♣ P

Blickling

Buckinghamshire Arms
By Blickling Hall
☎ (01263) 732133
12–3, 6–11
**Adnams Bitter, Broadside;
guest beers** H
Very nice two-bar pub, in an
old building by Blickling Hall.
The turned handpump
handles in the snug are

unusual. Like the Hall, it is
apparently haunted.
🏰 Q 🐾 ❀ 🛏 ◖ ▶ ♣ P

Bradenham

Lord Nelson
1 Hale Road ☎ (01362) 820738
12–4, 7–11
Courage Directors H
Friendly village local near the
green. Meals served in
summer. ◖ ▶ ♣ P

Briston

Green Man
Hall Street ☎ (01263) 861449
11–11
**Greene King XX Mild, IPA,
Abbot** H; **guest beer**

Long-established, popular village pub which serves reasonably priced food. Large log fires ensure a warm welcome. 🜂 ❀ ◐ ◑ ♣ P

Brockdish

Greyhound
The Street ☎ (0137 975) 775
12–2 (not Mon & Tue), 7–11
Greene King IPA, Abbot (both summer); **Woodforde's Wherry** [G]
Small, friendly pub where the beer is still served from the cellar. Background classical music. Eve meals Wed–Sat.
🜂 ❀ ◐ ◑ ♣ P ⊬

Brooke

White Lion
49 The Street ☎ (01508) 550443
12–3, 5.30–11; 12–11 Sat
Adnams Bitter; Bass Worthington BB; Fuller's London Pride; M&B Highgate Dark; Whitbread Boddingtons Bitter; guest beers [H]
Attractive pub, just off the main Norwich road, facing the meres. No food Mon.
🜂 ❀ ◐ ◑ ♿ ▲ ♣ P

Burnham Market

Hoste Arms
The Green ☎ (01328) 738257
11–3, 6–11
Ruddles County; Webster's Yorkshire Bitter; Woodforde's Wherry; guest beers [G]
Very popular, 19th-century hotel, in an historic village. Guest ales can be pricey.
🜂 Q 🐎 ❀ 🛏 ◐ ◑ ♿ P ⊬

Caister-on-Sea

Ship
Victoria Street
☎ (01493) 728008
11–11
Greene King IPA; Morland Old Speckled Hen; Whitbread Boddingtons Bitter [H]
Friendly locals' pub, hidden away in the back streets. The comfortable wood-panelled bar displays nautical memorabilia. Family/pool room. 🜂 🐎 ❀ ◐ ◑ ♿ ♣ P

Cantley

Cock Tavern
Manor Road ☎ (01493) 700895
11–3.30 (4 Sat), 7–11
Adnams Bitter; Samuel Smith OBB; Woodforde's Wherry; guest beers [H]
Friendly local with a good selection of food and ales. One bar serves several drinking areas, separated by beams. Popular with all ages. Darts, crib and petanque teams.
🜂 🐎 ❀ ◐ ◑ ▲ ♣ ⌓ P

Carleton St Peter

Beauchamp Arms
Buckenham Ferry OS350044
☎ (01508) 480247
11–3 (not winter Mon–Fri), 6–11
Adnams Bitter; Draught Bass; Woodforde's Wherry; guest beer (summer) [H]
Attractive pub and restaurant, with extensive boat moorings on the south bank of the River Yare. Good fishing, and pleasant walks nearby.
Q 🐎 ❀ ◐ ◑ ♿ ▲ ♣ P

Castle Acre

Ostrich
Stocks Green ☎ (01760) 755398
12–3, 7 (6 summer)–11
Greene King XX Mild, IPA, Abbot [H]
Attractive, 16th-century coaching inn on the Peddars Way. Situated in an historic village with a ruined priory and castle, it caters for locals and tourists with good meals.
🜂 Q 🐎 ❀ 🛏 ◐ ◑ ▲ ♣ P

Cley next the Sea

George & Dragon
High Street ☎ (01263) 740652
11–3, 6–11; 12–2, 7–10.30 Sun
Greene King IPA, Abbot [H]
A place where ale and bird watching come together, there being a scrape just over the sea wall and a hide upstairs. George & Dragon memorabilia in the bar. A third beer in summer. 🜂 ❀ 🛏 ◐ ◑ P

Three Swallows
Newgate Green
☎ (01263) 740526
11–3, 6–11
Greene King IPA; Tetley Bitter (summer) [H]
Wonderfully situated pub beneath Cley church, and overlooking the Glaven valley towards Wiveton. The bar has an ornate carved front, which is offset by the simple decor. An unusual attraction is the croquet lawn. No eve meals winter. 🜂 ❀ 🛏 ◐ ◑ ▲ ♣

Colkirk

Crown
Crown Road ☎ (01328) 862172
11–2.30, 6–11; 12–2.30, 7–10.30 Sun
Greene King XX Mild, IPA, Rayments Special, Abbot [H]
Popular pub with two wood-panelled bars, boasting a fine grandfather clock in the restaurant area. Very good food. 🜂 ❀ ◐ ◑ ♣ P

Coltishall

Red Lion
Church Street
☎ (01603) 737402
11–3, 5–11
Adnams Bitter; Brakspear Bitter; Greene King Abbot; Morland Old Speckled Hen; Whitbread Boddingtons Mild, Flowers Original; guest beer [H]
Pub popular with locals, as well as holidaymakers, dating from the 16th century: two bars on two levels, plus a well-designed children's play area. A Woodforde's house beer is also sold. ❀ ◐ ◑ ♣ P

Colton

Ugly Bug Inn
High House Farm Lane (signed from A47)
☎ (01603) 880794
11–3, 5.30–11
Adnams Bitter; Greene King IPA, Abbot; guest beers [H]
Originally a barn, converted to a house, then tastefully to a pub. Pre-war advertisements adorn the walls.
🜂 ❀ 🛏 ◐ ◑ ♿ ♣ P

Cromer

Bath House
The Promenade
☎ (01263) 514260
11–3, 6.30–11 (may extend summer)
Greene King Abbot; guest beers [H]
Originally a seawater bath house (hence the name), now a seafront hotel with a characterful bar.
🜂 ❀ 🛏 ◐ ◑ ▲ ⇌ ♣

Deopham

Victoria
Church Road
☎ (01953) 850783
12–2.30 (not Mon & Tue), 7–11
Adnams Bitter; Greene King Abbot; Woodforde's Wherry [H]; **guest beers**
Popular, friendly village pub with a comfortable atmosphere. Very good food includes vegetarian and children's dishes. Quiz and petanque teams fielded.
🜂 ◐ ◑ ♣ P

Dersingham

Feathers Hotel
Manor Road (B1140)
☎ (01485) 540207
11–2.30, 5.30–11
Adnams Bitter; Bass Charrington IPA; Fuller's London Pride; guest beer [H]
Traditional Carrstone hotel with panelled rooms and open

fires. Good bar and restaurant food caters for the whole family, a public/games bar is housed in the old stables and there are extensive gardens and a play area.
🏠 ☻ 🛏 ◖ ▮ 🍴 ㅌ ▲ ♣ P

Dickleburgh

Crown

The Street ☎ (01379) 741475
12–3, 7–11; 11–11 Sat
Adnams Bitter, Old H; guest beer (summer)
Comfortable, beamed, 16th-century pub with some good furniture and a large garden.
🏠 ☒ ☻ ◖ ▮ P ✗

East Barsham

White Horse Inn

Fakenham Road
☎ (01328) 820645
11–3, 7–11; 11–11 summer
Greene King Abbot; Whitbread Boddingtons Bitter; Woodforde's Wherry H
17th-century inn with a comfortable atmosphere. Five clocks display times around the world and lots of artefacts adorn the interior.
🏠 ☻ 🛏 ◖ ▮ ♣

Eccles

Old Railway Tavern (Eccles Tap)

Station Road
2–2.30, 5.30–11
Adnams Bitter G**; Greene King IPA** H**, Abbot** G
'Back to basics' pub, with a relaxed atmosphere. Mind your head! Snacks served.
🏠 Q ☻ ⇌ (Eccles Rd) ♣ ▭ P

Erpingham

Spread Eagle

Eagle Lane ☎ (01263) 761591
1–3, 6.30–11
Woodforde's Mardler's Mild, Wherry, Norfolk Nog, Baldric, Headcracker H
16th-century pub in a picturesque Norfolk village. The large lawn at the rear is pleasant in summer. The house beer (Spread Eagle) is brewed by Woodforde's.
🏠 ☒ ☻ ◖ ▮ ㅌ ▲ ♣ P

Gayton

Crown

Lynn Road (B1145)
☎ (01553) 636252
1–3, 6–11
Greene King XX Mild, IPA, Rayments Special, Abbot H
Lovely old village pub, opposite the church: two bars, a noted restaurant and a

games/family room. Huge log fires in the main bar.
🏠 Q ☒ ☻ ☻ ◖ ▮ ♣ P

Geldeston

Wherry

7 The Street ☎ (01508) 518371
11–3, 7 (6 summer)–11
Adnams Bitter, Old, Extra, Broadside, Tally Ho H
Two-bar pub, near the River Waveney, at the southern end of the Broads. Parts date from the 1670s. Phat is played Mon.
🏠 Q ☻ ◖ ▮ ▲ ♣ P

Gorleston-on-Sea

Dock Tavern

Dock Tavern Lane
☎ (01493) 442255
11–11
Adnams Broadside; Whitbread Boddingtons Bitter H**; guest beers**
Friendly pub, popular with the locals. Many photos of Old Gorleston are displayed alongside the hull of a Walker's skiff above the bar. Note the mark of the 1953 floods near the door. Local cider. Q ☒ ☻ ◖ ▮ ♣ ▭

New Entertainer

Back Pier Plain
☎ (01493) 441643
11–11
Adnams Mild, Bitter, Old, Extra, Broadside; guest beers H
Old Lacon's pub with one long bar and a friendly atmosphere, popular with the locals. Selection of reading material.
Q ◖ ㅌ ♣

Short Blue

47 High Street
☎ (01493) 602192
10.30–11
Scott's Golden Best, Blues and Bloater; Tetley Bitter H
Town-centre pub with a nicely carved, wooden bar and photographs of Old Gorleston on display. Q ☻ ◖ ▮

Great Cressingham

Windmill Inn

Water End (signed off A1065)
☎ (01760) 756232
11–2.30, 6.30–11; 12–2.30, 7–10.30 Sun
Adnams Bitter, Broadside; Draught Bass; Greene King IPA; Samuel Smith OBB; guest beer H
Original oak-beamed pub with three bars and four other drinking areas, including a conservatory. It has a large garden (ask for horseshoes and Aunt Sally), and full camping and caravanning facilities; safe for kids.
🏠 Q ☒ ☻ ◖ ▮ ▲ ♣ P

Great Yarmouth

Clipper Schooner

Friars Lane (off South Quay)
☎ (01493) 854926
11–11
Adnams Mild, Bitter, Old, Broadside, Tally Ho; guest beers H
1930s, ex-Lacon's pub close to the docks and the old town wall. Comfortable and friendly, it serves hot food all day. ☒ ☻ ◖ ▮ ㅌ ♣ P

Mariners Tavern

69 Howard Street South
☎ (01493) 332299
11–2.30, 8–11; closed Mon–Wed eve & Sun
Bass Worthington BB, Draught Bass; M&B Highgate Dark; guest beers H
Comfortable bar lounge/restaurant, hosting folk music the first Thu eve of each month, plus four small beer festivals a year. It has an attractive, old-looking exterior, although only built in the 1950s by Lacon's.
Q ☻ ◖ ▮ ☒ ⇌ ♣ P ✗

Try also: **Oliver Twist**, North Market Rd; **Red Herring**, Havelock Rd (both Free)

Griston

Waggon & Horses

Church Road
☎ (01953) 883847
11–3, 6.30–11
Greene King IPA, Rayments Special, Abbot H
Large, comfortable, village pub, displaying brewery mirrors. Good food is always available. Q ☻ ◖ ▮ ▲ ♣ P

Hainford

Chequers

Stratton Road
☎ (01603) 891657
11–3, 6.30–11
Morland Old Speckled Hen; guest beers H
Thatched and beamed pub which, although food-oriented, still has some charm. No electronic machines or bright lighting. A strong ale is added in winter. 🏠 ☻ ◖ ▮ ▲ ♣ P

Hales

Chequered Flag

Yarmouth Road
☎ (01508) 548468
12–3, 7–11
Tetley Bitter; Tolly Cobbold Mild, Original H
Long, two-bar pub featuring collections of old cigarette cards and old photos of the pub. Bowling green. ☒ ☻ ◖ ▮
▲ (Raveningham) ♣ P

Norfolk

Harleston

Cherry Tree
74 London Road
☎ (01379) 852345
11–2.30, 6–11
Adnams Mild, Bitter, Old, Extra, Broadside H
Wonderful, two-bar pub, unspoilt by modernisation and refurbishment. An old iron range is a feature of the lounge bar. The sort of pub to linger in. ♨ Q ✿ ♿ ▲ ♣ P

Hedenham

Mermaid
Norwich Road
☎ (0150 844) 480
11–3, 5–11; 11–11 Sat
Adnams Bitter; Draught Bass; Greene King IPA H
Comfortable, refurbished country pub, which has retained much of its original character, with a large open fire offering a warm welcome.
♨ ✿ ◖ ▶ ▲ ♣ P

Hemsby

Kings Head
North Road ☎ (01943) 730568
11–3, 6–11; 11–11 Sat
Morland Old Speckled Hen; John Smith's Bitter; Woodforde's Wherry; guest beers (summer) H
Pleasant, 18th-century village pub with oak beams and real fires in the bar and dining room. Well-attended quiz Sun eve. The Asian board game of Carrom is also played.
♨ Q ✿ ◖ ▶ ♿ ▲ ♣ P

Hethersett

King's Head
36 Old Norwich Road
☎ (01603) 810206
11–2.30, 5.30 (5 Fri, 6 Sat)–11
Courage Directors; Marston's Pedigree; Morland Old Speckled Hen; John Smith's Bitter; Wadworth 6X; guest beer H
Lovely, old two-bar local, with timber beams much in evidence. Food is available but does not dominate. Note the bottle collection in the small bar. A good bus service (including Sun) runs between Norwich and Wymondham. Eve meals Fri and Sat.
♨ Q ✿ ◖ ▶ ♿ ♣ P

Heydon

Earle Arms
The Street ☎ (01263) 87376
11 (12 winter)–3, 6 (7 winter)–11
Adnams Bitter, Old; Morland Old Speckled Hen H

An unusual unspoilt free house and bistro in a cul-de-sac village. Classical background music. Beware the fake Scrumpy Jack handpump. A third Adnams beer is also available.
♨ ✿ ◖ ▶ ▲ ⌂ P ✕

Hilborough

Swan
☎ (01760) 756380
11 (10.30 Sat)–2.30, 6–11; 12–2, 7–10.30 Sun
Draught Bass; Greene King IPA, Abbot H**; Tolly Cobbold Mild** G**; guest beers**
Friendly, roadside free house. It stocks a constantly changing guest beer and unusual malt whiskies. ♨ Q ✿ ♣ P

Holkham

Victoria
Park Road ☎ (01328) 710469
11–3, 7–11 (11–11 summer)
Greene King IPA; Marston's Pedigree
Children are welcome in this circa 1820 pub on the edge of the Holkham estate. Popular with tourists, the restaurant has a fine view over the marshes. A bar area adjoins the restaurant and there is another small bar.
♨ Q ✿ ⊨ ◖ ▶ ♣ P

Horsey

Nelson Head
The Street (just off B1159)
☎ (01493) 393378
11–2.30 (3 Sat), 7 (6 summer)–11
Woodforde's Wherry, Nelson's Revenge (summer) H
Friendly, one-bar country pub with nautical artefacts; popular with visitors to the marshes and Horsey Mill, and within easy walking distance of the Broads and beach. Austrian food is a speciality.
♨ Q ⛄ ✿ ◖ ▶ ♣ P

King's Lynn

Duke's Head Hotel (Lynn Bar)
Tuesday Market Place
☎ (01553) 774996
11–2.30, 6–11
Adnams Bitter; Draught Bass; Courage Directors; guest beers H
Small, friendly hotel bar.
Q ⊨ ◖ ▶ ≋ ♣ P

London Porterhouse
78 London Road
☎ (01553) 766842
11.30–2.30, 6–11; 12–11 Sat
Greene King IPA, Abbot G
Small, busy local, near the

historic South Gate, which is featured in prints of old King's Lynn on display. The only gravity dispensed beer in the area. Q ✿ ≋ ♣

Seven Sisters
Extons Road ☎ (01553) 766707
12–3, 7–11
Younger IPA; guest beers H
Popular pub with a pool table. The restaurant serves good value food. Close to the Walks football ground. ◖ ▶ ♣

Larling

Angel
On A11 ☎ (01953) 717963
11–3, 5–11 (11–11 if busy)
Adnams Bitter; Greene King IPA; guest beer H
Soon to be bypassed, but don't miss this genuine local with a real public bar and always an ale to tempt the enthusiast. One mile from the Snetterton Circuit. ♨ ✿ ⊨ ◖ ▶ ≋ (Harling Rd) ♣ P

Letheringsett

Kings Head
Holt Road ☎ (01263) 712691
11–3, 5.30–11
Adnams Bitter; Draught Bass; Greene King IPA, Abbot H
Comfortable, old beamed pub in a delightful garden setting, adjoining old brewery buildings. Take a quiet walk from the watermill nearby, along the River Glaven. Families welcome.
♨ Q ✿ ◖ ▶ ▲ ♣ P

Middleton

Gate Inn
Hill Road, Fair Green (A47)
☎ (01553) 840518
12–3, 7 (5 Fri)–11
Draught Bass; Greene King IPA H
Cosy cottage pub with two bars, good, home-cooked food and a real fire in a brick hearth. ♨ Q ✿ ◖ ▶ ♣ P

Mundesley

Royal Hotel
Paston Road ☎ (01263) 720096
11–2.30, 6–11
Adnams Bitter; Greene King IPA, Abbot; guest beer H
Comfortable, beamed bar displaying pictures of Nelson. Popular with the locals.
♨ ⛄ ✿ ⊨ ◖ ▶ ▲ P

Mundford

Crown Hotel
Crown Road ☎ (01842) 878233
11–11

230

John Smith's Bitter; Webster's Yorkshire Bitter; Woodforde's Wherry, Nelson's Revenge, Norfolk Nog Ⓗ
Multi-roomed, 17th-century coaching inn, at the village centre. Exceptional food in the bar and restaurant.
🏚 ❀ 🍴 ◐ ▣ ♠ P

Neatishead

White Horse
The Street ☎ (01692) 630828
12–2.30, 7 (6 summer)–11
Greene King IPA; Tolly Cobbold Mild, Original Ⓗ
Classic rural Norfolk pub, near Neatishead Staithe.
🏚 ❀ 🍴 ◐ ♠ P

New Buckenham

King's Head
Market Place ☎ (01953) 860487
11.30–2.30, 7–11
Wadworth 6X; Whitbread Boddingtons Bitter; guest beer Ⓗ
Simple, two-roomed pub on the village green; handy for the annual fair. No food Mon.
🏚 ❀ ◐ ♠

North Walsham

Scarborough Hill House Hotel
Yarmouth Road (1 mile from town) ☎ (01692) 402151
11–3, 7–11
Tolly Cobbold Original; Whitbread Boddingtons Bitter; guest beer (occasional) Ⓖ
Hotel with a bar and dining room, adorned with brasses and agricultural implements, set in large grounds in rural surroundings.
Q ❀ 🍴 ◐ ♠ A ♣ P

Northwold

Crown
High Street ☎ (01366) 727317
12–2.30, 6–11; 11–11 Sat
Greene King Abbot, IPA; guest beers Ⓗ
Traditional, 18th-century village pub. Good food is served daily. 🏚 ❀ ◐ ♠ P

North Wootton

Red Cat Hotel
Station Road ☎ (01553) 631244
11–2.30, 6.30–11
Adnams Bitter; Bass Worthington BB Ⓗ
Pleasant village hotel deriving its name from a mummified cat in the bar. The house beer 'Red Cat' is brewed by Woodforde's.
🏚 Q ❀ 🍴 ◐ ◐ P ✗

Norwich

Adam & Eve
17 Bishopgate (behind cathedral)
☎ (01603) 667423
11–11
Adnams Bitter; Ruddles Best Bitter, County; John Smith's Bitter Ⓗ
Beautiful plaster and timber pub with low ceilings in its two bars. Noticeable orientation towards food between 12 and 7. The snug is used by non-smokers at lunchtime. Twee muzak.
🍴 ❀ ◐ ➤ P ✗

Alexandra Tavern
16 Stafford Street (between Earlham and Dereham road, ½ mile from centre)
☎ (01603) 627772
10.30–11
Chalk Hill Old Tackle; Courage Best Bitter; Marston's Pedigree; Morland Old Speckled Hen; Wadworth 6X Ⓗ
Two-bar, Victorian corner pub, the popular public bar attracting a sociable clientele. One of the very few outlets for Chalk Hill Brewery.
🏚 Q ♠ ◐

Champion
101 Chapelfield Road (by St Stephen's roundabout)
11–3, 7–11
Adnams Bitter, Old, Extra, Tally Ho; Wadworth 6X Ⓗ
Cosy and comfortable pub with three enclosed, small areas off one central bar, furnished with old upholstery. Note the Lacon's windows.
♠

Coach & Horses
82 Thorpe Road (near station)
☎ (01603) 620704
11–11
Chalk Hill Tap Bitter, CHB, Old Tackle; Fuller's London Pride; guest beers Ⓗ
Pub renovated with care to include Norwich's newest brewery. It has one large bar area with wood floors, a lovely fire and a solarium at the back. No food Sun eve.
🏚 ◐ ➤ ♠ ◐ P

Eaton Cottage
75 Mountpleasant (½ mile from RC cathedral)
☎ (01603) 53048
11–3, 5.30–11; 11–11 Sat
Marston's Pedigree; Samuel Smith OBB; John Smith's Bitter; guest beers Ⓗ
A 19th-century corner pub, which is unusual in not being knocked through, retaining a snug. ❀ ♠ P

Fat Cat
49 West End Street (just off A1074) ☎ (01603) 624364
12 (10.30 Sat)–11
Adnams Bitter; Fuller's London Pride; Wells Bombardier; Woodforde's Mardler's Mild, Nelson's Revenge Ⓗ; guest beers Ⓖ / Ⓗ
Excellent Victorian, traditional pub with a good range of local and unusual beers; several of the strong ones are served on gravity dispense. A must for the connoisseur. Q ❀ ◐

Freemasons Arms
27 Hall Road
☎ (01603) 623768
11–3 (Sat), 6 (7.30 Sat)–11
Woodforde's Mardler's Mild, Wherry, Nelson's Revenge, Norfolk Nog; guest beers Ⓗ
Busy, single bar in a good drinking area, very popular at lunchtimes (snacks available). The guest beer is from Woodforde's. ♠

Mill Tavern
2 Millers Lane (opp. Waterloo Park) ☎ (01603) 410268
11.30–2.30 (3 Sat), 6.30–11
Adnams Mild, Bitter, Old, Broadside Ⓗ
The one long bar area in this down-to-earth boozer, with its old Joanna, dartboard and crib team, leads to a newly opened garden. ❀ ♿ ♠ P

Mustard Pot
101 Thorpe Road
☎ (01603) 32393
12–3, 5.30–11; 12–11 Fri & Sat
Adnams Bitter, Old; Marston's Pedigree; guest beers Ⓗ
Large, recently refurbished pub with a pleasant, relaxed atmosphere. ❀ ◐ ♿ ➤ P

Plasterers' Arms
43 Cowgate (off Magdalen St, opp. Anglia Sq)
10.30–11
Adnams Bitter, Extra, Broadside; Everards Old Original; Ind Coope Burton Ale; Mansfield Riding Mild Ⓗ
Dark and scruffy pub lit by twinkling fairy lights and covered with curios. High quality lunches are served Mon–Sat. See the Terry Storer memorial plaque. Q ◐

Pottergate Tavern
23 Pottergate (near City Hall)
☎ (01603) 614589
10.30–11
Greene King XX Mild, IPA, Rayments Special, Abbot Ⓗ; guest beers
Single-bar, split-level pub which has remained largely untouched since its construction in the 1930s. A

231

Norfolk

good place for a lunchtime drink in the city. 🍴 ♣ ⏖

Reindeer
10 Dereham Road
☎ (01603) 666821
11–11
Reindeer Moild, RPA, Gnu Bru; guest beers H
Cosmopolitan city pub where six guest beers are always available. Very popular at weekends, it is attached to Norwich's oldest brewery. Less than half the house beers are now kept under gas.
Q 🏛 🍴 ♣ ⏖ P

Rosary Tavern
95 Rosary Road (near yacht and rail stations)
☎ (01603) 666287
11–11
Adnams Bitter; Draught Bass; Bateman XXXB; Marston's Pedigree; Woodforde's Wherry H; **guest beers** G
Very friendly, cosy pub with several guest beers served direct from the cellar. A good selection of traditional pub games is available. The house beer (Rosary) is brewed by Woodforde's. No food Sun.
⏖ 🏛 🍴 ≢ ♣ ⏖ P

St Andrew's Tavern
4 St Andrew's Street (opp. multi-storey car park)
☎ (01603) 614858
11–11; closed Sun
Adnams Bitter, Extra; guest beers H
Pub with a variety of drinking areas. Five guest beers are stocked, including a mild. Eve meals Thu–Sat. 🏛 🍴 ▶ ≢

Tap & Spile
73 Oak Street (inside inner ring road) ☎ (01603) 620630
12–11
Beer range varies H
Chain pub serving a selection of up to ten ales and one real cider in its three bars, at very reasonable prices. No food Sun. 🏚 🍴 ♣ ⏖ P

Trafford Arms
61 Grove Road
☎ (01603) 628466
11–11
Adnams Bitter; Tetley Bitter; Whitbread Boddingtons Bitter; Woodforde's Mardler's Mild; guest beers H
Newly free Inntrepreneur pub run by a landlord committed to selling a range of real ales including local brews. The single bar has a dining area. The Barley Boy house bitter is brewed by Woodforde's.
🍴 ▶ ⏖ P

Windmill
Knox Road (B1140, near prison) ☎ (01603) 34531

11.30–2.30 (3.30 Sat), 6 (6.30 winter)–11
Greene King XX Mild, IPA, Abbot H
Pub where there is a definite contrast between the quiet and comfortable lounge and the much larger, brightly-lit public bar, but there is no longer a price differential (the lounge prices were dropped). No food Sun. 🏛 🍴 ♣ P

Old Buckenham

Ox & Plough
The Green ☎ (01953) 860004
12–2 (2.30 summer), 5–11; 11–11 Sat
Adnams Bitter; Greene King IPA; guest beer H
Single bar in a welcoming pub overlooking the large village green. One area is set aside for pool. 🏚 🏛 🍴 ▶ 🚻 ♣ P

Old Hunstanton

Ancient Mariners
Golf Course Road (A149)
☎ (01485) 534411
11–3, 6–11; 11–11 Sat & summer
Adnams Bitter, Broadside; Draught Bass; guest beer H
Large bar, part of the Le Strange Arms Hotel, nevertheless retaining a pub-like atmosphere. It features low beams, nautical decor, intimate drinking areas for adults and a room and garden for children; superb for families. Sea views.
🏚 ⏖ 🏛 🛏 🍴 ▶ 🚻 ♣ P

Ormesby St Margaret

Grange Hotel
On A149, towards Caister
☎ (01493) 731877
12–11
Bass Worthington BB; Courage Directors; Elgood's Cambridge Bitter; John Smith's Bitter; Woodforde's Wherry H
Hotel situated on the east coast, just five miles from Gt Yarmouth. It makes an ideal base for business or holidaymakers, with Caister heliport nearby, as well as local beauty spots and places of interest. Pets corner.
🏚 Q ⏖ 🏛 🛏 🍴 ▶ ♣ P

Jolly Farmers
10 West Road
☎ (01493) 730471
11.30–11
Adnams Bitter; Ruddles Best Bitter, County; Webster's Yorkshire Bitter H
Busy local, worth seeking out. Good food is always available and holidaymakers are made welcome. Children's play area outside. 🏛 🍴 ▶ ♣ P

Outwell

Red Lion
6 Wisbech Road (A1112)
☎ (01945) 773368
11–2.30 (not Mon–Fri in winter), 7–11; 11–11 Sat
Elgood's Cambridge Bitter H
Overlooking the church and Welle Creek, a modern brick front hides an early 19th-century local. One quiet village bar has a large fireplace and beams; two others have the jukebox, pool table etc.
🏚 Q 🚻 ♣ P

Oxborough

Bedingfeld Arms
Off A134 ☎ (01366) 328300
12–3, 5–11
Courage Directors; Morrells Bitter; S&N Theakston Best Bitter; Whitbread Boddingtons Bitter H; **guest beers**
Popular pub with both locals and visitors to Oxborough Hall. The friendly owners serve good food. Large garden. 🏚 🏛 🍴 ▶ 🅰 ♣ P

Reedham

Railway Tavern
Havaker ☎ (01493) 700340
12–3, 7–11; 11–11 Fri & Sat
Adnams Bitter; Greene King IPA, Abbot; Scott's Blues and Bloater; Tetley Bitter; Woodforde's Wherry; guest beers H
Children are welcome in this friendly, village local where good food is served in the small restaurant. This 150-year-old Grade II-listed building boasts a comfortable atmosphere, and a wide selection of guest beers. Local cider in summer.
🏚 🏛 🛏 🍴 ▶ 🚻 🅰 ≢ ⏖ P

Reepham

Kings Arms
Market Place ☎ (01603) 870345
11.30–3, 5.30–11
Adnams Bitter, Broadside; Draught Bass; Fuller's London Pride; Greene King IPA H
Large, popular pub at the centre of a small town.
🏚 ⏖ 🏛 🍴 ▶ 🚻 ✂

Old Brewery House
Market Square
☎ (01603) 870881
11–3, 6–11 (11–11 summer)
Adnams Bitter; Draught Bass; Greene King Abbot; Reepham Velvet Stout; Whitbread Boddingtons Bitter H

Pleasant and comfortable bar in an old hotel which overlooks the market place.
Q 🍺 ⚙ 🛏 ◁ ▷

Ringstead

Gin Trap

High Street ☎ (01485) 25264
11–2.30, 7 (6 summer)–11
Adnams Bitter; Draught Bass; Greene King Abbot; Woodforde's Norfolk Nog; guest beer H
Petanque is a feature of this country village pub which boasts a collection of animal traps. It has a split-level bar and a pleasant garden. Next to an art gallery.
🏚 Q ⚙ ◁ ▷ ♣

Sedgeford

King William IV

Heacham Road
☎ (01485) 571765
11–3, 6 (6.30 winter)–11
Adnams Bitter; Bass Worthington Dark, Draught Bass; Greene King IPA H
Out-of-the-ordinary village local, noted for its good value food. Local Kingfisher cider.
🏚 Q ⚙ ◁ ▷ & ♣ ➪ P

Smallburgh

Crown

North Walsham Road
☎ (01692) 536314
12–3 (4 Sat), 5.30 (7 Sat)–11
Draught Bass; Greene King IPA, Abbot; Tetley Bitter; Tolly Cobbold Mild H
Thatched, beamed building which dates from the 15th century and features a large open fire, and tables and chairs made from wooden barrels. A friendly local, it offers good food in an attractive dining room (no meals Sun eve).
🏚 Q 🍺 ⚙ 🛏 ◁ ▷ ▲ ♣ P

Southery

Jolly Farmers

60 Feltwell Road
☎ (01366) 377327
11–2.30, 6–11
Adnams Bitter; Greene King IPA, Abbot H
Spacious 1960s pub, unusual to find in a village. A welcome is extended to all the family, with very reasonably priced drinks and food. ⚙ ◁ ▷ P

South Walsham

Ship

18 The Street ☎ (01603) 270553
11–3, 6–11; 11–11 Sat
Adnams Bitter; Ruddles Best Bitter; Woodforde's Wherry; guest beer H

Cosy village pub with a traditional brick and beam interior in both bars. Children's play area in the garden. 🏚 🍺 ⚙ ◁ ▷ ♣ P

Try also: Fur & Feather, Woodbastwick (Woodforde's)

Stalham

Kingfisher

High Street ☎ (01692) 581974
11–2.30, 6–11
Adnams Bitter; Draught Bass; Woodforde's Wherry H
Modern, family-run hotel with a comfortable bar, situated in a small country town, near the sea and the Broads.
🛏 ◁ ▷ ♣ P

Try also: Butcher's Arms, E Ruston (Free)

Stanhoe

Crown

Burnham Market Road (B1155)
☎ (01485) 518330
11–3, 6–11
Elgood's Cambridge Bitter H, **GSB** G
Small village local with a friendly welcome. Try the excellent, home-cooked food. Small caravan park for CC members. 🏚 Q ⚙ ◁ ▷ ♣ P

Stiffkey

Red Lion

44 Wells Road
☎ (01328) 830552
11–2.30, 6–11
Greene King IPA, Abbot; Woodforde's Wherry; guest beers H
Large pub with open fires and a restaurant, re-opened in 1990 after 20 years as a private house. The unspoilt village is in an area popular with walkers.
🏚 Q 🍺 ⚙ ◁ ▷ 🍴 & ▲ ♣ P

Stowbridge

Heron

Station Road ☎ (01366) 384147
11–3, 7–11
Adnams Bitter; Draught Bass; Greene King IPA, Abbot; guest beers H
Friendly, riverside pub ideal for holidaymakers and anglers. The cosy, welcoming interior features a wood-burning stove, a pool bar and a function room.
🏚 🍺 ⚙ ◁ ▷ ♣ P

Strumpshaw

Shoulder of Mutton

Norwich Road
☎ (01603) 712274
11–11

Adnams Bitter, Old, Extra H; **guest beer**
Popular local with a large single bar and a restaurant. The spacious outdoor drinking area hosts barbecues in summer.
🏚 🍺 ⚙ ◁ ▷ & ♣ P

Swaffham

Norfolk Hero

48 Station Street
☎ (01760) 723923
11.30–11
M&B Brew XI; guest beers H
Quiet, two-bar pub, a short distance from the town centre.
🏚 Q 🍺 ◁ ▷ ♣ P

Swanton Morley

Darbys

Elsing Road ☎ (01362) 637647
11–2.30, 6 (7 Sat)–11
Adnams Bitter, Broadside; Woodforde's Wherry; guest beers H
Pub converted from two old cottages but retaining much of their original character, with beams and bricks exposed in the bar. Pleasant atmosphere and a friendly welcome. No-smoking family room.
🏚 Q 🍺 🛏 ◁ ▷ & ▲ P ↯

Thetford

Albion

Castle Street ☎ (01842) 752796
11–2.30, 6–11; 12–2, 7–10.30 Sun
Greene King Abbot, IPA H
Small, comfortable and friendly, flint-faced pub in an older part of town, close to Castle Hill ancient monument. It sells by far the cheapest pint in the area. Q ⚙ ◁ ♣ P

Try also: Bell Hotel, King St (Free)

Thompson

Chequers

Griston Road (B1075, left at Griston crossroads) OS923969
☎ (01953) 483360
11–3, 6–11
Adnams Bitter; Ind Coope Burton Ale; guest beer H
Unspoilt, 16th-century, thatched pub, well off the beaten track. Enjoying a fine reputation amongst the locals, it is extremely busy all year. Of its three bars, two feature very low ceilings. Kingfisher cider. Q 🍺 ⚙ ◁ ▷ ♣ ➪ P

Thorpe St Andrew

Gordon

88 Gordon Avenue
☎ (01603) 34658
11–3, 7–11

233

Greene King IPA, Abbot; Ind Coope Burton Ale; Tetley Bitter H
Large, suburban, family pub popular with the locals: a mock Tudor building dating from 1934. Q ✿ ♣ P

Tibenham

Greyhound
The Street ☎ (0137 977) 676
7–11; 12–3, 7–11 Sat
Beer range varies H
Unspoilt, two-bar village pub, well worth finding. The house beer (K9) is brewed by Woodforde's. Children are welcome in summer.
🏠 ♒ ✿ ▲ ♣ P

Titchwell

Three Horseshoes
Main Road ☎ (01485) 210202
11–3, 7 (6 summer)–11
Adnams Bitter; Draught Bass; guest beer H
An inn in the true sense, offering food, drink and accommodation. Its old-style interior includes a restaurant, serving genuine, home-cooked food. It overlooks the RSPB reserve.
🏠 ✿ 🛏 ◖ ▲ ♣ P

Try also: Lifeboat, Thornham (Free)

Toft Monks

Toft Lion
Beccles Road ☎ (01502) 677702
11.30–2.30, 6.30–11
Adnams Bitter, Old; Draught Bass; guest beers (summer) H
Comfortable, friendly local. Its single bar displays old farm implements and good, home-cooked food is available.
🏠 ♒ ✿ 🛏 ◖ ♦ ♣ P

Upton

White Horse
17 Chapel Road
☎ (01493) 750696
11–11
Adnams Bitter or Broadside; Woodforde's Wherry or Nelson's Revenge; guest beer G
Quiet village pub near the River Bure, with a stone-flagged floor and two large wood burners in its one long bar with two rooms off. The landlord runs a minibus for hire. 🏠 ♒ ✿ ◖ ♣ ○ P

Walcott

Lighthouse Inn
Coast Road ☎ (01692) 650371
11–3, 6.30–11

Adnams Bitter; Tetley Bitter; Wadworth 6X H
Single-bar pub, very popular; families are welcome. It hosts barbecues and a children's disco Tue eve in summer. Good value food (separate dining room).
🏠 ♒ ✿ ◖ ▲ ♣ P

Walpole Cross Keys

Woolpack Inn
Sutton Road ☎ (01553) 828327
12–3, 7–11
Adnams Bitter, Old, Broadside; guest beer H
Pleasant country inn on the old A17. Friendly landlady. No food Mon or Tue eves.
🏠 Q ♒ ✿ ◖ ♣ P

Warham

Three Horseshoes
69 The Street ☎ (01328) 710547
11–2.30 (3 summer), 6–11; 11–11 Sat
Greene King IPA, Abbot; Woodforde's Wherry; guest beers G
Old village pub with a basic decor and some unusual artefacts, including a 1921 electric pianola. Food is cooked with local produce.
🏠 Q ♒ ✿ 🛏 ◖ ▲ ♣ P

Weasenham All Saints

Ostrich
☎ (0132 874) 221
11–3, 7–11
Adnams Bitter, Broadside H
The slightly scruffy exterior belies a cosy, one-bar pub which also sells fruit and veg in the bar. Worthington White Shield is available. Outside toilets. 🏠 Q ✿ ♣ P

Wells-next-the-Sea

Crown Hotel
The Buttlands
☎ (01328) 710209
11–2.30, 6–11; 12–2.30, 7–10.30 Sun
Adnams Bitter; Marston's Pedigree; Tetley Bitter (summer) H
A coaching inn since the 18th century; a fine hotel, facing a tree-lined green. The Tudor building has a Georgian facade. 🏠 ♒ ✿ 🛏 ◖ ▲ 👦 P

West Rudham

Dukes Head
Lynn Road ☎ (01485) 528540
11–3, 6.30–11; 12–2.30, 7–10.30 Sun
Adnams Bitter; Woodforde's Wherry; guest beer H
There are no electronic machines in this old pub,

which was extended (upwards) in the 17th century, giving rise to an unusual flint, brick and Carrstone facade. The interior is cosy, with a half-panelled back bar.
🏠 Q ✿ ◖ ♣ P

Wighton

Sandpiper
High Street ☎ (01328) 820752
11–2.30, 6.30–11 (11–11 July & Aug)
Adnams Bitter; Elgood's Cambridge Bitter; Samuel Smith OBB; Woodforde's Wherry; guest beers H
Pub where a central fireplace, with a brick chimney, separates the bar from the family room. The entrance leads through a games room.
🏠 Q ♒ ✿ 🛏 ◖ ▲ ♣ P

Wimbotsham

Chequers
Church Road
☎ (01366) 774407
11.45–3, 6.30–11; 11.45–11 Sat
Greene King XX Mild, IPA, Abbot H
Lively local, overlooking the green.
Q ♒ ✿ ◖ ▲ 👦 ♣ P

Winterton-on-Sea

Fisherman's Return
The Lane ☎ (01493) 393305
11–2.30 (3 Sat), 7 (6 summer)–11 (11–11 summer Sat)
Adnams Bitter; Draught Bass; M&B Highgate Dark; John Smith's Bitter; guest beers H
Popular, two-bar local near the beach, serving good value food. The lounge bar has a cosy feel, with beams and brasses.
🏠 Q ♒ ✿ 🛏 ◖ ♣ P

Woodton

King's Head
Hempnall Road
☎ (0150 844) 329
12–2, 7–11
Draught Bass; Greene King IPA, Abbot H
A former row of cottages which has been converted into a pub. A dining area is at one end, pool and pinball at the other. 🏠 ✿ ◖ ▲ ♣ P

Wymondham

Feathers
Town Green ☎ (01953) 605675
11–2.30, 7 (6 Fri & Sat)–11
Adnams Bitter; Greene King Abbot; Marston's Pedigree; guest beers H
Busy, friendly local with a single, beamed bar, serving a good choice of home-cooked food. ✿ ◖ ▶ ⇌ ○

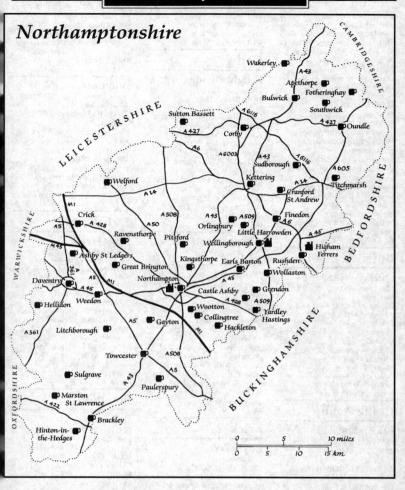

Northamptonshire

*Abington Park, Northampton; **Cannon**, Wellingborough; **Nene Valley**, Higham Ferrers*

Apethorpe

Kings Head
Kings Cliffe Road
☎ (01780) 470627
11–2.30, 6–11
Marston's Pedigree; Oakham Old Tosspot; S&N Theakston Best Bitter, XB, Old Peculier H
Stone pub in a conservation village. Originally built for farm and estate workers. Unusual courtyard.
🛏 ❀ ◑ ▶ ৬ ♣ P

Ashby St Ledgers

Old Coach House Inn
Off A361 ☎ (01788) 890349
12–2.30, 6–11; 12–11 Sat
Chiltern Beechwood, Three Hundreds; Everards Old Original; Jennings Cumberland Ale; Whitbread Flowers Original; guest beers H
Classic country pub which offers more each year. Real fires and wood panels for the winter; new garden for the summer. Beer festivals in March and Oct. Three guest beers. Award-winning food.
🛏 Q ☞ ❀ 🛏 ◑ ▶ ♣ P

Brackley

Greyhound Inn
101 High Street (A43)
☎ (01280) 703331
12–2.30, 7–11
Greene King Rayments Special; Tetley Bitter; guest beers H
Pub where a snug front

Northamptonshire

lounge has an L-shaped bar which leads to a games room (pool team) and a restaurant at the rear. Mexican dishes a speciality. Fifty whiskies to delight malt fans. Function room upstairs and a family room.
🏬 ⚄ ❀ ⬩ ◗ ✦

Red Lion

11 Market Place (A43)
☎ (01280) 702228
11–3, 5.30–11; 11–11 Fri & Sat
Wells Eagle, Bombardier; guest beers H
Stone-built pub dating from the 16th century, situated on the corner of the market square. A public bar with a pool table leads to a rear lounge and snug with an inglenook. Fortnightly music in the licensed barn bar in the rear garden.
🏬 ⚄ ❀ ⬩ ◗ ✦

Bulwick

Queen's Head

Main Street ☎ (01780) 450272
11–3, 6–11
Bateman XXXB; Greene King Abbot; guest beers H
Grade II-listed building in a quiet village now bypassed by the A43. Good food in the bar and restaurant. Interesting bank note collection.
🏬 ⚄ ❀ ⬩ ✦ P

Try also White Swan, Harringworth (Free)

Castle Ashby

Falcon Hotel

Off Bedford Road
☎ (01604) 696200
12–3, 7 (6 summer)–11
Adnams Mild, Extra; Hook Norton Old Hooky H
Traditional, 16th-century country hotel which is privately owned on the Marquess of Northampton's estate. Fourteen letting bedrooms and a cellar bar. Mild is now a regular feature.
⚄ ❀ ⬩ ◗ ▶ P

Collingtree

Wooden Walls of Old England

25 High Street (off A508, near M1 jct 15) ☎ (01604) 762427
11.30–3, 6–11
Brakspear Bitter; S&N Theakston Mild, Best Bitter, XB; Whitbread Boddingtons Bitter; guest beers H
Welcoming village local which dates back 600 years. Cromwell's officers drank the pub dry before the Battle of Naseby and refused to pay! Originally called the Ship, this

excellent two-roomed pub is a pleasant alternative to the motorway services.
🏬 ⚄ ❀ ⬩ ◗ ✦ P

Corby

Knights' Lodge

Towerhill Road
☎ (01536) 742602
12–3 (4 Fri & Sat), 6–11
Everards Beacon, Tiger, Old Original; guest beers H
Early 17th-century, stone-built pub on the site of a 12th-century knights' lodgings. Surrounded by modern housing, it is a veritable oasis in an ex-steel town. Reputed to have eight ghosts. Note the graffiti dated 1860 on a staircase window. The stairs lead to an upstairs restaurant.
🏬 ❀ ⬩ ◗ P

Cranford St Andrew

Woolpack

17 St Andrews Lane (off old A604) ☎ (01536) 78256
10.30–3, 6–11
Tetley Bitter; Whitbread Flowers Original H
Excellent, stone-built gem tucked away down a dead-end lane, filled with beams and probably the best display of brassware in the county (hung around the inglenook). A separate room has Northants skittles. Note the derelict cars in the car park.
🏬 ⚄ ❀ ✦ P

Crick

Royal Oak

Church Street
☎ (01788) 822340
7–11; 12–3, 7–11 Sat
Marston's Bitter, Pedigree; Taylor Landlord; guest beers H
Unusual pub with three rooms on separate levels (served by a central bar), plus a lounge with a huge satellite TV screen. The back bar has a games room attached. Folk music on Tue. Two real fires make it very cosy in winter.
🏬 ⚄ ❀

Try also Fox & Hounds, Clay Coton (Free)

Daventry

Coach & Horses

Warwick Street
☎ (01327) 76692
11–2.30, 5 (4.30 Fri)–11; 12–3, 7–11 Sat
Ind Coope Burton Ale; Marston's Pedigree; Tetley Bitter; guest beer H
Old coaching inn close to the town centre with a surprisingly large garden.

Very friendly feel: more a village local than a town pub. Quiz night Sun; jazz in the stable every other Thu. The sort of pub you have to be dragged out of. No meals weekends. 🏬 ❀ ⬩ ⚅

Dun Cow

Brook Street ☎ (01327) 71545
10.30–2.30, 5–11
Greenalls Davenports Bitter, Original H
Very busy, town-centre pub with a head cracking beam between bars. The large bar has a pool table; the small lounge has an open fire. A separate meeting room is entered from under the coaching arch. Folk club last Sun of the month. 🏬 ❀ ⬩ P

Earls Barton

Stags Head

25 High Street (off village centre) ☎ (01604) 810520
11–3 (4 Sat), 6–11; 12.30–3, 7–10.30 Sun
Home Bitter; S&N Theakston Best Bitter, XB, Old Peculier H
Grade-II listed, olde-worlde village pub. Its central beam is reputed to be a ship's timber, possibly floated up the River Nene. Function room for 50–60 people. New patio in the garden; large car park. No meals Sun.
🏬 ⚄ ❀ ⬩ ⚅ ✦ P

Finedon

Bell

Bell Hill ☎ (01933) 680332
11–2.30, 5.30–11
Vaux Samson; Wards Best Bitter; guest beers H
Classic pub entered by a Gothic design period archway in local ironstone. The spacious bar retains a cosy atmosphere and has a glowing log burner in winter months. An inglenook, beams and subtle lighting add to the feel. Lounge and restaurant at the rear. No eve meals Sun or Mon. 🏬 ⚄ ❀ ⬩ ◗ ✦ P

Fotheringhay

Falcon

Main Street ☎ (0183 26) 254
11–3, 6–11
Adnams Bitter; Elgood's Cambridge Bitter; Greene King IPA, Abbot; Ruddles Best Bitter, County H
Good beer and good food are the watchwords of this 18th century country pub set in the centre of historic Fotheringhay (Mary Queen of Scots connections). Cosy tap room and larger lounge; excellent restaurant.
🏬 ⚄ ❀ ⬩ ◗ ⚅ ⚄ ✦ P

Gayton

Eykyn Arms
20 High Street
☎ (01604) 858361
12–2, 7 (5.30 summer)–11
**Hall & Woodhouse
Tanglefoot; Morland Old
Speckled Hen; Wells Eagle,
Bombardier** Ⓗ
Friendly, unspoilt village local
with thriving skittles and darts
teams. The quiet front lounge
is decorated with planes and
ships; separate pool room and
an adjacent covered patio.
Now trades as a free house.
🚃 Q 🚲 🕸 ◖▶ ♣ P

Try also Queen Victoria, High
St (Free)

Great Brington

Fox & Hounds
Althorpe Coaching Inn (on
A428) ☎ (01604) 770651
12–2.30, 5.30–11; 12–11 Sat
**S&N Theakston Best Bitter,
XB, Old Peculier; guest
beers** Ⓗ
350-year-old coaching inn with
flagstone floors, original
beams and some panels. The
olde-worlde interior is split
into three areas, each with
character and style. Log fires
create a welcoming
atmosphere. Six guest beers
(pricey though). Live music
occasionally. 🚃 Q 🕸 ◖▶ P

Grendon

Crown
34 Manor Road (in village
centre) ☎ (01933) 663995
11–3, 6.30–11
**Marston's Pedigree; guest
beers** Ⓗ
Listed old stone pub with a
large public bar popular with
young and old alike. Cosy
lounge with a log fire and
exposed beams. Old boxing
prints adorn the walls. Good,
home-cooked food served in
the separate restaurant (no eve
meals Sun/Mon). Four
ever-changing guest beers.
🚃 Q ◖▶ ♣ P

Try also Half Moon, Main St
(Wells)

Hackleton

White Hart
80 Main Road (B526)
☎ (01604) 870271
11–3, 6–11
**Ruddles Best Bitter; S&N
Theakston XB; Webster's
Yorkshire Bitter** Ⓗ
Stone-built pub, the history of
which dates back to 1739. The

bar has a large inglenook and
Northants skittles; the two-tier
lounge has a 40-ft well built
into the bar. The excellent food
is all home-made (no food Sun
eve). Large safe garden to the
rear. Q 🕸 ◖▶ ♣ P

Hellidon

Red Lion
Catesby Road ☎ (01327) 61200
12–3, 7–11
**Bass Worthington BB,
Draught Bass; Marston's
Pedigree** Ⓗ
Low stone pub set in open
countryside: several rooms, all
beamed, with wooden panels,
generally catering for older
clients with a fairly formal
atmosphere. Food is very
popular. Golf course close by.
🚃 🕸 🚲 ◖▶ ▷ P

Hinton-in-the-Hedges

Crewe Arms
On A43 ☎ (01280) 703314
12–2.30, 6.30–11
**Hook Norton Best Bitter;
Marston's Pedigree; Morland
Old Speckled Hen; guest
beers** Ⓗ
Lovely, stone pub with open
fires and wood beams, two
beer gardens and a function
room for 80, tucked away at
the centre of a remote village.
Three bars, all with their own
character, and an à la carte
restaurant. Selection of fruit
and country wines.
🚃 Q 🕸 ◖▶ ♣ P

Kettering

Talbot
Meadow Road
☎ (01536) 514565
11–3, 5–11; 11–11 Sat
Marston's Bitter, Pedigree Ⓗ
Very friendly town pub with
letting rooms, redecorated
without altering the basic
structure. Marston's adjacent
lounges and a public bar with
pool, darts and other games.
Good jukebox. Marston's
Head Brewer's Choice also
available. Q 🕸 🚲 ◖ 🚆 ♣

Three Cocks
Lower Street ☎ (01536) 512569
10.30–3, 5–11
**Banks's Mild; Marston's
Bitter, Pedigree** Ⓗ
19th-century town pub with
an attractive painted frontage,
near the town centre.
Marston's Head Brewer's
Choice also available. ◖ ♣

Try also Cherry Tree, Sheep St
(Wells); **Old Market Inn**,
Market Place (S&N)

Kingsthorpe

Queen Adelaide
50 Manor Road
☎ (01604) 714524
11–2.30 (3 Sat), 5.30–11
**Banks's Bitter; Morland Old
Speckled Hen; Wadworth 6X;
Webster's Yorkshire Bitter** Ⓗ
Busy local in old Kingsthorpe
village, a Grade-II building
dating back to 1640. The public
bar retains its original ceiling,
panelling and old photographs
of Kingsthorpe; separate
Northants skittles room.
Home-cooked lunches Mon–
Sat (Sandra's omelettes are a
speciality). Q 🕸 ◖ ♣ P

Try also King William IV,
Green End (Courage)

Litchborough

Red Lion
4 Banbury Road
☎ (01327) 830250
11.30–3 (not Mon), 6.30–11
Banks's Bitter Ⓔ; **Marston's
Pedigree** Ⓗ
Three-room pub offering
Northants skittles and pool,
plus one little bar with a real
fire. Very popular with locals
from early eve. Black beams
add to the atmosphere. A very
successful local.
🚃 🕸 ◖▶ ♣ P

Little Harrowden

Lamb
Orlingbury Road
☎ (01933) 673300
11–2.30 (3 Sat), 6–11
**Adnams Broadside; Mansfield
Riding Mild; Wells Eagle,
Bombardier; guest beer** Ⓗ
Pleasant village local with oak
beams in the lounge and a
traditional bar with Northants
skittles. Advance booking
recommended for diners (Sun
roast served, but no food Sun
eves). Live music. Ask the
landlord for an explanation of
the Jean Dosser trophies
award. 🚃 Q 🕸 ◖▶ 🚆 ♣ P

Marston St Lawrence

Marston Inn
☎ (01295) 711906
12–2 (not Mon), 7–11
**Hook Norton Best Bitter, Old
Hooky, Twelve Days; guest
beer** Ⓗ
Former village butcher's shop
now extending into an
adjoining cottage terrace. The
three small, interconnecting
rooms have an accent on
excellent home-cooking. Large
safe gardens to the front and

Northamptonshire

rear. No food Sun night or Mon lunch.
🏠 Q ✿ ◑ ▶ ♣ P

Northampton

Barn Owl
Olden Road, Rectory Farm (follow A4500 then signs to Rectory Farm)
☎ (01604) 416463
12–3, 6–11
Greene King IPA, Rayments Special, Abbot H
Popular, award-winning, estate pub. Bar billiards played. ✿ ◑ ▶ ♿ ♣ P

Brewers Arms
1 Gas Street ☎ (01604) 36900
12–3, 7–11; 12–11 Sat
Banks & Taylor Shefford Bitter; guest beers H
Two-room pub with a comfortable lounge, popular with bikers. Unusual wooden bar floor. Up to five guest beers. Northants skittles played. Regular bands.
✿ ⇌ ♣ ○

Cricketers
43 Hervey Street (off Kettering Rd, A43) ☎ (01604) 35009
6–11; 11–11 Fri & Sat
Wells Eagle, Bombardier; guest beers H
Back-street, mid-terraced local with a long association with a soccer team. Bands, comics and curries feature Fri night. A good basic boozer. 🏠 ♣ ♠

Crown & Cushion
276 Wellingborough Road (A4500) ☎ (01604) 33937
11–11
Banks's Bitter; Ruddles Best Bitter H
Town pub with a mixture of local and passing trade. Friendly atmosphere in a large, U-shaped bar with a busy games area in one corner. Well maintained garden, with safe play equipment. ✿ ♣

Orlingbury

Queens Arms
11 Isham Road
☎ (01933) 678258
11.30–2.30, 5.30–11
Fuller's London Pride; Hook Norton Best Bitter; Marston's Pedigree; Morland Old Speckled Hen; guest beers H
Recently refurbished rural local, originally dating back to the 1750s. A real beer drinkers' local, according to the landlord. This has earned him the Northants CAMRA *Pub of the Year* award for 1994. Lunchtime food Mon–Fri. Five regular guest beers.
🏠 ✿ ◑ P

Oundle

Ship Inn
18–20 West Street (100 yds from centre) ☎ (01832) 273918
11–3, 6–11; 11–11 Sat
Draught Bass; Marston's Pedigree; Wadworth 6X; guest beer H
Stone-built, multi-roomed pub, a former tea room with low beams. Live music nights Fri. Extensive food menu (small no-smoking dining area).
🏠 ✿ 🚪 ◑ ▶ ♿ ♣ ○ P ⚲

Try also **Rose & Crown**, Market Place (Free)

Paulerspury

Barley Mow
53 High Street
☎ (01327) 33260
12–3, 7–11
Everards Tiger; Marston's Pedigree; Ruddles Best Bitter; Webster's Yorkshire Bitter H
Open-plan pub with an L-shaped bar with plenty of atmosphere. Games room upstairs and a restaurant in the old maltings to the rear. The large inglenook houses log fires. Lunches Sat/Sun only. 🏠 ✿ 🚪 ◑ ▶ P

Pitsford

Griffin
High Street ☎ (01604) 880346
12–2.30 (not Mon), 6–11
S&N Theakston Best Bitter, XB; guest beer H
Listed, stone-built village pub, friendly and relaxing. Lunches served Tue–Sat. ✿ ◑ ♣ P

Ravensthorpe

Chequers
Church Lane ☎ (01604) 770379
11–3, 6–11; 11–11 Sat
Fuller's London Pride; Samuel Smith OBB; Thwaites Bitter; guest beer H
One of the county's few free houses, set in rolling countryside and well worth finding. A beamed, single L-shaped bar is adorned with bric-a-brac, creating a warm, cosy atmosphere. Excellent value food and beer. Family room across the courtyard.
Q ⛄ ✿ ◑ ▶ ♣ P

Rushden

Rushden Historical Transport Society
Rushden Station, Rectory Road (look for railway signal on town-centre one-way system)
☎ (01933) 318988

7.30–11; 12–2.30, 7.30–10.30 Sun
Fuller's Hock, London Pride; guest beers H
Midland Railway station building saved by locals after the 1962 branch line closure. An atmospheric gas-lit bar has been created from the former ladies' waiting room and is stuffed with transport memorabilia. Bar and open day activities extend into a carriage parked at the platform edge. Adjoining museum. Under the remote threat of demolition for roadworks. 50p daily membership. 🏠 Q ✿ P

Try also **Feathers**, High St; **King Edward VII**, Queen St (both Wells)

Southwick

Shuckburgh Arms
Main Street
☎ (01832) 274007
11–2.30, 6–11
Adnams Extra; Hook Norton Best Bitter; Thwaites Craftsman; guest beers G
16th-century thatched village local with extraordinary character: a snug, friendly lounge with an inglenook and a larger public bar with Northants skittles in the passage. Totally unspoilt.
🏠 Q ✿ ▲ ♣ P

Sudborough

Vane Arms
Main Street
☎ (01832) 733223
11.30–3 (not Mon), 5.30 (6 Sat)–11
Beer range varies H
Deservedly popular, old thatched village free house of great character. Beams abound in both the basic bar and the plusher lounge. Small upstairs restaurant. At least eight guest beers, plus a house beer from Nene Valley. Draught Kriek and Frambozen, too. No eve meals Mon.
🏠 ✿ 🚪 ◑ ▶ ♿ ♣ ○ P

Sulgrave

Star
Manor Road (opp. Sulgrave Manor)
☎ (01295) 760389
11–2.30, 6–11
Hook Norton Mild, Best Bitter, Old Hooky, Twelve Days; guest beers H
Well-run village local across the road from the ancestral home of George Washington. The single bar has stone-flagged floors, wooden beams and lots of interest on the walls, and attracts a more

Northamptonshire

mature clientele (no jukebox or noisy games). No eve meals Sun in winter.
🍴 Q ✿ 🚲 ◖ ▶ P

Sutton Bassett

Queens Head
Main Street (B664)
☎ (01858) 463530
11.45–3, 6.30–11
Adnams Bitter; Tetley Bitter; guest beers H
Fairly unspoiled rural hostelry catering for the full range of customer demands (although lacking pub game facilities). Basically two adjoining rooms with a restaurant upstairs. Piano in the back room and at least four guest beers. Beer festival Oct. 🍴 ✿ ◖ ▶ P

Titchmarsh

Dog & Partridge
6 High Street
☎ (01832) 732546
12–2.30 (4 Sat), 6 (6.30 Sat)–11
Adnams Broadside; Morland Old Speckled Hen; Wells Eagle, Bombardier H
18th-century pub in a peaceful village off the A605, with one large bar incorporating quiet and games areas. Good locals' pub, very welcoming.
🍴 ✿ ઙ ▲ ♣ P

Towcester

Plough
Market Square, Watling Street (A5) ☎ (01327) 50738
11–3, 5–11; 11–11 Sat
Adnams Broadside; Wells Eagle, Bombardier H
Pub fronting the small market square: a small bar at the front leads to a larger seated area at the rear. Excellent value food.
🍴 ◖ ▶

Wakerley

Exeter Arms
Main Street (between A47 and A43, on Duddington side)
OS955995 ☎ (0157 287) 817
12–2.30, 6–11
Adnams Broadside; Bateman XB; Marston's Pedigree H
Friendly, 17th-century, stone pub, reputedly haunted, near Wakerley Woods (popular for walks). No food Mon except bank hols. Separate bar and lounge. Customers come from afar. 🍴 Q ✿ ◖ ▶ ♣ P

Weedon

Globe Hotel
High Street (A45/A5 jct)
☎ (01327) 40336
11–11
Marston's Bitter, Pedigree; Taylor Landlord; Webster's Yorkshire Bitter H
Very popular hotel with a pleasant atmosphere, catering for all ages. Predominantly a hotel, but the bar retains the bonhomie of a good local. Care taken to ensure customer satisfaction.
🍴 Q ઙ 🚲 ◖ ▶ ઙ P

Heart of England
High Street (A45)
☎ (01327) 340335
11–11
Hook Norton Best Bitter; S&N Theakston Best Bitter, XB; Whitbread Boddingtons Bitter; guest beers H
Well-maintained pub, offering a large garden with play equipment for children, and a dining area. The low bar was built in 1740. Next to the Grand Union Canal. One wheelchair-adapted bedroom.
🚲 ◖ ▶ ઙ

Try also **Wheatsheaf**, High St (Banks's)

Welford

Shoulder of Mutton
12 High Street (A50)
☎ (01858) 575375
12–2.30, 7–11
Bass Worthington BB, Draught Bass; guest beer H
Welcoming, 17th-century local with a single bar divided by arches. The games room doubles as a family room when the weather prevents use of the extensive play facilities in the garden. The good value menu caters for children's and vegetarian tastes (no meals Thu).
🍴 ઙ ✿ ◖ ▶ ♣ P

Wellingborough

Cannon
Cannon Street
☎ (01933) 279629
11–11
Cannon Light Brigade, Pride, Fodder, Old Nosey; Wells Eagle; guest beers H
Home-brew pub on the edge of town, with a large U-shaped bar. Bar billiards played.

Snacks lunchtime.
🍴 ✿ ⇌ ♣ P

Vivian Arms
153 Knox Road
☎ (01933) 223660
11–2.30 (3 Sat), 6 (7 Sat)–11
Wells Eagle, Bombardier; guest beer H
Friendly back-street local: a cosy lounge with a real fire, a wood-panelled bar, plus a large games room.
🍴 ✿ 🍺 ⇌ ♣

Wollaston

Boot
35 High Street
☎ (01933) 664270
11–2.30, 6–11; 12–2.30, 7–10.30 Sun
Draught Bass; Tetley Bitter H
Unchanged and unspoilt local: a whitewashed, thatched, listed pub with a warm welcome and a fire to match. Two front rooms act as the bar; the room to the rear houses Northants skittles. Well worth finding—conversation is always on the menu. Snacks available. 🍴 Q ♣ P

Wootton

Wootton Workingmen's Club
23 High Street
☎ (01604) 761863
12–2.30, 7.30–11; 12–2.30, 7.30–10.30 Sun
Greene King IPA; Wells Eagle; guest beers H
One of the best selections of real ales in the area, confirmed by the collection of pump clips behind the bar. East Midlands CAMRA *Club of the Year* 1993, but more a pub than a club, with exposed stonework, bookshelves and a coal effect fire. Live entertainment. CIU entry restrictions apply. Live entertainment.
♣ P

Yardley Hastings

Red Lion
189 High Street (off Bedford Rd) ☎ (01604) 696210
11–2.30 (3 Fri & Sat), 6–11
Adnams Broadside; Wells Eagle H
Village local with a welcoming atmosphere in a low-beamed lounge and a separate bar, with Northants skittles in a former gents' loo! A regular *Guide* entry. No food Sun.
🍴 Q ✿ ◖ 🍺 ♣ P

Updates to the *Good Beer Guide* are published in CAMRA's newspaper, *What's Brewing*. Join CAMRA and receive a free copy each month.

Border, *Tweedmouth*;
Hexhamshire, *Hexham*;
Longstone, *Belford*

Northumberland

---

holidaymakers, tourists and
diners as well as locals.

Victoria Hotel
Front Street ☎ (01668) 214431
11–11
**Longstone Bitter; Stones Best
Bitter; Tetley Bitter; guest
beers** H
An aristocrat amongst pubs:
excellent food and
accommodation in an
imposing hotel, frequented by
a cross-section of northern
Northumberland society.

Berwick-upon-Tweed

Free Trade
Castlegate ☎ (01289) 306498
12–3, 7–11 (may vary)
Vaux Lorimers Best Scotch H
The best pint of Lorimers
Scotch in the country, served
in a classic Victorian pub. It
features a screen at the
entrance, basic furnishing, a
friendly licensee and
somewhat unpredictable
opening hours. Q

Hen & Chickens
15 Sandgate ☎ (01289) 306314
11–11
**McEwan 70/-, 80/-; S&N
Theakston Best Bitter; guest
beers** H
Fine town-centre local with the
added charm of being the only
Berwick pub open all day.
Popular on match days with
supporters of Berwick
Rangers.

Blyth

Flying Horse
78 Waterloo Road
☎ (01670) 353314
11–11
**Ruddles County; Webster's
Yorkshire Bitter; guest
beers** H
Comfortable local offering an
interesting selection of guest
beers.

Oddfellows Arms
91 Bridge Street
☎ (01670) 356535
11–3, 6–11; 11–11 Fri & Sat
**Stones Best Bitter; guest
beers** H
Small, cosy, three-roomed pub
near the quayside. A nautical
air is presented by an array of
pictures of Blyth in bygone
years and ships associated
with the port. A listed
building, it stands near the
former (imposing) police
courts. The licensee is keen to
support local charities. Dogs
welcome.

Acomb

Miners Arms
Main Street ☎ (01434) 603909
11–11
**Federation Buchanan's Best
Bitter, Special, Original;
Morrells Varsity; Robinson's
Bitter; guest beers** H
Traditional stone-built village
pub. The good food includes a
vegetarian option.

Allendale Town

Kings Head
Market Square (B6303)
☎ (01434) 683681
11–11
**S&N Theakston Best Bitter,
XB, Old Peculier; guest
beers** H
Welcoming pub in a friendly
town, high up in the Pennines.

Alnwick

Tanners Arms
Hotspur Place
☎ (01665) 802553

12–3 (not Mon or Tue), 7–11
**Belhaven Sandy Hunter's Ale,
80/-; guest beer** H
Splendidly eccentric town-
centre local with a no-frills
atmosphere and comfortable
surroundings.

Ashington

Bubbles
58a Station Road
☎ (01670) 850800
11–3, 5.30–11; 11–11 Fri & Sat
Beer range varies H
Down a side-street, off the
main shopping area, lies one
of the few pubs to be found in
the heart of northern clubland.
Constantly changing beers and
annual beer festivals make it
worth seeking out but it can
get very noisy and full.

Bamburgh

Castle Hotel
Front Street ☎ (01668) 214351
12–3, 6–11
**Vaux Lorimers Best Scotch,
Samson** H
Popular pub in an historic
seaside town, frequented by

Top House

Marlow Street
☎ (01670) 356731
11–11
S&N Theakston Best Bitter, XB; guest beer H
Prominent town-centre pub with many original features. Good for conversation. ⚶

Carterway Heads

Manor House Inn

On A68, 6 miles S of Corbridge
☎ (01207) 55268
12–3, 6–11
Butterknowle Bitter; Hadrian Centurion; guest beers H
A warm welcome awaits at this charming country inn with its splendid views over the Derwent valley. There is usually a guest porter or stout available along with a good and varied food menu; also guest ciders.
⚶ Q ✿ ⚶ ◖ ▶ ⇨ P

Corbridge

Dyvels

Station Road ☎ (01434) 633566
7–11 (may vary summer)
Draught Bass; Stones Best Bitter; Taylor Landlord; guest beers H
An ideal base for exploring the Roman Wall, with always a warm welcome from both the landlord and customers. Note: closed lunchtimes.
⚶ Q ✿ ⚶ ≠

Wheatsheaf Hotel

St Helens Street
☎ (01434) 632020
11–11
Wards Best Bitter; guest beers H
Excellent country hotel and restaurant; warm and welcoming.
⚶ ✿ ⚶ ◖ ▶ ⊞ P

Cramlington

Brockwell Seam

Northumbrian Road
☎ (01670) 732071
11–11
Bass Worthington BB, Draught Bass; guest beer H
Fine new pub with friendly staff and regulars. It hosts events and live entertainment most eves. The landlord is qualified in sign language. Eve meals until 8pm. ✿ ◖ ▶ & P

Plough

Middle Farm
☎ (01670) 737633
11–3, 6–11; 11–11 Fri & Sat
S&N Theakston XB; guest beers H
Converted farm buildings in the old village centre, now

refurbished into a separate bar and lounge. It always has a welcoming atmosphere, and interesting guest ales for the area. ✿ ◖ ⚶ & ≠

Craster

Jolly Fisherman

Haven Hill ☎ (01665) 576218
11–3, 6–11; 11–11 Sat
Wards Best Bitter H
Welcoming pub in a tiny village famous for its seafood. Try the crab sandwiches. Marvellous sea views.
⚶ ◖ ▶ P

Dipton

Dipton Mill Inn

Dipton Mill Road (off B6306, 2 miles S of Hexham)
☎ (01434) 606577
12–3, 6–11
Hadrian Gladiator; Hexhamshire Shire Bitter, Devil's Water, Whapweasel; S&N Theakston Best Bitter H
An excellent advertisement for the Hexhamshire Brewery: welcoming and cosy, with coal fires throughout. A former CAMRA Northumberland *Pub of the Year*, noted for its food. The family room is basic.
⚶ Q ✿ ✿ ◖ & ♣ P

Falstone

Blackcock Inn

☎ (01434) 240200
11–3, 6.30–11; 11–11 Sat & occasionally summer
Whitbread Boddingtons Bitter, Castle Eden Ale; guest beers H
Historic pub near Kielder Reservoir. Popular with watersports enthusiasts and walkers, it is always friendly and cosy.
⚶ Q ✿ ✿ ⚶ ◖ ▶ & ▲ ♣ P

Great Whittington

Queens Head Inn

☎ (01434) 672267
12–3, 6–11
Courage Directors; Hambleton Bitter; guest beers H
One of the county's oldest inns, dating back to the 15th century and set in lovely countryside, close to Hadrian's Wall. ⚶ Q ✿ ◖ ▶ & P

Haltwhistle

New Inn

West Road ☎ (01434) 320455
11–3.30, 7–11
Vaux Lorimers Best Scotch; guest beers H
Interestingly-shaped bar, full of character. ≠

Railway

Station Road ☎ (01434) 320269
11–11
Webster's Yorkshire Bitter; Whitbread Boddingtons Bitter; guest beer H
Comfortable, cosy local, near the Roman remains. Very friendly. ⚶ ≠

Hedley on the Hill

Feathers Inn

☎ (01661) 843607
6–11; 12–3, 6–11 Sat
Whitbread Boddingtons Bitter; guest beers H
Hilltop pub, offering a base for walking. Warm and friendly with an excellent atmosphere.
⚶ Q ✿ ◖ ▶ P

Hexham

Globe Inn

Battle Hill ☎ (01434) 603742
11–11
S&N Theakston Best Bitter; guest beer H
Bustling, traditional pub in the heart of town. Unspoilt and cosy. ⚶ ≠

Heart of All England

Market Street
☎ (01434) 603375
11–11
McEwan 80/-; S&N Theakston Mild, Best Bitter H
Spacious pub, looking out over the market square. Close to the abbey, it is popular with tourists and shoppers, particularly for meals. ◖ ≠

Tap & Spile

Battle Hill ☎ (01434) 602039
11–11
Beer range varies H
Busy, two-roomed pub with a wide, changing range of ales: a market town pub popular with customers connected with agriculture and other trades at lunchtimes. Live music Mon nights. Q ◖ ≠

High Horton

Three Horse Shoes

Hathery Lane
☎ (01670) 822410
11–11
Draught Bass; Ind Coope Burton Ale; Marston's Pedigree; Tetley Bitter; guest beers H
Large, friendly pub, hosting occasional beer festivals.
✿ ✿ ◖ & ♣ P

Langley

Carts Bog Inn

Off A686 ☎ (01434) 684338
12–3 (not Mon, except bank hols), 7–11

Northumberland

Federation Buchanan's Best Bitter; Whitbread Boddingtons Bitter; guest beers H
Isolated pub on the moor edge, built in 1730 on a site where brewing had taken place since 1521. Local musicians play on the second Thu of the month, also spontaneously on other summer eves. Mini-beer festivals are held. Quoits and camping in the pub grounds.
🏚 ❀ ◑ ▶ ᕘ & ♣ P

Longhorsley

Linden Pub
In grounds of Linden Hall Hotel ☎ (01670) 516611
11–3, 6–11
Whitbread Boddingtons Bitter, Castle Eden Ale; guest beer H
Secluded country pub in an attractively converted granary. Summer barbecues are held in the courtyard, also giant chess. Children are always welcome (toy corner).
Q ❀ ᕘ ◑ ▶ & P

Milecastle

Milecastle Inn
Military Road (B6318, 1½ miles N of Haltwhistle)
☎ (01434) 320682
12–2.30 (3 summer), 6.30 (6 summer)–11
Tetley Bitter; guest beers H
Very popular with walkers, this small cosy pub has three rooms—one serving as a restaurant. 🏚 Q ❀ ◑ ▶ P

Morpeth

Joiners Arms
3 Wansbeck Street
☎ (01670) 513540
11–11
Draught Bass; Ruddles Best Bitter; S&N Theakston XB; John Smith's Bitter; guest beer H
Large, two-roomed pub. A wheelchair ramp is available on request. Q & ⇌ ♣

Tap & Spile
Manchester Street
☎ (01670) 513894
12–2.30 (3.30 Wed), 4.30–11; 11–11 Fri & Sat
Beer range varies H
Everything one expects from a Tap & Spile: a good beer range and plenty of atmosphere in two contrasting bars. ▣

White Swan
18 Newgate Street
☎ (01670) 513532
11–11

Vaux Samson, Double Maxim; Wards Best Bitter; guest beer H
Large, pleasant, open-plan pub, well-decorated, with partitions separating off smaller areas. A wheelchair ramp is available on request.
◑ ▶ & ⇌ ♣

Netherton

Star Inn
On B634 ☎ (01669) 30238
11–2, 7–11 (may vary winter)
Whitbread Castle Eden Ale G
Remote, unspoilt, marvellous pub set in beautiful countryside, ideal for walkers. Time has stood still here. Note the disused cockfighting pit opposite the pub. 🏚 Q ❀

Newton on the Moor

Cook & Barker
½ mile off A1
☎ (01665) 575234
11–11
S&N Theakston XB; Whitbread Castle Eden Ale; Younger No.3; guest beers H
Friendly, large, multi-roomed pub and restaurant with a welcoming atmosphere. Displays of foreign notes abound.
🏚 Q ❀ ᕘ ◑ ▶ P ⅟

Prudhoe

Halfway House
Edgewell ☎ (01661) 832688
11–3.30, 6–11; 11–11 Fri & Sat
Beer range varies H
Pleasant, two-roomed pub with a large, open-plan lounge and a small, old-fashioned, lower-priced bar.
Q ◑ ▣ ♣ P

Ridsdale

Gun Inn
On A68 ☎ (01434) 270223
11–11
Whitbread Castle Eden Ale H
Extended, stone-built pub benefiting from good views over the valley.
🏚 Q ⅚ ❀ ᕘ ◑ ▶ ᕘ ♣ P

Rothbury

Railway Hotel
Bridge Street
☎ (01669) 20221
11–11
Ruddles Best Bitter; Tetley Bitter; guest beer H

Two-roomed pub with a friendly atmosphere.
🏚 Q ᕘ ◑ ▣

Turks Head
High Street
11–11
Wards Best Bitter H
Basic, multi-roomed pub, popular with the locals.
🏚 ◑ ▶ ▣

Seahouses

Olde Ship Hotel
Main Street ☎ (01665) 720200
11–3, 6–11
Longstone Bitter; S&N Theakston Best Bitter, XB H
Fine pub with maritime memorabilia, providing the absolute antithesis to the touristy side of Seahouses. A popular and historic retreat which demands a visit.
🏚 Q ᕘ ◑ & ᕘ P

Tweedmouth

Angel Inn
11 Brewery Bank
☎ (01289) 303030
12–3, 7–11
Border Old Kiln; guest beers H
The only tied house belonging to the local Border Brewery: a centre for brewery visits and a showcase for Old Kiln Bitter and the many occasional Border brews. Enjoy the comfortable, characterful, friendly atmosphere. Q ᕘ P

Wooler

Anchor Inn
10 Cheviot Street
☎ (01668) 281412
11–3, 7–11 (may vary summer)
Vaux Lorimers Best Scotch, Samson H
Cosy, friendly pub popular with walkers enjoying the beautiful Northumbrian countryside. 🏚 Q ❀ ᕘ

Wylam

Boathouse
Station Road ☎ (01661) 853431
12–3 (not Mon), 6–11; 11–11 Sat
Draught Bass; Ind Coope Burton Ale; Marston's Pedigree; Taylor Landlord; Tetley Bitter; Younger No.3; guest beer H
Two-roomed pub, adjacent to the station and next to Wylam Bridge. Lunches served Sat and Sun only.
🏚 Q ❀ ⇌ ♣ P

Protect your pleasure — Join CAMRA (see page 528)

Nottinghamshire

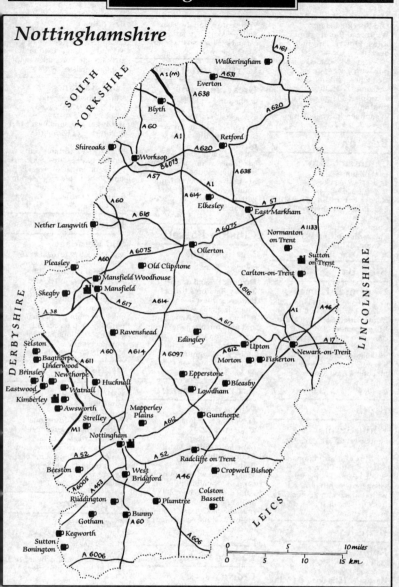

 Fellows, Morton & Clayton, Nottingham; **Hardys & Hansons,** Kimberley; **Mansfield,** Mansfield; **Springhead,** Sutton on Trent

---

Awsworth

Gate Inn
Main Street (off A6096)
☎ (0115) 9329821
12–3 (4 Sat; not winter Tue–Thu), 7–11
Hardys & Hansons Best Mild,

Best Bitter E
Superb, old, traditional pub, once owned by Offilers of Derby (closed 1966). Near the site of the once-famous 40 bridges—see photos in the passage. Separate pool room.
Q ⊛ ◖ 🍴 ♣ P

Bagthorpe Underwood

Red Lion
Church Lane ☎ (01773) 810482
12–3, 6–11; 12–11 Sat in summer

Nottinghamshire

Marston's Pedigree; Morland Old Speckled Hen; Whitbread Boddingtons Bitter, Flowers Original; guest beers H

300-year-old, beamed village pub with a separate eating area where children are welcome. Friendly, welcoming atmosphere; large garden and children's play area. Barbecues in summer. Independent guest beers. ❀ ◖ ▶ P

Beeston

Commercial Inn
19 Wollaton Road
☎ (0115) 9254480
11–2.30 (5 Sat), 5.30–11
Hardys & Hansons Best Mild, Best Bitter, Kimberley Classic H
Comfortable, friendly local. The bar has pictures of old Beeston. Skittle alley.
❀ ◖ ⊟ & ♣ P

Bleasby

Waggon & Horses
Gypsy Lane ☎ (01636) 830283
11–3 (not Mon in winter), 6–11
Home Bitter; S&N Theakston XB; guest beer H
200-year-old pub converted from a farmhouse, nestling in the shadow of the church. Separate room for pool. No lunchtime food Mon; no eve food Sun–Tue.
🚶 Q ❀ ◖ ▶ A ⇌ ♣ P

Blyth

White Swan
Font Street ☎ (01909) 591222
12–3, 7–11
Whitbread Boddingtons Bitter, Castle Eden Ale H
Small, beamed pub on the village green. Modernised with character and noted for fresh fish meals (no food Sun eve). 🚶 ❀ ◖ ▶ & P

Brinsley

Robin Hood
Hall Lane ☎ (01773) 713604
12–3, 6.30 (7 winter)–11
Hardys & Hansons Best Mild, Best Bitter E
Village pub of character in DH Lawrence country, rumoured to be haunted by a former licensee. Disco Fri; guest singers Sat. Two skittle alleys.
Q ❀ ⊟ ♣ P

Bunny

Rancliffe Arms
Loughborough Road
☎ (0115) 9844727
11.30–2.30, 6–11
Mansfield Riding Mild, Riding Bitter, Old Baily H

Large, imposing, roadside, 17th-century inn: two bars with a separate restaurant. The car park is on a sharp bend.
🚶 ❀ ◖ ▶ ♣ P

Carlton-on-Trent

Great Northern
Ossington Road (200 yds W of A1) ☎ (01636) 821348
12–2.30, 5.30–11
Mansfield Riding Bitter; Springhead Bitter; guest beers H
Pub adjacent to the main east coast railway line and popular with train spotters. The bar has railway artefacts. Large family room, well stocked with games. Also an outdoor play area.
🚶 🏃 ❀ ◖ ▶ ⊟ & ♣ P ⚹

Colston Bassett

Martins Arms
School Lane ☎ (01949) 81361
12–2.30, 6–11
Draught Bass; Bateman XB, XXXB; Marston's Bitter, Pedigree; guest beers H
Charming village free house, full of character. An original and high quality menu is on offer in both the bar and restaurant. No food Sun and Mon eves. Magnificent carved fireplace in the main lounge.
🚶 Q ❀ ◖ ▶ P

Cropwell Bishop

Wheatsheaf
11 Nottingham Road
☎ (0115) 9892247
12–3, 6–11; 11–11 Sat
Mansfield Riding Mild, Riding Bitter, Bitter, Old Baily H
Village local with a lounge, a bar and a small front room. Parts date back over 500 years and are haunted. The speciality is Chinese food—for pre-booked parties of eight or more only.
🚶 🏃 ❀ ▶ ⊟ ♣ P

East Markham

Crown
High Street ☎ (01777) 870870
Courage Directors; Marston's Pedigree; John Smith's Bitter; Webster's Yorkshire Bitter; guest beers H
Beamed country pub attracting local custom but also trade from the A57/A1.
❀ ◖ ▶ & A P

Eastwood

Greasley Castle
1 Castle Street, Hilltop (off B6010) ☎ (01773) 761086
11–4, 6–11; 11–11 Fri & Sat

Hardys & Hansons Best Mild, Best Bitter E
Street-corner, Victorian local on a one-way street: an open bar and a lounge. Extremely busy Fri and Sun nights, with live local artistes. ❀ ⊟ ♣

Lord Raglan
Newthorpe Common (off B6010) ☎ (01773) 712683
11–3, 5.30 (6.30 Sat)–11
Hardys & Hansons Best Mild, Best Bitter E, Kimberley Classic H
Friendly, comfortable pub serving local estates. Spacious games-oriented bar; weekend sing-along in the olde-worlde lounge. Wed night quiz. Good food. Beer garden and swings for children. 🚶 ❀ ◖ ⊟ ♣ P

Edingley

Old Reindeer
Main Street ☎ (01623) 882253
12–3, 6–11; 12–11 Sat; closed Tue
Mansfield Riding Mild, Riding Bitter, Bitter, Old Baily H
Delightful, family-run, 18th-century rural local. Ducks and chickens roam the garden, whilst the tap room houses an ornate collection of chamber pots. Regular barbecues in summer. 🚶 ❀ A ♣ P

Elkesley

Robin Hood
High Street ☎ (01777) 838259
11–3.30, 6.30–11
Whitbread Boddingtons Bitter, Trophy; guest beers H
Popular village local also attracting passing trade from the A1 and selling some of the finest pub food along the Great North Road.
🚶 ❀ ◖ ▶ ⊟ & ♣ P

Epperstone

Cross Keys
Main Street ☎ (0115) 9663033
11.45–2.30 (not Mon), 6–11; 12–2.30, 7–10.30 Sun
Hardys & Hansons Best Mild, Best Bitter E, Kimberley Classic H
Delightful, white-painted village pub in a pleasant, rural setting: a simply-furnished public bar, a rear snug and a lounge displaying CAMRA accolades. Impromptu folk sessions. Award-winning food (no meals Sun and Mon eves, or Mon lunch).
🚶 Q 🏃 ❀ ◖ ⊟ A ♣ P

Everton

Blacksmiths Arms
Chapel Lane ☎ (01777) 817281
12–2 (3 Sat), 7–11

Home Bitter; S&N Theakston Best Bitter, XB, Old Peculier; Younger Scotch; guest beer H
Rambling village pub with many interesting features and a restaurant.
🚶 ♿ ❀ ◗ ♣ P

Fiskerton

Bromley Arms
Main Street ☎ (01636) 830789
11–3, 7–11 (11–11 summer)
Hardys & Hansons Best Mild, Best Bitter, Kimberley Classic H
Picturesque, 17th-century, three-roomed village local by the Trent. Excellent home-cooked food, with vegetarian dishes a speciality. Anglers' breakfasts by prior arrangement. Function room.
🚶 Q ❀ ◗ ♦ ⊟ ▲ ♣ P

Gotham

Sun Inn
The Square ☎ (0115) 9830484
11.30–2.30, 6–11; 12–2, 7–10.30 Sun
Everards Mild, Beacon, Tiger, Old Original; guest beer H
Comfortable and friendly local in a small village. Food is served in the lounge, with the bar reserved for conversation and games. 🚶 ❀ ◗ ♦ ♣

Gunthorpe

Tom Brown's
Trentside ☎ (0115) 9663642
11–3, 6–11; 11–11 Sat & summer
Home Bitter; S&N Theakston Best Bitter, XB, Old Peculier; guest beers H
Former schoolhouse now an excellent free house. High quality food in the bar and restaurant; a low price ale is always available. Good moorings. No bar food Sat/Sun eves. 🚶 ❀ ◗ ▲ P

Hucknall

Red Lion
High Street ☎ (0115) 9632174
0.30–3.30, 6–11; 10.30–11 Fri & Sat
Home Mild, Bitter; Whitbread Boddingtons Bitter H
Former coaching inn, now a typical town-centre local, rightly popular. Four separate rooms. Q 🍺 ⊟ ≠ ♣ P

Kegworth

Station Hotel
Station Road (between Kegworth and Sutton Bonington) ☎ (01509) 672252
1.30–2.30, 6–11; 11.30–11 Sat
Bass Worthington BB,

Draught Bass; M&B Mild; guest beer H
Pub built in 1847 as a hotel for the now-closed station, now a traditional, country inn, catering for lovers of home-cooked food (no food Sun eve). Large garden with a fine view. 🚶 Q ❀ 🛏 ◗ ♣ P

Kimberley

Nelson & Railway
Station Road ☎ (0115) 9382177
11–3, 5–11; 11–11 Fri & Sat
Hardys & Hansons Best Mild E, Best Bitter, Kimberley Classic H
Unspoilt village pub adjacent to the brewery. The lively wood-panelled bar adjoins a carefully restored, beamed lounge and dining area. Excellent food (no meals Sun eve). Twenty years in the *Guide*. ❀ 🛏 ◗ ♦ ♣ P

Queens Head
Main Street ☎ (0115) 9328117
10.30–11
Hardys & Hansons Best Mild, Best Bitter E
Convivial, street-corner local with a boisterous bar, snug and an upstairs lounge featuring live music. Don't forget to admire the landlord's tie, selected from his collection of over 400. ⊟ ♣

Lowdham

Old Ship Inn
Main Street ☎ (0115) 9663049
11.30–2.30, 5.30–11; 11.30–11 Sat
Courage Directors; John Smith's Bitter; guest beer H
Warm and friendly, popular village pub, originally a coaching house but well renovated. An eating area is provided at the end of the lounge. No food Sun eve.
🚶 🍺 ◗ ♦ ⊟ ≠ ♣ P

Mansfield

Boothy's Club
2 West Hill Drive (ring road near cinema) ☎ (01623) 23729
11–11
Adnams Bitter; Mansfield Riding Bitter, Bitter, Old Baily; Wells Bombardier; guest beers H
Large private club on the ring road: a large concert hall and a lounge. Membership easily obtainable. Q ◗ ♣ P

Plough
180 Nottingham Road ☎ (01623) 23031
11–11
Marston's Pedigree; Morland Old Speckled Hen; Whitbread Boddingtons Bitter; guest beers H

Large, one-roomed pub with eight ales. Friendly landlord. Quiz Mon; live music Thu. Good value food till 6pm. Handy for the football. ❀ ◗ P

Ram
Littleworth ☎ (01623) 656071
11–11
Mansfield Riding Bitter, Bitter, Old Baily H
Lively pub next to Mansfield Brewery, popular with locals and employees. Home-cooked food at reasonable prices (no meals Sun). Separate tap room with pub games.
Q ❀ ◗ ♦ ♿ ♣ P

Tap & Spile
39 Leeming Street ☎ (01623) 21327
11.30–3.30, 5.30–11
Big Lamp Bitter; Daleside Bitter; Hadrian Gladiator; Moorhouse's Pendle Witches Brew; Rudgate Battleaxe; guest beers H
Two-roomed town pub just off the market. Sympathetically renovated, it offers traditional games in the back room. Children welcome in the no-smoking snug. Annual beer festival.
Q 🍺 ◗ ♦ ♣ ⌂ P ✗

Westfield Hotel
Westfield Lane (off A6009, near fire station) ☎ (01623) 25090
11–11
Mansfield Riding Mild, Riding Bitter, Bitter H
Lively, friendly town pub hosting frequent games nights. Specify handpumped when ordering beer. No food Sun, or Fri–Sun eves. ❀ ◗ ♦ ⊟ ♣ P

Mansfield Woodhouse

Greyhound Inn
High Street ☎ (01623) 643005
12–4, 7–11
Home Mild, Bitter; S&N Theakston Mild, Best Bitter, XB, Old Peculier H
Typical village local, popular with all ages: a lounge bar and a tap room. ❀ ♣ P

Mapperley Plains

Travellers Rest
Plains Road (B684) ☎ (0115) 9264412
11–11
Home Bitter; S&N Theakston Mild, Best Bitter, XB, Old Peculier; guest beers H
Comfortable roadhouse close to the highest point in the county, with a 'Pop Inn' family room. The excellent home cooking includes

children's specials. No food
Sun eve.
🏛 ᗑ ❀ ◖ ▶ ♣ P

Morton

Full Moon Inn

Main Street ☎ (01636) 830251
11–3, 6–11
**S&N Theakston Best Bitter,
XB, Old Peculier; guest
beers** H
Traditional, oak-beamed pub,
offering excellent food, with a
new theme every month (can
be crowded with diners). Note
the rhyme beside the entrance.
Handy for riverside walks.
🏛 Q ❀ ◖ ▶
≢ (Fiskerton) P

Nether Langwith

Jug & Glass

Queens Walk
☎ (01623) 742283
11.30–4, 7–11
**Hardys & Hansons Best
Bitter** E, **Kimberley Classic** H
Unpretentious, 15th-century
inn by the village stream. The
site dates from the 12th
century. 🏛 ❀ ◖ ▶ ⊟ ♣ P

Newark-on-Trent

Crown & Mitre

53 Castlegate
☎ (01636) 703131
11.30–3, 7–11; 11–11 Sat (& summer
Fri)
**Marston's Pedigree; John
Smith's Bitter; Wards Best
Bitter; guest beers** H
Single bar in a comfortable
split-level pub which is now
popular for real ciders. Pool,
darts and doms played
upstairs; skittles at the back.
Function room (also used for
Sun lunch).
🏛 ᗑ ❀ ◖ ≢ (Castle) ♣ ⬤

Mail Coach

13 London Road
☎ (01636) 605164
11–3, 5.30 (7 Sat)–11
**Ind Coope Burton Ale; Tetley
Bitter; Thwaites Bitter; guest
beers** H
Busy pub dating from 1778,
located opposite the former
Holes brewery and hosting
musical acts at weekends.
Jenga and the ball-round-the-
maze game are popular. Real
cider in summer months. No
food Sun. 🏛 ❀ ⊟ ◖ ▵
≢ (Castle) ♣ ⬤ P

Old Malt Shovel

25 Northgate ☎ (01636) 702036
11.30–3, 7 (5 Fri)–11
**Everards Old Original; Taylor
Landlord; Wards Best Bitter;
guest beers** H
Welcoming single room pub.
A former bakery, it is now

famed for its Mexican eves
and snail racing! Higher
gravity guest beers a
speciality. Beware: the
Scrumpy Jack is not traditional
cider. 🏛 ❀ ◖ ▵
≢ (Castle/Northgate)

Wing Tavern

13 Bridge Street
☎ (01636) 702689
11–3 (2.30 Tue & Thu), 7–11
**S&N Theakston Best Bitter,
XB, Old Peculier; Younger
No.3** H
The sounds of dominoes and
table skittles predominate in
this well-hidden local with a
small, single bar and a
separate pool room. A handy
retreat from the busy market
place. ❀ ≢ (Castle) ♣

Newthorpe

Ram Inn

Beauvale (off B600/B6010 via
Dovecote Rd)
☎ (01773) 713312
11–4, 6–11; 11–11 Sat
**Hardys & Hansons Best Mild,
Best Bitter** E, **Kimberley
Classic** H
Friendly locals' pub, popular
for darts and quizzes. Good
food. 🏛 ❀ ◖ ▶ ⊟ ♣ P

Normanton on Trent

Square & Compass

East Gate ☎ (01636) 821439
12–3, 6–11
**Adnams Bitter; Stones Best
Bitter; guest beers** H
Popular, low-beamed pub on
the edge of the village. Good,
home-cooked food in the bar
or in the small restaurant
(housing a collection of
shotguns). Ninepins played.
🏛 ᗑ ❀ ⊟ ◖ ▵ ♣ P

Nottingham

Bell Inn

18 Angel Row (W side of
Market Square)
☎ (0115) 9475241
10.30–11; 10.30–2.30, 5.30–11 Sat;
12–2, 7–10.30 Sun
**Draught Bass; Eldridge Pope
Royal Oak; Jennings Bitter;
Marston's Pedigree; S&N
Theakston XB, Old Peculier;
guest beers** H
Popular, timber-framed,
15th-century inn, owned by
the Jackson family since 1898.
Cellar tours by appointment.
Regular jazz Sun lunch and
Sun–Tue eves. Guest beers in
the back room. Q ❀ ◖

Boat Inn

9 Priory Street, Lenton
☎ (0115) 9786482
11–2.30, 6 (5.30 Fri)–11; 12–3, 6.30–11
Sat

Home Mild, Bitter E; **S&N
Theakston XB; Younger No.3;
guest beer**
One-roomed local with a
friendly atmosphere and wood
panelling with inlaid mirrors.
Close to Queens Medical
Centre. ❀ ◖ ♣

Coopers Arms

3 Porchester Road,
Thorneywood (off Carlton Rd)
☎ (0115) 9502433
11.30–3.30 (not Wed; 11.30–2.30 Tue
& Fri; 11.30–4.30 Sat), 6 (5.30 Fri, 7
Sat)–11
Home Mild, Bitter E
Four-roomed, 1890s, locals'
pub with a skittle alley.
Function room. Q ᗑ ♣ P

Fellows, Morton & Clayton

54 Canal Street
☎ (0115) 9506795
11–11
**Samuel Fellows Bitter,
Matthew Clayton's Strong
Ale; Whitbread Castle Eden
Ale; guest beers** H
Converted canalside buildings
with several split-level areas.
The brewhouse is visible at the
rear. Friendly and convivial, it
can get busy at weekends. No
parking during the working
day. Well-respected guest beer
policy. ❀ ◖ ≢ ⬠ P

Fox at Sneinton

Dale Street ☎ (0115) 9504736
11–2.30, 6–11
**Ind Coope Burton Ale; Taylor
Landlord; Tetley Bitter** H
Popular drinkers' pub with a
lively bar, separate lounge and
upstairs games room. Very
handy for visiting Green's
Windmill and Museum.
❀ ⊟ ♣

Limelight

Wellington Circus (part of
Nottingham Playhouse)
☎ (0115) 9418467
11–11
**Adnams Bitter; Bateman
Mild; Exmoor Gold;
Marston's Pedigree; S&N
Theakston XB; Whitbread
Boddingtons Bitter; guest
beers** H
Ex-theatre bar offering a
selection of nine, ever-
changing cask ales. Large
choice of meals, with a
vegetarian menu and a
separate restaurant. Music
every Sun night (no food Sun).
Q ❀ ◖ ▶ ♣ ✂

Lincolnshire Poacher

161–163 Mansfield Road (600
yds N of Victoria Centre)
☎ (0115) 9411584
11–3, 5 (6 Sat)–11
**Bateman Mild, XB, Valiant,
XXXB, Victory; Marston's
Pedigree; guest beers** H

Well-established drinkers' house. A good range of ales and draught ciders, and over 80 malt whiskies, make it usually busy. Fresh food and snacks available daily, except Sat/Sun eves. Occasional spontaneous folk eves.
Q ◁ ▶ & ♣ ↺

Magpies
Meadow Lane
☎ (0115) 9863851
11–3, 5–11
Home Mild, Bitter E; **S&N Theakston XB** H
Pub on the eastern edge of the city, handy for both football clubs, the cricket ground and racecourse. Pool table and Sky TV. ☻ ◁ ▶ ⊟ ⇌ ♣ P

March Hare
248 Carlton Road, Sneinton
☎ (0115) 9504328
11.30–2.30, 6–11; 12–2.30, 7–10.30 Sun
Courage Directors; John Smith's Bitter H
Pub where the post-war brick exterior hides a welcoming interior: a functional bar with pool and a comfortable lounge. Q ◁ ⊟ ♣ P

Plainsman
149 Woodthorpe Drive, Mapperley ☎ (0115) 9622020
10.30–2.30 (3 Sat), 6–11; 12–2.30, 7–10.30 Sun
Hardys & Hansons Best Bitter E, **Kimberley Classic** H
Welcoming and unpretentious pub of character. Quiz night Thu. ◁ ⊟ ♣ P

Portland Arms
24 Portland Road (N of centre via Canning Circus and off A610) ☎ (0115) 9782429
11.30–3, 7–11
Hardys & Hansons Best Bitter E, **Kimberley Classic** H
Cosy, friendly, back-street local, now open-plan but retaining a sense of its Victorian past. Quiz nights. Good value cobs. ☻ ♣

Queens Hotel
2 Arkwright Street (opp. station) ☎ (0115) 9864685
11–2.30, 5.30–11; 11–11 Fri; 11–4, 7–11 Sat
Greenalls Shipstone's Mild, Bitter, Original; Stones Best Bitter; Tetley Bitter H
Town pub with a Victorian-style bar and a comfortable lounge. ⋈ ◁ ▶ ⊟ ⇌ ♣ P

Red Cow
Windmill Lane, Sneinton
☎ (0115) 9501632
11.30–3, 6–11
Courage Best Bitter, Directors; Mansfield Bitter; Marston's Pedigree; Ruddles Best Bitter; Wilson's Bitter H

Pub where a plain, drinkers' bar complements the plush lounge. To the rear is a large concert room and games area. Pool played. No quiet room Sat or Sun. Q ☻ ◁ ▶ ⊟ ♣

Tom Hoskins
12–14 Queens Bridge Road, The Meadows
☎ (0115) 9850611
11.30–2.30 (3 Sat), 5.30 (4.30 Fri, 5 Sat match days)–11
Bateman Mild; Hoskins Beaumanor Bitter, Penn's Ale, Old Nigel; guest beer H
One L-shaped bar decorated with brewery artefacts. Friendly, with a regular following for the country & western eves (Sat) and quiz nights (Sun). Sky TV is discreetly located. The Scrumpy Jack is not traditional cider. Lunches Mon–Fri, and Sat match days. ☻ ◁ ⇌

Trip to Jerusalem
1 Brewhouse Yard, Castle Road ☎ (0115) 9473171
11–3, 6–11; 11–11 summer Sat
Hardys & Hansons Best Mild, Best Bitter, Kimberley Classic; Marston's Pedigree H
Many languages are heard as the world visits the historic 'Trip'. The building is mostly formed from caves cut into the rock on which stands the castle—providing ideal beer cellars. A must for visitors.
⋈ Q ☻ ◁ ⇌

Old Clipstone

Dog & Duck
Main Road ☎ (01623) 822138
11–3, 6–11
Home Bitter; S&N Theakston XB; guest beers H
Friendly village local, enjoying some passing trade (Sherwood Forest and Centre Parks are within two miles).
⋈ Q ♿ ☻ ◁ ▶ ▲ ♣ P

Ollerton

White Hart
Station Road ☎ (01623) 822410
11.30–4, 7–11
Samuel Smith OBB H
Tucked away in the centre of the old village, a pub popular with locals and tourists.
♿ ☻ ◁ ▶ ⊟ ♣ P

Pleasley

Olde Plough
869 Chesterfield Road North (A617) ☎ (01623) 810386
11–3.30, 5.30–11; 11–11 Fri & Sat
Ind Coope Burton Ale; Mansfield Bitter, Old Baily; Stones Best Bitter, Tetley Bitter; Whitbread Boddingtons Bitter; guest beers H

One-roomed pub recently refurbished with new beams, etc. Noted for its food (not served Sun eve). At least two guest ales. Q ☻ ◁ ▶ & P ✗

Plumtree

Griffin Inn
Main Road ☎ (0115) 9375743
11–2.30, 5.30–11; 12–2, 7–10.30 Sun
Hardys & Hansons Best Mild, Best Bitter E, **Kimberley Classic** H
Substantial, Victorian, brick-built pub on a crossroads in a small village. The interior has been opened out but retains an intimate atmosphere. Good selection of main meals and snacks; no food Sun. Garden play area. Q ☻ ◁ ▶ ♣ P ✗

Radcliffe on Trent

Royal Oak
Main Road ☎ (0115) 9333798
11–11
Fuller's Chiswick; Marston's Pedigree; Morland Old Speckled Hen; Taylor Landlord; Whitbread Boddingtons Bitter, Castle Eden Ale; guest beers H
Inviting village local with a cosy and convivial lounge and a newly-extended public bar. At least ten cask ales. No food Sun eves. ⋈ ◁ ▶ ⊟ ⇌ ♣ P

Ravenshead

Little John Inn
Main Road ☎ (01623) 792670
11–11
Mansfield Riding Bitter, Bitter, Old Baily H
Large, traditional local with a public bar, and a skittle alley in a converted barn. Summer barbecues; restaurant.
⋈ ☻ ◁ ▶ ⊟ & ♣ P ✗

Retford

Clinton Arms
Albert Road (S of centre, off A638) ☎ (01777) 702703
11–11
Courage Directors; Marston's Pedigree; John Smith's Bitter; Webster's Green Label; guest beers H
Pub with a quiet lounge and a busy bar. Popular with sports fans. Regular live rock music. Food served all day.
Q ♿ ☻ ◁ ▶ ⊟ & ⇌ ♣ P

Market Hotel
West Carr Road, Ordsall
☎ (01777) 703278
11–3, 5–11; 11–11 Sat
Adnams Bitter; Draught Bass; Kelham Island Pale Rider; Morland Old Speckled Hen; Wadworth 6X; Whitbread Flowers Original H

Nottinghamshire

Pub with a separate restaurant and a large function room. Guest beers complement a choice of 12 regular ales. Retford's own mini-beer festival. ❀ ◁ ▶ ᴋ ⇌ P

Turks Head

Grove Street (just out of town square) ☎ (01777) 702742
11–3, 7–11
Vaux Samson; Wards Best Bitter H
Oak-panelled pub exuding a warm welcome. Very popular with ale enthusiasts. Lunches Mon–Sat; eve meals Thu–Sat. ♨ ❀ ⇔ ◁ ▶ ᴋ ♣ P

Ruddington

Three Crowns

23 Easthorpe Street
☎ (0115) 9213226
11.30–3, 6–11
Mansfield Riding Bitter, Bitter, Old Baily; Tetley Bitter; Whitbread Boddingtons Bitter; guest beer H
Known to its regulars as the 'Top House', a quiet, friendly village local, which can get busy at weekends. Handy for the Great Central Railway Walk. Q ❀ ◁

Selston

Horse & Jockey

Church Lane (off B6018)
☎ (01773) 863022
11–11
Draught Bass; Bateman XXXB; Courage Directors; Hook Norton Old Hooky; Taylor Landlord; Whitbread Boddingtons Bitter; guest beers G
Old village pub, dating back to 1664, that time has forgotten: three rooms with low, beamed ceilings. Local CAMRA *Pub of the Season* summer 1993. A small, friendly pub.
♨ Q ꙅ ❀ ◁ ᴋ ♣ P

Miners Arms

Inkerman Road (off B600 at Manor pub via Hanstubbin Rd) ☎ (01773) 862348
12–3, 7–11
Hardys & Hansons Best Mild, Best Bitter H
Friendly, two-room pub off the beaten track, with a welcoming, traditional atmosphere. Sandwiches lunchtimes. ♨ ❀ ♣ P

Shireoaks

Hewett Arms

Shireoaks Park, Thorpe Lane
☎ (01909) 500979
12–3, 6.30–11
Bateman XXXB; Marston's Pedigree; Morland Old

Speckled Hen; Ruddles County; John Smith's Bitter H
Converted early 18th-century coach house in the grounds of Shireoaks Hall, surrounded by coarse fishing waters. ♨ Q
ꙅ ❀ ◁ ▶ ⊟ ᴋ ᴀ ⇌ ➺ P

Skegby

Fox & Crown

116 Dalestorth Road (ring road) ☎ (01623) 552436
11–3, 6–11
Home Bitter; S&N Theakston XB, Old Peculier H
Refurbished modern pub and popular eating place. Children allowed in only if eating in the separate room. Q ❀ ◁ ᴋ P

Strelley

Broad Oak

Main Street ☎ (0115) 9293340
11–11
Hardys & Hansons Best Mild, Best Bitter H, **Kimberley Classic** H & G
Recently refurbished and extended, 17th-century, listed building with a hidden well. Ask for the Classic to be drawn direct from the cask. Meals end at 9pm; open Sun afternoon for diners. ❀ ◁ ▶ P

Sutton Bonington

Anchor Inn

Bollards Lane
☎ (01509) 673648
7 (12 Sat)–11
Banks's Mild; Marston's Pedigree H
Very welcoming, family-run village local: a single room but on a split level. Reputedly haunted by a previous landlord. Pool table.
♨ ❀ ♣ P

Upton

Cross Keys

Main Street ☎ (01636) 813269
11.30–2.30, 6–11; 12–2.30, 7–10.30 Sun
Bateman XXXB; Brakspear Bitter; Marston's Pedigree; Whitbread Boddingtons Bitter; guest beer H
Warm, friendly pub in an attractive village, serving excellent food in the bar and upstairs restaurant (open Fri/Sat eves and Sun lunch). Live folk music Sun eves.
♨ ❀ ◁ ▶ ᴋ ♣ P

Walkeringham

Three Horseshoes

High Street ☎ (01427) 890959
11.30–3, 7–11
Bass Worthington BB, Draught Bass; Stones Best Bitter; guest beer H

Comfortable village local providing interesting, value food. ❀ ◁ ▶ ᴀ ♣ P

Watnall

Queens Head

Main Road ☎ (0115) 9383148
11–3, 5.30–11
Home Mild, Bitter; S&N Theakston XB, Old Peculier H
Carefully renovated, characterful, 17th-century pub with a low, wood-panelled bar and a small, quiet, intimate snug. Part of the building is listed. No food Sat and Sun eves. ♨ ❀ ◁ ♣ P

Royal Oak

Main Road ☎ (0115) 9383110
11–3.30, 5.30–11; 11–4, 7 (6 summer)–11 Sat
Hardys & Hansons Best Mild, Best Bitter, Kimberley Classic H & E
Unusual, split-level, village local with a lounge upstairs. The log cabin at the rear (a former RAF officers' mess) is used for entertainment and functions. No food Sat–Mon. Sky TV available.
ꙅ ❀ ◁ ⊟ ♣ P

West Bridgford

Bridgford Wines

116 Melton Road (by petrol station) ☎ (0115) 9816181
5 (11 Sat)–11
Springhead Bitter; guest beers G
An off-licence for the drinks enthusiast, with four–six cask beers, plus bottled beers from around the world. Polypins for parties. ➺ P

Worksop

Manor Lodge

Mansfield Road (A60, follow signs) ☎ (01909) 474177
11–3, 5.30–11.30
Adnams Broadside; Draught Bass; Burton Bridge XL; Hardington Best Bitter; Steam Packet Poacher's Swag; Stones Best Bitter; guest beers H
Unusual, five-storey Elizabethan manor house in extensive grounds. Built in 1593, many original features remain intact. Safe children's play area. Folk club Fri.
♨ ꙅ ❀ ⇔ ◁ ▶ ᴀ ➺ P

Newcastle Arms

Carlton Road (200 yds from station) ☎ (01909) 485384
11.30–3, 5.30–11
Marston's Pedigree; Morland Old Speckled Hen; Ruddles Best Bitter, County; Webster's Yorkshire Bitter; guest beer H
Popular free house catering for all. ꙅ ❀ ◁ ▶ ᴀ ᴀ ⇌ ♣

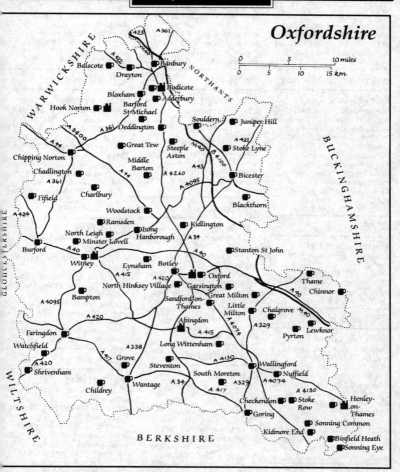

Oxfordshire

Brakspear, Henley-on-Thames; **Hook Norton**, Hook Norton; **Morland**, Abingdon; **Morrells**, Oxford; **Plough Inn**, Bodicote; **Wychwood**, Witney

Adderbury

White Hart
Tanners Lane (off Horn Hill Rd) ☎ (01295) 810406
11–2.30, 5–11
Whitbread Boddingtons Bitter; guest beers H
Tastefully furnished, 17th-century village inn; quiet and friendly. ♠ Q ❀ ⊭ ◑ ▶

Balscote

Butchers Arms
Shutford Road (off A422) ☎ (01295) 730750
12–3, 6–11
Hook Norton Best Bitter H

Classic, one-roomed village pub, popular with hikers and locals. ♠ Q ❀ ♣ P

Bampton

Romany
Bridge Street ☎ (01993) 850237
11–11; 12–4, 7–10.30 Sun; closed Sun
Archers Village; Hook Norton Mild, Best Bitter; Morland Bitter H; **guest beers** H / G
Superb village pub, popular with drinkers and diners alike: one large bar with a good, friendly atmosphere. Dine in the bar or restaurant (extensive good value menu). ♠ ❀ ⊭ ◑ ▶ & ♣

Banbury

Coach & Horses
Butchers Row
☎ (01295) 273552
10.30–3, 5–11
Hook Norton Mild, Best Bitter, Old Hooky, Twelve Days H
Friendly, one-room, conversational town-centre pub. ❀ ⊭ ⇌ ♣

Reindeer Inn
47 Parsons Street
☎ (01295) 264031
11–2.30, 5 (7 Sat)–11; closed Sun
Hook Norton Best Bitter, Old Hooky; Twelve Days; guest beers H

249

Superbly restored, 15th-century former coaching inn, with a relaxed atmosphere (tidy dress—no-one under 21). An historic Jacobean panelled room. ♨ Q ❀ ◖ ⇌ ⌂ P

Barford St Michael

George Inn
Lower Street (1 mile from B4031) ☎ (01869) 38226
12–2.30 (3 Sat), 6 (7 Sat)–11
Adnams Bitter; Wadworth 6X; guest beers H
300-year-old stone and thatch pub with a beamed ceiling, set in the Swere valley. Camping in the garden. Blues bands Mon eve. Note the painting of the Battle of Agincourt.
♨ ☎ ❀ ◖ ▶ ♣ P

Bicester

Littlebury Hotel
Kings End ☎ (01869) 252595
11–3, 5–11
Marston's Pedigree H
Welcoming, established family hotel. Home-cooked meals.
Q ☎ ❀ ⇤ ◖ ▶ ⇌ P

Binfield Heath

Bottle & Glass
Harpsden Road (off A4155, ½ mile NE of centre)
☎ (01491) 575755
11–3, 6–11
Brakspear Bitter H/E, **Old** H, **Special** H/E
Thatched, low-beamed, 17th-century, country pub with a flagstoned floor in the larger bar. Large garden and good home-cooked food (including vegetarian). No meals Sun eve. Q ❀ ◖ ▶ P

Blackthorn

Rose & Crown
Off B4011 ☎ (01869) 252534
12–3, 7–11
Morrells Bitter H
Splendid Victorian pub with a convivial atmosphere, wholesome bar snacks and an interesting jukebox. ♨ ❀ ♣ P

Bloxham

Red Lion Inn
High Street ☎ (01295) 720352
11–2.30, 7–11
Adnams Bitter; Wadworth 6X; guest beers H
Pleasant, friendly pub with two bars and a large garden. Extended lounge-dining area.
♨ Q ❀ ◖ ▶ ⊟ & A ♣ P

Bodicote

Plough
High Street ☎ (01295) 262327
11–3, 6–11; 12–2.30, 7–10.30 Sun

Bodicote Bitter, No. 9, Porter, Triple X H
Lively brew pub offering brewery tours (book). Home-cooked food in the lounge (Sun meals to order). ◖ ▶ ⊟

Botley

Fair Rosamund
Chestnut Road
☎ (01865) 243376
12–3, 7–11 (may open earlier summer)
Marston's Bitter, Pedigree H
Estate pub, built in the 1950s, consisting of three bars: a games room, a public bar and a comfortable lounge. Due for alterations. Q ❀ ♣ P

Burford

Lamb Inn
Sheep Street ☎ (01993) 823155
11–2.30, 6–11
Wadworth IPA, 6X, Old Timer H
Lovely, quiet locals' bar in a very smart hotel, complete with flagged floor, oak beams and antique furniture. This 14th-century, Cotswold stone inn was originally Garne's brewery tap. No food Sun.
♨ Q ❀ ⇤ ◖ ⌂

Chadlington

Tite Inn
Mill End (near A361)
☎ (01608) 676475
12–2.30, 6.30 (7 winter)–11 (closed Mon, except bank hols)
Archers Village; Hall & Woodhouse Badger Best Bitter; guest beers H
16th-century free house and restaurant. The delightful garden has country views. No jukebox, slot machines or pool. No-smoking garden room in summer. Children welcome.
♨ Q ❀ ◖ ▶ & A ♣ P

Chalgrove

Red Lion
High Street ☎ (01865) 890625
11.30–3, 6–11
Brakspear Bitter; Fuller's London Pride; guest beers H
Popular and attractive village pub which is 350 years old; a Grade II-listed building with several drinking areas; families welcomed. Wide range of good value, home-cooked food, including vegetarian (no food Sun eve). No-smoking dining room. ♨ ❀ ◖ ▶ & ♣

Charlbury

Rose & Crown
Market Street
☎ (01608) 810103
12–3, 5.30–11; 12–11 Fri & Sat

Archers Village H; **guest beers** H/G
Popular, one-room, town-centre pub with a small garden. Excellent rotation of guest beers. ♨ ❀ ⇌ ♣

Checkendon

Black Horse
Towards Stoke Row, left up a narrow lane OS667841
☎ (01491) 680418
11–2.30, 6.30–11
Brakspear Bitter; Old Luxters Barn Ale G
No food, no music, no indoor loos; not even a proper address! This family-run country pub is hidden away in the woods. A classic.
♨ Q ☎ ❀ A ♣ P

Childrey

Hatchet
High Street ☎ (01235) 751213
11.30–3, 7–11
Brains Dark; Fuller's London Pride; Morland Bitter; guest beers H
Former Morland house opened out into one bar with a warm welcome. The delicious, home-cooked food is good value. ❀ ◖ ▶ & A P

Chinnor

Kings Head
Station Road ☎ (01844) 351530
11–3, 6–11
Morrells Bitter, Mild, Varsity; guest beer H
Traditional, small, 300-year-old, oak-beamed, two-bar pub with a split-level lounge. The nearest pub in the village to the Ridgeway path. Meals Mon–Fri. ❀ ◖ ⊟ & ♣ P

Chipping Norton

Chequers
Goddards Lane
☎ (01608) 644717
11–2.30, 5.30–11
Fuller's Hock, Chiswick, London Pride, Mr Harry, ESB H
Friendly, traditional pub, close to the theatre; a winner of Fuller's *Town Pub* award. Eve meals finish at 8.30 (no food Sun). ♨ Q ❀ ◖ ▶ ♣

Deddington

Crown & Tuns
New Street ☎ (01869) 37371
11–3, 6–11
Hook Norton Mild, Best Bitter, Old Hooky H
Small, basic, Georgian coaching inn where Aunt Sally is played. In every edition of the *Guide*. ♨ ❀ ♣

Drayton

Roebuck Inn
Stratford Road (A422)
☎ (01295) 730542
11–2.30, 6–11
Fuller's London Pride; Hook Norton Best Bitter; Marston's Pedigree; Ruddles County; Whitbread Boddingtons Bitter; guest beers (occasional) H
17th-century, picturesque village pub known for food.
🏚 Q ❀ 🏠 ◖ ▶ & P

Eynsham

Queens Head
Queen Street ☎ (01865) 881229
12–2.30, 6.30–11
Morland Bitter, Old Speckled Hen; guest beers H
Unspoilt, 18th-century, two-bar pub; the public bar has a darts area at the rear. Very friendly atmosphere.
🏚 Q ❀ ♣

Faringdon

Bell
Market Place ☎ (01367) 240534
10.30–11
Hall & Woodhouse Tanglefoot; Wadworth 6X, Farmer's Glory, Old Timer; guest beers H
Rambling, popular, 16th-century inn, full of character. The large bar boasts a mural; the lounge is smaller. Flower-bedecked courtyard. Excellent family facilities; wheelchair WC.
🏚 Q ♿ ❀ 🏠 ◖ ▶ & P ✂

Folly
54 London Street
☎ (01367) 240620
10.30–2.30, 5.30–11
Morrells Bitter, Varsity H
Charming, homely little town pub without frills, at the foot of Faringdon Folly: a public bar and two lounges.
🏚 Q ❀ ⌑ ♣

Fifield

Merrymouth Inn
Stow Road (A424)
☎ (01993) 831652
11–2.30, 6–11; 12–2.30, 7–10.30 Sun
Donnington BB, SBA; guest beers H
Historic, 13th-century Cotswold inn with a beamed bar and stone floor, mentioned in the *Domesday Book*. Home-cooking.
🏚 Q 🏠 ◖ ▶ P

Garsington

Three Horseshoes
The Green ☎ (01865) 361395
11–3, 6.30–11 (11–11 summer)

Draught Bass; Morrells Bitter, Varsity H; **guest beers** G
A pub since 1801 in which a magnificent ship's keel supports the bar ceiling. Food is cooked to order by a French chef for the lounge and no-smoking conservatory restaurant. The huge garden features a children's play area.
🏚 ❀ ◖ ▶ ♣ P

Goring

Catherine Wheel
Station Road (off B4009 at Miller of Mansfield pub)
☎ (01491) 872379
11–2.30 (3.30 Sat), 6–11
Brakspear Mild, Bitter H, **Old** G, **Special, OBJ** H
The oldest pub in the village (over 500 years old). The L-shaped bar extends into the old blacksmith's forge—now the restaurant area. Popular with locals and tourists. Quiz and folk music eves. No food Sun eve. 🏚 ❀ ◖ ▶ ⇌ ♣ P

John Barleycorn
Manor Road (off B4009 at Miller of Mansfield pub)
☎ (01491) 872509
10–2.30, 6–11
Brakspear Bitter, Special H
Attractive, 16th-century, low-beamed inn with a cosy lounge. Extensive, good-value menu, with daily specials. Close to the Thames and the Ridgeway footpath.
Q ❀ 🏠 ◖ ▶ ⌑ ⇌ ♣

Great Milton

Bell Inn
The Green ☎ (01844) 279270
12–2, 7–11; 12–2, 7.30–10.30 Sun
Brakspear Bitter; Smiles Bitter; Uley Old Spot; guest beers H
Welcoming, 17th-century, country pub with good, home-made food. Beer festivals twice-yearly. Aunt Sally.
🏚 Q ❀ ◖ ▶ ⌑ & ▲ ♣

Great Tew

Falkland Arms
Off B4022 ☎ (01608) 683653
11.30–2.30 (not Mon), 6–11; 12–, 7–10.30 Sun
Donnington BB; Hall & Woodhouse Tanglefoot; Hook Norton Best Bitter; Wadworth 6X; guest beers H
Classic, thatched, 16th-century inn in a preserved village, featuring oak panels, oil lamps, settles and flagstoned floors, malt whiskies and fruit wines. A gem! No food Sun eve. 🏚 Q ❀ 🏠 ◖ ▲ ♣ ⌣

Grove

Volunteer
Station Road (A338)
☎ (01235) 769557
11–11
Archers Village; Draught Bass; Fuller's London Pride; Morland Bitter; Ruddles Best Bitter; Wadworth 6X H
Originally built to serve a station, this pub is now thriving, since being saved by a dedicated landlord. Noted for its food (served all day). Free minibus nightly to and from Wantage. ❀ ◖ ▶ ♣ P

Henley-on-Thames

Saracen's Head
129 Greys Road (off A4155; up hill ½ mile SW of A4130/A4155 jct) ☎ (01491) 575929
11–2.30 (3 Sat), 5.30–11
Brakspear Mild, Bitter, Old (winter), **Special** (summer), **OBJ** H
A friendly welcome in a popular, busy local which has an emphasis on pub games. Home-cooked snacks.
🏚 ❀ 🏠 ▲ ♣ P

Hook Norton

Pear Tree Inn
Scotland End
☎ (01608) 737482
12–2.30 (3 Sat; not winter Tue), 6–11
Hook Norton Mild, Best Bitter, Old Hooky H, **Twelve Days** G
Charming, 18th-century, one-room, brick-faced pub. Cosy log fires and beams feature. The large garden (with games) is ideal for children. Good food (last orders 8pm; no eve meals Tue or Sun).
🏚 Q ❀ 🏠 ◖ ▲ ♣ P

Juniper Hill

Fox
¼ mile E of A43, 3 miles S of Brackley ☎ (01869) 810616
12–2, 7–11
Hook Norton Best Bitter H, **Old Hooky** G
Friendly pub in the centre of a hamlet. It appeared as the Waggon & Horses in *Lark Rise to Candleford*. 🏚 Q ❀ ♣ P

Kidlington

Kings Arms
4 The Moors ☎ (01865) 373004
11–3, 6–11
Ind Coope ABC Best Bitter, Burton Ale; guest beers H
Very attractive, two-bar village local. Both the bar and lounge

Oxfordshire

are quite small, so they can get crowded, but the atmosphere is friendly and welcoming. Thatched toilets. Q ◑ ♣ P

Kidmore End

New Inn
Chalkhouse Green Road (off B481) ☎ (01734) 723115
11–3, 6–11
Brakspear Bitter, Old, Special, OBJ H
Attractive, two-bar pub with beams and wood panelling, opposite the village pond. The large garden has petanque and a fishpond. The extended Tap Room is drinks-oriented and has no music. Good, varied menu, with vegetarian options. The handpumps are gas pump-assisted (no gas contact with beer).
🍴 Q ♿ ⊛ ◑ ♣ ⌂ P ✗

Lewknor

Olde Leathern Bottel
High Street (off B4009, near M40 jct 6) ☎ (01844) 351482
11–2.30, 6–11
Brakspear Bitter, Old, Special H
Comfortable, inviting, family-run village pub with a friendly atmosphere and a large, well-kept garden. The food is good, home-made and well-priced (vegetarian options).
🍴 ♿ ⊛ ◑ ♣ ⊟ ♣ P

Little Milton

Plough
Stadhampton Road (A329) ☎ (01844) 278180
11–11
Morrells Bitter, Mild *or* **Graduate, Varsity; guest beer** H
17th-century, stone-walled and timber-beamed pub with a village atmosphere. Good value food, including vegetarian dishes, all day. Large, enclosed play area and garden. OAP discounts.
🍴 ♿ ⊛ ◑ ▲ ♣ P ✗

Long Hanborough

Bell
Main Road ☎ (01993) 881324
10.30–3, 6.30–11
Morrells Bitter, Mild; guest beer H
Traditional Cotswold stone inn and restaurant, near Blenheim Palace. The garden affords an exceptional view.
♿ ⊛ ◑ ⇌ ♣ P

Long Wittenham

Machine Man Inn
Fieldside (1 mile off A415, follow signs) ☎ (01865) 407835
11–3, 6.30–11

Eldridge Pope Blackdown Porter, Hardy Country, Royal Oak; guest beers H
Basic, friendly village local. The odd name comes from the machine mender who used to own it. The good value, home-made food includes vegetarian dishes (book Sun eve). Families welcome; ETB-approved accommodation. The Addlestones cider is top pressured. Interesting guest beers. 🍴 ⇌ ⊛ ◑ ♣ P

Middle Barton

Fox
27 Enstone Road (off A4260) ☎ (01869) 40338
12–2.30, 6–11
Samuel Smith OBB; S&N Theakston XB; Wychwood Best; guest beers H
Small, 15th-century, Cotswold stone pub featuring beams, a flagstone floor and a good atmosphere. Noted for good food, in the bar or restaurant. Summer beer festival.
🍴 Q ♿ ⊛ ◑ ▲ ♣ P

Minster Lovell

White Hart
Burford Road ☎ (01993) 775255
11–11
Courage Best Bitter; Donnington BB, SBA; guest beers H
Late 15th-century, roadside inn: one large bar with a small restaurant area (good food).
🍴 ♿ ⇌ ◑ ♣ ⌂ P

North Hinksey Village

Fishes
☎ (01865) 249796
10.30–2.30, 6–11
Morrells Bitter, Varsity, Graduate H
A popular lunch venue for nearby businesses, this largish pub serves a medieval village, now within the Oxford ring road. Often very busy, but there's always somewhere to sit. ♿ ⊛ ◑ ⊟ ♣ P ✗

North Leigh

Woodman
New Yatt Road (off A4095) ☎ (01993) 881790
12–3 (4 Sat), 6–11
Hook Norton Best Bitter; Wadworth 6X; Wychwood Shires; guest beers H
Small village pub offering home-made food. The large terraced garden hosts twice-yearly beer festivals.
🍴 Q ⊛ ⇌ ◑ ▲ ♣ ⌂ P

Nuffield

Crown
Gangsdown Hill (A4130) ☎ (01491) 641335
11–2.30, 6–11
Brakspear Bitter, Old (occasional), Special, OBJ H
Early 17th-century, low-beamed, cosy, waggoner's inn. Of the three rooms, two boast large inglenooks. Excellent range of good value, home-cooked food. Children welcome lunchtimes. Large garden. 🍴 Q ⊛ ◑ ▲ ♣ P

Oxford

Black Boy
91 Old High Street, Headington (off A420) ☎ (01865) 63234
11–3, 6–11; 11–11 Sat
Morrells Bitter, Mild, Varsity, Graduate; guest beer H
Friendly, popular local in Old Headington. The small saloon bar is a quiet retreat. Award-winning garden. No food Sun eve. Q ⊛ ◑ ⊟ ♿ ♣ P

Bookbinders Arms
17–18 Victor Street, Jericho ☎ (01865) 53549
10.30–3, 6–11
Morrells Bitter, Mild H
Traditional, friendly local. The single room is split into two areas, and is popular for games. No food Sun. ◑ ♿ ♣

Butchers Arms
5 Wilberforce Street, Headington ☎ (01865) 61252
11.30–2.30, 5.30 (4.30 Fri & Sat)–11
Fuller's Hock, Chiswick, London Pride, Mr Harry, ESB H
Former Halls pub, now a thriving back-street local, serving good food. Families welcome lunch and early eve. Quiz Sun night. 🍴 ⊛ ◑ ♿ ♣

Cricketers Arms
43 Iffley Road (A4158) ☎ (01865) 726264
12–3, 6.30–11
Morland Bitter, Old Masters, Old Speckled Hen; S&N Theakston XB; guest beer H
Traditional, friendly, two-bar local. The lively public bar hosts jazz Tue eve and blues Sun lunch. The lounge offers a more relaxed atmosphere. Range of vegetarian meals, but no food Sun eve. ⊛ ◑ ⊟ ♣

Fir Tree Tavern
163 Iffley Road (A4158) ☎ (01865) 247373
12–3, 5.30–11; 12–11 Sat
Morrells Bitter, Mild, Varsity; guest beer H

Small, split-level Victorian pub popular with locals and students. Piano player Wed and Sun eve; jam session Tue eve; quiz Thu eve. Freshly-made pizzas; cider in summer. Children welcome until 8pm.
🌇 ❀ ◑ ▶ ♣ ⇗

Kings Arms
40 Holywell Street
☎ (01865) 242369
10.30–11
Morland Bitter; Wadworth 6X; Younger No. 3; Young's Bitter, Special, Winter Warmer H
Large, busy, city-centre pub, still an Oxford institution, despite no longer being a free house. The atmospheric Dons' Bar at the rear is worth trying—if you can get a seat. Opens 10.30am Sun for snacks.
🌇 Q 🌇 ❀ ◑ ▶ ♿ ♣ ✗

Marlborough House
60 Western Road, Grandpont (off A4144) ☎ (01865) 243617
11.30–2.30, 6–11; 11.30–11 Sat
Ind Coope ABC Best Bitter, Burton Ale; Tetley Bitter H
Friendly, back-street local on the site of the city's first station. Popular with students. Pool room upstairs. Can get rather smoky. 🌇 ❀ ◑ ♣

Marsh Harrier
40 Marsh Road, Cowley (off B480) ☎ (01865) 775937
12–2.30, 6–11; 12–11 Fri & Sat
Fuller's London Pride, Mr Harry, ESB H
Small, friendly, two-bar pub. Garden events in summer.
🌇 ❀ 🅗 ◑ ♣

Old Tom
101 St Aldates (A420)
☎ (01865) 243034
10.30–3, (5.30 Fri & Sat)–11
Morrells Bitter, Mild, Varsity H
Small, comfortable, 17th-century, city-centre pub, popular with locals, students and tourists. Lively, but friendly atmosphere. It takes its name from the bell at Christchurch College. Eve meals finish early; no food Sun eve. No-smoking area at lunchtime. Q ❀ ◑ ▶ ⇌ ✗

Royal Oak
42–44 Woodstock Road (A4144) ☎ (01865) 54230
11–11
Ind Coope ABC Best Bitter, Burton Ale; Tetley Bitter; Wadworth 6X H
Popular, multi-roomed, former 17th-century coaching inn, just north of the city centre. Much altered, it retains some character and appeals to most tastes. 🌇 Q 🌇 ❀ ◑ ▶ ♿ ♣

Three Goats Heads
3–5 St Michael's Street
☎ (01865) 721523
11–11
Samuel Smith OBB, Museum H
City-centre pub on two levels, situated next to the Oxford Union. Tastefully decorated, with much wood and tiling in evidence, it was previously commended in CAMRA's *Pub Preservation* awards and serves some of the cheapest beer in central Oxford. ◑ ▶ ⇌

Victoria Arms
Mill Lane, Old Marston (¼ mile down drive, W off Mill Lane) ☎ (01865) 241382
11.30–2.30, 6–11 (11.30–11 May–Oct)
Hall & Woodhouse Tanglefoot; Wadworth IPA, 6X, Farmer's Glory, Old Timer; guest beers H
Formerly known as the Ferry, this large riverside pub is popular with punters and tourists. The garden and patio have room for over 100 people and a children's play area.
🌇 Q ❀ ◑ ▶ ♿ ♣ P ✗

Pyrton

Plough
Knightsbridge Lane (off B4009, N of Watlington)
☎ (01491) 612003
11.30–2.30, 6 (7 Tue)–11; closed Mon eve
Adnams Bitter; Brakspear Bitter; Fuller's ESB H
Attractive, 17th-century, thatched pub in a quiet country village. Popular for its extensive menu of home-cooking, served in the bar and restaurant (where families are welcome at lunchtime).
🌇 ❀ ◑ ▶ A ♣ P

Ramsden

Royal Oak
High Street ☎ (01993) 868213
11.30–2.30, 6.30–11.30
Archers Village; Banks's Bitter; Hook Norton Best Bitter, Old Hooky; guest beers H
17th-century, former coaching inn with a courtyard. The restaurant serves high quality local produce and the long-serving staff help create an efficient, friendly atmosphere.
🌇 Q ❀ 🅗 ◑ ▶ ♿ ♣ P

Sandford-on-Thames

Fox Inn
25 Henley Road (off A423)
☎ (01865) 777803
12–2.30, 7 (6 summer)–11; 12–2.30, 7–10.30 Sun
Morrells Bitter, Mild (winter),

Varsity (spring/summer) H, **College** G
Roadside local in the same family for 75 years, and 17 consecutive years in the *Guide*. Probably the cheapest Morrells in Oxfordshire. Limited parking. 🌇 Q ❀ 🅗 ♣ P

Shrivenham

Prince of Wales
High Street ☎ (01793) 782268
11.30–3, 6–11
Hall & Woodhouse Tanglefoot; Wadworth IPA, 6X; guest beer H
Cosy, 17th-century, stone-built coaching inn with beams. No food Sun eve. Limited parking.
🌇 Q ❀ ◑ ▶ ♣ P

Sonning Common

Bird in Hand
Peppard Road (B481)
☎ (01734) 723230
11–2.30, 6–11
Courage Best Bitter; Fuller's London Pride; Ruddles County H
Friendly roadside pub with a cosy atmosphere. The good value food is served in the bar or restaurant. A large, attractive garden and outdoor drinking area (with caged animals) back onto woodland. No food Sun eve. Q ❀ ◑ ▶ P

Sonning Eye

Flowing Spring
Henley Road (A4155)
☎ (01734) 693207
11.30–3, 5–11 (11–11 summer)
Fuller's Chiswick, London Pride, Mr Harry, ESB H; **guest beer** (summer)
Traditional ale house with a piano. It runs several special events and has friendly rugby, soccer and cricket teams. Quiz Sun eve. The only pub in the country with this name. No food Sun eve. 🌇 ❀ ◑ ▶ ♣ P

Souldern

Fox
Fox Lane (off B4100, 2 miles S of Aynho) ☎ (01869) 345284
11–3, 5 (6 Sat)–11
Bass Worthington BB; Draught Bass; Fuller's London Pride; Hook Norton Old Hooky H
Friendly Cotswold stone pub in the village centre. Noted for its food—served in the bar and restaurant (not Sun eve).
🌇 Q ❀ 🅗 ◑ ▶ ♣ P

South Moreton

Crown
High Street (off A4130/A417)
☎ (01235) 812262

Oxfordshire

11–3, 5.30–11
Adnams Bitter; Hall & Woodhouse Tanglefoot; Wadworth IPA H, **6X** G; guest beer
Friendly, village local, popular for meals, including vegetarian. New no-smoking family room. Quiz night Mon; regular theme nights. Water coolers are used on the 6X on gravity behind the bar.
🏚 Q ⛺ ❀ ◑ ▮ ♣ P ⊬

Stanton St John

Star Inn
Middle Road (100 yds off B4027) ☎ (01865) 351277
11–3, 6.30–11; 12–2.30, 7–10.30 Sun
Hall & Woodhouse Tanglefoot; Wadworth IPA, 6X, Farmer's Glory, Old Timer H
17th-century inn retaining some original features. Tasty home-cooked food, with numerous vegetarian dishes, is served at reasonable prices. Popular, no-smoking family room.
🏚 ⛺ ❀ ◑ ▮ ♣ P ⊬

Steeple Aston

Red Lion
South Street (off A4260) ☎ (01869) 340225
11–3, 6–11
Hall & Woodhouse Tanglefoot; Hook Norton Best Bitter; Wadworth 6X H
Friendly, discerning pub with a library in the cosy bar. Bar lunches are served, except Sun; the dining room is used for eve meals Tue–Sat.
🏚 Q ❀ ◑ ▮ P

Steventon

Cherry Tree
High Street ☎ (01235) 831222
11.30–2.30, 6 (6.30 Sat)–11
Brakspear Bitter; Wadworth IPA, 6X, Farmer's Glory, Old Timer; guest beer H
Comfortable, inviting roadside tavern of character, offering an inventive menu of high quality, home-made food. Popular with local businesses for lunch. 🏚 ❀ ◑ ▮ P

Stoke Lyne

Peyton Arms
½ mile from B4100
☎ (01869) 345285
11–2.30 (not Mon), 5.30–11
Hook Norton Mild, Best Bitter, Old Hooky G
Small, basic village local, unchanged by time—a real rural gem!
🏚 Q ❀ ▮ ♣ P

Stoke Row

Cherry Tree
Off B481 ☎ (01491) 680430
11–3, 6–11
Brakspear Mild, Bitter, Special, OBJ G
Low-beamed, attractive village local close to the famous Maharajah's Well. Families are welcome in the lounge and pool rooms (swings in the garden). Bar snacks available (not Mon). 🏚 ⛺ ❀ ▮ ♣ P

Thame

Rising Sun
High Street ☎ (01844) 214206
11–2.30, 6–11
Adnams Extra; Hook Norton Best Bitter; Wadworth 6X; guest beers H
Attractive, 16th-century, oak-beamed building with an overhanging first floor. Its cosy atmosphere is enhanced by low ceilings. Lots of board games. An excellent, home-cooked menu includes a vegetarian option (last orders 10.45pm). 🏚 ❀ ◑ ▮ ♣ ⌂

Six Bells
44 Lower High Street
☎ (01844) 212088
11–3, 6–11
Fuller's Hock, Chiswick, London Pride, ESB H
Warm, comfortable old two-bar pub featuring some 16th-century ship's timbers. The lounge bar ceiling has straps to assist perpendicular drinkers. Regular quizzes.
Q ❀ ❀ ◑ ▮ ⊞ ♣ P

Wallingford

Coach & Horses
12 Kinecroft (off High St, 400 yds W of A329/A4130 jct)
☎ (01491) 825054
11.30–2.30 (3 Fri & Sat), 6–11
Fuller's Hock, Chiswick, London Pride, Mr Harry H, **ESB, Golden Pride** G
Cosy, two-bar pub overlooking the Kinecroft common (which acts as its garden). Popular with locals and shoppers, it serves good value food (not Sun/Mon eves). 🏚 ◑ ▮ ⊞ ♣ ❀

Wantage

Royal Oak
Newbury Street (A338)
☎ (01235) 763129
12–2.30 (not Mon–Thu), 5.30–11
Draught Bass; Fuller's London Pride; Hall & Woodhouse Badger Best Bitter H, **Tanglefoot** G; **Wadworth 6X** H; guest beers H/G
Boisterous pub with two large bars. Poets and peasants, hoi-polloi and Hooray Henries—they all enjoy an atmosphere of convivial camaraderie. No food Sun. The guest beers change frequently. 🏚 ◑ ⊞ ♿ ♣

Shoulder of Mutton
38 Wallingford Street (A417)
☎ (01235) 762835
11–3 (may extend), 6–11
Morland Bitter H
A rare, untouched Morland town pub. Apart from a new bar counter and new inside toilets, little has changed over the years. Definitely no frills.
🏚 Q ❀ ❀ ♿ ♣

Watchfield

Royal Oak
Oak Road (off Shrivenham Rd)
☎ (01793) 782668
12–2.30, 6.30–11
Courage Directors; Ushers Best Bitter, Founders H
Friendly, ivy-covered village local with a low ceiling, dating back to the 18th century.
❀ ◑ ▮ ♣ P

Witney

House of Windsor
31 West End (B4022)
☎ (01993) 704277
12–3.30 (not Mon), 6 (7 Sat)–11
Hook Norton Best Bitter; Wadworth 6X; guest beers H
Popular town pub offering a varied, well-chosen selection of guest beers. It has a very comfortable single bar, but mind the doors to the bar when entering. 🏚 ◑ ▮ ♣

Three Horse Shoes
Corn Street ☎ (01993) 703086
11–2.30, 6.30–11; 11–11 Sat; 12–2.30, 7–10.30 Sun
Adnams Broadside or Wells Bombardier; Morland Bitter H
16th-century Cotswold inn with exposed beams and a stone floor, covered with oriental rugs, and antique furniture, including a grandfather clock.
🏚 Q ⛺ ❀ ◑ ▮

Woodstock

Black Prince
2 Manor Road, Old Woodstock (A44) ☎ (01993) 811530
12–2.30, 6.30–11
Archers Village; S&N Theakston XB, Old Peculier; guest beer H
16th-century pub of great character with a suit of armour in the bar. The garden lies on the banks of the River Glyme. Good meals: Mexican food is a speciality. 🏚 ❀ ◑ ▮ P

Shropshire

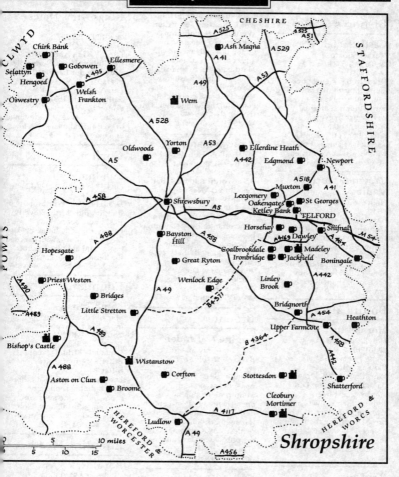

Shropshire

All Nations, Madeley; **Fox & Hounds**, Stottesdon; **Hanby**, Wem; **Hobsons**, Cleobury Mortimer; **Three Tuns**, Bishop's Castle; **Wood**, Wistanstow

---

Ash Magna

White Lion
E of, and off A525, Whitchurch bypass ☎ (01948) 663153
12–2 (not Mon), 6–11
Bass Worthington BB, Draught Bass; M&B Highgate Dark; guest beers ⓗ
A central bar separates the two rooms of this neat village pub which displays many real ale mementos in the public bar and hickory-handled golf clubs in the lounge. Bar billiards and skittles; bowling green. No food Sun.
🏨 Q ❀ ⓓ ▸ ⊟

Aston on Clun

Kangaroo Inn
☎ (015887) 263
12–3, 7–11
Bass Worthington BB, Draught Bass; M&B Highgate Dark; guest beer ⓗ
The landlord's time in Australia is mirrored in the mementos in this pub's large public bar. There is also a lounge and eating area, and a large garden. The village Arbor tree is decorated each May, continuing the ancient custom of tree dressing.
🏨 ⓓ ▸ ♣ P

Bayston Hill

Compasses
Hereford Road
☎ (01743) 722921
12–3 (not winter Mon–Fri), 5–11; 12–11 Fri & Sat
Draught Bass; M&B Highgate Dark, Brew XI; guest beer ⓗ
Set on a rise as the main A49 passes through the village, this pub features a snug and a recently extended bar. Note the huge collection of carved wooden elephants. Lunchtime snacks available.
Q ❀ ⊟ ⓵ ♣

Shropshire

Bishop's Castle

Castle Hotel
Market Square
☎ (01588) 638403
12–3, 6.30–11
Draught Bass; guest beers H
Fine country town hotel. The front entrance leads to a snug bar with much original woodwork in evidence. There is a larger room off and a public bar at the rear. Good selection of games; popular with locals. Large garden.
🛏 Q ❀ 🛏 ◑ ♣ ⏺ P

Crown & Anchor Vaults
High Street ☎ (01588) 638966
11–11
Bass Worthington BB, Draught Bass; Coach House Innkeepers Special Reserve; Tetley Bitter; guest beers H
Victorian-style drinking house, usually offering at least five hand-pulled beers, with occasional changes to the range. 🛏 ❀ ◑ ▶ ♣

Boningale

Horns Inn
Holyhead Road (A464)
☎ (01902) 372347
12–3, 6.30 (7 Mon, 5.30 summer)–11
Banks's Mild; Bass Worthington BB, Draught Bass; Hook Norton Old Hooky; guest beers H
18th-century, drovers' inn with timbered bars and real fires. The dining room (supper licence), offers an extensive menu with a good vegetarian selection. Three guest beers.
🛏 Q ◑ ▶ 🛏 P

Bridges

Horseshoes
OS394964 ☎ (0158 861) 260
12–2.30 (later Sat; not Mon), 6–11
Adnams Bitter, Old (winter); **Eldridge Pope Blackdown Porter** (not winter); **Marston's Pedigree; guest beers** H
Pub adjacent to one of the few roads that lead off the Long Mynd and near a privately-owned youth hostel. This attractive, rendered building is busy with walkers. One main bar and a side room displaying pictures for sale, and selling eggs and other local products.
🛏 Q ❀ ◑ ♣ ⏺ P ✕

Bridgnorth

Bear
Northgate (B4373 in High Town) ☎ (01746) 763250
11 (10.30 Fri & Sat)–2.30, 5.15 (6 Sat)–11; 12–2.30, 7.30–10.30 Sun

Batham Best Bitter; Holden's Mild; Ruddles Best Bitter; Whitbread Boddingtons Bitter; guest beers H
Grade II-listed, ancient inn, adjacent to the historic Northgate. Up to six real ales are available to wash down the excellent lunches (not served Sun). A gourmet night is held in the lounge each Thu (book). 🛏 Q ❀ 🛏 ◑ ⏺
≠ (SVR, summer) P

Railwayman's Arms
SVR Station, Hollybush Road (off B4364) ☎ (01746) 764361
11–11 (11–2.30, 7–11 winter)
Bass Worthington BB; Batham Best Bitter; M&B Highgate Dark; Wood Special; guest beers H
Bar located on the platform of a Victorian railway station, boasting an interesting collection of railwayana. The Severn Valley Railway runs throughout the summer. A good range of guest beers, hot snacks and locomotives.
🛏 ❀ ಠ A
≠ (SVR, summer) ♣ ⏺ P

Broome

Engine & Tender
Off Clun–Craven Arms road, B4367/8 ☎ (0158 87) 275
12–3, 7–11
Draught Bass; Wood Parish; guest beers H
Multi-roomed pub now open-plan with the exception of the function room, used for folk night. Broome Halt is a request stop. Camping is on the pub's own site; caravans allowed. Q ◑ A
≠ (Broome Halt) ♣ P

Chirk Bank

Bridge
☎ (01691) 773213
11–3, 6–11
Banks's Mild, Bitter E; **Camerons Strongarm** (summer) H
Welcoming old local on the Welsh border, in attractive surroundings. It lies on the old Holyhead road, by the Llangollen Canal. Q ❀ 🛏 ◑
▶ ಠ A ≠ (Chirk) ♣ P

Cleobury Mortimer

Bell Inn
Lower Street ☎ (01299) 270305
11–3, 7 (6 Sat)–11
Banks's Mild, Bitter E; **guest beer** H
Pub, with a multi-level lounge and an old-fashioned bar, plus a pool room and a private snooker club room (day membership). 🛏 Q 🍺 ♣ ⏺

Kings Arms Hotel
Church Street
☎ (01299) 270252
11.30–11
Greene King Abbot; Hobsons Best Bitter; Hook Norton Best Bitter; Taylor Landlord; guest beers H
Large, single-roomed inn dating back to 1530, with a central fireplace. The restaurant serves a wide range of well-priced meals. No food Sun eve. 🛏 🛏 ◑ ▶ ⏺ P

Corfton

Sun Inn
On B4368 ☎ (01584) 861239
11–2.30, 6–11
Draught Bass; Whitbread Boddingtons Mild, Flowers IPA; guest beers H
Family-run inn, dating back to the 17th century, with exposed beams and a dining area off the lounge. Large garden.
🛏 Q ❀ ◑ ▶ ঌ ಠ A ♣ P ✕

Edgmond

Lamb Inn
Shrewsbury Road (B5062, 1½ miles from Newport)
☎ (01952) 810421
12–2.30 (3.30 Sat), 7–11
Greenalls Mild, Davenports Bitter, Original; Tetley Bitter H
Large country pub with three bars, a dining room, a pool room and a function room, frequented by all ages. Good value food (book Sun lunch).
🛏 ❀ 🛏 ◑ ▶ 🍺 ♣ P

Ellerdine Heath

Royal Oak
1 mile off A53, 2 miles off A442 OS603226
☎ (01939) 250300
11–3, 5–11; 11–11 Fri & Sat
Brains SA; Hanby Black Magic Mild, Drawwell; Wood Parish; guest beers H
CAMRA regional *Pub of the Year* 1994. This friendly, rural pub is nicknamed the 'Tiddly', because of its small bar. Varied selection of good food at very reasonable prices (not served Mon eve or Tue lunch). Cider in summer; camping by arrangement only.
🛏 ❀ ◑ ▶ A ♣ ⏺ P

Ellesmere

White Hart
Birch Road ☎ (01691) 622333
12–3 (varies weekends), 7–11
Banks's Mild; Marston's Bitter, Pedigree H
Interesting, Grade II-listed pub in Shropshire's Lake District.
Q ❀ 🍺 ঌ A ♣ P

Gobowen

Cross Foxes

The Cross ☎ (01691) 670827
11–11
Banks's Mild; Marston's
Bitter, Pedigree H
Old, established, welcoming
village local, by the station.
Marston's Head Brewer's
Choice. Q ❀ ৬ ▲ ⇌ ♣ P

Great Ryton

Fox

E of A49 at Dorrington
OS490032 ☎ (01743) 718499
12–3, 7 (6.30 summer)–11
Draught Bass; guest beers H
One main, L-shaped bar, plus
a restaurant. This pub's
slightly elevated position
affords good views towards
the South Shropshire hills.
Two guest beers most of year,
but generally just one in
winter. Supper licence.
❀ ◑ ▶ ♣ P

Heathton

Old Gate Inn

Between Bobbington and
Claverley OS813924
☎ (01746) 710431
12–3, 7–11; 12–3 (2.30 winter), 7–10.30
Sun
Enville Ale; HP&D Entire;
Tetley Bitter; guest beer H
Busy, popular, 16th-century
country pub with excellent
food (outstanding puddings).
The outdoor area features a
barbecue and a sandpit.
Still the only HP&D inn in
Shropshire.
🏠 ❀ ◑ ▶ ⊟ P

Hengoed

Last Inn

3 miles N of Oswestry, off
B4579 ☎ (01691) 659747
7–11; 12–3, 7–10.30 Sun
Draught Bass; Whitbread
Boddingtons Bitter; Wood
Special; guest beers H
Rural pub with separate
family and games rooms. Sun
lunch is served, but no food
Tue eve. Weston's cider on
gravity. 🏠 Q ⛻ ◑ ▶ ৬ ⌂ P

Hopesgate

Stables Inn

Off A488 ☎ (01743) 891344
11.30–2.30, 7–11; closed Mon
Felinfoel Double Dragon;
Tetley Bitter; Wood Wallop;
guest beer H
Outstanding pub offering
lovely views of the hills, and a
warm atmosphere. Excellent
meals in the dining room. The

attractively furnished bar
features a massive log fire. Eve
meals Wed–Sat.
🏠 Q ❀ ◑ ▶ P

Jackfield

Boat Inn

☎ (01952) 882178
12–3, 6–11 (12–2.30, 7–11 winter)
Banks's Mild, Bitter E
Cosy, compact, riverside pub.
Note the original
Coalbrookdale range and the
flood level markers on the
door. Access across the river is
via a footbridge. Good value
food; Weston's cider.
🏠 Q ❀ ◑ ▶ ▲ ♣ ⌂ P

Linley Brook

Pheasant Inn

Britons Lane (off B4373)
☎ (01746) 762260
12–2.30, 6.30 (7 winter)–11
Hook Norton Mild; Mitchell's
Best Bitter; guest beers H
Two-roomed pub in an
attractive, rural setting: well
worth finding for its cosy
lounge and good food. Two
guest beers. Children are only
allowed in the garden.
🏠 Q ❀ ◑ ▶ ⊟ ৬ ♣

Little Stretton

Green Dragon

☎ (01694) 722925
11–3 (extends summer weekends),
6–11
Wadworth 6X; Whitbread
Boddingtons Mild, Bitter;
Wood Parish H
Well-appointed pub in idyllic
surroundings, at the foot of
Ashes Hollow, which leads on
to the Long Mynd walking
area. 🏠 Q ❀ ◑ ▶ ▲ P

Ludlow

Bull Hotel

14 Bull Ring ☎ (01584) 873611
11–11
Banks's Mild; Marston's
Bitter, Pedigree H
Do not be fooled by the plain
front of this classic coaching
inn (the original was
destroyed by fire in 1795), as
through the arch is the half-
timbering of the Tudor era.
One long bar with various
corners and levels. Host of the
Ludlow Fringe Festival.
Marston's Head Brewer's
Choice. 🏠 ❀ ◑ ▶ ⇌

Church Inn

Buttercross ☎ (01584) 872174
11–11
Ruddles County; Webster's
Yorkshire Bitter; guest beers
(summer) H

Tucked away in Ludlow's
pedestrian area, on one of the
town's most ancient sites, this
upmarket inn stands near the
church of St Lawrence, the
largest and most majestic in
Shropshire. Q 🛏 ◑ ▶ ⇌

Newport

Shakespeare Inn

Upper Bar ☎ (01952) 811924
11–11
Draught Bass; Banks's Mild;
S&N Theakston Best Bitter,
XB, Old Peculier; guest
beer H
Old, single-bar, market town
pub, frequented by all ages.
Excellent floral display in
spring and summer. Pool
room. P

Oldwoods

Romping Cat

Near Bowmere Heath
☎ (01939) 290273
12–3 (not Fri), 7–11; 12–2, 7–10.30 Sun
Whitbread Castle Eden Ale;
guest beers H
A genuine welcome is always
found at this homely country
pub which has a reputation as
a supporter of charities. Q ♣

Oswestry

Golden Lion

Upper Church Street
☎ (01691) 653747
12–3, 6.30–11
Marston's Bitter, Pedigree H
Cosy, long-established local
with an attractive garden, an
outlet for Marston's Head
Brewer's Choice. No food
Mon. Q ❀ ◑ ▶ ♣ P

Priest Weston

Miners Arms

OS293973 ☎ (0193 872) 352
11–3, 6–11
Bass Worthington BB,
Draught Bass H
Remote, classic country pub,
still largely unspoilt. It draws
walkers visiting the nearby
stone circle. The well can be
viewed en route to the toilet.
Folk singing on the first Wed
of the month; annual folk
festival. 🏠 ❀ ◑ ▶ ♣ ⌂ P

Selattyn

Cross Keys

Ceiriog Road (B4579)
☎ (01691) 650247
Hours vary (please phone)
Banks's Mild, Bitter H
17th-century gem of a village
pub with various rooms, just
off Offa's Dyke footpath.
🏠 Q ⛻ ❀ 🛏 ৬ ▲ ♣ P

Shropshire

Shatterford

Red Lion
Bridgnorth Road (A442)
☎ (01299) 861221
11.30–2.30, 6.30–11
Banks's Mild, Bitter E**; Draught Bass; Batham Best Bitter; guest beers** H
Friendly roadside inn with an oak-beamed lounge, and a dining room at the rear. Wheelchair access and toilet facilities are available through the dining room. One car park is in Worcestershire.
🏨 ❀ ◗ ▶ ☖ & P ⊬

Shifnal

Old Bell
Church Street
☎ (01952) 463300
12–3, 5.30–11
Draught Bass; Stones Best Bitter; guest beers H
16th-century coaching inn, with a dining room and two bars. Two doors from Little Nell's curiosity shop. Open all day Sun for food.
❀ ⋈ ◗ ▶ ⇌ ♣ P

White Hart
High Street
☎ (01952) 461161
12–3, 6–11; 11–11 Fri & Sat
Ansells Bitter, Mild; Enville Ale; Ind Coope Burton Ale; guest beers H
Highly regarded black and white, half-timbered, oak-beamed, 16th-century coaching inn. Cosy and very friendly, it sports seven handpumps, offering three guest beers. Good food selection.
Q ❀ ◗ ☖ ⇌ ♣ P

Shrewsbury

Albion Vaults
Castle Foregate
☎ (01743) 354906
11–3, 5.30–11; 11–11 summer
Burtonwood Mild, Bitter, Top Hat H
Former Ansells pub opposite the station, displaying some Shrewsbury in steam photos. Home-cooked meals finish at 7.30.
Q ⋈ ◗ ▶ ⇌ ♣ ⊬

Castle Vaults
16 Castle Gates
☎ (01743) 358807
11.30–3, 6–11; 11–11 Sat; 7–10.30 Sun, closed Sun lunch
Marston's Pedigree; Ruddles Best Bitter; guest beers H
Free house in the shadow of the castle, specialising in home-cooked Mexican food, served in an open bar area (no meals Sun). Up to six guest beers are constantly changing. Occasional beer festivals held. Roof garden.
🏨 Q ❀ ⋈ ◗ ▶ ⇌ ♨

Coach & Horses
Swan Hill
☎ (01743) 365661
10.30–11
Draught Bass; guest beers H
Unspoilt, Victorian pub in a quiet part of town. The bar is wood-panelled, with a partitioned area at the side; the lounge is used as a restaurant, 12–3 daily. Two, changing guest beers. Q ❀ ◗ ⇌

Dolphin
48 St Michaels Street
☎ (01743) 350419
12–3, 5.30–11; 12–11 Fri & Sat
Beer range varies H
Early Victorian, gaslit drinking house, with a porticoed entrance. Up to six hand-pulled beers are served; no lager, even in bottles. No under-21s. Q ⇌ ♣

Loggerheads
Church Street
☎ (01743) 355457
10.30–11
Draught Bass; M&B Mild; Stones Best Bitter; guest beer H
Cosy, side-street pub with four rooms; one has a shove-ha'penny board and strong sporting links. Don't miss the room on the left with its scrubbed-top tables and high-backed settles, formerly for men only. No food Sun.
Q ◗ & ⇌ ♣

Nags Head
Wyle Cop
☎ (01743) 362455
11–11
Beer range varies H
Often lively, historic house with considerable architectural interest, including lots of wood mouldings. Reputed to be haunted. Three or four beers from Carlsberg-Tetley stocked. Jetty at the rear.
❀ ⇌ ♣

Proud Salopian
Smithfield Road (50 yds from Welsh Bridge)
☎ (01743) 236887
11–11; 7–10.30 Sun, closed Sun lunch
Draught Bass; Whitbread Boddingtons Bitter; guest beers H
Set across a busy road from the River Severn, which has the beer floating at times of high flood. Thomas Southam—the Shrewsbury brewer—was the actual Proud Salopian. Five guest beers are available, including a mild.
◗ & ⇌ ♣

Three Fishes
4 Fish Street ☎ (01743) 344793
11.30–11
Morland Old Speckled Hen; Taylor Landlord; Whitbread Boddingtons Bitter, Flowers Original; guest beers H
Timber-framed building set among other buildings of the same era in a narrow side street. Recently refurbished to include more timberwork in its one room. ◗ ⊬

Stottesdon

Fox & Hounds
High Street (3 miles off B4363 at Billingsley)
☎ (0174 632) 222
12–3 (not Mon–Fri), 7–11
Fox & Hounds Wust Bitter, Bostin, Gobstopper; guest beers H
Small brew pub at the heart of the county. The skittle alley at the rear is for hire; quoits also played. Lunches served Sat.
🏨 ▲ ♣ P

Telford: *Coalbrookdale*

Coalbrookdale Inn
12 Wellington Road
☎ (01952) 433953
12–3, 6–11
Cannon Royall Millward's Musket Mild; Courage Directors; guest beers H
Lively local, close to the Museum of Iron, offering an extensive range of guest beers on seven handpumps (over 400 by 1993). Good welcome. Local CAMRA *Pub of the Year* 1993. Excellent home-cooked meals (not served Sun; eves until 8pm).
🏨 ❀ ◗ ▶ ♣ P

Dawley

Three Crowns Inn
Hinkshay Road (off B4373 at Finger Rd garage)
☎ (01952) 590868
11–3 (4 Fri & Sat), 6.30–11
Marston's Bitter, Pedigree H
Small, town pub with a U-shaped lounge, part of which is given over to darts and pool. Friendly, relaxed atmosphere. Marston's Head Brewer's Choice. ❀ ◗ ♣ P

Horsehay

Travellers Joy
Woodhouse Lane OS673069
☎ (01952) 501802
12–3, 7 (6.30 summer)–11
Draught Bass; Hook Norton Old Hooky; M&B Highgate Dark; Stones Best Bitter; guest beers H

Family-owned free house, with a comfortable, open-plan interior and a sheltered garden. Good value food at all sessions (except Sun eve). A warm welcome is extended to well-behaved children. Two guest beers change regularly.
🏠 ⚜ 🛏 🕽 ♣ P

Ironbridge

Crown Inn

10 Hodge Bower (off A4169 Madeley Hill; follow Belmont Rd) ☎ (01952) 433128
12–3, 7–11
Banks's Mild, Bitter E
Traditional local in a scenic spot above the historic Ironbridge gorge, offering good food (eve meals Mon and Tue are for pre-booked parties only). The silverware testifies to the popularity of the games room. ⚜ 🕽 🌢 ♣ P

Golden Ball

1 Newbridge Road (up A4169, Madeley Hill, ½ mile, 1st right into Jockey Bank)
☎ (01952) 432179
12–3, 6–11 (12–11 summer Sat)
Draught Bass; Courage Directors; Ruddles Best Bitter; John Smith's Bitter; guest beer H
Multi-roomed pub on different levels, great for intimate liaisons or group meetings. Very good, international menu. Originally a brewhouse, it has kept a licence and the same name since 1728, with a number of original features intact. 🏠 ⚜ 🛏 🕽 🌢 ♣ P

Horse & Jockey

15 Jockey Bank (½ mile up Madeley Hill, A4169)
☎ (01952) 433798
12–3, 6.30–11
Bass Worthington BB, Draught Bass; guest beer H
Two-roomed pub comprising a small bar and a larger lounge catering for diners. It features a wealth of beams and breweriana, testifying to the demise of many British breweries. ⚜ 🕽 🌢 ♣

Ketley Bank

Lord Hill Inn

Main Road (off A442/B5061 or Greyhound interchange)
☎ (01952) 613070
12–2.30 (3 Sat), 7 (5 Thu & Fri)–11
Draught Bass; Hook Norton Best Bitter; Mansfield Riding Mild; guest beers H
Pub fronted by a conservatory, part of which is a new family room. Very popular, but the atmosphere can be smoky when crowded. Occasional beer festivals. The village

bakery and mortuary were contained in the cellars.
🏠 ⚜ ⚜ 🛏 🗲 (Oakengates)
♣ P ⚞

Leegomery

Malt Shovel Inn

Hadley Park Road (off A442 at Leegomery roundabout)
☎ (01952) 242963
12–3, 5–11
Banks's Mild; Marston's Bitter, Pedigree H
Two-roomed pub: a small bar and a comfortable lounge, which gives the impression of someone's front room. Bar lunches Mon–Fri. A Marston's Head Brewer's Choice outlet.
🏠 Q 🕽 🍺 ♣ P

Madeley

All Nations

Coalport Road
☎ (01952) 585747
12–3 (4 Sat), 7–11
All Nations Pale Ale H
One-bar pub overlooking Blists Hill Museum; one of the four brew pubs left before the modern resurgence. Always popular, not least because of its prices, with no other draught products available. Accessed by the road opposite the museum. ⚜ 🌢 ♣ P

Muxton

Shropshire

Muxton Lane (signed off A518, Telford–Newport road)
OS724133 ☎ (01952) 677866
11–11
Bass Worthington BB, Draught Bass; M&B Highgate Dark; guest beer H
Comfortable, informal bar where families are welcome, serving a golf and leisure complex. Games area; regular entertainment in a marquee. Good value food. One guest beer changes frequently.
Q ⚜ 🕽 🍺 ♣ P ⚞

Oakengates

Duke of York

Market Street
☎ (01952) 612741
11–11
Banks's Mild, Bitter; Draught Bass; Ruddles County H
Busy, lively, two-bar, main street pub. ⚜ 🍺 🍺 🛵
🗲 (Oakengates) ♣ P

St Georges

Albion Inn

Station Hill
☎ (01952) 614193
12–3 (4.30 Sat), 5 (7 Sat)–11

Marston's Bitter, Pedigree H
Well-restored pub in Victorian style, complete with a black-leaded range, stencilled ceiling and period furnishings. Good food. An outlet for Marston's Head Brewer's Choice. ⚜ 🛏
🕽 🗲 (Oakengates) ♣ P

Upper Farmcote

Lion O'Morfe

Off Bridgnorth–Stourbridge road; follow signs for Claverley
☎ (01746) 710678
11.30–2.30 (4 Sat), 7–11
Banks's Mild, Bitter E;
Draught Bass; guest beers H
Country pub with a lounge, a small bar, a pool room and a no smoking conservatory (families welcome). Very popular, it serves excellent food (eve meals Mon–Thu until 9pm). Function room.
🏠 ⚜ 🛏 🕽 🍺 ♣ P ⚞

Welsh Frankton

Narrow Boat Inn

Ellesmere Road
☎ (01691) 661051
11–3, 7–11
Tetley Bitter; guest beers H
Welcoming pub beside the Shropshire Union (Llangollen) Canal. Three real ales are always available.
⚜ 🕽 🌢 P

Wenlock Edge

Wenlock Edge Inn

Hilltop (B4371)
☎ (0174 656) 403
12–2.30, 7–11; closed Mon
Hobsons Best Bitter; Robinson's Bitter; Webster's Yorkshire Bitter; guest beer H
Good atmosphere in a welcoming, family-run pub on top of the beautiful Wenlock Edge. Children are welcome if eating; all food is freshly prepared and home-cooked.
🏠 Q ⚜ 🕽 🍺 P

Yorton

Railway

OS505239 ☎ (01939) 28240
11.30–3, 6–11
Whitbread Castle Eden Ale; Wood Parish, Special; guest beer H
Pub owned by the same family for many years, which is reflected in the unchanging atmosphere, much appreciated by the locals. This friendly, simple bar, with a large front lounge, lies by the recently reprieved station.
🏠 Q ⚜ 🗲 ♣ P

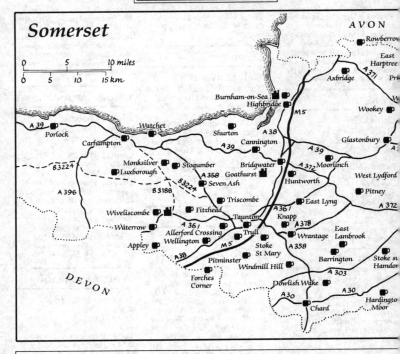

Somerset

0   5   10 miles
0   5   10   15 km

AVON

Rowberro

East Harptree

Axbridge

Pri

Wookey

Burnham-on-Sea
Highbridge

M5

Glastonbury

A

Porlock
A 39
Watchet
Shurton
Cannington
A 38
A 39

Carhampton

B3224
Monksilver
Luxborough
Stogumber
A 358
Bridgwater
Goathurst
Seven Ash
A 372
Moorlinch
West Lydford
Pitney

Wiveliscombe
A 396
B 3188
A 36 /
B3224
Triscombe
Huntworth
East Lyng
A 372
Fitzhead
Taunton
Knapp
A 378
East Lambrook
A 361
Waterrow
Allerford Crossing
Trull
Wrantage
A 358
Appley
Wellington
M5
Stoke St Mary
Barrington
Stoke su Hamdon
A 38
Pitminster
Windmill Hill
A 303
Forches Corner
Dowlish Wake
A 30
Hardingto Moor
A 30
Chard

DEVON

Ash Vine, Trudoxhill; **Berrow**, Burnham-on-Sea; **Bridgwater**, Goathurst; **Cotleigh**, Wiveliscombe; **Cottage**, West Lydford; **Exmoor**, Wiveliscombe; **Oakhill**, Oakhill

---

Allerford Crossing

Victory Inn
(½ mile S of B3227) OS182249
☎ (01823) 461282
11–3, 6–11
Cotleigh Tawny; Hall & Woodhouse Tanglefoot; Morland Old Speckled Hen; Ringwood Fortyniner; John Smith's Bitter; Wadworth 6X; guest beers H
Large pub which caters for all tastes with usually 11 real ales served. Good value food can be enjoyed either in the restaurant or in one of the several bar areas. Two gardens, one ideal for families, with a play area, some animals and a purpose-built family room. Cider in summer.
🏨 Q 🌲 🏠 ◑ ▶ ♣ ⇔ P ⅍

Appley

Globe Inn
2½ miles N of A38 at White Ball Hill OS071215
☎ (01823) 672327

11–3 (not Mon), 6.30–11
Cotleigh Tawny; Furgusons Dartmoor Best Bitter H
Fascinating old pub, well worth finding. The bar is a hatchway in a flagstoned corridor, with several comfortable rooms leading off in all directions. Large beer garden and car park. Good value food every day. Campsite opposite. Skittles played.
🏨 Q 🌲 🏠 ◑ ▶ ▲ ♣ ⇔ P

Axbridge

Lamb Inn
The Square
☎ (01934) 732253
11.30–2.30 (3 Sat), 6.30–11
Draught Bass; Butcombe Bitter; Wadworth 6X; guest beer H
Rambling pub, now owned by Butcombe, opposite King John's hunting lodge. Large terraced garden; the unusual bar is made of bottles. Well worth a visit. Thatcher's cider.
Q 🏠 🍴 ◑ ▶ 🍺 ⅙ ▲ ♣ ⇔

Barrington

Royal Oak
Off B3168 ☎ (01460) 53455
12–2.30 (not winter Mon), 6.30–11; 12–11 Sat
Berrow 4Bs; guest beers H
Old stone pub in a pretty village; CAMRA Somerset *Pub of the Year 1994*, situated a couple of miles from the A303. Up to six guest beers are available at any time, along with a good range of continental beers and malt whiskies. The good value tasty food makes it popular with locals and visitors alike. Try it!
🏨 Q 🏠 ◑ ▶ 🍺 ⅙ ♣ ⇔ P

Bridgwater

Commercial Inn
Redgate Street (near station)
☎ (01278) 426989
11–2.30, 7–11; 12–2.30, 7–10.30 Sun
Butcombe Bitter; Whitbread Boddingtons Bitter, Flowers IPA; guest beer H
Modernised, popular local with a bar area (pool table)

plus a lounge and a skittle alley. ❀ ◗ ⑃ ⇌ ♣ P

Fountain Inn

1 West Quay (near Town Bridge) ☎ (01278) 424115
11.30 (11 Fri & Sat)–3, 6.30–11
Butcombe Bitter; Hall & Woodhouse Tanglefoot; Wadworth IPA, 6X, Farmer's Glory; guest beers H
Enlarged, one-bar local, newly decorated with bric-a-brac. It attracts a good mix of ages and has a good atmosphere. No food Sun. ◗ ⑃ ⇌ ♣

Bruton

Blue Ball

2 Coombe Street (A359)
☎ (01749) 812315
11–2.30 (3.30 Sat), 5.30–11
Marston's Pedigree; Smiles Best Bitter; guest beer (occasional)
Pub with a thriving public bar with character, plus a quiet, comfortable lounge.
🚲 Q ⇌ ◗ ▶ ⑃ ⇌ ♣ ⇌

Burnham-on-Sea

Royal Clarence Hotel

31 The Esplanade
☎ (01278) 783138
11–11
RCH PG Steam, Pitchfork, Old Slug Porter, East St Cream, Firebox; guest beers H
Large seafront hotel with its own brewery (not now on

---

site). Guest beers are always available, plus the range of RCH brews. Beer festivals held each Feb and Oct.
Q ⇌ ❀ ⇌ ◗ ▶ ⑃ ⇌ 🚶 ♣ P

Cannington

Malt Shovel

Blackmore Lane (off A39)
☎ (01278) 653432
11.30–3, 6.30–11
Butcombe Bitter; John Smith's Bitter; guest beers H
Warm and friendly pub on the outskirts of the village, with a cosy, wood-panelled bar and a relaxing lounge. Skittles played but no electronic music or games, etc. Lane's and Rich's cider.
🚲 Q ⇌ ❀ ⇌ ◗ ▶ 🚶 ♣ ⇌ P

Carhampton

Butchers Arms

On A39 ☎ (01643) 821333
11–3, 6–11; 11–11 Sat
Cotleigh Tawny; Ushers Best Bitter; Wadworth 6X H
Village local offering a good range of games and activities, the only pub in West Somerset that carries on the ancient tradition of wassailing apples for cider making. Rich's cider sold. Recommended for families, with good children's activities. Pets welcome.
🚲 Q ⇌ ❀ ⇌ ◗ ▶ ⑃ 🚶 ♣ ⇌ P

Castle Cary

Horse Pond

The Triangle ☎ (01963) 350318
10.30–2.30, 5.30–11
Courage Best Bitter; Marston's Pedigree; John Smith's Bitter; guest beer H
Large, simply-furnished town pub with several rooms, including a separate games room. Live music Sat nights. No eve meals Mon.
🚲 ⇌ ❀ ⇌ ◗ ▶ ⑃ ♣ ⇌ P

Chard

Old White Horse

15 Silver Street
☎ (01460) 62201
11–3 (3.30 Sat), 5 (6.30 Sat)–11; 11–11 Fri
Wadworth 6X; guest beers H
Pub offering wood-panelled, walk-through bar areas, including a snug. Pool, darts and quiz nights, plus live music on the last Sat of each month. No food Sun. Burrow Hill cider.
🚲 Q ❀ ◗ ▶ ⑃ ⇌ P

Chelynch

Poacher's Pocket

½ mile N of A361 at Doulting
☎ (01749) 880220

11.30 (12 Mon)–2.30, 6.15 (6 Sat)–11
Butcombe Bitter; Oakhill Best Bitter; Wadworth 6X; guest beer H
Part-14th-century pub in a small village, mostly given over to food, but remaining popular as a locals' drinking pub. The large garden is well-patronised on summer weekends. Wilkins cider.
🚲 Q ❀ ◗ ▶ ♣ ⇌ P

Corton Denham

Queens Arms Inn

3 miles S of A303
☎ (01963) 220317
12–2.30 (3 summer), 6.30 (7 Mon)–11
Bridgwater Coppernob; Exmoor Ale; guest beers H
Comfortable, rural pub in superb walking country. It features guest traditional ciders and a chalkboard listing guest ales of the month, plus a good choice of specials on the food menu.
🚲 Q ❀ ⇌ ◗ ▶ 🚶 🚶 ⇌ P

Dowlish Wake

New Inn

☎ (01460) 52413
11–3, 6–11
Butcombe Bitter; S&N Theakston Old Peculier; Wadworth 6X H
Popular village pub with two bars and a good-sized garden which caters for families. A good range of home-cooked food includes Swiss specialities. Near Perry's cider farm. 🚲 Q ⇌ ❀ ⇌ ◗ ▶
⑃ ♣ ⇌ P

East Harptree

Castle of Comfort

On B3134, ½ mile N of B3135
☎ (01761) 221321
12–2.30, 7–11
Draught Bass; Butcombe Bitter; guest beers (weekends) H
Stone-built coaching inn on the former Roman road. Two bars serve up to four ales (over 250 beers to date). Ask the landlord about the real ale ghost. Good value food; live music Fri. Q ❀ ◗ ▶ ♣ P

East Lambrook

Rose & Crown

Off A303 ☎ (01460) 240433
11.30–2.30, 7.30–11
Bass Worthington BB; M&B Highgate Dark; Otter Bitter; guest beers H
Cosy, oak-beamed, traditional, two-bar village pub, one of the few in Somerset to stock a permanent traditional mild. Good value food; Burrow Hill cider. 🚲 Q ⇌ ❀ ◗ ▶ 🚶 🚶 ♣ ⇌ P

Somerset

East Lyng

Rose & Crown
On A361 ☎ (01823) 698235
11–2.30, 6.30–11
Butcombe Bitter; Eldridge Pope Hardy Country, Royal Oak H
Old whitewashed pub on the A361, in the centre of this hamlet, with a comfortable and civilised atmosphere. The bar is full of antique furniture, old prints and sofas. A small restaurant area leads off to one side. The attractive garden is a blaze of colour in summer.
🏚 Q ⌘ 🛏 ◑ ▶ & ♣ P

Emborough

Old Down Inn
At A37/B3139 jct
☎ (01761) 232398
11.30–3, 7–11
Draught Bass H
Atmospheric coaching inn, circa 1640, with a diversity of rooms and old furniture. It was burnt down in 1886, but fortunately rebuilt! No food Sun. Campsite opposite.
🏚 Q 🛏 ◑ ▶ ▲ ♣ P

Faulkland

Tucker's Grave Inn
On A366, 1 mile E of village.
☎ (01373) 834230
11–2.30, 6–11
Draught Bass; Butcombe Bitter G
The burial site of a suicide in 1747, a former cottage that has doubled as an inn for over 200 years. Three old-fashioned rooms without a bar counter; the barrels sit in the centre room. The story of the unfortunate Edward Tucker can be found above the parlour. Cheddar Valley cider.
🏚 Q ⌘ 🎱 ▲ ♣ ⌂ P

Fitzhead

Fitzhead Inn
Off B3227 ☎ (01823) 400667
12–3, 7–11
Cotleigh Tawny; guest beers H
Cosy village pub with a growing reputation for good quality and good value food. Usually three guest beers available, plus Bollhayes cider.
🏚 Q ⌘ ◑ ▶ & ♣ ⌂

Forches Corner

Merry Harriers
OS182171
☎ (01823) 421270
12–2.30, 6.30–11
Exmoor Gold; Hall & Woodhouse Badger Best

Bitter (summer), **Tanglefoot** (summer); **Otter Bitter** H
Isolated, but friendly old inn on the Somerset/Devon border, high on the Blackdown Hills. Brass abounds. Regular live music. The large garden has a children's play area and the pub has its own campsite (caravans welcome).
🏚 ⌘ 🛏 ◑ ▶ & ▲ ♣ ⌂ P

Glastonbury

Who'd A Thought It
17 Northload Street
☎ (01458) 834460
11–2.30, 6–11; 12–2.30, 7–10.30 Sun
Draught Bass; Eldridge Pope Hardy Country, Blackdown Porter; Palmers IPA H
Town-centre free house with a warm, friendly atmosphere, decorated with pre-war railway and rural artefacts. Live music fortnightly; good food. Wheelchair WC.
🏚 Q ⌘ 🛏 ◑ ▶ & ▲ P

Hardington Moor

Royal Oak
Moor Lane (follow signs from Yeovil to Crewkerne and A30 to Hardington)
☎ (01935) 862354
12–3 (not Mon), 7–11
Bateman XXXB; Butcombe Bitter; guest beer H
Former farmhouse offering a warm and friendly atmosphere in a rural setting. A large choice of snacks and meals, plus Taunton Traditional and Bridge Farm cider are usually available. Camping by arrangement.
🏚 Q ⌘ ◑ ▶ ▲ ♣ ⌂ P

Highbridge

Coopers Arms
24 Market Street (by station)
☎ (01278) 783562
11–3, 5.15–11; 12–3, 7.30–10.30 Sun
Palmers IPA; guest beers E
Modernised pub with two lounge areas and a public bar with darts and a skittle alley. The beers are listed on chalkboards (usually six available). Coopers Brue and Best are house beers (origin unknown). ⌘ 🎱 ⇌ ♣ P

Huntworth

Boat & Anchor
½ mile from M5 jct 24
☎ (01278) 662473
11.30–3.30, 6.30–11; 11–11 Sat
Cotleigh Tawny; Eldridge Pope Hardy Country; RCH East St Cream H
Canalside, family-owned, rural free house where the large,

pleasant garden has a children's play area.
🏚 Q ⌘ 🛏 ◑ ▶ & ♣ P

Knapp

Rising Sun Inn
Off A361, then follow pub signs OS301254
☎ (01823) 490436
11–2.30, 6.30–11
Draught Bass; Exmoor Ale; Whitbread Boddingtons Bitter H
15th-century inn: a fine example of a Somerset longhouse with many original features, including two inglenooks. The winner of many national awards for its extensive fish menu, it has a busy weekend food trade (eve meals also in the restaurant). No food Sun eve. Local cider in summer.
🏚 Q ⌂ ⌘ 🛏 ◑ ▶ ▲ ⌂ P

Leigh upon Mendip

Bell
High Street ☎ (01373) 812316
12–3, 7–11
Butcombe Bitter; Oakhill Best Bitter; Wadworth 6X H
Much altered and extended village inn, now comfortably furnished, with an emphasis on the food trade. (Separate restaurant but food is served throughout the pub.) Friendly locals' atmosphere at the bar.
🏚 ⌘ ◑ ▶ P

Luxborough

Royal Oak of Luxborough
☎ (01984) 40319
11–2.30, 6–11
Bateman XXXB; Cotleigh Tawny; Exmoor Gold G**; Whitbread Flowers IPA; guest beers** H
Rural gem, set deep in a fold of the Brendon Hills and known locally as the Blazing Stump. Folk club Fri; quiz Tue. Good home-made food; Rich's and Cheddar Valley cider.
🏚 Q ⌘ ⌂ ◑ ▶ ▲ ♣ ⌂ P

Monksilver

Notley Arms
On B3288 ☎ (01984) 56217
11.30–2.30, 6.30–11
Courage Directors; Exmoor Ale; Ushers Best Bitter; Wadworth 6X H
Village pub in a very rural spot, a centre for walking the Brendon Hills. Noted locally for its award-winning food, large, child-friendly garden and family room. Thatcher's

cider in summer. Closed first two weeks in Feb.
🏚 Q ㅎ ⊛ ◑ ▯ ⚲ ♣ ⌒ P

Moorlinch

Ring of Bells

Pit Hay Lane
☎ (01458) 210358
12–2 (not Mon), 7–11; 12–11 Sat
Draught Bass; Bridgwater Coppernob; Oakhill Best Bitter; guest beers H
Lively, friendly village local with two large rooms: a quiet lounge and a busy games room. Situated near the local vineyard. At least two guest beers are usually available, plus Wilkins cider. Good food.
🏚 Q ⊛ ◑ ▯ A ♣ ⌒ P

Try also: **King William**, Catcott (Free)

Nettlebridge

Nettlebridge Inn

On A367, 1 mile N of Oakhill
☎ (01749) 841360
11.30–2.30, 6–11
Oakhill Best Bitter, Black Magic, Yeoman H
Big roadside pub in a pretty valley on the edge of the Mendips. It serves as the brewery tap for the nearby Oakhill brewery. Priority is given to good value food in the single, large main bar.
⊛ ㅁ ◑ ▯ P

North Brewham

Old Red Lion

On Maiden Bradley–Bruton road OS722368
☎ (01749) 850287
12–2.30, 6–11
Butcombe Bitter; guest beer H
Stone-built former farmhouse in an isolated rural setting. The bar is in the old dairy, with flagged floors. Two regular guest beers, plus Thatcher's cider.
🏚 Q ⊛ ◑ ▯ ♣ ⌒ P

Norton St Philip

Fleur de Lys

High Street (B3110)
☎ (01373) 834333
11–2.30, 5–11; 11–11 Sat
Bass Charrington IPA, Draught Bass; Oakhill Best Bitter; Wadworth 6X H
Ancient stone building, parts of which may date from the 13th century, which has undergone extensive, but mainly sympathetic, refurbishment. Unfortunately, the resited bar now blocks the old passageway through which the pub ghost was said to pass.
🏚 Q ㅎ ⊛ ◑ ▯ ♣ P

Pitminster

Queens Arms

Off B3170, at Corfe
☎ (01823) 421529
11–3, 5–11
Draught Bass; Cotleigh Tawny; guest beers H
Very popular village pub with two bars and a function room/bar. It normally stocks five guest beers, plus a good range of food (vegetarian dishes a speciality). Cider in summer.
🏚 Q ⊛ ㅁ ◑ ▯ ▯ A ♣ ⌒ P

Pitney

Halfway House

On B3153 ☎ (01458) 252513
11.30–3, 5.30–11
Butcombe Bitter; Cotleigh Tawny G; **Oakhill Best Bitter** H; **guest beers** G
Old village pub: real fires, flagstone floors and rudimentary wooden furniture. It always has six–nine beers available most from South-West micros. Try the home-cooked curries (no food Sun). Dogs and children welcome. A real gem.
🏚 Q ㅎ ⊛ ◑ ▯ ♣ P

Try also: **Rose & Crown**, Huish Episcopi (Free)

Porlock

Ship Inn

High Street
☎ (01643) 862507
10.30–3, 5.30–11
Draught Bass; Cotleigh Old Buzzard; Courage Best Bitter; guest beer (summer) H
13th-century thatched inn mentioned in *Lorna Doone*, within walking distance of the sea and moor. With its old bar, a stone floor and a log fire, it is a pub for conversation (no piped music). Separate games room. Vegetarian meals and Perry's cider available.
🏚 Q ㅎ ⊛ ㅁ ◑ ▯ A ♣ ⌒ P

Priddy

New Inn

☎ (01749) 676465
11.30 (12 Mon)–2.30, 7–11; 12–2.30, 7–10.30 Sun
Draught Bass; Eldridge Pope Hardy Country; Wadworth 6X H
15th-century farmhouse on the village green, with flagged bars: a warm and friendly pub, enjoying a reputation for good food, including a choice of vegetarian meals. Popular at weekends. Wilkins cider.
🏚 ⊛ ㅁ ◑ ▯ ▯ ▯ ▯ ♣ ⌒ P

Rode

Bell Inn

13 Frome Road (A361)
☎ (01373) 830356
11–3, 6–11
Nethergate IPA, Bitter, Old Growler H
Two-bar pub, converted from several cottages. The restaurant specialises in seafood.
🏚 Q ⊛ ◑ ▯ ▯ ♣ P

Rowberrow

Swan Inn

☎ (01934) 852371
12–2.30, 6–11
Draught Bass; Butcombe Bitter; Wadworth 6X; guest beer H
Former cider house, converted from three stone cottages, now two bars with fake beams and a big fireplace. No food Sun.
🏚 Q ⊛ ◑ ▯ P

Rudge

Full Moon

1 mile N of A36 bypass at Standerwick OS829518
☎ (01373) 830936
12–3 (not Mon), 6–11
Draught Bass; Butcombe Bitter; Wadworth 6X H
Splendid, 300-year-old building, greatly extended in 1991, but retaining most of its original features, including stone floors. The emphasis is on the food trade, the skittle alley, families and accommodation. Country and western music Sun eve (when no food is served). 🏚 Q
ㅎ ⊛ ㅁ ◑ ▯ ▯ A ♣ ⌒ P

Seven Ash

Quantock Cottage Inn

On A358 ☎ (01823) 432467
12–3, 6–11; closed Mon, except bank hols
Bridgwater Coppernob; Cotleigh Tawny H; **guest beer** (summer)
Comfortable, family-run pub on the busy road to Minehead, with good family facilities. Cider in summer. 🏚 Q
ㅎ ⊛ ㅁ ◑ ▯ ▯ A ♣ ⌒ P

Shepton Mallet

Horseshoe Inn

Bowlish (A371, ½ mile W of centre) ☎ (01749) 342209
12–2.30, 6–11
Draught Bass; Wiltshire Stonehenge; guest beer H
Stone pub on the western outskirts of town. Much of the lounge is now set up as a

Somerset

restaurant area; for the more down-to-earth pub-goer, there is also a splendid, popular, well-equipped public bar. No food Sun eve.
🍴 ℞ ◖ ▮ ✦

Kings Arms

Leg Square ☎ (01749) 343781
11.30–2.30, 6–11
Ansells Bitter; Ind Coope Burton Ale; guest beer H
Much-altered, 17th-century pub of character in an area of town known as the Dustbowl. A pleasant courtyard/patio is sheltered on two sides by a conservatory.
❀ ⛵ ◖ ▮ ⊞ ✦ P

Shepton Montague

Montague Inn

Off A359, S of Bruton
OS675316 ☎ (01749) 813213
12–3 (not Mon–Fri), 5.30–11
Butcombe Bitter; Marston's Pedigree; guest beer (summer) G
Remote but convivial country pub. Thatcher's cider served.
🍴 Q ❀ ⌂ P

Shurton

Shurton Inn

Follow signs to Hinckley Point power station
☎ (01278) 732695
11–2.30, 6–11
Exmoor Ale; Hall & Woodhouse Badger Best Bitter; guest beer H
Lively and busy village pub with regular and varied music in the eve. A guest beer and Lane's cider are usually available. Camping for CC members.
🍴 Q ⛵ ❀ ◖ ▮ ▲ ✦ ⌂ P

Sparkford

Sparkford Inn

Off A303 ☎ (01963) 440218
11–2.30, 6.30–11
Bass Worthington BB, Draught Bass; Wadworth 6X; guest beer H
15th-century coaching inn retaining many of its original features, with separate rooms and corridors. A large function room is available, staging a country and western special at least once a month (Sat). A good family pub.
🍴 Q ⛵ ❀ ◖ ▮ ⊞ ♿ ▲ P

Stogumber

White Horse Inn

☎ (01984) 56277
11–2.30, 6–11
Cotleigh Tawny; Exmoor Ale H

Traditional pub, opposite the 12th-century church in a picturesque village. The restaurant and accommodation are in an old, adjoining market house. Sheppy's cider is available in summer. Handy for the West Somerset Railway.
🎮 Q ❀ ⛵ ◖ ▮ ♿ ▲ ✦ ⌂ P

Stoke St Mary

Half Moon

Off A358 at Henlade
☎ (01823) 442271
11 (11.30 Wed–Sat)–2.30, 6–11
S&N Theakston Best Bitter; Wadworth 6X; Whitbread Boddingtons Bitter H
Popular, renovated country pub with a stone-flagged bar and a no-smoking dining area.
Q ⛵ ❀ ◖ ▮ P

Stoke sub Hamdon

Half Moon Inn

Off A303, below Ham Hill
☎ (01935) 824890
12–2.30, 6.30–11; 12–11 Sat
Whitbread Best Bitter, Flowers Original; guest beers H
Popular village local which concentrates on real ales (always four guests). Live bands play every Sat eve (mainly blues). Local East Chinnock farmhouse cider served. Free car park nearby.
❀ ⛵ ♿ ▲ ✦ ⌂

Taunton

Masons Arms

Magdalene Street
☎ (01823) 288916
10–3, 5 (6 Sat)–11
Draught Bass; Exe Valley Dob's Best Bitter; guest beers H
Comfortable, one-bar pub with a relaxing atmosphere, situated off the main streets. Fresh food is always available, including grillstone steaks.
Q ❀ ◖ ▮ ✦

Minstrel's

Castle Bow ☎ (01823) 337780
10–3, 7–11; 10–11 Sat
Draught Bass; Eldridge Pope Hardy Country; guest beer H
Comfortable and popular, town-centre, L-shaped bar, situated under the Castle Hotel. The entrance is by the arch in Castle Bow. Live music three nights a week.
🍴 ⛵ ◖ ≉

Pen & Quill

Shuttern (opp. law courts)
☎ (01823) 256982
11–3, 5.30–11 (11–11 May–Dec)

Draught Bass; Butcombe Bitter; Whitbread Boddingtons Bitter, Flowers IPA H
Friendly, popular town pub with olde-worlde decor. Lunchtime live jazz is performed on the first Sun in the month. Annual weekend jazz festival. Q ◖ ▮ ♿

Wood Street Inn

Wood Street ☎ (01823) 333011
11–11 (may vary)
John Smith's Bitter; Wadworth 6X; guest beer H
Popular and lively, back-street pub, once tied but now a free house. Regular live bands play at weekends. The decor is basic, but there's a good atmosphere. Park opposite.
❀ ⛵ ♿ ≉ ✦

Triscombe

Blue Ball

1 mile off A358
☎ (01984) 618242
11–3, 7–11
Butcombe Bitter; Cotleigh Tawny; Exmoor Ale; Morland Old Speckled Hen H
17th-century, thatched pub at the foot of the Quantock Hills. Ideally situated for walkers, it boasts an extensive, picturesque garden. Dominoes and skittles are played; good food (no meals Sun eve). Generally busy on summer weekends.
Q ⛵ ❀ ⛵ ◖ ▮ ✦ P

Trudoxhill

White Hart

½ mile S of A361 at Nunney
Catch ☎ (01373) 836324
12–3, 7 (6.30 Fri & Sat)–11
Ash Vine Trudoxhill, Bitter, Challenger, Black Bess Porter, Tanker, Hop & Glory; guest beer H
Comfortable, open-plan village pub with exposed beams and a large fireplace. The Ash Vine brewery is at the rear. Thatcher's cider.
🍴 ❀ ◖ ▮ ⌂ P

Trull

Winchester Arms

Church Road
☎ (01823) 284723
12–3, 7 (6 summer)–11
Draught Bass; Bridgwater Coppernob; Butcombe Bitter; John Smith's Bitter; guest beer H
Busy village local with several drinking areas, serving good quality food; situated on the outskirts of Taunton. Both skittles and bar skittles are played. Q ❀ ◖ ▮ ✦ P

Upton Noble

Lamb Inn
Church Street (off A359)
☎ (01749) 850308
12–2.30, 6.30–11; closed Mon
Butcombe Bitter; guest beer H
Former 17th-century cottages, with fine views over Alfred's Tower and the surrounding countryside. No food Sun eve. Inch's cider.
♨ Q ❀ ◁ ▶ ♠ ♣ ◔ P

Watchet

West Somerset Hotel
Swain Street ☎ (01984) 634434
11–11
Cotleigh Harrier; Courage Directors; John Smith's Bitter; guest beer H
Enterprising, friendly family-run, former coaching inn serving the local community as well as tourists. Activity holidays are arranged. Situated near the West Somerset Railway station and the harbour.
♿ ❀ ⛴ ◁ ▶ ♠ ⇌ ♣

Waterrow

Rock Inn
On B3227 ☎ (01984) 623293
11–2.30, 6–11
Cotleigh Tawny; Exmoor Gold; John Smith's Bitter (summer) H
Interesting old inn, set hard against a rockface, which forms the rear wall of part of the bar area (public-style at one end with a lounge and restaurant at the other). Sheppey's cider is available in summer.
♨ Q ⛴ ◁ ▶ ♠ ♣ ◔ P

Wellington

Ship Inn
39 Mantle Street
☎ (01823) 662106
11–3, 6–11
Gibbs Mew Salisbury, Wake Ale, Deacon, Bishop's Tipple H
Friendly town local with a cosy atmosphere. Close to the local cinema, it is home to a local folk club. Skittles played.
❀ ⛴ ◁ ▶ ♿ ♣

Wells

Rose & Crown
7 St Johns Street
☎ (01749) 677556
11–3, 6.30–11
Courage Directors; John Smith's Bitter; Ushers Best Bitter, Founders H
Locals' pub just off the town centre; one of the best in town.
♨ ❀ ⊞ ♣ ◔

Wincanton

Bear Inn
12 Market Place (off A303)
☎ (01963) 32581
11–2.30, 5.30–11; 11–11 Sat
Draught Bass; Marston's Pedigree; guest beer H
Large, former coaching inn with several drinking areas, plus a substantial games and function room. Weekly archery takes place in the skittle alley. Guest beers always include a session, as well as a stronger, beer. ♨ Q ⛴ ◁ ▶ ♣ P

Windmill Hill

Square & Compass
Off A358, Ashill bypass
OS310165 ☎ (01823) 480467
11.30–2.30, 6.30–11
Draught Bass; Exmoor Ale; Whitbread Boddingtons Bitter, Flowers Original H
Pleasant country pub offering a good, varied menu, including vegetarian meals. The dining room welcomes children and there is a play area in the garden. Parking for caravans next door. Walkers welcome.
♨ Q ❀ ♿ ◁ ▶ ♠ ♣ P

Witham Friary

Seymour Arms
On minor road off B3092, by the old railway station
☎ (01749) 850742
11–3, 6–11
Ushers Best Bitter H
Old village local, unspoilt by progress, featuring a central serving hatch and a fine garden. Rich's cider is available on gravity dispense.
♨ Q ❀ ⊞ ♠ ◔

Wiveliscombe

Courtyard Hotel
10–12 High Street
☎ (01984) 623737
11.30–3, 7–11
Archers Best Bitter; Cotleigh Tawny H**; guest beers** H / G
Small, quiet bar with household furnishings, plus a new underground cellar bar which has the beers on gravity (at least four guests available). Inch's and Thatcher's cider.
Q ⛴ ◁ ▶ ◔

Wookey

Burcott Inn
☎ (01749) 673874
11–2.30 (3 Sat), 6–11
Butcombe Bitter; guest beers H
Deservedly popular, roadside pub with a friendly atmosphere, offering over 40 different guest beers per year (always two available). The L-shaped bar has a copper serving top and there is a small games room. The good-sized garden boasts an old cider press. Good quality food (no eve meals Sun or Mon).
♨ Q ♿ ❀ ◁ ▶ ♿ ♠ ♣ P

Wrantage

Canal Inn
On A372 ☎ (01823) 480210
12–3, 7–11
Exmoor Ale; Whitbread Flowers Original; guest beer H
Friendly local offering good food and an outdoor children's play area. Skittles and darts are played. Lane's local cider.
♨ ❀ ◁ ▶ ♠ ♣ ◔ P

Yeovil

Armoury
1 The Park ☎ (01935) 71047
12–2.30 (11–3 Fri & Sat), 6.30–11
Adnams Broadside; Butcombe Bitter; Wadworth 6X, Farmer's Glory; guest beer H
Lively, simply furnished town pub, formerly an armoury. Snacks and salads are available lunchtimes, Mon–Sat.
Q ❀ ◁ ♿ ♠ P

OPENING HOURS

Permitted opening hours in England and Wales are 11–11, though not all pubs choose to take advantage of the full session and many close in the afternoons. Some pubs have special licences and there are sometimes special local arrangements for market days and other events. Standard Sunday hours are 12–3, 7–10.30. Scottish licensing laws are more generous and pubs may stay open longer.

Staffordshire

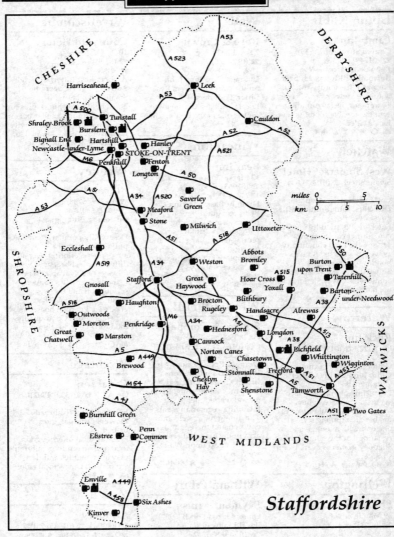

Staffordshire

 Burton Bridge, *Burton upon Trent;* **Enville,** *Enville;*
Forrester & Firkin, *Stafford;* **Lichfield,** *Lichfield;*
Marston's, *Burton upon Trent;* **Rising Sun,** *Shraley*
Brook; **Titanic,** *Burslem*

Abbots Bromley

Bagot Arms
Bagot Street (B5234)
☎ (01283) 840371
11–2.30, 6–11
Marston's Pedigree Ⓗ
18th-century coaching inn
specialising in good food (no
meals Mon). Marston's

Head Brewer's Choice beers
are stocked. ◖ ◗ P

Alrewas

George & Dragon
120 Main Street
☎ (01283) 791476
11.30–2.30 (3 Sat), 5.15–11; 12–2.30,
7–10.30 Sun

Marston's Pedigree Ⓗ
Popular village-centre inn with
a welcoming atmosphere and
a good reputation for home-
cooked meals. Marston's Head
Brewer's Choice beers are
available. Beware: Symonds
Scrumpy Jack cider is not real.
No food on Sun. No leather
jackets.
🛏 ❀ ◖ ◗ ৬ ♣ P

Barton-under-Needwood

Top Bell

Barton Gate ☎ (01283) 712510
12–3, 6–11; 12–11 Sat
**Burtonwood Bitter,
Forshaw's, Top Hat** H
Typical country pub with oak
beams, which encourages live
music Wed, Fri, Sat and Sun.
Quizzes on Tue; no food on
music nights. ♨ ⇆ ◁ ▸ ♣ P

Bignall End

Plough

Ravens Lane (½ mile E of
Audley on B5500)
☎ (01782) 720469
12–3 (6 Sat), 7–11
**Banks's Bitter; Camerons
Strongarm; Marston's
Pedigree; guest beers** H
Smart, roadside hostelry
which caters for local and
passing trade in two rooms
with a split-level lounge. Good
range of bar snacks and meals.
Constantly changing guest
beers. ❀ ◁ ▸ ♣ P

Blithbury

Bull & Spectacles

Uttoxeter Road (B5014)
☎ (0188 922) 201
12–3, 6–11
**Ind Coope Burton Ale;
Lichfield Steeplejack;
Marston's Pedigree** H
15th-century country pub near
Blithfield Reservoir. Popular
for food (not served Mon).
❀ ◁ ▸ ♣ P

Brewood

Swan

Market Square
☎ (01902) 850330
11–3, 7–11
Draught Bass H**; M&B
Highgate Dark** E**; S&N
Theakston XB; Stones Best
Bitter; guest beer** H
One-roomed, lounge pub with
mostly original wooden beams
and two snug areas. Skittle
alley upstairs, above the car
park entrance. ♨ ◁ ♣ P

Brocton

Chetwynd Arms

Cannock Road (A34)
☎ (01785) 661089
11.30–3, 5.45–11; 11–11 Sat
Banks's Mild, Bitter E**;
Camerons Strongarm;
Marston's Pedigree** H
Bustling, main-road pub at the
northwestern boundary of
Cannock Chase. No meals Sat
eve or Sun. ❀ ◁ ▸ ⊟ ♧ ♣ P

Burnhill Green

Dartmouth Arms

Snowdon Road
☎ (0174 65) 268
12–2.30, 7–11
**Ansells Bitter, Mild; Ind
Coope ABC Best Bitter,
Burton Ale; guest beer** H
Popular village pub, renowned
for its home-made meals,
served in a small restaurant
area (book at busy times; no
food Sun eve/Mon lunch).
Children's meals are served in
the garden area. The guest
beer comes from Carlsberg-
Tetley. ♨ ❀ ◁ ▸ P

Burton upon Trent

Anglesey Arms

Bearwood Hill Road, Winshill
(off A50) ☎ (01283) 564791
10.30–2.30, 5.30–11; 10.30–11 Sat;
12–2.30, 7–10.30 Sun
**Banks's Mild; Marston's
Bitter, Pedigree, Owd
Rodger** H
Popular, urban local with a
lounge and a conservatory/
family room. It boasts the
oldest bowling green in Burton
and holds regular quiz nights.
Marston's Head Brewer's
Choice. ⇆ ⊟ ♧ ♣ P

Beacon Hotel

227 Tutbury Road (A50)
☎ (01283) 568968
11–3, 6–11
Draught Bass E**; Ind Coope
Burton Ale; guest beers** H
Large, three-roomed, family-
run pub with a children's
room and a safe garden. The
landlord is a member of the
Guild of Master Cellarmen,
rare for a Bass licensee.
Q ⇆ ⊜ ⋈ ◁ ▸ ⊟ ♧ ♣ P

Blue Posts

High Street ☎ (01283) 533427
11–11; 12–2.30, 7–10.30 Sun
**Bass Worthington BB,
Draught Bass; M&B Highgate
Dark, Brew XI; Morland Old
Speckled Hen; Ruddles
County** H
A Marston's house before Bass
acquired the premises around
1886. Known as the Blue
Stumps before a refit in 1994
turned it into a 'Traditional
Ale House' with an emphasis
on cask beers. ◁

Boathouse

The Dingle (off Ferry St)
☎ (01283) 538831
12–2.30, 7–11
**Draught Bass; Greene King
Abbot; Marston's Pedigree;
Morland Old Speckled Hen;
Ruddles County; S&N
Theakston Old Peculier** H
Pub on a bank of the Trent,
beside the ferry bridge, with a

garden play area for children.
Q ❀ ◁ ▸ ♧ ▲ P

Burton Bridge Inn

24 Bridge Street (A50, by Trent
Bridge) ☎ (01283) 536596
11.30–2.15, 5.30–11; 12–2, 7–10.30
Sun
**Burton Bridge Summer Ale,
XL, Bridge Bitter, Porter, Top
Dog Stout, Festival; guest
beer** H
Small, friendly, brewery tap
where no music or machines
detract from the fine beers
brewed here. Wooden pews,
award-covered walls and good
conversation prevail. No food
Sun. Q ◁ ♣

Cooper's Tavern

Cross Street (off Station St)
☎ (01283) 532551
12–2.30, 5 (7 Sat)–11
**Draught Bass; Hardys &
Hansons Best Mild** G**, Best
Bitter** H**, Kimberley
Classic** G**; Marston's
Pedigree** H
Former Bass Brewery annexe,
now a traditional ale house
with a renowned tap room—
note the stillage casks, barrel
tables and the 'top bench' seat.
A must for visitors.
Q ◁ ⇌ ♣

Derby Inn

18 Derby Road
☎ (01283) 543674
11–3, 5.30–11
Marston's Pedigree H
Small, busy pub with a
comfortable lounge. Fresh
vegetables on sale. ❀ ♣ P

Duke of York

Victoria Street
☎ (01283) 568118
10.30–11
Marston's Pedigree H
Original locals' bar with a
recently added smart lounge: a
very friendly centre for the
local community. Good, cheap
food (eves till 8pm). No meals
Sun. ❀ ◁ ▸ ⊟ ♣ P

Roebuck Hotel

Station Street
☎ (01283) 568660
11–11; 11–3, 6–11 Sat
**Ansells Bitter, Mild; Ind
Coope ABC Best Bitter,
Burton Ale; Tetley Bitter;
guest beer** H
Ind Coope's busy, one-room
tap, just across the road from
the brewery. One guest beer is
generally available; over 350
different guest beers have been
served. Often very busy at
weekends. Eve meals end at
8pm. ❀ ⋈ ◁ ▸ ⇌ ♣

Star & Garter

104 Grange Street (200 yds
behind Town Hall)
☎ (01283) 567569
11–2.30 (3.30 Fri & Sat), 5.30–11

Marston's Pedigree H
Large, friendly, two-room pub with an outsales area opposite the entrance. The upstairs function room is the home of Burton Folk Club (Fri eve). Basic good value food—try the ½ yard hot dog (no meals Sun). ◖ ≋ ♣

Swan Hotel

Trent Bridge, Winshill
☎ (01283) 563552
11.30–2.30 (3 Sat), 6–11
Hardys & Hansons Best Bitter, Kimberley Classic H
100 years old in 1994, a pub built as an hotel, with the shop next door the original bar. Note the rooftop illuminated brewery sign. ❀ ⇔ ♣ P

Thomas Sykes Inn

Anglesey Road
☎ (01283) 510246
11.30–3, 5–11; 11.30–11 Fri
Draught Bass; Burton Bridge Bitter; Heritage Bitter; Marston's Pedigree; guest beers H
Classic ale house, situated in the former stables and wagon sheds of the old Thomas Sykes Brewery. Stone-cobbled floors, high ceilings and breweriana create a truly traditional atmosphere. Q ❀ P

Cannock

Shoal Hill Tavern

Sandy Lane ☎ (01543) 503302
12–2.30, 7–11
Home Bitter; S&N Theakston Mild, Best Bitter, XB, Old Peculier H
Large, comfortable pub on the border of town and countryside, especially popular in summer. ❀ ⊞ P

Cauldon

Yew Tree

Off A52/A523
☎ (01538) 308348
11–3, 6–11
Draught Bass; Burton Bridge Bitter; M&B Mild H
One of the finest pubs in the country, dating back to the 17th century. Its superb collection of antiques includes working polyphonia, a pianola, grandfather clocks and sundry Victoriana. Look out for the 'Acme' dog carrier and the huge old yew tree.
Q ☺ ❀ ♿ ▲ ♣ P

Chasetown

Uxbridge Arms

2 Church Street
☎ (01543) 674853
12–3, 6–11; 12–11 Sat

Bass Worthington BB, Draught Bass; M&B Highgate Dark; guest beers H
Popular, street-corner local with a games room. Two guest beers. ❀ ◖ ▮ ⊞ ♣ P

Cheslyn Hay

Woodman

Little Wood Lane, Littlewood (off A354) ☎ (01922) 413686
12–3, 6.30–11; 11–11 Sat
S&N Theakston Mild, Best Bitter, XB, Old Peculier H
Friendly, family-run pub, a former brew house with its own spring. The eating area has proved successful (meals extensions eves and Sun).
☺ ❀ ◖ ▮ ⊞ ♿ ♣ P

Ebstree

Hollybush

Ebstree Road OS854959
☎ (01902) 895587
12.30–2.30 (11.30–3 Sat), 6–11
Ansells Bitter; Ind Coope Burton Ale; Tetley Bitter H
Pleasant country pub, half a mile west of the Staffs and Worcester Canal. No meals Sun eve. The mild has, sadly, been lost. ⇔ ❀ ◖ ▮ ⊞ ♣ P

Eccleshall

George Hotel

Castle Street ☎ (01785) 850300
11–11
Ind Coope Burton Ale; Tetley Bitter; Whitbread Boddingtons Bitter; guest beer H
Enterprising hotel soon to start brewing. The site has been occupied at various times by a coaching inn, a draper's shop and an undertaker's.
⇔ ☺ ⇔ ◖ ▮ ♿ ♣ ⎈ P ⚥

Enville

Cat Inn

Bridgnorth Road (A458)
☎ (01384) 872209
12–3, 7–11; closed Sun
Enville Bitter, Ale, Gothic; S&N Theakston XB, Old Peculier; guest beer H
Part-16th-century country inn with a games room and an upstairs restaurant. Boules is played. The brewery tap of the Enville Brewery (1½ miles away). ⇔ Q ❀ ◖ ▮ ♿ ♣ P

Freeford

Whittington Arms

Tamworth Road (A51, 2 miles from Lichfield)
☎ (01543) 432340
11–11

Morland Old Speckled Hen; Wadworth 6X; guest beers H
Boarding kennels converted in 1993; now a large pub specialising in family dining, with a good selection of ales.
❀ ◖ ▮ ♿ P

Gnosall

Boat

Wharf Road ☎ (01785) 822208
11 (11.30 winter)–11
Marston's Bitter, Pedigree H
Popular pub next to Bridge 34 on the Shropshire Union Canal. Meals are served Easter–end Sept (except Sun).
⇔ ❀ ◖ ▮ ♿ ♣ P

Royal Oak

Newport Road (A518)
☎ (01785) 822362
11–11
Ansells Bitter; Ind Coope Burton Ale; Tetley Bitter H
Hospitable village local with a narrow, basic bar and a comfortable lounge. Acorn Bitter is brewed by Coach House. ❀ ◖ ▮ ⊞ ♣ P

Great Chatwell

Red Lion

2 miles E of A41 OS792143
☎ (01952) 691366
12–3 (not Mon), 6 (7 winter, 5 summer Sat)–11
Draught Bass; S&N Theakston XB; Tetley Bitter; guest beers H
Recently renovated country pub in a small village, with a games and family room. Excellent children's play area. Good value food.
⇔ ☺ ❀ ◖ ▲ ♣ P

Great Haywood

Clifford Arms

Main Road ☎ (01889) 881321
12–4, 7–11; 12–11 Fri; 11–11 Sat
Bass Worthington BB, Draught Bass; guest beers (occasional) H
Former coaching house, rebuilt in 1934, close to the Trent and Mersey Canal. Eve meals Tue–Sat.
⇔ Q ❀ ◖ ▮ ⊞ ▲ ♣ P

Handsacre

Crown

24 The Green (A513)
☎ (01543) 490239
11.30 (11 Thu–Sat)–3, 6–11
Bass Worthington BB, Draught Bass; M&B Highgate Dark H
Characterful, canalside, two-roomed local, incorporating a games room where children are welcome. No food Sun. Q ❀ ◖ ⊞ ♣ P

Harriseahead

Royal Oak
High Street ☎ (01782) 513362
7–11; 12–3, 7–11 Sat; 12–2.30, 7–10.30 Sun
Courage Directors; John Smith's Bitter; guest beers H
Busy, two-roomed free house with a smallish bar and a larger lounge (no price difference). It is popular with people of all ages, which adds to its appeal. Several different guest ales each week make this the best choice in the area. Handy for Mow Cop Folly (NT). ⊛ ♣ P

Haughton

Bell
Newport Road (A518)
☎ (01785) 780301
11.30–3, 6–11
Brains Dark; Marston's Pedigree; Whitbread Boddingtons Bitter; guest beer H
One-roomed village free house. ♨ ⊛ ◖ ▶ ♣ P

Hednesford

Queens Arms
Hill Street ☎ (01543) 878437
12–3, 6.30 (7 Sat)–11
Bass Worthington BB, Draught Bass; M&B Highgate Dark E
Welcoming, two-roomed pub of traditional nature, well-supported by locals. The excellent food is well-priced.
♨ Q ⊛ ◖ ⊞ ⇌ ♣ P

Hoar Cross

Meynell Ingram Arms
1 mile W of A515 at Newchurch OS133234
☎ (01283) 575202
12–3, 6–11; 11–11 Sat
Marston's Pedigree; Whitbread Boddingtons Bitter H
Extended former estate pub in rural surroundings, displaying hunting memorabilia. No food Sun eve. ♨ Q ⊛ ◖ ▶ ♣ P

Kinver

Cross
Church Hill ☎ (01384) 872435
11–3, 7–11; 11–11 Sat
Banks's Hanson's Mild, Bitter E
Popular local with a smart lounge, next to a restored Tudor house and near the Staffs and Worcs Canal.
♨ ▱ ⊛ ◖ ♣ P

Plough & Harrow
High Street
☎ (01384) 872659
12–3 (not winter Mon–Thu; 4 Fri), 7–11; 12–11 Sat
Batham Mild, Best Bitter H
Three-roomed pub, known locally as the 'Steps', 500 yards from the Staffs and Worcs Canal.
♨ ▱ ⊛ ◖ ▶ ⊞ ♣ P

Leek

Swan
2 St Edward Street
☎ (01538) 382081
11–3, 7–11
Bass Worthington BB, Draught Bass; M&B Highgate Dark; guest beer H
16th-century coaching inn, opposite St Edward's church, with a three-room layout. The comfortable lounge is mainly given over to non-smoking diners at lunchtimes. An ever-changing guest beer and a range of malt whiskies are available. Q ⊛ ◖ ▶ ♣

Lichfield

George & Dragon
28 Beacon Street
☎ (01543) 263554
11–3, 5.30–11; 11–11 Sat
Banks's Mild, Bitter E; Marston's Pedigree
Traditional, two-roomed local near the cathedral. ♣ P

Greyhound
Upper St John Street
☎ (01543) 262303
11.45–3, 5–11; 11.30–11 Fri & Sat
Ansells Bitter; Draught Bass; guest beers H
Busy local with an extended lounge area, offering regular rotating premium guest beers and quiz nights.
▱ ◖ ▶ ⊞ ⇌ (City) ♣ P

King's Head
Bird Street ☎ (01543) 256822
11–11; 11–3.30, 7–11 Sat
Marston's Bitter, Pedigree H
The oldest surviving pub in the city, first listed in 1408. Today, it consists of an oak-beamed bar, a lounge, and a large conservatory. Very busy weekends, it serves very good lunches.
◖ ⇌ (City) ♣

Scales
24 Market Street
☎ (01543) 410653
11–11
Bass Worthington BB, Draught Bass; Lichfield Steeplejack; M&B Highgate Dark; guest beers H
Completely renovated city-centre ale house. Its name, which relates to a defunct local racecourse, was only retained after a local campaign. Two guest beers. No food Sun lunch. ⊛ ◖ & ⇌ ♣

Longdon

Swan With Two Necks
40 Brook End (off A51)
☎ (01543) 490251
12–2.30, 7–11; 12–2, 7–10.30 Sun
Ansells Bitter, Mild; Burton Bridge Bitter; HP&D Entire; Ind Coope Burton Ale; guest beers H
400-year-old pub run by a French landlord in an award-winning village. The guest beer changes at weekends. No food Sun. ♨ Q ⊛ ◖ ▶ P

Marston

Fox
1 mile NW of Wheaton Aston OS935140 ☎ (01785) 840729
12–2.30 (3 Sat), 7 (6 summer)–11
Lloyds Derby; Mansfield Old Baily; Wells Eagle; Wood Special; guest beers H
Quiet, gimmick-free, country free house, especially popular with cyclists. Meals are served in the barn restaurant (snacks available in the pub). The beer range may vary.
♨ Q ⊛ ⊞ & ▲ ♣ ⌴ P

Meaford

George & Dragon
100 yds S of A34 Meaford roundabout ☎ (01785) 818497
12–2.30 (3 Sat), 6–11
Burtonwood Mild, Bitter, Forshaw's H
Large, main-road hostelry with a spacious, wood-panelled lounge bar. The ex-Beefeater restaurant upstairs caters for parties.
♨ ⊛ ◖ ▶ & ♣ P

Milwich

Green Man
On B5027 ☎ (01889) 505310
12–3, 6 (5.30 Fri)–11; 12–11 Sat
Bass Worthington BB, Draught Bass; guest beers H
Welcoming village pub near a tiny 1833 schoolhouse. A schedule of previous landlords (since 1792) is displayed in the bar. Many malt whiskies are available. No meals Sun eve or Tue; other eves till 8pm.
♨ ⊛ ◖ ▲ ♣ P

Moreton

Rising Sun
2 miles E of A41
☎ (01952) 691255
12–5, 7–11; 12–11 Sat
Banks's Mild; Marston's Bitter H
Friendly, rather isolated country pub, where the snug serves as a family room.

Staffordshire

Marston's Head Brewer's Choice beers are featured.
🏠 ⛺ 🌜 ◖ ◗ ▲ ♣ P

Newcastle-under-Lyme

Albert
1 Brindley Street
☎ (01782) 615525
12–3 (4 Fri & Sat), 7–11
Burtonwood Bitter, Top Hat H
Small, one-roomed local out of the town centre. Pictures of old Newcastle and clay pipes adorn the walls. One of few pubs still to have a piano. ♣

Crossways
Ironmarket ☎ (01782) 616953
11–11
Courage Directors H **&** G**; Vaux Extra Special; Wards Mild** H
Large pub opposite Queens Garden, on the outskirts of town: a substantial lounge with a smaller bar-cum-games room (chess available), popular with crossword followers. The house beer, Bear Cross, is brewed by Coach House.
🍴 ◖ ♣ ○

Victoria
King Street ☎ (01782) 627010
11–3 (4 Sat), 5 (7 Sat)–11
Draught Bass; Whitbread Boddingtons Bitter H
Victorian two-roomed local, convenient for the town centre and the New Victoria Theatre. Bar snacks and morning coffee are available. Q ❀ 🍺 ♣

Norton Canes

Railway Tavern
Norton Green Lane
☎ (01543) 279579
12–2 (3 Sat), 7–11
Ansells Bitter, Mild; Ind Coope Burton Ale; Tetley Bitter H
Village pub with a bowling green and an enthusiastic following. Cosy bar. ❀ ♣ P

Outwoods

Village Tavern
Signed from A518 (1 mile)
OS788182 ☎ (01952) 691216
12–3 (2 winter), 6 (7.30 winter)–11
Hanby Drawwell; Marston's Pedigree; Ruddles County; guest beers H
CAMRA Staffordshire *Pub of the Year* 1993. This small country inn is off the beaten track, but worth finding. Families are made very welcome.
🏠 Q ❀ ◖ ◗ ▲ ♣ P

Penkridge

Boat
Cannock Road (B5012, by Bridge 86 on Staffs and Worcs Canal) ☎ (01785) 714178
12–3, 6.30–11
Ansells Bitter; HP&D Entire; Ind Coope Burton Ale; Marston's Pedigree H
Comfortable, homely canalside pub with plenty of brass on display and bar skittles in the corridor. Sun eve meals served in summer only.
❀ ◖ ◗ ☖ ▲ ≈ ♣ P

Cross Keys
Filance Lane (by Bridge 84 on Staffs and Worcs Canal)
OS925134 ☎ (01785) 712826
11–3.30 (4 Sat), 6.30 (5 Fri)–11
Banks's Mild; Bass Worthington BB, Draught Bass; M&B Highgate Dark E
Modernised pub, attracting much canal trade. Barbecues in the garden; no food Sun eve.
❀ ◖ ◗ ♣ P

Littleton Arms Hotel
St Michael's Square (A449)
☎ (01785) 712287
11–11
Bass Worthington BB, Draught Bass; M&B Highgate Dark; guest beer H
Large, town-centre hotel with several linked lounge bar areas and a restaurant. A beer festival is held in the Grade II-listed stables.
🍴 ◖ ◗ ☖ ≈ P ✂

Railway
Clay Street (A449)
☎ (01785) 712685
12–2.30 (11.30–4 Sat), 7–11
Banks's Mild; M&B Highgate Dark; Tetley Bitter H **/** E
Pub whose frontage comprises the lounge and restaurant areas; the public bar is situated in a separate, former coach house building, to the rear. The bar has a games area with ¾-size snooker table, and only here is Highgate Dark available. The house beer in the lounge is brewed by Coach House. 🏠 ❀ 🍴 ◖ ◗ 🍺 ☖
≈ ♣ ○ P

Penn Common

Barley Mow
Pennwood Lane (off Wakeley Hill) OS949902
☎ (01902) 333510
12–2.30, 6.30–11; 11–11 Sat
Holden's Mild; HP&D Entire; Ind Coope Burton Ale; Marston's Pedigree; guest beer H
Hidden gem, circa 1630, with a warm welcome. The garden, with a playground, is very

popular in summer. The guest beer is a best bitter from Ind Coope. Near Penn Golf Course. 🏠 ❀ ◖ ◗ ○ P

Rugeley

Red Lion
Market Street
☎ (01889) 570328
11–4, 6–11; 11–11 Sat
Banks's Mild, Bitter E
Small, three-roomed pub with bags of atmosphere. It has pool and darts rooms and a cosy bar. ❀ ♣ P

Saverley Green

Hunter
Sandon Road OS970385
☎ (01782) 392067
12–3, 7–11
Burtonwood Mild, Bitter, Forshaw's, Top Hat; guest beers H
Cosy country pub offering great hospitality and occasional beer festivals. Eve snacks. 🏠 ⛺ ❀ ◖ ▲ ♣ P

Shenstone

Bull's Head
Birmingham Road
☎ (01543) 480214
11.30–11; 12.30–3, 7–10.30 Sun
Bass Worthington BB, Draught Bass; M&B Highgate Dark, Brew XI; guest beer H
18th-century, refurbished pub, a former courthouse reputedly haunted by a 'grey lady'. Popular with office staff lunchtime and diners eves.
🏠 Q ⛺ ❀ ◖ ◗ ☖ ≈ P ✂

Railway
Main Street ☎ (01543) 480503
12–3, 5–11; 12–11 Fri & Sat
Banks's Mild; Marston's Bitter, Pedigree H
Typical village pub built to serve the Birmingham–Lichfield railway in the 1800s. The lounge and bar are frequented by locals. Imaginative food menu; Marston's Head Brewer's Choice. Q ❀ ◖ ◗ ≈ ♣ P

Shraley Brook

Rising Sun
Knowle Bank Road (200 yds from B5500) ☎ (01782) 720600
12–3 (may vary), 7–11; 11–11 Sat
Rising Sun Rising, Setting, Sun Stroke, Total Eclipse; guest beers H
Free house with a brewery at the rear. Sunlight and Solar Flare are also occasionally available, plus a very wide range of ciders, malt whiskies and foreign bottled beers. A folk club meets upstairs.
🏠 Q ❀ ◖ ◗ ☖ ♣ ○ P

Six Ashes

Six Ashes
On A458 ☎ (01384) 221375
12–3, 6–11
Banks's Mild, Bitter E
Comfortable, two-roomed
rural hostelry. No food Mon.
Wheelchair access is via the
rear door. 🏿 ❀ ◑ ▶ ᴕ ♣ P

Stafford

Bird in Hand
Mill Street ☎ (01785) 52198
11–11; 11–4, 7–11 Sat
**Courage Best Bitter,
Directors; John Smith's Bitter;
guest beer** H
Popular and enterprising,
town-centre pub with a bar,
snug, lounge and games room.
Children are welcome in the
lounge until 9pm. Occasional
cider; no meals Sun.
🏿 ❀ ◑ ᴕ ≋ ♣ ◔

Stafford Arms
Railway Street
☎ (01785) 53313
12–2.30, 5 (6.30 Sat)–11
**Titanic Best Bitter, Lifeboat,
Premium, Captain Smith's;
guest beers** H
Since becoming Titanic Inns'
second house, this fine, one-
roomed pub opposite the
station has added the Titanic
range to the three guest beers
from independent brewers.
Basic meals lunchtime (not
Sun), and Mon–Fri eves till
8pm. A must. ◑ ▶ ≋ P

Sun
7 Lichfield Road
☎ (01785) 42208
11.30–2.30 (11–3.30 Sat), 7 (6.30
summer)–11
**Bass Worthington BB,
Draught Bass; guest beer** H
Pleasant, multi-roomed,
town-centre pub with an
olde-worlde restaurant. The
reference library is useful. No
meals Sun eve.
ᴥ 🏿 ◑ ▶ ᴕ ≋ ♣ P

Telegraph
Wolverhampton Road (A449)
☎ (01785) 58858
11–11
**Bass Worthington BB,
Draught Bass; M&B Highgate
Dark; Stones Best Bitter;
guest beer** H
Good, honest local with a
lounge and bar, not far from
the town centre. Good value
meals are served (no food Sun
eve). ◑ ▶ ᴕ ♣ P

Trumpet
Radford Bank (A34, by Bridge
98 on Staffs and Worcs Canal)
☎ (01785) 42825
11–3, 6–11; 11–11 Fri & Sat

Draught Bass H
Main-road, canalside pub. Eve
meals in summer only.
❀ ◑ ▶ ᴕ ᴕ ♣ P

Stoke on Trent:
Burslem

Bull's Head
14 St John's Square
☎ (01782) 834153
11.30 (12 Sat)–3, 5.30 (6.30 Sat)–11;
11.30–11 Fri
**Titanic Best Bitter, Lifeboat,
Premium, Captain Smith's,
Wreckage** H
Town-centre house which has
recently reverted to two
rooms. It usually offers three
guest beers, always from
independent breweries.
🏿 Q ❀ ᴕ ᴕ ♣

George Hotel
Swan Square ☎ (01782) 577544
11.30–2.30, 5.30–11
**Marston's Bitter, Pedigree;
Morland Old Speckled Hen** H
Fine pseudo-Georgian
building, circa 1928,
refurbished. The bar is open to
non-residents—ideal for a
quiet drink—but smart casual
dress is required. Special rates
on accommodation for
CAMRA members.
Recommended food.
Q ᴥ ◑ ▶

Leopard Hotel
Market Place ☎ (01782) 837578
11–11
**Bass Worthington BB,
Draught Bass** H
Large, historic, multi-roomed
town-centre pub, dating back
to 1760. It appeared as the
Tiger in Arnold Bennett's
books. Q ◑ ᴕ ♣

Post Office Vaults
Market Place ☎ (01782) 811027
11–11
**Bass Worthington BB,
Draught Bass; M&B Highgate
Dark; Marston's Pedigree;
Ruddles County** H
Small, one-roomed pub near
the town hall. It offers a large
range of beers, considering the
size of the bar.

Fenton

Malt'n'Hops
295 King Street (A50)
☎ (01782) 313406
12–3, 7–11
**Burtonwood Mild, Top Hat;
guest beers** H
A warm welcome awaits at
this well-run establishment,
which is often packed at
weekends. A consistent
winner of the local CAMRA
Pub of the Year award, with at
least 15 different beers sold

each week. Bursley Bitter is
brewed by Burtonwood.
≋ (Longton) ♣

Hanley

Coachmakers
65 Lichfield Street
☎ (01782) 262158
11–11
**Bass Worthington BB,
Draught Bass** H
Classic, small, mid-terraced,
town pub: three rooms and a
corridor are served from a tiny
bar. A very friendly local.
🏿 Q ᴕ ♣

Golden Cup
65 Old Town Road
☎ (01782) 212405
11–11
**Bass Worthington BB,
Draught Bass** H
Friendly local boasting
splendid bar fittings, rebuilt in
1910. Its ornate Edwardian
exterior proudly proclaims
'Bass only'. The last beer house
in Hanley to obtain a liquor
licence, now famous for its
'Big Breakfast'. ❀ ◑ ᴕ ♣

Hartshill

Jolly Potters
296 Hartshill Road
☎ (01782) 45254
11–3 (4 Sat), 6 (7 Sat)–11; 11–11 Fri
**Draught Bass; M&B Mild;
guest beer** H
An increasingly rare example
of a typical Potteries town-
centre pub. Situated in a
conservation area, it has four
small rooms and a central
corridor. Q ❀ ᴕ ᴕ ♣

Longton

Royal Oak
143 Uttoxeter Road, Normacot
(A50) ☎ (01782) 336323
11–11
**Bass Worthington BB,
Draught Bass; M&B Highgate
Dark** H
Lively local with an
occasionally boisterous
clientele. ❀ ≋ ♣ P

Penkhull

Marquis of Granby
51 St Thomas's Place
☎ (01782) 47025
11–3 (4 Thu–Sat), 6.30–11
**Banks's Mild; Marston's
Bitter, Pedigree** H
Corner pub opposite the
village church, with a large,
comfortable lounge. Public bar
games are very popular, as is
the garden. Marston's Head
Brewer's Choice beers are
available. ❀ ◑ ᴕ ♣ P

Staffordshire

Terrace
148 Penkhull New Road
☎ (01782) 47631
11–11; 11–4, 7–11 Sat
Bass Worthington BB, Draught Bass H
Modern pub on a steep hill within walking distance of the town centre. The lounge is very popular with older people, while the public bar has an emphasis on games.
❀ ⌔ & ♣ P

Tunstall

Globe
High Street ☎ (01782) 839816
11–3, 4.30 (6.30 Sat)–11; 12–2.30, 7–10.30 Sun
Draught Bass H
No-nonsense, street-corner local at the lower end of town: a traditional long bar and a smaller snug with a serving hatch. It is somewhat basic (outside gents') but full of local character. ⌔ ♣

White Hart
43 Roundwell Street
☎ (01782) 835817
11–5, 7–11; 11–11 Fri & Sat
Banks's Mild; Marston's Bitter, Pedigree H
Friendly, street-corner drinkers' pub on the edge of the town centre. The single room is split into two areas. The only Marston's house in town. Q ❀ ⌔ ♣

Stone

Pheasant
Old Road OS902352
☎ (01785) 814603
11.30–4, 6–11; 11.30–11 Fri & Sat
Bass Worthington BB, Draught Bass H
Friendly local, immaculately maintained and improved over 13 years by the present landlord. The dining room extension is now open (eve meals Fri and Sat; no food Sun). ❀ ⌔ ▶ ⌔ ⇌ ♣

Stonnall

Old Swan
Main Street ☎ (01543) 374314
12–3, 5.30–11; 12–11 Fri & Sat
Draught Bass; M&B Highgate Dark; guest beers H
Traditional, family, village pub; a games venue for locals. The quiet garden holds barbecues. Q ❀ ⌔ ▶ & ♣ P

Royal Oak
Main Street ☎ (01543) 373929
12–2.30 (not Mon, except bank hols), 5.30–11
Courage Directors; Marston's Pedigree; Ruddles County; John Smith's Bitter; guest beer H

The oldest hostelry in Stonnall is said to be haunted by a previous owner's wife. Regular, changing guest beers.
❀ ⌔ ⌔

Tamworth

Market Vaults
7 Market Street
☎ (01827) 69653
11–11
Banks's Mild, Bitter E
Modernised, town-centre pub, popular at weekends. No eve meals Fri and Sat; book Sun lunch. ❀ ⌔ ▶ ⇌

Tatenhill

Horseshoe
Main Street ☎ (01283) 564913
11–3, 5.30–11
Marston's Pedigree, Owd Rodger (winter) H
Old village pub with beamed ceilings, tastefully altered to provide well-defined areas for drinking and/or eating. Popular for meals (but no food Sun eve). Marston's Head Brewer's Choice beers are stocked. ❀ Q ⛱ ❀ ⌔ ▶ P

Two Gates

Bull's Head
Watling Street (A5/A51 jct)
☎ (01827) 287820
12–2.30 (3 Sat), 7–11; 12–2.30, 7–10.30 Sun
Banks's Mild; Marston's Pedigree H
Busy, friendly local where darts, dominoes and football are all supported. Good, inexpensive food is available Mon–Sat lunch. Marston's Head Brewer's Choice. Q ❀ ⌔ & ⇌ (Wilnecote) ♣ P

Uttoxeter

Black Swan
Market Street
☎ (01889) 564657
11 (10.30 Sat)–11
Bass Worthington BB, Draught Bass H
17th-century listed building of great character. Visitors are made welcome by the Scottish landlord. ⌔ ⇌ ♣ P

Vaults
22 Market Square
☎ (01889) 562997
11–3, 5.30 (5 Fri & Sat)–11
Draught Bass H
Busy old pub of character.
⌔ ⇌ ♣

Weston

Saracen's Head
Weston Road (A518)
☎ (01889) 270286
11–11

Banks's Mild; Bass Worthington BB, Draught Bass E; **guest beer** H
Open-plan, country pub running a courtesy bus for regulars and parties of six or more diners. No-smoking area for dining.
❀ ❀ ⌔ ▶ ⌔ ♣ P

Woolpack
The Green ☎ (01889) 270238
11.30–3, 6–11; 11–11 Fri & Sat
Marston's Bitter, Pedigree; guest beer H
This 17th-century 'inn on the green' has been carefully extended, retaining separate drinking and eating areas. A good selection of quality home-cooked food is offered at competitive prices (no meals Sun eve).
❀ ❀ ⌔ ▶ ⌔ ♣ P

Whittington

Bell
Main Street ☎ (01543) 432377
12–3, 6–11
Draught Bass; Ind Coope Burton Ale; Tetley Bitter H
Traditional, beamed, village pub with a large garden to the rear and a children's play area. Popular at weekends.
❀ Q ⛱ ❀ ⌔ ▶ ♣ P

Dog Inn
Main Street ☎ (01543) 432252
11–3, 5–11
Ansells Bitter, Mild; Draught Bass; Ind Coope Burton Ale; Tetley Bitter H
16th-century coaching inn offering bar and restaurant menus and modern B&B facilities.
❀ ⇌ ⌔ ▶ & ♣ P

Wigginton

Old Crown
Main Road ☎ (01827) 64588
11.30–2.30, 6–11
S&N Theakston Mild, Best Bitter, XB, Old Peculier; guest beer H
Village local where a warm welcome is guaranteed. Very reasonable prices, plus regularly changing guest beers. Local CAMRA Pub of the Year 1994.
❀ ⌔ ▶ P

Yoxall

Crown
Main Street
☎ (01543) 472551
11–3, 5.30–11
Marston's Pedigree H
Attractive pub with a lounge, a bar and a conservatory area for families. No food is served Sun. ⛱ ❀ ⌔ ▶ & ♣ P

BEERS OF THE YEAR

Chosen by CAMRA tasting panels, by votes from the general public at beer festivals and by a poll of CAMRA members, these are the *Good Beer Guide* Beers of the Year. Each was found to be consistently outstanding in its category and took its place in the Champion Beer of Britain contest at the Great British Beer Festival at Olympia in August 1994. These beers have also been awarded a tankard symbol in the breweries section of this book.

DARK AND LIGHT MILDS

Bateman Dark Mild
Coach House Gunpowder Mild
Hoskins & Oldfield HOB Mild
Hydes' Anvil Light
M&B Highgate Dark
Tolly Cobbold Mild

OLD ALES AND STRONG MILDS

Adnams Old
Hadrian Emperor Ale
Malton Owd Bob
Sarah Hughes Original Dark
    Ruby Mild
Summerskills Indiana's Bones
Young's Winter Warmer

BITTERS

Big Lamp Bitter
Caledonian Deuchars IPA
Everards Beacon Bitter
Hardington Traditional Bitter
Judges Barristers Bitter
Nethergate Bitter

BARLEY WINES

Gibbs Mew The Bishop's Tipple
Marston's Owd Rodger
Parish Baz's Bonce Blower
Robinson's Old Tom
Woodforde's Headcracker

BEST BITTERS

Concertina KW Special Pride
Fuller's London Pride
Hadrian Centurion Best Bitter
Otter Ale
Taylor Landlord
Titanic Premium Bitter

PORTERS AND STOUTS

Bateman Salem Porter
Coach House Blunderbus
    Old Porter
Elgood's North Brink Porter
Hambleton Nightmare
Oakhill Black Magic

STRONG BITTERS

Butterknowle High Force
Coach House Posthorn
    Premium Ale
Fuller's ESB
Hop Back Summer Lightning
Moorhouse's Pendle
    Witches Brew
Young's Special

BOTTLE-CONDITIONED BEERS

Bass Worthington White Shield
Courage Imperial Russian Stout
Eldridge Pope Thomas
    Hardy's Ale
Gale's Prize Old Ale
King & Barnes Festive
Shepherd Neame Spitfire

Suffolk

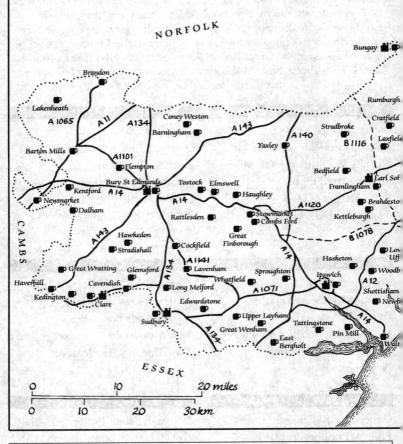

NORFOLK

Bungay

Brandon

Lakenheath

A1065

A11

A134

Coney Weston

Barningham

A143

Rumburgh

Cratfield

Stradbroke

Laxfiel

A140

Yaxley

B1116

Barton Mills

A1101

Flempton

Bury St Edmunds

Tostock

Elmswell

Haughley

Bedfield

Earl Soh

Framlingham

Kentford

A14

Newmarket

Dalham

A14

Rattlesden

Stowmarket

Combs Ford

Great Finborough

A1120

Kettleburgh

Brandesto

B1078

Lov

Uff

Hawkedon

Stradishall

Cockfield

A1141

Lavenham

Whatfield

A14

Sproughton

Hasketon

Ipswich

A12

Woodb

Great Wratting

Glemsford

A134

A1071

Shottisham

Newb

Haverhill

Cavendish

Long Melford

Edwardstone

Kedington

Clare

Sudbury

A134

Upper Layham

Great Wenham

Tattingstone

East Bergholt

Pin Mill

Pin Mill

A14

Walt

ESSEX

| 0 | 10 | 20 miles |
| 0 | 10 | 20 | 30km |

Adnams, *Southwold;* **Earl Soham,** *Earl Soham;* **Green Dragon,** *Bungay;* **Greene King,** *Bury St Edmunds;* **Green Jack,** *Oulton Broad;* **Mauldons,** *Sudbury;* **Nethergate,** *Clare;* **Scott's,** *Lowestoft;* **Tolly Cobbold,** *Ipswich*

Aldeburgh

White Hart
High Street ☎ (01728) 453205
11–3, 6–11 (may extend); 11–11 Sat
Adnams Bitter, Extra, Broadside H
Lively, one-bar pub in a popular coastal town. Wood panelling and pictures line the walls; cheery welcome. May be busy at weekends.
🏰 ✿ ▲ ♣

Try also: Cross Keys, Crabbe St (Adnams)

Barningham

Royal George
Church Road
☎ (01359) 221246
11–2.30, 7–11
Greene King XX Mild, IPA, Abbot H
Attractive, thatched pub at the village centre. Its spacious interior has exposed beams and gets busier at weekends. A mainly home-prepared menu is served (no food Sun).
Q ✿ ◁ ▶ ♣ P

Barton Mills

Bull Inn
The Street ☎ (01638) 712230
11–11
Adnams Bitter; Draught Bass; Greene King IPA; guest beer H
Imposing old coaching inn, not as near to the main road as in yesteryear, but still easily reached from the A11 trunk road. A family-run pub offering full hotel facilities.
✿ ⊨ ◁ ▶ P

Bedfield

Crown

Church Lane (leave A1120 in
Earl Soham) ☎ (01728) 628431
11.30–3, 6–11; 11–11 Sat
Greene King IPA; guest beer H
Village local with a friendly
welcome. 🚲 ❀ ◖ ♣ P

Blaxhall

Ship

☎ (01728) 688316
11–3 (not Mon), 7–11
**Adnams Bitter; Tolly
Cobbold Mild** H
Traditional narrow bar with a
pool table and a piano. The
attached dining room offers a
good value menu. Occasional
folk sessions. ❀ ◖ ▶ 🛦 ♣ P

Try also: **Oyster**, Butley
(Adnams)

Bramfield

Bell

The Street ☎ (0198 684) 395
11–2.30, 6.30–11
Adnams Mild, Bitter G
Basic, down-to-earth, two-bar
pub with a Ring the Bull game
in the public bar. Note the
thatched church with a round
detached tower opposite.
Q ❀ ◖ 🛱 🛦 ♣ P

Brandeston

Queens Head

The Street ☎ (01728) 685307
11.30–2.30, 5.30 (6 Mon & Sat)–11
**Adnams Mild, Bitter, Old,
Broadside** (summer) H
Excellent all round country
pub with a family room, a
large lounge and a quiet back
bar for drinkers only.
Extensive garden with play
equipment and camping
facilities. Good value meals.
🚲 Q 🛏 ❀ ❀ ◖ ▶ 🛱 🛦 ♣ P

Brandon

Five Bells

Market Hill ☎ (01842) 813472
11–2.30, 5–11; 11–11 Fri & Sat
Greene King XX Mild, IPA H
Busy, small town pub (the
patio drinking area gives a
good view of market
activities). Eve meals Fri and
Sat. Q ❀ ◖ 🛦 ⇌ ♣ P

Try also: **Crown**, Crown St
(Greene King)

Bungay

Chequers Inn

23 Bridge Street
☎ (01986) 893579
12–3, 5–11; 11–11 Fri & Sat
**Adnams Bitter; Bass
Charrington IPA, Draught
Bass; guest beers** H
Comfortable, one-bar pub with
an ever-changing range of
unusual guest ales for the area.
A hospitable landlord and
friendly locals help make this
an exceptionally good bar.
Wheelchair access at the rear.
Q ❀ ◖ 🛦 🛦 P

Green Dragon

Broad Street ☎ (01986) 892681
11–3, 5–11 (may vary); 11–11 Fri & Sat
**Adnams Bitter; Green Dragon
Chaucer, Bridge St, Dragon;
guest beer** H
Two-bar town house which
has a lively atmosphere. The
beer range is dominated by
house brews. A third room
provides sanctuary when the
bars are crowded.
🚲 Q 🛏 ❀ ◖ ▶ 🛦 🛦 ♣ P

Bury St Edmunds

Black Boy

69 Guildhall Street
☎ (01284) 752723
11–3, 5–11
**Greene King XX Mild, IPA,
Abbot** H
15th-century pub near the
town centre, popular
lunchtime with shoppers.
Good value food. The games
room is decorated with
caricatures. Occasional pub
theatre upstairs. Q ◖ ▶ ⇌ ♣

Elephant & Castle

21 Hospital Road
(Parkway/Westgate St jct)
☎ (01284) 755570
11–2.30 (3 Sat), 5 (7 Sat)–11
**Greene King XX Mild, IPA,
Abbot** H
Homely, two-bar pub with a
garden and terrace suitable for
children. Family atmosphere.
No eve meals Sun. ❀ ◖ ▶ P

Fleetwood's

25 Abbeygate Street (1st floor;
Lower Baxter St jct)
☎ (01284) 705703
11–3, 5–11; 11–11 Sat
**Ballard's Wassail; Fuller's
London Pride; Morland Old
Speckled Hen; Smiles Best
Bitter; guest beers** H
Friendly bar close to the
historic town centre and
abbey, offering a good
selection (at least four) of ales
from breweries throughout the
country. Wide selection of
good value lunchtime food.
Busy weekends. ◖ P

Ipswich Arms

Station Hill ☎ (01284) 703623
12–2.30 (3 Fri, Sat & summer), 6–11
Greene King IPA H
Interesting, semi-circular,
19th-century light brick pub
on a busy corner. The early
photograph (1871) in the
lounge was taken from the top
of a nearby church spire—the
highest in Suffolk. Note: a cask
breather is used on the Mild
and Abbot. ❀ ◖ ▶ ⇌ ♣ P

Queens Head

39 Churchgate Street
☎ (01284) 761554
11–2.30, 5–11; 11–11 Sat
**Draught Bass; Tolly Cobbold
Original; guest beers** H
White brick, 18th-century
coaching inn with plenty of
history beneath a Victorian-
style refurbishment. Good
selection of East Anglian beers
alongside national brews. Busy
with the young at weekends.
◖ ▶

Rose & Crown

48 Whiting Street (Westgate St
jct) ☎ (01284) 755934
11–11; 11–3, 7–11 Sat

Suffolk

Greene King XX Mild, IPA, Abbot H
Unspoilt town local, close to the brewery and used by all ranks of Greene King staff. The mild outsells the bitter. Family-run for many years.
Q ◑ ⊟ ≋ ♣

Cavendish

Bull Inn
High Street ☎ (01787) 280245
11–3, 6–11
Adnams Mild, Bitter, Broadside H
Beamed village pub dating from 1530. An excellent range of freshly prepared food is available both in the bar and in the dining area (no food Mon). Friendly. ♨ Q ☀ ◑ ◗

Clare

Bell
Market Hill ☎ (01787) 277741
11–11
Greene King IPA; Nethergate IPA, Bitter, Old Growler H
Fine, timber-framed, 16th-century hotel of character offering a cosy bar area and a comfortable lounge with antique furnishings. Full hotel and restaurant services.
☀ ⇤ ◑ ◗ P

Try also: **Cock**, Callis St (Adnams)

Cockfield

Three Horseshoes
Stows Hill (A1141)
☎ (01284) 828177
12–2.30, 6–11
Greene King IPA H
Thatched, 14th-century former hall house and court. The striking lounge bar boasts an exposed crown post and tie beam circa 1350. The good village public bar menu provides an excellent selection of home-made food, including traditional puddings (no eve meals Tue–Sun, Oct–April). Note: a cask breather is used on the Mild and Abbot.
♨ ⚘ ◑ ◗ ♣ P

Combs Ford

Gladstone Arms
1 mile from Stowmarket town centre on Needham road
☎ (01449) 612339
11–2.30, 5–11
Adnams Bitter, Old, Broadside; Morland Old Speckled Hen H
Much improved pub with areas to suit most tastes. A good games venue.
♨ ☀ ♣ P

Coney Weston

Swan
Thetford Road
☎ (01359) 221295
12–2.30, 5–11
Greene King IPA, Abbot H
Simple, Edwardian village pub with good regular trade, especially early eves. Off the beaten track. ♨ Q ☀ ⊟ P

Cratfield

Poacher
Bell Green ☎ (01986) 798206
12–3, 6–11; 11–11 Sat
Adnams Bitter, Broadside; Greene King IPA, Abbot H
Former post office and off-licence, now a pub packed with curios, including a miniature bottle collection.
♨ ☀ ◑ ◗ ⅙ ▲ ♣ ⏚ P

Dalham

Affleck Arms
☎ (01638) 500306
11–2.30, 6.30–11
Greene King IPA, Abbot H
Elizabethan thatched pub beside the River Kennet, well-used by walkers on weekends. ♨ Q ☀ ◑ ◗ ⊟ P

East Bergholt

Royal Oak (Dicky)
East End ☎ (01206) 298221
11.30–2.30, 6–11
Greene King IPA, Abbot H
Excellent rural pub which may be difficult to find (follow signs to Grange camping site). The friendly single bar is well-supported by local characters. The covered patio at the rear is popular for summer barbecue eves. Snacks lunchtime. ♨ ☀ ⅙ ▲ ♣ P

Eastbridge

Eels Foot
☎ (01728) 830154
11–3, 6–11; 11–11 Fri & Sat
Adnams Mild (summer) G, **Bitter, Old, Extra** H
Classic smugglers' inn overlooking the marshes and the RSPB's Minsmere reserve. Popular in summer. No eve meals Wed.
♨ Q ☀ ◑ ◗ ▲ ♣ P

Edwardstone

White Horse
Mill Green (off A1071)
☎ (01787) 211211
11.30–2, 6–11
Greene King XX Mild, IPA H, **Abbot** G

Traditional pub featuring games. Good value meals Thu–Sat. Sun lunch bookings are advisable. Local cider.
♨ ☀ ◑ ⊟ ▲ ♣ ⏚ P

Elmswell

Railway Tavern
School Road ☎ (01359) 241275
11–2.30, 6–11; 11–11 Sat
Greene King XX Mild, IPA, Abbot H
Fine old pub with a good, friendly atmosphere. All pub games are played. Good children's play area. Barbecues summer Sat. Pictures of steam trains adorn the bar. No lunches Sun; eve meals Mon and Sat. ♨ ☀ ◑ ≋ ♣ P

Try also: **Fox**, Station Rd (Greene King)

Flempton

Greyhound
The Green ☎ (01284) 728400
11–2.30, 5–11; 11–11 Sat
Greene King IPA H
Traditional village local quietly positioned behind the church, just off the A1101. The popular public bar has a tiled floor; the lounge is smart. Large, enclosed garden for families. Note: a cask breather is used on the Mild and Abbot.
♨ Q ☀ ◑ ⊟ ♣ P

Framlingham

Railway Inn
Station Road ☎ (01728) 723693
12 (11 Sat)–3, 5.30 (6 Sat)–11
Adnams Bitter, Old, Extra H
Pub where the public bar, though basic, always offers a friendly welcome. The plush lounge boasts a Victorian fireplace and fine decor.
♨ Q ☀ ⊟ ▲ ♣ P

Try also: **Queens Head**, Dennington (Free)

Glemsford

Crown
Brooke Street
☎ (01787) 281111
11–2, 5–11
Greene King IPA H
Friendly village local, a former brew pub full of history, with a well-kept, enclosed garden. Highly commended in *Floral Pub of the Year* awards locally. Function room over an old stable block. ♨ Q ☀ P

Great Finborough

Chestnut Horse
High Road (B1115)
☎ (01449) 612298
11–3, 6–11

Greene King XX Mild, IPA, Abbot H
Fine, friendly village local attracting a wide range of people and featuring sewing machine table bases, a collection of cigarette lighters and a large, open brick fireplace. The 1993 *Greene King in Bloom* winner. Excellent food (no eve meals Tue or Sun). ⚲ ⊛ ◖ ▶ ▲ ♣ P

Great Wenham

Queens Head
On Capel St Mary road
☎ (01473) 310590
12–2.30, 6.30–11
Adnams Bitter; Greene King IPA, Abbot; guest beers H
Red brick, Victorian, cottage-style, one-bar house with a small, separate, no-smoking dining room (25 home-made, authentic Indian curries). Food is served at every session. English meals also available.
⚲ ⊛ ◖ ▶ ▲ ♣ P

Great Wratting

Red Lion
School Road ☎ (01440) 783237
11–11
Adnams Mild G, **Bitter, Old, Extra** H
Welcoming village pub with a traditional bar and a separate restaurant, serving good, home-cooked food. No eve meals Sun/Mon. Whale bones form an arch over the entrance. ⚲ ⊛ ⌂ ◖ ▶ ♣ P

Hasketon

Turks Head
Low Road ☎ (01394) 382584
11–3, 5.30–11
Draught Bass; Tolly Cobbold Mild, Bitter, Old Strong H
Converted into a public house during the 17th century, this small, quiet establishment is packed with curios and antiques. No food Sun eve or Mon. ⚲ Q ⊛ ◖ ▶ ▲ ♣ P

Haughley

Railway Tavern
Station Road (1 mile E of centre) ☎ (01449) 673577
11–2.30, 5.30 (6.30 Sat)–11
Greene King XX Mild, IPA, Abbot; guest beer H
19th-century former railway tavern, beside an old station on the London–Norwich line: a friendly local. No food Mon eve. ⚲ ☢ ⊛ ◖ ▶ ♣ P

White Horse
New Street ☎ (01359) 240349
12–2.30, 7–11

Greene King XX Mild, IPA, Abbot H
Pleasant, 400-year-old country pub, found just off the A45. Folk club every fourth Thu in the month. Bar food lunchtime, except Sun and Mon. ⚲ Q ⊛ ◖ ▶ P

Haverhill

Queens Head
Queen Street ☎ (01440) 702026
11–11
Courage Best Bitter; Nethergate Bitter, Old Growler; Ruddles Best Bitter; Wadworth 6X H
Town-centre pub, now a listed building with a lively, friendly atmosphere. ⊛ ◖ ♣

Hawkedon

Queens Head
Rede Road ☎ (01284) 89218
12–3, 6–11; 12–11 Sat
Greene King IPA; Mauldons Bitter H; **Woodforde's Wherry** G; **guest beer** H / G
Classic village bar, near the church, dating in part from the 14th century, with low ceilings, heavily moulded beams, a large inglenook and comfy chairs. Interesting, genuinely home-made meals; the menu changes regularly.
⚲ Q ⊛ ◖ ▶ P

Ipswich

County
24 St Helen's Street
☎ (01473) 255153
11–11
Adnams Mild, Bitter, Old, Extra, Tally Ho (Xmas) H
Large, two-bar pub near the town centre. The sedate lounge/dining area serves cheap food; the bar is more upbeat. A winner of the Adnams *Cellar of the Year* award. ◖ ▶ ⊞ ⓓ ♣

Greyhound
9 Henley Road
☎ (01473) 252105
11–2.30, 5–11; 11–11 Sat
Adnams Mild (summer), **Bitter, Old, Extra, Broadside; guest beers** H
Popular two-bar town pub whose main bar always seems busy. The small front bar is normally quieter and has an assortment of wooden furniture. Interesting guest ales. Q ⊛ ◖ ▶ ♣ P

Plough
2 Dogs' Head Street (by old cattle market bus station)
☎ (01473) 288005
11–3, 5–11; 11–11 Fri & Sat; 7–10.30 Sun, closed Sun lunch

Adnams Bitter; Black Sheep Best Bitter; Crouch Vale Millennium Gold; Mauldons Bitter; Nethergate Bitter; Tolly Cobbold Original H
Former theme pub, sympathetically restored, offering ten ever-changing real ales from all over the country, plus fruit wines. Friendly.
Q ☢ ◖ ▶ ⓓ ♣ ⌂ ✂

Tap & Spile
76 St Helen's Street
☎ (01473) 211270
11–3, 5–11; 11–11 Thu–Sat
Beer range varies H
Formerly the Dove Inn, and retaining many of its features, this compact, three-room pub has had a busy first year, with over 250 different ales tried. Good lunch menu. Occasional live music. Wheelchair WC.
Q ☢ ⊛ ◖ ⓓ ♣ ⌂ P

Try also: Brewery Tap, Cliff Quay (Tolly Cobbold)

Kedington

White Horse
White Horse Lane
☎ (01440) 63564
11.30–2.30, 5–11 (11.30–11 summer)
Greene King Mild, IPA, Abbot H
Friendly village pub featuring good food and a large garden, with summer barbecues. No meals Sun. ⊛ ☢ ◖ ▶ ♣ P

Kentford

Cock
Bury Road ☎ (01638) 750360
11–3 (not Mon), 5.30–11; 11–11 Sat
Greene King IPA, Abbot H
Large country pub partly from the 1600s, with three bars. Very welcoming landlady. Good for families with its large garden and play area.
⚲ Q ⊛ ◖ ▶ ▲ ♣ P

Kettleburgh

Chequers
Easton Road ☎ (01728) 723760
Greene King IPA; Marston's Pedigree; Tolly Cobbold Mild H
One time home of the Deben brewery, pulled down during the last century. The current pub was built in 1912. The garden extends down to the River Deben. Vibrant, friendly bar. ⚲ Q ⊛ ◖ ▶ P

Lakenheath

Plough
Mill Road ☎ (01842) 860285
11–2.30, 6–11
Greene King IPA H
Popular pub in a busy village.

Its fine flint exterior, typical of the locality, conceals a spacious bar and a pool room. A long-standing *Guide* entry. Note: a cask breather is used on the Mild. ❀ ♣ P

Try also: Half Moon, High St (Greene King)

Lavenham

Angel

Market Place ☎ (01787) 247388
11–3, 6–11
Adnams Bitter; Courage Directors; Nethergate Bitter, Old Growler (winter); **Ruddles County; Webster's Yorkshire Bitter** H
Impressive, 14th-century coaching inn overlooking the market cross and guildhall. Pick a quiet time and ask to see the medieval vaulted cellars. Very relaxed atmosphere; classical background music played with live classical piano on Fri nights. Quality menu.
🏨 Q ☎ ❀ 🍴 ◖▶ ♣ P

Laxfield

Kings Head/Low House

Gorams Mill Lane
☎ (01986) 798395
11–3, 6–11
Adnams Mild, Bitter, Old, Extra, Broadside; guest beers (summer) H
Classic 15th-century pub with a proper tap room with high-back settles. Beer is served from the back cellar: there is no bar. Four-pint jugs are offered at reduced rates. An excellent pub.
🏨 Q ☎ ❀ ◖▶ ⚲ ♣ ⌂ P

Long Melford

George & Dragon

Hall Street ☎ (0178 73) 71285
11–11
Greene King IPA, Rayments Special, Abbot H
Family-run former coaching inn with a lounge-style single bar and a restaurant. Good choice of home-cooked food.
🏨 ❀ 🍴 ◖▶ P

Lower Ufford

White Lion

The Street ☎ (01394) 460770
11.30–2.30, 6.30–11
Tolly Cobbold Mild, Bitter, Old Strong; Whitbread Flowers Original G
Delightful, small, one-bar pub offering a very friendly atmosphere. A large chimney stack divides the bar area. All beers are on gravity stillage at the back of the bar, whilst

---

daily specials keep the menu interesting. River at the rear.
🏨 Q ☎ ❀ ◖▶ ⚲ ♣ P

Lowestoft

Prince Albert

Park Road ☎ (01502) 573424
11–3, 7–11; 11–11 Sat
Adnams Mild, Bitter, Old, Broadside H
Modern, back-street pub comprising three rooms. Food is home-made (no meals Sun).
❀ ◖▶ ♣ P

Welcome

182 London Road
☎ (01502) 585500
10.30–4, 7.30–11
Adnams Bitter, Old, Extra (summer); **Bass Worthington BB; Greene King IPA, Abbot** H
Traditional, main street tavern, where the long single room is bedecked with mementoes of Lowestoft's maritime heritage. Simple hospitality with a warm welcome. ⚓ ♣

Newbourn

Fox

The Street ☎ (01473) 736307
11–3, 5.30–11
Greene King IPA; Tolly Cobbold Bitter G
Pub with its origins in the 14th century, featuring a tiled floor, oak beams and a real fire, with no electronic games or music. It also houses the only skittle alley left in a Suffolk pub. No-smoking family room.
🏨 Q ☎ ❀ ◖▶ ⚲ ▲ ♣ P ⌿

Try also: Ship, Levington (Pubmaster)

Newmarket

Five Bells

16 St Mary's Square
☎ (01638) 664961
11–3, 6–11; 11–11 Fri & Sat
Greene King XX Mild, IPA, Abbot H
Traditional, one-bar local with much team participation in various activities. Attractive garden at the rear with children's amusements. Limited parking.
🏨 ❀ ◖▶ ♣ P

Pin Mill

Butt & Oyster

☎ (01473) 780764
11–3, 7–11; 11–11 Sat & summer
Draught Bass; Tolly Cobbold Mild, Bitter H / G, **Original, Old Strong, Tollyshooter** H
Classic riverside pub featured in just about everything from Arthur Ransome's books to the BBC's *Lovejoy*. It is also a

---

perennial *Guide* entry and was CAMRA's regional *Pub of the Year* 1992. Not to be missed.
🏨 Q ❀ ◖▶ P

Try also: Bakers Arms, Harkstead (Pubmaster)

Rattlesden

Five Bells

High Street ☎ (01449) 737373
11–11
Adnams Bitter; Hook Norton Old Hooky; Morland Old Speckled Hen; Ridleys IPA; Wadworth 6X; Whitbread Boddingtons Bitter H
Small, relaxed drinking pub next to the church and overlooking the village: one bar rotating a good range of varying beers. Dog friendly.
🏨 Q ❀ ♣ P

Rumburgh

Buck

Mill Road ☎ (0198 685) 257
11–2.30, 5.30–11
Adnams Bitter; Greene King IPA; guest beer (occasional) H
Historic inn, refurbished and extended to give a number of interlinked areas which maintain their individual identities. 🏨 ❀ ◖▶ ♣ P

Shottisham

Sorrel Horse

☎ (01394) 411617
11–2.30, 6.30–11
Tolly Cobbold Mild, Bitter, Old Strong; guest beer G
A traditional basic bar greets the traveller at this picturesque, thatched pub. Low beams and a bar billiards table provide adequate furnishings. Interesting menu.
🏨 Q ◖▶ ⚲ ♣ P

Sibton

White Horse

Halesworth Road (off A1120 at Peasenhall garage)
☎ (0172 879) 337
11.30–2.30, 7–11
Adnams Bitter, Broadside H
16th-century inn with a raised gallery and a separate dining room (well-behaved children welcome). Large garden and play area. Occasional cider.
🏨 ❀ 🍴 ◖▶ ⚲ ♣ ⌂ P

Southwold

Lord Nelson

East Street ☎ (01502) 722079
10.30–11
Adnams Mild, Bitter, Old, Broadside, Tally Ho H
Always busy, a friendly pub serving the cheapest beer in

town, close to sea cliffs. Note the collection of 250 soda syphons around the one room. 🏚 🛏 ◐ ▶ ♿ ⚑ ♣

Try also: All other Adnams pubs in Southwold

Sproughton

Beagle
Old Hadleigh Road (dead-end road off B1113, close to A1071 jct) ☎ (01473) 730455
11–2.30, 5–11
Adnams Mild, Bitter, Broadside; Greene King IPA, Abbot; Mauldons Bitter; guest beers H
Excellent two-bar pub which can be difficult to find: originally four cottages, converted in 1986. Children over five welcome.
🏚 Q 🛏 ❀ ◐ ♿ ♣ P

Stowmarket

Royal William
52 Union Street (up Stowupland St from station) ☎ (01449) 674553
11–3, 6–11
Greene King XX Mild, IPA, Abbot, Winter Ale G
A good example of a small town pub still serving beer by gravity dispense from a room behind the bar. A popular games venue. ❀ ◐ ▶ ▲ ⇌ ♣

Stradbroke

Queens Head
Queen Street ☎ (01379) 384384
11–3, 6.30–11
Adnams Bitter, Old, Extra (summer); **Greene King IPA, Abbot** H
Pub where the spacious interior is divided by a large fireplace. Naval memorabilia in the lounge; large collection of board games. Barbecues in summer.
🏚 ❀ 🛌 ◐ ▶ ♿ ▲ ♣ P

Stradishall

Cherry Tree
Bury Road (A143) ☎ (01440) 820215
11.30–2.30, 6–11
Greene King IPA, Abbot H
Farmhouse converted to pub use in the 1940s, offering good food in the two bars and a restaurant for CC members. Camping for CC members. 🏚 ❀ ◐ ▶ ▲ P

Sudbury

Waggon & Horses
Alton Square ☎ (01787) 312147
11–3, 6.30–11; 11–11 Sat & summer
Greene King IPA H
Revitalised back-street pub

with a public bar, a games room, a restaurant and a snug. The architecture incorporates several different styles and ages. Next to the site of the old Phoenix brewery. Note: a cask breather is used on the Mild and Abbot. Eve meals Mon–Wed, if booked.
🏚 🛏 ❀ 🛌 ◐ ⇌ ♣ P

Tattingstone

White Horse
White Horse Hill (½ mile N of village, over Leamons Hill bridge) ☎ (01473) 328060
11–3, 7–11
Greene King IPA; Tetley Bitter; Tolly Cobbold Mild, Bitter H
Pub where the timbered bar area has an adjoining dining room and the comfortable family room is well-stocked with games. Good value food.
🏚 🛏 ❀ ◐ ▶ ♣ P

Tostock

Gardeners Arms
Church Road ☎ (01359) 70460
11.30–2.30, 7–11
Greene King IPA, Rayments Special, Abbot H
Old building with original beams near the village green. The basic public bar has church pews and a tiled floor; the comfortable lounge has a large, open fireplace. Good food (no meals Sun lunch or Mon/Tue eves). Steel quoits played. 🏚 ❀ ◐ ▶ 🛌 ♣ P

Upper Layham

Marquis of Cornwallis
On B1070 ☎ (01473) 822051
11–3, 6–11 (11–11 Sat in summer)
Adnams Bitter, Extra; guest beer (summer) H
Warm and cosy, 16th-century inn which specialises in food. The large garden slopes down to the River Brett.
🏚 Q 🛏 ❀ 🛌 ◐ ▶ ▲ P

Walberswick

Bell
☎ (01502) 723109
11–11
Adnams Bitter, Old, Extra, Broadside H
600-year-old, classic inn by the sea, with high-back settles and flagstone and brick floors. Fine views; large garden.
🏚 Q 🛏 ❀ 🛌 ◐ ▶ ♿ ▲ ♣ P

Try also: Ship, Dunwich (Free)

Walton

Tap & Spile
303 High Street
☎ (01394) 282130

11–4, 5.30–11; 11–11 Fri & Sat
Adnams Bitter; guest beers H
Very friendly pub with an excellent play area for children, good bar snacks and numerous, interesting guest beers. Still referred to as the Half Moon. 🏚 Q ❀ ♣ P

Whatfield

Four Horseshoes
The Street ☎ (01473) 827971
11–2.30, 5.30–11
Adnams Bitter, Broadside; Greene King IPA; Nethergate Bitter; guest beers H
Traditional, two-bar pub where the landlord's interest in Napoleonic history is evident. 🏚 ❀ ◐ ▶ 🛌 ♣ P

Woodbridge

Kings Head
Market Square
☎ (01394) 387750
11–3, 7–11
Adnams Bitter, Old, Extra, Broadside; Whitbread Boddingtons Bitter H
Busy, two-bar pub, very popular with young drinkers.
🏚 Q ❀ ◐ ▶ ⇌

Seckford Arms
Seckford Street
☎ (01394) 384446
11–11
Adnams Bitter; Draught Bass; Nethergate Old Growler; Scott's Blues and Bloater H
Family-run free house, with two comfortable bars and additional rooms (one 16th-century). South American food a speciality. Welcoming landlord. Q 🛏 ❀ ◐ ▶ ⇌

Tap & Spile
New Street
☎ (01394) 382679
11–3, 5.30–11; 11–11 Sat
Adnams Bitter; Marston's Pedigree; Wells Eagle; guest beers H
Unpretentious boozer, formerly the Mariners Arms. Beers regularly change, with 261 sampled in three years. Jazz and folk sessions on Mon and Wed. Q ❀ ⇌ ♣ ⌣ P

Yaxley

Bull
Ipswich Road
☎ (01379) 783604
11–3, 5–11; 11–11 Fri & Sat
Adnams Bitter; Nethergate Old Growler; Woodforde's Wherry; guest beers (summer)
16th-century, genuine free house with bags of character beneath its high, beamed roof. Good food.
Q ❀ 🛌 ◐ ▶ ▲ ♣ P

279

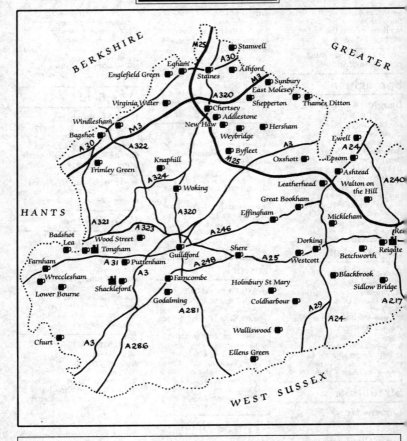

🏰 **Cyder House**, *Shackleford;* **Hogs Back**, *Tongham;*
Pilgrim, *Reigate*

Addlestone

Magnet
21 Station Road (B3121)
☎ (01932) 847908
11–11
Greene King IPA, Abbot H
First licensed around 1869, this
pub's name originally referred
to a magnet, drawing in
custom. Today, the inn sign
shows the famous old boys'
comic of that name. A pleasant
and comfortable pub.
🏨 Q ⊛ ◁ ⇌ ♣

Ashford

District Arms
180 Woodthorpe Road
☎ (01784) 252160
11–3, 5.30–11; 11–11 Sat
**Courage Best Bitter,
Directors; John Smith's Bitter;
guest beers** H

Cosy, one-roomed pub,
usually quiet. The food is
recommended.
🏨 Q ◁ ▷ ♣ P

Ashtead

Brewery Inn
The Street (A24)
☎ (01372) 272405
11–3, 5.30–11
**Ind Coope Friary Meux Best
Bitter, Burton Ale; King &
Barnes Sussex; Tetley Bitter;
guest beer** H
Pub on the site of George
Sayer's Ashtead Brewery.
Although always busy, it still
offers room for a quiet pint.
⊛ ◁ ▷ ⇌ ♣ P

Badshot Lea

Crown Inn
Pine View Close (off A324)
☎ (01252) 20453

10.30–11
**Fuller's Hock, Chiswick,
London Pride, Mr Harry,
ESB** H
Traditional, low-ceilinged,
friendly local, known
for its good value food
(not served Sun eve).
Q ⊛ ◁ ▷ ♣ P

Bagshot

Foresters Arms
173 London Road (A30)
☎ (01276) 472038
11–3, 5.30–11
**Courage Best Bitter; guest
beer** H
Comfortable and deceptively
roomy local with a convivial
atmosphere and a skittle
alley. Four guest beers
change regularly.
No food Sun.
Q ⊛ ◁ ♣ P

Surrey

Guide for 21 consecutive years.
No food Mon eve. ❀ ◖ ▸ P ✕

Bletchingley

William IV

Little Common Lane (off A25)
☎ (01883) 743278
11–3, 6–11
**Bass Charrington IPA,
Draught Bass; Fuller's
London Pride; Hancock's HB;
Harveys BB; Pilgrim
Progress** H
Traditional country inn, away
from the village centre with
two small bars. Well known
locally for its food.
Q ❀ ◖ ▸ ⌺ P

Byfleet

Plough

104 High Road (off A245)
☎ (01932) 353257
11–3, 5.30–11
**Courage Best Bitter; guest
beer** H
A single bar offering friendly
local conversation and at least
five imaginative beers, often
including Ringwood and Hogs
Back brews. An excellent
home-cooked supper is served
Wed only. No food Sun.
🏠 Q ❀ ◖ ⇌ ♣ P

Caterham

King & Queen

34 High Street (B2030)
☎ (01883) 345438
11–3, 5–11; 11–11 Sat
**Fuller's Hock, Chiswick,
London Pride, Mr Harry,
ESB** H
This 400-year old building was
originally three cottages, but
was turned into a pub in the
1840s. Several linked drinking
areas. No food Sun.
🏠 Q ❀ ◖ ▸ ♣ P

Chertsey

Coach & Horses

14 St Ann's Road (B375)
☎ (01932) 563085
11–11
**Fuller's Chiswick, London
Pride, ESB** H
Interesting, corner, tile-hung
building dating from 1860, but
recently refurbished.
🏠 ⌺ ◖ ▸ ♣ P

Crown Hotel

London Street (B375)
☎ (01932) 564657
11–11
**Young's Bitter, Special,
Winter Warmer** H
A former coaching inn: the
present structure dates from
1899 and the large interior is in
the Young's 'built to last' style.
A 30-bed extension and

conservatory have been added.
❀ Q ❀ ❀ ⌺ ◖ ▸ ⬤ ⇌
♣ P ✕

Churt

Crossways Inn

Crossways Road (A287)
☎ (01428) 714323
11–3, 6 (5.30 summer)–11
**Courage Best Bitter; Hogs
Back TEA; S&N Theakston
XB; guest beer** H
First-class village local with
two good, contrasting bars and
a strong real ale following.
Many pub games. No food
Sun; quiz night Sun.
Q ❀ ◖ ⌺ ♣ P

Coldharbour

Plough Inn

Coldharbour Lane OS152441
☎ (01306) 711793
11.30–3, 6 (7 winter)–11
**Adnams Broadside; Gibbs
Mew Bishop's Tipple; Hall &
Woodhouse Badger Best
Bitter; Ringwood Old
Thumper; Wadworth 6X;
guest beers** H
Family-run free house in good
walking country, on the slopes
of Leith Hill. Ten beers plus a
cider are always available.
Good, traditional home
cooking. Children welcome
weekends and summer
lunchtimes.
🏠 ❀ ❀ ⌺ ◖ ▸ ♣ ⌂

Dorking

Bush

10 Horsham Road (A2003, 400
yds S of one-way system)
☎ (01306) 889830
11–2.30 (3 Sat), 6–11
**Brakspear Bitter; Fuller's
London Pride; Harveys BB;
Thwaites Bitter; guest beer** H
Friendly, well-run local with
its own marbles ring. Good
value, interesting food is
served, plus occasional
barbecues. Eve meals Tue–Sat.
❀ ◖ ▸ ♣

Kings Arms

45 West Street (A25, one-way
system) ☎ (01306) 883361
11–11
**Ind Coope Friary Meux Best
Bitter; King & Barnes Sussex;
Marston's Pedigree; Tetley
Bitter; Wadworth 6X; guest
beer** H
Originally three farmworkers'
cottages which became a
coaching inn in the 16th
century. One central bar offers
several drinking areas. The
guest beer (from
independents) changes
regularly. Eve meals Tue–Sat.
❀ ◖ ▸ ⇌ (West) ♣ P

Betchworth

Dolphin

The Street ☎ (01737) 842288
11–3, 5.30–11
**Young's Bitter, Porter,
Special, Winter Warmer** H
Attractive 16th-century inn in
a picturesque setting by the
church, featuring a solid
flagstone floor and inglenooks.
A magnet for walkers. Good
food. 🏠 Q ❀ ◖ ▸ ♣ P

**Try also: Royal Oak,
Brockham (Friary Meux)**

Blackbrook

Plough at Blackbrook

Blackbrook Road OS181466
☎ (01306) 886603
11–2.30 (3 Sat), 6–11
**King & Barnes Sussex,
Broadwood, Old, Festive** H
Two-bar country pub with a
justifiable reputation for food.
The Blackbrook Bar displays
saws on the ceiling and a
collection of 600 ties. In this

Surrey

Queens Head

Horsham Road (A25, one-way system) ☎ (01306) 883041
11–11
Fuller's Chiswick, London Pride, ESB H
Family-run pub fielding darts and pool teams. No food Sun.
⊛ ◖ ♣ P

East Molesey

Europa

171 Walton Road (B369)
☎ (0181) 979 5183
11–11
Courage Best Bitter, Directors; Marston's Pedigree; John Smith's Bitter H
Pub with three distinctive bars which stages live folk music on the last Sat in the month. Happy hour 5–7 Mon–Sat, 12–1, 7–8 Sun.
Q ⊛ ◖ ♿ ♣

Effingham

Plough Inn

Orestan Lane
☎ (01372) 458121
11–2.45, 6–11
Young's Bitter, Special, Winter Warmer H
One of Young's finest, and all the better for being off the beaten track. Quality food.
Q ⊛ ◖ ▶ ♿ P

Egham

Crown

38 High Street (off A30)
☎ (01784) 432608
11–3, 5.30–11
Courage Directors; S&N Theakston Mild, Best Bitter, XB, Old Peculier H
A pub has stood on this site since 1560. Unusually for the area, the present pub retains a separate public bar. No food Sun ⊛ ◖ ≱ ♣ P

Ellens Green

Wheatsheaf Inn

Off A281, signed Rudgwick
OS098359 ☎ (01403) 822155
11–3, 6–11
King & Barnes Mild, Sussex, Broadwood, Old, Festive H
17th-century, country roadside pub boasting low beams, brasses and wooden seating. The children's garden has play equipment, and even their own toilets. No food Sun eve.
♨ Q ⊛ ◖ ▶ ♿ ♠ ♣ P

Englefield Green

Happy Man

12 Harvest Road (off A30)
☎ (01784) 433265
11–11

Courage Directors; John Smith's Bitter; Tetley Bitter H
Small pub, popular with students from the local college. Built in 1929, it has a good, homely atmosphere. Good value food is always available.
⊛ ◖ ▶ ♣

Epsom

Barley Mow

12 Pikes Hill ☎ (01372) 721044
11–3, 5.30–11
Fuller's Hock, London Pride, Mr Harry, ESB H, **Golden Pride** G
Back-street local that attracts all types. The rear conservatory backs on to a pleasant garden. Q ⊛ ◖ ▶

Kings Arms

144 East Street (A24)
☎ (01372) 723892
11–3, 5.30–11; 11–11 Sat
Young's Bitter, Porter (summer), **Special, Winter Warmer** H
A basic public bar and a plush lounge shield this pub's attractive garden from the busy A24. No food Sun.
⊛ ◖ ♿ ♣ P

Ewell

King William IV

19 High Street (B2200)
☎ (0181) 393 2063
11–11
Ind Coope Friary Meux Best Bitter, Burton Ale; Tetley Bitter H
Inviting local which stages frequent quizzes and live music. Note the original etched windows. No food Sun.
⊛ ◖ ♿ ≱ (West/East) ♣ P

Farncombe

Cricketers

37 Nightingale Road
☎ (01483) 420273
12–3 (3.30 Fri & Sat), 5.30–11
Fuller's Hock, Chiswick, London Pride, Mr Harry, ESB H
Splendid, friendly local which is usually crowded, especially on Mon quiz night. Wide range of customers.
⊛ ◖ ▶ ≱ ♣

Farnham

Hop Blossom

Long Garden Walk, Castle Street ☎ (01252) 710770
12–2.30, 4.45–11; 11–11 Fri & Sat
Fuller's London Pride, ESB H
Live and recorded jazz both feature regularly at this idiosyncratic back-street pub. Drinkers vie for elbow room

---

with gnomes, inflatables and other manifestations of the landlord's sense of humour.
◖ ≱ ♣

Lamb

43 Abbey Street (off A287)
☎ (01252) 714133
11–3, 6–11
Shepherd Neame Master Brew Bitter, Best Bitter, Porter, Bishops Finger H
Friendly, no-nonsense, cosy back-street local with a roaring log fire, two big dogs and excellent value food. Can be smoky. No food Tue eve or Sun. ♨ ⊛ ◖ ▶ ≱ ♣

Shepherd & Flock

22 Moor Park Lane (on A31 Bourne Mill roundabout)
☎ (01252) 716675
11–3, 5.30–11; 11–11 Sat
Courage Best Bitter; Fuller's London Pride; John Smith's Bitter; guest beer H
This pleasant and well-run, cottage-like pub and restaurant, although on a large roundabout, has a peaceful air. Up to eight real ales available. Live music Sat. Eve meals Tue–Sat. ⊛ ◖ ▶ ♣ P

Frimley Green

Old Wheatsheaf

205 Frimley Green Road (A321) ☎ (01252) 835074
11–3, 5–11; 11–11 Sat
Morland Bitter, Old Masters, Old Speckled Hen; guest beer H
100-year-old village local, now refurbished into a single bar with wood-panelled alcoves. Good lunch trade. The bookable skittle alley becomes a family room Sun lunchtimes. No food Sun. ⊛ ◖ ♣ P

Godalming

Anchor Inn

110 Ockford Road (A3100)
☎ (01483) 417085
12–3, 5.30 (6 Sat)–11
Draught Bass; Brakspear Bitter; Hall & Woodhouse Tanglefoot; Hogs Back TEA; guest beer H
Very busy, comfortable pub with a large L-shaped bar area, serving regularly changing guest beers, plus occasional ciders in summer. ⊛ ◖ ≱ ♣

Red Lion

Mill Lane ☎ (01483) 415207
11–11; 11–3, 6.30–11 Sat
Courage Best Bitter, Directors; Wadworth 6X; guest beer H
Large, two-bar, town-centre pub, comprising a games-oriented public and a quiet

lounge bar. Lively and popular, it has an imaginative guest beer policy. No food Sun eve. ✿ ◖ ◖ ◗ ⊕ ⇌ ♣

Great Bookham

Anchor

161 Lower Road (off A246, via Eastwick Rd)
☎ (01372) 452429
11–2.30 (4 Sat), 5.30–11
Courage Best Bitter, Directors; Pilgrim Surrey H
500-year-old local that only looks its age on the inside. Two fireplaces maintain a cosy atmosphere. No food Sun.
✿ Q ✿ ◖ ◗

Guildford

Kings Head

27 Kings Road (A320)
☎ (01483) 68957
11–3, 5–11
Fuller's Hock, Chiswick, London Pride, ESB H
Extended, multi-roomed pub with bare-board flooring. Friendly local atmosphere with good value beer and food (no meals Sun eve). Busy at lunchtime with students.
✿ ◖ ◗ ⇌ (London Rd) ♣ ✂

Sanford Arms

58 Epsom Road (A246)
☎ (01483) 572551
11–2.40, 5.30–11; 11.30–3.10, 6–11 Sat
Courage Best Bitter; Wadworth 6X; guest beer H
Friendly, wood-panelled local, with well-separated bars. The garden has an aviary and a small conservatory. The guest beer (from independent breweries) changes regularly. No food Sun eve. Q ✿ ◖ ◗ ⊕ ⇌ (London Rd) ♣

Spread Eagle

46 Chertsey Street (A320)
☎ (01483) 35018
10.30–2.30 (3 Fri, 3.30 Sat), 5–11
Courage Best Bitter, Directors; John Smith's Bitter; Young's Special; guest beer H
Close to the town centre, this popular pub serves good value lunches (Mon–Sat). An adventurous guest beer policy guarantees an interesting choice; nearly 250 different guests in three years. Busy weekend eves. ◖ ⇌ ♣ P

Hersham

Bricklayers Arms

6 Queens Road (off A317)
☎ (01932) 220936
11–11
Courage Best Bitter; Fuller's London Pride; Hall & Woodhouse Tanglefoot; Marston's Pedigree;

Wadworth 6X; Webster's Yorkshire Bitter H
Cosy Victorian pub retaining two bars, and offering spectacular floral displays in summer. No food weekend eves. ✿ ⋈ ◖ ◗ ⊕ ⅙ ♣

Royal George

130 Hersham Road (off A244)
☎ (01932) 220910
11–3, 5.30–11; 11–11 Sat
Young's Bitter, Special, Winter Warmer H
Traditional, family-oriented, post-war local with two spacious bars, displaying nautical memorabilia.
✿ Q ✿ ◖ ⊕ ⅙ ♣ P

Holmbury St Mary

Kings Head

Pitland Street (off B2126, follow signs to 'MSSL')
☎ (01306) 730282
11–3, 6–11; 11–11 Sat
Brakspear Bitter; Fuller's London Pride; Ringwood Best Bitter, Old Thumper; guest beer H
Very good village local with unusual church-arched doors and wooden pews. The imaginative layout includes a games/TV area. The large garden benefits from lovely views. The beer range may vary. No eve meals Sun.
✿ ✿ ◖ ◗ ♣ P

Knaphill

Garibaldi

136 High Street
☎ (01483) 473374
11–11
Beer range varies H
Small, two-bar pub with an interesting and changing range of guest beers. Good children's playground in the garden. No food Sun. Q ✿ ◖ ⊕ ♣ P

Leatherhead

Plough

93 Kingston Road
☎ (01372) 377608
11–3, 5.30–11; 11–11 Sat
Hogs Back TEA; Tetley Bitter; guest beers H
Pleasant, wood-panelled pub sitting on a roundabout. The two guest beers change frequently. No food Sun, quiz day. ◖ ◗ ⇌ ♣ P

Lower Bourne

Spotted Cow

3 Bourne Grove (signed off Farnham–Tilford road)
☎ (01252) 726541
11.30–2.30, 6–11
Adnams Old; Brakspear Special; Courage Best Bitter;

John Smith's Bitter H
Tucked away down a narrow lane and in an extensive garden, a pub with an accent on food. Occasional live music, normally jazz. Another guest beer is possible in summer. Eve meals Tue-Sat.
Q ✿ ◖ ◗ P

Merstham

Inn on the Pond

Nutfield Marsh Road (½ mile N of A25) OS303515
☎ (01737) 643000
11.30–3, 5.30 (6 Sat)–11
Greene King Abbot; Hogs Back TEA; Pilgrim Surrey; guest beer H
A pub since 1988, although the building is much older, boasting original beams, two real fires and a large conservatory. Several clubs meet here and there is a bookable squash court. No food Sun eve. ✿ ✿ ◖ ◗ P

Mickleham

King William IV

Byttom Hill (off A24, southbound) ☎ (01372) 372590
11–3, 6–11
Adnams Bitter; Hall & Woodhouse Badger Best Bitter; Hogs Back TEA; Whitbread Boddingtons Bitter H
Pub which perches precariously on a hillside, opposite Norbury Park. Its extensive menu (no meals Mon eve) includes a range of vegetarian delights.
✿ Q ✿ ◖

New Haw

White Hart

New Haw Road (A318)
☎ (01932) 842927
11.30–3, 5.30 (5 Sat)–11
Courage Best Bitter, Directors; John Smith's Bitter H
Friendly pub dating from the 1850s, built on the banks of the Wey Navigation. Sup in the comfortable bar or in the pleasant canalside garden.
Q ✿ ♣ P

Oxshott

Bear

Leatherhead Road (A244)
☎ (01372) 842747
11–3, 5.30–11
Young's Bitter, Special, Winter Warmer H
Open-plan pub with a large conservatory, where children are allowed; comfortably-appointed. Extensive menu of home-cooked food.
✿ Q ⅔ ✿ ◖ ◗ ♣ P

Surrey

Oxted

Crown Inn
53 High Street, Old Oxted (off A25) ☎ (01883) 717853
12–3, 6–11
Adnams Bitter; Fuller's London Pride; King & Barnes Sussex; Pilgrim Porter H
Dating in part from the 16th century, this pub has bars on two levels, with a family room at the top (open at weekends). The large, safe garden features petanque. No eve meals Sun.
🏠 ❀ ◖ ♣ ♠

George Inn
52 High Street, Old Oxted (off A25) ☎ (01883) 713453
11–11
Adnams Bitter; Draught Bass; Fuller's London Pride; Harveys Sussex; Morland Old Speckled Hen; Wadworth 6X H
Friendly, well-renovated, 500-year-old pub serving excellent food. Only one bar, but plenty of comfortable seating areas. 🏠 Q ❀ ◖ ▶ P

Puttenham

Good Intent
62 The Street (off B3000 near church) ☎ (01483) 810387
11–2.30, 6–11; 11–11 Sat
Courage Best Bitter; Wadworth 6X; guest beer H
Very pleasant, comfortable, 16th-century former coaching inn offering interesting guest beers and bar meals. Popular with locals, diners and walkers from the nearby North Downs Way. Eve meals Tue–Sat.
🏠 ❀ ◖ ▶ ♣ ⌂ P

Redhill

Home Cottage
Redstone Hill (A25)
☎ (01737) 762771
10.30–11
Young's Bitter, Porter, Special, Winter Warmer H
Victorian pub at the back of the station. Note the ancient bank of handpumps in the front bar. Children welcome in the conservatory.
🏠 ❀ ◖ ▶ ≈ ♣ P

Reigate

Nutley Hall
8 Nutley Lane (just off the town centre, by northern car park) ☎ (01737) 241741
11–11
King & Barnes Mild, Sussex, Broadwood, Old, Festive H
An active drinkers' pub which has its own cricket and football teams; sometimes very

busy at weekends. King & Barnes seasonal ales are stocked. ❀ ◖ ▶ ≈ ♣ P

Yew Tree
99 Reigate Hill (A217)
☎ (01737) 244944
11–11
Courage Best Bitter, Directors; John Smith's Bitter; Wadworth 6X; Young's Bitter H
Pub enjoying busy lunch and early eve trade and offering comfortable, wood-panelled surroundings. The food is good value. 🏠 ❀ ◖ ▶ P

Shackleford

Cyder House Inn
Peperharow Lane OS935453
☎ (01483) 810360
11–3.30, 5.30–11
Hall & Woodhouse Badger Best Bitter; Ringwood Fortyniner; Wadworth 6X; guest beer H
In the heart of good walking country, a popular, well-run, pub-brewery which can be crowded with diners for Sun lunch. Six beers, including one home-brewed beer, plus cider in summer.
🏠 Q ❀ ◖ ♣ ⌂ P

Shepperton

Barley Mow
67 Watersplash Road (off B376 at Shepperton Green)
☎ (01932) 225580
11–11
Adnams Broadside; Courage Best Bitter; Webster's Yorkshire Bitter; guest beer H
Friendly neighbourhood local which, although only one bar, provides separate areas in which to drink or have a meal. Quiz nights. 🏠 ❀ 🚐 ◖ ▶ P

Shere

Prince of Wales
Shere Lane ☎ (01483) 202313
11–2.30, 6–11
Young's Bitter, Porter, Special, Winter Warmer H
Pub in a delightful village with a pretty stream. A small public bar, dominated by pool, contrasts with a more sedate lounge, often used by diners. Excellent children's facilities.
🏠 Q ♿ ❀ ◖ 🍴 ♣ P

Sidlow Bridge

Three Horseshoes
Ironsbottom (off A217)
OS249463 ☎ (01293) 862315
11.45–2.30 (3 Fri & Sat), 7 (6 Fri)–11; 11.45–11 summer Sat
Fuller's London Pride, ESB; Harveys BB; Morland Old Speckled Hen; guest beer H

Small rural pub which welcomes helicopters (phone in advance) but not motorcyclists; the home of many devoted regulars. Large garden. No food Sun eve.
◖ ▶ ♣ P ✗

Staines

Hobgoblin
14 Church Street
☎ (01784) 452012
11–11
Wychwood Shires, Best, Dr Thirsty's Draught, Black Wych, Hobgoblin; guest beers H
Since its transformation into Wychwood's first tied house, this pub has gone from strength to strength. Now deservedly SE CAMRA *Pub of the Year*, offering both public bar and lounge areas.
🏠 ◖ ♿ ≈ ♣

North Star
52 Kingston Road (off A308)
☎ (01784) 450736
11–11
Adnams Bitter; Courage Best Bitter, Directors; Wadworth 6X; guest beer H
Named after an old GWR loco of 1837, a well-designed, open-plan pub, popular with all. Excellent food. Q ❀ ◖ ≈

Stanwell

Wheatsheaf
Town Lane (B378)
☎ (01784) 253372
11–11; 11–4, 7–11 Sat
Courage Best Bitter, Directors; Marston's Pedigree H
Small, traditional village pub with a big welcome. Its low-beamed interior can become cheerfully populous at times. Q ❀ ◖ ▶ P

Sunbury

Hare & Hounds
132 Vicarage Road (½ mile from Sunbury Cross, signed Feltham) ☎ (01932) 761478
11–11
Fuller's Chiswick, London Pride, ESB H
Large roadside inn with two bars. The spacious garden has children's games. Pool and darts also available.
🏠 ❀ ◖ ▶ ≈ ♣ P

Thames Ditton

Angel
Portsmouth Road
☎ (0181) 398 4511
10.30–3.30, 5.30–11; 11–11 Sat
Courage Best Bitter, Directors; Wadworth 6X; Young's Bitter H

Set opposite Giggs Hill Green, a bay-windowed pub boasting low ceilings and exposed beams. Q ♿ 🏠 🍴 ➡ ♣ P

Titsey

Botley Hill Farmhouse
Limpsfield Road, Warlingham (B269) ☎ (01959) 577154
11–11
Greene King XX Mild, IPA, Abbot; Pilgrim Progress; Shepherd Neame Master Brew Bitter, Spitfire, Bishops Finger; guest beer H
A converted farmhouse, originally owned by King Henry VIII, which is now a country pub/restaurant (good food). 🏠 Q 🏠 🍴 ▶ P

Tongham

Hogs Back Brewery
Manor Farm, The Street (A3014) ☎ (01252) 782328
9–6 (8 Wed for tours)
Hogs Back Mild, TEA, Blackwater Porter, Hop Garden Gold, Rip Snorter, Olde Tongham Tastie G
Brewery off-licence selling most of the Hogs Back range (CAMRA discount). Extensive choice of foreign bottled beers, too. ⌂ P

Virginia Water

Stag & Hounds
Wellington Avenue (off B389) ☎ (01344) 842253
11–11
Morland Bitter, Old Masters; guest beer H
Built in the 1840s and rebuilt in 1925, a pub popular with ramblers, golfers and families in summer. The guest and Morland beers change regularly. Q 🏠 🍴 ▶ ♣ P

Walliswood

Scarlett Arms
Walliswood Green Road OS119382 ☎ (01306) 627243
11–2.30, 5.30–11
King & Barnes Mild, Sussex, Broadwood, Old, Festive H
A classic pub, which was converted 87 years ago from two cottages, built in 1620. It features low beams, an inglenook, and a stone-flagged floor. 🏠 Q 🏠 🍴 ▶ ♣ P

Walton on the Hill

Chequers
Chequers Lane ☎ (01737) 812364
11–3, 5.30–11; 11–11 Fri & Sat
Young's Bitter, Porter, Special, Winter Warmer H

Dating from around 1800, this building at one time housed a brewhouse and bakery. Four different drinking areas are now set around a central bar. The rear section, with a tiled floor, has the feel of a public bar. 🏠 Q 🏠 ▶ 🍴 ♿ ♣ P

Warlingham

Hare & Hounds
Limpsfield Road (B269) ☎ (01883) 623952
11–11
Fuller's London Pride; Harveys BB; M&B Highgate Dark; Stones Best Bitter H
Lively local with many societies and charity fund-raising events. One horseshoe-shaped bar. No food Sun. 🏠 🏠 🍴 ♣ P

Westcott

Prince of Wales
Guildford Road (A25) ☎ (01306) 889699
11–3, 5.30 (6 winter)–11
Fuller's Hock, Chiswick, London Pride, ESB H
One-bar pub whose separate games room offers darts and two pool tables. 🏠 🍴 ▶ ♣ P

Weybridge

Old Crown
83 Thames Street (off A317) ☎ (01932) 842844
10.30–11
Courage Best Bitter, Directors; Wadworth 6X H
Grade II-listed, 16th-century pub with a weatherboarded facade, divided into several rooms. Fish is a speciality (meals served all day Sat). Q 🏠 🍴 ▶ ♣ P

Prince of Wales
11 Cross Road, Oatlands Park ☎ (01932) 852082
11–11
Adnams Bitter; Fuller's London Pride; Tetley Bitter; Wadworth 6X; Whitbread Boddingtons Bitter H
Popular, cosy pub with traditional decor. The restaurant has a good value menu (no food Sun eve). No children allowed in the garden. Q 🏠 🍴 ▶ P

Windlesham

Windmill Inn
London Road (A30) ☎ (01276) 472281
11–3, 5–11; 11–11 Fri & Sat
Adnams Broadside; Gibbs Mew Bishop's Tipple; Hampshire Pendragon; Hop Back Summer Lightning; Woodforde's Headcracker H

An enterprising pub which usually fields ten or more beers, with regular beer festivals. A long, single bar serves two comfortable areas. Occasional gravity-dispensed beers. Q 🏠 🍴 ▶ P

Woking

Mayford Arms
Guildford Road ☎ (01483) 761018
11–2.30 (3 Sat), 5.30–11
Greene King XX Mild, IPA, Rayments Special, Abbot, Winter Ale H
Early 20th-century pub which has a games room plus a dining area. Children appreciate the garden. A new bypass has boosted local trade. No food Sun eve. 🏠 🛏 🍴 ♣ P

Wood Street

White Hart
White Hart Lane ☎ (01483) 235939
11–3, 5.30–11
Draught Bass; Brakspear Bitter; Ruddles County; Young's Special H
Picturesque village pub with a beamed interior: one large, square bar with an adjacent restaurant. Eight beers are usually available; summer mini-beer festivals. Q 🏠 🍴 ▶ ♿ ▲ ♣ P

Wrecclesham

Bat & Ball
Bat & Ball Lane, Boundstone (off Upper Bourne Lane, off Sandrock Hill Rd) OS833444 ☎ (01252) 794564
12–11
Brakspear Bitter; Fuller's London Pride; Young's Special; guest beer H
Secluded free house with good family facilities. Excellent home-made food (not served Sun); a changing range of seven real ales. Q ♿ 🏠 🍴 ♣ P

Sandrock
Sandrock Hill Road (B3384) ☎ (01252) 715865
11–11
Batham Mild, Best Bitter; Brakspear Bitter; Cheriton Pots Ale; Taylor Landlord; guest beer H
A recent CAMRA regional *Pub of the Year*, this comfortable, functional pub is seldom surpassed for beer range and quality: eight beers usually available. Good food, too (no meals Sun). 🏠 Q 🏠 🍴 ♣ P

East Sussex

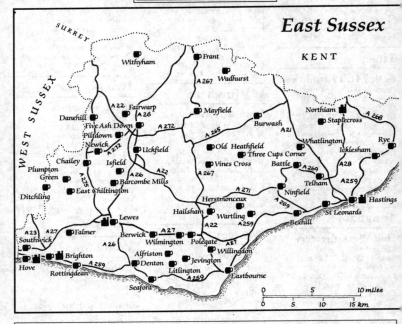

East Sussex

 First In, Last Out, *Hastings;* **Harveys,** *Lewes;*
Hedgehog & Hogshead, *Hove;* **Kemptown,** *Brighton;*
Rother Valley, *Northiam*

Alfriston

Market Cross/
Smugglers
Waterloo Square
☎ (01323) 870241
11–2.30 (3 Sat), 6.30–11
**Courage Best Bitter,
Directors; Harveys BB, Old** H
In the centre of a very
attractive, tourist-oriented
village, this pub has real
atmosphere, with its huge
inglenook, large collection of
early kitchen implements, and
pleasant, no-smoking
conservatory. It really does
have two names—and,
allegedly, two ghosts.
Q ✿ ● ▷ ♣ ☼

Barcombe Mills

Anglers Rest
Mill Road (1 mile W of A26)
OS428150 ☎ (01273) 400270
11.30–2.30 (3 Sat), 6–11
**Harveys BB, Old; guest
beers** H
Single-bar pub in a rural
location, next to an old railway
station and close to the River
Ouse. Garden play area and
extensive collection of
miniatures. No meals Sun eve.
✿ ▷ ● ▷ ▲ ♣ P

Battle

1066
High Street
☎ (01424) 773224
10–3, 5–11; 10–11 Fri, Sat & summer
**Wadworth 6X; Whitbread
Boddingtons Bitter,
Fremlins Bitter;
guest beers** H
Busy and lively, split-level
pub near the abbey. The
folk/blues club Sun eves often
features big names. Function
room and restaurant upstairs.
Is this still Britain's only
year-named pub?
✿ ✿ ● ▷ ▲ ⇌ ♣

Squirrel
North Trade Road
(A271, 1¾ miles from centre)
☎ (01424) 772717
11–3, 5–11; 11–11 Sat & summer
**Fuller's London Pride; Greene
King Abbot; Harveys BB;
Shepherd Neame Bishops
Finger; Wadworth 6X; guest
beers** H
A welcome addition to the
Guide: a pub with a friendly
atmosphere and always a
good range of beers. Good
food; separate restaurant.
Pool/family room.
✿ ⛺ ✿ ● ▷ ▲ ♣ P ⚄

Berwick

Cricketers Arms
100 yds S of A27 near Alfriston
(Drusilla's Island) OS519053
☎ (01323) 870469
11–3, 6–11
Harveys BB, Old G
Totally unspoilt country pub
with several rooms, just off the
main road, but completely
rural in situation and outlook.
The gravity dispense and lack
of emphasis on food are real
rarities in this area (eve meals
Thu–Sat only in winter).
Harveys seasonal brews also
sold. ✿ Q ✿ ● ▷ ⚄ ♣ P

Bexhill

Sportsman
15 Sackville Road
☎ (01424) 214214
10.30–11
**Eldridge Pope Royal Oak;
Harveys BB; King & Barnes
Festive; Webster's Yorkshire
Bitter** H
Small, cosy town-centre pub
with an outgoing landlady and
sociable locals. Suntrap beer
gardens. The only pub in town
selling a decent range of beers.
✿ ● ⇌

Brighton

Albion
28 Albion Hill (behind the former Tamplins brewery) ☎ (01273) 604439
11–11
Brakspear Bitter; Marston's Pedigree; Whitbread Boddingtons Mild, Bitter; guest beer H
Unspoilt corner local situated on a steep hill, causing an unusual split-level bar. Described as friendly in the 1930s, and it still is! A very popular games venue, which has appeared in every *Guide* since 1977. The guest beer is almost always from an independent brewer. ❀ ♣

Basketmakers Arms
12 Gloucester Road (300 yds SE of station) ☎ (01273) 689006
11–3, 5.30–11; 11–11 Fri & Sat
Gale's BBB, Best Bitter, 5X, HSB H
Popular and lively, back-street pub with live music on Sun nights. The interior is a cornucopia of old tins and other ephemera. Note: all cider is keg. ◖ & ⇌

Bugle
24 St Martins Street (N of the Level, off Lewes Rd, behind the church) ☎ (01273) 607753
11–3, 6–11; 11–11 Fri & Sat
Courage Best Bitter, Directors; Harveys BB; Young's Special H
Hard to find but well worth seeking out: a real local as yet unrestored, with a central bar area giving rise to a number of cosy corners, often busy. ❀

Evening Star
56 Surrey Street (200 yds S of station) ☎ (01273) 328931
11–3.30, 5–11; 11–11 Fri & Sat
Arundel ESB; Brewery on Sea Spinnaker Bitter; Cheriton Diggers' Gold; Cotleigh Harrier SPA; Hogs Back TEA; Otter Bitter; guest beers H
Back to the roots, real ale pub with church pews, a wooden floor and no electronic games. Background music at a reasonable volume. Billed as Brighton's permanent real ale festival, with nine pumps pulling well over 600 different beers since opening in March 1992. No food Sun. ◖ ⇌ ↺

Greys
105 Southover Street (up steep hill, E of the Level) ☎ (01273) 680734
11–3, 5.30–11; 11–11 Fri & Sat
Brakspear Bitter; Wadworth 6X; Whitbread Flowers Original; Young's Special H

Very much part of the local music scene, a pub with its small bar adorned with posters for local events. Live bands somehow squeeze in Sun lunch and Mon eve. Food, which includes vegetarian, is recommended. Small selection of bottled Belgian beers sold. ❀ ◖

Hand in Hand
33 Upper St James Street, Kemptown (E of centre) ☎ (01273) 602521
11–11
Hall & Woodhouse Badger Best Bitter, Tanglefoot; Kemptown Budget Bitter, Best Bitter, Celebrated Staggering Ale, SID H
Popular, one-bar corner local, home to Brighton's only brewery, featuring fascinating decor and excellent food. Probably the smallest brew pub in the country. ◖

Hobgoblin
31 York Place ☎ (01273) 602519
11–11
Courage Best Bitter, Directors; Wychwood Best, Hobgoblin H
Large, two room, ex-Charrington, main road pub with bare boards and walls decorated with old photos and breweriana, including mirrors and enamel adverts. The music catering for the mainly student clientele can be loud in the eve. Crowded happy hour 7–8, Mon–Sat. ♨ ◖ ▸ &

Lamb & Flag
9 Cranbourne Street (near clock tower) ☎ (01273) 326415
10.30–11; closed Sun
Fuller's London Pride; Kemptown Budget Bitter H
Comfortable bar near the Western Rd shopping area. Popular at lunchtimes with shoppers and office workers; quieter in the eve. ◖ ⇌

Lion & Lobster
24 Sillwood Street (100 yds S of Norfolk Sq) ☎ (01273) 720223
11–3, 5.30–11; 11–11 Fri & Sat
Beer range varies H
Large, street-corner pub with a regularly changing selection of five beers. Popular with a varied clientele. ◖ ▸

Lord Nelson
36 Trafalgar Street (200 yds E of station) ☎ (01273) 682150
10.30–3, 5.30–11
Harveys XX Mild (summer), **Pale Ale, BB, Old, Armada** H
Two-bar, town-centre pub split by snob screens. Renowned for its good food and busy at most times. Trafalgar Ale—a Harveys house beer—is served

on Oct 25th (Trafalgar Day) and other Harveys seasonal beers are also served.
Q ❀ ◖ ⇌ ♣

Preston Brewery Tap
197 Preston Road ☎ (01273) 508700
11–11
Courage Best Bitter; Ruddles County; Wadworth 6X; guest beers H
Friendly local on the main road to London, offering a wide range of modern pub games, regular happy hours and a good range of food (no meals Sun). Taped music at above moderate volume. Generally two guest ales sold. ❀ ◖ ▸ ⇌ (Preston Pk)

Sir Charles Napier
50 Southover Street (up steep hill, E of the Level) ☎ (01273) 601413
11–3, 6–11
Gale's XXXD, BBB, Best Bitter, 5X, HSB H
Corner site local, long since opened into one bar. Look out for photographs of former licensees and locals, plus various items of breweriana. Well-behaved children are welcome to use the area separated by a large screen. Bulmers cider.
↺ ❀ ◖ ♣ ↻

Sussex Yeoman
7 Guildford Road (150 yds W of station) ☎ (01273) 327985
11–3, 5–11; 11–11 Fri & Sat
Arundel Best Bitter; Bateman XXXB; Fuller's London Pride; Harveys BB; guest beers H
Beards free house very handy for the station but located on a steep hill. Hot food is available at most times (speciality sausage selection). Four guest beers. ◖ ▸ ⇌ ♣

Walmer Castle
45 Queens Park Road (top of steep hill, E side of town) ☎ (01273) 682466
5.30–11; 12–3, 5.30–11 Fri; 11–11 Sat
King & Barnes Sussex, Broadwood, Festive, Old H, **Christmas Ale** G
Busy, corner site, split-level, three-bar pub (one available until 9pm for families). The wood panelling recalls the brown café style. Many of the performing arts supported, with live music on the first Wed of every month and poets/folk music Tue night.
↺ ❀ ◖ ♣

Burwash

Bell
High Street (A265, E end of village) ☎ (01435) 882304
11–3, 5.30–11 (11–11 May–Oct)

East Sussex

Harveys BB; guest beers H
Superb old pub, full of
character, with over 20 years
continuous entry in the *Guide*.
It stands in a pretty village
and close to Rudyard Kipling's
house (Batemans—NT)
🏚 Q 🌣 🍴 🐾 ◗ ♠ ▭ P

Chailey

Horns Lodge
South Chailey (A275)
☎ (01273) 400422
11–3, 6–11
**Harveys BB; John Smith's
Bitter; guest beers** H
Single-bar pub with dining
and family areas, plus a large
garden with a marbles ring. A
proud winner of many games
trophies. No meals Sun eve.
🏚 🐾 🌣 ◗ ♠ P

Danehill

Coach & Horses
School Lane (¾ mile NE of
village, off A22) OS412286
☎ (01825) 740369
11–2.30, 6–11; 12–2.30, 7–10.30 Sun
Harveys BB; guest beers H
Sympathetically restored
bustling local in a picturesque
setting. Separate restaurant;
garden overlooking the valley.
Cider in summer.
🏚 Q 🌣 ◗ ◗ 🖚 🔥 ♠ ▭ P

Denton

Flying Fish
42 Denton Road
☎ (01273) 515440
11–3, 6 (5 Fri)–11
Harveys XX Mild, BB H; **guest
beer** G
Originally a 16th-century barn,
but now a pub of many years
standing, with two bars and a
pool room. A pleasant 'rural'
local, but check the tide tables,
as it can flood at high water
(hence the interesting stillage
arrangement built into the
bar!). No food Sun.
🏚 🌣 ◗ ◗ ♠ P

Ditchling

White Horse
16 West Street
☎ (01273) 842006
11–11
**Adnams Extra; Fuller's
London Pride; Harveys BB;
guest beers** H
Single-bar village local with a
warm welcome, reputedly
haunted and close to Anne of
Cleves's house. The good
range of bar meals and
snacks includes vegetarian
options. Guest beers include
Old Ale in winter.
🏚 🌣 ◗ ◗ ♠ P

Eastbourne

Alexandra Arms
453 Seaside (A259, 2½ miles E
of centre) ☎ (01323) 720913
11–3, 5–11 (11–11 summer)
**Fuller's London Pride;
Harveys BB; S&N Theakston
Old Peculier; Smiles Best
Bitter; guest beers** H
Two-bar local in the east end
of town, with a friendly
welcome. Good value meals
are served at every session,
except on Sun eve (daily
specials). The large garden
recently won a *Town Pub
Garden of the Year* award.
🏚 🌣 ◗ P

Hogshead
South Street (top of Gildredge
Rd, opp. station)
☎ (01323) 723017
11–11
**Harveys BB; Wadworth 6X;
Whitbread Boddingtons
Bitter, Flowers Original; guest
beers** H
Theme pub with atmosphere,
featuring wooden floors and
lots of pine. Popular with the
young and students, and hosts
occasional mini-beer festivals.
Beer is available in jugs, often
at a discount. ◗ ➹

Hurst Arms
76 Willingdon Road (A22, 1½
miles N of centre)
☎ (01323) 721762
11–11
**Harveys Pale Ale, BB,
Armada** H
Unusual, red-brick local
featuring a large public bar
and a smaller saloon, the latter
rather like a front room. It has
been in this guide consistently
since 1978. Harveys seasonal
ales also stocked. Q 🌣 ◗

Lamb Inn
High Street, Old Town (A259
W of centre) ☎ (01323) 720545
11–3, 5.30–11
**Harveys XX Mild, Pale Ale,
BB, Armada** H
Fine old town building with
lots of beams. Three bars on
one floor and two cellars on
different levels, the lower
dating from 1290 with an
underground passage to the
nearby church. Excellent cellar
tours available by prior
arrangement. Harveys
seasonal beers sold.
Q 🐾 🌣 ◗ ◗ P

New Inn
1 Grange Road (opp. town
hall) ☎ (01323) 735363
11–11
**Draught Bass; Harveys BB;
M&B Highgate Dark;
Morland Old Speckled Hen;
guest beers** H

Recently extensively altered
pub with a chequered past.
The new landlord has plans
for original beer selection for
the area. 🏚 ◗ ◗ 🔥 ➹

East Chiltington

Jolly Sportsman
Chapel Lane (off B2116)
OS372153 ☎ (01273) 890400
11.30–2.30, 6 (7 winter)–11; closed
Mon
**King & Barnes Sussex; John
Smith's Bitter; Wadworth 6X;
guest beers** (summer) H
A rural centre of local life, well
tucked away but worth
finding, affording good views
of the Downs and Weald.
Popular with ramblers and, on
summer Suns, families.
Although the bar area is quite
small, there are separate areas
for dining and pool. No food
Tue eve. 🌣 ◗ ◗ ♠ P

Fairwarp

Forester's Arms
Off B2026 ☎ (01825) 72808
11–3, 6–11
**King & Barnes Mild, Sussex,
Broadwood, Old, Festive** H
Traditional pub with a low,
beamed ceiling and a fine set
of brassware in a cosy,
spacious, L-shaped bar with
an eating area and discreet
music. Particularly attractive
to weekend walkers in the
adjacent Ashdown Forest.
Imaginative, reasonably-priced
food. 🏚 Q 🌣 ◗ ◗ 🔥 ♠ P

Falmer

Swan
Middle Street, North Falmer
☎ (01273) 681842
11–2.30, 6–11
**Gibbs Mew Bishop's Tipple;
Palmers IPA; Shepherd
Neame Master Brew Bitter,
Bishops Finger; guest beers** H
Traditional, L-shaped, three-
bar village local with an
interesting mixture of
architecture. Run by the same
family since 1903. At least five
ales generally available.
Q 🌣 ◗ ➹

Five Ash Down

Fireman's Arms
E of A26 ☎ (01825) 732191
11.30–2.30, 6–11; 11.30–11 Sat
**Harveys BB; S&N Theakston
Best Bitter; Younger IPA;
guest beers** H
Friendly local with an
interesting cross-section of
regulars. The landlord is a
steam railway enthusiast and a
traction rally is held at the pub
on New Year's Day. No eve

meals Tue. Cider in summer.
🏠 👥 ◁ ▶ 🍺
🚃 (Buxted) ♣ ◠ P

Frant

Abergavenny Arms

On A267 ☎ (01892) 750233
11–3, 6–11
Beer range varies H
Large old country pub on two
levels with lots of genuine
beams. The lounge was used
as a courtroom in the 18th
century, with cells in the
cellar. Good quality food,
providing excellent value.
🏠 Q 👥 🛏 ◁ ▶ 🍺 ◠ P

Hailsham

Grenadier

High Street ☎ (01323) 842152
10–11
**Harveys XX Mild, BB, Old,
Armada** (summer) H
Popular, two-bar town pub: an
imposing building with a
tastefully renovated interior.
(Spot the original gas lamp
fittings.) In the same family for
over 40 years and now close to
the Cuckoo Trail long distance
foot and cycle path. Harveys
seasonal beers also sold.
👥 ◁ 🛏 ♣ P

Hastings

First In, Last Out

14 High Street, Old Town
☎ (01424) 425079
11 (10 Sat)–11
**Adnams Broadside; FILO
Crofter, Cardinal** H
Home-brew pub buried in an
historic old part of Hastings,
offering central heating with a
difference—the fireplace is in
the centre of the pub. The
beers are amongst the cheapest
in the area and are
distinctively different. Not to
be missed. 🏠 Q ◁

Stag Inn

14 All Saints Street (off The
Bourne, Old Town, near
seafront) ☎ (01424) 425734
12–3, 6 (7 Mon)–11; 12–11 Sat
**Shepherd Neame Master
Brew Bitter, Best Bitter,
Spitfire, Bishops Finger**
(summer), **Porter** H
Ancient smugglers' pub with a
warm welcome for everyone.
Unique features include its
own game (Loggits), a
collection of mummified cats
and a beer mat-catching dog.
A must if you like malt
whisky. Cheap beer early eves.
🏠 Q 🍴 👥 🛏 ◁ ▶ ▲ ♣

Herstmonceux

Welcome Stranger

Chapel Row (100 yds S of

A271, on road to church)
OS639112 ☎ (01323) 832119
7–11; 12–3, 7–11 Sat
Harveys BB, Old H
A superb example of a simple
country pub, which almost
defies description and has
been virtually unaltered in
living memory. Beer is served
through a hatch into the very
small bar room. Well worth
the search (but not open
lunchtimes Mon–Fri).
🏠 Q 👥 🛏 ♣ P

Hove

Farm Tavern

13 Farm Road (off Western
Rd) ☎ (01273) 325902
11–11
Harveys BB; guest beers H
Six beers in a small local,
where the decor is a great
improvement on its former
Courage days. Bar snacks
served until 3pm. Full
measures! Q 🍴 ♣

Grenadier

200 Hangleton Road (off A27,
towards Devils Dyke)
☎ (01273) 735901
11–11
**Bass Worthington BB,
Draught Bass; Fuller's
London Pride; Young's
Special; guest beers** H
Large, modern pub, very
popular with the local
community, offering an
extensive range of guest beers
(at least four).
👥 ◁ 🛏 🚃 (Portslade) ♣ P

Icklesham

Queens Head

Parsonage Lane (off A259,
opp. church) ☎ (01424) 814552
11–3, 6–11; 11–11 Sat
Beer range varies H
Tile-hung country pub with a
magnificent mahogany public
bar and superb views from the
garden. A warm friendly
welcome is guaranteed and a
large collection of old farming
implements adorns the walls.
Boules pitch outside.
🏠 👥 ◁ ▶ ▲ 🛏 ◠ P ✂

Isfield

Laughing Fish

Station Road (W of A26)
☎ (01825) 750349
11–3, 6–11
**Harveys Pale Ale, BB, Old;
guest beer** H
Friendly village pub next to
the Lavender Line station, two
miles from Bentley Wildfowl
Park and Motor Museum. Its
porch was built by the
Canadian Army and an
underground stream cools the

cellar. No meals Mon eve.
🏠 👥 👥 ◁ ▶ ♣ P

Jevington

Eight Bells

High Street ☎ (01323) 484442
11–2.30, 6–11; 12–2, 7–10.30 Sun
**Adnams Broadside; Courage
Best Bitter; Harveys BB; John
Smith's Bitter; Wadworth 6X;
guest beers** H
Pub ideally situated for
walkers, just north of the
South Downs Bridleway. One
bar has an inglenook and a
wonderful antique cash
register; the other is modern
but comfortable. Recently
enlarged beer range.
🏠 Q 👥 ◁ ▶ ♣ P

Lewes

Black Horse Inn

55 Western Road
☎ (01273) 473653
11–2.30, 6–11
**Brakspear Bitter; Fuller's
London Pride; Harveys BB,
Old; Smiles Best Bitter; guest
beer** H
Two-bar local selling a good
selection of ales, generally
including one guest beer.
Originally a coaching inn built
in 1810, it boasts numerous
pictures of old Lewes.
Q 👥 🛏 ◁ P

Dorset Arms

22 Malling Street
☎ (01273) 477110
11–3, 6–11
**Harveys Pale Ale, BB, Old,
Armada** H
Smart, plush, two-bar pub
with a separate restaurant and
a family room.
👥 👥 ◁ ▶ 🛏 ♣

Gardener's Arms

45 Cliffe High Street
☎ (01273) 474808
11–3, 5.30–11; 11–11 Sat
Beer range varies H
Simple, two-bar, street-corner
local with an ever-changing
beer range (up to eight beers at
any one time). The selection of
taped music is played at a
volume which permits
conversation. Occasional live
music. ◁ ▶ 🚃 ♣ ◠

Lewes Arms

1 Mount Place (off High St)
☎ (01273) 473152
11–11
**Butcombe Bitter; Elgood's
North Brink Porter; Gibbs
Mew Bishop's Tipple;
Harveys BB, Old** H
A good selection of beers in a
Beards pub located in the
Castle's shadow. Three bars
include one devoted to games.
🏠 ◁ 🚃 ♣

East Sussex

Litlington

Plough & Harrow

☎ (01323) 870632

11–2.30 (later if busy), 7 (6.30 Fri & Sat)–11 (11–3, 6.30–11 summer)

Hall & Woodhouse Badger Best Bitter, Hard Tackle, Tanglefoot; Harveys BB; Wells Eagle, Bombardier; guest beer H

Smart, attractive pub with a wide beer range and a busy food trade. The bar is decorated with (mainly Southern) railway memorabilia. Unusual guest beers for the area often include a beer from the Gribble brew pub. Can be very busy, especially Sun lunchtime.
Q ✿ ◖ ▮ ▸ & P

Mayfield

Rose & Crown

Fletching Street (200 yds E of High St, at bottom of hill)

☎ (01435) 872200

11–2.30, 5.30–11

Greene King Abbot; Harveys BB; Ringwood Best Bitter; guest beers H

Country inn with varying levels and different character in each area. The large inglenook has seating. Excellent beer choice for the locality (frequent rare guest beers). A winner of awards for food and accommodation.
🚶 Q ☎ ✿ 🛏 ◖ ▮ ▸ ⊟ ▲ ♣ ♙

Newick

Crown

Church Road (S off A272)

☎ (01825) 723293

11–11

Adnams Bitter; Greene King Abbot; Harveys BB; guest beers H

One-bar village local, once a hotel and retaining an archway for coaches. Popular with the rugby club. Regular games, quizzes and competitions. No food Sun.
🚶 Q ◖ ♣ P

Ninfield

United Friends

The Green (A271)

☎ (01424) 842462

12–2.30 (not Mon), 6–11; 11–11 Sat

Fuller's London Pride; Greene King Abbot; Harveys BB; guest beers H

Genuine free house with an enthusiastic landlord who provides a good range of interesting beers (the blackboard lists what's due and when). Warm and friendly welcome.
☎ ✿ 🛏 ◖ ▮ & ▲ ♣ P

Old Heathfield

Star

Church Street (off B2096)

☎ (01435) 863570

11.30–3, 6–11

Harveys BB; King & Barnes Sussex; Young's Special; guest beer H

Ancient stone building with lots of character, actually in the village churchyard and an inn for 600 years. Restaurant quality food at restaurant prices, supplemented by a good beer range. Reputedly haunted. 🚶 Q ✿ ◖ ▮ ♣ P

Piltdown

Peacock

Shortbridge (B2102)

☎ (01825) 762463

11–2.30, 5.30–11

Courage Directors; Harveys BB; Whitbread Boddingtons Bitter, Flowers Original H

Picturesque, oak-beamed pub with an inglenook and a separate restaurant (elegant menu). A popular young people's meeting place near the site of the Piltdown Man hoax. Gardens front and rear.
🚶 ✿ ◖ ▮ P

Plumpton Green

Fountain

Station Road ☎ (01273) 890294

10.30–2.30, 6–11 (may vary)

Young's Bitter, Special, Porter, *or* **Winter Warmer** H

Young's most southerly tied house, which has its origins in a bakehouse and has appeared in every *Good Beer Guide*. The landlord has received many awards. 🚶 ≈ ♣ P

Polegate

Junction Tavern

99 Station Road (A27, just E of centre) ☎ (01323) 482010

11–11

Adnams Bitter; Harveys BB; S&N Theakston Old Peculier; Wells Bombardier; guest beers H

A country pub in town: originally a run-down Courage pub, now extensively restored by Beards. Separate uncarpeted public bar (same prices though), with two coal fires and lots of reading material—now known locally as the Library. Park opposite.
🚶 Q ✿ ◖ ▮ & ≈ ♣ P

Rottingdean

Black Horse

65 High Street

☎ (01273) 302581

10.30–2.30, 6–11

Harveys BB; guest beers H

Traditional, three-bar village local with a sports-oriented public bar, a cosy snug and a plush saloon. Beware the fake handpump for keg cider. Good choice of five guest beers.
🚶 ◖

Rye

Ypres Castle

Gun Gardens (down steps to the rear of Ypres Tower)

☎ (01797) 223248

11–11

Hook Norton Best Bitter, Old Hooky; King & Barnes Sussex; guest beers H

Not immediately obvious, this unspoilt pub (familiar from a dozen films) is well worth seeking out, with access on foot only. Superb views of the harbour from the safe garden. Good food all day (fresh fish a speciality). Warm welcome.
🚶 Q ☎ ✿ ◖ ▮ ♣

St Leonards

Horse & Groom

Mercatoria (off A259, one block behind seafront)

☎ (01424) 420612

11–3, 5.30–11

Courage Best Bitter, Directors; Harveys Pale Ale, BB; Marston's Pedigree; guest beer H

Smart, well-kept pub decorated with sporting prints, well tucked-away in the heart of old St Leonards and worth seeking out for its pleasant, comfortable atmosphere. ◖ ▮

New George & Dragon

Tower Road (off A21/A2100)

☎ (01424) 434055

11–3, 6–11; 11–11 Fri & Sat

Arkell's 3B; Fuller's London Pride; Harveys BB; guest beers H

Renamed and revitalized, back-street pub off the main shopping area of St Leonards. Six or more beers are always available in this oasis of choice, a real locals' pub which makes everyone welcome.
Q ✿ & ♣

Seaford

White Lion Hotel

74 Claremont Road (A259 jct)

☎ (01323) 892473

11–2.30, 6–11

Fuller's London Pride; Harveys BB, Old; Shepherd Neame Bishops Finger H

Comfortable and spacious bars within a hotel: a games bar off a saloon. The food range is extensive and is displayed on a blackboard (no meals Sun

eve). A good base for walkers on the South Downs. Note the photograph of the *Fawlty Towers* cast!
🍺 ❀ 🏠 ◑ ▮ ⚐ ♣ P

Southwick

King's Head
Fishersgate Terrace (A259, coast road) ☎ (01273) 422908
11–3, 5–11; 11–11 Fri & Sat
Hall & Woodhouse Badger Best Bitter, Hard Tackle, Tanglefoot; Harveys BB H
Lively pub overlooking the harbour. A bargain beer is often available, but enthusiastic darts and pool players can sometimes dominate.
❀ ◑ ⚐ (Fishersgate) ♣

Staplecross

Cross Inn
On B2165 in village centre ☎ (01580) 830217
11–2.30 (3 Sat), 6–11
Bass Worthington BB; Fuller's London Pride; Harveys BB; Rother Valley Level Best H
Fine village local, full of beams, offering a large, comfy inglenook to warm by in winter.
🍺 Q 🍴 & ▮ ♣ P

Telham

Black Horse
Hastings Road (A2100) ☎ (01424) 773109
11–3, 5.30–11
Shepherd Neame Master Brew Bitter, Best Bitter, Spitfire, Bishops Finger H
Attractive, weatherboarded pub with lots of beams. Games room on the first floor; skittle alley in the attic. Boules played in summer. An annual music weekend is held in a marquee every Spring Bank Hol, and special beers are often brewed for the event. Warm welcome.
🍺 ❀ ◑ ▮ & ▮ ♣ P

Three Cups Corner

Three Cups Inn
On B2096, between Heathfield and Battle ☎ (01435) 830252
11–3, 6.30–11
Arkell's 3B; Harveys BB; guest beers H
Traditional country pub with a an inglenook and a cosy interior; popular with the locals. Pub game addicts will not be disappointed. Good food, with home-made pies the speciality.
🍺 🍴 ❀ ◑ ▮ & ♣ P

Uckfield

Alma Arms
Framfield Road (B2102, E of centre) ☎ (01825) 762232
11–2.30, 6–11; 12–2, 7–10.30 Sun
Harveys XX Mild, Pale Ale, BB, Old, Armada H
Traditional town pub with a public bar, a comfortable saloon and a family room: in the same family for generations. A rare chance to sample the full Harveys range. Small garden.
Q 🍺 ❀ ◑ 🍴 & ⚐ ♣ P ✗

Vines Cross

Brewers Arms
☎ (01435) 812288
11–2.30, 6–11
Fuller's London Pride; Harveys BB; guest beers H
Welcoming country pub in a hamlet near Horam, offering a comfortable public bar and a cosy saloon. Genuine home cooking; excellent value. Home of a past world champion Tug of War team (spot the trophy).
🍺 🍺 ❀ ◑ ▮ ♣ P

Wadhurst

Greyhound
St James Square (B2099) ☎ (01892) 783224
11–2.30, 6–11; 11–11 Sat
Bass Charrington IPA, Draught Bass; Fuller's London Pride; Ruddles County; guest beer H
Tastefully refurbished high street pub with a friendly, homely atmosphere and an impressive inglenook. Excellent quality meals in the bar or restaurant. Mini-beer fests held each bank hol.
🍺 Q ❀ ◑ ▮ & ♣ P

Wartling

Lamb at Wartling
On minor road between Pevensey roundabout and Herstmonceux castle OS658092 ☎ (01323) 832116
11–2.30, 7–11; 11–3, 6–11 Sat & summer
Bass Charrington IPA, Draught Bass; Fuller's London Pride H
Two real fires warm this village local which has a separate restaurant but also serves bar food. Lots of beams. Warm welcome guaranteed.
🍺 Q 🍺 ❀ ◑ ▮ ♣ P

Whatlington

Royal Oak
On A21 ☎ (01424) 870492

11–3, 6–11; closed Tue
Harveys Pale Ale; Marston's Pedigree; Young's Special; guest beer H
Magnificent country inn dating from 1490 and displaying a list of innkeepers from 1509. Its classic interior includes an 80-ft well and the old pub sign (blown down in the great storm of 1987). Welcoming atmosphere; high quality food (the landlord owns a butcher's shop).
🍺 Q ❀ ◑ ▮ P

Willingdon

Red Lion
99 Wish Hill (just off A22) ☎ (01323) 502062
11–2.30, 5.30–11; 12–2.30, 7–10.30 Sun
King & Barnes Sussex, Broadwood, Old, Festive H
Single-bar village local, recently modernised but retaining a warm atmosphere. Good value food. Handy for the South Downs and mentioned in Orwell's *Animal Farm*. No food Sun.
❀ ◑ ▮ ♣ P

Wilmington

Giant's Rest
100 yds off A27 ☎ (01323) 870207
11–11 (closed Mon in winter)
Adnams Broadside; Harveys BB; King & Barnes Old; guest beers H
Originally a village cottage pub, relocated to an Edwardian house in the 1920s, and featuring a ship's maple wood floor, a log fire and frequent exhibitions of paintings by local artists. Rare guest beers; varied food menu of high quality. Comfortable, cheery atmosphere. Near the Long Man of Wilmington.
🍺 Q ❀ 🍴 ◑ ▮ & ▮ ♣ ⌂ P ✗

Withyham

Dorset Arms
On B2110, Groombridge to Hartfield road ☎ (01892) 770278
11.30 (11 Sat)–3, 5.30 (6 Sat)–11
Harveys XX Mild, Pale Ale, BB H
16th-century farmhouse, an inn since the early 18th century, and now a fine example of a Sussex local, with a good cross-section of regulars and an excellent choice of fine food. The good rustic location allows al fresco eating and drinking in clement weather. 🍺 Q ❀ ◑ ▮ ⌂ P

291

West Sussex

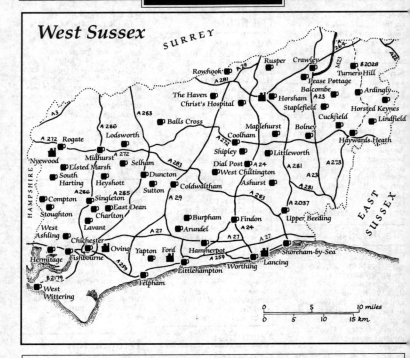

West Sussex

🏰 **Arundel**, Ford; **Ballard's**, Nyewood; **Brewery on Sea**, Lancing; **Gribble**, Oving; **King & Barnes**, Horsham

---

Ardingly

Oak Inn
Street Lane (towards church)
☎ (01444) 892244
11–3, 6–11
Draught Bass; Wadworth 6X; guest beers H
Classic, low-beamed pub dating from the 16th century with brass ornamentation. Conveniently close to Ardingly showground. Highly rated à la carte menu available 7–9.45pm.
Q ❀ ⬤ ▶ ♣ P

Arundel

Swan
27 High Street
☎ (01903) 882134
11–11
Arundel Best Bitter, Stronghold, Old Knucker; guest beers H
Centrally located and close to the castle, this former *Guide* regular has been sympathetically restored as the new Arundel Brewery's first tied house. The framed but ageing picture of a swan in the bar is actually the previous

pub sign, dating back to 1850.
🍴 ⬤ ▶ ⇌

Try also: White Hart, High St (Free)

Ashurst

Fountain
On B2135, S of Partridge Green
☎ (01403) 710219
11–2.30, 6–11
Courage Best Bitter, Directors; John Smith's Bitter; Young's Special; guest beers H & G
16th-century pub with a skittle alley which doubles as a function room (occasional live music). The extension, recently opened, caters for diners.
🍴 Q ❀ ⬤ ▶ ♣ P

Balcombe

Cowdray Arms
London Road (B2036/B2110 jct) ☎ (01444) 811280
11–3, 5.30–11
Harveys BB; guest beers H / G
Popular roadhouse with ample parking and a good selection of guest ales. Yearly beer festival Apr–May. The

conservatory is a no-smoking area. Q ❀ ❀ ⬤ ▶ ♣ ✗

Balls Cross

Stag
Kirdford Road (back lane from Petworth to Kirdford)
OS987263 ☎ (01403) 820241
11–3, 6–11
King & Barnes Mild, Sussex, Old, Festive H
16th-century country pub with a stone floor, an inglenook and a pleasant atmosphere. No food Sun eve. It is still used as a polling station.
🍴 Q ❀ ❀ ⬤ ▶ ♣ P

Bolney

Eight Bells Inn
The Street ☎ (01444) 881396
11.30–3, 6–11; 11–11 Sat
King & Barnes Sussex; S&N Theakston Best Bitter, Old Peculier H
400-year-old traditional village pub just off the A23, the centre of village life. The only pub known to play the French game of Javelot—team challenges welcome; tuition given. Families made

welcome. Various beers from Brewery on Sea, Arundel and Pilgrim also served.
🏚 Q ⚅ 🏶 🛏 ◑ ▮ ♣ P ⚲

Burpham

George & Dragon
☎ (01903) 883131
11–2.30, 6–11
Arundel Best Bitter; Courage Directors; Harveys BB; guest beers H
Popular free house in a pleasant village, offering regular changes to the menu and beer range. No meals Sun eve. 🏚 Q 🏶 ◑ ▮ & P

Charlton

Fox Goes Free
¾ mile E of A286 at Singleton
☎ (01243) 811461
11–3, 6–11
Arundel Best Bitter; Ballard's Wassail; Wadworth 6X; Whitbread Boddingtons Bitter; guest beers H
16th-century building that has always been a pub, with an undulating old brick floor and an inglenook. The first WI meeting in England was held here. The family room still retains the stalls from stabling for Goodwood racehorses. Interesting menu. Cider in summer. 🏚 Q ⚅ 🏶 🛏 ◑ ▮ & ▲ ♨ P ⚲

Chichester

Chequers
203 Oving Road (B2144, off A27) ☎ (01243) 786427
11–11
Greene King Abbot; Hop Back Summer Lightning; Whitbread Boddingtons Mild, Bitter, Flowers IPA H
Popular local with two bars and a games room. Petanque often played on summer eves; quiz nights Sun eve.
🏶 ◑ ▮ ♣ P

Rainbow Inn
56 St Paul's Road (B2178)
☎ (01243) 785867
10–11
Adnams Bitter; Ind Coope Friary Meux Best Bitter; guest beers H
Friendly local, a short walk from Northgate, offering a relaxed atmosphere and simple meals most of the day. Unusual guest beers make it a beer lover's dream. Extensive matchbox collection above the bar.
🏚 Q ⚅ 🏶 ◑ ▮ & ♣ P

Try also: **Chichester**, West St (Ind Coope)

Christ's Hospital

Bax Castle
On road from Southwater to Christ's Hospital OS148273
☎ (01403) 730369
11.30–2.30 (11–3 Fri & Sat), 5.30 (6 Sat)–11
Ansells Bitter; Draught Bass; Fuller's London Pride; John Smith's Bitter; guest beers H
Very small, one-bar pub with a separate restaurant, adjacent to the old railway line (now the Downs Link footpath, popular with walkers and cyclists). Situated behind the old railway bridge on a T-junction to Christ's Hospital.
🏚 Q ⚅ 🏶 ◑ ▮ ♣ P ⚲

Coldwaltham

Labouring Man
Old London Road
☎ (01798) 872215
11–3, 6–11
Draught Bass; Eldridge Pope Royal Oak; guest beers H
Friendly village pub on the western end of the Wild Brooks: a good location for country walks. The original thatched building burnt down in 1907. Eve meals Fri/Sat only. 🏚 🏶 ◑ ▮ ♣ P

Compton

Coach & Horses
The Square
☎ (01705) 631228
11–2.30, 6–11
Brakspear Bitter; King & Barnes Festive; Shepherd Neame Spitfire; Wadworth Farmer's Glory; Wells Bombardier; guest beers H
At the focal point of the village, overlooking the square with its well, this old ex-Watney pub features a pine-panelled main bar, and a skittle alley in the old stables. Good local trade, but also popular with cyclists and walkers. The lounge bar is a restaurant.
🏚 🏶 ◑ ▮ ♣

Coolham

Selsey Arms
Coolham Crossroads
☎ (01403) 741537
11–3, 5.30–11
King & Barnes Sussex; Wadworth 6X; Whitbread Strong Country; guest beer H
Basic one-bar pub with three separate rooms for drinking, each with its own fire. A sociable mix from surrounding villages gives this pub life.
🏚 Q 🏶 ◑ ▮ ♣

Crawley

Maid of Sussex
89 Gales Drive
☎ (01293) 525404
11–11
Courage Best Bitter, Directors; Webster's Yorkshire Bitter H
Large, friendly, well-run estate pub. Now in the *Guide* for 17 years. ⚅ 🏶 ◑ ▮ &
🚋 (Three Bridges) ♣ P

Sun
High Street ☎ (01293) 520030
11–3, 5.30 (6 Sat)–11
Courage Directors; Webster's Yorkshire Bitter; Young's Special H
Former roadside hotel now a friendly, two-bar town pub, popular with businessmen at lunchtime and locals in the eve. Despite a recent reprieve, it is still under threat from predatory office blocks. No food weekends or eves.
🏶 ◑ 🚋 ♣ P

White Hart
High Street ☎ (01293) 520033
10–11
Harveys BB, Armada H
Ever-popular, town-centre pub catering for a diverse clientele. Recent refurbishment has been in keeping with the pub's traditional values. Occasional live music. No food weekends. All Harveys seasonal beers sold as available.
🏶 ◑ 🚋 ♣ P

Cuckfield

White Harte
South Street ☎ (01444) 413454
11–3, 6–11
King & Barnes Sussex, Broadwood, Old, Festive H
Friendly, two-bar pub with an olde-world atmosphere. Genuine oak beams and an inglenook in the saloon; the contrasting public displays many old sporting photographs and trophies. The family room is only open in summer. No food Sun. Other King & Barnes beers may replace the above.
🏚 Q ⚅ 🏶 ◑ ▯ ♣ P

Dial Post

Crown
Worthing Road
☎ (01403) 710902
11–3, 5.30 (6 Sat)–11
Hall & Woodhouse Badger Best Bitter; Wadworth 6X; Webster's Yorkshire Bitter; guest beer H
A pub retaining its local ambience since the bypassing

of the village. A recently added games room ensures that players do not intrude on other customers but are still part of the pub. The guest beer changes regularly.
✠ ◖ ▶ ♣ P

Duncton

Cricketers
☎ (01798) 42473
11–3, 6–11
Hop Back Summer Lightning; Ind Coope Friary Meux Best Bitter, Burton Ale H
Friendly, Grade II-listed country pub, built in 1600 as a brewery. The single bar features cricketing memorabilia and a pianola. The attractive garden hosts weekend barbecues in summer, occasionally with music. No eve meals Sun/Mon in winter.
✠ Q ✤ ◖ ▶ ♣ P

East Dean

Hurdlemakers
Main Road ☎ (01243) 811318
11–2.30 (3 Sat), 6–11
Ballard's Mild, Wassail G; **Fuller's Chiswick; Morland Old Speckled Hen; Ruddles Best Bitter; guest beers** H
Friendly, well-run free house in the centre of this South Downs village; walkers welcome. Excellent garden with a covered patio; good range of food and good access to Goodwood racecourse and country park. Mind the duck crossing nearby. Wheelchair access is via the garden.
✠ Q ✤ ✤ ◖ ▶ ♣ ○

Elsted Marsh

Elsted Inn
SW of Midhurst, off A272
OS834207 ☎ (01730) 813662
11–3, 5.30–11
Ballard's Trotton, Best Bitter, Wassail; Fuller's London Pride; guest beers H
Welcoming, tastefully refurbished Victorian pub, the former home of Ballard's Brewery. Excellent food with imaginative home-cooked dishes, as well as traditional fare. The brewery at the rear now houses a picture gallery.
✠ Q ✤ ◖ ▶ ♣ P

Felpham

Old Barn
Felpham Road
☎ (01243) 821564
11–11
Arundel Best Bitter; Draught Bass; Greene King Abbot; guest beers H

Single-bar pub, equidistant from the village centre and the sea. Popular with visitors and locals. Up to four guest ales.
✠ ✤ ♿ ♣ P

Findon

Village House Hotel
Horsham Road
☎ (01903) 873350
10.30–11
Harveys BB; King & Barnes Sussex; Ruddles County; Tetley Bitter; Young's Special; guest beers H
16th-century village local where the bar is decorated with racing silks from local stables. Two guest ales.
✠ ✤ ✤ ✉ ◖ ▶ P

Try also: Gun, Horsham Rd (Whitbread)

Fishbourne

Bull's Head
99 Fishbourne Road (A259)
☎ (01243) 785707
11–3, 5.30–11; 11–11 most Sats
Fuller's London Pride; Greene King Abbot; Hop Back Summer Lightning; S&N Theakston Best Bitter; Young's Bitter; guest beers H
Extended 17th-century pub with a skittle alley, and separate restaurant and children's areas next to the bar. Barbecues in summer on the patio; wide range of home-cooked food, including Sun roasts. No meals Sun eve. Always two good guest beers. Convenient for the Roman palace and adjacent to a mill pond. Cider in summer.
✠ ✤ ✤ ◖ ▶ ⇄ ♣ ○ P ⚲

Hammerpot

Woodman's Arms
On A27 ☎ (0190 674) 240
10.30–3, 6–11
Gale's BBB, Best Bitter, HSB H
Originally woodmen's cottages, this 16th-century roadside pub was first licensed in the 18th century but did not have a full licence until the 1960s. It boasts a stone floor, inglenook and low beams (mind your head). Good food served every day.
✠ Q ✤ ◖ ▶ ♣ P

The Haven

Blue Ship
OS084306 ☎ (01403) 822709
11–3, 6–11
King & Barnes Sussex, Broadwood, Old H
One of the classic pubs of Britain: four small rooms, the

front one having a brick floor and an inglenook. No bar as such, with drinks served through a hatch in the top half of two doors. No eve meals Sun/Mon. K&B seasonal brews also sold.
✠ Q ✤ ✤ ◖ ▶ ♣ P

Haywards Heath

Star
1 Broadway ☎ (01444) 413267
11–11
Brakspear Bitter; Morland Old Speckled Hen; Wadworth 6X; Whitbread Boddingtons Mild, Bitter, Strong Country; guest beers H
Large L-shaped pub on the middle of one-way-system, with bare wood floors and wood panelling. One of the growing number of Hogshead ale houses, with 13 handpumps, all serving a different beer. Q ◖ ⇄ ○ P

Hermitage

Sussex Brewery
Main Road (A259 E of Emsworth) ☎ (01243) 371533
11–11
Hall & Woodhouse Badger Best Bitter, Hard Tackle, Tanglefoot; Wadworth 6X H
Merry and busy local: a small, old pub with plenty of atmosphere, featuring a separate dining room and a secluded garden. The daily menu specialises in over 30 varieties of sausages. House beer.
⇄ (Emsworth) ♣ P

Heyshott

Unicorn
☎ (01730) 813486
11–3, 6–11 (11–11 summer Sat)
Ballard's Trotton; Draught Bass; Whitbread Boddingtons Bitter; guest beer H
Beautifully-situated country pub on a spacious village green and popular with walkers, being close to the South Downs Way. A guest beer is usually available.
✠ ✤ ◖ ▶ ♿ ♣ P

Horsham

Dog & Bacon
North Parade
☎ (01403) 252176
11–2.30, 6–11
King & Barnes Mild, Sussex, Broadwood, Old H
Popular locals' pub in the Horsham suburbs, offering occasional theme eves. It attracts a good cross-section of people, with young and old mixing well. The small room at the front is used as a family

and dining room, and is designated no-smoking. No eve meals Sun/Mon. King & Barnes seasonal beers also served.

🕭 🌣 ◑ ▶ ♣ P ⊁

King's Arms

Bishopric (Guildford Rd)
☎ (01403) 253588
11–2.30, 6–11; 11–11 Fri & Sat
King & Barnes Sussex, Broadwood, Old, Festive H
100 yards from the King & Barnes Brewery, this comfortable two-bar pub, an 18th-century coaching inn, enjoys a village hostelry atmosphere. Popular with brewery workers and locals alike.

🕭 🌣 ◑ 🍴 & ⇌ ♣ ⊖

Stout House

29 Carfax ☎ (01403) 267777
10–4, 7.30–11; closed Tue eves
King & Barnes Sussex, Old, Festive H
As traditional as they come, this small, friendly pub is situated near the bandstand of the newly pedestrianised town centre. In this guide now for 12 consecutive years. Snacks lunchtimes. 🍴 & ⇌ ♣

Tanners Arms

Brighton Road
☎ (01403) 250527
11–2.30, 6–11
King & Barnes Mild, Sussex, Old H
Small pub on the south side of the town. The emphasis is on beer rather than food. Tiny snug bar; more extensive public bar, with a games area at the rear. A real local drinkers' pub. Q 🌣 ◑ ♣

Horsted Keynes

Green Man

☎ (01825) 790656
11–3, 6–11
Harveys BB; guest beers H
Village green pub with a strong local following and always a friendly welcome. A must for railway enthusiasts (close to the Bluebell railway). The landlord has been here 25 years. 🕭 🌣 ◑ ▶ 🍴 ♣ P

Lavant

Earl of March

Lavant Road (A286, 2 miles N of Chichester)
☎ (01243) 774751
10.30–3, 6–11
Ballard's Best Bitter; King & Barnes Broadwood; Ringwood Fortyniner, Old Thumper; guest beers H
Popular and roomy roadside pub with a splendid view of

the downs from the garden. Large range of Belgian beers at affordable prices. Game is prominent on the menu (large, home-cooked portions). Live rock band Thu eve; jazz Sun eve. The best value in the area, with three guest beers.
🌣 ◑ ▶ & ♣ ⊖ P

Lindfield

Linden Tree

47 High Street
☎ (01444) 482995
11–3, 6–11
Gale's HSB; Marston's Pedigree; Ringwood Old Thumper; Wadworth 6X; guest beers H
Small, friendly free house with a shop-like frontage, situated in a picturesque village. Seven real ales always on sale (range varies). The remains of a defunct brewery can be seen from the back garden. Can be rather smoky in winter months. No food Sun.
🕭 Q 🌣 ◑

Snowdrop

Snowdrop Lane (via Lyoth Lane from A272)
☎ (01444) 412259
11–2.30 (3 Fri & Sat), 6–11
King & Barnes Mild (summer), **Sussex, Broadwood, Old, Festive** H
Post-war pub housed in much older former farm cottages, in an appropriate rural location. The much extended saloon bar provides a large area for diners partaking from an extensive menu. The public bar provides a genuine 'local' atmosphere, with pub games. No food Sun or Mon eves. King & Barnes seasonal brews may replace the above beers.
🌣 ◑ ▶ 🍴 ♣ P

Littlehampton

Dew Drop Inn

96 Wick Street, Wick
☎ (01903) 716459
10.30–3, 5.30–11
Gale's BBB, 5X, HSB H
Small, friendly town house with an accent on games in the public bar. ◑ 🍴 ♣

Littleworth

Windmill

OS193205 ☎ (01403) 710308
11–3, 5.30 (6 Sat)–11
King & Barnes Mild (summer) G, **Sussex** H, **Old, Festive** G
Fine, out of the way local with a comfortable saloon bar, and a public bar with a strong rustic theme. No food Sun eve.
🕭 Q 🌣 ◑ ♣ P

Lodsworth

Halfway Bridge Inn

On A272 ☎ (0179 85) 281
11–3, 6–11; closed winter Sun eves
Brakspear Bitter; Gale's HSB; Whitbread Flowers Original; guest beers H
Early 18th-century coaching house, retaining much character in the several interconnecting rooms, all with real fires. Baldry's Railway Porter is rebadged Whitbread Porter. A roast half shoulder of lamb often features on an adventurous menu. 🕭 Q 🌣 ◑ ▶ & ♣ P

Try also: **Hollist Arms**, Lodsworth Village (Free)

Maplehurst

White Horse

Park Lane (between A281 and A272, S of Nuthurst)
☎ (01403) 891208
12–2.30 (3 Sat), 6–11
Brakspear Bitter; Harveys BB; King & Barnes Sussex; guest beers H
Pub whose landlord has enthusiasm for real ale and classic cars, hence its popularity with classic and vintage car buffs. It features a small, quiet comfortable bar with a real fire, and a main bar with an exceptionally wide bar top to prop up the regulars. Tasteful smoke-free conservatory for meals.
🕭 Q 🌣 ◑ ▶ ♣ ⊖ P

Midhurst

Bricklayer's Arms

Wool Lane (100 yds along West St) ☎ (01730) 812084
11–3, 5.30–11
Greene King IPA, Abbot H
400-year-old pub, originally built by shipwrights using old ships' beams. The roof is timbered out as upside-down boat. 🕭 🌣 ◑ ♣ P

Crown

Edinburgh Square (behind old fire station)
☎ (01730) 813462
11–11
Cheriton Diggers Gold, Porter; Fuller's London Pride H, **ESB** G; **Shepherd Neame Master Brew Bitter** H; **guest beers** G
Welcoming, traditional old pub where the superb hospitality makes it justifiably popular. Ever-changing range of guest beers on gravity in the cellar and in the back function hall (which is also used by live bands). Two annual beer festivals. 🕭 🌣 🍺 ◑ ▶ ♣

West Sussex

Royal Oak

Chichester Road (½ mile S of centre) ☎ (01730) 814611
11–11
Ballard's Best Bitter, Wassail; Ringwood Old Thumper; Whitbread Flowers IPA, Original H
Spacious, single-bar pub with partitions forming individual areas. Live music two nights a week. Large (32oz) steaks and grills are popular. The front and rear car parks are surrounded by a long, sloping lawn. Look out for Dwile Flonking Day in mid-July.
🏰 🏵 ◑ ▶ ⌂ P ⚲

Try also: Wheatsheaf, Rumbolds Hill (King & Barnes)

Pease Pottage

Grapes

Old Brighton Road (near M23 jct 11)
☎ (01293) 256359
11.30–2.30, 6 (5.30 Fri)–11
King & Barnes Sussex, Old, Festive H
The locals' pub in the area, part of which used to be a toll house on the London–Brighton road. Lined glasses used. No eve meals Sat or Sun. K&B seasonal ales also sold.
🏰 ♿ 🏵 ◑ ▶ ♣ P

James King

Old Horsham Road (300 yds from M23 jct 11)
☎ (01293) 612261
11–2.30 (3 Sat), 6–11
King & Barnes Sussex, Broadwood, Old, Festive H
Large roadside pub with a room at the rear used mainly for dining (children allowed). Separate à la carte restaurant—a popular midweek lunch venue for businessmen (restaurant closed Sun/Mon eves and Sat lunch). K&B seasonal beers served when available.
🏵 ◑ ▶ P

Rogate

Wyndham Arms

On A272
☎ (01730) 821315
11–3, 6–11
King & Barnes Sussex; Ringwood Best Bitter, Fortyniner, Old Thumper; guest beer G
Fine village inn dating from the 16th century and reputed to have a resident ghost. Dogs are most welcome and are offered a biscuit and a drink! Imaginative bar meal menu; highly recommended for B&B. Tiny car park.
🏰 Q 🛏 ◑ ▶ ♣ P

Rowhook

Chequers

☎ (01403) 790480
11–3, 6–11
Brakspear Bitter; Fuller's London Pride; Whitbread Flowers Original H; **guest beers** G
Large 15th-century village pub with beamed ceilings and a flagstone floor, plus a Civil War ghost. Recently refurbished restaurant. The pub is named after a 'chequer' tree in the garden, but the landlord can't find it.
🏰 🏵 ◑ ▶ ♣ P

Rusper

Plough

High Street
☎ (01293) 871215
11–3, 6–11
Courage Directors; Fuller's London Pride, ESB; guest beers H
Late-15th-century, low-beamed pub—duck or grouse if you are over 5½ft! Extensive range of guest ales; attractive large garden (ideal for families); variety of meals until 9pm; live music weekly. Upstairs room for meetings or functions.
🏰 Q 🏵 ◑ ▶ ♣ P

Selham

Three Moles Inn

1 mile S of A272 from Halfway Bridge OS935206
☎ (01798) 5303
11–2.30, 5.30–11; 11–11 Fri & Sat
King & Barnes Mild, Sussex, Broadwood, Old H
Small, isolated country pub, formerly a station hotel, where traditional games and hospitality are features. A highly recommended boozer, CAMRA Sussex *Pub of the Year* 1994. Beware of trains crossing the nearby long-demolished bridge after sessions!
🏰 Q 🏵 ♣ P

Shipley

Countryman

1½ miles SW of A24/A272 jct OS136214
☎ (01403) 741383
11–11; 11–2.30, 6–11 Mon
Courage Directors; Wadworth 6X; Young's Special; guest beer H
This pub's conversion to the free trade has done nothing to change the following which its regularly changing menu and pleasant country setting had already gained. A good area for country walks.
🏰 🏵 ◑ ▶ ♣ P

Shoreham-by-Sea

Marlipins

High Street ☎ (01273) 455369
10–4.30, 5.30–11
Bass Charrington IPA, Draught Bass; Harveys BB; Young's Special H
Excellent 16th-century town local, small and compact with many low beams, adjoining the town museum, which is even older. Good food (take-away pizzas); small garden at the rear. Pictures of old Shoreham in the bar. Busy at weekends. Q 🏵 ◑ ▶ ⇌

Red Lion

Old Shoreham Road
☎ (01273) 453171
11–11
Harveys BB; King & Barnes Sussex; John Smith's Bitter; Wadworth 6X; Young's Special; guest beers H
Duck your head as you enter this busy 16th-century pub which is popular at all times and has a reputation for good food. It also holds beer festivals with the pub opposite. Pleasant views from the front garden across the river and ancient toll bridge. Beware the Scrumpy Jack keg cider on fake handpump.
🏰 Q 🛏 🏵 ◑ ▶ P ⚲

Royal Sovereign

Middle Street
☎ (01273) 453518
11–11
Hall & Woodhouse Badger Best Bitter; Morland Old Speckled Hen; Whitbread Pompey Royal; guest beers H
Small, single-bar town pub, with original United Brewery leaded windows and green tiles. Always busy, especially at weekends. Q ◑ ⇌

Singleton

Horse & Groom

On A286 ☎ (01243) 811455
11–3, 7 (6 Sat & summer)–11
Ballard's Best Bitter; Courage Directors; John Smith's Bitter; guest beer H
Relaxed, family-run village local with a separate restaurant and an enclosed garden with swing boats and a trampoline. Home-made pizzas are an evening speciality (Thu–Sat). Handy for Goodwood races and the Downland Museum.
🏰 🛏 🏵 ◑ ▶ ♿ ♣ P

South Harting

Ship Inn

☎ (01730) 825302
11–3, 5.30–11

**Fuller's London Pride;
Palmers BB; guest beers** H
Friendly, 17th-century pub at
the centre of the village,
offering a separate bar for
dining and a good range of
meals (not available Sun in
winter). Garden with aviary.
The guest bitter is over 5%
ABV, and a guest mild is also
served. 🏚 ⊛ ◖ 🝙 ᕼ ♣ P

Staplefield

Jolly Tanners
Handcross Road
☎ (01444) 400335
11–3, 5.30–11
**Fuller's Chiswick, London
Pride; Thwaites Best Mild;
Wadworth 6X; guest beers** H
Welcoming inglenooked pub
opposite the village green.
Food is justifiably popular.
The unusual choice of mild for
the area has a growing band of
devotees.
🏚 Q ⊛ ◖ ᕼ ♣ P

Stoughton

Hare & Hounds
Off B2146, through
Walderton OS791107
☎ (01705) 631433
11–3, 6–11
**Adnams Broadside; Gale's
HSB; Mansfield Old Baily;
Ringwood Old Thumper;
Whitbread Boddingtons
Bitter; guest beers** H
A fine example of a Sussex
flint-faced building in a
secluded South Downs setting.
Popular and lively, with a
good local trade. Humorous
posters advertise the guest
beers. Good value food, with
fresh local seafood and game
specialities. Twentieth year in
the *Guide*.
🏚 Q ⊛ ◖ ᕼ ♣ P

Sutton

White Horse
OS979152 ☎ (0179 87) 221
11–2.30, 6–11
**Arundel Best Bitter; Bateman
XB; Courage Best Bitter,
Directors; Young's Bitter** H
Characterful Georgian village
inn. The saloon is comfortably
furnished, but bare boards
feature in the Village Bar.
Popular in summer with
walkers and visitors to the
Roman palace at Bignor.
🏚 Q 🛏 ◖ ᕼ ♣ P

Turners Hill

Red Lion
Lion Lane
☎ (01342) 715416
11–3, 6–11

**Harveys XX Mild, Pale Ale,
BB, Old** H
Unchanging village pub with
an interesting collection of
bottled beers. Its 20th entry in
the *Guide*. Pool room upstairs.
No food Sun. 🏚 ⊛ ◖ P

Upper Beeding

Bridge
High Street ☎ (01903) 812773
11–2.30, 5.30–11
King & Barnes Mild
(summer), **Sussex, Old,
Festive** H
Riverside village local, with a
friendly atmosphere. Three
drinking areas, one of which is
devoted to games. ⊛ ◖ ♣

West Ashling

Richmond Arms
Mill Lane (400 yds W of
B2146) ☎ (01243) 575730
11–2.30 (3 Sat), 5.30–11
**Brakspear Bitter; Fuller's
Chiswick; Greene King
Abbot; Marston's Pedigree;
Taylor Landlord; Whitbread
Boddingtons Bitter; guest
beers** H
Fine village local near the
duck pond, offering a choice of
home-cooked food at
reasonable prices. Bar billiards;
skittle alley. Always two guest
beers from small independent
breweries, plus a guest cider.
🏚 Q ⊛ ◖ ♣ ◡ P

West Chiltington

Elephant & Castle
Church Street
☎ (01798) 813307
11–11
**King & Barnes Mild, Sussex,
Broadwood, Old, Festive** H
Village pub with a lively
public bar and a Farmhouse
Lounge with basic seating and
blackboards for the day's
menu. Large garden.
⊛ ◖ ᕼ 🝙 ♣ P

Five Bells
Smock Alley OS092170
☎ (01798) 812143
11–3, 5.30–11
**King & Barnes Sussex; guest
beers** H
Spacious, one-bar pub near the
village, with an imaginative
selection of four guest ales
(232 different ales in the last
four years). A rare outlet for
real cider in this area. No eve
meals Sun/Mon.
🏚 Q ⊛ ◖ ◡ P

Queen's Head
The Hollows ☎ (01798) 813143
11–3, 6–11
**King & Barnes Sussex;
Wadworth 6X; Whitbread**

**Boddingtons Bitter, Flowers
Original; guest beer** H
400-year-old, two-bar pub at
the village centre. Collections
of coins, banknotes, golf balls
and bottles feature
everywhere. Clog and morris
dancing. 🏚 ⊛ ◖ ᕼ ♣ P

West Wittering

Lamb Inn
Chichester Road (B2179, 1 mile
N of centre) ☎ (01243) 511105
11–2.30, 6–11
**Ballard's Best Bitter, Wassail;
Bunces Benchmark, Best
Bitter; Hop Back Wilt; guest
beers** (summer) H
Traditional, friendly local close
to Chichester Harbour. Good
range of bar food available at
all times, except Sun eves in
winter. The separate
restaurant features seafood
specialities (book).
🏚 Q ⊛ ◖ 🝙 A P

Worthing

Alexandra
28 Lyndhurst Road
☎ (01903) 234833
11–11
**Draught Bass; Fuller's
London Pride; Harveys BB;
guest beer** H
Interestingly unimproved local
with a separate games room.
The emphasis is on service
rather than gimmickry.
🏚 ⊛ ♣

Vine
27–29 High Street, Tarring
☎ (01903) 202891
11–2.30 (3 Sat), 6–11
**Arundel Best Bitter; Ballard's
Best Bitter; Hall &
Woodhouse Badger Best
Bitter; Harveys BB; Hop Back
Summer Lightning; guest
beers** H
Popular local in a well-
preserved village street. The
former Parsons Brewery
stands at the rear. No food
Sun. Q ⊛ ◖ 🝙 ➔ (West
Worthing) P

Yapton

Maypole Inn
Maypole Lane (off B2132, ½
mile N of B2233 jct) OS977042
☎ (01243) 551417
11–2.30, 5.30–11
**M&B Highgate Dark;
Ringwood Best Bitter;
Whitbread Flowers Original;
Younger IPA; guest beers** H
Deservedly popular, two-bar
country pub with a continually
changing range of guest beers
from independent breweries.
Regular mini-beer festivals.
Meals are excellent value (not
served Sun or Tue eves).
🏚 Q ⊛ ◖ ᕼ 🝙 ♣ P

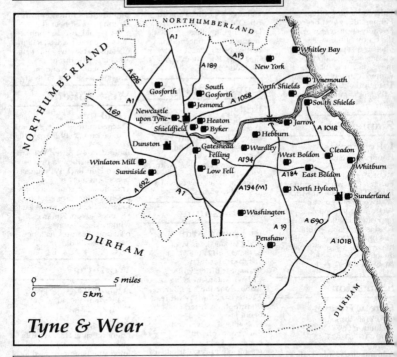

Tyne & Wear

Tyne & Wear

Big Lamp, *Newcastle upon Tyne*; **Federation**, *Dunston*; **Hadrian**, *Newcastle upon Tyne*; **Vaux**, *Sunderland*

Byker

Cumberland Arms
Byker Buildings
☎ (0191) 265 6151
11–11
Belhaven 80/-; Jennings Cumberland Ale; guest beers G
Totally unspoilt basic pub which is the home of many local bands and morris dancing teams. Up to eight beers on gravity at any one time. Live entertainment upstairs most nights; quieter ground floor bar and lounge. No frills, nothing fancy, just good cheer. ⌂ P

Free Trade Inn
St Lawrence Road
☎ (0191) 265 5764
11–11
McEwan 80/-; S&N Theakston Best Bitter, XB; Younger No.3 H
Split-level, basic pub with very loyal regulars. Huge windows give an excellent view upriver to the Tyne bridges. Live music Tue nights (when it gets even busier than usual). An outdoor seating area across the road allows a check to be kept on the quayside redevelopment. 🚲 ❀

Glendale Hotel
Potts Street
☎ (0191) 265 5174
11–11
Draught Bass; Stones Best Bitter; guest beers H
Comfortable, small bar and a larger lounge behind a shopping area. The varied clientele includes a loyal band of regulars. The licensee is very keen to offer a good range of guest beers.
⊖ (Byker/Chillingham Rd)

Ship Inn
Stepney Bank
☎ (0191) 232 4030
11–11
Whitbread Boddingtons Bitter, Castle Eden Ale, Flowers Original H
Small, cosy and comfortable, this unspoilt pub nestles under Byker Bridge, near the thriving local city farm. A wide range of drinkers from local industry and a craft centre ensures that every visit is interesting. ❀

Try also: Tap & Spile, Shields Rd (Pubmaster)

Cleadon

Cottage Tavern
North Street ☎ (0191) 536 7883
11–3, 5.30–11
Vaux Samson, Extra Special H
Typical Vaux 'farmhouse-style' village inn. Can be busy early eves. ❀ ♣

East Boldon

Grey Horse
14 Front Street
☎ (0191) 536 4186
11–11
Vaux Samson, Extra Special; guest beer H
Large village pub, a former coaching inn with a mock Tudor exterior. A winner of recent awards for its floral decor. Meals are very popular.
🚲 Q ♿ ❀ ⊙ ◗ 🍴 ♿ ♣ P

Felling

Old Fox
Carlisle Street
☎ (0191) 438 0073
11–4, 6 (7 Mon)–11; 12–11 Thu–Sat
Webster's Yorkshire Bitter; guest beers H

298

Single-roomed pub in three distinct areas, with always something going on, mainly organised by the friendly, keen owner. Warm welcome assured from staff and regulars. ♨ ❀ 🏠 🍺 🚭 ⊖

Wheatsheaf

26 Carlisle Street
☎ (0191) 438 6633
12–3, 7–11; 12–11 Fri & Sat
Big Lamp Bitter, Prince Bishop Ale; guest beers H
Basic, friendly, street-corner pub, the only tied house of Big Lamp Brewery, an interesting building offering a warm, friendly welcome to all. Cheap beer, excellent company and great atmosphere. ♨ ⊖

Gateshead

Borough Arms

82 Bensham Road
☎ (0191) 478 1323
12–3 (4 Fri), 6–11; 11–11 Sat
Courage Directors; Ruddles Best Bitter; guest beers H
Constantly-changing guest beers encourage repeat visits to this warm and welcoming pub. Two rooms, filled with friendly customers and excellent staff, ensure that each visit is a pleasure. ♨ ❀ 🍺 P

Station Hotel

Hills Street ☎ (0191) 487 3721
11–11
Beer range varies H
An excellent range of beers is always on offer in this comfortable, basic local: a small bar with an even smaller snug. Very popular, so it can get very busy, but it's always friendly and welcoming.
⊖ 🏠

Gosforth

Gosforth Hotel

High Street ☎ (0191) 285 6617
11–11
Marston's Pedigree; Tetley Bitter; guest beers H
Interesting street-corner pub near a busy shopping area. The lounge specialises in cask beers, with usually five guests on at any one time. The bar is popular with locals and shoppers taking advantage of the good quality lunches.
🍺 ⊖ (Regent Centre)

Try also: Earl Grey, High St (Vaux)

Heaton

Chillingham Arms

Chillingham Road
☎ (0191) 265 5915
11–3, 6–11; 11–11 Sat

Bass Worthington BB, Draught Bass; S&N Theakston Best Bitter, XB; Taylor Landlord; guest beers H
Impressive, double-fronted pub standing on the roadside: a large bar and a separate, larger lounge. Magnificent woodwork throughout; furnished to a high standard. Very popular with a wide cross-section of customers. Occasional mini-beer festivals.
🍺 🍴 ♿ ⊖ (Chillingham Rd)

Hebburn

Dougie's Tavern

Blackett Street
☎ (0191) 489 7622
11–11
Stones Best Bitter; Vaux Lorimers Best Scotch, Samson; guest beers H
Small, popular bar in the former industrial area of town. Busy at weekends. Good value meals served in the conservatory extension.
🍺 🍴 🍴 P

Jarrow

Jarrow Lad

Western Road
☎ (0191) 489 8039
1 (12 Fri & Sat)–4, 7–11
Vaux Samson; guest beer H
Basic but friendly pub on the outskirts of the town centre: a short walk from Metro and bus stations. 🍴 ⊖ P

Try also: Western, Western Rd (Pubmaster)

Jesmond

Legendary Yorkshire Heroes

Archbold Terrace (within office development near Scottish Life house)
☎ (0191) 281 3010
11–11
Ruddles Best Bitter; John Smith's Bitter; guest beers H
Thriving, popular bar, the flagship of a local pub chain. It usually has 12 beers on offer and often presents beer festivals too. Live music eves can be very crowded and noisy, but are always worth a visit. No meals weekends.
🍺 ⊖

Lonsdale

Lonsdale Terrace
☎ (0191) 281 0039
11–11
McEwan 80/-; Marston's Pedigree; S&N Theakston Best Bitter, XB H
Lively, ever-popular pub in a residential area. The bar is cosy and comfortable; the

lounge hums with activity and bustle. Can get very full, especially when there is live music on upstairs or at weekends.
🍺 🍴 ⊖ (West Jesmond)

Low Fell

Aletaster

706 Durham Road
☎ (0191) 487 0770
11–11
McEwan 80/-; Marston's Pedigree; S&N Theakston Best Bitter, XB, Old Peculier; Younger No. 3; guest beers H
Flagship pub of S&N's T&J Bernard chain, with one regular guest ale (Butterknowle Conciliation) plus one other guest. A very popular pub with 16 handpumps, including one for Bulmer's Traditional cider.
❀ ♿ 🏠 P

Newcastle upon Tyne

Bacchus

High Bridge ☎ (0191) 232 6451
11.30–11; 7–10.30 Sun, closed Sun lunch
Bass Worthington BB; S&N Theakston XB; Stones Best Bitter; Tetley Bitter; guest beer H
An unimposing entrance from a narrow lane leads into a large, well-refurbished, popular pub. Beautiful woodwork and some fine mirrors make drinking here a treat for the eyes, as well as the tastebuds. Can get very busy at weekends (no food Sat/Sun). 🍺 ⇌ (Central)
⊖ (Monument)

Broken Doll

Blenheim Street
☎ (0191) 232 1047
11–11
S&N Theakston Best Bitter, XB, Old Peculier; guest beer H
Once again the best S&N outlet in the city has cheated the bulldozers. Newcastle Planning Department would very much like to convert this popular and historic pub, a centre of live art and entertainment, into part of a 'tree-lined boulevard'.
❀ 🍺 ⇌ (Central) ⊖

Chapel Park

Hartburn Drive, Chapel Park, Westerhope ☎ (0191) 267 2858
11–3, 6–11; 11–11 Fri & Sat
Camerons Bitter, Strongarm H
Large, open-plan, modern pub in the middle of a large

Tyne & Wear

20-year-old estate. Games and quiet areas off the main bar. No food. Q & ♣ P

Cooperage

32 Close ☎ (0191) 232 8286
11–11
Ind Coope Burton Ale; Marston's Owd Rodger; Tetley Bitter; guest beers H
Set in one of the oldest buildings in Newcastle, this small cosy bar is always worth visiting. Huge wooden beams and exposed stone walls help to create a wonderful atmosphere, but it can get very busy, even more so when discos are being held upstairs. Good restaurant.
❀ ◖ ⇌ (Central) ❺ ⟲

Crown Posada

31 Side ☎ (0191) 232 1269
11 (12 Sat)–11
Draught Bass; Butterknowle Conciliation Ale; Hadrian Gladiator; S&N Theakston Best Bitter; Whitbread Boddingtons Bitter; guest beer H
One of Newcastle's finest pubs, steeped in history, with a wonderful ceiling and magnificent stained-glass windows. Smiling friendly service. Always worth a visit.
Q ⇌ (Central) ❺

Fitzgerald's

60 Grey Street
☎ (0191) 261 5038
11.30–11
Draught Bass; Butterknowle Conciliation Ale; S&N Theakston Best Bitter; guest beer H
Tastefully decorated pub on several levels, located in the heart of the city. Can be very busy eves and weekends.
◖ ⇌ (Central) ❺ (Monument)

Newcastle Arms

57 St Andrews Street
☎ (0191) 232 3567
Ind Coope Burton Ale; Tetley Bitter H
Impressive, yet still snug and cosy, pub. Some excellent mirrors, prints of the city in years gone by and an elaborate back bar fitting are features. Wide variety of customers from the nearby office and shopping centres. Very handy for the local China Town, and the football ground.
❺ (St James)

Rose & Crown

166–168 City Road (opp. Tyne-Tees TV)
☎ (0191) 232 4724
11–11; 12–2, 7–10.30 Sun
Draught Bass; Butterknowle Conciliation Ale; S&N Theakston Best Bitter, XB H

As yet unspoilt, two-roomed local near the quayside redevelopment area: a comfortable lounge overlooking the river and a basic, friendly bar. Warm welcome guaranteed from the staff and regulars. ❺ (Manors)

Tap & Spile

Nun Street
☎ (0191) 232 0026
11–11
Beer range varies H
An ever-changing range of ales in a large, ground floor bar and a basement (music several nights a week downstairs). Student night Mon with selected ale at £1 a pint. A recent local CAMRA *Pub of the Season*.
◖ ❺ (Monument) ⟲

New York

Shiremoor House Farm

Middle Engine Lane
☎ (0191) 257 6302
11–11
Draught Bass; S&N Theakston Best Bitter, Old Peculier; Stones Best Bitter; Taylor Landlord; guest beers H
Award-winning, very popular pub renowned for both its beer and food. Mini-beer festivals held. Q ❀ ◖ ▶ & A P

North Hylton

Shipwrights

Ferryboat Lane
☎ (0191) 549 5139
11–3, 7–11
Vaux Samson; Wards Best Bitter H
Quiet pub overlooking the River Wear, under the shadow of the A19 bridge. Popular bar meals. Eighteen consecutive years in the *Guide*. ㎲ ◖ ▶ P

North Shields

Chainlocker

Duke Street, New Quay (opp. ferry landing)
☎ (0191) 258 0147
11.30–4, 6–11; 11–11
Ind Coope Burton Ale; Taylor Landlord; Tetley Bitter; guest beers H
Classic, friendly pub with a real fire and good food. Quiz Wed; folk Fri. ㎲ ◖ ▶ ❺ ♣

Magnesia Bank

1 Camden Street
☎ (0191) 257 4831
11–11
Butterknowle Conciliation Ale; Ind Coope Burton Ale; Longstone Bitter; Taylor Landlord; Tetley Bitter;

Whitbread Boddingtons Bitter; guest beers H
Local CAMRA *Pub of the Year* 1994, featuring a happy hour 5–7 every day (with free bar snacks). Live music; friendly clientele. Lined glasses used.
㎲ ❀ ◖ ▶ ❺ ♣ P

Porthole

11 New Quay (100 yds from ferry landing)
☎ (0191) 257 6645
11.30–4, 6–11
Beer range varies H
An 1834 original pub on the banks of the Tyne, offering changing guest beers and displaying nautical memorabilia.
Q ⛴ ❀ & ❺ P

Prince of Wales

2 Liddle Street
☎ (0191) 296 2816
11–3, 7–11 (may vary; 11–11 summer)
Samuel Smith OBB, Museum H
The cheapest beer in North Shields is served in lined glasses at this traditional-style pub with real fires.
㎲ Q ⛴ ❀ ◖ ▶ ⊟ & ❺

Tap & Spile

184 Tynemouth Road
☎ (0191) 257 2523
11.30–11
Beer range varies H
There's always an excellent choice from 11 handpumps at this busy and popular Tap & Spile outlet.
Q ◖ ▶ & ❺ ♣ ⟲ P

Wooden Doll

103 Hudson Street
☎ (0191) 257 3747
11–3, 6–11; 11–11 Sat
S&N Theakston Best Bitter, Old Peculier; Taylor Landlord; Tetley Bitter H
Enjoy the good view over the harbour from this comfortable pub, renowned for its permanent exhibition of local artists' work. Live music; quiz Wed. Good food (no meals Sun eve). Q ◖ ▶ & P

Penshaw

Grey Horse

Village Green, Old Penshaw
☎ (0191) 584 4882
11–3 (4 Sat), 6 (5.30 Sat)–11
Tetley Bitter H
Busy and welcoming, traditional village pub, 14 years in the *Guide*, and packed at weekends. Situated near Penshaw Monument, a local landmark and folly. Excellent bar meals (no food Sun). ◖

Try also: Monument, Village Green (Vaux)

Shieldfield

Globe Inn

Wesley Street (next to tallest block of flats in area)
☎ (0191) 232 0901
11–11
Draught Bass; Stones Best Bitter; guest beer H
Pub with a bustling, lively bar and a more comfortable lounge. The regulars are very keen on sport and the bar can be very busy when sporting events are on TV. The lounge then becomes a haven of peace. The landlord and staff are always friendly and eager to please.
❀ ⊖ (Jesmond/Manors) P

South Gosforth

Brandling Villa

Station Road (near Gosforth roundabout)
☎ (0191) 285 6410
11–11; 11–3.30, 7–11 Sat
McEwan 80/-; S&N Theakston Best Bitter, XB; guest beer H
A small bar and a larger, comfortable lounge combine here to produce an excellent, traditional pub. ◖ ⊞ ⊖

South Shields

Alum House

Ferry Street (by ferry landing)
☎ (0191) 427 7245
11–11
Banks's Mild, Bitter; Camerons Bitter, Strongarm; Marston's Pedigree; guest beer H
The former William Woods brewery tap, now featuring an atmospheric cellar bar, with a wide choice of live music, and a more traditional lounge bar, with an unusual copper-clad bar top. Handy for the ferry and outdoor market. Eve meals end at 7pm; lunches served Tue–Fri only.
Q ◖ ▶ ⊖ P

Britannia

Charlotte Terrace (opp. Town Hall) ☎ (0191) 455 2781
12–11
McEwan 80/-; Marston's Pedigree; S&N Theakston Best Bitter, XB, Old Peculier; Younger No. 3; guest beer H
Splendid old pub renovated by T&J Bernard's chain in their kitchen style, selling a wide range of English ales and foreign bottled beers. On the edge of the town-centre circuit, so it tends to get busy at weekends. ◖ ▶ ⊖ ♣ ◠

Chichester Arms

Laygate (A194/B1298 jct)
☎ (0191) 456 1711
11–3, 5–11; 11–11 Sat
Ind Coope Burton Ale; Tetley Bitter; guest beers H

Comfortable pub near shops and a Metro interchange. The landlord is an Ind Coope *Master Cellarman*. The function room doubles as a dining area lunchtimes.
Q ◖ ⊞ ⊖ (Chichester)

Dolly Peel

137 Commercial Road
☎ (0191) 427 1441
11–11
Courage Directors; S&N Theakston XB; Taylor Landlord; Younger No. 3; guest beers H
Named after a legendary local fishwife, an award-winning, pioneering free house responsible for the real ale revival on South Tyneside. Two ever-changing guest ales.
Q P

Holborn Rose & Crown

East Holborn (opp. Middle Dock Gate)
☎ (0191) 455 2379
11–11
Draught Bass; S&N Theakston XB; Younger No. 3; guest beers H
Dockside pub, off the beaten track, with original bar fittings. Popular Thu night quiz. Unusual guest ales changed weekly. ▦ P

Scotia

Mile End Road
☎ (0191) 455 3495
11–11; 7–10.30 Sun, closed Sun lunch
McEwan 80/-; S&N Theakston Best Bitter, XB; Younger No. 3; guest beer H
Tastefully refurbished, corner-street local, comprising one long room with a small bar. Keen landlady. Q ⊖

Try also: Bamburgh, Bamburgh Ave (Whitbread); **Steamboat**, Milldam (Vaux)

Sunderland: *North*

Harbour View

Harbour View
☎ (0191) 567 1402
11–11
Bass Worthington BB; Draught Bass; guest beer H
Former *Guide* regular, almost totally rebuilt and refurbished; very busy on match days and during the illuminations period. Tasty free bar snacks daily. Fixed price guest ales.
▦ ❀ ◖ ▶

Sunderland Flying Boat

Sea Road, Fulwell
☎ (0191) 548 5961
11–11
Marston's Pedigree; Taylor Landlord; Tetley Bitter H

Popular, open-plan steakhouse within easy walking distance of the beach. Plenty of stained-glass dominates the decor in this pub named after the famous aeroplane. Can be quite busy on match days.
◖ ⇌ (Seaburn) P

Try also: St Hilda's (Club), Beaumont St, Southwick (Free)

Sunderland: *South*

Coopers Tavern

32 Deptford Road
☎ (0191) 567 1886
11–11
Vaux Lorimers Best Scotch, Samson, Double Maxim, Extra Special; Wards Best Bitter H
A Vaux licensee training centre: a cask-only, traditional ale house, tastefully refurbished and very popular. Other Vaux group beers are occasionally available on rotation. Q P

Fitzgerald's

12 Green Terrace
☎ (0191) 567 0852
11–11
Bass Worthington BB, Draught Bass; S&N Theakston Best Bitter, XB; guest beers H
Trendy city-centre 'circuit' pub close to the university. Good selection of real ales. Very popular with the town set.
◖ ▶ ⊞ ⇌

Ivy House

6 Worcester Street (side street behind Park Lane bus station)
☎ (0191) 567 3399
11–11
Vaux Samson; Wards Best Bitter; guest beer H
Back-street pub with a strong football following. Subdued lighting and loud music make this a popular students' haunt as well as a locals' bar. Charismatic landlord.
◖ ⊞ ⇌ ♣

King's Arms

Farringdon Row, Deptford
☎ (0191) 567 9804
11–2 (11.30–4 Sat), 7–11
Vaux Samson, Double Maxim; Wards Thorne Best Bitter H
Possibly Sunderland's oldest pub, just out of the city centre. The interior preserves many of the original features. Busy at weekends. Q

Museum Vaults

33 Silksworth Row
☎ (0191) 565 9443
12–11
Vaux Samson, Double Maxim *or* **Wards Best Bitter** H

Tyne & Wear

Just out of the city centre, one of the oldest pubs in Sunderland, which still retains many of the original features. Popular with students and often quite packed.
🏚 Q ✿ ⬘ ⇌ P

Saltgrass
36 Ayres Quay, Deptford
☎ (0191) 565 7229
11–3.30, 6–11; 11–11 Fri & Sat
Vaux Samson, Double Maxim, Extra Special; Wards Best Bitter H
Local CAMRA *Pub of the Year* 1992–93, and over ten years in the *Guide*: an excellent, friendly local in an industrial setting with a compact bar and a comfy lounge. Cheap drinks Tue before 9pm. Always busy.
🏚 ✿ ◖ ⬘

Tap & Spile
Salem Street ☎ (0191) 514 2810
12–3, 5.30–11
Butterknowle Conciliation Ale; Hambleton Goldfield, Stallion; Old Mill Bitter; S&N Theakston Old Peculier; guest beers H
Traditional ale house chain pub, situated just out of the town centre across Mowbray Park; popular with students and locals alike, with 11 varying ales on tap. Three rooms, all with bare floorboards and exposed brickwork. Annual in-house beer festival. Eve meals end at 8.30. 🏚 ◖ ❚ ⇌ ♣ ○

Try also: Brewery Tap, Dunning St (Vaux)

Sunniside

Potter's Wheel
Sun Street (A6076/A692 jct)
☎ (0191) 488 3628
11.30–3, 5.30–11; 11–11 Sat
Draught Bass; S&N Theakston Best Bitter; guest beers H
Fine, beautifully furnished pub with its main room divided into a number of distinct areas. Constantly changing guest beers ensure that each visit is a pleasure. A short stroll from the local steam railway. ✿ ◖ ❚ ⬘ P

Tynemouth

Fitzpatrick's
29 Front Street
☎ (0191) 257 8956
11–11

Bass Worthington BB; S&N Theakston Best Bitter, XB; Younger No. 3 H
The latest addition to Fitzgerald's chain of busy, attractive and comfortable pubs. ◖ ❚ ⬘ ⊖ P

Tynemouth Lodge Hotel
Tynemouth Road
☎ (0191) 257 7565
11–11
Draught Bass; Belhaven 80/-; S&N Theakston Best Bitter; guest beer H
18th-century, unspoilt, free house where full measures and a warm welcome are assured. No children; no hot food; no dogs; no music and no pub games. The best Bass in the area. 🏚 Q ✿ ⬘ ⊖ P

Wardley

Green
Whitemare Pool
☎ (0191) 495 0171
11–11
Draught Bass; Ruddles County; S&N Theakston Best Bitter, XB; guest beers H
Large, recently refurbished, food-oriented pub beside a golf course, with an ever-changing range of beers. Popular with several local sporting celebrities on Fri eves. Q ✿ ◖ ❚

Washington

Three Horse Shoes
Washington Road, Usworth
☎ (0191) 536 4183
12–3, 5.30–11; 12–11 Fri & Sat
Vaux Lorimers Best Scotch, Samson, Double Maxim; Wards Best Bitter; guest beer H
Large, isolated pub opposite the Nissan factory and handy for the aircraft museum: a plain bar and a plush lounge/eating area adorned with bric-a-brac. It can get packed whilst meals are being served. Annual in-house beer festival. ✿ ◖ ❚ ⬘ ♣ P

Try also: Sandpiper, Easby Rd (Whitbread)

West Boldon

Black Horse
Rectory Bank
☎ (0191) 536 1814

11–3, 7–11
Marston's Pedigree; Morland Old Speckled Hen; Stones Best Bitter; Whitbread Boddingtons Bitter, Fremlins Bitter; guest beer H
Large pub near the parish church, specialising in good quality meals (booking advisable). Frequently changing portfolio of guest ales. Q ◖ ❚ ⬘ P

Travelling Man
Newcastle Road
☎ (0191) 536 7642
11–3, 5.30–11
Vaux Extra Special; Wards Best Bitter H
Busy inn on the main road, just off the A19, attracting mainly passing trade.
Q ◖ ❚ ⬘ P

Whitburn

Jolly Sailor
1 East Street ☎ (0191) 529 3221
11–11
Bass Worthington BB, Draught Bass; guest beers H
Traditional pub with lots of small rooms, situated in one of Tyne & Wear's most attractive villages. Families welcome. Q ⛄ ◖ ⬘

Whitley Bay

Briar Dene
The Links ☎ (0191) 252 0926
11–11
Bass Worthington BB; S&N Theakston Best Bitter, XB, Old Peculier; Stones Best Bitter; guest beers H
Large, attractive pub with several areas, a splendid bar and sea views. Very popular mini-beer festivals are held.
Q ⛄ ✿ ◖ ❚ ♣ P

Winlaton Mill

Huntley Well
Spa Well Road, Blaydon
(A694) ☎ (0191) 414 2731
12–3, 7–11
Ind Coope Burton Ale; Tetley Bitter; guest beers H
Early 20th-century building with a friendly Geordie atmosphere: a former social club, built on the site of an old well. Dartboard and pool table in the bar. Situated near the start of the Derwent Walk, a renowned nature trail.
✿ ⬘ ♣ P

Updates to the *Good Beer Guide* are published in CAMRA's newspaper, *What's Brewing*. Join CAMRA and receive a free copy each month.

Warwickshire

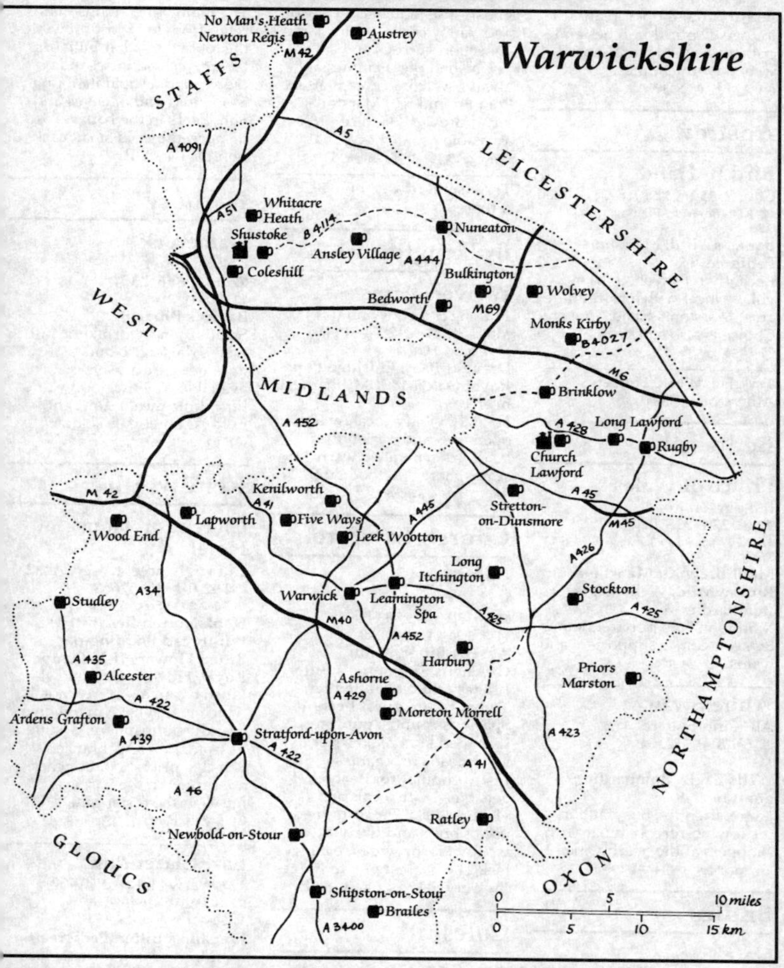

Church End, Shustoke; **Judges,** Church Lawford

Alcester

Three Tuns

34 High Street
☎ (01789) 765379
11–11
Exmoor Gold; Fuller's London Pride; Hobsons Best Bitter; Stanway Stanney Bitter; Wood Wonderful; guest beers H
High Street pub with antique-shop windows. It usually has eight draught beers on sale, and holds occasional beer festivals. It boasts its own newspaper and unique pub games devised by locals. Live music every week.
Q ♿ ⛺ ♣

Ansley Village

Lord Nelson Inn

Birmingham Road (B4114)
☎ (01203) 392305
12–3, 6.30–11
Draught Bass; Tetley Bitter; guest beers H
Large, roadside pub decorated to a naval theme on the Birmingham road out of Nuneaton.
♨ ♘ ❀ ◐ ◗ ⊞ ♣ P

Ardens Grafton

Golden Cross

Wixford Road OS114538
☎ (01789) 772420
11–2.30, 6–11
Draught Bass; M&B Highgate Dark; Tetley Bitter; guest beers H
Fine views over the Vale of Evesham to the Cotswolds can be enjoyed from this old, stone-built pub. Note the toys and dolls collection. It is rapidly building a reputation for unusual beers, alongside its well-established name for good food. Guest beers change weekly. ♨ Q ❀ ◐ ◗ ♣ P

Ashorne

Cottage Tavern

☎ (01926) 651410
7–11; 12–3, 7–11 Sat
Ansells Bitter, Mild H
Traditional, country public

house bar and open-plan lounge. Darts, dominoes and crib are played. Note: closed weekday lunchtimes.
🍺 Q ✹) & ♣

Austrey

Bird in Hand
Church Lane ☎ (01827) 830260
12–2.30 (not Mon–Fri in winter), 6.30–11
Banks's Mild; Marston's Pedigree H
Recently refurbished, friendly village local with a restaurant area. Marston's Head Brewer's Choice is also stocked.
Q ✹) & ♣ P

Try also: **White Horse**, Atherstone (Bass)

Bedworth

Prince of Wales
Bulkington Road
☎ (01230) 313302
12–2.30 (4.30 Mon & Fri), 7–11; 11–11 Sat
M&B Brew XI; Mansfield Riding Mild; Wells Eagle, Bombardier H
Mining village pub frequented by keen games supporters and teams. 🍺 ♣ P

White Swan
All Saints Square
☎ (01203) 312164
11–11
Wells Eagle, Bombardier; guest beer H
Large, friendly, busy pub in the town centre, popular with shoppers at the nearby open-air market. (🍺 ⇄ ♣ ♠

Brailes

Gate
Upper Brailes (B4035)
☎ (01608) 685212
12–2.30, 7 (6 Fri)–11
Hook Norton Mild, Best Bitter, Old Hooky, Twelve Days H
Friendly, old village local where children are always welcome. It stands next to the site of the former Brailes Brewery. No food Sun; Aunt Sally played.
🍺 ✹ ( ) & ♣ P

Try also: **George** (Hook Norton)

Brinklow

Raven
68 Broad Street
☎ (01788) 832655
11–2.30, 7–11
Banks's Mild; Marston's Bitter, Pedigree H
Locals', two-bar pub with a

ghost, situated beneath a Mott and Bailey castle, with a large collection of frogs and a pot-bellied pig. Families are always welcome except after 9pm Fri and Sat. Marston's Head Brewer's Choice available.
🍺 Q 🐕 ✹ ( ) 🍴 ♣ P

Try also: **Railway**, on B4027 (Free)

Bulkington

Weavers Arms
12 Long Street, Ryton (off Main St) ☎ (01203) 314415
11–4, 6 (5.30 Fri)–11
Draught Bass; Eldridge Pope Royal Oak; M&B Mild; guest beer H
Homely village local, where open fires and a friendly landlord generate a warm atmosphere. No food Sun.
🍺 Q ✹ (🍴 ♣

Church Lawford

Old Smithy
Village Green
☎ (01203) 542333
11–3, 5.30–11; 11–11 Sat
Ansells Bitter, Mild; Greenalls Shipstone's Bitter; Judges Old Gavel Bender; Tetley Bitter; guest beers H
Spacious country pub: an L-shaped lounge on several levels leads to a games room. Justly popular for its food, it gets busy with locals and visitors alike. The restrained use of brass and the dark woodwork provide a country feel. The nearest pub to Judges Brewery. 🍺 ✹ ( ) & ♣ P

Coleshill

Swan Hotel
High Street
11–11
Ansells Mild, Bitter; Ind Coope Burton Ale; Tetley Bitter H
16th-century coaching inn: a good quality hotel and restaurant. Some dress restrictions are imposed at weekends. 🍴 ( ) 🍴 P

Five Ways (Haseley Knob)

Case is Altered
Case Lane (off Rowington Rd nr A4177/A4141 jct) OS225701
☎ (01926) 484206
11–2.30, 6–11; 12–2, 7–10.30 Sun
Ansells Mild, Bitter; Ind Coope Burton Ale G**; Samuel Smith OBB** H**; Whitbread Flowers Original** G
Classic gem of a country pub.

The main bar contains many relics from long-lost breweries, the lobby has a bar billiards table which still uses old 6d pieces, and a separate lounge is open Fri and Sat eves and Sun. Beers in the bar are dispensed by old small cask pumps. 🍺 Q P

Harbury

Gamecock
Chapel Street
☎ (01926) 612374
12–3, 7–11
Banks's Bitter H
Small, friendly drinkers' pub where darts, crib and dominoes are always available. Try the good value lunchtime meals. Draught mild is sometimes sold.
🍺 Q ✹ (🍴 ♣

Kenilworth

Clarendon House Hotel
Old High Street (A429/A452 jct) ☎ (01926) 57668
11.30–2.30 (3 Fri & Sat), 6–11
Hook Norton Best Bitter; Whitbread Boddingtons Bitter, Flowers IPA, Pompey Royal, Flowers Original H
Plush bar in a restored hotel which manages to maintain a friendly atmosphere, despite its upmarket appearance. Sensible prices too. Lunches are served in the bar; eve meals in the restaurant.
Q 🍴 (P

Earl Clarendon
127 Warwick Road (A452)
☎ (01926) 54643
11.30–11
Marston's Bitter, Pedigree H
Popular and comfortable local in the main street. Lunchtime snacks are available Mon–Sat.
Q ✹ 🍺

Royal Oak
36 New Street (A429)
☎ (01926) 53201
12–2.30, 6–11; 12–11 Sat
Marston's Bitter, Pedigree H
Pub where one of the last locals' bars in town is complemented by a cosy lounge. Parking can be tricky. Snacks are available every day.
🍺 ✹ 🍺

Lapworth

Navigation
Old Warwick Road
☎ (01564) 783337
11–2.30, 5.30–11; 11–11 Sat
Draught Bass; Burton Bridge Bitter; M&B Highgate Dark, Brew XI; guest beer H

Canalside pub with a large garden, popular with fishermen and boaters. A wall display shows pumpclips of beers they have sold to date.
🏚 Q ❀ ◑ ▶ A ≈ ♣ P

Leamington Spa

Hope & Anchor

41 Hill Street ☎ (01926) 423031
11–11
Ansells Bitter, Mild; guest beer H
Archetypal Victorian street-corner local near the town centre. Pleasantly decorated, it has a single L-shaped bar, and always a friendly welcome. The guest beer comes from Carlsberg-Tetley's Tapster's Choice range. ♣

Red House

113 Radford Road
☎ (01926) 881725
11.30–2.30, 5–11; 11–11 Fri & Sat
Adnams Extra; Bass Worthington BB, Draught Bass; Hancock's HB H
Local community pub where good conversation abounds.
Q ❀ ♣

Somerville Arms

4 Campion Terrace
☎ (01926) 426746
11–2.30 (3 Fri & Sat), 5.30 (6 Sat)–11
Ansells Bitter, Mild; Ind Coope Burton Ale; Marston's Pedigree; Tetley Bitter; guest beer H
Two-roomed pub with a large public bar and a cosy lounge. The guest beer comes from Carlsberg-Tetley's Tapster's Choice list. Included in this *Guide* since 1978. 🍺 ♣

Try also: New Inn, Leam Tce (Whitbread)

Leek Wootton

Anchor

Warwick Road
☎ (01926) 53355
11–3, 6–11
Draught Bass; M&B Highgate Dark, Brew XI H
Deservedly popular pub, well-known for the quality of its lunches (served Mon–Sat in the lounge), but retaining a basic, village locals' bar.
🏚 Q ❀ ◑ 🍺 ₺ ᗡ P

Long Itchington

Harvester

Church Road
☎ (01926) 812698
11–3, 6–11
Hook Norton Best Bitter, Old Hooky; guest beer H
Popular country pub with a large bar and a restaurant

(booking advisable). A large tropical fish tank is a prominent feature. The guest beer changes regularly.
Q ◑ ▶ 🍺 ♣ P

Long Lawford

Sheaf & Sickle

1 Coventry Road
☎ (01788) 544622
12–3, 6–11; 11–11 Sat
Ansells Bitter, Mild; Marston's Pedigree; Tetley Bitter; guest beer H
Popular roadside local with many unusual features, a small comfy lounge and a bar leading into a games/family room. Twice the local CAMRA *Pub of the Year*, serving a record number of guest beers. The new restaurant is already renowned for its good portions and Balti meals (Tue).
🦽 ❀ ◑ ▶ ₺ ♣ P

Monks Kirby

Denbigh Arms

1 Main Street
☎ (01788) 832303
12–2.30 (not Mon), 7–11; 12–2.30, 7–10.30 Sun
Morland Old Speckled Hen; S&N Theakston Best Bitter, XB, Old Peculier; Young's Special H
Old village pub opposite a 13th-century church. Formerly a farmhouse-cum-inn, it is part of the Earl of Denbigh's estate. The no-smoking rooms are popular and the children's play area features animals. Folk music Fri nights. Book weekend meals.
🏚 Q 🦽 ❀ 🚗 ◑ ▶ 🍺 ₺ ♣ P ⊁

Moreton Morrell

Black Horse

2 miles from M40 jct 12
☎ (01926) 651231
11–2.30 (3 Sat), 7 (6.30 summer)–11
Hook Norton Best Bitter; Shepherd Neame Bishops Finger H
Friendly village local with a games area in the back bar; popular with students from the local agricultural college. Peaceful garden. ❀

Newbold-on-Stour

Bird in Hand

Stratford Road (A3400)
☎ (01789) 450253
12–2.30, 6–11; 11–11 Sat
Hook Norton Best Bitter, Old Hooky; guest beers H
Busy, friendly local, bought by Hook Norton from Whitbread. It comprises a main bar with an adjacent games room. Excellent food, specialising in

game dishes.
🦽 ❀ 🚗 ◑ ▶ ♣ P

Newton Regis

Queens Head

Main Road ☎ (01827) 830271
11–11
M&B Highgate Dark, Brew XI; guest beer H
Spacious, modernised, one-roomed pub in good surroundings. Food is available at all times and it can get busy for Sun lunch.
Q ❀ ◑ ₺ ♣ P

No Man's Heath

Four Counties

Ashby Road (B5493)
☎ (01827) 830243
11–2.30 (3 Sat), 6.30–11
Everards Old Original; Marston's Pedigree; Shepherd Neame Spitfire; Tetley Bitter; guest beer H
Former coaching inn on the border between four counties. It features three real fires, beamed ceilings and good, cheap pub food. Cider in summer.
🏚 Q ❀ ◑ ▶ ⌂ P ⊁

Try also: Horse & Jockey, Bentley (Bass)

Nuneaton

Fox

11a The Square, Attleborough
☎ (01203) 383290
11–11
Draught Bass; M&B Mild, Brew XI; guest beers H
Recently rebuilt, well-finished, traditional local, with a large, comfortable lounge and a popular bar. Cheap beer for the locality. Q ❀ 🍺 ₺ ♣

Griffin Inn

Coventry Road, Griff
☎ (01203) 312149
11–3, 5 (6 Sat)–11
Banks's Bitter; Draught Bass; S&N Theakston XB H
Old pub, very little altered, with a large garden play area. It retains a 16th-century vaulted brick ceiling in the cellar. In the heart of George Eliot country.
🏚 ❀ ◑ 🍺 ♣ P

Oddfellows Arms

Upper Abbey Street
☎ (01203) 385437
11–11; 12–3, 6–11 Tue & Thu
M&B Brew XI; Mansfield Riding Mild; Wells Bombardier H
Welcoming town pub: one large room, refurbished, but retaining its character. It has a small cosy snug and a games room at the rear. ❀ ♣

Warwickshire

Priors Marston

Holly Bush Inn
Holly Bush Lane
☎ (01327) 260934
12–3, 5.30–11; 12–11 Sat
Draught Bass; Hook Norton Best Bitter; Marston's Pedigree; S&N Theakston Old Peculier; guest beers H
Old stone pub with many individual areas (including a restaurant), once separate rooms. The main part is dominated by a large inglenook. Appealing atmosphere.
🏚 ⊛ ◖ & ♣ P

Try also: **Falcon**, Helidon Rd (Free)

Ratley

Rose & Crown
☎ (01295) 678148
12–3, 6–11
Hall & Woodhouse Tanglefoot; Ruddles County; Wells Eagle, Bombardier; guest beers H
Lovely country pub, built 900 years ago as a cottage for the stonemasons building the church. This friendly, family-run local is haunted by a Roundhead ghost from the Battle of Edgehill. Families welcome; Aunt Sally played.
🏚 ⊛ ◖ ▸ & ▲ ♣

Rugby

Alexandra Arms
72–73 James Street (behind John Barford car park)
11–2.30, 5.30 (7 Sat)–11
Home Bitter; S&N Theakston XB; Younger Scotch; Young's Special; guest beers H
Cosy, town-centre pub near the theatre. It has a large, well-equipped games room, and is popular with rock music fans. The L-shaped lounge is quiet.
Q ⊛ ◖ ⊞ ⇌ ♣

Half Moon
28–30 Lawford Road
☎ (01788) 574420
11–3.30, 5.30–11; 11–11 Fri; 10–11 Sat; 12–3, 7.30–10.30 Sun
Ansells Bitter, Mild; Ind Coope Burton Ale; guest beers H
Friendly and welcoming terraced pub close to the town centre. A recent refurbishment has only added to its appeal.
🏚 & ♣

Raglan Arms
50 Dunchurch Road
☎ (01788) 544441
12–2.30 (3 Mon & Fri; 11–3 Sat), 7–11
Bateman Mild; Fuller's London Pride; Marston's Bitter, Pedigree; Wadworth 6X H
Deceptively large, terraced pub close to Rugby School. A pub to sit and sup in with beers at very reasonable prices. No food or music.
Q ♣ P

Victoria Inn
1 Lower Hillmorton Road
☎ (01788) 544374
12–2.30 (4 Sat), 6 (7 Sat)–11
Draught Bass; M&B Highgate Dark, Brew XI; guest beer H
Victorian corner pub with original fittings, near the town centre. Pool and darts are played in the bar; the lounge is friendly. Trad jazz Mon eve. No food at weekends.
◖ ⊞ ⇌ ♣

Shipston-on-Stour

Black Horse
Station Road ☎ (01608) 661617
11–2.30, 6–11
Home Bitter; Ruddles Best Bitter; S&N Theakston XB; Webster's Yorkshire Bitter; guest beers H
Thatched pub dating back to the 12th century, now surrounded by modern housing. Originally a row of cottages for Cotswold sheep farmers, it has an interesting interior. An excellent children's room leads to the garden. Good value food.
🏚 ⋟ ⊛ ◖ ⊞ & ♣ P

Coach & Horses
16 New Street (A3400)
☎ (01608) 661335
11–11
Hook Norton Best Bitter; guest beers H
Friendly local, built 200 years ago, bought by Flowers in 1856 and sold off in 1992. It always has three or four guest beers, changing weekly. Occasional live music; cider in summer. A family room may be added.
🏚 ⊛ ◖ ▸ & ▲ ♣ ⌂

Shustoke

Griffin Inn
On B4114, sharp bend 1 mile E of village ☎ (01675) 481205
12–2.30, 7–11
Hook Norton Old Hooky; M&B Mild; Malton Pickwick's Porter; Marston Moor Brewers Pride; Marston's Pedigree; Stocks Old Horizontal H
Very popular, extended 17th-century pub. Note the fine inglenook and beamed ceilings. A minimum of seven beers available; no food Sun.
🏚 Q ⋟ ⊛ ◖ & P

Plough
The Green (B4114)
☎ (01675) 481557
12–2.30, 6.30–11
Draught Bass; M&B Mild, Brew XI H
Quiet, village local. No food Sun. 🏚 Q ◖ ▸ & ♣ P

Stockton

Crown Inn
High Street ☎ (01926) 812255
12–3, 7–11
Ansells Bitter, Mild; guest beers H
250-year-old country pub and restaurant with a homely atmosphere, much brass and oak beams. It stocks a selection of malt whiskies and English country wines, usually four guest beers from independent breweries, and cider in summer. Function barn.
🏚 Q ⊛ ◖ ▸ ♣ ⌂ P

Stratford-upon-Avon

Queen's Head
Ely Street ☎ (01789) 204914
11.30–11
Draught Bass; Hancock's HB; M&B Highgate Dark, Brew XI; guest beers H
Popular cosy, town-centre pub, dating back to the 16th century. A lively atmosphere prevails in its L-shaped bar. The regularly changed guest beers often come from small independent breweries. Weston's cider.
🏚 ⊛ ◖ ⇌ ⌂

Try also: **Olde Thatch**, Market Place (Whitbread)

Stretton-on-Dunsmore

Shoulder of Mutton Inn
12–3 (not Mon–Thu), 8–11; 12–3, 8–10.30 Sun
Draught Bass; M&B Mild, Brew XI; guest beers H
Unpretentious, unspoilt, 19th-century local with traditional values and ambience. It features a small, panelled snug in period decor and a tiled bar. An indoor rifle range in the bar plays host to a 75-year-old club. Jazz last Wed of the month.
🏚 Q ⊞ & ♣ P

Studley

Little Lark
108 Alcester Road (A435)
☎ (0152 75) 853105
12–3, 6–11

Ind Coope Burton Ale; guest beer H
Typical Mad O'Rourke-style pub on a printing theme. It presents live music once a week (Blue Grass) and imaginative meal specials include alligator, kangaroo, goat and emu! The pub is divided into three small rooms, served by a central bar. Look out for the cats. Lumphammer house beer is also sold. ▲ ❀ ◖ ▶

Warwick

King's Head
29 Saltisford ☎ (01926) 493096
10.30–3.30, 5.30–11
Ansells Bitter, Mild; guest beer H
Homely, 200-year-old pub with a lounge and a bar. The lounge gets busy weekday lunchtimes due to the very good value food. The guest beer changes regularly but follows a fairly limited rota. ▲ ◖ ⌷ ♣ P

Old Fourpenny Shop
27 Crompton Street
☎ (01926) 491360
12–2.30 (3 Fri & Sat), 5.30 (5 Fri)–11; 12–2.30, 7–10.30 Sun
M&B Brew XI; guest beers H
Popular pub, well-known for its varied guest beers (usually five on). CAMRA's Warwickshire *Pub of the Year* 1993, it is convenient for the racecourse. No food Sun. ⌷ ◖ ▶ ♣

Tilted Wig
11 Market Place
☎ (01926) 410466
12–3, 5–11; 11–11 Fri, Sat & summer; 12–3, 8–10.30 Sun
Ansells Bitter; Judges Barristers; Tetley Bitter H
Listed Georgian town pub: one large, light and airy bar, but the layout and decor produce three distinct 'rooms'. It is a popular place to observe the bustle of the market square. An additional Carlsberg-Tetley beer is usually available. No meals Sun eve. Limited parking at the rear.
❀ ◖ ▶ P

Woodman Inn
2 Priory Road (near police station)
☎ (01926) 492262
10.30–3 (3.30 Sat), 7–11
Draught Bass; guest beers H
Much altered and improved, town-centre free house, formed from two old cottages. It now comprises a single, simply furnished bar with two drinking areas. Popular for its lunch menu. Two guest beers are usually available.
Q ⌷ ◖ ⇌

Try also: **Samuels**, Coten End (Free)

Whitacre Heath

Railway
Station Road
☎ (01675) 464227
12–2.30, 5–11

Marston's Pedigree; Ruddles Best Bitter, County; John Smith's Bitter; Webster's Yorkshire Bitter H
Large, lively pub serving good value food. The large garden and playground are ideal for children. The guest beer changes weekly.
ਠ ❀ ◖ ▶ ⌷ ♣ P

Wolvey

Bulls Head
Church Hill (B4065, Coventry–Leicester road)
☎ (01455) 220383
11–30–3.30, 6–11
Marston's Bitter, Pedigree H
Recently refurbished village pub, with a carpeted bar and lounge, on the old A46. Completely rebuilt in the early 1960s.
❀ ⌷ ◖ ▶ ⌷ ⚅ ♣ P

Wood End

Old Royal Oak
Broad Lane (B4101)
☎ (01564) 742346
11–2.30 (3 Sat), 5.30 (6 Sat)–11
Draught Bass; Tetley Bitter; guest beers H
Small, one-roomed roadside inn on the Earlswood to Redditch road: comfortable, pleasant and seldom crowded. Guest beers come from a limited Pubmaster portfolio.
▲ ❀ ⇌ ♣ P

STOP GASSING

Like all real foods, real ale stops improving after a while and will go off. In order to prolong the life of beer, some companies use gas—CO_2, nitrogen, or a mixture. This forms a blanket, filling the space inside the cask not taken up with beer. By excluding oxygen from the beer, it holds off the natural process of ageing. The cask-breather is the most common means of doing this, a device which applies the gas at relatively low pressure.

However, CAMRA does not recommend any system which involves applying gas to beer. The cask-breather and similar systems are a technical fix for poor staff training and poor stock control. If brewers supply beer in the right sized containers, such devices are often completely unnecessary—the beer is sold before it has time to go off.

Natural ageing is part of the flavour development of a beer, and there is a widespread view within CAMRA that applied gas affects the taste and carbonation. Consequently, beers stored under cask-breather are not recommended in the Good Beer Guide, nor are pubs encouraged to use it.

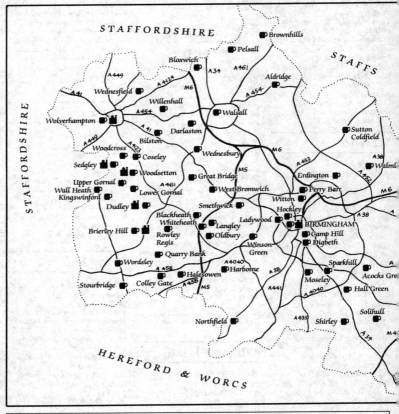

Aston Manor, *Birmingham*; **Banks's**, *Wolverhampton*; **Batham**, *Brierley Hill*; **British Oak**, *Dudley*; **Fowl & Firkin**, *Coventry*; **Holden's**, *Woodsetton*; **Sarah Hughes**, *Sedgley*

Aldridge

Lazy Hill
196 Walsall Wood Road (½ mile from centre)
☎ (01922) 52040
12–2.30 (3 Sat), 6–11
Ansells Bitter, Mild; HP&D Entire; Ind Coope Burton Ale; Marston's Pedigree; Tetley Bitter H
Large, three-roomed, 17th-century pub with a timber interior and a very friendly atmosphere. ♨ P

Barston

Bull's Head
Barston Lane
☎ (0167 544) 2830
11–2.30, 5.30 (6 Sat)–11
Draught Bass; M&B Brew XI; Tetley Bitter H

Traditional country pub, the centre of village life, partly dating back to 1490, with oak beams. No meals Wed eve or Sun. ♨ Q ❀ ◖ ▸ P

Bilston

Spread Eagle
Lichfield Street (A41)
☎ (01902) 403801
11.30–3.30, 7–11
British Oak Mild, Castle Ruin, Eve'ill Bitter, Col. Pickering's Porter, Dungeon Draught, Old Jones H
Three-roomed urban pub; a basic bar with wooden floorboards and excellent wooden-backed seats. British Oak's second tied house, but all British Oak beers are not always available. Ind Coope beers also sold. ◖ ▸ ⌂ ♣ P

White Rose
20 Lichfield Street, Swan Bank (A41)
☎ (01902) 493474
12 (11 Sat)–3, 7–11
Banks's Mild; M&B Highgate Mild, Brew XI E
Friendly pub where the locals will teach the Indian card game 'Seep' to visitors. Good for pool. ⌂ ♣

Birmingham: Acocks Green

Bernie's Off-Licence
908 Warwick Road
☎ (0121) 708 1664
12–2 (not Mon or Wed), 5.30–10; 12–2, 7–10 Sun
Beer range varies H
Off-licence offering a variety of cask beers.

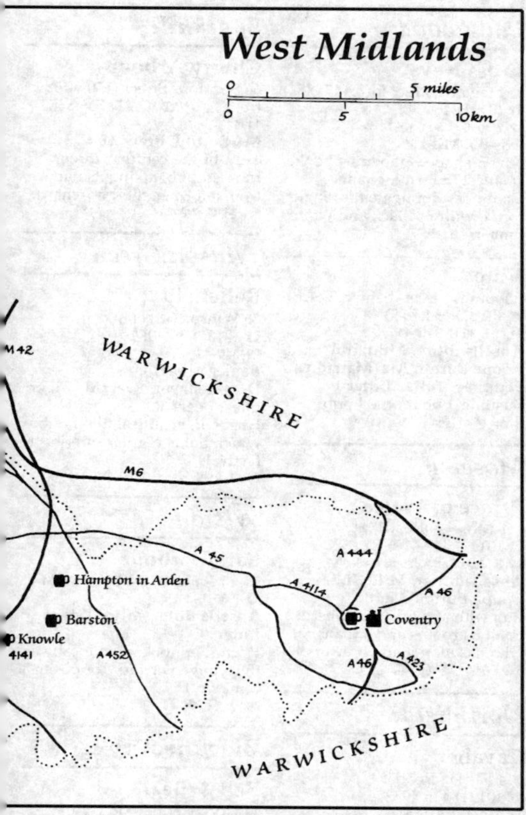

Camp Hill

Brewer & Baker
Old Camp Hill
☎ (0121) 772 8185
11–11
Banks's Mild, Bitter E; Camerons Strongarm H
Friendly, welcoming pub, with cheap and satisfying meals.
❀ ◐ ♿ ⇌ (Bordesley) ♣ P

City Centre

Australian
48 Bromsgrove Street
☎ (0121) 622 4256
10.30–11; 11–11 Sat
Greenalls Mild, Davenports Bitter, Original; Tetley Bitter; Wadworth 6X H
One-roomed pub with an island bar, popular with theatre-goers.
◐ ◗ ⊞ ♿ ⇌ (New St)

Flapper & Firkin
Cambrian Wharf, Kingston Row ☎ (0121) 236 2421
11–11
Firkin Mucky Duck Mild, Flapper, Dogbolter; Tetley Bitter H
Canalside pub formerly known as the Longboat, now having the character of other Firkin pubs. The upstairs and downstairs bars are always boisterous.
❀ ◐ ⇌ (New St/Moor St) ♣

Old Contemptibles
176 Edmund Street
☎ (0121) 236 5264
12–10.30 (11 Thu & Fri, 7 Sat); closed Sun
Draught Bass; M&B Highgate Mild, Brew XI; guest beers H
City-centre pub used by office workers lunchtimes; Birmingham CAMRA *Pub of the Year* 1993/4. No meals Sat eve or Sun; other eves till 8pm.
Q ◐ ◗ ⇌ (Snow Hill)

Prince of Wales
Cambridge Street
☎ (0121) 643 9460
11–3, 5–11; 11–11
Ansells Bitter, Mild; Ind Coope Burton Ale; Marston's Pedigree H
Always friendly pub, worth visiting, behind the convention centre and one of the few old buildings in the area. Eve meals end at 8pm.
Q ◐ ◗ ⇌ (New St) ♣

Village
152 Hurst Street
☎ (0121) 622 4742
12–11
Banks's Mild, Bitter; Camerons Strongarm; Marston's Pedigree H
Tastefully refurbished gay pub with good accommodation.
🛏 ❀ ⛟ ◐ ⇌ (New St)

Wellington
37 Benetts Hill
☎ (0121) 233 2439
11–11; closed Sun
Burton Bridge Summer Ale; Courage Directors; Marston's Pedigree; Ruddles County; guest beers H
Pub popular with students and business people.
◐ ⇌ (New St)

Digbeth

Adam & Eve
201 Bradford Street
☎ (0121) 693 1500
11–11; 7–10.30 Sun, closed Sun lunch
HP&D Mild; Marston's Pedigree; Wadworth 6X; guest beers H
Old corner pub where live bands play most nights. ◐

Lamp Tavern
157 Barford Street
☎ (0121) 622 2599
10.30–11
Marston's Pedigree; Stanway Stanney Bitter; Wadworth 6X; Whitbread Boddingtons Mild, Bitter; guest beers H
Very small lounge with a larger room at the back where live bands often play. A rare outlet in Brum for Stanway Ales. ◐ ⇌ (New St)

Spotted Dog
104 Warwick Street
☎ (0121) 772 3822
7–11; 12–3, 7–10 Sun
Ansells Bitter, Mild; HP&D Entire H
Back-street, Irish pub fielding rugby and netball teams.
Q ❀ ⇌ (New St)

White Swan
Bradford Street
☎ (0121) 622 2586
11–3, 6–11
Ansells Mild; Tetley Bitter H
Unspoilt, tiled corner pub with an Irish flavour. Q ♿
⇌ (New St/Moor St) ♣

Erdington

Beer Shop
55 New Street
☎ (0121) 384 3636
6 (5.30 Fri)–11; 12–11.30 Sat; 7–10 Sun, closed weekday & Sun lunch

West Midlands

Taylor Landlord; guest
beers ⌂
Off-licence with an ever-
changing range of ales, plus
bottled beers. ⇌

Hall Green

Baldwin

Baldwins Lane
☎ (0121) 744 3356
11–11
Ansells Mild; Courage Best
Bitter, Directors; Marston's
Pedigree; Morland Old
Speckled Hen; Ruddles Best
Bitter ⌂
Large bar and lounge with a
children's room, built on the
theme of half a ship; the other
half is the Three Magpies, a
half-mile away.
⦿ ❀ ◖ ⌺ & P

Harborne

Junction

212 High Street
☎ (0121) 426 1838
10.30–11
Draught Bass; M&B Mild,
Brew XI; guest beer ⌂
There is something for all in
this lively pub, hosting regular
activity nights. The bar
provides a quieter, traditional
contrast. Guest beers
promoted. ◖ ⌺ & ✦ P

New Inn

74 Vivian Road
☎ (0121) 427 5062
11–3, 5.30–11; 11–11 Sat
Banks's Mild, Bitter;
Camerons Strongarm ⌂
Former inn, well-refurbished
and providing a village pub
atmosphere in a busy suburb.
The new outdoor drinking
yard doubles as a spectator
area for the bowling green.
Wheelchair WC. Eve meals
end at 8pm. Q ❀ ◖ ▸ ⌺ &

Hockley

Black Eagle

Factory Road (near A41/B114
jct) ☎ (0121) 523 4008
11–3 (4 Sat), 5.30 (7 Sat)–11; 11–11 Fri
Ansells Bitter, Mild; guest
beers ⌂
Superb, friendly pub. Local
CAMRA *Pub of the Year* 1993.
🍴 Q ❀ ◖ ▸ ⌺

Church Inn

Hockley Hill
☎ (0121) 515 1851
12 (11 Sat)–11
Ansells Mild; Batham Best
Bitter; HP&D Entire; Tetley
Bitter ⌂
Renowned for its generous
portions of food, this is
Birmingham's only steady
outlet for Batham's beers.
Q ◖ ▸ ⌺ ✦

Ladywood

Cross Keys

81 Steward Street (off A457)
☎ (0121) 454 3058
12–2.30, 5 (7.30 Sat)–11
Ansells Mild ⌂
This L-shaped pub must be the
smallest in Birmingham.
Dominoes dominate the single
room, with its black and white
timbers. ◖ ✦

Vine

Rawlings Street (behind Tesco)
☎ (0121) 454 7943
11–3, 5.30 (7 Sat)–11
Ansells Bitter, Mild; Ind
Coope Burton Ale; Marston's
Pedigree; Tetley Bitter ⌂
Bustling, one-roomed pub.
◖ & ⇌ (Five Ways) ✦

Moseley

Prince of Wales

118 Moseley Road
☎ (0121) 449 4198
11–3 (3.30 Sat), 5.30 (6 Sat)–11
Ansells Bitter, Mild; Ind
Coope Burton Ale ⌂
Pub with a good atmosphere
in all its rooms and a manager
who has won many brewery
awards. 🍴 Q ⌺ ✦

Northfield

Cavalier

214 Fairfax Road
☎ (0121) 475 4083
11–11; 11–3, 6–11 Sat
Ansells Bitter, Mild ⌂
Pub with a quiet lounge
(crowded at weekends, when a
folk band appears), plus a
basic bar with a pool table.
❀ ⌺ ⇌ ✦ P

Old Mill

30 West Heath Road
☎ (0121) 475 1337
12–3, 6–11
Ansells Bitter, Mild; Ind
Coope Burton Ale; Tetley
Bitter ⌂
Popular local, set back from
the main road: a friendly bar
and a modern lounge. Bands
Thu; quiz/disco Sun. No
meals Sun. ❀ ◖ ⌺ ⇌ ✦ P

Perry Barr

Seventh Trap

Regina Drive (A34)
☎ (0121) 356 2092
11–11
Banks's Mild, Bitter ℰ;
Marston's Pedigree ⌂
Modern pub, built in the
1980s, offering good value
meals and waitress service.
Entertainments include quiz
nights. ❀ ◖ ▸ ⌺ & ⇌ ✦ P

Sparkhill

Cherry Arbour

66 Stratford Street (150 yds
from A41) ☎ (0121) 766 8452
11–11
M&B Mild, Brew XI ℰ
Turn-of-the-century, three-
roomed pub, taking its name
from a former cherry orchard.
❀ ⌺ & ⇌ P

Winson Green

Bellefield

36 Winson Street
☎ (0121) 558 0647
12–3, 5–11
Banks & Taylor
Dragonslayer; Everards Tiger;
guest beers ⌂
Unspoilt, beautiful, tiled pub
which holds regular mini-beer
festivals.
❀ ◖ ▸ & ✦ P

Witton

Safe Harbour

Moor Lane ☎ (0121) 356 4257
11–2.30, 5–11
Ansells Bitter, Mild; Tetley
Bitter ⌂
Friendly pub, known locally as
the 'Grave Diggers' (opposite a
cemetery).
❀ ◖ ⌺ ✦ P

Blackheath

Bell & Bear

71 Gorsty Hill Road (A4099, ¾
mile from town)
☎ (0121) 561 2196
11–11; 11–3, 6–11 Sat; 12–2.30,
7–10.30 Sun
HP&D Mild, Bitter, Entire;
Ind Coope Burton Ale;
Marston's Pedigree; Taylor
Landlord; guest beer ⌂
Rambling, one-room pub, very
comfortably furnished,
situated in an elevated
position with fine views. Food
all day, till 9pm (not Sun).
❀ ◖ ▸ ⇌ (Old Hill) P

Shoulder of Mutton

Halesowen Street, Rowley
Regis ☎ (0121) 559 4174
12–11
Burtonwood Bitter, Top
Hat ⌂
Single-roomed pub with cosy
nooks. Sun lunches. 🍴
⇌ (Rowley Regis) ✦ P

Waterfall

132 Waterfall Lane
☎ (0121) 561 3499
12–2.30, 5.30–11; 12–11 Sat
Batham Best Bitter; Enville
Ale; Everards Old Original;
Hook Norton Old Hooky;
Marston's Pedigree; guest
beers ⌂

A worthwhile ten-minute walk up from the station or down from the town to sample at least seven real ales. Regular quizzes and musical eves.
❀ ◑ ▶ ⊞ ≋ (Old Hill) P

Bloxwich

Knave of Hearts
Lichfield Road
☎ (01922) 405576
12–2.30 (3 Fri & Sat), 5 (6.30 Sat)–11
HP&D Mild, Bitter, Entire H
Large, two-roomed pub decorated with mock Victoriana. Its harsh exterior belies a pleasant atmosphere. A wide-ranging menu includes children's portions. No food Sun eve or Mon.
❀ ◑ ▶ ⊞ ♣ P

Royal Exchange
Stafford Road
☎ (01922) 479618
11–2.30, 5–11; 11–11 Fri & Sat;
12–2.45, 7–10.30 Sun
Banks's Mild; Marston's Bitter, Pedigree H
Busy, friendly pub, serving excellent food, plus occasional barbecues. Live music Wed eve. Marston's Head Brewer's Choice.
❀ ◑ ♣ P

Sir Robert Peel
Bell Lane (A4124/B4210 jct)
☎ (01922) 405512
12–2.30 (3 Sat), 5 (7 Sat)–11
Bass Worthington BB, Draught Bass; M&B Highgate Dark; Stones Best Bitter H
Large, roadside pub: a friendly bar, a plush lounge, and a restaurant (good value meals).
❀ ◑ ▶ ⊞ ≋ ♣ P

Brierley Hill

Bell
Delph Road (B4172)
☎ (01384) 72376
12–3, 6–11; 12–11 Fri
HP&D Mild, Entire; Tetley Bitter; guest beer H
Popular Victorian pub at the bottom of the famous Delph Nine locks. Regular summer barbecues. No food Sun.
🏨 ❀ ◑ ⊞ ♣ P

Blue Brick Tap House
Dudley Road, Round Oak (A461) ☎ (01384) 78448
11–11
Banks's Mild, Bitter; Camerons Strongarm; Marston's Pedigree; guest beers H
Large pub with a number of linked rooms, mostly gas lit. Hanson's Mild and Camerons Bitter are sold as house beers.
🏨 ❀ ◑ ♣ P

Vine (Bull & Bladder)
Delph Road (B4172)
☎ (01384) 78574
12–11
Batham Mild, Best Bitter H
Famous Black Country brewery tap on top of the Delph Run: a rambling, multi-roomed pub with a basic bar and a down-to-earth lounge. It is known as the Bull & Bladder on account of a former butcher's shop, now part of the brewery. Note the Shakespearian quotation on the facade. ⏦ ❀ ◑ ⊞ ♣ P

Woodside
67 Pedmore Road, Woodside (A4036) ☎ (01384) 77550
11–3, 5 (6 Sat)–11
Banks's Mild; Bass Worthington BB, Draught Bass; guest beers H
Smart pub near Merry Hill shopping centre, with two rooms and a restaurant.
Q ◑ ▶ ⊞

Brownhills

Prince of Wales
98 Watling Street
☎ (01543) 372551
12–3 (not Mon–Fri), 7–11; 12–2.30, 7–10.30 Sun
Ansells Bitter; Draught Bass; M&B Highgate Dark H
Small, single-roomed local, with a warm welcome.
🏨 Q ❀ ▲ ♣

Royal Oak
Chester Road, Shire Oak (A452) ☎ (01543) 452089
12–3, 6–11
Ansells Bitter, Mild; Ind Coope Burton Ale; Tetley Bitter; guest beers H
Known locally as the Middle Oak. A good example of a 30s roadhouse, it features a small but splendid bar, and a plush, comfortable lounge. It's best to book for eve meals on Fri/Sat.
❀ ◑ ▶ ⊞ ♣ P

Colley Gate

Round of Beef
33 Windmill Hill (A458)
☎ (01384) 67646
11 (10.30 Fri)–3, 5–11; 11–11 Sat
Banks's Mild, Bitter E
Comfortable, modernised local on the brow of the hill. The vibrant, friendly locals' bar houses a pool table; quieter lounge. Q ⊞ ♣ P

Coseley

Old Bush
Skidmore Road (off B4163)
☎ (01902) 492776
12–3.30 (4 Sat), 7–11

Holden's Mild, Bitter E, Special H
Lively, two-roomed local, much patronised by the senior drinker. No food Sat or Sun.
❀ ◑ ⊞ ≋ ♣ P

White House
1 Daisy Street, Daisy Bank (B4163) ☎ (01902) 402703
11–3, 6–11
HP&D Mild, Bitter, Entire; guest beers H
Popular, comfortable, free house on the Dudley–Bilston bus routes. Two guest ales. Good value food (not served Sun). 🏨 ❀ ◑ ▶ ≋ ♣

Coventry

Biggin Hall Hotel
Binley Road, Copsewood (A428, 3 miles E of centre)
☎ (01203) 451046
10.30–11; 10.30–3.30, 6–11 Sat
Banks's Mild; Marston's Bitter, Pedigree, Owd Rodger H
Built in 1923 in mock Tudor style, this large roadside pub is a gem. Recent redecoration has done little to spoil the welcoming atmosphere. Note the large oak centre table in the rear lounge.
🏨 Q ⏦ ❀ ◑ ⊞ ♣ P

Black Horse
Spon End ☎ (01203) 677360
10.30–3, 4.30–11
Draught Bass; M&B Mild, Brew XI; Tetley Bitter H
Popular, three-roomed, drinking place in an old area of Coventry. It attracts a lot of trade from the 'Spon End Crawl'. 🏨 ◑ ⊞ ♣ P

Boat
188 Blackhorse Road, Longford ☎ (01203) 361438
12–3, 7–11
Ansells Bitter, Mild; Draught Bass; S&N Theakston XB; guest beers H
Not quite canalside, but close; this pub has been in the same family for generations and seems unchanged for decades (although, in fact, it has been altered). 🏨 Q ❀ P

Broomfield Tavern
Broomfield Place, Spon End
☎ (01203) 228506
12–3 (4 Thu), 7–11; 12–11 Fri & Sat
Banks's Mild; Ruddles Best Bitter, County; guest beers H
Pub with a recently renovated public bar. Increasingly varied choice of guest beers. Quiz nights. ❀ ◑ ⊞ ≋ ♣ ◔

Greyhound
Much Park Street (near museum and university)
☎ (01203) 221274
12–11; 12–2.30, 6–11 Tue

Mansfield Riding Mild; Wells Eagle, Bombardier H
Thoroughly refurbished city-centre pub catering for a legal and business clientele, as well as students. ☎ ◖ ♣

Greyhound

Sutton Stop, Longford
☎ (01203) 363046
11–3, 6–11; 11–11 Fri & Sat
Draught Bass; S&N Theakston Mild, XB; Young's Special; guest beers H
Pub on a major canal junction, difficult to find. The bar is complemented by a small restaurant, famous for its pies.
🍴 Q ✿ ◖ ▮ 🚲 ◖ P

Malt Shovel

Spon End ☎ (01203) 220204
12–2.30 (3 Fri & Sat), 7–11
Ansells Bitter, Mild; Tetley Bitter; guest beers H
An original Heritage Inn where one bar serves inter-connected rooms; a congenial drinking place. It hosts events in the garden. Regular quizzes. Meals weekdays.
🍴 Q ✿ ◖ 🚲 ≉ ♣ ♠ P

Nursery Tavern

38–39 Lord Street, Chapelfields
☎ (01203) 674530
11–11
Ansells Mild; Coach House Gunpowder Mild; Courage Best Bitter; Wadworth 6X; Webster's Yorkshire Bitter; guest beers H
Lots of social events make this a real community pub. The back room (with dartboard) is suitable for children. Excellent barbecues. No food Sun.
✿ ◖ ♣

Old Windmill

Spon Street
☎ (01203) 252183
11.30–2.30, 6 (7 Sat)–11; 12–2, 7–10.30 Sun
Morland Old Speckled Hen; Ruddles Best Bitter, County; Samuel Smith OBB; Wadworth 6X; Webster's Yorkshire Bitter H
Multi-roomed, 16th-century pub, offering an excellent range of reasonably-priced lunches (not served Sun).
🍴 Q ◖ ◖ ◌

Rainbow Inn

73 Birmingham Road, Allesley
☎ (01203) 402888
11–11
Ansells Mild; Courage Best Bitter, Directors; guest beer H
17th-century coaching house which retains the feel of a village pub. Popular for its good value bar meals, the quieter lounge is reserved for diners eves (no food Sun). Weekly-changing guest beers.
Q ✿ ◖ ▮ ♣ P

Royal Oak

22 Earlsdon Street
☎ (01203) 674140
5–11
Ansells Mild; Draught Bass; Ind Coope ABC Best Bitter; Tetley Bitter; guest beers H
Very popular drinking house with large communal tables. Waiter service is available at the rear of the bar. 🍴 Q

Spittlemoore Inn

Lower Ford Street (near bus station) ☎ (01203) 221939
10–11
Judges Barristers; guest beers H
Basic, city-centre pub, offering an unusual menu (not served Sun). 🍴 ✿ ◖ ♣ ◌

Darlaston

Fallings Heath Tavern

Walsall Road (A4038)
☎ (0121) 526 3403
12–3, 7–11
Ansells Bitter, Mild; Tetley Bitter H
Friendly local with a busy bar and a quieter lounge. The children's room has been extended. 🚲 ✿ 🚲 ♣ P

Dudley

Lamp Tavern

116 High Street (A459)
☎ (01384) 254129
11–11
Batham Mild, Best Bitter, XXX H
There's always a friendly welcome in this lively local which has a plain bar, a comfortable lounge, an eating area and a function room. Once the Queens Cross brewery tap. Eve meals weekdays, till 8pm.
🍴 ✿ 🚲 ◖ ▮ 🚲 ♣ P

Old Priory

New Street (off market place)
☎ (01384) 455810
12–11
HP&D Mild, Entire; Tetley Bitter H
Former, early-19th-century home-brew house, known as the Britannia, now refurbished in comfortable Victorian style, with chaises-longues in the U-shaped drinking area.
🍴 ◖ ♣

Old Vic

King Street ☎ (01384) 236082
12–3, 5.30–11; 12–11 Fri & Sat
Home Bitter; S&N Theakston Mild, Best Bitter, XB, Old Peculier; guest beer H
Lively, town-centre pub with an island bar. Quizzes Mon; live bands Thu. ✿ ◖ & ♣

Great Bridge

Port'n'Ale

178 Horseley Heath (A461)
☎ (0121) 557 7249
12–3, 5 (6 Sat)–11
Batham Best Bitter; Blackbeard Stairway to Heaven; guest beers H
Three-roomed free house specialising in new and unusual guest beers.
✿ ◖ ▮ & ≉ (Dudley Port) ♣ ◌ P

Halesowen

Fairfield Inn

Fairfield Road, Hurst Green
11–3, 5.30–11
Banks's Hanson's Mild, Bitter E; Marston's Pedigree H
Popular, large roadhouse, with a lively bar, and a busy, smart lounge. No food Sun. ✿ ◖ ▮
≉ (Rowley Regis) ♣ P

Rose & Crown at Hasbury

Hagley Road, Hasbury (B4183)
☎ (0121) 550 2757
12–2.30 (3 Sat), 5.30 (6 Sat)–11
HP&D Mild, Entire; Tetley Bitter H
Deservedly popular inn. Various drinking areas radiate from a central bar. Excellent lunches (not served Sun).
🍴 ◖ ♣ P

Waggon & Horses

Stourbridge Road (A458)
☎ (0121) 550 4989
12–3, 7–11; 12–11 Fri & Sat
Enville Ale; Hobsons Best Bitter; guest beers H
Very friendly pub; a permanent beer festival offering 16 handpumps, usually all in use. Near Halesowen Town FC. ♣ ◌

Hampton in Arden

White Lion

High Street ☎ (01675) 442833
12–2.30, 5.30, (6 Sat)–11
Draught Bass; M&B Mild, Brew XI H
Small, friendly local with a restaurant. The basic public bar has remained unchanged for 50 years.
🍴 Q ✿ 🚲 ◖ ▮ 🚲 ≉ P

Kingswinford

Park Tavern

182 Cot Lane (500 yds from A4101) ☎ (01384) 287178
12–3, 5–11; 12–11 Fri & Sat
Ansells Bitter; Batham Best Bitter; Ind Coope Burton Ale; Tetley Bitter H

Pleasant, friendly, two-roomed local near Broadfield House Glass Museum. ❀ ⊞ ♣ P

Knowle

Vaults
St Johns Close
☎ (01564) 773656
12–2.30, 5 (6 Sat)–11
Ansells Mild; HP&D Bitter; Ind Coope Burton Ale; Tetley Bitter; guest beers H
Three-level basement pub; the top area offers some seclusion. Solihull CAMRA *Pub of the Year* 1992 and 1993. No food Sat eve. ◐ ◗ ♣

Langley

Crosswells
The Crosswells, High Street
☎ (0121) 552 2629
11–2.30 (3 Fri & Sat), 5.30 (5 Sat)–11
HP&D Mild, Bitter, Entire, Deakin's Downfall H
Friendly, comfortable, two-roomer near the mothballed HP&D Brewery. ⌂ ◐ ⊞ ⇌ (Langley Green) ♣

New Navigation
Titford Road (off A4123, near M5 jct 2) ☎ (0121) 552 2525
11.30–3, 6 (7 Sat)–11
HP&D Mild, Bitter, Entire; Tetley Bitter; guest beers H
Friendly pub in brewer's Tudor style, almost at the end of the Titford Canal. ⌂ ◐ ⇌ (Langley Green) ♣ P

Lower Gornal

Fountain Real Ale Bar
8 Temple Street (B4175, off A459) ☎ (01384) 834888
12–2.30 (not Mon–Wed), 7–11; 12–2.30, 7–10.30 Sun
Adnams Broadside; Everards Tiger; Hall & Woodhouse Tanglefoot; Shepherd Neame Bishops Finger; guest beers H
Comfortable free house with a dining room, 200 yards 'up the Zoar'. It was the last known brew house in Gornal. Beer festivals; good range of guest beers. ⌂ ❀ ◐ ◗ ⌓ P

Oldbury

Waggon & Horses
Church Street (off A4034)
☎ (0121) 552 5467
12–2.30 (3 Fri), 5 (6 Sat)–11; 12–2.30, 7–10.30 Sun
Adnams Bitter; Draught Bass; Batham Best Bitter; Everards Mild, Tiger, Old Original; guest beers H
Splendidly unspoilt, 19th-century pub, notable for its food, which includes Baltis. Note the tiled walls and copper ceiling. ⌂ ❀ ◐ ◗ ⇌ (Sandwell & Dudley)

Pelsall

Royal Oak
Norton Road ☎ (01922) 691811
11.30–3 (11–3.30 Sat), 5.30–11
Ansells Bitter, Mild; Ind Coope Burton Ale; Walker Bitter H
Canalside pub with an impressive cottage-style lounge and hand-painted tables. ❀ ◐ ◗ ⊞ ♿ ⛺ P

Quarry Bank

Sun Inn
218 High Street
☎ (01384) 66254
11–3, 6.30–11
Banks's Hanson's Mild, Mild, Bitter E
Large roadhouse, popular with locals and convenient for Merry Hill shopping centre. ♘ ❀ ◐ ⊞ ♿ ♣ P

Rowley Regis

Cock Inn
75 Dudley Road (B4171)
☎ (0121) 561 4273
12–3, 5–11
Banks's Mild E**; HP&D Mild, Bitter, Entire; Tetley Bitter** H
Popular, friendly pub in the Holts Victorian style. Enjoy the extensive views from its hilltop location. No food Sun eve. ⌂ ❀ ◐ ◗ ♿ ♣ P

Sir Robert Peel
1 Rowley Village (B4171)
☎ (0121) 559 2835
12–4, 7–11
Ansells Bitter, Mild; Draught Bass; Tetley Bitter H
The oldest building in Rowley village, formerly a police station, now a traditional three-roomed pub, licensed since 1840. One servery is in the entrance passage. Warm welcome. ⌂ Q ❀ ⇌ ♣

Sedgley

Beacon Hotel
129 Bilston Street
☎ (01902) 883380
12–2.30, 5.30–10.45; 11–3, 6–11 Sat; 12–2.30, 7–10.30 Sun
Hook Norton Best Bitter; Sarah Hughes Ruby Mild, Sedgley Surprise; M&B Mild; guest beers H
Lovingly restored Victorian brewery tap, home of Sarah Hughes Brewery. Tours Sun. ⌂ Q ♘ ❀ ♿ ♣ P

Bull's Head
27a Bilston Street (A463, just off A459) ☎ (01902) 679606
1 (12 Sat)–11 (may close afternoons Mon–Wed)
Holden's Mild, Bitter E**, Special** H
Two-roomed drinkers' pub. Live music Thu and Fri lunchtimes. ❀ ⊞ ♿ ♣ ⌓ P

Shirley

Bernie's Real Ale Off-Licence
266 Cranmore Boulevard (off A34, 2 miles from M42 jct 4)
☎ (0121) 744 2827
12–2 (not Mon), 5.30–10
Butcombe Bitter; Fuller's ESB; Marston's Pedigree; Oakhill Black Magic; Taylor Landlord; Titanic Premium H
Solihull's longest continuous entry, usually offering six beers, mainly from small breweries, plus two ciders. 'Try before you buy' system. ♿ ⌓

Lodge
Yardley Wood Road, Solihull Lodge ☎ (0121) 430 2727
12–2.30 (3 Sat), 6–11
Ansells Mild; HP&D Entire; Tetley Bitter H
In a residential area, this pub comprises a comfortable lounge, with an area for family meals, a split-level bar, and a pool table in an annexe. Half a mile from the Birmingham–Stratford Canal. ◐ ◗ ⊞ ♣ P

Red Lion
Stratford Road
☎ (0121) 744 1030
11–2.30 (3 Sat), 6.30–11
Ansells Bitter, Mild; HP&D Mild; Marston's Pedigree; Tetley Bitter; guest beer H
Main-road pub, with a modern facade. The lounge is split into three areas, and the bar is now a 'pool' room. The guest beers come from Carlsberg-Tetley. ◐

Smethwick

Ivy Bush
218 St Pauls Road
☎ (0121) 565 0929
11–11
Holden's Mild, Bitter H/E**, Special, XL** H
Former M&B pub, recently renovated, enjoying a friendly atmosphere. Summer barbecues; no food Sun. ♘ ◐ ♿ ⇌ (West) ♣

Solihull

Old Colonial
Damson Lane
☎ (0121) 705 9054
11.30–11; 11–3.30, 6.30–11 Sat
Draught Bass H**; M&B Mild, Brew XI** E**; guest beer** H
Ten-year-old, single-room pub with seven areas. The central area has a sliding roof. Families are welcome until

West Midlands

7pm. Many events hosted; monthly guest beer; weekday lunches. ⚑ ❀ ◖ & ♣ P ✕

Stourbridge

Mitre Inn
Lower High Street
☎ (01384) 395374
11–2.30, 7–11
Draught Bass; M&B Highgate Dark; Stones Best Bitter H
Large, multi-roomed town house whose upstairs function room has become a noted live music venue. Popular with the young at weekends.
◖ ▶ & ⇌ (Town)

Moorings Tavern
80 High Street, Amblecote (A491) ☎ (01384) 374124
12–3, 5–11
Draught Bass; S&N Theakston XB; Tetley Bitter; Whitbread Boddingtons Bitter; guest beers H
Lively one-roomer, just off the ring road, near the canal basin. The decor is, naturally, canal influenced. A wide range of good quality and value food is served (not Sun eve), plus a good choice of guest beers.
❀ ◖ ▶ ⇌ (Town) P

Old White Horse
South Road ☎ (01384) 394258
12–3, 5–11
Draught Bass; Courage Directors; Ruddles Best Bitter H
Part of the Harvester chain, but the lounge is popular with drinkers. Annual beer festival. Wheelchair WC.
❀ ◖ ▶ & ♣ P

Plough
154 Bridgnorth Road, Wollaston (A458)
☎ (01384) 393414
12–2.30 (3 Sat), 6–11
Draught Bass; M&B Mild; Stones Best Bitter H
Highly decorated old house with original windows; a keen sporting pub. The lounge is used lunchtimes and early eves for the excellent, good value food. Folk music Tue and Wed eves. ❀ ◖ ▶ & ♣ P

Robin Hood
196 Collis Street, Amblecote (A461) ☎ (01384) 440286
12–3, 6–11
Batham Best Bitter; Enville Ale; Everards Tiger; Fuller's ESB; Hall & Woodhouse Tanglefoot; guest beers H
Popular free house, offering a wide range of real ales and a varied menu. ⚑ ❀ ⌂ ◖ ▶

Royal Exchange
75 Enville Street
☎ (01384) 396726
12–11

Batham Mild, Best Bitter H
On a busy road, just off Stourbridge ring road, this two-roomed local has a lively bar and a small, quiet lounge to the rear. Q ❀ ▣ ♣ ⌂

Shrubbery Cottage
28 Heath Lane, Oldswinford
☎ (01384) 377598
12–2.30, 5–11; 12–2.30, 7–10.30 Sun
Holden's Mild, Bitter, Special; guest beer (occasional) H
Popular, one-roomed local near the college. Many events for charity.
❀ ◖ ⇌ (Junction) ♣ P

Sutton Coldfield

Blake Barn Inn
Blake Street ☎ (0121) 308 8421
11–2.30, 5.30–11.30; 11–11.30 Sat
Banks's Mild, Bitter E **; Camerons Strongarm; Marston's Pedigree** H
Popular pub appealing to all ages. Rural decor contrasts with the modern building.
❀ ◖ ▶ & ⇌ (Blake St) P ✕

Duke
Duke Street ☎ (0121) 355 1767
11.30–3, 5.30–11; 12–2.30, 7–10.30 Sun
Ansells Bitter, Mild; Ind Coope Burton Ale; Tetley Bitter H
Unspoilt, friendly local. Note the fine mahogany back bar.
Q ❀ ▣ ⇌ ♣ P

Laurel Wines
63 Westwood Road (near Sutton Park) ☎ (0121) 353 0399
12–2, 5.30–10.30 (11 Fri & Sat)
Batham Best Bitter; Burton Bridge Festival; Enville Gothic; Lichfield Steeplejack; Marston's Pedigree; guest beers G
Friendly off-licence with a good choice of real ales. ⌂

New Inns
Lichfield Road, Four Oaks
☎ (0121) 308 0765
11.30–2.30, 5.30–11; 11.30–11 Sat
Ansells Bitter; Tetley Bitter; guest beer H
Large, refurbished, single-roomed pub, with its own bowling green. ❀ ◖ &
⇌ (Butlers Lane) ♣ P

Upper Gornal

Britannia (Sally's)
109 Kent Street (A459)
☎ (01902) 883253
12–2.30 (not Mon–Thu), 7–11; 12–2.30, 7–10.30 Sun
Courage Directors; Morland Old Speckled Hen; Ruddles Best Bitter; Wood Wonderful; Wye Valley Brew 69; guest beers H

Former brew pub built in 1780, which boasts an untouched late-19th-century tap room, where beer is served from handpumps against the wall. The original brewhouse is intact and there are plans to brew again. ⚏ Q ❀ ♣ P

Wall Heath

Wall Heath Tavern
14 High Street (A449)
☎ (01384) 287319
11–3, 6–11
HP&D Entire; Tetley Bitter; guest beer H
Food-oriented pub with over a hundred choices: a friendly locals' bar stocking guest beers from Carlsberg-Tetley.
❀ ◖ ▶ ▣ & ♣ P

Walmley

Oak'n'Ash
Calder Drive (800 yds from A38/A4097 jct)
☎ (0121) 351 7443
11.30–3, 5.30–11; 11.30–11 Fri & Sat
Draught Bass; M&B Mild, Brew XI; guest beer H
Busy, modern estate pub with a bar and a comfortable lounge. Popular with locals.
Q ❀ ◖ ▣ & ♣ P ✕

Walsall

Hamemaker's Arms
87 Blue Lane West (A454)
☎ (01922) 28083
11.30–3, 6–11; 11–11 Sat
Banks's Mild, Bitter E **; Camerons Strongarm** H
Pleasantly modernised, 1930s pub with a well-laid-out bar and a warm, bright, comfortable lounge. The name refers to the brass collar hames worn by carthorses, a bygone local industry. No eve meals Sun, but Sun lunch till 4pm.
Q ❀ ◖ ▣ ⇌ ♣ P

Katz
23 Lower Rushall Street (near Safeway) ☎ (01922) 725848
12–2.30, 5.30–11 (7–10.30 Sat); closed Sun
HP&D Entire; Mansfield Riding Mild; Marston's Pedigree; Tetley Bitter; guest beer H
Two-bar pub, formerly the Victoria Hotel, nicknamed Katz. The old tower brewery is now a private house. No meals Sat eve. ❀ ◖ ▶ ▣

King Arthur
Liskeard Road, Parkhall (off A34, 2 miles S of centre)
☎ (01922) 31400
12–2.30, 5.30–11; 12–11 Sat
Courage Best Bitter; Ruddles Best Bitter, County; John Smith's Bitter H

Friendly pub with two substantial rooms in which families are welcome. Try the Indian food (not served Sun). A challenge to find, but worth the effort. ❀ ◖ ▶ ♣ P

New Fullbrook

West Bromwich Road
☎ (01922) 21761
11.30–11
Bass Worthington BB; M&B Highgate Dark, Brew XI E
1930s roadhouse-style pub with a large bar, a games room and a small, pleasant lounge. It boasts the world record for sales of Highgate Dark. ❀ ◖ ⊞ ⇌ (Bescot Stadium) P

Oak Inn

336 Green Lane (A34)
☎ (01922) 645758
12–2.30 (11.30–3 Sat), 7–11; 7–10.30 Sun, closed Sun lunch
Wiltshire Stonehenge Bitter; guest beers H
Pub with an island bar and a friendly atmosphere, popular with workers at lunchtime. No food Sat, Sun and Tue eves. ◖◖ ❀ ◖ ▶ ⇌ ♣ P

Tap & Spile

5 John Street ☎ (01922) 27660
12–3, 5.30 (7 Sat)–11; 12–3, 8–10.30 Sun
Ansells Bitter, Mild; Ind Coope Burton Ale; guest beers H
The tiled entrance to the 'Pretty Bricks' is a reminder of a style of pub architecture which has been sadly abused. Inside, too, it is a pub for the nostalgic. No food Mon eve or Sun. ◖◖ Q ◖ ▶ ⊞ ⇌ ♣

White Lion

Sandwell Street
☎ (01922) 28542
12–3, 7 (6 Sat)–11
Ansells Bitter, Mild; HP&D Bitter, Entire; Ind Coope Burton Ale; guest beers H
Large, three-roomer in a residential area near the town centre. Friendly welcome. No food Sun. ◖ ⊞ ♣

Wednesbury

Old Blue Ball

Hall End (off A462)
☎ (0121) 556 0197
12–3, 5–11; 11.30–4.30, 7–11 Sat
Bass Worthington BB; M&B Highgate Dark; Stones Best Bitter E; **guest beer** H
Friendly, three-roomed local: a typical example of a Black Country boozer. ❀ ⊞ ♣

Wednesfield

Broadway

Lichfield Road (A4124)
☎ (01922) 405872
12–3, 5 (6 Sat)–11

Ansells Bitter, Mild; Holden's Bitter; Ind Coope Burton Ale; Tetley Bitter; guest beer H
Pleasant, multi-roomed pub with wood panelling in the lounge. The back lounge features ornate plaster coving and partitions of stained-glass. Carlsberg-Tetley's 'Tapster's Choice' guest beer. No food Sun. ❀ ◖ ⊞ ♣ ♦ P

Dog & Partridge

High Street ☎ (01902) 723490
Banks's Mild, Bitter E; **Camerons Strongarm** H
The oldest house in Wednesfield (pre-1840). Note the well in the back room, real beams and wattle and daub construction on view. ❀ ♣

Pheasant

Wood End Road
☎ (01902) 725548
11–2.30 (3 Fri & Sat), 5.30 (7 Sat)–11
HP&D Mild, Bitter, Entire; Tetley Bitter H
Large, smart, suburban, one-roomed pub with an island bar, often busy. Lunches weekdays. HP&D seasonal beers. ◖◖ ❀ ◖ ♣ P

Pyle Cock

Rookery Street
☎ (01902) 732125
10.30–11
Banks's Mild, Bitter E
Excellent locals' boozer with lovely etched windows depicting a pyle cock. The family room is quite basic. Q ⊠ ⊞ ♣ P

West Bromwich

Churchfield Tavern

18 Little Lane West
☎ (0121) 558 5468
11–11
Banks's Hanson's Mild, Mild, Bitter E
Friendly, three-roomed local. Eve meals end at 8pm. ⊠ ❀ ◖ ▶ ⊞ ♦ ♣ P

Hall End Tavern

Vicarage Road
☎ (0121) 588 5954
11–11; 12–2.30, 7–10.30 Sun
Banks's Mild E; **M&B Mild; Stones Best Bitter** H
Friendly, basic local, hosting a Tue night quiz. ⊠ ❀ ⊞ ♣ P

Vine

Roebuck Lane (off A41, near M5 jct 1) ☎ (0121) 553 2866
11–3, 5–11; 11–11 Fri & Sat
Banks's Mild; M&B Mild; Brew XI E; **guest beers** H
Lively, tiny corner pub famous for its Indian food. ◖ ▶ ♣

Wheatsheaf

379 High Street (off A41)
☎ (0121) 553 4221

11–3, 5–11; 11–11 Fri & summer; 12–2.30, 7–10.30 Sun
Holden's Mild, Bitter E, **Special** H
Lively, two-roomed local at the Carter's Green end of West Bromwich High St. Eve meals are served Sat only; no food Sun. ❀ ◖ ⊞ ♣ ⌣

Whiteheath

Whiteheath Tavern

400 Birchfield Lane (400 yds from M5 jct 2, follow signs to Blackheath) ☎ (0121) 552 3603
12 (12.30 Sat)–3, 7.30–11
Ansells Bitter, Mild H; **Banks's Mild** E
Popular, friendly local, with a games-oriented bar. ⊞ ♣

Willenhall

Brewers Droop

44 Wolverhampton Street (behind Lock Museum)
☎ (01902) 607827
12–3, 6–11
Batham Best Bitter; Everards Old Original; Hook Norton Old Hooky; S&N Theakston Old Peculier; guest beers H
An unusual array of artefacts enhances the appeal of this popular local. Mini-beer festivals four times a year. No food Sun eve. ◖ ▶ ㅎ ♣

Falcon

Gomer Street West
☎ (01902) 633378
12–11
Banks's Mild; Samuel Smith OBB; guest beers H
Black Country local with a games-oriented public bar and a quieter lounge. Up to four guest beers are available at weekends—the choice is adventurous. ❀ ⊞ ♣

Kipper House

16 Upper Lichfield Street
☎ (01902) 606146
11–3, 6–11; 11–11 Fri & Sat
Ansells Mild; HP&D Entire; Ind Coope Burton Ale; Ruddles County; Tetley Bitter H
One of Mad O'Rourke's chain of pubs, based on a nautical theme, with seafood on the menu. It can get very busy at weekends and has live music every Tue eve. Lumphammer, the house beer, is brewed by Carlsberg-Tetley. ❀ ◖ ▶ P

Robin Hood

54 The Crescent (200 yds from A454) ☎ (01902) 6080066
12–3 (3.30 Sat), 7–11; 12.30–3, 5.30–11 Fri
Ansells Mild; Ind Coope Burton Ale; Tetley Bitter; guest beer H
Welcoming, small, one-roomed pub. ❀ ♣ P

West Midlands

Wolverhampton

Brewery Tap
Dudley Road (½ mile from ring road) ☎ (01902) 351417
12–11
HP&D Mild, Entire, Deakin's Downfall; Tetley Bitter; guest beer H
One-bar, multi-alcoved pub with the HP&D Brewery visible at the rear: a stylised HP&D 1980s 'Victorian' pub featuring Black Country decor. Carlsberg-Tetley 'Tapster's Choice' guest beer.
🏠 ◑ P

Clarendon
38 Chapel Ash (A41)
☎ (01902) 20587
11–11
Banks's Mild, Bitter E ; Camerons Strongarm H
Banks's brewery tap, recently 'spoiled by progress' with the loss of the public and corridor bars. No food Sun. ◑ P

Combermere Arms
Chapel Ash (A41)
☎ (01902) 21880
11–2.30, 6–11
Draught Bass; M&B Highgate Dark; Stones Best Bitter; Wadworth 6X H
Cunningly disguised as a terraced house: a small lounge, smoke room, games room and a corridor, all served by one bar. Hand-pulled Stones and Bass are rare in this area.
🏠 ❀ ◓ & ♣

Feathers
Molineux Street
☎ (01902) 26924
11–3, 5–11; 12–11 Fri; 11–11 Sat
Banks's Mild, Bitter E
Small, friendly local, handy for the university and football ground (closes Sat afternoon when Wolves are at home). The garden has won awards. Weekday lunches.
❀ ◑ ◪ ⇌ ♣

Great Western
Sun Street (off A4124, near railway bridge)
☎ (01902) 351090
11–11; 11–2.30, 5–11 Sat; 12–2.30, 7–10.30 Sun
Batham Best Bitter; Holden's Mild, Bitter, XB, Special H
Revitalised pub next to the old low level station, featuring railway memorabilia and a pleasant new lounge. CAMRA national *Pub of the Year* 1991. Excellent value Black Country food. 🏠 ◑ ⇌ ◯ P

Homestead
Lodge Road (off A449)
☎ (01902) 787357
11–2.30 (3 Sat), 6–11
Ansells Bitter, Mild; Ind Coope Burton Ale; Marston's Pedigree; guest beer H
Large, pleasant suburban pub with an excellent children's playground, a plush lounge and a basic bar. The guest beer is from Carlsberg-Tetley's 'Tapster's Choice'.
❀ 🏡 ◑ ▶ ◪ ♣ P

Lewisham Arms
69 Prosser Street (off A460)
☎ (01902) 53505
11.30–3, 6–11; 11–11 Sat
Banks's Mild, Bitter E
Glorious Victorian ale house with etched windows and iron balconies. The large, unspoilt bar caters for all, and there is a small smoke room. ◪ ♣

Newhampton Inn
Riches Street (off A41)
☎ (01902) 745773
11–11
Courage Best Bitter, Directors; Marston's Pedigree; Ruddles County; John Smith's Bitter; guest beer H
Busy, street-corner local with four, distinctly different rooms and a surprisingly large garden, with a bowling green. Regular jazz, folk and other music. Daily changed guest beers. 🏠 Q ❀ ◑ ◪ ♣ ◯

Paget Arms
Park Lane (off A460)
☎ (01902) 731136
12–3, 6–11; 12–11 Fri & Sat
Home Mild, Bitter; S&N Theakston Mild, XB, Old Peculier; guest beer H
Large estate pub with three spacious rooms of differing character. Note the clock built into the outside wall. Weekday lunches.
🏠 ❀ ◑ ◪ ♣ ◯ P

Posada
Lichfield Street
☎ (01902) 710738
11–2.30, 5–10.30; 11–10.30 Fri & Sat
HP&D Entire, Deakin's Downfall; Tetley Bitter; guest beer H
Town-centre, Victorian pub with its original bar, fittings and tiled front. The only HP&D outlet in the town centre, it is popular with students. Mild has been replaced by a Carlsberg-Tetley 'Tapster's Choice' guest beer. Closed Sat afternoon when Wolves are at home. Weekday lunches. ◑ ⇌ ♣

Stamford Arms
Lime Street (off Lea Rd)
☎ (01902) 24172
12–3, 6–11; 12–11 Sat
Banks's Mild, Bitter E
Many-roomed Victorian pub with an award-winning garden. The exterior tiling is worth a look. A hidden gem in an old part of town.
Q ☙ ❀ ◪ ♣

Swan
Bridgnorth Road (A454)
☎ (01902) 754736
11–3, 5–11; 11–11 Sat
Banks's Mild, Bitter E ; Camerons Strongarm H
Mostly original, Victorian pub with a lounge, bar and a snug.
🏠 Q ❀ ◪ ♣ P

Westacres
Finchfield Hill
☎ (01902) 757922
12–2.30 (3 Sat), 5.30 (6 Sat)–11
HP&D Mild, Bitter, Entire; Tetley Bitter H
Popular one-roomed, typical HP&D pub, recently altered internally to a Victorian theme, giving alcoves and separate areas. Over 21s only.
❀ ◑ ▶ P

Woodcross

Horse & Jockey
Robert Wynd
☎ (01902) 884552
12–3, 7–11
Draught Bass H; Banks's Mild, Bitter ; Marston's Pedigree; Tetley Bitter; guest beer H
Victorian-style, renovated local, hosting a keen darts and dominoes club. Eve meals Wed–Sat until 8.30; no food Sun.
🏠 ◑ ▶ ◪ ♣ P

Woodsetton

Park Inn
George Street (off A457/A4123) ☎ (01902) 882843
11–11
Holden's Mild, Bitter, XB, Special H
Boisterous brewery tap, frequented by all ages. All-weather barbecues are held Fri, Sat and Sun in the conservatory. 🏠 ☙ ❀ ◑ ▶ &
⇌ (Coseley/Tipton) ♣ P

Wordsley

Samson & Lion
140 Brierley Hill Road (B4180)
☎ (01384) 77796
12–11
Banks's Mild; Marston's Bitter, Pedigree H
Sympathetically restored hostelry next to Lock 4 on the Stourbridge Canal. It offers facilities for boaters and two skittle alleys. The garden houses a pigsty and aviary. Marston's Head Brewer's Choice beers. No meals Sun eve; barbecues in summer.
🏠 ☙ ❀ 🏡 ◑ ▶ & ♣ P

Wiltshire

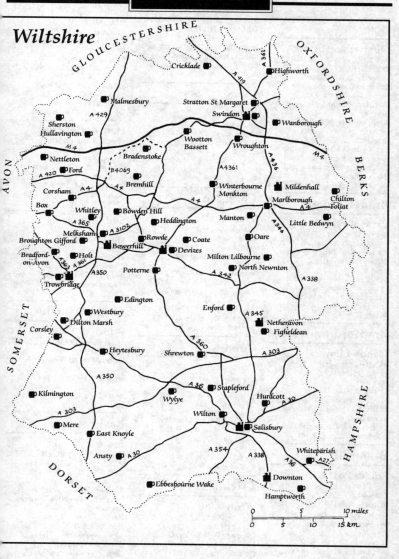

Cricklade
Highworth
Malmesbury
Stratton St Margaret
Swindon
Wanborough
Sherston
Hullavington
Wootton Bassett
Wroughton
Nettleton
Bradenstoke
Ford
Bremhill
Winterbourne Monkton
Mildenhall
Marlborough
Chilton Foliat
Corsham
Box
Whitley
Bowden Hill
Heddington
Manton
Little Bedwyn
Melksham
Broughton Gifford
Rowde
Coate
Oare
Holt
Bowerhill
Devizes
Milton Lilbourne
Bradford-on-Avon
Potterne
North Newnton
Trowbridge
Edington
Enford
Westbury
Netheravon
Dilton Marsh
Figheldean
Corsley
Heytesbury
Shrewton
Kilmington
Stapleford
Wylye
Hurdcott
Mere
Wilton
Salisbury
East Knoyle
Whiteparish
Ansty
Downton
Ebbesbourne Wake
Hamptworth

GLOUCESTERSHIRE
OXFORDSHIRE
AVON
BERKS
SOMERSET
HAMPSHIRE
DORSET

0   5   10 miles
0   5   10   15 km

Archers, Arkell's, Swindon; ***Bunces,*** Netheravon;
Foxley, Mildenhall; ***Gibbs Mew,*** Salisbury; ***Hop Back,***
Downton/Salisbury; ***Mole's,*** Bowerhill; ***Ushers,***
Trowbridge; ***Wadworth,*** Devizes

Ansty

Maypole Inn
Off A30 ☎ (01747) 870607
11–3, 6.30–11; closed Mon
**Butcombe Bitter; Fuller's
London Pride; Wadworth
6X** H
Comfortable pub situated near

Waldour Castle in a rural
setting. 🏕 Q ❀ 🛏 ◑ ▶ ▲ P

Bowden Hill

Rising Sun
32 Bowden Hill (1 mile E of
Lacock) ☎ (01249) 730363
11–2.30, 6–11

**Draught Bass; Mole's Tap,
Best Bitter, Landlords
Choice, Brew 97; guest
beer** H

Stone-flagged traditional pub
with fine views of the Avon
valley. The terraced garden
has a children's play area.
Live music Wed.
🏕 Q ❀ ◑ ♣ P

317

Wiltshire

Box

Quarrymans Arms
Box Hill (off A4) OS834693
☎ (01225) 743569
11–3, 7–11; 11–11 Thu–Sat
Draught Bass; Butcombe
Bitter; Wadworth 6X;
Wickwar Brand Oak; guest
beer H
An open-plan pub with
extensive views, worth the
detour. From Corsham turn
left off the A4 at the Rudloe
Park Hotel into Beech Road.
Then second right, and follow
the bends for 600 yards.
🛏 ❀ 🍴 🍺 🍴 🅰 ♣ ⌂ P

Bradenstoke

Cross Keys
Off B4069 ☎ (01249) 890279
7–11; 12–2, 7–11 Fri; 12–3, 7–11 Sat
Archers Best Bitter; Tetley
Bitter; Wadworth 6X; guest
beer H
Traditional, 200-year-old local
in a pretty village setting,
comprising two bars: a nice
lounge and a good public bar.
🛏 ❀ 🍺 🍴 ⌂ P

Bradford-on-Avon

Dandy Lion
35 Market Street
☎ (01225) 863433
10–3, 6–11
Draught Bass; Hall &
Woodhouse Tanglefoot;
Wadworth 6X, Old Timer;
guest beer H
Trendy, popular town-centre
pub/restaurant. 🍴 ▶ ➤

Bremhill

Dumb Post
Dumb Post Hill (off A4, W of
Calne) OS975727
☎ (01249) 813192
Archers Best Bitter;
Wadworth IPA, 6X H
Comfortable, friendly free
house offering the best value
beers in the area. No cooked
food Sun. 🛏 ❀ 🍴 ♣ P

Broughton Gifford

Bell on the Common
The Common (near B3107)
OS875642 ☎ (01225) 6782309
11–3, 6.30–11; 11–11 Sat
Wadworth IPA, 6X H
Handsome old village pub by
the common. The garden is
excellent for families.
🛏 ❀ 🍴 ▶ 🍺 🅰 ♣ P

Chilton Foliat

Wheatsheaf
On B4192 ☎ (01488) 682391
11–2.30 (3 Sat), 6–11

Morland Bitter, Old Masters,
Old Speckled Hen; guest
beer H
Friendly, two-bar country pub:
a former 13th-century
brewhouse. Cider in summer.
🛏 Q ❀ 🍴 ▶ 🍺 🅰 ⌂ P

Coate

New Inn
☎ (01380) 860644
12–2 (not Tue), 5–11
Wadworth IPA, 6X; guest
beer G
Proper village local where life
focuses on the public bar.
🛏 Q ❀ 🍺 🅰 ♣ P

Corsham

Two Pigs
38 Pickwick (A4)
☎ (01249) 712515
7–11; closed lunchtime, except Sun
Bunces Pigswill; guest
beers H
Main-road, stone-built pub
with wooden-clad walls, a
stone floor and a friendly,
lively atmosphere. Live blues
Mon eve (over-21s only). Local
CAMRA Pub of the Year 1993.
At least three ales. ❀ ⌂

Corsley

Cross Keys
Lye's Green (½ mile N of A362
at Royal Oak jct) OS821462
☎ (01373) 832406
12–3 (not Mon, Tue, Thu or Fri), 6.30
(7 Sat & Mon)–11
Draught Bass; Butcombe
Bitter; Mole's Best Bitter;
guest beer (occasional) H
A welcoming free house of
character: popular and
spacious. 🛏 ❀ 🍴 ▶ ♣ ⌂ P

Cricklade

White Lion
High Street ☎ (01793) 750443
11.30–3 (11–3.30 Sat), 6.30–11
Courage Best Bitter; Ushers
Best Bitter, Founders H
Country inn, in a 12th-century
Saxon town. An extensive
menu of home-made food is
available daily. Function room.
🛏 ❀ 🍴 🍴 ▶ 🍺 ♣ P

Devizes

Bell by the Green
Estcourt Street
☎ (01380) 723746
11–3, 6–11
Wadworth IPA, 6X; guest
beer H
Not so long ago, this pub was
not known for good real ale.
Thankfully, this has now
changed and it is a popular
pub. Skittle alley.
🍴 🍴 ▶ ♣ P

British Lion

9 Estcourt Street
☎ (01380) 729093
11–11
Beer range varies H
A convert to real ale, this pub
has one of the few
independent guest beer
policies in the area. Lion's
Pride, the house beer, is by
Coach House. ❀ ♣ ⌂ P

Hare & Hounds
Hare & Hounds Street
☎ (01380) 723231
11–2.30, 7–11
Wadworth IPA, 6X, Farmer's
Glory H
A proper pub and a Guide
regular; pub games feature
strongly. 🛏 ❀ 🍴 ♣ P

Old Crown
New Park Street
☎ (01380) 722692
11–11; 11–3, 6.30–11 Sat
Wadworth IPA, 6X H
Excellently refurbished pub,
now the closest to the brewery.
It can be very crowded. Skittle
alley. 🍴 ▶ 🍺

Dilton Marsh

Prince of Wales
High Street ☎ (01373) 865487
11–3, 7–11
Draught Bass; Wadworth 6X;
guest beer H
Simple, well-run, friendly,
open-plan local. Regular guest
beers are a feature. No food
Sun. 🍴 ➤ ♣ P

East Knoyle

Fox & Hounds
The Green (½ mile S of A303 at
Willoughby Hedge, signed)
OS807932 ☎ (01747) 830573
11–2.30, 6–11
Marston's Pedigree; Smiles
Bitter; Wadworth 6X; guest
beers H
Remote, 14th-century,
thatched, hillside inn with
panoramic views. The cosy
interior has three bars, a
children's room and skittle
alley. Popular with ramblers.
Good food. 🛏 Q 🐾 🍴 🍴
▶ 🍺 🅰 ♣ ⌂ P ⏚

Ebbesbourne Wake

Horseshoe Inn
Off A30, via Fovant OS242993
☎ (01722) 780474
11 (12 Mon)–2.30, 6.30 (7 Mon)–11
Adnams Broadside;
Ringwood Best Bitter, XXXX
Porter; Wadworth 6X; guest
beers G
This 18th-century inn offers a
friendly village atmosphere. It
stands at the foot of an old ox
drove and displays old
working tools in its two small

bars. No food Mon eve.
🏾 Q ❀ 🚗 ◖ 🅐 ♣ P

Edington

Lamb

Westbury Road (B3098)
☎ (01380) 830263
11–2.30 (3 Sat), 5.30 (6 Sat)–11
**Gibbs Mew Local Line,
Premium** H
Attractive village pub with
low-beamed ceilings. Two
bars, a dining room and a
function room. No meals Tue
eve. 🏾 ❀ ◖ ▶ 🔁 ♣ P

Enford

Swan

Longstreet ☎ (01980) 70338
12–2.30 (4 Sat), 7–11
**Hop Back Special; guest
beers** H
Cosy, unspoilt, thatched free
house with an unusual gantry
sign. Children are welcome in
the small bar for lunch. Good
value. 🏾 ❀ ◖ ▶ ♣ P

Figheldean

Wheatsheaf

High Street ☎ (01980) 70357
12–3, 7–11
**Draught Bass; Hop Back
Special; guest beers** H
Single bar with a large open
fire and alcoves, plus a family
room and a pleasant, large
garden. Usually four beers
stocked. 🏾 ⛌ ❀ ◖ ▶ ♣ P

Ford

White Hart

Off A420 ☎ (01249) 7822213
11–3, 5–11
**Draught Bass; Marston's
Pedigree; Smiles Best Bitter;
Exhibition; Wadworth 6X;
Whitbread Flowers IPA; guest
beers** H
Splendid old inn, full of
character. The outside
drinking area lies beside a
stream. Up to ten real ales. The
restaurant has a good
reputation.
🏾 Q ⛌ ❀ 🚗 ◖ ▶ ♿ ⌂ P

Hamptworth

Cuckoo

Hamptworth Road (take B3079
off A36, then 1st right, 1 mile)
OS243197 ☎ (01794) 390302
11.30–2.30, 6–11; 11.30–11 Sat & bank
hols
**Cheriton Pots Ale, Best Bitter;
Hop Back Summer Lightning,
Wheat Beer; Wadworth 6X,
Farmer's Glory; guest beers** G
Set on the edge of the New
Forest, this popular pub is
housed in a 300-year-old,
unspoilt, thatched cottage, and

has four rooms of public bar
standard. Busy in summer.
🏾 Q ⛌ ❀ ♿ 🅐 ♣ ⌂ P

Heddington

Ivy

Off A3102 ☎ (01380) 850276
11–3, 6.30–11
**Wadworth IPA, 6X, Old
Timer** G
Popular, thatched pub,
converted from three 400-year-
old cottages. Improvements
have been in keeping with its
general surroundings.
🏾 Q ⛌ ❀ ♿ 🅐 ♣ P

Heytesbury

Angel Inn

High Street ☎ (01985) 40330
11–3, 6 (6.30 winter)–11
**Marston's Pedigree;
Ringwood Best Bitter; guest
beer** H
17th-century coaching inn
with a highly regarded
restaurant. Strong local trade
is derived from the friendly
village, now bypassed.
🏾 Q ❀ 🚗 ◖ ▶ ♣ ⌂ P

Highworth

Wine Cellar

High Street ☎ (01793) 763828
12–3 (not Mon–Thu), 7–11
**Archers Village, Best Bitter;
guest beer** G
Quirky wine bar, hosting
occasional live music. ♣ ⌂

Holt

Old Ham Tree

Ham Green (B3107)
☎ (01225) 782581
11.15–3, 6.30–11
**Marston's Pedigree;
Wadworth 6X; guest beer** H
18th-century coaching inn of
character. A comfortable
lounge/restaurant contrasts
with a simple, friendly locals'
bar. Good variety of meals.
Q ❀ 🚗 ◖ ▶ 🔁 ♣ ⌂ P

Hullavington

Queens Head

The Street ☎ (01666) 837221
11.30–2, 7–11
**Archers Village; Wadworth
6X** H
Homely village local where
the open fires generate a warm
atmosphere. Skittle alley. No
food Sun. 🏾 Q 🚗 ♿ ♣ P

Hurdcott

Black Horse

Black Horse Lane (off A338)
☎ (01980) 611565
11–2.30, 6–11; 11–11 Sat

**Draught Bass; Gibbs Mew
Salisbury** H
Old building at the end of a
country lane, formerly three
cottages and a forge. Wattle
and daub upstairs; beamed bar
below. Q ❀ ◖ ▶ 🅐 P

Kilmington

Red Lion

On B3092 ☎ (01985) 844263
11–3, 6.30–11
**Butcombe Bitter; Marston's
Pedigree; guest beer** H
Unspoilt National Trust-
owned pub. The single bar has
a curtained-off area. Good
choice of hot and cold meals
(eves Fri and Sat only).
🏾 Q ❀ 🚗 ◖ ▶ ♣ ⌂ P

Little Bedwyn

Harrow

Off A4 ☎ (01672) 870871
11–2.30 (not Mon), 5.30 (6 Sat)–11
**Hook Norton Best Bitter;
guest beers** H
Cheerful, foody pub, owned
by a village co-operative. Its
decor reflects the nearby canal.
Beware, the cider is on blanket
pressure. No food Mon.
🏾 Q ❀ 🚗 ◖ ▶ ♣

Malmesbury

Smoking Dog

High Street
☎ (01666) 825823
11.30–3, 5.30–11; 11.30–11 Fri & Sat
Archers Best Bitter G; **Smiles
Best Bitter; Wadworth 6X;
guest beers** H
Lively, town-centre beer
drinkers' pub with a friendly
atmosphere. Home-made food.
🏾 Q ⛌ ❀ 🚗 ◖ ▶ ♣

Whole Hog

Market Cross
☎ (01666) 825845
11–11
**Archers Best Bitter; guest
beers** H
Former restaurant now a
popular wine, ale and food
house, providing a good view
of the old market cross. Two
guest beers, plus a house ale.
Q ◖ ▶ 🅐

Manton

Oddfellows Arms

High Street
☎ (01672) 512352
12 (11.30 Sat)–3, 6–11
**Wadworth IPA, 6X; guest
beer** H
Cosy little local with a friendly
atmosphere, a secluded garden
and a games room. No food
Sun eve.
🏾 Q ❀ ◖ ▶ ♣ ⌂ P

Wiltshire

Marlborough

Lamb
The Parade ☎ (01672) 512668
11–11
Wadworth IPA, 6X; guest beer G
Excellent, cheerful, noisy town pub. ✿ ⊨ ◑ ♣ ♦

Melksham

Red Lion
3 The City ☎ (01225) 702960
11–3, 5 (6 Sat)–11; 11–11 Fri
Draught Bass; M&B Highgate Dark; guest beer H
Stone-built pub of character. A popular, friendly local, refurbished. Q ✿ ♣ P

Mere

Butt of Sherry
Castle Street (B3095)
☎ (01747) 860352
11.30 (11 Sat)–3, 5–11
Draught Bass; Gibbs Mew Premium, Bishop's Tipple H
Traditional pub with a lively local trade. ⊨ ✿ ◑ ♣ ◔

Milton Lilbourne

Three Horseshoes
Off B3087 ☎ (01672) 62323
11.30–2.30 (not Mon), 6.30–11
Adnams Bitter; Wadworth 6X; guest beer H
Smart pub and restaurant with a well. No food Sun eve or Mon. ⊨ Q ✿ ◑ ♣ P

Nettleton

Nettleton Arms
☎ (01249) 782783
12–3, 7 (6.30 summer)–11
Archers Village; Draught Bass; Wadworth 6X; guest beer (summer)
One of the oldest buildings in the area, now a village pub, catering for all. No lunches winter Mon.
Q ✿ ⊨ ◑ ♦ & P

North Newnton

Woodbridge Inn
On A345 ☎ (01980) 630266
11–11
Wadworth IPA, 6X, Farmer's Glory, Old Timer; guest beer H
Pleasant, foody roadside inn with two comfortable bars. Angling rights on the Avon.
Q ✿ ⊨ ◑ ♦ & ♣ ♠ P

Oare

White Hart
☎ (01672) 62273
11.30–2.30, 7–11; 11–3, 6.30–11 Sat
Draught Bass; Wadworth IPA, 6X H
Fine traditional village pub.
⊨ Q ✿ ⊨ ◑ ♦ ⊞ ♣ P

Potterne

George & Dragon
High Street ☎ (01380) 722139
12–2.30, 6.30–11
Wadworth IPA, 6X; guest beers H
15th-century, thatched, village inn. Good food is a speciality. Skittle alley and a games room. Q ☽ ✿ ⊨ ◑ ♣

Rowde

George & Dragon
High Street ☎ (01380) 723053
12–3 (not Mon), 7–11
Wadworth IPA, 6X H
Pub described by *The Guardian* as 'unmucked about'. The food is first rate too! No eve meals Sun/Mon. ⊨ Q ◑ ♦ ⚲ ♣ P

Salisbury

Avon Brewery Inn
75 Castle Street (Amesbury road, near Market Sq)
☎ (01722) 327280
11–11
Eldridge Pope Dorchester, Hardy Country, Blackdown Porter (winter), **Royal Oak** H
Busy, Victorian, city-centre pub with a splendid bow front. The riverside garden boasts a petanque pitch. Try the excellent value traditional lunches. ✿ ◑ ♣

Maxwell's
26–27 Water Lane (off Fisherton St) ☎ (01722) 329140
11–3, 6–11; 7–10.30 Sun, closed Sun lunch
Hop Back GFB; Whitbread Boddingtons Bitter; guest beers (weekends) H
Spacious bar with a relaxed atmosphere. Good live music (jazz/blues) Fri and Sat eves.
✿ ◑ ♦ & ⚎ ♣

Royal George
Bedwin Street (300 yds N of Market Sq) ☎ (01722) 327782
11–3, 6–11
Gibbs Mew Salisbury, Premium, Deacon H
Part-12th-century, Grade II-listed pub. The Royal George was a sister ship of the Victory. Trad jazz Sun eve. Good atmosphere.
☽ ✿ ⊨ ◑ ♦ P

Village
33 Wilton Road (off St Paul's roundabout on A36)
☎ (01722) 329707
11–11
Hampshire King Alfred's, Pendragon; Hop Back Summer Lightning; Oakhill

Best Bitter; Taylor Landlord H**; guest beers** G
Relaxed pub with a cosy atmosphere. The Bunker Bar in the cellar has an art gallery. Popular with rail buffs. ⚎

Wyndham Arms
27 Estcourt Road (½ mile NE of centre) ☎ (01722) 331026
4.30 (4 Fri)–11; 12–11 Sat
Hop Back Mild, GFB, Special, Summer Lightning, Wheat Beer H
Small, back-street pub with a single bar and several drinking areas. The original home of Hop Back Brewery. ♣

Sherston

Rattlebone Inn
Church Street
☎ (01666) 840871
12–3, 5.30–11; 12–11 Sat; 12–3, 7.30–10.30 Sun
Smiles Best Bitter; Wadworth 6X; guest beer H
Old, friendly pub named after a local character. Rattlebone SPA is brewed by Archers; the pub also stocks local wine. Skittles, an unusual, six-sided pool table and boules feature.
⊨ Q ✿ ◑ ♦ ◔ P

Shrewton

Royal George
London Road (B3086, N of village) ☎ (01980) 620341
11–3, 6–11; 11–11 Sat
Ushers Best Bitter; Wadworth 6X; guest beer H
Part-16th-century chalk, flint and stone inn, which once housed a brewery. A pitcher of any beer is sold at one standard price. ⊨ Q ☽ ✿ ⊨ ◑ ♦ ⊞ ⚲ ♣ ◔ P

Stapleford

Pelican Inn
Warminster Road (A36)
☎ (01722) 790241
11–2.30 (3 Sat), 6–11
Otter Bitter; Ringwood Best Bitter, Fortyniner; guest beer H
Welcoming, 18th-century coaching inn where the restaurant area was once stables and a mortuary. Generous helpings of good food and pitchers of ale are offered. ⊨ ✿ ◑ ♦ ♣

Stratton St Margaret

Kingsdown
Kingsdown Road, Upper Stratton ☎ (01793) 823261
11–2.30, 6–11
Arkell's 2B, 3B, Kingsdown H

320

The Arkell's tap, recently extensively refurbished. No food Sun eve. Arkell's occasional beers served.
❀ ◐ ◑ ⊞ ♣ P

Swindon

Clifton Inn
Clifton Street
☎ (01793) 523162
11–2.30, 6–11
Arkell's 2B, 3B, Kingsdown H
Lively, cheerful back-street pub, between old and new Swindon. ❀ ♣ P

Duke of Wellington
27 Eastcott Hill
☎ (01793) 534180
12–2.30, 6.30–11
Arkell's 2B, 3B G
Small, welcoming pub near the town centre. No food Mon eve. Arkell's occasional beers served. ♕ ❀ ◐ ◑ ♣

Glue Pot
5 Emlyn Square
☎ (01793) 523935
11–11
Archers Village, Best Bitter, Black Jack, Golden, Old Cobleigh's; guest beer H
Bath stone, listed building in the railway village. The bar features high-backed booths. The Archers brewery tap.
Q ❀ ♿ ⇌ ♣

Kings Arms Hotel
Wood Street, Old Town
☎ (01793) 522156
11–3, 6–11
Arkell's 2B, 3B, Kingsdown, Noel Ale H
Large hotel bar in the Old Town area. Arkell's occasional beers served. ⛟ ◐ ◑ ♿ P

Rising Sun
6 Albert Street, Old Town
☎ (01793) 529916
11–11
Courage Best Bitter, Directors; Ushers Best Bitter, Founders H**, 1824** G
Busy, back-street pub, known as the Roaring Donkey. ♣ ⌓

Swiss Chalet
Chapel Street, Gorse Hill
☎ (01793) 535610
11–3, 5.30–11
Arkell's 2B, 3B, Kingsdown, Noel Ale H
Large single-bar pub with an Alpine flavour. Live music most eves. Arkell's occasional beers served. ◐ P

Trowbridge

Lamb Inn
Mortimer Street (opp. County Hall) ☎ (01225) 755947
11.30–2.30 (4 Sat), 7–11
Wadworth IPA, 6X H
Comfortable lounge bar, popular with council staff at lunchtimes. The lively public bar hosts bands Sat. No food Sat. ♕ ❀ ⛟ ◐ ⊞ ⇌ ♣ P

Wanborough

Black Horse
Callas Hill (crossroads S end of village) ☎ (01793) 790305
11–3, 5.30–11; 11–11 Sat
Arkell's 2B, 3B H**, Noel Ale** G
Past CAMRA regional *Pub of the Year*, a homely, cosy two-bar local with a down-to-earth welcome for all. No food Sun. In the same family for 36 years. Arkell's occasional beers served. ❀ ◐ ▲ ♣ P

Plough
High Street ☎ (01793) 790523
12–2.30, 5–11; 11–11 Fri & Sat
Archers Village; Draught Bass; Morland Old Speckled Hen; Wadworth 6X; Whitbread Boddingtons Bitter; guest beer H
Ancient, thatched pub with a long, beamed, stone-walled bar. No meals Sat lunch or Sun. ♕ Q ❀ ◐ ◑ ♣ P

Westbury

Crown Inn
Market Place ☎ (01373) 822828
11–2.30 (3 Mon), 5.30 (6 Sat)–11
Wadworth 6X; guest beer H
Welcoming, well-appointed local. It boasts a new function room and skittle alley. The guest beer changes fortnightly. No food Sun; eve meals Fri and Sat only. ❀ ◐ ⊞ ♣ ⌓ P

Oak Inn
Warminster Road (A350)
☎ (01373) 823169
12–3 (not Mon–Fri), 5.30 (6 Sat)–11
Draught Bass; Fuller's London Pride; Ringwood Best Bitter, Fortyniner H
A mock Tudor exterior conceals a 16th-century inn with more recent additions. Occasional beer festivals in the skittle alley. ♕ ❀ ⊞ ♣ P

Whiteparish

Parish Lantern
Romsey Road (A27)
☎ (01794) 884392
11.30–3, 6.30–11
Ringwood Best Bitter H**; guest beers**
A cottage and pub at the turn of the century, now one long room with a low ceiling and mock beams. No food Mon eve. ♕ Q ❀ ◐ ◑ ♿ ▲ ♣ P

Whitley

Pear Tree
Top Lane ☎ (01225) 709131
12–3, 7–11
Eldridge Pope Hardy Country; Hall & Woodhouse Badger Best Bitter; Wadworth 6X; guest beer (occasional) H
Delightful pub in an unspoilt village. The half-acre garden has a children's play area. Skittles nights; barbecues in summer. Upstairs restaurant.
Q ☋ ❀ ◐ ◑ ♿ ♣ P

Wilton

Bear Inn
12 West Street (A30)
☎ (01722) 742398
11–3 (3.30 Sat), 5–11
Hall & Woodhouse Badger Best Bitter H
Small, 16th-century pub with one bar. A convivial welcome is assured. ♕ ❀ ♣

Winterbourne Monkton

New Inn
Off A4361 ☎ (01672) 539240
11–3, 6–11
Adnams Bitter; Wadworth 6X; guest beer H
Neat, friendly little pub with a carpeted bar featuring china plates. ♕ ❀ ⛟ ◐ ◑ ♿ ♣ P

Wootton Bassett

Old Nick
Station Road ☎ (01793) 848102
11–11 (11.30 Fri & Sat)
Berrow 4Bs, Topsy Turvy; Courage Best Bitter; John Smith's Bitter; Wadworth 6X; guest beers H
Formerly the police station, now an extensive bar with police mementoes. The adjoining courthouse is a disco/pool room. Beerex held Nov. ♕ ◐ ◑ ♿ ♣ ⌓ P

Wroughton

Carters Rest
High Street ☎ (01793) 812288
11–3, 5.30–11; 11–11 Sat
Archers Village, Best Bitter, Black Jack, Golden; guest beers H
Edwardian building, tastefully refurbished. ♕ ◐ ♿ ▲ ♣ P

Wylye

Bell
High Street ☎ (0198 56) 338
11.30–2.30, 6–11 (11.30–11 summer); 12–2.30, 7–10.30 Sun
Hall & Woodhouse Badger Best Bitter; Wadworth 6X; guest beer H
14th-century coaching inn with a wealth of old beams. A vigilante group was formed here in 1798. Good food.
♕ Q ❀ ⛟ ◐ ◑ ♿ P

North Yorkshire

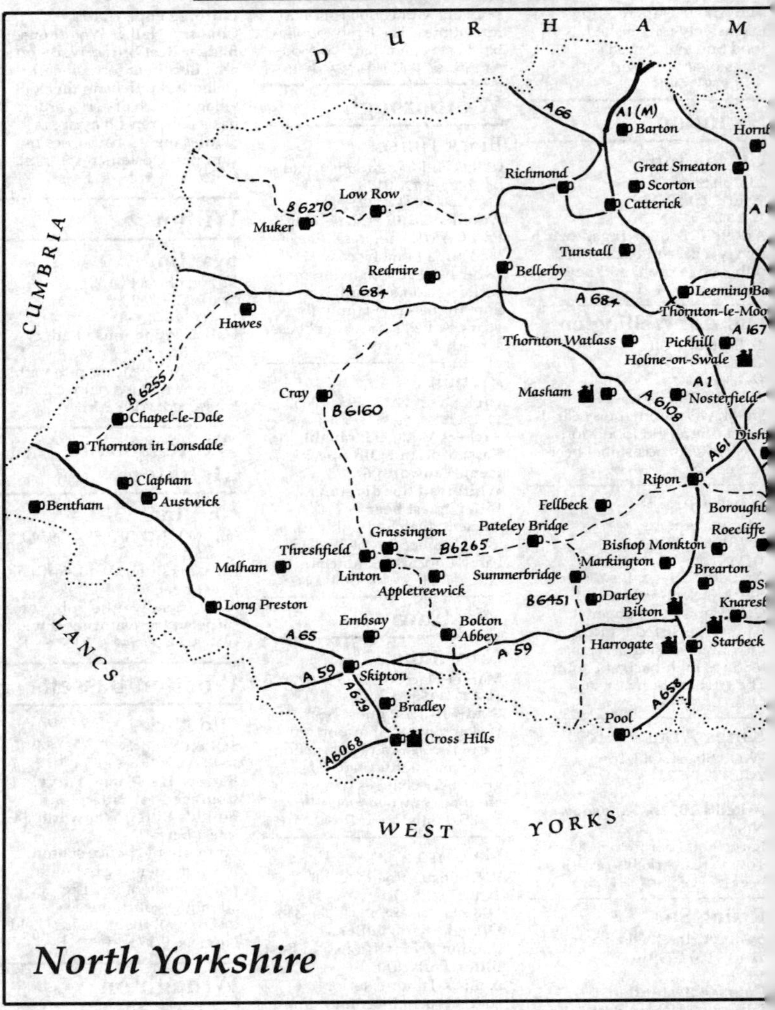

Black Sheep, *Masham;* **Wm. Clark,** *Scarborough;* **Cropton,** *Cropton;* **Daleside,** *Starbeck;* **Franklin's,** *Bilton;* **Hambleton,** *Holme-on-Swale;* **Lastingham,** *Pickering;* **Malton,** *Malton;* **Marston Moor,** *Kirk Hammerton;* **Old Bear,** *Cross Hills;* **Rooster's,** *Harrogate;* **Rudgate,** *Tockwith;* **Selby,** *Selby;* **Samuel Smith,** *Tadcaster;* **Whitby's,** *Whitby*

Acaster Malbis

Ship Inn

2 miles S of A64, 4 miles S of York ☎ (01904) 705609
11.30–3, 7–11; 11.30–11 Fri & Sat
Taylor Landlord; Tetley Mild, Bitter H

17th-century coaching inn beside the River Ouse, once an inn for bargees, now popular with boaters and campers (boating theme in the open bar). New function room; popular restaurant. Barbecues in summer on the terrace.
⛫ Q ❀ ⛟ ◐ ◗ ♿ ▲ ♣ P

Appletreewick

New Inn

☎ (01756) 720252
12–3 (not Mon), 7–11
John Smith's Bitter; Younger Scotch; guest beer H
Hospitable inn where the

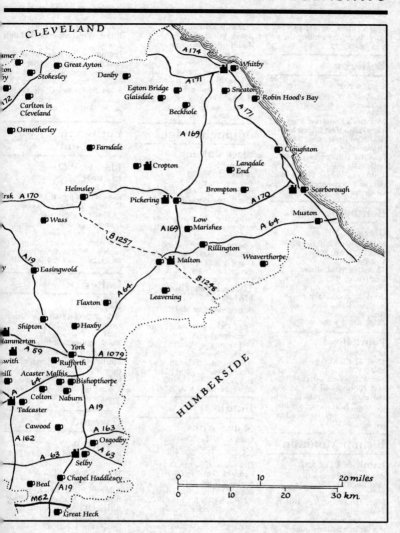

emphasis remains on beer.
Large range of foreign bottles;
Liefmans Kriek on draught.
The bar is in an L-shaped
room, with a separate room
across the hall. Gated garden
over the road.
🏠 ⛄ ❀ 🛏 🍴 ♣ ⌾ P

Austwick

Game Cock
☎ (0152 42) 51226
11–2.30, 6.30–11
Thwaites Bitter H
Plainly-furnished little bar,
decorated with memorabilia;
also a busy dining room and
verandah (children admitted),
overlooking the attractive
main street. No meals Mon
eve. 🏠 Q ❀ 🍴 ♣ P

Barton

King William IV
1 Silver Street
☎ (01325) 377256
12–3 (not Tue; 11.30–4 Sat), 6.30–11
**John Smith's Bitter,
Magnet** H
Recently extended roadside
local with a number of
separate spaces clustered
around a single serving area.
Excellent garden with play
equipment and quoits pitches.
🏠 ❀ 🍴 🛏 & ♣ P

Beal

Kings Head
Main Street ☎ (01977) 673487
7–11; 12–4, 7–11 Sat

**John Smith's Bitter; Tetley
Bitter** H
With its time-warp bar and
separate rooms, this pub is the
hub of village life in the eve.
Known locally as 'Fred's', it
has been in the same family
for almost half a century. Eve
meals served Sat. 🏠 ❀ ♣ P

Beckhole

Birchall Inn
1 mile from Goathland
☎ (01947) 896245
11–3, 7–11 (11–11 summer)
**S&N Theakston Mild
(summer), Best Bitter, XB** H
Rural gem, originally two
cottages, now a pub and
general store: a small front bar
and a larger room to the rear,

323

plus a garden on a terrace. A guest beer may replace the mild. ♨ Q ☎ ✿ ♣ ♠

Bellerby

Cross Keys
On A6108 ☎ (01969) 22256
11–3 (not winter Mon), 7–11; 11–11 Fri & Sat
Marston's Pedigree; S&N Theakston Best Bitter; John Smith's Bitter; guest beer (summer) H
Friendly village inn (c1760) with easy access to Swaledale and Wensleydale. Home-made pies and soups are specialities.
♨ ✿ 🛏 ◁ ▷ ▲ P

Bentham

Black Bull
Main Street, High Bentham
☎ (0152 42) 61213
11–3, 7–11
Thwaites Mild, Bitter, Craftsman H
Friendly village inn with three drinking areas. First prize-winner in Thwaites's cellar competition 1993.
♨ ✿ 🛏 ◁ ▷ ⇌ ♠ P

Punch Bowl
Low Bentham
☎ (0152 42) 61344
12–2 (not Mon), 6–11
Mitchell's Best Bitter H
18th-century, old-time village inn, extended in 1986 though the small neat rooms remain. Restaurant open weekends.
♨ ✿ ◁ ♣ P

Bishop Monkton

Lamb & Flag Inn
Boroughbridge Road
☎ (01765) 677322
12–3, 5.30–11
S&N Theakston Best Bitter; Tetley Bitter; guest beer H
Cosy, welcoming, two-roomed inn set in a picturesque village.
♨ ◁ ▷ ♣ P

Bishopthorpe

Ebor Inn
Main Street ☎ (01904) 706190
11–4, 6–11; 11–11 Fri; 10.30–11 Sat
Samuel Smith OBB, Museum H
Village pub which has kept its atmosphere even though modernised. Separate lounge; renowned restaurant. Popular with York race-goers.
Q ☎ ✿ ◁ ▷ 🍺 ⚘ ▲ ♣ P ✂

Bolton Abbey

Duke's Bar
Devonshire Arms Hotel
☎ (01756) 710441
11–11

Franklin's Bitter; Tetley Bitter; Whitbread Boddingtons Bitter; guest beers H
Spacious public bar, part of a country hotel complex, half a mile south of Bolton Abbey. Sporting memorabilia abounds. Popular with country sports enthusiasts.
♨ ✿ 🛏 ◁ ⚘ ▲ P

Boroughbridge

Black Bull Inn
St James Square
☎ (01423) 322413
11–3, 6.30–11; 11–11 Fri
Black Sheep Best Bitter; S&N Theakston Best Bitter; John Smith's Bitter H
Attractive 13th-century inn with separate drinking areas, including a comfortable lounge and a cosy snug. Pleasant, relaxed atmosphere. Popular for high quality meals. ♨ Q 🛏 ◁ ▷ ▲

Three Horseshoes Hotel
Bridge Street ☎ (01423) 322314
11–3, 5–11
S&N Theakston Best Bitter H; Vaux Samson E
Welcoming, unspoilt 1930s hotel with wood-panelling and stained-glass. Friendly atmosphere. A good place for meals and conversation.
♨ Q ☎ 🛏 ◁ ▷ ▲ ♣ P

Bradley

Slaters Arms
Crag Lane (back road to Farnhill) ☎ (01535) 632179
11–3.30, 6–11
Commercial Keighlian or Pennine Golden; John Smith's Bitter H
Pleasant village local dating from 1760, with a fine inglenook and a suntrap garden at the rear. The haunt of the local cricket team and an outlet for new Keighley-brewed beers. Popular with boaters from the nearby Leeds–Liverpool Canal.
♨ ✿ ◁ ▷ ♣ P

Brearton

Malt Shovel
Off B165 ☎ (01423) 862929
12–3, 6.30–11; closed Mon
Daleside Bitter; Old Mill Bitter; S&N Theakston Best Bitter; guest beer H
16th-century pub with stone walls and beams. Good food.
♨ Q ☎ ✿ ◁ ▷ ♣ ⌂ P

Brompton

Cayley Arms
Main Street ☎ (01723) 859372
11–11

Camerons Bitter; Tetley Bitter; Whitbread Castle Eden Ale H
Prominent wayside pub in an ancient village. A functional lounge is complemented by a hallway bar serving other areas. Sir George Cayley was an early aviation pioneer.
♨ ☎ 🛏 ◁ ▷ ▲ ♣ P

Carlton in Cleveland

Blackwell Ox
☎ (01642) 712287
12–3, 6.30–11
Bass Worthington BB, Draught Bass; guest beers H
Old village local with numerous rooms off a central bar. Thai meals are a speciality. Popular in summer with walkers and campers.
♨ Q ☎ ✿ 🛏 ◁ ▷ ▲ ♣ P

Catterick

Bay Horse
38 Low Green (100 yds from High St) ☎ (01748) 811383
12–3 (4 Sat), 7–11
Black Sheep Best Bitter; S&N Theakston Best Bitter; John Smith's Bitter, Magnet; guest beer H
Pub at the centre of a Georgian village, beside the beck. Warm atmosphere. ♨ ✿ ♣ P

Cawood

Ferry Inn
King Street (upstream side of swing bridge, off B1222)
☎ (01757) 268515
12–4, 6.30–11 (11–11 summer)
Adnams Bitter, Extra, Broadside; Mansfield Riding Bitter, Old Baily; Wells Bombardier H
Quiet village pub on the west bank of the River Ouse, with connections with Cardinal Wolsey. The large bar has a wood-burning stove; the garden leads down to the river.
♨ Q ☎ ✿ 🛏 ◁ ▷ ⚘ ▲ ♣ P

Chapel Haddlesey

Jug
Main Street ☎ (01757) 270307
12–3, 7–11; 11–11 Sat
Mansfield Bitter; S&N Theakston XB; guest beers H
250-year-old, small village inn, once also a blacksmith's shop, on the north bank of the River Aire. Welcoming atmosphere; friendly ghost. Try the Desperate Dan Cow Pie.
♨ Q ☎ ◁ ▷ ▲ ♣ P

Chapel-le-Dale

Hill Inn
☎ (0152 42) 41256
12–3, 6.30–11; 11.30–11 Sat
Dent Bitter; S&N Theakston Best Bitter, XB, Old Peculier; Whitbread Boddingtons Bitter H
Well-known, isolated pub on the Three Peaks Walk with bare floorboards and exposed stonework; a cosy bar, a pool room and a food bar (children welcome). Music Sat night; folk Sun lunchtime.
🏨 ❀ ◑ ▲ ♣ P

Clapham

New Inn
☎ (0152 42) 51203
11–3, 7–11
Dent Bitter; McEwan 80/-; John Smith's Bitter; Tetley Bitter; Younger No. 3 H
Large coaching inn, dated 1776: two lounge bars with oak panelling (1990 vintage). Separate restaurant (no-smoking: children welcome).
🏨 ❀ ◑ ▶ ▲ ♣ P

Cloughton

Red Lion Hotel
High Street ☎ (01723) 870702
11.30–2.30, 6–11
John Smith's Bitter; Tetley Bitter H
Village two-roomer with a small basic bar, popular with the locals, and a larger, functional lounge. Spacious garden with barbecue facilities.
🏨 ❀ 🍴 ◑ ▲ ♣ P

Colton

Olde Sun Inn
Main Street ☎ (01904) 744261
11.30–3, 7–11
Bass Worthington BB, Draught Bass; John Smith's Bitter; Stones Best Bitter H
Open-plan pub on several levels, furnished with Windsor chairs and old photographs of the area. The landlady signs for deaf visitors.
❍ ❀ ◑ ♣ P

Cray

White Lion
On B6160 ☎ (01756) 760262
1–3, 6–11; 11–11 Sat & summer
Moorhouse's Premier, Pendle Witches Brew; Tetley Mild, Bitter H
Welcoming, stone-flagged inn situated in fine walking country, with a log fire and Ring the Bull. Excellent range

of home-cooked meals (open daily 8.30–11am for food).
🏨 Q 🍴 ❀ 🍴 ◑ ▲ ♣ P ✗

Cropton

New Inn
Rosedale turn off A170 at Wrelton OS755890
☎ (01751) 417330
11–3, 6–11 (11.30–2.30, 7–11 winter)
Cropton King Billy, Two Pints, Scoresby Stout, Special Strong; Tetley Mild, Bitter H
An ideal pub to get snowed in—a free house with its own brewery at the top of a very steep hill. Nearby camp sites make it busy in summer, but don't spoil the relaxed atmosphere.
🏨 🍴 ❀ 🍴 ◑ ▶ ♿ ▲ ♣ ⌂ P ✗

Cross Hills

Old White Bear
6 Keighley Road
☎ (01535) 632115
11–11
Old Bear Bitter; guest beers H
Built in 1735, a large, four-roomed pub now further improved by a new restaurant. The Old Bear Brewery may be viewed through internal windows. Very popular with a wide range of people, it can get busy. Families welcome at lunchtime. Four guest beers from the Whitbread list.
🏨 Q 🍴 ❀ ◑ ♿ ♣ P

Dalton

Jolly Farmers of Olden Times
S of A168 ☎ (01845) 577359
7.30 (8.30 Mon)–11; 12–2 (not winter), 7.30–11 Sat; 12– 2, 7–10.30 Sun
Courage Directors; John Smith's Bitter; guest beers (summer) H
200-year-old, modernised village pub with some original beams retained. Join in the conversation at the bar to get the real feel of this pub. Lunches served when open.
🏨 Q ❀ 🍴 ▶ ♿ ▲ ♣ P

Danby

Duke of Wellington
West Lane
☎ (01287) 660351
11–3, 7–11 (11–11 summer)
Banks's Bitter (summer); Camerons Strongarm; Ruddles County; John Smith's Magnet H
Village local, a coaching inn dating from 1732 where walkers, hikers and families are welcome. Friendly locals. No-smoking residents' lounge.
🏨 Q 🍴 ❀ 🍴 ◑ ▶ ♿ ▲ ⇌ P

Darley

Wellington Inn
On B5451 at Darley Head
☎ (01423) 780362
11–11
Ind Coope Burton Ale; S&N Theakston Best Bitter; Tetley Mild, Bitter H
Much-extended Dales pub, including a cosy snug with an old range fire and settles. Real fires are a feature. Its lovely setting in Nidderdale makes this an excellent touring base. A guest beer sometimes replaces the Burton Ale.
🏨 ❀ 🍴 ◑ ▶ ♣ P

Dishforth

Crown Inn
Main Street ☎ (01845) 577398
12–2.30, 6.30–11
Hambleton Bitter; S&N Theakston Best Bitter; guest beer (weekends) H
Friendly, welcoming village pub. ❀ ▲ ♣ P

Easingwold

Station Hotel
Knott Lane (off Raskelf Rd)
☎ (01347) 822635
11–2.30, 5–11; 11–11 Fri & Sat
Hambleton Bitter; John Smith's Bitter; Tetley Bitter; guest beers H
A recent local newspaper *Pub of the Year*, this Victorian building serves real ale in a real rail setting. Extensive range of foreign bottled beers, plus Belgian beers on tap.
🏨 🍴 ❀ 🍴 ◑ ▶ ♿ ♣ ⌂

Egton Bridge

Postgate Inn
Off A171 ☎ (01947) 85241
11–11
Camerons Bitter; Tetley Bitter; Whitbread Flowers IPA; guest beer (summer) H
Attractive hotel overlooking a rustic railway station. Children's and vegetarian menus are offered. Named after Friar Postgate, a local martyr. 🏨 Q 🍴 ❀ 🍴 ◑ ▶ 🍴 ⇌ ♣ P

Embsay

Elm Tree Inn
5 Elm Tree Square
☎ (01756) 790717
11.30–3.30, 5.30–11
Cains Bitter; Morland Old Speckled Hen; Pennine Golden; guest beers H
Very popular village pub, for both beer and food. One large room houses the main bar, and a small side room is tastefully

furnished with old-fashioned pew-type seats. Pennine Golden is sold as Eh Bah Gum. Ever-changing guest beers.
Q ❀ ◑ ▶ ᴊ P ⅍

Farndale

Feversham Arms
Church Houses OS669974
☎ (01751) 433206
11–3, 7–11 (11–11 summer); closed Mon eve in winter
Tetley Bitter H
Small inn in a remote hamlet in Farndale, popular with walkers. The bar has a stone-flagged floor and a cast iron range. Separate restaurant.
🏕 Q ❀ 🚤 ◑ ▶ ♣ P

Fellbeck

Half Moon
On B6265 ☎ (01423) 711560
12–3, 6.30–11
S&N Theakston Best Bitter; Taylor Landlord; Younger Scotch H
Excellent roadside inn between Pateley Bridge and Ripon, close to Brimham Rocks. Pleasant lounge area and a small, friendly bar. Self-catering cottages to let.
🏕 Q ᴤ ❀ 🚤 ◑ ▶ ▲ ♣ P

Flaxton

Blacksmith's Arms
Main Street ☎ (01904) 468210
12–3, 7–11
S&N Theakston Best Bitter, Old Peculier; guest beers H
Three-roomed village local, keen on guest beers. Jovial landlord. 🏕 ᴤ ❀ ◑ ▶ P

Glaisdale

Angler's Rest
Top of hill off A171
11–3, 6–11 (varies summer)
Camerons Strongarm; S&N Theakston Best Bitter; Tetley Bitter H
Very friendly hilltop pub, formerly called the Three Blast Furnaces but known locally as the Middle House. Popular with walkers and campers. The beer range may vary. 🏕 Q ᴤ ❀ 🚤 ◑ ▶ 🍴 ▲ ⇌ P

Grassington

Black Horse
Garrs Lane (off the square)
☎ (01756) 752770
11–11
Black Sheep Best Bitter; Ruddles Best Bitter; S&N Theakston XB, Old Peculier; John Smith's Bitter; Tetley Bitter H
Welcoming and friendly bar in a family-run hotel, with a

large, open fire. Separate dining room. 🏕 ❀ 🚤 ◑ ▶ ▲

Great Ayton

Buck
1 West Terrace (over stone bridge) ☎ (01642) 722242
11–11
Morland Old Speckled Hen; Whitbread Boddingtons Bitter, Trophy, Flowers Original H
Old, riverside coaching pub from the 1700s, recommended for meals. ᴤ ❀ ◑ ▶ 🍴 ▲ ♣

Great Heck

Bay Horse Inn
Main Street ☎ (01977) 661125
12–3, 7–11; 11–11 Fri & Sat
Tetley Bitter; Whitbread Boddingtons Bitter H
Cosy country pub occupying three old cottages, close to the marina on the Aire and Calder Canal. ◑ ▶ P

Great Smeaton

Bay Horse
On A167 ☎ (01609) 881466
12–3, 6.30–11
Ruddles County; John Smith's Bitter; guest beer H
Small free house in the middle of a row of cottages, with two linked rooms: a functional bar and a soft-furnished lounge.
🏕 ❀ ◑ ▶ ♣

Harrogate

Gardeners Arms
Bilton Lane (3 miles NE of centre) ☎ (01423) 506051
12–3 (not Wed), 6–11
Samuel Smith OBB H
Traditional 18th-century country pub, unspoilt by modernisation, retaining small rooms, open fires and low beams. Small selection of home-cooked meals till 8pm, Mon–Fri. 🏕 Q ❀ ◑ ▶ ▲ P

Hales Bar
Crescent Road
☎ (01423) 569861
11–11
Bass Worthington BB, Draught Bass; Stones Best Bitter H
Excellent town-centre pub with a warm welcome in its small, friendly public bar and larger, gas-lit lounge, featuring old barrels, unusual, bar-top gas cigar lighters and stuffed birds. Good, cheap food.
Q ◑ ▶ ⅙ ⇌

Hawes

Board Hotel
Main Street ☎ (01969) 667223
11–4.30, 6–11; 11–11 Tue

Jennings Bitter, Cumberland Ale, Sneck Lifter H
Typical Dales pub dating from the 19th century.
🏕 Q ❀ 🚤 ◑ ▶ ♣

Haxby

Cottage Inn
The Village ☎ (01904) 763949
11.30–2 (3 Sat), 6–11
S&N Theakston Best Bitter; John Smith's Bitter; Tetley Bitter H
Large pub converted from a cottage. The oversized lounge is popular but lacks bar area. The conservatory is ideal for families. No eve meals Sun.
ᴤ ❀ ◑ ▶ P ⅍

Helmsley

Royal Oak
Market Place
☎ (01439) 70450
11–11
Banks's Bitter; Camerons Bitter; Marston's Pedigree; guest beer H
Lively pub with regular live music. A very popular area for tourists. ◑ ▶ P

Helperby

Golden Lion
Main Street ☎ (01423) 360870
6 (12 Sat)–11
Taylor Best Bitter; Tetley Bitter; guest beers H
All that is best in a country pub, including atmosphere and good food, with the bonus of two guest ales, plus an additional beer in summer.
🏕 ❀ ▶ ▲ ♣ ◔

Hornby

Grange Arms
☎ (01609) 881249
12–3, 7–11 (closed Mon, except bank hols)
S&N Theakston XB, Old Peculier; John Smith's Bitter, Magnet; guest beers H
Pleasant, whitewashed and pantiled village pub with a snug little bar and a dining room. 🏕 ❀ ◑ ▶ 🍴 ♣ P

Hutton Rudby

Station Hotel
49 Enterpen (Potto road, 400 yds from green)
☎ (01642) 700266
7–11; 12–3, 7–11 Sat
S&N Theakston Best Bitter; John Smith's Magnet H
Traditional local with a strong local patronage. It has always been a real ale pub and still avoids serving meals.
🏕 ❀ ♣

Knaresborough

Blind Jack's

Market Place ☎ (01423) 869148
11.30–3, 6–11; 11.30–11 Wed–Sat
Beer range varies H
Created in 1991 in a Georgian
listed building, this intimate
gem is full of character and
named after a local hero.
CAMRA's 1992 *New Pub
Design* award-winner: a single
bar, a small snug and upstairs
dining rooms. No music.
Q ◖ ▶ A ⇌ ♠

Half Moon

Abbey Road ☎ (01423) 863022
11–3 (not Mon–Thu), 5.30 (7.30 Fri &
Sat)–11
**Mansfield Riding Bitter, Old
Baily** (occasional) H
Small but friendly, one-
roomed lounge with a pool
table in an alcove. Ideal for a
drink between visiting Mother
Shipton's Cave and the House
in the Rock. A ♠

Marquis of Granby

York Place (A59)
☎ (01423) 862207
11–3, 6–11; 11–11 Wed & Sat
Samuel Smith OBB H
Twin-roomed, Victorian-style
pub opposite the local
swimming baths. A ⇌ ♠

Mitre

Station Road ☎ (01423) 863589
11–11
**Daleside Bitter; John Smith's
Bitter; Tetley Bitter; guest
beer** H
Large, comfortable, split-level
lounge with an adjoining pool
room and snug/TV lounge.
Separate downstairs bistro bar.
❀ ⌷ ◖ ▶ & ⇌

Langdale End

Moorcock Inn

OS938913 ☎ (01723) 882268
11–2.30 (2 Sat; not Mon–Thu in
winter), 8 (7 Fri & Sat)–11
**Malton Double Chance;
Whitby's Woblle** H
Rural gem, recently rescued
with a sympathetic renovation.
Somewhat remote, it can be
either quiet or packed.
🍺 Q ❀ A ♠

Leavening

Jolly Farmers

Main Street ☎ (01653) 658276
12–3 (later if busy), 7–11; closed Thu
lunch Nov–May
**Ind Coope Burton Ale; John
Smith's Bitter; Tetley Bitter;
guest beers** (summer) H
Genuinely unspoilt, 17th-
century pub, popular with
locals, hikers, cyclists and the
like. Welcoming and friendly,

it offers local guest beers in
summer. Renowned for
locally-caught game dishes at
reasonable prices (no food Sun
eve). Excellent views. A must!
🍺 ❀ ⌷ ◖ ▶ ♠ P

Leeming Bar

Motel Leeming

At A1/A684 jct
☎ (01677) 423611
11–2.30, 6–11 (sometimes 11–11
Mon–Fri); 12–2.30, 7–10.30 Sun
Hambleton Bitter H
Very welcoming stop-off point
for travellers, who mix well
with locals in the comfortable
and relaxing bars and
restaurant. Awarded *Ale
Keeper of the Year* 1994 by the
local CAMRA branch.
Q ⌂ ❀ ⌷ ◖ ▶ & P

Linton

Fountaine Inn

☎ (01756) 752210
12–3, 7–11 (11.30–3, 6–11 summer)
**Black Sheep Best Bitter,
Special Strong; Jennings
Bitter, Sneck Lifter** (winter);
Younger Scotch H
Superbly set pub, next to a
bubbling beck with an old
packhorse bridge, overlooking
the village green. Low-beamed
and cosy, with a separate
dining area, it also has a
partitioned section with a
large open fire. Splendid food.
🍺 Q ❀ ◖ ▶ A ♠ P

Long Preston

Maypole

On A65 ☎ (01729) 840219
11–3, 5.30–11
**Taylor Best Bitter; Whitbread
Boddingtons Bitter; Castle
Eden Ale; guest beer** H
Typical village pub facing the
maypole green: two rooms
featuring open fires, plus a
separate dining room.
Comprehensive menu. Cider
in summer.
🍺 Q ⌷ ◖ ▶ ⇌ ♠ ⌂ P

Low Marishes

School House Inn

3 miles N of A64/A169 jct
☎ (01653) 668247
11–3, 6.30–11
**Adnams Broadside; Malton
Double Chance; Mansfield
Bitter, Old Baily; guest
beers** H
Tidy pub with good facilities
for all the family, both inside
and out. Ukers, a violent form
of ludo, is a local favourite.
Home of the Ryedale Beerfest
(first weekend in Sept).
Excellent food.
🍺 ⌂ ❀ ◖ ▣ A ♠ P

Low Row

Punch Bowl Inn

☎ (01748) 886233
11–3, 6–11 (11–11 summer)
**S&N Theakston Mild, Best
Bitter, XB, Old Peculier; John
Smith's Bitter; Younger No. 3;
guest beers** H
Welcoming village inn, built in
1638. Budget accommodation
and meals are provided for
outdoor activity groups.
Frequent live music events
and beer festivals. Over 100
single malt whiskies on sale.
🍺 ⌂ ❀ ⌷ ◖ ▶ A ♠ P

Malham

Lister Arms

☎ (01729) 830330
12–3, 7–11
**Ind Coope Burton Ale;
Younger Scotch; guest
beers** H
Popular village pub dating
from 1702, partly opened out
into three areas. Fine garden to
the rear. Hikers are always
welcome. Two guest beers in
winter, three in summer.
Liefmans Kriek on tap, plus a
large range of bottles and malt
whiskies. Cider in summer
and at Xmas only.
🍺 ❀ ⌷ ◖ ▶ A ♠ ⌂ P

Malton

Crown Hotel
(Suddaby's)

Wheelgate ☎ (01653) 692038
11–3 (4 Sat), 5.30–11; 11–11 Fri
**Malton Pale Ale, Double
Chance, Pickwick's Porter,
Owd Bob; guest beers** H
Neat hotel offering a full range
of local beers. The functional
bar is complemented by a
conservatory-style extension.
🍺 Q ⌂ ⌷ ◖ ⇌ ♠ P

King's Head Hotel

Market Place ☎ (01653) 692289
11–3 (extends market days), 6–11
**Stones Best Bitter; Wards Best
Bitter; guest beers** H
Pub whose ivy-clad facade
overlooks the market square: a
comfortable front bar and a
rear farmer's bar. ◖ ▶ ⇌

Markington

Yorkshire Hussar

High Street ☎ (01765) 677715
11–3, 6–11
**Black Sheep Best Bitter; John
Smith's Bitter; Whitbread
Boddingtons Bitter** H
Unspoilt village pub near a
well-known equestrian centre.
Meals in summer only.
Q ❀ ◖ ▶ A ♠ P

North Yorkshire

Masham

White Bear
Wellgarth ☎ (01765) 689319
11–11
S&N Theakston Mild, Best Bitter, XB, Old Peculier H
Friendly, two-roomed village pub with a true locals' feel to the bar. Situated in the courtyard of Theakston's offices and adjacent to the Black Sheep brewery. Excellent home cooking. Live music Sat eves. ♨ ❀ ⇔ ◁ ▶ ♣ P

Muker

Farmer's Arms
☎ (01748) 886297
11–3, 6.30–11 (11–11 summer)
Butterknowle Bitter; S&N Theakston Best Bitter, XB, Old Peculier H
Village local opened into a single room but retaining old character, with massive stone flags and an open fire.
♨ Q ⇄ ❀ ⇔ ◁ ▶ ▲ ♣ P

Muston

Ship
West Street ☎ (01723) 512722
11.30–2.30, 7 (5.30 summer)–11
Draught Bass; Camerons Bitter; Ind Coope Burton Ale; Tetley Bitter; Whitbread Castle Eden Ale H
One-room pub split by a low wall to create a family dining area. A popular venue for food. ❀ ◁ ▶ ⅃ ▲ ♣ P

Naburn

Blacksmith's Arms
Main Street ☎ (01904) 623464
12–3.30, 7–11; 11–11 Fri, Sat & Easter–Oct
S&N Theakston Best Bitter, XB; Younger Scotch; guest beers H
Interesting village pub on the bank of the Ouse. The interior retains the feel of four rooms, although opened out.
♨ Q ⇄ ❀ ⇔ ◁ ▶ ⅃ ▲ ♣ P

Nosterfield

Freemason's Arms
Main Road (B6267, 3 miles E of Masham) ☎ (01677) 470548
12–3 (not Mon), 7–11
Black Sheep Best Bitter; S&N Theakston Best Bitter; Tetley Bitter; guest beers (occasional) H
Re-opened/refurbished country inn with a stone-flagged bar area and interesting wartime memorabilia. Excellent, home-cooked meals (not served Mon). ♨ Q ❀ ▶ P

Osgodby

Wadkin Arms
Main Street ☎ (01757) 702391
11–3, 6–11
Vaux Bitter, Samson H
Typical village pub with real fires, real beams and bright lights. Popular with the elderly. Smoky atmosphere.
♨ Q ❀ ♣ P

Osmotherley

Golden Lion
6 West End ☎ (01609) 883526
11–3 (not Mon, except bank hols), 6–11
John Smith's Bitter; guest beers H
Attractive, old pub in the centre of the village. Strong emphasis on food. Candles and fresh flowers make for a welcoming interior. Children welcome at lunchtime. The guest beers are usually from the Courage list. ♨ Q ❀ ◁ ▶

Pateley Bridge

Harefield Hall Hotel
Harrogate Road
☎ (01423) 711429
11–3, 7–11 (11–11 summer)
S&N Theakston XB, Old Peculier; Younger Scotch H
Large hotel and restaurant set in attractive grounds by the River Nidd. The spacious bar is tastefully decorated; games room. ❀ ⇔ ◁ ▶ P

Pickering

Black Swan Hotel
Birdgate ☎ (01751) 72286
10.30–3, 6–11; 10.30–11 Mon & summer
Courage Directors; Ruddles County; John Smith's Bitter; guest beers H
Former coaching inn, still popular with travellers, as well as enjoying a lively local trade. ♨ ⇔ ◁ ▶ ♣ P

Pickhill

Nag's Head Country Inn
☎ (01845) 567391
11–11
Hambleton Bitter; S&N Theakston Best Bitter, XB, Old Peculier; Younger Scotch H
Cosy country inn with excellent food and accommodation, and featuring a unique meteorological station. It's happy hour every night.
♨ Q ❀ ⇔ ◁ ▶ ▲ ♣ P

Pool

Hunters Inn
Harrogate Road, Riffa (A658)
☎ (01532) 841090
11–11
Beer range varies H
Warm, friendly pub with a mixed clientele and a grand view over the Wharfe valley. Eight constantly changing beers are served. Formerly a café, it is now renowned for its excellent pork pies.
♨ ❀ ♣ P

Redmire

Kings Arms
☎ (01969) 22316
11–3, 6–11 (11–11 bank hols)
S&N Theakston Best Bitter, XB; John Smith's Bitter; Magnet; Village White Boar; guest beers H
Wonderfully cosy hostelry bursting with atmosphere and conversation. The food is home-cooked and as good as the beer. The patio boasts views of Wensleydale.
♨ Q ❀ ⇔ ◁ ▶ ▲ ♣ P

Richmond

Black Lion
12 Finkle Street (off market place) ☎ (01748) 823121
11–11
Camerons Strongarm; Ind Coope Burton Ale; Tetley Bitter; Whitbread Flowers Original H
Old, residential coaching inn with traditional bars. Good local trade.
♨ Q ⇄ ⇔ ◁ ▶ ♣ P ⅃

Rillington

Coach & Horses
☎ (01944) 758373
11–2.30, 6–11
Tetley Bitter; Younger Scotch; guest beers H
Coaching inn with its roots in the *Domesday Book*. Prominently situated on the A64, it offers generous meals in a friendly environment.
⇄ ❀ ◁ ▶ ▲ ♣ P

Ripon

One Eyed Rat
Allhallowgate
☎ (01765) 607704
6–11; 12–3, 6–11 Sat
Black Sheep Best Bitter; Taylor Landlord; Whitbread Boddingtons Bitter; guest beers H
Cosy, popular terraced pub, offering a large garden and serving three guest beers.
♨ Q ❀ ⅃ ♣

Golden Lion

Allhallowgate
☎ (01765) 602598
12–3, 7–11
**Black Sheep Best Bitter;
Hambleton Goldfield; S&N
Theakston Best Bitter; John
Smith's Bitter** H
Traditional family eating pub.
Excellent food; friendly
atmosphere; plenty of
conversation. Q ⊛ ◑ ▶ ♣

Wheatsheaf

Harrogate Road (A61 S of
centre) ☎ (01765) 322578
11–3, 6.30–11
**Vaux Samson; Wards Best
Bitter** H
Old inn displaying intricate
carving. Small, separate dining
room. Sunken garden with
peacocks. ⌂ Q ⊛ ◑ ▶ P

Robin Hood's Bay

Laurel Inn

Halfway down bank into
village ☎ (01947) 880400
12–11
**Marston's Pedigree; Ruddles
Best Bitter; S&N Theakston
Old Peculier; John Smith's
Bitter** H
Small, friendly local in a
picturesque cliffside village.
⌂ Q ☎ ⊛ ♣

Victoria Hotel

Station Road (top of village)
☎ (01947) 880205
11.30–3, 6.30–11; 11–11 Fri, Sat &
summer
**Camerons Bitter,
Strongarm** H; **guest beers**
Large hotel built in 1897, with
an imposing garden and views
over the village and bay. A
modern family room has a
pool table. Local artists' work
is displayed for sale in the bar.
⌂ ☎ ⊛ ⊨ ◑ ▶ ⊞ ▲ ♣ P

Roecliffe

Crown Inn

☎ (01423) 322578
11.30–3, 6.30–11
**Bass Worthington BB; John
Smith's Bitter; Tetley Bitter** H
Pleasant village inn with a
friendly welcome. Run by the
same family for over 30 years,
it has a reputation for good
food. Basic tap room (the
handpumps are in the
comfortable lounge).
⌂ Q ⊛ ⊨ ◑ ▶ ▲ ♣ P

Rufforth

Tankard Inn

Wetherby Road (B1224)
☎ (01904) 738621
11–3, 6–11; 11–11 Sat
Samuel Smith OBB H
Compact, two-roomed, village
local in Sam Smith's 'panelled'
style, complete with matching
windows. The bar features old

village photographs.
⌂ Q ⊛ ◑ ▶ ♣ P

Scarborough

Alma Inn

1 Alma Parade (lane behind
Barclay's Bank)
☎ (01723) 375587
11.30–2.30 (3 Thu & Fri, 4.30 Sat),
7–11
**Tetley Bitter; Younger Scotch,
IPA, No. 3; guest beers** H
Tastefully extended, busy pub,
just off the main street. Varied
clientele; interesting old local
photos and Victoriana;
extensive menu. ⊛ ◑ ⅍ ≷

Angel Inn

North Street ☎ (01723) 365504
11–3, 5.30–11; 11–11 Fri & Sat
**Camerons Bitter; Tetley
Bitter** H
Cosy local, very crowded at
weekends. Games-oriented,
with photographic mementos
of the landlord's international
rugby league career. ≷ ♣

Britannia Inn

Eastborough ☎ (01723) 374201
11–3, 6–11
Bass Mild, Draught Bass H
Clean, basic, old town pub,
popular with locals. Darts in
the main room, pool table
upstairs. ≷ ⊛ ♣

Highlander

15–16 The Esplanade
☎ (01723) 365627
11–11
**Wm. Clark Mild, Thistle, No.
68; Tetley Bitter; Younger
IPA; guest beers** H
Large open bar overlooking
Scarborough's South Bay: a
whisky drinker's Mecca
(comprehensive collection of
malts). Warm, friendly
atmosphere. ⌂ ☎ ⊨ ◑ ▶ ⅍

Hole in the Wall

Vernon Road
☎ (01723) 373746
11.30–3.30 (3 Sat), 7–11
**Malton Double Chance; S&N
Theakston Best Bitter, XB,
Old Peculier; guest beers** H
Thriving alehouse, just off the
town centre, convenient for
the spa. No food Sun.
Q ◑ ≷ ♣

Leeds Arms

26 St Marys Street (up from
Princess Sq) ☎ (01723) 361699
11.30–3.30 (4 Sat), 7–11
**Bass Mild, Worthington BB,
Draught Bass; guest beer** H
Unspoilt, busy locals' pub of
great character, worth hunting
out. Old local photographs
line the walls. Q ♣

Shakespeare Inn

St Helens Square (opp. indoor
market) ☎ (01723) 363203
11–4, 7–11 (11–11 summer)

Tetley Bitter, Imperial H
Friendly town-centre pub. The
open-plan bar provides a good
venue for watching rugby
league. ≷ ♣

Tap & Spile

94 Falsgrave Road
☎ (01723) 363837
11–11
**Big Lamp Bitter; guest
beers** H
Pub recently Tap & Spiled, to
form a welcome addition to
the local real ale scene. Three
rooms (one non-smoking) with
plenty of exposed stonework
and planking floors.
Q ♉ ⊛ ◑ ≷ ♣ ⅍

Scorton

White Heifer

☎ (01748) 811357
11–11
**Black Sheep Best Bitter; S&N
Theakston Best Bitter; John
Smith's Bitter, Magnet;
Village White Boar; guest
beers** (occasional) H
A haven for the ale drinker in
two small lounges with open
fires, facing the largest raised
village green in the UK.
⌂ Q ⊛ ⅍ ♣ P

Seamer

King's Head

12 Hilton Road (between
Maltby and Stokesley)
☎ (01642) 710397
7–11; 12–3, 7–11 Sat
**McEwan 80/-; S&N Theakston
XB; Younger Scotch** H
Four cosy rooms built around
one bar. With no screaming
jukebox, this is a pub for a
quiet drink and a chat.
⌂ Q ♉ ⊞ ▲ ♣ P

Selby

Abbey Vaults

James Street (S side of market
place) ☎ (01757) 702857
11–11
**Mansfield Riding Bitter,
Bitter, Old Baily** H
Pub with open-plan bars,
partitioned at one end for a
restaurant and recently
refurbished in Edwardian
decor. One outer wall was
formerly the wall of the abbey
tithe barn. ⊛ ◑ ⅍ ≷ ♣ P

Albion Vaults

New Street ☎ (01757) 213817
12–11
**Old Mill Mild, Bitter,
Porter** H
Reputedly Selby's oldest pub,
with welcoming staff, a
comfortably furnished bar and
a lively tap room. Good value
lunches. ⊛ ◑ ⅍ ≷ ♣

North Yorkshire

Cricketers Arms

Market Place ☎ (01757) 702120
11–11; 11–3.30, 5.30–11 Tue & Wed
Samuel Smith OBB H
Town pub popular with
younger locals, where the
open-plan lounge bar extends
the full length of the building
and seating is partitioned into
alcoves. Wheelchair access at
the rear. ♨ Q ✿ ◑ ও ⇌

Shipton

Dawnay Arms

Main Street ☎ (01904) 470334
11.30–2.30, 6–11
**Camerons Bitter, Strongarm;
Tetley Bitter** H
Roomy, roadside pub, four
miles north of York: a large,
comfortable lounge with a
basic locals' bar to the rear.
Popular with hungry townies,
but beer remains the priority.
No food Wed.
Q ✿ ⊯ ◑ ♣ P

Skipton

Royal Shepherd

Canal Street (via alley off High
St) ☎ (01756) 793178
11–4, 5–11; 11–11 Fri & Sat
**Marston's Pedigree;
Robinson's Hartleys XB;
Whitbread Boddingtons
Bitter, Trophy, Castle Eden
Ale; guest beer** (occasional) H
A regular *Guide* entry, popular
for its quiet canalside location,
friendly welcome and, in
summer, award-winning
garden. Note the canal-
themed, stained-glass window
in the larger main bar; there's
also a back bar and a snug to
the side. Q ✿ ◑ ⇌ ♣

Sneaton

Wilson Arms

Beacon Way (B1416)
☎ (01947) 602552
12–3, 7–11 (11–11 Easter–end of
summer)
**S&N Theakston Best Bitter,
XB; John Smith's Bitter; guest
beer** H
Grade II-listed, reputedly
haunted, large village pub.
Traditional Sun lunch served.
♨ Q ठ ✿ ⊯ ◑ ▷ ♣ P

Staveley

Royal Oak

Main Street ☎ (01423) 340267
12–3, 6.30–11
**Rudgate Viking; John Smith's
Bitter; Tetley Bitter** H
Attractive village local next to
the church, with a restaurant
well-known for its spit-roast
eves (no food Sun/Mon).
♨ Q ठ ✿ ◑ ▷ ♣ P

Stokesley

White Swan

1 West End ☎ (01642) 710263
11.30–3 (4 Sat), 5.30 (7 Sat)–11
**Butterknowle Conciliation
Ale; Whitbread Castle Eden
Ale; Younger No. 3; guest
beers** H
Cosy oak-panelled bar in a
traditional pub, with
agricultural memorabilia on
the walls. No meals; no
jukebox. The owner promotes
real ales and at least five are
available. ♨ Q ✿ ♣ ◔

Summerbridge

Flying Dutchman

Main Street ☎ (01423) 780321
11.30 (12 winter)–2.30, 6–11
Samuel Smith OBB H
Stone-built village inn named
after a famous racehorse.
Comfortable lounge. Good
prices. No meals Sun eve in
winter. ♨ ✿ ⊯ ◑ ▷ ♣ P

Tadcaster

Angel & White Horse

Bridge Street ☎ (01937) 835470
11–2.30, 5 (7 Sat)–11
**Samuel Smith OBB,
Museum** H
Large town pub attached to
Sam Smith's brewery, with
brewery history photos in the
oak-panelled bar. The brewery
shire horses are stabled in the
coachyard, which also serves
as an outdoor drinking area.
Eve meals for groups by prior
arrangement.
♨ Q ✿ ◑ ▲ ♣

Thirsk

Cross Keys

Kirkgate (just NW of market
place) ☎ (01845) 552250
11–11
**John Smith's Bitter,
Magnet** H
No-frills drinker's pub: an
L-shaped bar plus a pool
room. ♣ P

Thornton in Lonsdale

Marton Arms

☎ (0152 42) 41281
12–3 (not Mon–Fri in winter), 6–11
**Dent Bitter; Jennings Bitter;
S&N Theakston Best Bitter;
Thwaites Craftsman; guest
beers** H
Pre-turnpike coaching inn,
dated 1679 but reputedly
older: a large, comfortable
oak-beamed lounge and a
restaurant offering good home
cooking. Eleven guest beers.
♨ ✿ ⊯ ◑ ♣ ◔ P

Thornton-le-Moor

Black Swan

☎ (01609) 774117
12–2.30, 7–11
**Hambleton Bitter; John
Smith's Bitter, Magnet** H
Large village pub with a
separate games room. Good
selection of reasonably priced
meals. Q ✿ ◑ ▷ ▲ ♣ P

Thornton Watlass

Buck Inn

☎ (01677) 422461
11–2.30, 6–11; 11–11 Sat
**Black Sheep Best Bitter; S&N
Theakston Best Bitter; John
Smith's Bitter; Tetley Bitter;
Village White Boar; guest
beers** H
A picturesque village green
provides the setting for this
bar, lounge dining area and
function room, catering for all
tastes in food.
♨ Q ठ ✿ ⊯ ◑ ▷ ও ♣ P

Threshfield

Long Ashes Inn

Just off B6160
☎ (01756) 752434
11–3 (4 summer), 6.30 (5.30
summer)–11
**Moorhouse's Pendle Witches
Brew; S&N Theakston Mild,
Best Bitter; Tetley Bitter;
guest beers** H
Three split-levels, stone floors
and beamed ceilings create a
varied and pleasant
atmosphere in this converted
lodge. Next to an extensive
caravan park with a leisure
centre. ♨ ठ ✿ ◑ ▷ ও ♣ P

Old Hall Inn

On B6160 ☎ (01756) 752441
11–3, 6–11
**Moorhouse's Pendle Witches
Brew; S&N Theakston Best
Bitter; Taylor Best Bitter,
Landlord; Younger Scotch** H
Smart roadside country inn
supporting a varied clientele:
an open lounge, with a
coal-fired range, and a
separate dining room, offering
top-quality, wide-ranging
meals (no food Sun eve, or
Mon). Attractive garden. ♨ Q
ठ ✿ ⊯ ◑ ▷ ▲ ♣ ◔ P

Tunstall

Bay Horse Inn

Tunstall Road (off A1, near
Catterick) ☎ (01748) 818564
12–3, 7–11
Samuel Smith OBB H
Homely, open-beamed village
pub, holding regular
entertainment. Small caravan
site—ideal for visitors to the
Dales. ♨ Q ✿ ◑ ▷ ▲ ♣ P

Wass

Wombwell Arms
2 miles from Coxwold
☎ (01347) 868280
12–2.30, 7–11; closed Sun eve & Mon in winter
Black Sheep Best Bitter; Taylor Landlord; guest beer H
18th-century inn with a relaxed, country atmosphere and log fires. Excellent food.
🏠 Q 🛏 ◖▶ ♣ P

Weaverthorpe

Star Inn
☎ (0194 43) 273
7–11; 12–3, 7–11 Sat
John Smith's Bitter; Taylor Landlord; Tetley Bitter; Webster's Yorkshire Bitter H
Country inn with a bar for everyone. The front lounge is popular with diners, while the bar is used by locals.
🏠 � ❀ 🛏 ◖▶ ▲ ♣ P

Whitby

Duke of York
Church Street
☎ (01947) 600324
11–3, 7–11; 11–11 Sat & summer
Courage Directors; John Smith's Bitter, Magnet H
Harbourside pub with a magnificent view, situated at the foot of the 199 steps leading to the abbey. Popular in folk week. 🛏 ◖▶ 🍺 ♣

George Hotel
Baxtergate (opp. station)
☎ (01947) 602565
12–11
Bass Worthington BB, Draught Bass; Stones Best Bitter; Tetley Bitter; Whitby Wobble; guest beer H
Large, renovated Victorian hotel with a split-level lounge sporting suspended brass musical instruments. Pool room. 🏠 🛏 ◖▶ 🍺 ♣

Wighill

White Swan
High Street ☎ (01937) 832217
11–3, 6–11
S&N Theakston Best Bitter; Old Peculier; Stones Best Bitter; Tetley Bitter H
Multi-roomed pub of great character, served by two separate bars. Eve meals Thu–Sat; lunches only Sun.
🏠 � ❀ ▶ P

York

Ackhorne
9 St Martins Lane (off Micklegate) ☎ (01904) 629820
12–3, 5.30–11

Black Sheep Best Bitter; guest beers H
A 'local heroes' themed pub, based on Sir Thomas Fairfax. Always four beers from small independent Yorkshire breweries available, plus a Marston Moor house beer. 🍺

Blue Bell
53 Fossgate ☎ (01904) 654904
12–3, 5.30 (7 Sat)–11
Vaux Bitter, Samson, Extra Special; Wards Best Bitter H
Intimate late-Victorian gem: two cosy rooms and a drinking corridor. ♣

Brown Cow
36 Hope Street (off Walmgate)
☎ (01904) 634010
11.30–11
Taylor Best Bitter, Landlord H
Slightly off the usual tourist track, this most easterly of Taylor's tied houses is a small, two-roomed, friendly local, frequented by all sorts.
Q ❀ ♣

Fox
168 Holgate Road
☎ (01904) 798341
11–11
Tetley Bitter H
Pub with historical and railway connections. Note the model train in the Sprinter Room. Q ❀ ◖ & 🍺 ♣ P

John Bull
11 Layerthorpe
☎ (01904) 621593
11.30–3, 5.30–11; 11–11 Fri & Sat
Malton Double Chance; guest beers H
John Bull continues to represent the best of British—real beer, real food and a real fire, all in real 1930s surroundings. Despite all this, there are plans to demolish the pub to increase car parking space for the adjacent garage. A Marston Moor house beer is also available. 🏠 Q ❀ ⬭

Lighthorseman
124 Fulford Road
☎ (01904) 624818
12–11
Thwaites Bitter, Craftsman H
Splendid Victorian building, its public bar being York's nearest approximation to a big city gin palace. � 🛏 ◖ P

Maltings
Tanners Moat
☎ (01904) 655387
11.30–11
Draught Bass; Black Sheep Best Bitter; guest beers H
Enterprising free house with a changing range of guest beers from small independents. Quality control in action. No food Sun. ◖ 🍺 ⬭

Minster Inn
24 Marygate ☎ (01904) 624499
11–11
Bass Worthington BB, Draught Bass; Ruddles Best Bitter; John Smith's Bitter H
Popular local near the city centre, where the multi-room layout allows for quiet conversation. Look for the error on the old pub sign in the passageway. Q 🍺 🍽

Royal Oak
17 Goodramgate
☎ (01904) 653856
11.30–11
Camerons Bitter; Ind Coope Burton Ale; Tetley Bitter H
Traditional town pub within a stone's throw of the Minster. Definitely a pub for students, although the landlord does his best to welcome everyone. Good access for wheelchairs downstairs. Q � ◖▶ & 🍽

Spread Eagle
98 Walmgate ☎ (01904) 635868
11–11
S&N Theakston Best Bitter; Taylor Landlord; guest beers H
York's original free house, still packing them in. A good choice of guest beers (usually from local independents), a full range of snacks and meals, and high-speed service.
❀ ◖▶ P

Wellington Inn
47 Alma Terrace (off Fulford)
☎ (01904) 645642
11–3, 6 (5.30 Fri)–11; 11–11 Sat
Samuel Smith OBB, Museum H
Unspoilt, attractive pub dating back to the 1860s, with a public bar, snug and a games room. Floral arrangements enhance the appearance in summer. One of the cheapest pints in York. 🏠 � ❀

York Arms
High Petergate
☎ (01904) 624508
11–11
Samuel Smith OBB, Museum H
Friendly town pub with a small front bar and a cosy rear lounge. Smoke-free dining room upstairs lunchtimes. Eve meals served till 7.30 (not Sun). 🛏 ◖ & 🍺 ♣

York Beer Shop
28 Sandringham Street (off Fishergate) ☎ (01904) 647136
11 (4.15 Mon, 10 Sat)–10; 12–2, 7–10 Sun
Old Mill Bitter; Rooster's Yankee; Taylor Landlord; guest beers H
Off-licence serving draught beer and a wide range of bottled beers. ⬭

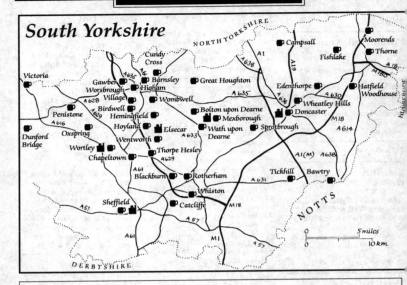

South Yorkshire

(map showing: Victoria, Curdy Cross, Gawber, Worsbrough Village, Barnsley, Great Houghton, Campsall, Moorends, Thorne, Fishlake, Higham, Wombwell, Edenthorpe, Hatfield Woodhouse, Penistone, Birdwell, Hemingfield, Bolton upon Dearne, Mexborough, Wheatley Hills, Doncaster, Dunford Bridge, Oxspring, Hoyland, Elsecar, Wath upon Dearne, Sprotbrough, Wortley, Wentworth, Chapeltown, Thorpe Hesley, Blackburn, Rotherham, Tickhill, Bawtry, Sheffield, Whiston, Catcliffe, NORTH YORKSHIRE, NOTTS, DERBYSHIRE, HUMBERSIDE; scale 5 miles / 10 km)

Concertina, *Mexborough;* Frog & Parrot, *Kelham Island, Sheffield;* South Yorkshire, *Elsecar;* Stocks, *Doncaster;* Wards, *Sheffield;* Wortley, *Wortley*

Barnsley

Shaw Inn
Racecommon Road
☎ (01226) 294021
12–11
**Morland Old Speckled Hen;
John Smith's Bitter;
Whitbread Flowers Original;
guest beers** H
No-frills pub catering for all ages: the best example of a traditional pub in the town centre. Value-for-money guest beers; folk club Mon.
⌣ ✿ ◑ ♣ P

Bawtry

Turnpike
High Street ☎ (01302) 711960
11–3, 6–11
Stocks Best Bitter, Select, St Leger Porter; guest beers H
Pub converted from a wine bar. The interior is of wood, glass and brick, with a flagstone floor. Good value varied menu (eve meals Tue–Thu). Weekly guest beers.
🍴 ✿ ◑ ▶

Birdwell

Cock Inn
Pilley Hill (off A61 towards Pilley) ☎ (01226) 742155
12–3, 7–11
Draught Bass; Whitbread Boddingtons Bitter H

Popular, 200-year-old village local in Yorkshire stone, with a slate floor, a superb fireplace and much brass. Extensive garden with a quality play area. Quiz Thu. No meals Sun eve. 🍴 Q ⌣ ✿ ◑ ▶ ♣ P

Blackburn

Crown
Blackburn Road (½ mile from Meadowhall, beside M1)
☎ (01709) 560498
11–3.30 (4.30 Fri & Sat), 7 (7.30 Fri, 6 Sat)–11
Stones Best Bitter; Tetley Bitter H
Late-Victorian building with an open-plan interior and a large, semi-circular bar. ✿ ◑
≢ (Meadowhall) ♣ P

Bolton upon Dearne

Cross Daggers Inn
Church Street (150 yds off B6098) ☎ (01709) 892299
12–4, 7–11
John Smith's Bitter; guest beer H
Built in 1923 and virtually unspoiled, a pub with many rooms, including a games room with snooker. Corridor drinking area. Gents' hairdressing Sat and Sun lunch; quizzes Tue, Thu and Sun lunch.
🍴 Q ◑ ✿ & ≢ ♣ P

Campsall

Old Bells
High Street ☎ (01302) 700423
11–2.30, 5.30–11
Ruddles Best Bitter; John Smith's Bitter, Magnet; Tetley Bitter H
Situated in an old part of the village, T'Bells has a lounge, a small smoke room and a tiny snug plus two restaurants.
Q ✿ ◑ & ♣ P

Catcliffe

Waverley
Brinsworth Road
☎ (01709) 360906
12–3.30 (11.30–4.30 Sat), 6–11; 12–2.30, 7–10.30 Sun
Ruddles County; John Smith's Magnet; Taylor Landlord; guest beers H
Large free house renowned both for its beer range (constantly changing) and children's facilities (very large children's room with an entertainer every Fri eve 8–9pm). Extensive grounds. No lunches Sun.
⌣ ✿ ◑ ▶ ♣ P

Chapeltown

Norfolk Arms
White Lane ☎ (0114) 2468414
12–11
Vaux Samson; Wards Best Bitter H

Old pub with sympathetic modernisation and sports and games involvement. No food Sat eve or Sun.
☎ ❀ ◖ ▶ ♿ ▲ ⇌ ♣ P

Prince of Wales
80 Burncross Road
☎ (0114) 2467725
11–3 (4 Sat), 5.30 (6.30 Sat)–11; 12–2.30, 7–10.30 Sun
Wards Best Bitter H / E
Traditional pub with a rear public bar. Good, home-cooked food; active fundraising. Keen on sports.
Q ❀ ◖ ▲ ⇌ ♣ P

Cundy Cross

Mill of the Black Monks
Grange Lane ☎ (01226) 242244
11–11
S&N Theakston Best Bitter, XB, Old Peculier; John Smith's Bitter; guest beers H
A CAMRA conservation award winner: an 800-year-old monastic mill displaying artefacts unearthed during restoration. Live music Tue; jam session Wed. Excellent garden. ⛺ ❀ ◖ ▶ P

Doncaster

Hallcross
33–34 Hallgate (by Odeon cinema) ☎ (01302) 328213
11–11; 11–4, 6.30–11 Sat
Stocks Best Bitter, Select, St Leger Porter, Old Horizontal; guest beer H
Pub displaying a collection of mirrors and old photos of the area. In summer, sit in the yard and watch the next brew being made. ❀ ◖ ⌂

Leopard
1 West Street ☎ (01302) 363054
11–11
Courage Directors; Marston's Pedigree; Ruddles County; John Smith's Bitter; guest beers H
Lively street-corner boozer with a superb tiled frontage. The beers may vary but guest beers are selected from all over the country at customers' suggestion. Live music most weekends upstairs. ⇌ ♣ P

Masons Arms
Market Place ☎ (01302) 364391
10.30 (11 Mon, Wed & Thu)–4, 7.30–11; 12–3, 7.30–10.30 Sun
Tetley Bitter H
Tetley Heritage Inn, 200 years old, displaying photos of old Doncaster. Q ❀ ⊟ ⇌

Olde Crown
Greyfriars Road
☎ (01302) 325190

11–3, 6–11; 11–11 Sat
Bass Worthington BB; Stones Best Bitter; guest beers H
Welcoming oasis in the shadow of St George's church, featuring a monthly guest beer and also a regular mild. Good value meals (no meals Sat/Sun eve). Live music. A gem.
Q ❀ ⋈ ◖ ▶ ⇌ ♣ P

Railway
West Street ☎ (01302) 349700
11–11
John Smith's Bitter, Magnet; Stones Best Bitter H
Thriving street-corner pub with a large, busy public bar and cosy 'snug'-like lounge. Popular with railway workers and noted for its friendly atmosphere. Lined glasses. No food Sun. ◖ ⇌ ♣

Salutation
South Parade
☎ (01302) 342736
12–11; 12–3, 6–11 Sat
Ind Coope Burton Ale; Marston's Pedigree; Tetley Bitter, Imperial; guest beers H
On the edge of the town centre, past the Odeon cinema; a pub first shown as an inn in 1754. It still retains some old world charm and has framed brewery memorabilia. Quiz Tue; live music Sun night. Can get very busy Fri–Sat eves. No food Sat/Sun. ⋈ ◖ P

White Swan
Frenchgate ☎ (01302) 366573
11–11
Wards Thorne Best Bitter H, **Best Bitter** H & E
Friendly, town-centre pub which features the highest bar in Britain in the front tap room. A tiled passageway leads to a comfortable lounge. Good value lunches. ◖ ⇌ ♣

Dunford Bridge

Stanhope Arms
Off A628 ☎ (01226) 763104
11–3 (not Mon), 7–11
Black Sheep Best Bitter; Ruddles Best Bitter; John Smith's Bitter; Wilson's Mild H
Multi-roomed, former shooting lodge situated in a picturesque valley next to the Woodhead tunnel entrance. An alternative Pennine Way passes the front door.
Q ❀ ⋈ ◖ ▶ ♿ ▲ ♣ P

Edenthorpe

Eden Arms
Edenfield Road (by Tesco)
☎ (01302) 890468
11.30–3, 5 (6.30 Sat)–11
Tetley Bitter, Imperial H
Popular new pub, built in

1990, with a spacious, split-level lounge. A Big Steaks house (up to 32oz) which serves a large selection of good value meals, with a children's menu. ❀ ◖ ▶ ♿ P ⅌

Fishlake

Hare & Hounds
Church Street
☎ (01302) 841208
12–3, 7–11; 12–2.30, 7–10.30 Sun
Mansfield Riding Bitter, Old Baily H
A pub with a spacious, horse-brassed lounge and a smaller public bar where pool and dominoes dominate. Both feature old photos of this historic village. The landlord was Mansfield *Host of the Year* 1993. ❀ ◖ ▲ ♣ P

Gawber

New Inn
Redbrook Road
☎ (01226) 294962
11.30–3.30, 7–11; 11–11 Fri & Sat
Vaux Samson; Wards Thorne Best Bitter H
Popular, two-roomed 1930s local with a large beer garden (barbecues). ❀ ◖ ▶ ♣ P

Great Houghton

Old Hall Inn
High Street ☎ (01226) 758706
12–3.30 (5 Sat), 7–11
Hardys & Hansons Best Bitter H
Three-roomed pub on the site of an old coaching inn, with the church behind. Busy clientele: quizzes Tue and Thu, disco Sat and darts league Mon. A courtesy coach is available.
⋈ Q ❀ ⊟ ♿ ♣ P

Hatfield Woodhouse

Robin Hood & Little John
Main Street ☎ (01302) 840213
10.30–4, 6–11
Draught Bass; Stones Best Bitter H
Friendly village local, busy at weekends. The garden attracts families. ❀ ◖ ⊟ P

Hemingfield

Lundhill Tavern
Beech House Road (off A633, ½ mile along Lundhill Rd)
☎ (01226) 752283
12–5.30, 7–11
John Smith's Bitter; South Yorkshire Barnsley; Stones Best Bitter; Taylor Landlord; guest beers H

South Yorkshire

Pub off the beaten track and steeped in local coal mining history, sporting a collection of brass blow lamps. Quiz Tue, Wed and Sun. No meals Sun eve or Mon; restaurant upstairs. Q ❀ ◑ ▶ ♣ P

Higham

Engineers Arms
Higham Common Lane (off A635) ☎ (01226) 384204
11–3, 7–11
Samuel Smith OBB H
Village local with a superb tap room and a plush lounge. The beer garden is next to a cricket field. Q ❀ ◑ ♣ P

Hoyland

Furnace Inn
163 Milton Road (off B6097)
☎ (01226) 742000
12–3 (11.30–3.30 Sat), 6.30–11;
12–2.30, 7–10.30 Sun
Vaux Samson H; **Wards Thorne Best Bitter, Best Bitter** E
Welcoming, stone-built pub by an old forge pond, a winner of awards for *Superloo, Wards in Bloom* and cellarmanship. Coal mining souvenir plates are displayed. Quiz night Tue.
Q ❀ ≱ (Elsecar) ♣ P

Mexborough

Concertina Band Club
9a Dolcliffe Road
☎ (01709) 580841
12–4, 7–11; 12–2, 7–10.30 Sun
Concertina Best Bitter; Mansfield Bitter; John Smith's Bitter; Wards Best Bitter; guest beers H
Visitors are welcomed at this small, friendly club. Brewing began on the premises in 1992 (beer choice varies). Lined glasses used. ≱ ♣

Falcon
Main Street ☎ (01709) 571170
11.30–4 (4.30 Fri, 5 Sat), 7–11; 12–2.30, 7–10.30 Sun
Old Mill Mild, Bitter, Bullion, Porter H
Pub with a large, smart lounge with raised seating areas (disco and live entertainment some eves) and a tap room with games. Wheelchair access is via the outside passage.
❀ ◑ & ≱ ♣

George & Dragon
81 Church Street (off A6023)
☎ (01709) 584375
12–4, 7–11; 12–11 Fri & Sat
Vaux Bitter, Samson, Double Maxim; Wards Best Bitter H
Welcoming, cosy, one-roomed pub with a central bar and many prints of old Mexborough. Friendly atmosphere; pleasant garden,

popular with families. Lined glasses used. ❀ ≱ P

Moorends

Moorends Hotel
156 Marshlands Road
☎ (01405) 812170
Wards Thorne Best Bitter H
Built in 1927 to serve a bygone mining community, a pub known locally as Uncle Arthur's, after a key figure in the 1936 miners' strike. Live entertainment Thu–Sat nights.
🎰 ❀ ♣ P

Oxspring

Waggon & Horses
Sheffield Road (B6462/B6449 jct) ☎ (01226) 763259
12–3 (summer only), 7 (7.30 winter)–11; 12–11 Sat all year
Bass Worthington BB, Draught Bass; John Smith's Bitter; Stones Best Bitter; guest beers (occasional) H
Converted farmhouse, 150 years old, with nooks, crannies and beamed ceilings. Warm, welcoming and full of character. Good value meals in the bar, restaurant and new function barn. 🎰 ❀ ◑ ▶ ♣ P

Penistone

Cubley Hall
Mortimer Road, Cubley Village (1 mile from Penistone)
☎ (01226) 766086
11–3, 6–11
Greenalls Original; Ind Coope Burton Ale; Tetley Bitter, Imperial; guest beers H
Former gentleman's residence in a country setting; multi-roomed with original decor. The adjacent carvery also sells real ale. Extensive grounds with a kids' play area. Food all day Sun.
Q 🛏 ❀ 🎰 ◑ & ▲ ♣ P ⊬

Rotherham

Belvedere
Moorgate ☎ (01709) 374126
11–11
Marston's Pedigree; Whitbread Boddingtons Bitter, Castle Eden Ale H
Spacious, but not large, pub in one of the most pleasant areas of Rotherham. Central wooden bar; conservatory (children welcome till 8pm). A meeting place for students. No food Sun. ❀ ◑ & P

Bridge Inn
Greasbrough Road (near bus station) ☎ (01709) 363683
10.30–3, 6–11
Draught Bass; John Smith's Magnet; Stones Best Bitter H & E

An example of mock early English architecture, built in the 1930s next to the 14th-century Chapel on the Bridge. Three bar areas, plus a lounge. No meals weekends. ◑ ≱ ♣

Britannia
Lindley Street
☎ (01709) 382708
11–11
Bass Worthington BB H; **Stones Best Bitter** E
Double-fronted pub in brick and mock marble with a large, open-plan tap room side and a comfortable lounge area. Sandwiches available. ♣ P

Moulder's Rest
110–112 Masbrough Street, Masbrough ☎ (01709) 560095
12–3, 6 (5 Fri, 7.30 Sat)–11; 12–3, 7.30–10.30 Sun
Stones Best Bitter H & E
Large, main-road corner pub, two minutes' from the football ground. It features a well-patronised tap room, a snug and a through lounge. Big on games. No food weekends. One other Bass ale served.
🎰 ◑ ▶ ≱ ♣ P

Tut 'n' Shive
9 Wellgate ☎ (01709) 364562
11–11; 7–10.30 Sun, closed Sun lunch
Whitbread Boddingtons Bitter; guest beers H
Alehouse-style pub with rough and ready, DIY decor. The games room has two ten pin bowling alleys and two pool tables. No food Sun. Beware of the fake handpump for pressurised cider. ◑ ≱

Wilton
255 Kimberworth Road, Kimberworth
☎ (01709) 551100
11.30–3.30 (5.30 Sat), 6.30–11
Stones Best Bitter E
Friendly local: a through lounge and a tap room with pool, darts, satellite TV and games. Quiz nights. One other Bass beer is also sold. ♣

Woodman Inn
Midland Road (by bus depot, off A629) ☎ (01709) 561486
12–3, 7–11; 12–2, 7–10.30 Sun
Stones Best Bitter; guest beers H
Former Bentley's house with an orthodox tap room and a snug lounge. Built as a 'local' in 1853, but the housing has been cleared. Always a friendly welcome. Separate snooker room. ❀ ♣

Sheffield: *Central*

Bath Hotel
66 Victoria Street (off Glossop Rd) ☎ (0114) 2729017

12–3, 6.30 (5 Fri, 7.30 Sat)–11; 7.30–10.30 Sun, closed Sun lunch
Ind Coope Burton Ale; Tetley Bitter; Wards Best Bitter; guest beer H
Tetley Heritage pub converted from Victorian cottages to a small, friendly, two-roomed local. The original ground lease prohibits the use of the site as an alehouse, or for other noxious activities! Lunches Mon–Fri. ◑ ♣

Brown Bear
109 Norfolk Street
☎ (0114) 2727744
11–11
Courage Directors; Marston's Pedigree; Ruddles County; John Smith's Bitter, Magnet; guest beer H
Rare, traditional-style, two-roomed pub: a popular meeting place patronised by the cast and audience from the nearby theatres. Theatrical memorabilia. ❀ ◑ ⇌ ♣

Fagans
69 Broad Lane
☎ (0114) 2728430
11.30–3, 5.30–11; 11–11 Fri & Sat
Ind Coope Burton Ale; Tetley Bitter H
Lively, popular pub with a small snug. Impromptu folk music sessions. Q ❀ ◑ ♣

Fat Cat
23 Alma Street
☎ (0114) 2728195
12–3, 5.30–11
Kelham Island Bitter; Marston's Pedigree; S&N Theakston Old Peculier; Taylor Landlord; guest beers H
Sheffield's first real ale free house, opened in 1981: two comfortable rooms (one non-smoking), a corridor drinking area and an upstairs function room used for overspill. Kelham Island brewery is situated in the grounds. At least four guest beers. ▨ Q ❀ ◑ ◐ ⠶

Harlequin
26 Johnson Street
☎ (0114) 2729864
12–4, 7–11
Wards Best Bitter H
Genuinely traditional, street-corner pub, noted for the pot-bellied stove in the tap room. Separate pool room. ▨ ❀ ⇌ (Midland) ♣

Lord Nelson
166 Arundel Street
☎ (0114) 2722650
12–11; 12–5, 7.30–11 Sat
Hardys & Hansons Best Bitter H
Recently refurbished street-corner local in an area of small workshops. Upstairs games/function room. ◑ ⇌ ♣

Moseley's Arms
West Bar ☎ (0114) 2721591
11–11; 11–3, 7–11 Sat
Draught Bass; Stones Best Bitter H
Superbly renovated pub just off the city centre. Three comfortably furnished rooms, with a friendly atmosphere. Function room upstairs with pool.
◑ ▨ ⅃ (Midland) ♣

Red Deer
18 Pitt Street ☎ (0114) 2722890
11.30 (12 Sat)–3, 5 (7.30 Sat)–11; 11.30–11 Fri; 7.30–10.30 Sun, closed Sun lunch
Alloa Arrol's 80/-; Ind Coope Burton Ale; Tetley Mild, Bitter, Imperial; Wards Best Bitter; guest beer H
Friendly, one-roomed local close to the university. Excellent home-cooked meals. Display of paintings for sale. Quiz Sun eve. No-smoking area lunchtime. ❀ ◑ ◗ ⠶

Red House
168 Solly Street
☎ (0114) 2727926
11–11; 12–4, 7.30–11 Sat
Wards Thorne Best Bitter, Best Bitter H
Renovated traditional local, retaining three drinking areas, one with darts and pool. Regular folk sessions. Lunches Mon–Fri. Q ◑ ♣

Rutland Arms
86 Brown Street
☎ (0114) 2729003
11.30 (12 Sat)–3, 5 (7.30 Sat)–11; 12–3, 8–10.30 Sun
Ind Coope Burton Ale; Marston's Pedigree; Tetley Bitter; Younger No. 3 H
City-centre gem in a resurgent cultural corner. Behind the distinctive Gilmour's frontage lies a comfortable lounge. Cosmopolitan clientele. Eve meals till 7pm, Mon–Fri.
Q ❀ ▨ ◑ ◗ ⇌ P

Tap & Spile
42 Waingate ☎ (0114) 2726270
11.30–3, 5.30–11; 11.30–11 Sat; 7–10.30 Sun, closed Sun lunch
Beer range varies H
Large, tastefully refurbished ex-Gilmour's street-corner pub. A large bar with exposed brickwork and bare boards, and a smaller sideroom (non-smoking at lunchtime). Up to ten beers and two ciders. Q ◑ ⇌ ♣ ⌣ ⠶

Washington
79 Fitzwilliam Street
☎ (0114) 2754937
11.30–3, 6.30–11; 12–2, 7–10.30 Sun
Ind Coope Burton Ale; Tetley Mild, Bitter H
Pub with two comfortably furnished rooms. A popular meeting place. Lunches Mon–Fri. Q ◑ ▨ ♣

Sheffield: *East*

Alma Inn
76 South Street, Mosborough (behind Eckington Hall)
☎ (0114) 2484781
11.30–3.30, 6.30 (7 winter)–11
Wards Thorne Best Bitter H, **Best Bitter** E
Two-roomed, traditional and friendly local, with a central bar. A worthy find, off the beaten track. Small play area for children. Q ❀ ▨ ♣ P

Carbrook Hall
537 Attercliffe Common
☎ (0114) 2440117
12–3, 5 (7 Sat)–11; 11–11 Fri
Draught Bass; John Smith's Magnet; Stones Best Bitter H
Large, three-roomed pub having links with the Civil War. A building on this site can be traced back to 1176. Reputedly haunted. Lunches weekdays and Sun; early eve meals Mon–Fri. Q ❀ ◑ ◗
⇌ (Meadowhall) P

Cocked Hat
75 Worksop Road, Attercliffe
☎ (0114) 2448332
11–11; 11–3, 7–11 Sat
Marston's Bitter, Pedigree; guest beers H
Popular Victorian pub next to the Don Valley Stadium. Weekday lunches. Guest beers from Marston's. ▨ ❀ ◑ ♣

Enfield Arms
95 Broughton Lane, Carbrook
☎ (0114) 2425134
11.30 (11 Sat)–11
Bass Worthington BB; Stones Best Bitter; Tetley Bitter H
Three-roomed, street-corner local with a large games area, all served by a central bar. Opposite Sheffield Arena, and good value. ⛴ ◑ ﹠ ♣ P

Red Lion
145 Duke Street
☎ (0114) 2728296
12–4, 7–11
Burtonwood Bitter, Forshaw's H
Three separate rooms, including a pool room, plus a central bar, make up this traditional and welcoming locals' pub. Q ❀ ﹠ ⇌ ♣

Sheffield: *North*

Cask & Cutler
1 Henry Street (Infirmary Rd/Penistone Rd jct)
☎ (0114) 2721487
12–3, 5.30–11; 12–11 Fri & Sat
Beer range varies H
A little gem. A warm welcome is assured in this free house of ever-changing beers (up to six independents). All food is home-cooked. Q ◑ ◗ ﹠ ♣ ⌣

South Yorkshire

Mill Tavern
2–4 Earsham Street
☎ (0114) 2756461
11–4, 7–11
Old Mill Bitter, Bullion, Porter H
A single bar serves all areas of this large pub which displays a collection of lorries made out of cornflake packets. Warm atmosphere. Food only on Thu and Fri. ◗ ♣

Morrisey's East House
18 Spital Hill ☎ (0114) 2726916
12–11
Taylor Landlord; Whitbread Boddingtons Bitter; guest beers H
A second life for this old, friendly pub which had fallen on hard times. Long and narrow, with a central bar, it offers acoustic live music, an active hiking and caving group, and excellent exotic vegetarian meals.
◗ ◗ ♿ ♣ ⊙

Robin Hood
Little Matlock, Greaves Lane, Stannington ☎ (0114) 2344565
11.30–3, 7–11
Stones Best Bitter E
Old, large pub with a children's play area outside and a collection of stuffed animals inside. Good value bar meals. Children's parties a speciality. Q ❀ ◗ ◗ ♣ P

Staffordshire Arms
40 Sorby Street (300 yds from A6135/B6082 fork)
☎ (0114) 2721381
11–11
Stones Best Bitter E
Visiting this back-street hostelry is like walking back in time. It offers one of the cheapest pints in Sheffield and many social and sports events. Real community spirit. Q ♣

Sheffield: *South*

Dore Junction
Dore Station, Abbeydale Road South ☎ (0114) 2620675
11–3, 5.30–11
Marston's Pedigree; S&N Theakston Best Bitter, Old Peculier; guest beers H
Victorian station converted into a pleasant pub and restaurant, decorated with period railway memorabilia.
Q ◗ ◗ ♿ ⟐ (Dore) P

Earl of Arundel & Surrey
528 Queens Road
☎ (0114) 2551006
11–11
Taylor Landlord H; **Wards Best Bitter** H & E; **guest beers** H

Listed corner pub near Bramall Lane football ground; a games venue with a mixed clientele. Attached is the city's poundhouse for stray livestock, giving the landlord the title of Pinder. No meals Sun. ◗ ♣ P

Fleur de Lys
Tutley Hall Lane
☎ (0114) 2361476
11–11
Bass Worthington BB; Stones Best Bitter H
Large, popular pub on the edge of the city: two oak-panelled rooms, the larger having an eating area at the rear. Handy for the Derbyshire moors. ⨌ Q ❀ ◗ ◗ ♣

Old Mother Redcap
Prospect Road, Bradway
☎ (0114) 2360179
11.30–3, 5.30–11; 11.30–11 Sat
Samuel Smith OBB H
Modern stone building in the style of an old farmhouse with mullion windows. Inside is a single L-shaped room divided into small areas. Friendly atmosphere. Eve meals Thu and Fri only. Q ❀ ◗ ◗ ♣ P

Shakespeare
106 Well Road, Heeley
☎ (0114) 2553995
12–3.30 (4.30 Sat), 5.30 (7 Sat)–11
Stones Best Bitter; Tetley Bitter, Imperial; guest beers H
Three drinking areas in an imposing pub with a view over Sheffield and a cosy atmosphere. Wheelchair access at the side. ❀ ♿ ♣ P

Small Beer Real Ale Off-Licence
57 Archer Road (off A621)
☎ (0114) 2551356
11 (10.30 Sat)–10; 12–2, 7–10 Sun
Bateman XXXB; Exmoor Gold; Taylor Landlord; guest beers H
Small but well-stocked off-licence also selling a wide range of continental beers.

Sheffield: *West*

Banner Cross
791 Ecclesall Road (A625, 2 miles S of city centre)
☎ (0114) 2661479
11.30–11
Ind Coope Burton Ale; Tetley Bitter; guest beer H
Busy local with a panelled lounge and a large tap room. Upstairs games room with snooker. ❀ ◗ ♣

Cherry Tree Inn
2 Carterknowle Avenue (off Carterknowle Rd)
☎ (0114) 2585051
12–11

Bass Worthington BB, Draught Bass; Stones Best Bitter; guest beer H
Friendly, traditional local, built in 1961: one bar, with a raised drinking area. Quiz nights, games and fund raising activities. No music. Everyone welcome. Q ❀ ♣ P

Fox & Duck
223–227 Fulwood Road (A57)
☎ (0114) 2663422
11–11
Courage Directors; John Smith's Bitter, Magnet H
Busy pub in the Broomhill shopping centre. A large bar serves several areas, all traditionally furnished.
❀ ◗ ♣

Lescar
303 Sharrowvale Road
☎ (0114) 2663857
12–11
Draught Bass; Stones Best Bitter; guest beers H
Pub split into three bars. The public is cheerful and friendly, while the lounge is quiet but homely. The large back room has a stage, used for a comedy club. Food is good value. Excellent Sun lunches.
Q ❀ ◗ ♣

Old Grindstone
3 Crookes ☎ (0114) 2660322
11–11
Taylor Landlord; Vaux Samson H; **Wards Best Bitter** H & E; **guest beer** H
Spacious, busy pub. The Victorian design lounge has a raised area, and the oak-panelled games room is based on a gentleman's club, offering snooker. Meals till 7.30pm. Quiz Thu eve. The guest beer changes weekly. ❀ ◗ ◗ ♿ ♣

Old Heavygate
114 Matlock Road
☎ (0114) 2340003
12–3.30, 7–11
Hardys & Hansons Best Bitter, Kimberley Classic H
Pub dating from 1696, with some original beams in the Oak Room. The lounge features potted plants.
Q ❀ ♣ P

Royal Hotel
114 Walkley Street (corner of Cundy St, off South Rd)
☎ (0114) 2322457
2–5 (summer only), 7–11; 12–5, 7–11 Fri & Sat all year
S&N Theakston Best Bitter, Old Peculier; Whitbread Boddingtons Bitter H
Street-corner local with etched Tennants windows and leaded lights above. The snug has unusual 3-D effect framed plaques, the bar area has photos of old Walkley and the games room is decorated with newspaper clippings of sporting events. Q ❀ ♣

Sprotbrough

Boat Inn
Nursery Lane
☎ (01302) 857188
11–3, 6–11 (11–11 summer Sat)
Courage Directors; John Smith's Bitter, Magnet H
17th-century former coaching house where Sir Walter Scott wrote *Ivanhoe*. Refurbished in 1985 to expose beams and a stone floor. Set between woodlands and the River Don. Bar and restaurant meals, but no food Sun eve. ❀ ◑ ▶ ♿ P

Ivanhoe
Melton Road ☎ (01302) 853130
11–11
Samuel Smith OBB, Museum (summer) H
Attractive pub in large grounds adjoining the cricket pitch. A large lounge and conservatory, plus a public bar with games. Excellent outdoor play area. ❧ ❀ ◑ ▶ ♿ ♣ P

Thorne

Churchills
Horsefair Green (off A614)
☎ (01405) 812320
11–3, 7–11
Tetley Bitter H
Pub annexed to the Belmont Hotel. A popular eating place.
❀ ⊨ ◑ ▶ ≽ (South) P

Thorpe Hesley

Horse & Tiger
Brook Hill ☎ (0114) 2468072
11–3, 6–11; 11–11 Sat & bank hols
Stones Best Bitter; Tetley Bitter H
Friendly and lively locals' pub, restored to its former glory. Its unique name derives from an incident involving a travelling circus years ago. ❀ ♣ P

Tickhill

Carpenters Arms
Westgate ☎ (01302) 742839
11.30–3, 6 (6.30 Sat)–11
Vaux Bitter, Samson, Double Maxim H
Appealing pub with a lounge, a bar and a large, no-smoking family room. No food Sun or Mon. Award-winning garden.
Q ❧ ❀ ♣ P ⌀

Royal Oak
Northgate ☎ (01302) 742351
11.30–3 (5 Sat), 6 (5.30 Thu & Fri)–11
Whitbread Boddingtons Bitter, Trophy; guest beers H
Friendly local with a comfortable lounge and a bar. Two guest beers. Home-made lunches, as well as eve meals on Thu, Fri and Sat (children's menu). ❀ ◑ ▶ ♿ ♣ P

Scarbrough Arms
Sunderland Street
☎ (01302) 742977
11–3, 6–11
Courage Directors; Ruddles County; John Smith's Bitter, Magnet; guest beers H
Popular local with three rooms of differing character. Guest beers from independent breweries vary weekly. Home-made lunches (not served Sun). Lined glasses used. ⩲ ❀ ◑ ♿ ♣ P

Three Crowns
Northgate ☎ (01302) 745191
12–3 (summer only), 7–11
Tetley Bitter; Whitbread Boddingtons Bitter; guest beers H
Formerly the Buttercross, this quiet, friendly old pub is now known by its original name. Guest beers from independent brewers. ❀ ♣

Victoria

Victoria Inn
On A616 ☎ (01484) 682785
12–2 (Fri, Sat & Sun only), 7–11
S&N Theakston Best Bitter; Tetley Bitter H
A 1950s timewarp. Nothing has changed at this welcoming roadside pub. Enjoy a toastie from the vintage grill. Children not allowed. ⩲ Q P

Wath upon Dearne

Staithes
Doncaster Road
☎ (01709) 873546
12–11
Draught Bass; John Smith's Bitter, Magnet; Stones Best Bitter; guest beer H
An old railway sidings building renovated to introduce old-style cottage features. Brass and water jug collections. ⩲ Q ❧ ❀ ◑ ▶ P

Wentworth

Rockingham Arms
Main Street ☎ (01226) 742075
11–3, 5.30–11; 11–11 Sat
S&N Theakston Best Bitter, XB, Old Peculier; Younger Scotch, No. 3 H
200 years old, a former coaching inn, offering five open fires, a bowling green and a family room. Live entertainment Mon–Fri in 'The Barn'. ⩲ ❧ ❀ ⊨ ◑ ▶ P

Wheatley Hills

Wheatley Hotel
Thorne Road ☎ (01302) 364092
10–11
Courage Directors; Ruddles County; John Smith's Bitter, Magnet H
Large but friendly hotel with a comfortable lounge divided by impressive sliding doors. Well equipped children's play room and garden. The separate restaurant serves excellent value, home-cooked 'two for the price of one' meals Thu, Fri and Sat eves. ❧ ❀ ⊨ ◑ ▶ P

Whiston

Golden Ball
Turner Lane ☎ (01709) 378200
11.45–3, 5–11; 11.45–11 Fri & Sat
Ind Coope Burton Ale; Taylor Landlord; Tetley Bitter, Imperial; guest beer H
Picture postcard pub offering a pleasant outside drinking area. Full of olde-worlde charm, with an extensive bar menu, a restaurant and two real fires.
⩲ ❀ ◑ ▶ ♣ P

Wombwell

Royal Oak Hotel
13 Church Street
☎ (01226) 752158
12–11
Whitbread Boddingtons Bitter; guest beers H
Originally a Clarksons pub, with a set of old brewery windows. Quiet and friendly during the week; noisier Fri; live music Sat. Eight guest beers, including mild.
❀ ⊨ ◑ ≽ ♣

Worsbrough Village

Edmunds Arms
25 Worsbrough Village (off A61) ☎ (01226) 206865
11–3, 5 (6 Oct–Apr)–11
Samuel Smith OBB H
Splendid inn, opposite an historic church: a lounge, tap room and restaurant offering good value food (no bar meals Mon eve). ❀ ◑ ▶ ♣ P

Wortley

Wortley Arms Hotel
Halifax Road (A629)
☎ (0114) 2882245
12–2.30, 5.30–11 (extends in summer); 12–11 Sat
Coach House Blunderbus; Stones Best Bitter; Wortley Bitter, Earls Ale, Countess Ale; Younger IPA; guest beer H
16th-century coaching house opposite the church. Popular with walkers, it has a comfortable lounge, a public bar, a no-smoking snug, a restaurant. Folk nights. Wortley beers are brewed in the cellar. ⩲ Q ❧ ❀ ⊨ ◑ ♿ ♣ P ⌀

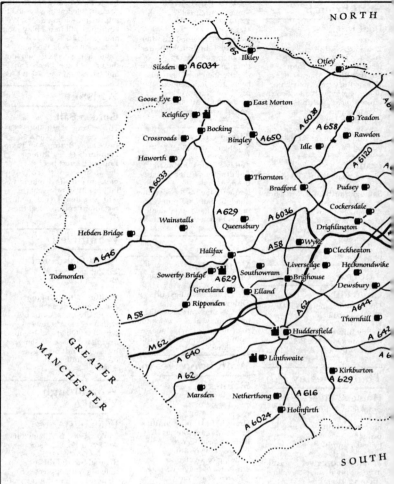

West Yorkshire

 Clark's, Wakefield; *Commercial*, Keighley; *Eastwood's*, Huddersfield; *Fox & Newt*, Leeds; *Goose Eye*, Keighley; *Linfit*, Linthwaite; *Pennine*, Keighley; *Ryburn*, Sowerby Bridge; *Steam Packet*, Knottingley; *Taylor*, Keighley; *Tomlinson's*, Pontefract

---

Aberford

Arabian Horse
Main Street
☎ (0113) 2813312
11–2.30, 5–11; 11–11 Sat
S&N Theakston Best Bitter; Younger Scotch, No. 3 Ⓗ
Pub adjacent to the green in one of Leeds's most attractive villages; an 18th-century inn with open fires in the lounge and separate rear games room. Fine collection of horse brasses. ⚄ 🛏 ◗ ♣ P

Bingley

Brown Cow
Ireland Bridge (50 yds over bridge on Harden Rd from A650 jct) ☎ (01274) 569482
11.30–3, 5.30–11
Taylor Golden Best, Best Bitter, Landlord, Ram Tam Ⓗ
Wood panelling and stained-glass give a rural feel to this riverside pub. A la carte dining is a speciality.
⚄ ❀ 🛏 ◗ ▶
⇌ (Bingley) P

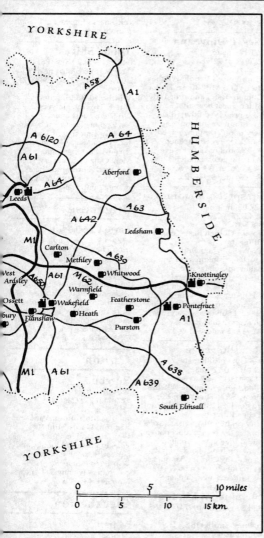

S&N Theakston Best Bitter; Taylor Landlord; Tetley Bitter; guest beers H
Split-level pub on the Leeds Country Way, within a slice of a golf course. Flooding necessitated building of the low front wall and tortuous entrance route. DJ and quiz most eves. Excellent family room. Live music outside on summer Sats. ☎ ☼ ❀ ♣ P

Castle
20 Grattan Road
☎ (01274) 393166
11–11; 7–10.30 Sun, closed Sun lunch
Adnams Extra, Broadside; Mansfield Riding Mild, Riding Bitter, Bitter; Wells Bombardier; guest beers H
Built in Yorkshire stone, in a style appropriate to its name, this open-plan alehouse offers beers from independent brewers, with regular guests from local micro-brewers. Bar meals may be introduced.
≠ (Forster Sq/Interchange)
P (eves only)

Corn Dolly
110 Bolton Road (500 yds from Forster Sq station)
☎ (01274) 720219
11.30–11
Moorhouse's Premier; S&N Theakston Best Bitter, XB; Whitbread Boddingtons Bitter; guest beers H
Beamed ceilings, a roaring, open fire, huge lunchtime sandwiches and four ever-changing guest beers have won this popular pub many awards, including local CAMRA *Pub of the Year*. Home-cooked meals Mon–Fri. Classic jukebox; C&W Wed and Sun nights.
🏨 ☼ ◑ & ≠ ♣ P

Cricketers Arms (Slip)
51 Chapel Street, Eccleshill
☎ (01274) 639798
11–11
Whitbread Boddingtons Bitter, Trophy, Castle Eden Ale, Flowers Original; guest beers H
Comfortable, suburban pub with stonework a feature, inside and out. Originally part of a row of terraced houses. Games area; nearly separate quieter snug. Good views from the garden. Occasional mini-beer festivals. Barbecues in summer. ☼ ♣ P

Duchess of Kent
26 Sackville Street
☎ (01274) 725003
11–11
Tetley Bitter H
Old-fashioned pub with thriving games rooms. ☼
≠ (Interchange/Forster Sq)
♣

Bocking

New Inn
Halifax Road (A629 near A6033 jct) ☎ (01535) 643191
4 (11 Sat)–11
Black Sheep Best Bitter; Mansfield Riding Bitter; Taylor Golden Best; Whitbread Boddingtons Bitter H
Popular two-room, open-plan, local where the comfortable decor comprises stained-wood and Yorkshire stone. Breakfasts served from 9.30am Sat. Bus stop outside.
& ≠ (KWVLR Haworth)
♣ P

Bradford

Bedford Arms
2 Wakefield Road (100 yds from Interchange)
☎ (01274) 733837
11–11
Tetley Bitter H
Friendly, honest pub with a distinct Irish flavour. A basic lounge and a separate pool room. ≠ (Interchange) ♣

Blue Pig
Fagley Road, Lower Fagley (narrow road at the end of Fagley Rd) OS193351
☎ (0113) 2562738
12 (3 winter Tue–Thu)–11

West Yorkshire

Fighting Cock
21–27 Preston Street,
Listerhills (off Thornton Rd)
☎ (01274) 726907
11.30–11
**Black Sheep Special Strong;
Marston's Pedigree; Old Mill
Bitter; Samuel Smith OBB;
S&N Theakston Old Peculier;
Taylor Golden Best,
Landlord; Vaux Extra Special;
guest beers** H
Back to basics, back-street
Mecca for ale drinkers. One of
the first pubs of this type,
opening 13 years ago. Food
(only hot at lunchtime)
includes massive 'docker's
wedge' sandwiches. A major
contributor to charity.
🚃 🍴 ⌂

Gaping Goose
5–6 Slack Bottom Road,
Wibsey (off Buttershaw Lane)
☎ (01274) 601701
12–3, 7–11
**Black Sheep Best Bitter; S&N
Theakston Old Peculier;
Taylor Landlord; Tetley
Bitter; Whitbread Trophy** H
Intimate, friendly, two-roomed
local displaying a large
collection of brassware in the
pleasant lounge. 🏵 ♿ ♣ P

Idle Cock
1190 Bolton Road (A6176, 2
miles from centre)
☎ (01274) 639491
11.30–11
**Black Sheep Special Strong;
Marston's Pedigree; Old Mill
Bitter; Samuel Smith OBB;
Taylor Landlord; Wards
Thorne Best Bitter; guest
beers** H
Recently extended, deservedly
popular pub, winner of a local
CAMRA *Pub of the Season*
award in 1993. Excellently
priced and portioned pub
grub. A charity fundraising
venue. Quiz Tue. 🏵 🍴 ▶ ⌂

Mail Coach
32 Huddersfield Road, Odsal
(200 yds from rugby stadium)
☎ (01274) 671857
7–11; 12–3, 7–11 Fri; 12–11 Sat
Vaux Bitter, Samson H
Three-roomed pub, recently
refurbished. Very busy on
Northern match days.
🚃 🛏 ♣ P

Melborn Hotel
104 White Abbey Road (B6144,
1 mile from centre)
☎ (01274) 726867
11–11
**Mansfield Riding Bitter;
Tetley Bitter; guest beers** H
Down to earth, friendly pub
with both a large tap room
and a music room.
Breweriana and musical gear
adorn the walls (live music

Thu–Sun eves).
🏵 🛏 🍴 ♿ ♣ P

New Beehive Inn
171 Westgate
☎ (01274) 721784
11.30–11
**Moorhouse's Pendle Witches
Brew; Old Mill Bitter; Taylor
Golden Best, Landlord; Tetley
Bitter; guest beers** H
Well-preserved Edwardian,
gas-lit inn: an atmospheric and
very popular multi-roomed
pub. Large newly opened
cellar bar. Live jazz Fri eve.
Wide range of malt whiskies.
🚃 Q 🛏 🏵 🍴 ▶ ♿
🚆 (Forster Sq) ♣ P

Prospect of Bradford
527 Bolton Road
☎ (01274) 727018
3–5, 7–11
**Taylor Golden Best; Tetley
Bitter** H
Ex-Waller's pub with a
spacious drinking area and
panoramic views over
Bradford (watch City play
free). Excellent function room
with a bar (good value buffet).
Organist sing-along Wed, Fri,
Sat and Sun eves. Nearer the
city centre than it looks.
🚃 🚆 (Forster Sq) ♣ P

Rams Revenge
1–3 Upper Millergate
☎ (01274) 720283
11.30–11; 11.30–5, 7–11 Sat
**Moorhouse's Pendle Witches
Brew; S&N Theakston XB;
Taylor Best Bitter, Landlord;
Tetley Bitter** H
City-centre pub on the site of a
former toll booth, court house
and dungeon (now only the
dungeon remains). Two pubs
in one (the Cobbles Bar opens
at weekends when busy). 🍴
🚆 (Interchange/Forster Sq)

Shoulder of Mutton
28 Kirkgate ☎ (01274) 726038
11–11
**Samuel Smith OBB,
Museum** H
Small, multi-roomed, city-
centre pub with a famous
suntrap garden. High quality,
good value lunches. 🏵 🍴
🚆 (Forster Sq/Interchange)
♣

Steve Biko Bar
Bradford University,
Richmond Building (D Floor),
Richmond Road
☎ (01274) 733466
11 (5 Sat)–11; 7–10.30 Sun, closed
Sun lunch
**S&N Theakston Best Bitter,
XB, Old Peculier; Taylor
Landlord; Whitbread Eden
Bitter, Castle Eden Ale; guest
beers** H
Large, open-plan bar with
plenty of seating. Can be noisy

in the eve. Hot snacks eves;
cold snacks lunchtime. Usually
four guest beers. ♣ ⌂ ♿

Tut 'n' Shive
49 Duckworth Lane (B6144,
2 miles from centre, near
infirmary) ☎ (01274) 547372
11–11
**Whitbread Boddingtons
Bitter, Trophy, Flowers
Original; guest beers** H
Very popular, basic pub with a
friendly atmosphere. Groups
travel from far afield to see the
friendly host. Jug night every
Mon. Quiz games every Tue
and Wed. Three guest beers
from independents. A charity-
oriented pub. 🍴 ♿ ♣

Brighouse

Forte Crest Hotel
Clifton Village (1 mile from
centre near M62 jct 25)
☎ (01484) 400400
11–11
Taylor Landlord H
Purpose-built, four-star hotel,
with one massive lounge area
leading into the restaurant.
Prices match the status of the
establishment, but bar snacks
are reasonably priced.
Q 🏵 🛏 🍴 ▶ ♿ P ♿

Carlton

Rosebud
Westfield Road
☎ (0113) 2822236
12–3 (4 Sat), 5.30 (7 Sat)–11
**John Smith's Bitter; Vaux
Samson; Wards Mild** H
Wayside local in a pretty
village: a pleasant lounge and
a friendly, small tap room.
Board games played;
occasional live music. Lunches
Mon–Fri. 🚃 Q 🏵 🍴 ♣ P

Cleckheaton

Marsh
28 Bradford Road (A638)
☎ (01274) 872104
11.30–3 (5 Fri), 7–11
**Old Mill Mild, Bitter,
Bullion, Porter** H
Floral fabrics and wallpaper
abound in this refurbished
ex-Tetley house, with a
mahogany bar and wall
panelling. Bizarre brick wall in
the pool room. Raised
drinking area. No food Sat.
🍴 ♣ P

Cockersdale

Valley
68 Whitehall Road (A58)
☎ (0113) 2852483
11.30–3, 5.30–11; 11.30–11 Sat
Samuel Smith OBB H

Tastefully decorated roadside inn with a good value menu and a wide range of regulars. Sporty pool room; quiet meeting room; separate lounge and a busy bar/lounge. An ideal place to end a walk on the Leeds Country Way. No eve meals Sat/Sun/Wed; other eves till 7.30.
🏠 ❀ ◖ ▶ ♣ P

Crossroads

Quarry House Inn

Lees Moor (near A629/A6033 jct) ☎ (01535) 642239
12–3, 7–11 (11.30 supper licence)
Ind Coope Burton Ale; Taylor Landlord, Porter (winter); **Tetley Bitter** H
Family-run converted farmhouse in open country, with extensive views. The bar is a former church pulpit and is set in a small, cosy area. Now ten years in the *Guide*. Excellent food.
🏠 ❀ ◖ ▶ ◖ ▲ P

Dewsbury

John F Kennedy

2 Webster Hill (A644, near bus and rail stations)
☎ (01924) 455828
7–11
Taylor Landlord; Tetley Bitter; guest beer H
It's not pretty, it's not trendy, it's not quiet, but it is an intriguing Dewsbury institution, popular with young and old alike. ◖ ⇌ ♣

Market House

8 Church Street (200 yds N of bus station) ☎ (01924) 457310
11–11
S&N Theakston Best Bitter; Tetley Mild, Bitter H
Pub with an excellent tap room at the front, dominated by an imposing bank of handpumps. A drinkers' corridor leads to a back lounge, served by a small hatch. This Tetley Heritage pub is a haven for those who like to chat and drink.
🏠 Q ◖ ⇌ ♣

Drighlington

Waggon & Horses

28 Wakefield Road
☎ (0113) 2853585
7 (6 Fri)–11; 12–4, 6–11 Sat
Tetley Bitter; guest beer (occasional) H
Three-roomed, revitalized local, with a friendly atmosphere and enthusiastic sports teams. Returned to real from fizz by the current licensee, who has also added occasional guest beers, which

account for the steady increase in trade (and opening hours). Children welcome in the pool room. Lunches Sat on request.
◖ ♣ P

East Morton

Busfeild Arms

Main Road ☎ (01274) 564453
11–11
Bass Worthington BB, Draught Bass; Stones Best Bitter; guest beer H
18th-century, stone-built ex-farmhouse in a small attractive village east of Keighley. Sympathetically modernised in wood and stone with two separate rooms. Popular for lunchtime meals. Quiz Thu. ❀ ◖ ♣ P

Elland

Colliers Arms

66 Park Road (A6025)
☎ (01422) 372007
11.30–3, 5.30 (5 Fri)–11; 11.30–11 Sat
Samuel Smith OBB, Museum H
Two-roomed cottage pub with a conservatory overlooking the canal (own moorings). Attractive small garden. Eve meals: winter Fri/Sat till 8pm; summer Thu–Sat till 8.30pm.
🏠 ▷ ❀ ◖ ▶ ◖ ♣ P

Featherstone

Sun Inn

Ackton Lane ☎ (01977) 702055
12–3.30, 6–11
Morland Old Speckled Hen; John Smith's Bitter; Whitbread Boddingtons Bitter, Flowers IPA, Trophy; guest beer H
Typical, friendly local, tastefully refurbished into three separate drinking areas. Wed/Thu quiz nights; Mon pool knockout. A quiet retreat.
Q ❀ ◖ ▶ ◖ P

Flanshaw

Flanshaw Hotel

Flanshaw Lane
☎ (01924) 290830
11.30–11
John Smith's Bitter; Tetley Bitter; guest beers H
Large estate pub, well-renovated and still retaining separate rooms. Up to three guest beers at competitive prices. Quiz Thu; entertainers weekends. Book for eve meals.
❀ ◖ ▶ ◖ ◖ ⇌ (Westgate) P

Goose Eye

Turkey Inn

West Lane from Keighley: turn

for Laycock then for Goose Eye ☎ (01535) 681339
12–3 (not Mon; 12–5 Sat), 5.30 (7 Sat)–11
Goose Eye Bitter, Wharfedale; Ind Coope Burton Ale; Tetley Bitter H
200-year-old country pub with a relaxing atmosphere. Two alcoves with real fires, a tap room and a dining room (steak night Thu; no food Mon). Quiz Wed. Children welcome till 8pm. 🏠 ▷ ❀ ◖ ▶ ♣ P

Greetland

Greetland Community & Sporting Association

Rochdale Road
☎ (01422) 370140
12–3 (Wed only), 7–11; 12–11 Sat; 12–3, 7–10.30 Sun
Taylor Best Bitter; Tetley Bitter; guest beers H
Club which caters for all ages, with a single, friendly bar where athletic types sample the variety of guest beers. There can be a 50p admission charge for non-members. A Hambleton beer is also served.
▲ ♣

Star Inn

1 Lindwell (off B6113)
☎ (01422) 373164
12–4 (not Tue), 7–11; 12–3, 7–10 Sun
Wards Thorne Best Bitter, Best Bitter H
Popular local: a well-lit busy tap room and a cosy lounge with subdued lighting. The Calderdale Way is nearby.
❀ ♣

Halifax

Brown Cow

569 Gibbet Street, Highroad Well (1½ miles W of centre)
☎ (01422) 361640
11.30–3, 5–11; 11–11 Fri & Sat
Whitbread Trophy, Castle Eden Ale H
Busy local holding quizzes. Large collection of cows. Lunches Mon–Fri. ◖ ◖ ♣

Clarence Hotel

77 Lister Lane
☎ (01422) 363266
11.30–11 (12.30am supper licence Thu–Sat)
Bass Worthington BB; Fuller's London Pride; Stones Best Bitter; Tetley Bitter; guest beer H
Busy street-corner local on the fringe of the town centre: four drinking areas in open-plan style and an upstairs function room. Active sports following. Daily happy hours: 12–1.30 and 5–7 (5–9 Fri).
❀ ◖ ◖ ⇌ ♣ P

341

West Yorkshire

Pump Room
35 New Road (250 yds left from station) ☎ (01422) 381465
11–11
Black Sheep Special Strong; Marston's Pedigree; John Smith's Magnet; Taylor Landlord; Tetley Bitter; Whitbread Boddingtons Bitter; guest beers H
Traditional-style alehouse with a collection of taps and other breweriana. Home to a golfing society, football club and quiz team. Daily happy hour and good food. Nine regular and three guest beers, plus a house beer. ☀ ♨ ▶ ≠ ⌂ P

Shears Inn
Paris Gates, Boys Lane (behind flats, near the Shay, between mills and down into the mill yard) ☎ (01422) 362936
11.45–4.30, 7–11; 11.45–11 Fri & Sat
Taylor Golden Best, Best Bitter, Landlord; Younger Scotch, No. 3; guest beer H
Difficult to find, but worth it. The dark, satanic mills that surround it are probably more recent than the pub itself. A convenient place to stop along the Hebble Trail footpath (the Hebble brook runs by the car park). No meals at weekends. ♨ ☀ ◗ ≠ ♣ P

Sportsman
Bradford Old Road, Ploughcroft (¼ mile E of A647, 1 mile N of centre) ☎ (01422) 367000
12–3, 6–11; 12–11 Sat
Old Mill Bitter; S&N Theakston Old Peculier; Taylor Landlord; Tetley Bitter; guest beer H
Popular hill-top free house with expansive views. Squash, solarium and sauna are all available; all-weather ski-slope attached. Folk club Thu; five quiz nights. The brewer of the house beer is kept secret. No meals Mon eve. ♨ ☎ ☀ ◗ ♿ ♣ P

Sportsman Hotel
48–50 Crown Street ☎ (01422) 355704
11–11
Tetley Bitter; guest beer H
Lively town local with an Edwardian frontage. Four drinking areas adjoin the bar. The pool room is adorned with rugby league memorabilia. Rock jukebox. The guest beer is reasonably priced. ≠ ♣

Haworth

Fleece Inn
67 Main Street ☎ (01535) 642172
11–11
Taylor Golden Best, Best Bitter, Landlord, Ram Tam H
Welcoming 300-year-old coaching inn on a cobbled street. Three rooms with a stone-flagged bar area. Family room available till 3pm. Steak night Tue. No wheelchair access to ladies' WC. ♨ ☎ ◗ ♿ ▲ ≠ (KWVLR)

Haworth Old Hall
Sun Street (bottom of Main St, opp. park) ☎ (01535) 642709
11–11
Draught Bass; Stones Best Bitter; Taylor Golden Best; Tetley Bitter H
Three-roomed, 17th-century, Tudor-style building with open stonework, oak beams and mullioned windows. Friendly atmosphere; large garden; à la carte restaurant (good Sun lunches; no bar lunches Sun). No wheelchair access to ladies' WC. ☎ ☀ ♨ ◗ ▶ ▲ ≠ (KWVLR) P

Heath

Kings Arms
Heath Common ☎ (01924) 377527
11.30–3.30, 6–11.30
Clark's Bitter, Festival; Taylor Landlord; Tetley Bitter H
Historic inn on the village green. The multi-roomed interior features wood panelling, gas lighting and flagged floors. Warm and atmospheric on cold eves. Cask ale is also available in the excellent restaurant. No children after 8.30pm. ♨ Q ☎ ☀ ◗ ▶ ♿ P

Hebden Bridge

Fox & Goose
9 Heptonstall Road (A646) ☎ (01422) 842649
11.30–3, 7–11
Goose Eye Bitter; Ruddles Best Bitter; guest beers H
Small but cosy pub with a keen landlord. Guest beers change and are listed on a blackboard outside. Q ◗ ▶ ≠

Hare & Hounds
Lane Ends, Chiserley, Old Town OS005280 ☎ (01422) 842671
12 (7 Mon)–11 (7–11 Tue–Thu in winter; may close if quiet)
Taylor Golden Best, Best Bitter, Landlord H
Cosy, homely hillside pub above Hebden Bridge and near the automobile museum. ♨ Q ☀ ◗ ▶ ♣ P

Nutclough House Hotel
Keighley Road (A6033 ¼ mile from centre) ☎ (01422) 844361
12–3 (Tue–Fri, summer only), 6–11; 12–11 Sat

S&N Theakston Best Bitter; Taylor Landlord; Thwaites Bitter; guest beers H
Roomy and comfortable pub, attracting a varied clientele. Regular live music. Three guest beers. ♨ ☀ ◗ ▶ ≠ ♣ P

Shoulder of Mutton
38 New Road, Mytholmroyd (B6138) ☎ (01422) 883165
11.30–3, 7–11; 11.30–11 Sat
Whitbread Boddingtons Bitter, Flowers IPA, Trophy, Castle Eden Ale; guest beers H
Popular roadside local with a display of toby jugs and china. Two guest beers. No eve meals Tue. ♨ ◗ ▶ ▲ ≠ (Mytholmroyd) ♣ P

Heckmondwike

Old Hall
New North Road (400 yds NW of the green) ☎ (01924) 404774
11.30–2, 6–11
Samuel Smith OBB H
A late medieval, timber-framed, aisled house, later encased in stone and enlarged, this pub still retains a plaster ceiling from c 1640. Joseph Priestley, discoverer of oxygen, lived here as a boy. Quizzes Tue and Thu. ☀ ◗ ▶ P

Holmfirth

Rose & Crown (Nook)
Victoria Square (alley behind Barclay's Bank) ☎ (01484) 683960
11.30–11
Samuel Smith OBB; Stones Best Bitter; Taylor Best Bitter, Landlord, Ram Tam; Tetley Mild; guest beers H
Legendary, basic, traditional boozer with an extensive range of beers, a stone floor and a legendary landlord. Not visible from the road and difficult to find the first time. ♨ ☎ ☀ ♣

Horbury

Calder Vale
Millfield Road (400 yds from Southfield Lane) ☎ (01924) 275351
12–3.30, 6.15–11
John Smith's Bitter; guest beer H
Traditional working-class boozer in a large Victorian building on the outskirts of Horbury. Built in 1884 for the Fernandes brewery, this pub retains some of the atmosphere of a bygone age. Hard to find but well worth the effort. Q ☀ ♣ P

Navigation

Broadcut Road (600 yds from
Denby Dale Rd)
☎ (01924) 274361
11–11

**Taylor Landlord; Tetley
Bitter, Imperial; guest beer** H
Popular canalside pub on the
Calder and Hebble
Navigation, tastefully
decorated with historic
memorabilia. Free moorings.
The garden is popular with
families. A must for folk of all
ages. ♨ Q ♒ ❀ ◖ ● & P

Huddersfield

Albert Hotel

38 Victoria Lane (by central
library) ☎ (01484) 421065
11–11

**Bass Light, Draught Bass;
Stones Best Bitter; Taylor
Landlord; guest beer** H
Split-level, Victorian building,
tastefully refurbished around
the original, fine etched-glass
and mahogany bar.
Established and budding poets
regularly gather to recite their
work. No lunches Sun. ◖ ≢

Ale Shoppe

205 Lockwood Road,
Lockwood (A616, 1 mile S of
centre) ☎ (01484) 432479
11–9; 12–3 Sun

**Eastwood's Best Bitter; Taylor
Best Bitter or Landlord; guest
beer** (occasional) H
Off-licence that is a rare local
outlet for Huddersfield-
brewed Eastwood's ale.
Extensive range of specialist
beer-making supplies for the
home brewer. Huge variety of
British and European bottled
beers. Open 9–9 (12–6 Sun),
but only licensed at above
times. ≢ (Lockwood)

Black Horse

107 Occupation Road, Lindley
(2½ miles NW of centre)
☎ (01484) 425816
6–11; 12–3, 6.30–11 Fri; 11–11 Sat

**Mansfield Riding Bitter, Old
Baily** H
Former Bentley & Shaw's
Lockwood brewery house
which still retains its original
green-tiled entrance. A small,
homely pub overlooked by
Lindley clock tower. Discos Fri
and Sun. ❀ & ♣

Electricians Arms

159–161 Manchester Road,
Longroyd Bridge (A62 near
ring road jct) ☎ (01484) 429779
12–2, 7.30–11; 12–11 Sat; 12–3,
7.30–10.30 Sun

**Courage Directors; Ruddles
County; S&N Theakston XB,
Old Peculier; John Smith's
Bitter; guest beer** H

Long, stone-built pub with a
cosmopolitan crowd, from
boffins to bikers. Unusual
games. ♨ ❀ ♣ ◌

Marsh Liberal Club

Glenfield, 31 New Hey Road,
Marsh (A640, 1 mile from
centre) ☎ (01484) 420152
12–2 (not Mon), 7–11; 11–11 Sat

**Mansfield Old Baily; Samuel
Smith OBB; Taylor Best
Bitter; Tetley Mild, Bitter;
guest beers** H
Club founded in 1883, but
moved to this Grade II-listed,
former mill owner's house in
1930. Extensive range of guest
beers. Good collection of beer
bottles and pump clips. Show
this guide or a CAMRA
membership card at the bar to
be signed in. Q ♒ ❀ P

Rat & Ratchet

40 Chapel Hill (A616 near ring
road jct) ☎ (01484) 516734
12 (3 Mon–Wed, 11.30 Fri) –11

**Adnams Bitter; Bateman
Mild; Mansfield Riding
Bitter, Old Baily; Taylor Best
Bitter, Landlord; guest
beers** H
Bare boards alehouse usually
sporting more than a baker's
dozen of beers on the bar. Also
regularly holds its own beer
festivals, when even more
brews are on offer. The
jukebox can be loud. Wed
is curry night.
❀ ◖ ≢ ◌ P

Shoulder of Mutton

11 Neale Road, Lockwood (off
B6108, near A616 jct, 1 mile S
of centre)
☎ (01484) 424835
7 (3 Sat)–11

**Draught Bass; Taylor Best
Bitter, Landlord; Tetley Mild,
Bitter; Thwaites Bitter; guest
beer** H
A genuine free house for many
years, with a traditional
atmosphere, sited at the head
of a cobbled street. One of the
rare breed of pubs where, over
the years, subtle alterations
have taken place without
destroying the innate charm.
❀ ≢ (Lockwood) ♣

Slubbers Arms

1 Halifax Old Road, Hillhouse
(just off A641, ¾ mile from
centre) ☎ (01484) 429032
11.30–3.30, 6.30 (7 Sat)–11

**Marston's Pedigree; Taylor
Best Bitter; guest beer** H
150-year-old beer house which
has grown into an odd-shaped
pub by absorbing adjoining
cottages, creating a genuine
period feel—much better than
brewer's Victorian. Spot the
lavatory cistern in memory of
the old loos. ♨ Q ◖ ♣

Zeneca Recreation Club

509 Leeds Road (A62, 3 miles
NE of town) ☎ (01484) 514367
12–11

**Taylor Best Bitter; Tetley
Mild, Bitter; guest beers** H
Twice winner of CAMRA's
Club of the Year award: a large
club with three lounges, two
bars, eight snooker tables,
bowls, tennis, hockey, croquet,
etc. Can be hired for functions.
Show this guide or CAMRA
membership to the doorman to
be signed in. ❀ ◖ ♣ P

Idle

Brewery Arms

Louisa Street (off High St)
☎ (01274) 610546
12–11

**Bass Worthington BB; Tetley
Bitter; guest beers** H
Former Liberal club which has
survived the closure of the
adjacent Trough brewery: a
large lounge with a separate
pool room at the rear and a
snug. It can be noisy and
lively, but a welcome is
assured. Eve meals till 7.30.
❀ ◖ ● ♣ P

Brewery Tap

51 Albion Road
☎ (01274) 613936
11.45–3 (4 Sat), 6.30 (7 Sat)–11

**Whitbread Flowers IPA,
Castle Eden Ale** H
Former bakery and previously
a Trough brewery tied house:
one room with a large central
bar area. Live rock music Tue
and Sat. Guest beers may be
available. ❀ & ♣

New Inn

High Street ☎ (01274) 613136
11.30–3.30, 7–11

**S&N Theakston Best Bitter;
Tetley Bitter** H
Popular local at the top of the
aptly-named High Street. The
two-section lounge includes a
TV for Sky; the upstairs games
room can be used for
meetings. ❀ ◖ & ♣ P

Springfield Hotel

179 Bradford Road
☎ (01274) 612710
11–11

Vaux Samson H
Roadside local on the edge of a
large housing estate. Two
small rooms: a lounge with
pool and a tap room popular
with darts players. Other Vaux
products may be tried.
❀ ♣ P

Ilkley

Midland Hotel

Station Road ☎ (01943) 607433
11–11

West Yorkshire

Courage Directors; Marston's
Pedigree; John Smith's Bitter;
guest beers H
Very convenient for bus and
train stations, and next to the
King's Hall, a pub with two
rooms, one of which is games-
oriented. Some nice
railwayana. The lounge is
warm and comfortable.
Q ◁ ⇌ ♣ P

Keighley

Albert Hotel
Bridge Street (South St)
☎ (01535) 602306
11–5.30, 7–11; 11–11 Fri & Sat
Taylor Golden Best, Best
Bitter, Landlord, Ram Tam
(winter) H
One of Taylor's longest
serving tenants, offering value
for money Taylor's ales in a
large and popular Victorian
hotel: a long, narrow front
room and a large pool room.
Note the mural and the
half-motorcycle on the wall.
Small car park. ⇌ ♣ P

Boltmakers Arms
117 East Parade
☎ (01535) 661936
11.30–11; 11–4.30, 7–11 Sat
Taylor Golden Best, Best
Bitter, Landlord; Tetley
Bitter H
Very popular, one-room,
split-level local, which can get
very busy, especially at
weekends. Good selection of
malt whiskies. ⇌ ♣

Cricketers Arms
Coney Lane (off East
Parade/Worth Way)
☎ (01535) 669912
11–11
Taylor Golden Best, Best
Bitter, Landlord (summer),
Ram Tam (winter) H
Small, one-room, friendly
local, nestling between two
mills. Tastefully renovated by
the present licensee. Try the
traditional northern snacks
Sun lunchtime. ⓱ ⇌ ♣

Grinning Rat/Rat Trap
2 Church Street
☎ (01535) 609747
11–11; Rat Trap 8–midnight (2am
Thu–Sat, 8–midnight Sun)
Commercial Keighlian;
Kelham Island Pale Rider;
Taylor Landlord; Whitbread
Boddingtons Bitter; guest
beers H
Centrally-located and popular,
large, multi-level, traditional
alehouse with up to 17 bitters
available at weekends, plus a
mild and two ciders. Live
music Thu night. The Rat Trap
is the adjoining night club,
with two bars and late-night
extensions. Food Mon–Sat
12–2.30. ◁ ⓱ ⇌ ⌂

Red Pig
Church Street
☎ (01535) 605383
12–3, 7–11; 12–11 Fri & Sat
Commercial Keighlian;
Taylor Golden Best,
Landlord; guest beers H
Welcoming former Trough
pub, centrally located and very
popular, exhibiting local
artists' work. Good range of
Belgian bottled beers and malt
whiskies. Sandwiches Fri and
Sat lunchtime only. Guest
beers come from northern
independents. ⌕ ⇌ ♣

Volunteer Arms
Lawkholme Lane (behind
the Cavendish pub in
Cavendish St)
☎ (01535) 600173
11–11
Taylor Golden Best, Best
Bitter, Ram Tam (winter) H
Compact local with two
rooms, the smaller used
mainly for games. ⇌ ♣

Keighley to Oxenhope and Back

Keighley and Worth Valley Buffet Car
Stations at Keighley, Ingrow
West, Oakworth, Haworth and
Oxenhope
☎ (01535) 645214; talking
timetable ☎ (01535) 647777
Runs Sat & Sun Mar–Nov
Beer range varies H
Volunteer-run railway buffet
car giving changing views of
the Worth Valley. Usually one
or two beers available, refilled
several times a day. The train
is available to hire for
weddings, etc., with beer to
requirements.
⌕ (Ingrow, Oakworth,
Oxenhope) Q ♠ (Oxenhope)
⇌ (Keighley) P (Keighley,
Ingrow, Oxenhope) ⍾

Kirkburton

Royal
64 North Road (½ mile E of
A629/B6116 jct)
☎ (01484) 602521
11.30–2.30 (not Mon), 5–11; 11.30–11
Sat
Ind Coope Burton Ale; Taylor
Landlord; Tetley Mild, Bitter;
guest beers (occasional) H
Large Victorian pub, now
completely refurbished. The
opened-out and tastefully
decorated lounge has a
welcoming real fire; separate
games and function rooms.
Background music, but no
jukebox. Customers of all ages.
Eve meals Wed–Sat.
⌕ ⓱ ◁ ▶ ♣ P

Knottingley

Steam Packet Inn
2 Racca Green (follow A645
from station, ½ mile E)
☎ (01977) 674176
11–11
Steam Packet Gamekeeper,
Chatterley, Foxy, Bit o Black,
Bargee, Brown Ale, Poacher's
Swag, Giddy Ass; guest
beers H
Large, multi-roomed pub
alongside the canal. Home of
Steam Packet brewery (tours
by arrangement). ⌕ ⓱ ♣ P

Ledsham

Chequers Inn
Claypit Lane (1 mile W of A1
from A63 fork)
☎ (01977) 683135
11–3, 5.30–11; 11–11 Sat; closed Sun
S&N Theakston Best Bitter;
John Smith's Bitter; Younger
Scotch, No. 3 H
Unspoilt, ivy-clad village inn
with a stone-fronted bar
serving a multitude of
genuine, oak-beamed small
rooms. Excellent restaurant
upstairs. A gem—not to be
missed. ⌕ Q ⓱ ◁ ▶ ♣ P

Leeds

Beer Exchange
121 Woodhouse Street,
Woodhouse ☎ (0113) 2341658
12–3, 5.30 (7 Sat)–11
Marston Moor Cromwell,
Brewers Pride, Brewers
Droop; guest beers H
Former derelict pub which
became Leeds CAMRA *Pub of
the Year* within 12 months of
reopening and has sold over
300 guest beers (always six at a
time, plus a cask stout). The
refurbishment has added style
and character to a central bar
serving three areas. No eve
meals Sat/Sun. Q ◁ ♣ ⍾

Beer Paradise
Unit 11, Bridgewater Road,
South Accommodation Road
(trading estate by iron river
bridge) ☎ (0113) 2359082
10–6 (8 Thu & Fri); 12–3 Sun; closed
Mon
Massive supermarket-style
warehouse outlet offering a vast
range of beers for public sale
at very keen prices. It
specialises in Belgian beer.
This *Guide* is a registered
member: please show at the
checkout. ⓱ P

Central
88 Wellington Street
☎ (0113) 2453927
11–11; 11–3, 7–11 Sat
Ind Coope Burton Ale; Tetley
Mild, Bitter H

Birthplace of the Leeds branch of CAMRA. An L-shaped single room with a raised seating area at the back, which doubles as a dining area for good value meals at lunchtime, and a stage in the eve for music. ◑ ≈ ♠

Chemic Tavern

9 Johnston Street, Woodhouse (½ mile from university)
☎ (0113) 2440092
11–3, 5.30–11; 11–11 Sat
Ind Coope Burton Ale; Marston's Pedigree; Tetley Bitter, Imperial; guest beer H
Victorian, stone-fronted house, which gives way to two relaxing, low-ceilinged, wood-panelled bars. An unspoilt premises, with no electronic diversions (save the TV in the tap room for sports). Good banter, with student and local clientele harmonising. Note the 5s and 3s inlaid boards. Q ♠ P

City of Mabgate

45 Mabgate (off Regent St)
☎ (0113) 2457789
12–11
Marston's Pedigree; Morland Old Speckled Hen; Whitbread Boddingtons Bitter, Trophy; guest beers H
Built in 1840, formerly a Dutton's house with a tiled exterior and a genuine, old interior. Well worth seeking out in the shadow of the York Road flyover. Popular with the more mature customer, but welcoming to all. No food Sat. ⚏ ◑ ⌘ ♠

Duck & Drake

43 Kirkgate (between Kirkgate market and parish church)
☎ (0113) 2465806
11–11
Home Bitter; Old Mill Bitter; S&N Theakston Best Bitter, XB, Old Peculier; Taylor Landlord; guest beers H
Basic, two-roomed, wooden-floored alehouse, situated beside the railway bridge. A dozen real ales and real music make it popular with old and young alike. Live music Tue, Thu and Sun. No meals weekends. ⚏ ◑ ≈ ♠ ⌂

Eagle Tavern

North Street, Sheepscar
☎ (0113) 2457146
11–3, 5.30–11
Taylor Mild, Golden Best, Best Bitter, Landlord, Ram Tam; guest beers H
The Eagle is synonymous with good beer and has won many awards, including CAMRA regional *Pub of the Year* 1993. Well on its way to its 1000th guest beer—and all through two handpumps. ⚏ ◑ ♠ ⌂

Grove Inn

Back Row, Holbeck (between Hilton Hotel and M1)
☎ (0113) 2439254
11.30–11; 11.30–4, 7–11 Sat
Draught Bass; Courage Directors; Ruddles Best Bitter, County; John Smith's Bitter, Magnet H
Unchanged Yorkshire corridor pub which has played host to acoustic music (rock, blues, jazz and folk) for 33 years. Saved from demolition (car park planned) by campaigning and the property trend. Local business trade at lunchtime gives way to frustrated musicians at night. No food Sat. ⚏ ✿ ◑ ≈ ♠ P

Highland (Laddie)

38 Cavendish Street, Burley
☎ (0113) 2428592
11.30–11
Tetley Mild, Bitter H
Real back-street gem, well worth seeking out near Park Lane College. The single boat-shaped bar is always busy. Games room off. ⚏ ◑ ≈ ♠

Londoner

Lovell Park Road, Little London (near Merrion Centre)
☎ (0113) 2453666
11–11
Marston's Pedigree; Tetley Bitter; guest beers H
New Tetley Festival Ale House, with lots of dark wood, chalk boards and unusual beer-related inscriptions on the lintels. Etched-glass partitions make for a cosy atmosphere. ✿ ◑ ♪ ♠ P

Mulberry

Hunslet Road (A61)
☎ (0113) 2457621
11.30–11
S&N Theakston Mild (occasional), Bitter, XB; guest beers H
Roadside pub with a split-level interior, which used to serve local industry. Times change, as does the clientele. No meals weekends. Excellent potential for guest beers now S&N is classed as a 'national'. ◑ P

Nag's Head

20 Town Street, Chapel Allerton
☎ (0113) 2624938
11–3, 5.30–11; 11–11 Fri & Sat
Samuel Smith OBB H
White-painted, 17th-century pub in Georgian manor house style, offering a large lounge, busy tap/games room and a no-smoking area at lunchtime. No food weekends. ✿ ◑ ♠ P ✗

New Inn

18 Elland Road, Churwell
☎ (0113) 2533468
11–11
Moorhouse's Pendle Witches Brew; Morland Old Speckled Hen; S&N Theakston XB; Whitbread Boddingtons Bitter, Trophy, Castle Eden Ale; guest beers H
Popular roadside pub known to the locals as 'Bottom 'Ole' (being the lowest of three pubs on the hill). Inside is a stone-flagged floor and partitioned drinking areas with a separate games room. Regular mini-beer festivals and usually two guest beers. ✿ ◑ ♨
≈ (Churwell) ♠ P

New Roscoe

Bristol Street, Sheepscar
☎ (0113) 2460778
11.30–11
Ruddles County; John Smith's Bitter; Tetley Bitter; guest beer H
A Gaelic atmosphere prevails in this former club with three rooms, including a large, plush lounge filled with brass/antiques, which hosts bands. A facade of the old Roscoe leads to a quiet snug. Large, boisterous tap room. The house beer is brewed by Moorhouse's. No food weekends. ◑ ♨ ♠ P

Old Kings Arms

The Green, Horsforth
☎ (0113) 2581189
11–11
Marston's Pedigree; Tetley Mild, Bitter; guest beers H
Large, stone-built Victorian pub converted into Tetley's first Festival Ale House in Leeds. At least four guest beers at a time; regular mini-beer festivals. No food Sun. ◑ ⌘ ♨ ♠

Old Unicorn

Stocks Hill, off Town Street, Bramley ☎ (0113) 2565488
11.30–4, 5.30–11
Black Sheep Best Bitter; Tetley Mild, Bitter; Younger No. 3; guest beers H
200-year-old free house overlooking Bramley centre. Once a brewhouse, it is now extended into adjacent cottages, with the open interior busy with a mixed local clientele. ✿ ◑ ♪ ♨ ♠ P

Old Vic

17 Whitecote Hill, Bramley
☎ (0113) 2561207
11–3 (not Tue, 11–4 Sat), 7–11
Taylor Golden Best, Landlord; Tetley Bitter; guest beers H
Formerly a vicarage, then a social club, now a popular free

house, set back in its own grounds. Two lounges, a games room and a function room. ⚔ Q ◁ ⊞ & ♣ P

Prince of Wales

Mill Hill ☎ (0113) 2452434
11–11
Black Sheep Best Bitter; Courage Directors; Marston's Pedigree; John Smith's Bitter H
Bustling city-centre local popular with workers and travellers from the nearby station. A comfy lounge with brass decorations and a separate pool area. Note the exterior decor with etched windows. ⚔ ◁ ⊞ ⚍ ♣

Victoria Family & Commercial

Great George Street (behind town hall) ☎ (0113) 2451386
11–11; 12–2, 7–10.30 Sun
Tetley Mild, Bitter H
19th-century hotel, originally built for visiting judges and lawyers. A splendid, large, genuine Victorian lounge and three smaller, comfy rooms, deservedly popular with locals, office staff and students. Beautiful wood panelling. No food Sun.
Q ◁ ⊞ & ⚍

West Yorkshire Playhouse

Quarry Hill Mount
☎ (0113) 2442141
12–2.30, 6.30–11 (may vary); closed Sun
Ind Coope Burton Ale; Tetley Bitter H
Theatre bar in the shadow of the new national DSS complex, catering for a theatre buff clientele in the Huntsman bar and Wild Oats restaurant. National award-winner for disabled facilities.
Q ⌛ ◁ ▶ & ⚍

Whitelock's First City Luncheon Bar

Turks Head Yard, Briggate
☎ (0113) 2453950
11–11
S&N Theakston Best Bitter; Younger Scotch, No. 3 H
Central Leeds architectural gem with beer prices reflecting the tourist trade. Unchanged, with brass, old mirrors and a small marble bar in evidence. The tiny lower bar has a small restaurant, whilst the Upper Yard Bar (open only eves) has a flagged floor. No meals Sun eve. ⚔ Q ⊛ ◁ ▶ ⚍

Woodies

104 Otley Road, Headingley
☎ (0113) 2757838
11–11
Black Sheep Best Bitter; Marston's Pedigree; Taylor

Landlord; Whitbread Boddingtons Bitter, Trophy, Castle Eden Ale H
Back to basics pub with lots of bare wood. Open-plan, split-level and popular with all types, especially students. Beware fake Scrumpy Jack handpump. No food Sun.
⊛ P

Wrens

61 New Briggate
☎ (0113) 2458888
11–11
Ind Coope Burton Ale; Tetley Mild, Bitter, Imperial; guest beer H
Popular with theatre-goers and thespians, a pub with a true public bar and a no-smoking room, a friendly atmosphere and pleasant surroundings. Hanging baskets outside. No food Sun.
◁ ⊞ ⚍ ♣ ✂

Linthwaite

Sair Inn

Lane Top, Hoyle Ing (off A62)
☎ (01484) 842370
7–11; 12–3, 7–11 (Sat)
Linfit Mild, Bitter, Special, English Goldfield, Stout, Old Eli, Leadboiler; guest beer H
19th-century brew pub which recommenced brewing 13 years ago. Stone-flagged floors, roaring real fires and a domestic menagerie.
⚔ ♣ ↺

Liversedge

Black Bull

37 Halifax Road (A649, 400 yds from A62)
☎ (01924) 403779
12 (11.30 Sat)–4, 7–11
Black Sheep Special Strong; Clark's Burglar Bill; Hambleton Goldfield; Old Mill Bitter; Stones Best Bitter; Tetley Bitter; guest beers H
Arthur is a no nonsense landlord who believes that pubs are for supping ale—hence the only food is sandwiches at lunchtime. A number of walls have been removed but the pub still retains a super tap room at the front. ⊛ ♣ P

Marsden

Tunnel End Inn

Reddisher Road (400 yds S of station) ☎ (01484) 844636
12–3 (ring to confirm Mon–Fri), 7.30–11
Ind Coope Burton Ale; Tetley Mild, Bitter H
Friendly, three-roomed pub near the Standedge canal tunnel and picnic area. Parties welcome weekday lunchtime

by prior arrangement. Sun lunches served. ⚔ ⌛ ⚍ ♣

Methley

New Bay Horse

Main Street ☎ (01977) 553557
12–5, 6 (7 Mon)–11
Tetley Bitter; guest beer H
Pub recently extended to form a very large children's room and a second smart lounge, all to the owner's own design—but after consultation with the locals. Big brewers please note. Wonderfully varied, but reasonable menu (eve meals end at 8pm; no food Mon/Sun eves). ⌛ ⊛ ◁ ▶ & ♣ P

Netherthong

Clothiers Arms

106 School Street (off B6107, 1 mile from Holmfirth)
☎ (01484) 683480
12–3.30, 7–11; 12–11 Fri & Sat
Ryburn Mild; Stones Best Bitter; Taylor Landlord; Tetley Mild, Bitter; guest beer H
Friendly village local decorated with beer and brewery memorabilia, offering a wide selection of beers at reasonable prices. Ryburn Bitter and Ryburn Luddite alternate as an extra guest beer. No food Sun/Mon. ◁ ♣

Ossett

Brewers Pride

Low Mill Road (bottom of Healey Rd) ☎ (01924) 273865
12–3, 5.30–11; 11–11 Fri & Sat
Taylor Landlord; guest beers H
Edwardian stone-fronted pub, very popular in spite of its location by the river, railway and Healey Mills. The three-room interior has interesting decor and breweriana. Home-cooked lunches (not served Sun). Live music outside in summer, with barbecues.
⚔ ⊛ ◁ ♣ ↺

Coopers Arms

Intake Lane (near bus station)
☎ (01924) 263038
12–3, 5–11; 12–11 Thu–Sat (& Mon–Wed in winter)
Thwaites Bitter, Craftsman H
Rejuvenated Thwaites pub with an ever-expanding growth in clientele, mainly due to its reputation for beer and a warm welcome. Entertainment at weekends; parties catered for. ⌛ ♣ P

George

64 Bank Street (by new police station) ☎ (01924) 264754
11–3, 7–11; 11–11 Fri & Sat

Ind Coope Burton Ale; Taylor Landlord; Tetley Mild, Bitter; guest beer H
Refurbished and extended pub, catering for most with a large, open-plan bar, yet still retaining a locals' tap room. Fortnightly guest beer from the Allied stable. Eve meals: Mon 7–9.30 only.
🏮 ◗ 🍴 ♣ P

Little Bull

99 Teall Street (½ mile from Queens Drive)
☎ (01924) 273569
12–3 (4 Sat), 6 (7 Sat)–11
Thwaites Bitter, Craftsman H
Very friendly and popular local with reasonable prices: a comfortable, L-shaped lounge and a small but lively tap room. Regular quiz and games nights. A gem. 🏮 ◗ 🍴 ♣ P

Otley

Bay Horse

20 Market Place (B6451)
☎ (01943) 461122
11–11
Tetley Mild, Bitter, guest beers H
Tiny pub sandwiched between shops. Friendly atmosphere; guest beers from independent breweries. Pies and pasties available. 🏮 ♣

Junction

44 Bondgate (old A660)
☎ (01943) 463233
11–3, 5.30–11; 11–11 Fri & Sat
S&N Theakston XB, Old Peculier; Taylor Best Bitter, Landlord; Tetley Bitter H
Busy, one-roomed corner pub with a tiled floor, wooden-beamed ceiling and panelled walls. Bric-a-brac displayed. A popular local. 🏮 ◗ ♣

Red Lion

33–35 Kirkgate (old A660)
☎ (01943) 463233
11–11
Courage Directors; John Smith's Bitter, Magnet H
Well-kept pub near the market square: four rooms in semi-open plan style, served from one bar. Large whisky collection. ◗

Pontefract

Greyhound

Front Street ☎ (01977) 791571
12–4, 7–11
Ruddles Best Bitter; S&N Theakston XB; John Smith's Bitter H
Popular, friendly pub at the end of town: a comfortable, traditional bar with a collection of local pub memorabilia. Regular live

music, especially on bank hols. 🏮 ➤ (Tanshelf)

Liquorice Bush

8 Market Place
☎ (01977) 703843
11–4, 7–11
Wards Thorne Best Bitter; guest beers H
Edge of town-centre pub, formerly an hotel: one large room split into three drinking areas, plus a small side room. Popular at weekends (no food Sun). ◗ 🍴 ➤ (Baghill/Monkhill) ♣

Tap & Spile

28 Horsefair (near bus station)
☎ (01977) 793468
11–2.30, 4.30–11; 11–11 Fri & Sat (may vary in summer)
Beer range varies H
Victorian-style alehouse, with three separate drinking areas, one lounge-style. Eleven rotating guest beers. Wakefield CAMRA *Pub of the Year* 1993. Varied clientele. No food Sun. 🏮 ◗ 🍴 ➤ (Baghill/Monkhill) ♣ ▭ P

Pudsey

Butchers Arms

Church Lane ☎ (0113) 2564313
11–3 (3.30 Sat), 5.30 (5 Fri, 7 Sat)–11
Samuel Smith OBB H
Typical Yorkshire stone pub providing a warm and friendly welcome. Busy, with an open interior, 1980s furniture and decor. Separate dining area. 🏮 ◗ 🍴 ♣

Masons Arms

Lowtown ☎ (0113) 2577857
11–11; 11–3.30, 6.30–11 Sat
Tetley Bitter; Whitbread Boddingtons Bitter, Best Bitter H
A fine example of a Victorian pub in the Yorkshire house style. Original Bentley's Yorkshire Brewery windows front an unaltered interior of three rooms. An old map shows all pubs in Pudsey c 1850. Q 🏮 ♣ P

Purston

White House

Pontefract Road
☎ (01977) 791878
11–4, 7–11
Samuel Smith OBB H
Small, open-plan pub, very popular with locals. Comfortable surroundings; collection of rugby league photographs. 🏮 ◗ 🍴 ♣ P

Queensbury

Pineberry Inn

Brighouse & Denholme Road, Mountain ☎ (01274) 882168
11.30–4, 6–11

Black Sheep Special Strong; Morland Old Speckled Hen; Webster's Green Label, Yorkshire Bitter H
High, olde-worde pub with beautiful country views and beamed rooms. Wide range of meals at every session (all home-made). Goat in the garden. 🏮 Q 🏮 ◗ ◗ & P

Rawdon

Emmott Arms

Town Street ☎ (0113) 2506036
11–11
Samuel Smith OBB, Museum H
Old pub with a traditional tap room with a range-type fire, a cosy, comfortable lounge, and an upstairs restaurant. Dark wood and low ceilings add to the relaxed atmosphere. Friendly and knowledgeable bar staff. No eve meals Sun/Mon. Q 🏮 ◗ ♣ P

Ripponden

Blue Ball

Blue Ball Lane, Soyland (off A58, near Baitings reservoir) OS011192 ☎ (01422) 823603
12–3 (not Tue), 7–11
Bass Worthington BB, Draught Bass; S&N Theakston Old Peculier; Taylor Golden Best, Landlord; guest beers H
Moorland inn dating from 1672, with panoramic views over the reservoir. Cosy and welcoming. Regular folk music and sing-alongs. Upstairs restaurant.
🏮 ⚄ 🏮 ⌂ ◗ & P

Old Bridge Inn

Priest Lane ☎ (01422) 822595
12–4, 5.30–11; 12–11
Black Sheep Special Strong; Ryburn Bitter; Taylor Golden Best, Best Bitter H
Ancient hostelry with a timbered structure in a picturesque setting by a pack horse bridge. Pumps are mostly unlabelled and the landlord promotes local independent breweries, so the range may vary. No meals Sat eve, or Sun. 🏮 Q 🏮 ◗ ◗ P

Silsden

Bridge Inn

Keighley Road
☎ (01535) 653144
12–3, 5–11; 11–11 Fri & Sat
Black Sheep Best Bitter; John Smith's Bitter; guest beer H
Canalside pub which predates the canal, being first recorded in 1660. The original drinking rooms are now the cellar and toilets. The outside drinking

West Yorkshire

area was the original main road. Parking for boats only. ♿ ❀ ◑ ▷ ⇌ (Steeton & Silsden) ♣

South Elmsall

Barnsley Oak
Mill Lane (½ mile from A638/B6428 roundabout)
☎ (01977) 643427
12–3.30 (5 Sat), 7–11
John Smith's Bitter H
Sixties estate pub on the edge of a mining village, offering panoramic views of the Elms valley from the conservatory. Free sausages, scallops, etc. Sun eves. Q ♿ ❀ ◑ ⇌ ♣ P

Southowram

Shoulder of Mutton
14 Cain Lane ☎ (01422) 361101
12–3, 7–11
Marston's Pedigree; Morland Old Speckled Hen; Ruddles County; John Smith's Bitter; guest beers H
Village local noted for the range of guest beers (up to five each week). ⌂ ◑ ♣ ○

Try also: Pack Horse (Vaux)

Sowerby Bridge

Moorings
No. 1 Warehouse, Canal Basin (off Wharf St, A58)
☎ (01422) 833940
11.30–3, 5.30–11; 11.30–11 Sat
Moorhouse's Premier; S&N Theakston Best Bitter, XB; Younger Scotch; guest beer H
Bar-cum-restaurant located in a converted canal warehouse, enjoying views over Sowerby Bridge basin. Good range of world, and especially Belgian, beers. No-smoking family room. ♿ ❀ ◑ ▷ ⇌ P ✄

Puzzle Hall Inn
21 Hollins Mill Lane (400 yds from A58) ☎ (01422) 835547
11–11
Vaux Samson, Double Maxim; Wards Best Bitter H
Tiny, two-roomed pub of mixed architectural styles, dominated by the tower of the former Puzzle Hall brewery behind. Jazz Tue nights and occasional folk/blues. Modern art gallery in the gents'. Guest Vaux beer. Meals till 8pm. ⌂ Q ❀ ◑ ▷ ⇌ ♣ ○ P

William IV
80 Wharf Street
☎ (01422) 833584
11.30–11
Ryburn Bitter, Luddite; Tetley Bitter; Whitbread Boddingtons Bitter, Eden Bitter; guest beer (weekends) H

Comfortable free house on the main street, offering an increasing beer range. Strong support from enthusiasts for traditional pub games and quizzes. Yorkshire Day (Aug 1st) morris dancing competition. ❀ ⇌ ♣ P

Thornhill

Savile Arms
12 Church Lane (B6117)
☎ (01924) 463738
5.30–11; 12–4, 7–11 Sat
Black Sheep Best Bitter; Old Mill Mild, Bitter; Tetley Bitter H
Small, genuine, 600-year-old village pub with much original woodwork, close to the 1447 chapel of St Michael (full of monuments). Lunches Sat. Q

Thornton

Blue Boar
354 Thornton Road (B6145)
☎ (01274) 833298
4 (1.30 Fri, 12 Sat)–11
Taylor Golden Best, Best Bitter, Landlord H
Pub with an open-plan main bar and a separate pool room. Collection of miniatures behind the bar. Quiz Sun. ♣

Todmorden

Fountain
Victoria Road, Meadowbottom (off A646 opp. Centre Vale Park) ☎ (01706) 812921
5 (12 Fri & Sat)–11
Jennings Mild; Tetley Bitter H
Very much a locals' pub in 1970s Tetley style, with a large lounge and a small separate tap room. Conservatory to the rear with 'old colonial'-style wickerwork chairs. Regular quizzes. A second Jennings beer is also served. ❀ ⌂ ◑ ⇌ P

Masons Arms
1 Bacup Road, Gauxholme (A6033/A681 jct)
☎ (01706) 812180
7 (7.30 Sat)–11; 12–3, 7.30–10.30 Sun
John Smith's Bitter; Thwaites Bitter; Wilson's Mild H
Cosy pub nestling under a railway bridge. The unusual snug has sycamore-topped tables, reputedly once used for post-mortems. Easy access from the canal towpath. Lunches served Sun. ⌂ ❀ ♿ ⇌

Staff of Life
550 Burnley Road, Knotts Bend (A646 1½ miles N of centre) ☎ (01706) 812929

12–3, 5–11; 12–11 Sat
Jennings Bitter, Cumberland Ale, Sneck Lifter; guest beers H
Atmospheric free house in a wooded gorge. The overhanging crag has supernatural connections. Four rotating guest beers. ⌂ ❀ ◑ ▷ P

White Hart
White Hart Fold, Station Road
☎ (01706) 812198
11.30–3.30 (not Tue), 7–11; 11–11 Fri & Sat
Tetley Mild, Bitter; guest beers H
Former Ramsden's pub with a brewers' Tudor-style exterior. Popular and spacious. Two guest beers. ❀ ◑ ⇌ ♣ P

Wainstalls

Cat i'th' Well Inn
Wainstalls Lane (¼ mile W of Wainstalls) OS042285
☎ (01422) 244841
12–3 (not winter weekdays), 7 (5.30 Fri)–11
Taylor Golden Best, Best Bitter, Landlord; Whitbread Boddingtons Bitter, Castle Eden Ale; guest beer H
Cosy, oak-panelled free house, delightfully situated in a wooded valley. The panelling came from the demolished Victorian 'castle' in the beautiful Luddenden Dene nearby. Quiz Mon. Lunches in summer. ❀ ◑ ▲ ♣ P

Withens Hotel
Cold Edge Road OS045307
☎ (01422) 244809
12–2 (Easter–Sept only), 7–11; 12–3, 7–11 Sat all year
Taylor Best Bitter, Landlord; guest beer (summer) H
The highest pub in the county with suitably expansive views over the Calderdale hills and beyond. Built in 1862 to serve passing quarrymen, it now caters for walkers, motorists, families, and people looking at the Ovenden Moor windfarm. No meals Sat eve. ⌂ ♿ ❀ ◑ ▷ P

Wakefield

Albion
94 Stanley Road (follow Peterson Rd from Kirkgate roundabout) ☎ (01924) 376206
11–4 (5 Sat), 7–11
Samuel Smith OBB H
Impressive 1920s estate pub at the edge of the town centre. Popular lunchtimes for fresh, home-cooked food. A collection of unusual teapots adorns the lounge. Friendly local clientele. ❀ ◑ ⊞ ⇌ (Kirkgate) ♣ P

Beer Engine
77 Westgate End
☎ (01924) 375887
12–11
Taylor Landlord; guest beers H
Popular, traditional alehouse with a stone-flagged floor and gas lighting. With up to six guest beers, changing very frequently, it has to be Wakefield's only true free house. Good atmosphere, catering for all types. ♨ ❀
⇌ (Westgate) ♣ ○

Elephant & Castle
109 Westgate (opp. station)
☎ (01924) 376610
11–11
Courage Directors; John Smith's Bitter H
Convivial city pub notable for its impressive Warwick Boroughbridge Ales facade. The elaborate exterior style is complemented inside by an extensive array of old brewery mirrors. Reasonably priced home-cooked food and accommodation. ♨ ⛺ ◑ ▮ ♿
⇌ (Westgate) ♣

Rainbow
40 Lower Warrengate
(opp. baths)
☎ (01924) 374433
11–11; 11–3.30, 5.30–11 Mon & Thu
John Smith's Bitter, Magnet; guest beer H
Welcoming town local with a comfortable lounge and a lively tap room. Busy lunchtimes with shoppers enjoying good value home-cooked food. When the lounge is closed (between 3 and 7pm) use the rear entrance to the tap room. No food Sun.
⛺ ◑ ▭ ⇌ (Westgate/Kirkgate) ♣ P

Redoubt
28 Horbury Road
☎ (01924) 377085
11–11
Tetley Mild, Bitter; guest beers H
Tetley Heritage pub whose low ceilings and small, cosy rooms infuse a relaxed, beery ambience; positioned on a busy junction a half-mile from the centre. ⛺ ⇌ (Westgate) ♣ P

Tut 'n' Shive
38 Teal Street (by market)
☎ (01924) 374191
11–11

Morland Old Speckled Hen; Moorhouse's Pendle Witches Brew; Whitbread Boddingtons Bitter, Castle Eden Ale; guest beers H
Formerly the Brunswick Hotel, now catering for all types and popular with students. The family room has automated ten pin bowling. Small garden. Snacks every day; full menu Mon–Sat 12–2. ⛺ ❀ ◑ ♿
⇌ (Westgate/Kirkgate) ♣ P

Wakefield Labour Club
18 Vicarage Street (near market hall) ☎ (01924) 371626
7–11; 11–3, 7–11 Sat; 12–2 Sun, closed Sun eve
Marston Moor Cromwell *or* **Taylor Golden Best; guest beers** H
Unpretentious and friendly club, known locally as the Red Shed. Cosmopolitan clientele. The only regular outlet for Marston Moor beers in the area. Show CAMRA membership card or this guide to be signed in. Wheelchair access at the side door.
Q ❀ ♿
⇌ (Westgate/Kirkgate) ♣ P

York Street
76 Lower York Street
☎ (01924) 371297
11.45–4, 7–11
Draught Bass; Stones Best Bitter; Taylor Landlord; guest beer H
Pub where photographs of old Wakefield adorn the walls, alongside banknotes from around the world. Popular with office workers at lunchtime. Close to Wakefield rugby union ground. Same landlord for the past 22 years. No food Sun. ❀ ◑ ♿ ♣ P

Warmfield

Plough Inn
45 Warmfield Lane (400 yds from A655) ☎ (01924) 892007
12–2, 7–11 (12–11 summer)
S&N Theakston Mild, Best Bitter, XB, Old Peculier; guest beers H
Unspoilt, 18th-century village inn overlooking the lower Calder valley, with low beamed ceilings and a small corner bar. Quiz Thu nights; lively piano sing-alongs Sat. Good bar meals—try the Old Peculier Pie. Barbecues in summer. Open all day Sun in summer for meals. Two changing guest beers.
❀ ◑ ▮ P

West Ardsley

British Oak
407 Westerton Road
☎ (0113) 2534792
12–3, 6 (7 Sat)–11
Whitbread Boddingtons Bitter, Castle Eden Ale, Flowers Original; guest beers H
Pub with a single room around a central bar, and a jovial host who, after a long battle with Whitbread, is still a tenant (not a lessee). A pub newsletter, live music, tasteless tie collection and zany waistcoats all add up to a unique atmosphere.
❀ ♿ ♣ P

Whitwood

Bridge Inn & Hotel
Altofts Lane
☎ (01977) 550498
11–11; 11–3, 7–11 Sat
S&N Theakston Mild, Bitter, XB, Old Peculier; Tetley Bitter; guest beers H
Large, recently-built free house/hotel attractively constructed in rustic style. The interior features reclaimed timber beams, exposed brickwork and stone-flagged floors. No-smoking dining room and separate restaurant and drinking areas. Friendly, comfortable atmosphere.
Q ⛺ ❀ ⛺ ◑ ▮ ♿ P

Wyke

Junction
459 Huddersfield Road
☎ (01274) 679809
12–11
Thwaites Bitter, Craftsman H
Two-roomed pub with a split lounge and a pool room. Good atmosphere. ❀ ♣

Yeadon

Tut 'n' Shive
The Green
☎ (0113) 2506052
11–11
Whitbread Boddingtons Bitter, Castle Eden Ale; guest beers H
Stone-built in 1728, a pub refurbished in Tut 'n' Shive company style, with a few surprises. Good value bar meals (vegetarian option).
❀ ◑ P

Protect your pleasure — Join CAMRA (see page 528)

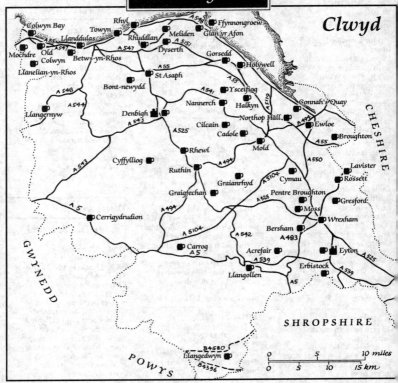

W A L E S

Clwyd

Clwyd

Dyffryn Clwyd, Denbigh; Plassey, Eyton

Acrefair

Duke of Wellington
Llangollen Road (A483)
☎ (01978) 820169
12–4 (not winter, except Fri), 7–11
(12–11 summer; 12–4, 7–11 summer
Mon)
**Banks's Mild; Marston's
Bitter, Pedigree** H
Popular, cosy pub near
Pont-Cysyllte Aqueduct. The
garden has swings and a
tractor.
🏠 Q ❀ ◖ ♣ P

Bersham

Black Lion
Y Adol, Bersham Road (B5099)
☎ (01978) 365588
11–4.30, 7–11
Hydes' Anvil Mild, Bitter E
Black and white local with a
cosy parlour-style main bar
plus overflow and pool rooms.
On the Clywedog Valley
Industrial Trail, and next to
the Bersham Heritage Centre.
 ❀ 🍺 ♿ ♣ P

Betws-yn-Rhos

Wheatsheaf Inn
☎ (01492) 60218
12–3, 6–11
**Crown Buckley Best Bitter;
Fuller's Chiswick; John
Smith's Bitter** H
Old village pub, extended to
the rear; on split-levels but
retaining a pleasant bar area at
the front. The choice of beers is
constantly changing.
Q ❀ 🛏 ◖ ▶ P

Bont-newydd

Dolben Arms
W of Trefnant OS015705
☎ (01745) 582207
7–11
S&N Theakston Mild, XB H
16th-century, country inn in a
picturesque valley, accessible
only by country lanes. The bar
is separated into restaurant,
lounge and games areas. Sun
lunch served (closed
lunchtime, except Sun).
Q ❀ ▶ ♣ P

Broughton

Offa's Dyke
Broughton Hall Road
☎ (01244) 532777
12–3.30, 5–11; 12–11 Fri & Sat
**Cains Bitter; Whitbread
Higsons Mild, Boddingtons
Bitter, Higsons Bitter** H
Estate pub in two parts:
a comfortable public bar
with TV, pool and darts,
and a low-lit, mellow
lounge with a conservatory.
No meals Sat.
Q ♿ ❀ ◖ 🍺 ♣ P

Cadole

Colomendy Arms
Gwernaffield Road (off A494)
☎ (01352) 85217
7 (12 Fri & Sat)–11
**Burtonwood Bitter; Dent
Bitter, Ramsbottom; guest
beers** H
Excellent village local. A
footpath leads to Loggerheads
Country Park.
🏠 Q ♿ ❀ ▲ ♣ P

Carrog

Grouse Inn
On B5437, ½ mile off A5
☎ (0149 083) 272
12–4.30, 7–11
Lees GB Mild, Bitter H
Homely pub in the Dee Valley
above Llangollen. The single
bar comprises three drinking
areas; the lounge is like a
private front room. ⚑ ❀ ⌂
◖ ▶ ▲ ♣ P

Cerrigydrudion

White Lion
Near B5105/B4501 jct
☎ (0149 420) 202
11–3, 6–11
Lees GB Mild, Bitter H
Rural pub with a
camping/caravan site in the
grounds. Good value food and
accommodation. ⚑ Q ⊜ ⌂
◖ ▶ ▢ ▲ ♣ P

Cilcain

White Horse
2 miles S of A541 OS177652
☎ (01352) 740124
12–3, 7–11
Ansells Bitter; Ind Coope
ABC Best Bitter, Burton
Ale H
Pub in a walking area, close to
Moel Famau Country Park.
Antique handpumps are
displayed in the bar. A
pleasant lounge is divided into
three areas.
⚑ Q ◖ ▶ ▢ ▲ ♣ P

Colwyn Bay

Park Hotel
128 Abergele Road
☎ (01492) 530661
11–11
Bass Worthington BB; M&B
Mild; Stones Best Bitter H
Popular local with a friendly
atmosphere. The large, single
room has TV and a pool table.
A good drinkers' pub! ⇋ ♣

Toad Hall
West Promenade
☎ (01492) 532726
11.30–3, 6–11
Banks's Mild; Marston's
Bitter, Pedigree H
Seafront, first-floor bar and
restaurant.
⚑ ⊜ ❀ ◖ ▶ ⇋ ♣ P

Wings Sports & Social Club
Imperial Buildings, Princes
Drive ☎ (01492) 530682
11–3, 7–11; 12–2, 7–10.30 Sun
Lees GB Mild, Bitter E
On the first floor of the
Imperial Hotel, a large lounge
with a bar and a small dance

floor. There are also TV, games
and snooker rooms. ⊜ ▲ ⇋

Connah's Quay

Sir Gawain & the Green Knight
Golftyn Lane
☎ (01244) 812623
11.30–3, 5.30–11; 12–11 Sat; 12–3,
7.30–10.30 Sun
Samuel Smith OBB H
Converted farmhouse with an
aviary, close to Dee Estuary
Bird Sanctuary. Frequented by
students. ❀ ◖ ♣ P

Cyffylliog

Red Lion
Off B5105 at Llanfwrog
☎ (01824) 716664
6.30 (11 summer)–11
Lees GB Mild, Bitter H
Unspoilt village pub with a
bar, pool room, and a lounge,
offering good value food and
accommodation. Situated in a
picturesque valley.
⚑ Q ❀ ⌂ ◖ ▶ ▢ ▲ ♣ P

Cymau

Olde Talbot Inn
Cymau Lane (1 mile off A541)
OS298561 ☎ (01978) 761410
12–4 (not Mon–Wed, 5 Sat), 7–11
Hydes' Anvil Dark Mild,
Bitter E
Excellent little games-oriented
pub in a hilltop village, with
an intimate, low-ceilinged
lounge. A rare outlet for
Hydes' Dark. ❀ ◖ ▶ ♣ P

Denbigh

Pot Black
Lenton Pool ☎ (01745) 815676
11–11
Ansells Mild; Coach House
Coachman's; Tetley Walker
Dark Mild, Bitter; guest
beer H
Snooker and social club with
seven tables, formerly the Drill
Hall. Visitors are welcome. ♣

Dyserth

New Inn
Waterfall Road
☎ (01745) 570482
11.30–3, 5–11; 11–11 Sat
Marston's Bitter, Pedigree H
Low-ceilinged, cosy village
pub catering for local and
summer trade.
⚑ ⊜ ❀ ◖ ▶ ▲ ♣ P

Erbistock

Cross Foxes
Overton Bridge (A528)
☎ (01978) 780380

Marston's Bitter, Pedigree H;
guest beer
Olde-worlde style inn with a
warm atmosphere. The fish
dishes are excellent. Superb
views from the garden to the
River Dee. ⚑ Q ⊜ ❀
◖ ▶ ▢ ▲ ♣ P

Ewloe

Boar's Head
Holywell Road (just off A55)
☎ (01244) 531065
12–3, 6–11
Greenalls Mild, Bitter H
Comfortable, traditional pub
that is a shrine to brass, and
which has avoided Greenalls'
attempts to 'modernise' it.
Worthington White Shield is
available. Q ◖ P

Eyton

Plassey
Off B5426 ☎ (01978) 780277
7.30–11; 12.30–3, 7.30–11 Sat; 12.30–3,
7–10.30 Sun
Plassey Bitter, Cwrw Tudno,
Dragon's Breath H
Thriving caravan and campsite
with its own brewery: a Mecca
for real ale lovers who
frequent the Treetops Bar
(closed Nov–Feb) or restaurant
(open all year). Wheelchair
access to the restaurant only.
⊜ ❀ ▶ ▲ P

Ffynnongroew

Railway
Main Road ☎ (01745) 560447
12–4, 7–11; 11–11 Sat
Vaux Bitter; Wards Mild H
Friendly village local.
⚑ ❀ ▲ ♣ P

Glan yr Afon

White Lion
Glan yr Afon Road (S of A548
at Ffynnongroew) OS118817
☎ (01745) 560280
12–3 (not Mon & Tue), 6–11
Ruddles Best Bitter, County;
guest beer H
Once home of Welsh
playwright Emlyn Williams,
this excellent old pub retains
much of its original character.
Very good food is served at
reasonable prices (not Mon or
Tue). Local CAMRA Pub of the
Year 1993; worth the trouble to
find. ⚑ Q ❀ ◖ ▶ ▢ ♣ ⌂ P

Gorsedd

Druid Inn
Just off A5026, near Holywell
OS153767 ☎ (01352) 710944
7–11
Marston's Pedigree;
Whitbread Boddingtons
Bitter; guest beers H

Clwyd

Interesting, many-roomed country pub. The bar has an ancient two-pull handpump on display. Sun lunch served.
🏚 Q ❀ ▶ P ⅊

Graianrhyd

Rose & Crown
Llanarmon Road (B5430)
☎ (0182 43) 727
12–11
Marston's Pedigree; Whitbread Boddingtons Bitter, Flowers IPA H
Welcoming pub. The two areas are served by one bar. Good food. 🏚 ❀ ◑ ▶ ▲ ♣ P

Graigfechan

Three Pigeons
On B5429 ☎ (01824) 703178
6.30–11
Draught Bass; guest beers G
Extended, 17th-century pub affording fine views over the Vale of Clwyd. Regular music includes Welsh (and Irish) nights. A skittle alley is available for parties. Sun lunch is served plus eve meals Fri/Sat.
🏚 Q ☙ ❀ ◑ ▶ ▲ ♣ P

Gresford

Griffin
The Green
1–4.30 (12–4 Sat), 7–11
Greenalls Mild, Bitter H
Unspoilt village local off the beaten track. The only sound heard is the gentle hum of conversation. Q ❀ ♣ P

Halkyn

Britannia Inn
Pentre Road ☎ (01352) 780272
11–3, 5.30–11; 11–11 Sat
Lees GB Mild, Bitter H, **Moonraker** H / G
500-year-old stone pub, with four rooms, popular with locals. The conservatory restaurant has a superb view over the Dee Estuary.
🏚 ☙ ❀ ◑ ▶ ♿ ▲ ♣ P

Holywell

Glan yr Afon Inn
Milwr (off old A55)
☎ (01352) 710052
11.30–2.30, 6–11
Courage Directors; Ruddles Best Bitter; Webster's Yorkshire Bitter H
17th-century inn where the restaurant enjoys a reputation for good value (no eve meals Mon). ☙ ❀ ◑ ▶ ♿ ▲ P

Red Lion
High Street ☎ (01352) 710097
11–11

Ansells Mild; Tetley Walker Bitter; guest beers H
Friendly, town-centre pub. The bar divides the games and small lounge areas. Guest beers come from Carlsberg-Tetley's list. 🏚 ♣

Lavister

Nag's Head
Old Chester Road (B5445)
☎ (01244) 570486
11.30–3, 5.30–11
Thwaites Bitter; Whitbread Boddingtons Mild, Bitter; guest beers H
Large, comfortable roadside pub in a small village. Bowling green. Guest beers are from the Whitbread range.
🏚 ❀ ◑ ▶ ♣ P

Llanddulas

Dulas Arms Hotel
Abergele Road
☎ (01492) 515747
12–2.30 (not winter Mon or Tue, 3 summer), 7 (6 summer)–11; 12–3, 6–11 Sat (11–11 summer Sat)
Lees GB Mild, Bitter, Moonraker H
Large lounge, an adjoining bar, a snug, a restaurant and a large family room in a pub which holds a beer festival Aug Bank Hol. Children's adventure playground.
Q ☙ ❀ ⛢ ◑ ▶ ♿ ♣ P ⅊

Valentine Inn
Mill Street ☎ (01492) 518189
12–3, 5.30–11 (may vary); 12–2, 7–10.30 Sun
Banks's Mild; Draught Bass; M&B Mild H
Tastefully renovated, small village inn with a tiny public bar. The comfortable lounge features an inviting fire. Eve meals in summer only (until 8pm). 🏚 Q ❀ ◑ ▶ ♿ ▲ ♣

Llanelian-yn-Rhos

White Lion Inn
☎ (01492) 515807
11–3, 6–11
Ruddles Best Bitter; John Smith's Magnet; Wilson's Mild; guest beers H
Olde-worlde village pub, with a bar, snug, lounge and a dining extension.
🏚 Q ⛢ ◑ ▶ ♿ ▲ ♣ P

Llangedwyn

Green Inn
On B4396 ☎ (01691) 828234
11–3, 6–11
Whitbread Boddingtons Bitter; guest beers H
17th-century former drovers' pub in a picturesque valley: an open lounge and a cosy slate-flagged area, with an

---

inglenook. Extensive, good value menu. Three guest beers, plus cider in summer.
🏚 Q ❀ ◑ ▶ ♿ ♣ ⌂ P

Llangernyw

Stag Hotel
On A548 ☎ (01745) 76213
7–11; 12–3, 7–11 Sat
Draught Bass; Marston's Pedigree H
Classic village pub: all that's good in a traditional pub.
🏚 Q ❀ ⛢ ▶ P

Llangollen

Cambrian Hotel
Berwyn Street (A5)
☎ (01978) 860686
1 (12 summer)–3.30, 7–11
Ind Coope Burton Ale; Tetley Walker Bitter H; **guest beer** (occasional)
Friendly, family-run hotel. The unspoilt back bar is old-fashioned without being olde-worlde. Meals in summer. Q ☙ ⛢ ▶ ▲ ♣ P

Wynnstay Arms
Bridge Street ☎ (01978) 860710
11–11 (may close winter weekday afternoons)
Ind Coope Burton Ale H
Comfortable, welcoming hotel with a cosy bar and a restaurant. Close to the River Dee, it boasts a large, enclosed garden. The menu caters for children. 🏚 Q ☙ ❀ ⛢ ◑ ▶ ♿ ♣ P

Meliden

Red Lion
Meliden Road (off A547)
☎ (01745) 852565
12 (11.30 Sat)–3, 6–11
Draught Bass; S&N Theakston Best Bitter, Old Peculier; Stones Best Bitter H
Cosy, friendly pub, unspoilt by refurbishment. Eve meals in summer only.
Q ❀ ◑ ▶ ▲ P

Mochdre

Mountain View
7 Old Conwy Road
☎ (01492) 544724
11–3, 6–11; 11–11 Sat
Burtonwood Mild, Bitter, Forshaw's, Top Hat H
Village pub with a large, friendly lounge. The locals' bar has a pool table and a jukebox. Pleasant atmosphere; good food. Q ❀ ◑ ▶ ▲ ♣ P

Mold

Boar's Head
Chester Street
☎ (01352) 758430
11.30–3 (5 Fri & Sat), 7–11

Ind Coope Burton Ale; Tetley Walker Bitter H
Well-modernised, town-centre pub with a horseshoe-shaped bar. Handy for the bus station.
❀ ◑ & ♣ P

Moss

Bird in Hand
Woodland Road (track off B5433) OS303538
☎ (01978) 755809
7–11
Hydes' Anvil Bitter E
Idiosyncratically furnished pub. A ¾-size snooker table is available in the back room. Splendid views from the sun lounge at the front. No food Mon. Closed Mon–Sat lunch.
Q ❀ ▶ ♣ P

Nannerch

Cross Foxes
Off A541 ☎ (01352) 741293
6–11
S&N Theakston XB; Younger Scotch H
Village pub with an excellent locals' bar, housing a large fireplace. The lounge is in two areas. ⚑ Q & ♣ P

Northop Hall

Boar's Head
Village Road ☎ (01244) 815995
11.30–3, 5.30–11; 11.30–11 Sat
Burtonwood Bitter H
Traditional Welsh village pub locally known as the 'Top Monkey' ('monkey' being the colloquial name for a mineshaft). ⚑ Q ❀ ♣ P

Old Colwyn

Marine Hotel
Abergele Road
☎ (01492) 515484
11.30–11
Draught Bass; M&B Mild H
Large public house with three bars, a pool room and a restaurant. Q ⌂ ◑ ▶ ⊟ ♣ P

Pentre Broughton

Cross Foxes
High Street ☎ (01978) 755973
11–3, 7–11; 11–11 Sat
Burtonwood Bitter H
Deceptively spacious, two-bar local where local scenes adorn the walls. Outdoor drinking in the car park. ⚑ ❀ ♣ P

Rhewl (Ruthin)

Drovers Arms
On A525 ☎ (01824) 703163

12–3 (not Mon), 7 (6 Fri & Sat)–11
Dyffryn Clwyd Comfort; Ruddles Best Bitter H
Pleasant, welcoming roadside pub with various drinking areas and comfortable dining space. Children are welcome.
❀ ◑ ▶ ⊟ ♣ P

Rhuddlan

New Inn
High Street ☎ (01745) 591305
11–3, 5.30–11; 11–11 Fri & Sat
S&N Theakston Best Bitter, XB, Old Peculier H
Pleasant pub, with a central bar serving a lounge, small snug and a dining room. Very popular. Q ❀ ⌂ ◑ ▶ A P

Rhyl

White Horse
Bedford Street
☎ (01745) 334927
11–11
John Smith's Bitter; guest beers H
Back-street pub, frequented by all ages. It holds two beer festivals annually, and over 100 guest beers featured in 1993. One of few outlets for real cider in N Wales.
& A ⇌ ♣ ○

Rossett

Butcher's Arms
Chester Road
☎ (01244) 570233
12–11
Burtonwood Bitter, Top Hat H
Friendly, roadside pub which encourages a local following in its popular public bar and plush lounge. Reasonably priced, home-cooked food. No meals Sun eve. ❀ ◑ ▶ ♣ P

Ruthin

Wine Vaults
St Peter's Square
☎ (01824) 422067
12–3.30, 5–11; 12–11 Fri & Sat
Robinson's Best Bitter H
Well-established pub with a locals' lounge-type bar and a pool room. Q ❀ ⌂ ♣ P

St Asaph

Gamekeeper
Lower Street ☎ (01745) 583514
12–3, 7–11
Banks's Hanson's Mild, Mild, Bitter; Camerons Strongarm H
Recently modernised pub with a lounge, a public bar, and a restaurant. ❀ ⌂ ◑ ▶ P

Towyn

Morton Arms
Sandbank Road (200 yds from A548) ☎ (01745) 330211
11–11
Bass Worthington BB, Draught Bass; M&B Mild; guest beers H
Modern, open-plan, seaside pub and restaurant. Regular summer entertainment.
ॐ ❀ ◑ ▶ & A ♣ P

Wrexham

Cross Foxes
5 Abbott Street
☎ (01978) 261199
11–11
Tetley Walker Bitter; guest beers H
Down-to-earth pub, next to the High Street and popular with bikers. The guest beer varies fortnightly. 60s jukebox.
⚑ ❀ ⇌ (Central)

Horse & Jockey
Hope Street ☎ (01978) 351081
11–6 (5 Sat), 7 (6 Sat)–11
Ind Coope Burton Ale; Tetley Walker Dark Mild, Bitter; guest beer H
Listed building with a thatched roof, popular with city workers. Real ale trade is increasing, with a different guest every weekend. No food Sun. ◑ & ⇌ (Central) ♣

Oak Tree
Ruabon Road
☎ (01978) 261450
12–5, 6.30–11; 12–11 Sat
Marston's Bitter, Pedigree H
Comfortable local, just outside the town centre; a former farmhouse. Floral displays decorate the unusual frontage.
Q ❀ ⊟ ♣ P

Railway Inn
17 Railway Road, Rhosddu
☎ (01978) 311172
12–3, 7–11; 11–11 Sat
Banks's Mild; Marston's Bitter, Pedigree H
Friendly pub near the Plas Coch development. A plush, narrow lounge adjoins the popular public bar and the garden has a play area.
❀ ◑ ⇌ (General) ♣ P

Ysceifiog

Fox
N of A541, W of Mold
OS152715 ☎ (01352) 720241
7–11; 12–3, 7–11 Sat
Ansells Mild; Bass Worthington BB; Tetley Walker Bitter; guest beer H
Classic village pub in a remote setting. ⚑ Q ॐ ❀ ⊟ ♣ P

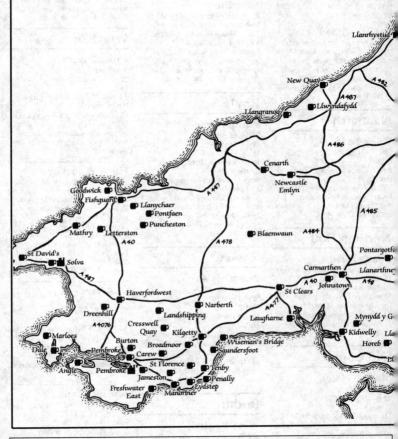

Dyfed

 Aberystwyth, Llanrhystud; **Crown Buckley, Felinfoel,** Llanelli; **Pembroke,** Pembroke; **Solva,** Solva

Aberystwyth

Arts Centre Bar
Penglais Hill (university campus, off A487)
☎ (01970) 622882
12–2, 7–11; closed Sun/Mon
Felinfoel Bitter, Dark, Double Dragon; guest beers Ⓗ
The bar of a popular arts centre, affording good views over the town and adjoining a wholefood café. Two guest beers available at any one time, with the range constantly varying. Cider in summer. Admission charge Wed eve.
◑ ▮ & ▲ ⌂ P

Fountain Inn
Trefechan (A487, opp. fire station) ☎ (01970) 612430
12–11
Hancock's HB; M&B Highgate Dark; guest beers Ⓗ
Old, friendly pub near the harbour: four small rooms decorated with photographs of the old town and items of nautical interest. Very amusing pub sign! One hundred vodkas on offer. Excellent selection of vegetarian food. ◑ ▮ ▯ ≈ ♣

Mill Inn
Mill Street (near roundabout)
☎ (01970) 612306
12–3, 6–11; 12–11 Sat
Aberystwyth Dinas Draught; Ansells Mild; Greenalls

Shipstone's Bitter; Tetley Bitter; guest beers Ⓗ
Busy town-centre pub, offering up to six guest beers at any one time (selection changes frequently). Popular with locals and students. Beware the Addlestones cider on a fake handpump. ≢

Angle

Hibernia Inn
Main Street ☎ (01646) 641517
11–3, 6.30–11
Bass Worthington BB; Hancock's HB; guest beer (summer) Ⓗ
Large, cosy local run by one of

---

the Angle lifeboat crew, hence the strong naval theme. A good family pub near the beach. Good pub grub.
🏚 Q ⛄ ❀ ◖ ▮ ⅃ ⅄ ♣ P

Blaenwaun

Lamb Inn
☎ (01994) 448440
Hours vary
Young's Bitter; guest beer Ⓗ
Traditional country local in an isolated hamlet. Friendly welcome. ❀ ♣ P

Broadmoor

Cross Inn
☎ (01834) 812287
11–11
Bass Worthington BB, Draught Bass Ⓗ
Pub with a small public bar, a larger food-oriented lounge, a family room and a big playground garden. Treasure hunts in winter, and other activities.
🏚 Q ⛄ ❀ ◖ ▮ ⅃ ♣ P

Burton

Jolly Sailor
Burton Ferry Road
(Haverfordwest side of Cleddau Bridge)
☎ (01646) 600378
11–3, 6–11 (11–11 summer)
Bass Worthington BB; Ind Coope Burton Ale; Tetley Bitter Ⓗ
If you're into water sports, this is the pub for you, with one of the best views of the Milford estuary. Parking for boats, too. Large garden; adventure playground.
🏚 Q ❀ ◖ ▮ ⅃ ⅄ ♣ P

Bynea

Lewis Arms
Yspitty Road ☎ (01554) 772878
12–3, 6–11
Felinfoel Bitter, Dark Ⓗ
Village pub also serving an industrial estate. ❀ ◖ ≢ P

New Plough
76 Cwmfelin Road
☎ (01554) 777187
11.30–3.30, 6.30–11 (midnight supper licence)
Crown Buckley Dark, Best Bitter; guest beer Ⓗ
Pleasant village pub with an adjoining restaurant. Children's play area in the garden. ❀ ◖ ▮ ≢ ♣

Caio

Brunant Arms
1 mile NE of A482
☎ (0155 85) 483
12–3, 7 (6 summer)–11 (may be 12–11 summer)

Hook Norton Best Bitter, Old Hooky; guest beer Ⓗ
Friendly pub, full of character, in the centre of the UK's second largest parish. Vast number of pub games. Close to the Dolaucothi Gold Mines.
🏚 ❀ ⅄ ◖ ▮ ⅃ ⅄ ♣ P

Capel Bangor

Tynllidiart Arms
On A44 ☎ (01970) 84248
11–2.30, 6–11 (closed Sun in winter)
Aberystwyth Dinas Draught, Premium; guest beers Ⓗ
304-year-old cottage inn, once connected to the mailcoach trade: two small bars. Choice of bottled Belgian beers, plus draught cider in summer.
🏚 ◖ ▮ ♣ ⌒

Carew

Carew Inn
On A4075 ☎ (01646) 651267
12–3, 5–11; 11–11 Sat
Bass Worthington BB; Crown Buckley Rev. James Ⓗ
Large rural pub revamped in 1994 in pine. The local clientele are farmers and tradesmen. Cheap beer in winter. Welsh spoken here. Eve meals Tue–Sat only in winter.
🏚 Q ⛄ ❀ ⅄ ◖ ▮ ⅄ ♣ P

Carmarthen

Boar's Head
Lammas Street
☎ (01267) 222789
11–11
Felinfoel Bitter, Dark, Double Dragon; guest beer Ⓗ
17th-century coaching inn refurbished. Excellent food.
Q ⅄ ◖ ▮ ≢ P

Mansel Arms
Mansel Street
☎ (01267) 236385
11–11
Bass Worthington Dark, BB; guest beers Ⓗ
Pub alongside the market, popular with locals. ❀ ◖ ≢

Queens Hotel
Queen Street ☎ (01267) 231800
11–11
Bass Worthington BB, Draught Bass; M&B Highgate Dark; guest beers Ⓗ
Convivial, town-centre pub, popular with all age groups. The cellar is renowned for its Bass. Snacks lunchtime.
Q ❀ ≢ ♣

Cenarth

Three Horseshoes
☎ (01239) 710119
11–11

Dyfed

Draught Bass; Crown Buckley Dark, Best Bitter, Rev. James; guest beer ⓗ

With the garden overlooking the famous Cenarth Falls, this is a very popular inn. Thatched brewhouse at the rear (non-productive). Good food. Close to the Coracle Museum on the River Teifi.
🏚 Q ⛄ ❀ ◑ ▶ ᕦ ▲ ♣ ◠ P

Cresswell Quay

Cresselly Arms
☎ (01646) 621210
11–3, 5–11
Hancock's HB ⓖ
Famous little gem that has not changed much since 1900 when sail boats unloaded at the quay. Beer is served via the jug. A side of Welsh bacon hangs from the parlour ceiling, giving a feeling of being in gran's kitchen, Aga and all.
🏚 Q ❀ ▲ ♣ P

Cwmann

Ram Inn
On A482, 1 mile from Lampeter ☎ (01570) 422556
11–11
Draught Bass; Fuller's London Pride; guest beer ⓗ
Originally a drovers' hostelry dating back to the 16th century. Now very much a traditional pub, with a superb display of Welsh love spoons. A must. 🏚 ❀ ◑ ▶ ᕦ P

Dale

Griffin
☎ (01646) 636227
11 (6 winter)–11
Bass Worthington BB; Felinfoel Double Dragon; guest beers ⓗ
Pub on the edge of the bay, popular with water sports enthusiasts. One guest beer in winter, two in summer. Parking can be a problem.
🏚 Q ◑ ▶ ▲ ♣ ◠

Dreenhill

Denant Mill Inn
Off B4327, 2½ miles from Haverfordwest
☎ (01437) 766569
12–3, 6–11 (may vary in winter)
Beer range varies ⓗ/ ⓖ
A pub fast becoming a legend with beer and food connoisseurs, set in an old water mill. No regular beers but a merry-go-round from all over the UK, plus a selection of Belgian beers. Excellent food and accommodation.
🏚 Q ⛄ ❀ 🏠 ◑ ▶ ᕦ ▲ ♣ P

Fforest

Bird in Hand
24 Carmarthen Road (old A48)
☎ (01792) 882460
11.30–11
Bass Worthington Dark, BB, Draught Bass; guest beers ⓗ
Country inn enjoying a good local trade. Families welcome. No food Sun eve in winter. Happy hour 12–7pm Mon–Thu. ❀ ◑ ▶ ♣ P

Fishguard

Old Coach House
High Street ☎ (01348) 873883
11–11
Bass Worthington BB; Whitbread Flowers IPA; guest beer (summer) ⓗ
Renovated old town pub run by young people for young people. The open-plan design is clean and light, with a family area in a nook. Cider in summer, but beware Addlestones cider on a fake handpump. Two restaurants. Wheelchair access to ladies' WC only. ❀ ◑ ▶ ᕦ ▲ � ◠

Ship Inn
Newport Road, Lower Town (A487) ☎ (01348) 874033
11–3, 7–11; 12–2, 7–10.30 Sun
Bass Worthington Dark, BB ⓗ & ⓖ
An excellent haven by the original harbour. Marine nick-nacks dominate this low-ceilinged, beamed pub, famous for hosting film crews from *Moby Dick* and *Under Milk Wood*. Snacks. 🏚 ♣

Foelgastell

Smiths Arms
Off A48 ☎ (01269) 842213
11–11
Crown Buckley Best Bitter; Whitbread Boddingtons Mild, Flowers Original ⓗ; guest beer ⓖ
Cosy, friendly pub in a quiet village, a minute or so off the main holiday route. Interesting menu. 🏚 ❀ ◑ ▶ ♣ ◠ P

Freshwater East

Freshwater Inn
On B4584 ☎ (01646) 672329
12–3, 7–11
Bass Worthington BB, Draught Bass; guest beer (summer) ⓗ
Little gem of a local set on cliffs. Modernised to a high standard, featuring a large bar with five handpumps, a games room and a large-windowed restaurant. Beer festival Easter.
🏚 Q ⛄ ❀ 🏠 ◑ ▶ ▲ ♣ P ⤫

Goginan

Druid Inn
On A44 ☎ (01970) 84650
11–3, 5.30–11; closed Sun
Banks's Mild, Bitter; guest beers ⓗ
Pub set into the hillside in a former lead-mining village. Selection of Romanian vodkas and bottled Czech lagers on sale. 🏚 ❀ ◑ ▶ ᕦ ♣ P

Goodwick

Glendower Hotel
The Square ☎ (01348) 872873
11–11
Crown Buckley Best Bitter, Rev. James ⓗ
Large, well-kept hotel bar, near the Irish ferry.
Q ⛄ ❀ 🏠 ◑ ▶ ▲
� (Fishguard Harbour) ♣

Haverfordwest

George's
24 Market Street (off High St)
☎ (01437) 766683
11–3, 7–11
Marston's Pedigree; guest beers ⓗ
Modernised pub in the old part of town (steep climb), retaining some originality with its nooks and settles. Good and varied menu. Homely and friendly. Q ❀ ◑ ▶ �

King's Arms Hotel
Dew Street ☎ (01437) 763726
11–3, 5.30–11
Beer range varies ⓗ
Olde-worlde town pub, recently renovated back to life. A log burner and a flagged floor are features. Some 150 different ales sold in six months. 🏚 Q ◑ � ♣

Pembroke Yeoman
Hill Street (near St Thomas's Green) ☎ (01437) 762500
11–11
Draught Bass; Ruddles County; Whitbread Boddingtons Bitter; guest beers ⓗ
Old, homely local, Victorian in character. In the old part of town and not usually seen by visitors. Large cellar bar. Varied menu; good choice of beers. 🏚 Q ❀ ◑ ▶ ♣

Horeb

Waun-Wyllt
Off B4309 ☎ (01269) 860209
12–3, 7 (6 Fri, 5.30 Sat)–11
Felinfoel Double Dragon; S&N Theakston Best Bitter; guest beers ⓗ
Excellent free house in idyllic countryside. Q ❀ ◑ ▶ 🍺 P

Jameston

Tudor Lodge
☎ (01834) 871978
3–11; 12–11 Sat & summer
Bass Worthington BB, Draught Bass (summer) H
A beautiful house in spacious grounds, with a comfortable lounge and restaurant, a locals' bar, a large family room, and a large playground with a mini-assault course. Excellent range of food.
⚒ Q ☎ ❀ ♨ ◁ ▶ ▲ ♣ P

Johnstown

Friends Arms
St Clears Road
☎ (01267) 234073
11–11
Ansells Mild; Ind Coope Burton Ale; Tetley Bitter H
Old village tavern which once doubled as a blacksmith's. Sensibly modernised into a friendly local. ❀ ◁

Kidwelly

Boot & Shoe
2 Castle Street
☎ (01554) 891341
11–3.30, 6.30–11
Felinfoel Bitter, Dark, Double Dragon H
Small, friendly local. ◁ ▶ ♣

Kilgetty

Kilgetty Arms
☎ (01834) 813219
11–3, 6–11; 11–11 Sat
Felinfoel Bitter, Dark H
Traditional, two-roomed local with a welcome. The quiet lounge is used as a family room at lunchtime. ⚒ Q ❀ ◁ ▶
⊞ ♨ ▲ ⇌ ♣ P

Landshipping

Stanley Arms
Off A4075 OS013117
☎ (01834) 891227
12–3, 6–11
Bass Worthington BB; Crown Buckley Best Bitter, Rev. James; guest beer (summer) H
An excellent find in an idyllic rural setting: a rambling, stone pub with flagged floors. Home-cooking is the order of the day. Beers change often in summer. Live music weekends.
⚒ Q ☎ ❀ ◁ ▶ ▲ ♣ ⊃ P

Laugharne

Brown's Hotel
King Street ☎ (01994) 427320
11–11

Crown Buckley Best Bitter H
Friendly village pub filled with Dylan Thomas memorabilia. No-smoking area in summer only. ▲ ♣ ✀

Letterston

Harp Inn
31 Haverfordwest Road (A40)
☎ (01348) 840061
11–3, 5.30–11; 11–11 Sat
Ind Coope Friary Meux Best Bitter, Burton Ale; Tetley Bitter H
Warm, friendly, modernised country inn and restaurant, near the superb coastline and the Preseli mountains.
⚒ Q ❀ ◁ ▶ ♨ ♣ P

Llanarthney

Paxton Inn
On B4300 ☎ (01558) 668705
4 (11 Sat)–11
Bass Worthington BB; guest beers G
Traditional, 250-year-old pub, full of character and curios. Live music four nights a week. Guest beers vary; five in high season, up to 12 at festivals. Food all day Sun. ◁ ▶ ♨ ▲ P

Llandeilo

Three Tuns
1 Market Street
☎ (01558) 823978
3.30 (2 Fri, 12 Sat)–11; closed Sun
Bass Worthington BB; Ind Coope Burton Ale; Tetley Mild, Bitter H
Friendly back-street fun pub, dating from the 1770s. Quiz Wed; karaoke Thu; live music Fri nights. Popular with all age-groups and reputedly haunted. ⚒ ⊞ ♨ ⇌
⇌ (not winter Sun) ♣

White Horse Inn
125 Rhosmaen Street (off A483, through archway at top of main street) ☎ (01558) 822424
12–3, 5–11; 12–11 Fri, Sat & summer
Archers Best Bitter; Bass Worthington Dark, BB; Shepherd Neame Spitfire; Wadworth 6X; guest beers H
17th-century coaching inn with a courtyard. A fishing theme is prominent; anglers welcome. Friendly atmosphere; renowned for good food. Usually two guest beers.
⚒ Q ❀ ♨ ◁ ▶ ♨
⇌ (not winter Sun) ♣ ⊃

Llandovery

Bear Inn
Market Square ☎ (01550) 20728
11–11
Bass Worthington Dark, BB, Draught Bass H

Busy, three-bar, town-centre pub, popular with all ages. About 200 years old.
⊞ ◁ ▶ ♨ ▲
⇌ (not winter Sun) ♣

Red Lion
Market Square ☎ (01550) 20813
11–3 (not Wed), 5.30–11 (may close early); closed Sun
Crown Buckley Mild, Best Bitter, Rev. James G
As pubs used to be: friendly and basic, with no bar counter. In the same family for over a century. ⚒ Q ▲ ⇌

Llandybie

Red Lion
The Square ☎ (01269) 851202
11–3, 6–11; 12–3 Sun, closed Sun eve
Draught Bass; Whitbread Boddingtons Bitter, Flowers Original H
Attractive, stylish pub offering a good welcome to families. Pleasant bilingual atmosphere.
⚒ ☎ ❀ ⊞ ◁ ▶ ⇌ P ✀

Llanelli

Bull Inn
Ann Street ☎ (01554) 756283
11–11
Crown Buckley Dark, Best Bitter H
Pub where a large collection of horns reflects the name. A locals' pub with a good atmosphere. ⇌ ♣ P

Island House
Island Place ☎ (01554) 778378
11.30–3, 6.30–11; 11.30–11 Thu–Sat
Bass Worthington Dark, BB, Draught Bass; guest beer H
Locals' pub in the town centre, with exposed beams in the bar. Weekly guest beers. Q ⇌

Thomas Arms Hotel
Thomas Street
☎ (01554) 772043
12–11
Crown Buckley Best Bitter, Rev. James H
Plush Crown Buckley showpiece pub: various function rooms and a relaxed, roomy lounge bar. ⊞ ◁ ▶ P

Llangadog

Carpenters Arms
Queens Square
☎ (01550) 777359
12–2.30, 5.30–11; 12–11 Sat
Draught Bass; Whitbread Boddingtons Bitter H
A popular pub with all age groups in a village on the edge of the Brecon Beacons National Park.
⚒ ☎ ❀ ◁ ▶ ♨
⇌ (not winter Sun) ♣

Dyfed

Llangranog

Ship Inn
☎ (01239) 654423
11–11 (12–3, 7–11 Nov–Easter)
Brains Dark; Ind Coope Burton Ale; Ruddles Best Bitter; Wadworth 6X; Whitbread Flowers Original; guest beer H
This 350-year-old inn overlooks the beach in this picturesque village on the Heritage Coast. Good food.
🏠 Q ✿ 🛏 ◖ ▶ & ▲ ♣ P

Llannon

Red Lion
Heol y Plas ☎ (01269) 841276
5 (12 Sat)–11
Felinfoel Bitter, Dark, Double Dragon H
Pub dating back to at least the 17th century and rumoured to have a secret tunnel leading to the neighbouring church, as well as a ghost. 🏠 Q ➍ ▶ P

Llanychaer

Bridge End Inn
On B4313 ☎ (01348) 872545
11–3, 6–11 (varies in winter)
Beer range varies H
Pub in a hidden valley, with an enthusiastic landlord who specialises in different ales in summer. A large, barn-like lounge is decorated with country implements.
🏠 Q ◖ ▶ ▲ ♣

Llwyndafydd

Crown Inn
☎ (01545) 560396
12–3, 6–11 (7–10.30 winter; closed Sun eve in winter)
Whitbread Boddingtons Bitter, Flowers Original; guest beers H
Known as the Hidden Inn, due to its relative remoteness, this pub has a deserved reputation for excellent fare. Situated near the secluded cove at Cwmtydu, it is extremely popular. Bookings wise in summer. Q ✿ ◖ ▶ ▲ P

Lydstep

Lydstep Tavern
☎ (01834) 871521
12–3, 6.30–11 (may close some weekdays Dec–Easter)
Bass Worthington BB; Tetley Bitter H
Welcoming pub in what used to be the post office of a small village with a large caravan park. Pleasant garden. On the main Tenby–Pembroke bus route and excellent for cliff walks. Meals in summer.
➍ ✿ ◖ ▲ ♣ P

Manorbier

Castle Inn
☎ (01834) 871268
11–11
Bass Worthington BB; guest beers H
Welcoming, low-ceilinged pub near the Norman castle and within easy reach of the sands. Activities throughout the week. Custom-built Indian arm-wrestling table in the bar.
🏠 Q ➍ ✿ ◖ ▶ ▲ ♣

Marloes

Lobster Pot
Off Dale Road
☎ (01646) 636233
11–11
Beer range varies H
Village pub with a warm atmosphere, where games teams are very evident. The bar is decked out with lobster pots. The beer range varies, with up to five ales sold.
🏠 ✿ ◖ ▶ & ▲ ♣ ◠ P

Mathry

Farmers Arms
Off A487 ☎ (01348) 831284
11–11
Bass Worthington BB, Draught Bass; guest beer (summer) H
Rural pub with a timbered interior: a monks' brewhouse back in 1291, atop an ancient hill settlement. Guinness prints adorn the walls. Fresh seafood a speciality.
✿ 🛏 ◖ ▲ ♣ ◠ P

Mynydd y Garreg

Prince of Wales
☎ (01554) 890522
12–3 (usually not Mon), 5.15–11 (may extend)
Beer range varies H
Interesting pub with every nook and cranny filled with bric-a-brac. Normally six real ales. No-smoking in the restaurant. No lunches Sun or Mon. Under-14s not allowed.
🏠 ✿ ◖ ▶ & ▲ ♣ P

Narberth

Kirkland Arms
St James Street
☎ (01834) 860423
11–11
Felinfoel Bitter, Double Dragon H
Always popular local where 'Del's Bar' has been extended through the old hallway without losing any of its character. Opposite the rugby ground and convenient for the excellent local museum. No meals Sun.
➍ ✿ ◖ 🍴 & ▲ ♣ P

Newcastle Emlyn

Ivy Bush
Emlyn Square
☎ (01239) 710542
11.30–2.30, 5.30–11; 11–11 Fri & Sat
Bass Worthington BB, Draught Bass H
Centrally-situated, market town pub with a cosy fireside front bar and a pleasant atmosphere. Bar skittles played. 🏠 Q ➍ ✿ ◖ ♣ P

New Quay

Black Lion Hotel
Glanmor Terrace
☎ (01545) 560209
12–3, 6–11 (11–11 July–Aug)
Brains SA; Whitbread Boddingtons Mild, Bitter, Flowers Original H
The old bar of this hotel dates from 1680 and contains memorabilia of New Quay. Poet Dylan Thomas was a regular and the restaurant bears his name. Live folk/blues music Fri or Sat (Mar–Oct). Good food. The garden overlooks Cardigan Bay and includes a boules pitch. 🏠 Q ✿ ◖ ▶ ♣ P ⊬

Pembroke

Old Cross Saws Inn
109 Main Street
☎ (01646) 682475
11–11
Crown Buckley Best Bitter, Rev. James; Pembroke Main Street; guest beers H
A rugby-followers' local, larger inside than it looks from the outside. Well-placed for sight-seeing.
✿ 🛏 ◖ ▶ & ⇌ ♣

Pembroke Dock

Ferry Inn
Pembroke Ferry (underneath Cleddau Bridge)
☎ (01646) 682947
11.30–2.45 (3.45 Mon), 6.30 (7 Mon) 11
Draught Bass; Hancock's HB H
Pub at the landing point of the Cledda river ferry before the bridge was built. Popular with yachtsmen, water skiers and holidaymakers alike. Large menu (best to book for food); carvery Sun. Wide selection of single malt whiskies.
🏠 Q ✿ ◖ ▶ ▲ ♣ P

First & Last
London Road
(A477)☎ (01646) 682687
11–11
Bass Worthington BB; guest beers H
Lively local, still lit by gas, in

which you can be served by
the oldest licensee in Wales.
Live music Sat. Guest beers
change regularly, and the pub
is one of the cheapest places to
drink in the Dock. No food
Sun. ✿ ◖ ⇌ ♣ P

Penally

Cross Inn

Opp. station. ☎ (01834) 844665
12–3, 7–11; 12–11 Sat & summer
Bass Worthington BB H;
guest beers G
Stripped wood and slate floors
give an airy feel to this
welcoming hillside pub which
offers panoramic views across
to Caldey Island. The centre of
village activities. Handy for
cliff walks. Q ✿ ◖ ♠ ⇌ ♣

Pontargothi

Cresselly Arms

On A40 ☎ (01267) 290221
11–3, 6.30–11
Marston's Pedigree;
Whitbread Flowers
Original H
Handsomely furnished, pretty
main-road pub near lovely
river walks. Beautiful
waterscape from the
restaurant. ⚏ ⏖ ✿ ◖ ♠ P

Pontfaen

Dyffryn Arms

Off A187/B4313
☎ (01348) 881305
Hours vary
Draught Bass or Ind Coope
Burton Ale G
A 1920s front room where
time has stood still, popularly
known as Bessie's. Beer is
served by the jug and
conversation is obligatory. Set
in the Gwaun valley, between
the Preseli mountains and
Fishguard. No visit to Wales is
complete without a call here.
⚏ Q ✿

Puncheston

Drovers Arms

Off A40, E of Letterston
☎ (01348) 881469
11–11
Bass Worthington BB;
Draught Bass; guest beer
(summer) H
Family-run, conversational
pub with a flag-floored public
bar, a lounge bar and a large
function room. Lots of outside
space, safe for children. Warm
welcome.
Q ⏖ ✿ ◖ ♠ ♣ P

Rhandirmwyn

Royal Oak

☎ (0155 06) 201
11–3, 6–11

Fuller's London Pride;
Ruddles Best Bitter;
Wadworth 6X; guest beers H
Friendly, family-owned pub,
formerly a 15th-century
mansion on a drovers' road.
Popular with locals and
visitors alike. Excellent views
of the Tywi valley. A good
centre for walkers, campers
cyclists and ornithologists
(RSPB reserve nearby).
⚏ Q ✿ ⛺ ◖ ♠ ♣ P

Saundersfoot

Old Chemist Inn

The Strand ☎ (01834) 813982
11–11
Bass Worthington BB,
Draught Bass; guest beers
(summer) H
This pub is so near the beach
the sea hurls stones into the
garden on stormy nights! The
bars are elevated, giving
excellent sea views, and there
is access to the sands from the
garden. Eve meals in summer.
⚏ Q ⏖ ✿ ◖ ♠ 🍴 ♣

St Clears

Corvus Inn

Station Road ☎ (01994) 230965
11–11
Bass Worthington BB; Brains
SA; guest beers H
Comfortable pub in a largish
village. The lounge is set aside
for meals. ◖ ♠ ♣

St David's

Farmers Arms

Goat Street ☎ (01437) 720328
11–11
Whitbread Boddingtons
Bitter, Flowers Original H
19th-century, stone-built pub
with beams, a flagstone floor
and an original fireplace.
Popular with local fishermen,
farmers and lifeboatmen.
Excellent home-cooked meals.
⚏ Q ⏖ ✿ ◖ ♠ ♣

St Florence

New Inn

High Street ☎ (01834) 871315
11–3, 5.30–11; 11–11 Sat (supper
licence)
Brains Bitter G
Charming pub nestling in the
centre of a picturesque floral
village, handy for all the
attractions of Pembrokeshire
but not over-run by tourists.
⚏ Q ✿ ◖ 🍴 ♠ ♣ P

Solva

Ship Inn

Main Street (A487)
☎ (01437) 721247
11–11

Bass Worthington BB,
Draught Bass; Solva Ramsey
Bitter; guest beers H
Small, 300-year-old pub
popular with locals and
holidaymakers, in a lovely
Pembrokeshire fishing village.
Ramsey Bitter comes from the
brewhouse (set up in 1993).
Park on the quay and see the
story and remains of the first
lighthouse. Meals in summer.
⚏ Q ⏖ ✿ ◖ ♠ ♣

Tenby

Crown Inn

Lower Frog Street
☎ (01834) 842796
12–11
Brains Dark; Courage
Directors (summer); John
Smith's Bitter
Near the seafront and just
within the town walls, this
local is less frenetic than many
in high summer and warmly
welcoming in winter. The
exposed stone walls are
adorned with photographs of
some of Pembrokeshire's less
obvious beauty spots. Meals in
summer only. ✿ ◖ ⇌ ♣

Hope & Anchor

St Julian's Street
☎ (01834) 842131
11–3, 7–11 (11–11 summer)
Bass Worthington BB; Crown
Buckley Rev. James; guest
beers H
Nautically-themed pub very
close to the harbour, with a
strong adherence to dominoes,
crosswords, quizzes, darts and
pool. Popular and cheerful all
year round. Meals in summer.
⏖ ✿ ◖ ♠ & ⇌ ♣

Tenby & District
Ex-Servicemen's Club

Ruabon House, South Parade
☎ (01834) 842258
11–3, 7 (6 summer)–11; 12–2, 7–10.30
Sun
Bass Worthington Dark, BB H
Large club opposite the town
walls which welcomes
temporary members. Snooker
room with two tables; upstairs
function room with bingo, etc.
Families allowed at lunchtime
only. Q ⏖ ⇌ ♣

Wiseman's Bridge

Wiseman's Bridge Inn

☎ (01834) 813236
11–3, 7–11 (11–11 summer)
Bass Worthington BB,
Draught Bass; Hancock's HB;
guest beers (summer) H
Excellent pub perched on the
very edge of the beach, with
its own camping site, but no
overt tourist trappings. Good
sea views from the garden and
function room.
⚏ Q ⏖ ✿ 🏠 ◖ ♠ & ♠ ♣ P

359

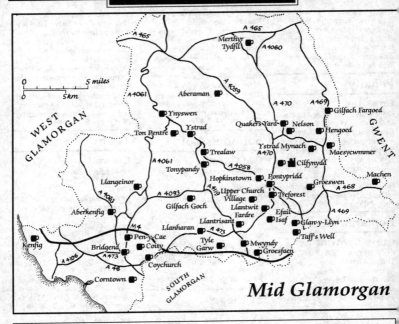

Mid Glamorgan

 Reckless Eric's, Cilfynydd

Aberaman

Temple Bar Vaults
Cardiff Road (B4275)
☎ (01685) 876137
12–4, 7–11 (may vary)
**Brains SA; Crown Buckley
Rev. James; Felinfoel Dark;
Wadworth 6X** Ⓗ
Small, friendly local, in the
same family for 107 years: a
homely bar, full of bric-a-brac,
and a pool room. The beers
may vary. ⚨ Q ⌹ ♣ P

Aberkenfig

Swan
128 Bridgend Road
☎ (01656) 725612
11–3.30 (4 Sat), 6–11; 12–2.30, 7–10.30
Sun
Brains Dark, Bitter, SA Ⓗ
Pleasant village pub, serving
good food (no meals Mon eve
or Sun). ⌹ ▶ ⇌ (Sarn) P

Bridgend

Famous Pen y Bont
Inn
Derwyn Road ☎ (01656) 652266
11.30–3, 5.30–11; 11–11 Sat
**Brains SA; Marston's
Pedigree; Whitbread
Boddingtons Bitter, Best
Bitter; guest beer** Ⓗ
Popular town-centre pub with
a beamed ceiling. ⌹ ▶ ⇌

Old Castle Inn
90 Nolton Street
12–4, 6–11; 12–11 Fri & Sat
**Bass Worthington BB,
Draught Bass** Ⓗ
Warm and friendly town local,
comfortably furnished, with
exposed stone walls. ⚨ Q ⌹

Cilfynydd

Commercial Hotel
Cilfynydd Road (A4054)
☎ (01443) 402486
11–11 (11.45 supper licence)
**Bass Worthington BB;
Hancock's HB** Ⓗ
Large, bustling village pub
offering pub games (snooker)
and live music. Comfortable
lounge areas and a restaurant.
No meals Mon eve. ⌹ ▶ ₲ ♣

Coity

Six Bells
120 Heol West Plas
☎ (01656) 653192
12–11
**Bass Worthington BB;
Hancock's HB** Ⓗ
Friendly, comfortable two-bar
village local, opposite the
ruins of Coity Castle. ❀ ♣ P

Corntown

Golden Mile
Corntown Road
☎ (01656) 654884

11.30–3, 5–11
**Bass Worthington BB,
Draught Bass; guest beer** Ⓗ
Old converted farmhouse with
a stone fireplace and beams.
Separate restaurant area. A
smart and comfortable pub
with a more basic public bar.
⚨ Q ❀ ₲ ▶ ♣ P

Coychurch

Prince of Wales
Main Road ☎ (01656) 860600
12–11
**Banks's Mild, Bitter;
Marston's Pedigree** Ⓗ
Pleasant, unpretentious village
local. Exposed stone walls
throughout. A rare Banks's
outlet for the area. Q ⌹ ₲

White Horse
Main Road ☎ (01656) 652583
11.30–4, 5.30–11; 11.30–11 Fri & Sat
Brains Dark, Bitter, SA Ⓗ
Pub with a plush, restaurant-
style, lounge and a
comfortable public bar.
Q ❀ ⌹ ▶ P

Efail Isaf

Carpenter's Arms
Heol Ffrwd Phillip
☎ (01443) 202426
12–5, 7–11; 11–11 Wed, Fri & Sat (may
vary)

Bass Worthington BB, Draught Bass; Brains Bitter ℍ
Very popular village local, with a comfortable lounge and a basic bar. 🏮 ♣ P

Gilfach Fargoed

Capel
Park Place ☎ (01443) 830272
12–4, 7–11; 12–11 Fri & Sat
Courage Best Bitter; John Smith's Bitter; guest beers ℍ
Traditional large valleys pub with lots of original features.
Q 🏮 ☕ ◑ ⌸ ⥱ ♣ P

Gilfach Goch

Griffin
Hendreforgan (600 yds S of A4093) OS988875
12–11 (may close afternoons)
Brains SA ℍ
Exceptional traditional pub, remotely situated in a small valley bottom, with interesting old bric-a-brac. Hard to find, being at the end of a half-surfaced lane and not signed, but well worth the effort. Cosy and friendly. Q 🏮 ♣ P

Glan-y-Llyn

Fagin's Ale & Chop House
Cardiff Road ☎ (01222) 811800
11–11
Brains Bitter; Felinfoel Double Dragon; Hardington Bitter; Ind Coope Burton Ale; Wadworth 6X; Whitbread Boddingtons Bitter ℍ; guest beers ⑥
Old terraced cottage pub, full of atmosphere. Its range of ales is constantly changing and features independent breweries, plus a house beer brewed by Crown Buckley. Separate restaurant. No food Sun eve. CAMRA regional Pub of the Year 1993. 🏮 ◑ ⌸ ⥱

Groesfaen

Dynevor Arms
Llantrisant Road
☎ (01222) 890530
11–3, 5.30–11; 11–11 Sat
Draught Bass; Hancock's HB; guest beer ℍ
Smart village pub, popular with all ages. One bar, with areas for regular live music and conversation. 🏮 ◑ ◗ ♣ P

Groeswen

White Cross Inn
Groeswen (on hillside 1 mile N of A468) OS128870
☎ (01222) 851332
12–3.30, 6–11; 11–11 Sat (midnight supper licence)

S&N Theakston Best Bitter; Whitbread Boddingtons Mild, Bitter, Flowers IPA, Original; Younger No. 3 ℍ
Deceptively large pub with a small bar and two additional rooms, the larger allowing for live entertainment. The patio has a view of Caerphilly Castle. Children welcome.
🏚 Q 🏮 ☕ ⊠ ◑ ⓓ ⚒ ♣ P

Hengoed

Junction Inn
9 Kings Hill ☎ (01443) 812192
12–4 (4.30 Fri & Sat), 7–11
Bass Worthington BB; Hancock's HB; guest beer ℍ
Immaculately appointed local, featuring railway memorabilia. Close to the viaduct. Eve meals Thu–Sat. ◑ ▶ ⌸ ⥱ ♣

Hopkinstown

Hollybush
Tŷ Mawr Road
☎ (01443) 402325
11.30–5, 6.15–11
Bass Worthington BB; Hancock's HB; guest beer ℍ
Small sports-oriented bar and a comfortable lounge in a main road pub. ◑ ▶ ⓓ ♣ P

Kenfig

Prince of Wales
Ton Kenfig (off B4283)
☎ (01656) 740356
11.30–4, 6–11.30
Bass Worthington BB, Draught Bass ℍ; guest beers ⑥
Old, well-preserved pub in scenic surroundings in historic Kenfig. Six guest beers.
🏚 Q ☕ 🏮 ◑ ▶ ⓓ ⚒ ♣ P

Llangeinor

Llangeinor Arms
400 yds N of A4093
☎ (01656) 870268
11–11
Bass Worthington BB; Hancock's HB; guest beer ℍ
Isolated hilltop pub with superb views, featuring oak beams and antique artefacts. Large conservatory. Meals all day. 🏚 Q ☕ 🏮 ◑ ▶ P

Llanharan

High Corner House
☎ (01443) 238056
11–11
Draught Bass; Brains Bitter; Wadworth 6X; Whitbread Boddingtons Bitter, Flowers Original, Porter (occasional) ℍ
Large Brewers Fayre pub which caters well for children.
🏮 ◑ ▶ P

Llantrisant

Penny Farthing
Cardiff Road, Southgate
☎ (01443) 228838
12–3, 6–11
Beer range varies ℍ
Modern estate pub with a single open-plan bar. Usually one Courage beer and one guest on sale. No food Sun.
Q 🏮 ◑ ▶ P

Llantwit Fardre

Bush Inn
Main Road ☎ (01443) 203958
2.30 (12 Sat)–11
Bass Worthington BB, Draught Bass; Hancock's HB; guest beers ℍ
Small, quiet village local which fills very quickly. Small car park. Q ◑ ▶ ♣ P

Machen

White Hart Inn
Nant y Ceisiad (100 yds N of A468 under railway bridge, to the right) ☎ (01633) 441005
12–2 (may vary), 6.30–11
Felinfoel Dark, Bitter; guest beers ℍ
Mid Glam CAMRA Pub of the Year 1991 and 1992: a rambling pub with extensive wood panelling, some saved from a luxury liner. Excellent range of guest beers from independent brewers. Two or three mini-beer festivals per year. Small restaurant (no lunches Sat).
🏚 Q 🏮 ◑ ▶ P

Maesycwmmer

Maesycwmmer Inn
Main Road ☎ (01443) 814385
12–4, 7–11
Brains SA ℍ
Small bar and a comfortable lounge in a pub adjacent to the eastern end of Hengoed viaduct. No lunches Sat.
◑ ▶ ⌸ ⥱ (Hengoed) ♣ P

Merthyr Tydfil

Lantern
Bethesda Street, Georgetown
☎ (01685) 383683
12–5, 7–11; 12–11 Sat
Bass Worthington BB, Draught Bass; guest beer ℍ
Comfortable pub which dates back 200 years: a single horseshoe-shaped bar with a raised dining area. Live music Thu and Sat. 🏮 ◑ ▶ ▲ ⥱

Mwyndy

Barn at Mwyndy
100 yds E of A4119
☎ (01443) 222333

12–2.30, 5.30 (7 Sat)–11; 12–2.30,
7–10.30 Sun

Felinfoel Double Dragon; Hancock's HB; Wadworth 6X; guest beers H

A conversion from an old barn: a meetings room on the upper level, two bars on the lower, where agricultural artefacts abound. Renowned for meals (not served Sun eve). Mixed couples and families only Sat eve. 🏚 Q 🛇 🕸 ◑ 🚶 ♣ P ⚹

Castell Mynach Inn

Llantrisant Road, Groesfaen (A4119, ½ mile N of M4 jct 34) ☎ (01443) 222298
11–11

Draught Bass; Hancock's HB H

Popular, prominent local, well served by main roads. Eve meals Wed–Sat. Q ◑ ▶ P

Nelson

Dynevor Arms

Commercial Street (near bus station) ☎ (01443) 450295
11.30–11; 11.30–4.30, 6.30–11 Tue & Thu

Bass Worthington BB; Hancock's HB; M&B Brew XI H

Former brew pub and mortuary, over 200 years old, used by farmers after market. Busy public bar. 🍺 ▲ ♣ P

Pen-y-Cae

Tŷ'r Isha

Off A4061/A4063 ☎ (01656) 725287
11–4, 6–11; 11–11 Sat

Draught Bass; Hancock's HB H

Popular, converted 15th-century farmhouse, formerly also a court house. 🏚 🕸 ◑ ▶ ▲ 🚶 (Sarn) ♣ P

Pontypridd

Bunch of Grapes

Ynysangharad Road (off A470 at Ynysybwl jct, behind B&Q retail park) ☎ (01443) 402934
11–11

Bass Worthington BB; Brains Bitter, SA; Hancock's HB; John Smith's Bitter; guest beer H

Large, comfortable pub with a popular restaurant. 🕸 ◑ ▶ P

Llanover Arms

Bridge Street (off A470 at Ynysybwl jct) ☎ (01443) 403215
11–11

Bass Worthington BB; Brains Dark, Bitter, SA; guest beer H

Bustling town pub with three bars. Near Ynysangharad Park. 🕸 🍺 ♣ P

Quakers Yard

Glantaff Inn

On A4054 ☎ (01443) 410822
12–4, 7–11

Courage Best Bitter, Directors; Ruddles Best Bitter; John Smith's Bitter H

Comfortable, popular inn with a warm, friendly atmosphere. Interesting collection of water jugs. No eve meals Sun. Upstairs restaurant. Q 🕸 ◑ ▶ ▲ 🚶 P

Taff's Well

Taff's Well Inn

Cardiff Road (A4054, N end of village) ☎ (01222) 810324
12–11

Tetley Bitter; guest beer H

Comfortable and friendly, open-plan pub. 🕸 ◑ 🚶 ♣ P

Ton Pentre

New Inn Hotel

Church Road ☎ (01443) 434660
11–2.30, 5.30–11; 11–11 Sat

Bass Worthington BB; Cains Bitter; Hancock's HB H

Unmissable local landmark, with all exterior walls painted cherry red: a large, friendly but basic free house. 🚶 ♣

Tonypandy

Paddy's Goose Inn

Trealaw Road (150 yds from station, Trealaw side) ☎ (01443) 434679
11–2.30, 5.30–11

Bass Worthington BB; Samuel Smith OBB H

Small, traditional valleys workingman's pub. Basic, but comfortable. 🍺 🚶 ♣ P

Trealaw

Ynyscynon Hotel

Ynyscynon Road ☎ (01443) 433084
11–11

Brains Bitter; Whitbread Best Bitter, Flowers Original H

Pub with a spacious public bar with two dartboards and a pool table, plus a comfortable lounge. ◑ 🍺 P

Treforest

Otley Arms

Forest Road ☎ (01443) 402033
11–11

Bass Worthington BB; Brains SA; Crown Buckley SBB, Rev. James H

Bustling suburban pub, popular with locals and students alike. ◑ 🚶 ♣ P

Tyle Garw

Boar's Head

Coed Cae Lane (½ mile off A473) ☎ (01443) 225400
12–4, 7–11

Beer range varies H

Small, simply furnished, unspoilt local with a friendly atmosphere. Forest walks opposite. Normally two guest beers served. Q 🕸 ♣

Upper Church Village

Farmer's Arms

St Illtyd's Road ☎ (01443) 205766
11–11

Bass Worthington BB, Draught Bass; Hancock's HB; guest beer H

Busy village pub where the open-plan single bar still retains a cosy atmosphere. The menu is largely home-made and includes Sat morning breakfasts. No meals Sun. Eve meals on request. 🕸 ◑ P

Ynyswen

Crown Hotel

Ynyswen Road ☎ (01443) 772805
3.30 (12 Fri & Sat)–11

Courage Best Bitter H**, Directors** H/ G**; Ushers Founders** H**; guest beers** H / G

Popular and welcoming main road local: a comfortable lounge and a separate bar, which features a red telephone box. 🏚 🍺 🚶 ♣

Ystrad

Greenfield

13 William Street ☎ (01443) 435953
11–11

Bass Worthington BB, Draught Bass H

Traditional Rhondda terraced pub that has extended into an adjoining house: a bar and a lounge. 🏚 🕸 ◑ ▶ 🍺 🚶 (Ystrad Rhondda) ♣

Ystrad Mynach

Olde Royal Oak

Commercial Street (A469) ☎ (01443) 814196
12–3, 5.30–11; 12–11 Sat

Bass Worthington BB, Draught Bass; Hancock's HB H

Unmistakeable brewers' Tudor pub with a busy public bar enjoying local trade. Good food. Q ◑ ▶ 🍺 ▲ 🚶 P

South Glamorgan

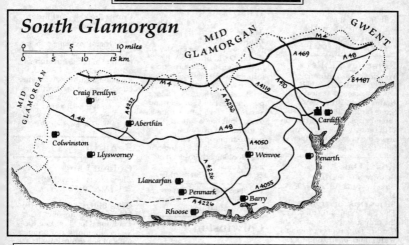

 Brains, Bullmastiff, Cardiff

Aberthin

Hare & Hounds

On A4222, just N of
Cowbridge ☎ (01446) 774892
11.30–11
Bass Worthington BB Ⓗ,
Draught Bass Ⓖ; **Hancock's
HB** Ⓗ
Traditional village inn with a
friendly atmosphere: a small
cosy bar and a comfortable
family room. The beer garden
and play area are enclosed and
safe for children. Limited
parking. 🏨 Q 🎭 🏵 ⅙ ♣ P

Barry

Castle Hotel

Jewel Street ☎ (01446) 701035
12–11
Brains Dark, Bitter, SA Ⓗ
Large, back-street local with
four rooms downstairs and an
upstairs function room. The
lounge is adorned with prints
of old Barry.
Q ⊟ ⥵ (Docks) ♣

Cardiff

Angel Tavern

Westgate Street
☎ (01222) 232633
11–3, 5–11
**Crown Buckley Rev. James;
guest beers** Ⓗ
The cellar bar of the Angel
Hotel, attracting a mixed
clientele. Very busy Tue and
Thu (student nights) and on
match days (opposite the
Arms Park). Hosts the S Wales
element of the Celtic Beer
Festival. 🛌 ⅆ ⥵ (Central)

Black Lion

High Street, Llandaff
11–11
Brains Dark, Bitter, SA Ⓗ
Traditional Brains house on a
busy road near the cathedral.
Popular with locals;
comfortable lounge.
Occasional eve meals.
Q ⅆ ⊟ ⥵ (Fairwater)

Butcher's Arms

Llandaff Road, Canton
☎ (01222) 227927
11–11
Brains Dark, Bitter, SA Ⓗ
Typical back-street boozer.
Although next door to Chapter
Arts Centre, the trendies avoid
this pub, which enjoys a
more mature clientele instead.
⊟

City Arms

10–12 Quay Street (off St Mary
St) ☎ (01222) 225258
11–11
Brains Dark, Bitter, SA Ⓗ
Simple, two-bar pub,
contrasting with other city-
centre 'leisure experiences'.
Q ⊟ ⥵ (Central)

King's Castle

Cowbridge Road East
☎ (01222) 230291
11–11
**Brains Bitter; Whitbread
Boddingtons Bitter, Flowers
IPA, Original** Ⓗ; **guest
beers** Ⓖ
Large, busy pub with one,
almost circular, room. The
clientele is mainly young, but
not totally. Guest beers usually
come from the Whitbread list.
Loud music sometimes. Good
choice of food nearby.

Kiwi's

Wyndham Arcade, 21–23 St
Mary Street ☎ (01222) 229876
12 noon–2am; 7–10.30 Sun, closed
Sun lunch
Hancock's HB; guest beers Ⓗ
Pub situated halfway along an
arcade, and handy for
shoppers. Noisy and busy in
the eves. Admission charge
after 9pm Thu–Sat (disco
upstairs). Good range of
international bottled beers (not
all bottle-conditioned though).
⥵ (Central)

Maltster's Arms

75 Merthyr Road, Whitchurch
☎ (01222) 624326
12–4, 5.30–11; 11–11 Wed–Sat
Brains Dark, Bitter, SA Ⓗ
Small, real local with a piano
sing-song Sat night and
skittles and darts matches
Mon–Fri. Many charity
activities.
Q ⊟ ⅆ ▯ ⊟ ⅙ ♣

Miller's Tavern

3 Brook Street, Riverside
☎ (01222) 297605
11–11
**Brains Dark; Ind Coope
Burton Ale; Tetley Bitter** Ⓗ
Large corner pub just outside
the city centre: a basic bar, a
smart lounge and a skittle
alley. Live bands Fri; karaoke
Sat. Function room upstairs.
ⅆ ⊟ ⥵ (Central)

Old Arcade

12 Church Street
☎ (01222) 231740
11–11
Brains Dark, Bitter, SA Ⓗ
Bustling city-centre pub in the
stand-up tradition. The
proximity of Cardiff Arms

363

Park has lent it a rugby theme, with framed shirts on the walls. No food Sun. The lounge is closed Mon–Wed eves. ◐ ⊞ ⇌ (Central)

Rompney Castle

Wentloog Road, Rumney (B4239) ☎ (01222) 793991
11–11; 11–3.30, 5.30–11 Mon
Brains Dark, Bitter, SA H & E
Stone-built, half-timbered, three-bar pub dating from the 17th century. Electric pumps serve the beer in the upper lounge. ❀ ◐ ⊞ ♣ P

Royal Oak

Broadway (E end of Broadway) ☎ (01222) 473984
11–11
Brains Dark, Bitter H, **SA** G
This *Guide* stalwart still offers the only gravity-served SA in Cardiff. Four rooms provide a wide choice of surroundings. The bar usually has sport on TV; occasional loud music in the lounge. ❀ ⊞

Three Arches

Heathwood Road
☎ (01222) 753831
11–11
Brains Dark, Bitter, SA H
One of the local brewer's largest pubs: a 1950s-built, recently refurbished house. Warm, friendly and comfortable, with a variety of clientele in its three bars. Upstairs function room; good skittle alley; darts and cards in the public bar. No food Sun. Q ❀ ◐ ⊞ ⇌ (Heath High/Low Level) P

Tŷ Mawr Arms

Graig Road, Lisvane (1 mile N of B4562) OS184842
☎ (01222) 754456
12–3, 6–11 (may vary in summer and on bank hols)
Courage Directors; Hancock's HB; Wadworth 6X; guest beers H
300-year-old listed building in extensive grounds with panoramic views and resident peacocks. The ceiling beams were ships' timbers. A former local CAMRA *Pub of the Year*, serving up to three guest beers. Over 21s only, unless part of a group. No eve meals Sun. ♨ ⛺ ❀ ◐ ◗ P

Vulcan Hotel

10 Adam Street, Adamsdown
☎ (01222) 461580
11–11
Brains Dark, Bitter H
The oldest working pub in Cardiff, an interesting building, outside and in. Good value food and a warm welcome. Can close early on winter eves. No meals Sun. ◐ ◗ ⇌ (Queen St) ♣

Wharf

Schooner Way, Atlantic Wharf (½ mile S of Centre)
☎ (01222) 480700
11–3, 5.30–11; 11–11 Sat and May–Oct
Brains Dark, Bitter, SA H
Impressive, new pub beside a former dock. The large bar is attractively decorated with prints, etc. of the docks. Bands play here Fri and Sat eves and Sun lunch. Two family rooms, one resembling a station platform. An upstairs restaurant is open lunch and eves, except Sat lunch and Sun eve. Booking advisable. Bar meals lunchtime. ♨ ❀ ◐ & ⇌ (Bute Rd) P

Try also: Guildhall Tavern, St Mary St (Free); **Ninian Park**, Leckwith Rd (Brains)

Colwinston

Sycamore Tree

Off A48 ☎ (01656) 652827
12–3 (extends weekends & summer), 6.30–11
Draught Bass; Hancock's HB; guest beer H
Welcoming village pub, refurbished but retaining much of its original character. Known for its good food. ♨ Q ❀ ◐ & ♣ P

Craig Penllyn

Barley Mow

1½ miles N of A48 OS978773
☎ (01446) 772558
12–3 (not Mon), 6–11
Bass Worthington BB; Hancock's HB; guest beers H
1993 S Glam CAMRA *Pub of the Year*: a friendly, cosy, three-roomed village pub, always popular with diners and drinkers. Two regularly changed guest beers. Separate restaurant; children welcome in the lounge. No food Sun eve. Beware low doorways. ♨ Q ❀ ◐ ◗ ▲ ♣ P

Llancarfan

Fox & Hounds

☎ (01446) 781297
11–3, 6.30–11; 11–11 Fri & Sat
Brains Bitter; Ruddles Best Bitter; John Smith's Bitter; guest beers H
Former CAMRA regional *Pub of the Year*: the focal point of the village. The rectangular bar has separate drinking areas; restaurant upstairs (no eve meals Sun). Two or three guest beers. ♨ Q ❀ ◐ ◗ ♣ P

Llysworney

Carne Arms

On B4268 ☎ (01446) 773553

12–3, 6–11
Crown Buckley Best Bitter; Ruddles County; Wadworth 6X H
Very friendly village pub, built in 1776 as a vicarage. The traditional interior features original oak beams and an inglenook. Families welcome. Large range of malt whiskies, an excellent menu and a huge beer garden with a play area. The beer range may vary. ♨ Q ❀ ◐ ◗ & ▲ ♣ P

Penarth

Golden Lion

Glebe Street (off A4160)
☎ (01222) 701574
12–11
Cains Bitter; Hancock's HB; Stones Best Bitter H
Traditional local serving the local community and popular with all age groups. Walls are adorned with plates. Q ⇌ (Penarth/Dingle Rd)

Penmark

Six Bells

☎ (01446) 710229
12–11
Hancock's HB H
Friendly, traditional country pub: a public bar with a darts area and Hancock's memorabilia, and a separate lounge. No eve meals Sun. New restaurant extension planned. ♨ Q ❀ ◐ ◗ ♣ P

Rhoose

Highwayman

Fon Mon (W of the airport at the end of a country lane) OS058673 ☎ (01446) 710205
6.30–11
Brains Bitter H
Large country pub displaying Guinness memorabilia (complete with Toucan figure) and serving Dublin-brewed Guinness. Popular for good value food—try the 'Condemned Man's Meal' if you dare! ♨ ❀ ◐ ◗ P

Wenvoe

Wenvoe Arms

Old Port Road
☎ (01222) 591129
11.30–3.30, 5.30–11; 11–11 Fri & Sat
Brains Dark, Bitter, SA H
Convivial locals' pub which looks after its regulars through organised golf and boules events: a venue for sporty types. Real fires in both bars. No meals in the bar or upstairs restaurant Sun–Tue eves. ♨ ❀ ◐ ◗ ⊞ ♣ P

West Glamorgan

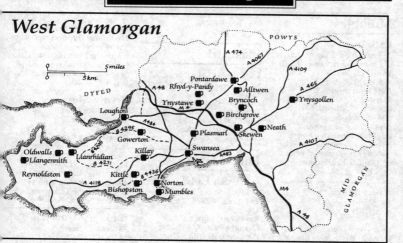

Alltwen

Butchers Arms
Alltwen Hill ☎ (01792) 863100
12–3, 6.30–11
**Courage Directors; Everards
Old Original; John Smith's
Bitter; Wadworth 6X; guest
beers** Ⓗ
A rarity in the area: a genuine
free house. The restaurant
provides views over the
Swansea Valley and is
recommended. Excellent
selection of single malt
whiskies. 🏚 Q ❀ ◖ ▶ & P

Birchgrove

Bridgend Inn
265 Birchgrove Road (off M4
jct 44) ☎ (01792) 321878
12–11
**Brains Dark; Marston's
Pedigree; John Smith's Bitter;
Wadworth 6X** Ⓗ
Local pub with a bar, a pool
room and a cosy lounge.
Families are welcome. Eve
meals to order.
Q ❀ ◖ ▶ & ♣ P

Bishopston

Joiners Arms
50 Bishopston Road
☎ (01792) 232658
12–11
**Brains Dark; Courage Best
Bitter, Directors; John Smith's
Bitter; guest beers** Ⓗ
Excellent free house serving
locals and Gower visitors
alike. It offers good value food
and always at least two guest
beers. Special 'beer months'
feature a vast range of
different beers. Occasional
cider. 🏚 ❀ ◖ ▶ ⌣ P

Bryncoch

Dyffryn Arms
Neath Road (A474)
☎ (01639) 636184
12–3, 7–11
**Whitbread Boddingtons Mild,
Bitter, Castle Eden Ale** Ⓗ
Well-run, rural pub, with a
fine display of old local photos
and a good collection of water
jugs. Good quality meals are
served in the bar and
restaurant (no meals Sun eve).
Large children's outdoor play
area. ❀ ◖ ▶ P

Gowerton

Welcome to Gower
Mount Street ☎ (01792) 872611
11.30–11
**Crown Buckley Dark, Best
Bitter, Rev. James** Ⓗ
Single-roomed pub, offering
good value meals. ◖ ▶ ⇥ P

Killay

Railway
Gower Road ☎ (01792) 203946
11.30–3.30, 5.30–11;
11.30–11 Fri & Sat
**Crown Buckley Dark, Best
Bitter, Rev. James** Ⓗ
Set in Clyne Valley Park, this
pub has a strong railway
theme (it stands on the old
Swansea–Gowerton line).
Bulmers cider. ❀ ◖ 🍴 ⌣ P

Kittle

Beaufort Arms
☎ (01792) 234521
12–11
**Crown Buckley Best Bitter,
Rev. James** Ⓗ
Pleasant pub and restaurant

(Mrs B's), featuring pictures
of old Swansea and the
surrounding area.
❀ ◖ ▶ P

Llangennith

King's Head Hotel
☎ (01792) 386212
11–11
**Crown Buckley Dark, Best
Bitter, Rev. James** Ⓗ
Village local with splendid
views over Rhossili Bay,
catering for the nearby holiday
park. ❀ ◖ ▶ 🍴 P

Llanrhidian

Welcome to Town
☎ (01792) 390015
11–3, 6–11 (varies with seasons)
Wadworth 6X Ⓗ
Country pub, opposite the
village green, open for
morning coffee. ❀ ◖

Loughor

Red Lion
Glebe Road (A4070)
☎ (01792) 892983
12–11
Felinfoel Dark, Bitter Ⓗ
Welcoming local where the
spacious lounge boasts a small
collection of old radio sets.
◖ 🍴 P

Reverend James
180 Borough Road (just off
A484) ☎ (01792) 892943
12–11
**Crown Buckley Dark, Best
Bitter, SBB, Rev. James** Ⓗ
Comfortable village inn and
restaurant. Note the
memorabilia concerning the
history of Crown Buckley.
🏚 ❀ ◖ ▶ 🍴 P

West Glamorgan

Mumbles

Park Inn
23 Park Street (right at church in Oystermouth, then 1st left)
☎ (01792) 366738
11.30-3.30, 5.30-11
Bass Worthington BB; Marston's Pedigree; Ruddles County; Wadworth 6X Ⓗ
Old-fashioned local with nautical decor; a popular, bright, but cosy free house, offering a variety of ales. The welcome is warm and genuine in its single bar/lounge.
Q ◑ ▶ &

Vincent's
580 Mumbles Road
☎ (01792) 368308
12-11
Bass Worthington BB, Draught Bass; guest beer Ⓗ
Seafront pub on a Spanish theme. It offers good value food and a regularly changed guest beer. ◑

Neath

Star
Pen-y-Dre ☎ (01639) 637745
12.30-4.30, 6-11; 12.30-11 Sat
Bass Worthington Dark, Draught Bass; Hancock's HB Ⓗ
Friendly local with two rooms, one of which is a snug. Conversation is the main theme, with occasional impromptu sing-alongs. Lunchtime bar snacks.
Q ⇌ P

Norton

Beaufort Arms
1 Castle Road (right by Norton House Hotel, off Mumbles)
☎ (01792) 406420
11.30-3, 5.30-11; 11-11 Fri & Sat
Bass Worthington Dark, BB, Draught Bass Ⓗ
Old-fashioned country pub, frequented by locals and tourists alike, with a split lounge and bar. The bar has all traditional pub games, and is fitted out in acres of wood, adorned with Toby jugs. The lounge is very smart, warm and cosy. ⚶ Q ❀ ◑ & ♣

Oldwalls

Greyhound
☎ (01792) 390146
11.30-11
Draught Bass; Hancock's HB; guest beers Ⓗ
Large free house set in the heart of Gower, benefiting from good views from the garden. An excellent restaurant specialises in

seafood. Guest beers are always available.
⚶ ❀ ◑ ▶ ⊞ ♣ P

Plasmarl

Commercial
Neath Road ☎ (01792) 771120
11.30-11
Brains Dark; Courage Best Bitter; John Smith's Bitter; guest beer (occasional) Ⓗ
Homely local, with a warm welcome. ❀ ⊞ ♣

Pontardawe

Ivy Bush Hotel
103 High Street (B4603)
☎ (01792) 862370
2.30-11
Bass Worthington BB, Draught Bass Ⓗ
Popular local with a large, traditional bar. A folk club meets upstairs. ⊞ ♣

Reynoldston

King Arthur Hotel
Higher Green
☎ (01792) 391099
11.30-11
Bass Worthington BB, Draught Bass; Felinfoel Double Dragon; Hancock's HB Ⓗ
Large village pub and restaurant. The bar features open wood fires and there is a games room. Various entertainments are presented throughout the year.
⚶ ❀ ◑ ▶ ♣ P

Rhyd-y-Pandy

Masons Arms
A few miles N of M4 jct 46
☎ (01792) 842535
11.30-11; 11.30-3, 6-11 Mon
Bass Worthington BB; Courage Best Bitter; Marston's Pedigree Ⓗ
Pleasant country pub, somewhat difficult to find but worth the effort. ⚶ ❀ ◑ ▶ P

Skewen

Crown
216 New Road
☎ (01792) 813309
11-11
Brains Dark, MA, SA Ⓗ
Friendly local; still the only pub to offer MA (a brewery mix of Bitter and Dark) on a regular basis. ⊞ ♣

Swansea

Adam & Eve
207 High Street
☎ (01792) 655913

11.30-4, 5.30-11; 11.30-11 Fri & Sat; 12-2.30, 7-10.30 Sun
Brains Dark, Bitter, SA Ⓗ
Traditional three-roomed pub. The rear bar was recently refurbished to a high standard. Good value food is served Mon–Sat. Occasional live bands. ◑ ⊞ ⇌

Bryn-y-Mor
Bryn-y-Mor Road
☎ (01792) 466650
11.30-11
Ansells Bitter; Ind Coope Burton Ale; Tetley Bitter; guest beer (occasional) Ⓗ
Lively locals' bar with pool and darts, plus live music Wed and Sun eves. Guest beers come from the Tetley range. No food Sun. ❀ ◑ ⊞ ♣

Builders Arms
36 Oxford Street
☎ (01792) 476189
11-11; closed Sun
Crown Buckley Dark, Best Bitter, Rev. James Ⓗ
Split-level lounge bar close to the Grand Theatre and Vetch Field football ground. Parties are catered for either in the dining area or on the upstairs balcony. Eve meals available by prior arrangement. Q ◑ &

Cockett
Waunarlwydd Road, Cockett
☎ (01792) 582083
11.30-11
Crown Buckley Dark, Best Bitter Ⓗ
Village local with a large bar and games area, plus a smaller, comfortable lounge. Boxing memorabilia is displayed in the bar.
❀ ◑ ⊞ ♣ P

Cross Keys
St Mary Street
11-11
Bass Worthington Dark, BB; guest beer Ⓗ
Well-appointed, city-centre pub. Its restaurant caters for a wide variety of tastes. A guest beer from the Bass range is usually available, changing every six weeks or so. ◑ ▶ ⇌

JC's
University College Swansea, Singleton Park
☎ (01792) 205678
12-11 (term time only)
Marston's Pedigree; Morland Old Speckled Hen; Whitbread Boddingtons Bitter, Castle Eden Ale Ⓗ
Well-appointed bar catering for students and locals. Various promotions are held throughout the year and the beer range may vary (Whitbread Cask Collection). Coffee and snacks are also available. Excellent value.
Q ♣ ✂

King's Arms

26 High Street
☎ (01792) 642216
12–11
**Courage Directors; Ruddles
Best Bitter; John Smith's
Bitter** H
Comfortable, one-roomed bar
which offers a carvery-style
Sun lunch. ◑ ⇌

Queens Hotel

Gloucester Place
☎ (01792) 643460
11–11
**Crown Buckley Best Bitter;
S&N Theakston Mild, Best
Bitter, Old Peculier** H
One-roomed lounge bar on the
edge of the marina. Numerous
photos depict the maritime
history of the area. Excellent
Sun lunches are served. The
outside drinking area is on the
pavement (tables set out).
❀ ◑ ₺ ⇌

St George

30 Walter Road
☎ (01792) 469317
11.30–11
**Bass Worthington Dark, BB;
Felinfoel Double Dragon** H
Lounge bar, just outside the
city centre; the only outlet for
Felinfoel in the city. Regular
events include live music Sun
eve and a quiz (Tue). Q ◑ ₺

Singleton Hotel

1 Dillwyn Street
☎ (01792) 655987
11.30–3, 6.30–11; 7–10.30 Sun, closed
Sun lunch

**Brains Dark; Courage
Directors; Ruddles Best
Bitter; John Smith's Bitter;
Ushers Founders** H
Comfortable lounge bar,
handy for the Grand Theatre.
Live entertainment Tue,
and Thu–Sat. Bulmers cider.
⌂

Star

1070 Carmarthen Road,
Fforestfach
☎ (01792) 586910
12–11; 12–4, 7–11 Wed
**Crown Buckley Dark, Best
Bitter** H
Friendly pub catering for the
nearby industrial estate and
locals alike. Large games area.
❀ ◑ ▶ ₩ ♣ P

Vivian Arms

104a Gower Road, Sketty
(Sketty Cross)
☎ (01792) 203015
12–11
Brains Dark, Bitter, SA H
Pub whose locals' bar holds
regular quiz nights. The
comfortable, spacious lounge
offers excellent home-cooking
weekdays, with curry a
speciality. ❀ ◑ ₩

Westbourne Hotel

1 Bryn-y-Mor Road
☎ (01792) 459054
12–11
**Bass Worthington Dark,
Draught Bass; Hancock's HB;
guest beers** H

Striking street-corner pub,
close to the Guildhall. The
landlord is famous for the
quality of his Bass and
currently presents some of the
best genuine guest ales in
Swansea. Bar skittles played.
❀ ◑ ₩ ♣

Ynysgollen

Rock & Fountain Inn

Glyn Neath Road (A465)
☎ (01639) 642681
12–3, 6–11
**Bass Worthington BB; Tetley
Bitter; guest beers** H
Pleasant country pub adjacent
to the A465. The restaurant
offers a varied menu, catering
for a wide range of tastes.
Usually one or two guest
beers are on sale. Relaxed
atmosphere.
❀ ◑ ▶ P

Ynystawe

Millers Arms

634 Clydach Road
☎ (01792) 842614
12–11
**Brains Dark; Whitbread
Flowers IPA, Castle Eden Ale;
guest beer** H
Comfortable, relaxing mainly
locals' pub serving good value
food. The small garden
overlooks a riverside walk.
The guest beer comes from the
Whitbread range.
❀ ◑ ▶ ₺ P

EUROWHINES

Does beer get a fair deal in Europe? For a start, there is a
minimum tax on beer across the European Union, but no
minimum tax on wine. Indeed, a ruling in Europe forced the
UK to cut taxes on wine and to raise them on beer, despite the
fact that some countries don't tax wine at all. On another
occasion, when ingredients listing for alcoholic drinks was
debated in the European Parliament, the wine lobby wanted it
to apply to every drink except wine. (This despite the
antifreeze scandal...) Fortunately this was defeated.
Furthermore, the European Union spends over a billion
pounds a year subsidising wine production—much of which
is undrinkable or, it has been claimed, a source of fraud.

All this ignores the fact that the consumption of beer and wine
across Europe is about the same (in terms of the numbers of
drinks taken)—and the balance will tilt to beer production and
beer drinking when Austria, Finland, Norway and Sweden
join the European Union.

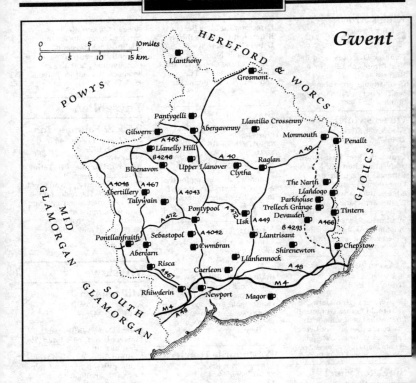

Gwent

Gwent

Abercarn

Old Swan
58 Commercial Road
☎ (01495) 243161
12–11
Courage Best Bitter; Ushers Best Bitter, Founders Ⓗ
Friendly valley pub where the area's mining heritage is remembered in photos. Separate pool room; a cosy lounge leads off the bar. Good value food. Camping available at the Cwmcarn Forest Drive. Snuff available at the bar.
🏨 ✿ ◑ ◗ ⊟ ▲ ♣

Abergavenny

Coach & Horses
Cross Street
10.30–11
Brains SA; Wadworth 6X; Whitbread Flowers IPA Ⓗ
Basic town boozer situated near the bus station. Now free of a tie, and the landlord's efforts are rewarded by this first entry in the *Guide*. One of the few local pubs that is open all day, but whenever you arrive you will get a warm welcome.
✿ ⇌ ⇔ ♣

Hen & Chickens
Flannel Street
☎ (01873) 853613
10.30–4, 7–11; 10–11 Tue; 10.30–11 Fri & Sat
Bass Worthington BB, Draught Bass; guest beer Ⓗ
An institution for many years, the 'Chicks' remains as popular as ever. A frequently changing guest beer has complemented the already large sales of Bass in this real ale mecca, while 'real' Worthington has virtually eliminated its keg equivalent. No food Sun. Q ☾ ◑ ♣

Somerset Arms
Victoria Street (Merthyr Rd jct)
☎ (01873) 852158
12–3 (not Wed; 12–2 winter); 7–11
Draught Bass; Felinfoel Bitter; guest beer Ⓗ
Popular family-run pub just outside the central area of town which has burst onto the local real ale scene over the last couple of years. Excellent reputation for beer, food (no meals Sun eve) and reasonably-priced accommodation. Superb summer floral displays.
🏨 Q ✿ ⛵ ◑ ◗ ⊟ ♣

Try also: Station, Brecon Rd (Free)

Abertillery

Clynmawr Hotel
Tŷ Bryn Road (off Gladstone St/A467) ☎ (01495) 212323
2 (1 Sat)–11
Crown Buckley Best Bitter Ⓗ
A short climb from the main road is rewarded in a public bar with a strong games tradition. There is also a lounge, skittle alley and a family room. ☾ ✿ ⊟ ♣

Blaenavon

Cambrian Inn
Cambrian Row
☎ (01495) 790327
6 (12 Sat)–11
Brains Dark, Bitter, SA; guest beers Ⓗ
Traditional locals' pub with a separate pool room and a comfortable lounge. Excellent guest beers—usually two every week. A stalwart of this guide. Q ⊟ ♣

Rifleman's Arms
1 Rifle Street (Abergavenny Road) ☎ (01495) 792297
12–3.30, 6–11 (12–11 summer)
Brains Bitter; Wadworth 6X; Whitbread Flowers IPA Ⓗ

Recently refurbished, small pub, ideally placed for Big Pit Mining Museum. Good food, but watch out for the dragon in the garden. ☎ ❀ ◑ ▶ P

Caerleon

Angel Hotel
Goldcroft Common
☎ (01633) 420264
12–11
Bass Worthington BB, Draught Bass; Hancock's HB; guest beer H
Popular outlet at the end of the village green: a quiet, relaxing lounge with a more boisterous bar. Home to local sports teams and close to the Roman remains. A good location from which to start a local crawl. Taunton cider. No eve meals Fri/Sat.
🚪 ❀ ◑ ▶ ❖ ⏥ P

Tabard Brasserie
High Street ☎ (01633) 422822
12–3 (not Sat & Sun), 6.30–11
Hardington Bitter, Moonshine; guest beers H
Small, friendly bar with an adjoining bistro and an upstairs restaurant. The beer range has now been extended to five handpumps (the widest changing range of guest beers in the area). Good reputation for high quality food. Norbury's perry is on sale.
Q ❀ ◑ ▶ ⏥ P ✗

Chepstow

Coach & Horses Inn
Welsh Street (near town arch)
☎ (01291) 622626
11–3, 6–11
Draught Bass; Brains SA; Crown Buckley Best Bitter, Rev. James; John Smith's Bitter; guest beer H
A regular *Guide* entry and a former Gwent CAMRA *Pub of the Year*: a popular bar with a good mix of clientele, attracting also occasional visits from the race-going fraternity. Beer festival in July. The house ale is brewed by Crown Buckley. Lunches served weekdays. ❀ ◑ ❂ ❄ ❖

Try also: Bridge Inn, Bridge St (Free)

Clytha

Clytha Arms
On old Raglan/Abergavenny Road, off B4598
☎ (01873) 840206
11.30–3 (not Mon), 6–11; 11–11 Sat
Hook Norton Best Bitter, Wadworth 6X; guest beers H
Gwent CAMRA *Pub of the Year* 1993: a country inn renowned for its food. Five beers

regularly available, often including a dark mild. The large mural in the gents' must be seen. Spacious garden; children welcome. One bedroom has a four-poster.
🚪 Q ❀ 🚲 ◑ ▶ ⏥ P

Cwmbran

Blinkin' Owl
Oxtens, Coed Eva
☎ (01633) 484749
12–4 (5 Sat), 6 (6.30 Sat)–11
Brains Dark, Bitter, SA H
Friendly estate pub, the best Brains outlet in Gwent. The basic bar and comfortable lounge both offer good food, or you can take it away.
Q ❀ ◑ ▶ ❂ ❖ P

Bush Inn
Graig Road, Upper Cwmbran (off Upper Cwmbran Rd)
☎ (01633) 483764
11–3, 7 (6 Fri & Sat)–11
Courage Best Bitter; guest beer H
A very lively pub at weekends, with disco, karaoke, etc.: two rooms, comfortably and impressively furnished. Excellent value for money Sun lunches (book well in advance). Book also for all eve meals. Parking limited.
🚪 ❀ ◑ P

Rose & Crown
Victoria Street
☎ (01633) 866700
11–11
John Smith's Bitter; guest beer H
Popular pub not far from the sports stadium: a small public bar and a larger lounge bar, where weekend discos and karaoke make for boisterous eves. ❀ ❂ ❖ P

Try also: Commodore Hotel, Llanyravon (Free)

Devauden

Masons Arms
On B4293 ☎ (0129 15) 315
11.30–2.30 (not Mon–Thu), 6.30–11
Draught Bass H
Unspoilt, friendly old pub with three rooms served by a small bar and impressive coal fires in winter. Check opening times if planning a visit.
🚪 ❀ ❖ P

Gilwern

Bridgend Inn
Main Road ☎ (01873) 830939
12–3, 7–11; 12–11 Fri, Sat & summer
Morland Old Speckled Hen; Ruddles Best Bitter; guest beers H
Pleasant canalside pub with a good range of independents'

ales. The open-plan interior includes a cosy fireside corner and a small dining area. Good varied menu. A popular watering hole for passing trade enjoying the fine scenery of the Clydach Gorge.
❀ 🚲 ◑ ▲ ❖ P

Corn Exchange Inn
Crickhowell Road
☎ (01873) 830337
11.30–3, 5–11 (11–11 summer)
Draught Bass; Brains SA; Hancock's HB H
Pub with a congenial atmosphere, comprising a pleasant bar and a tastefully decorated lounge. Good food is served in the cosy dining room (book for Sun lunch). Brains SA occasionally gives way to other guest ales.
❀ ◑ ▶ ❂ ▲ P

Grosmont

Angel
Main Street ☎ (01981) 240646
12–3, 7–11
Crown Buckley Best Bitter, Rev. James; Hancock's HB H
Old pub in an historic village with an impressive church and a castle. A good stop for walkers on the Three Castles Walk, or for those who like to visit pubs in charming, timeless villages. Rev. James is renamed 'Rev. Pope', in honour of the local vicar.
🚪 ❀ 🚲 ◑ ▶ ❖

Llandogo

Sloop Inn
On A466 ☎ (01594) 530291
11–3, 6–11; 11–11 Fri & Sat
Draught Bass; Hook Norton Best Bitter; Wye Valley Bitter H
Smart roadside inn with a large public bar with beams resembling ships' masts. The lounge faces the river and is popular with diners. Very comfortable accommodation.
🚪 ❀ 🚲 ◑ ▶ ❂ ▲ P

Llanelly Hill

Jolly Colliers
OS221123 ☎ (01873) 830408
12–4, 6.30–11
Beer range varies H
Excellent value food and a warm welcome in a hard-to-find village pub, near Clydach. Popular with all sorts. Sun lunches are served (book).
🚪 ❀ ▶ ❂ ▲ ❖ ⏥ P

Llanhennock

Wheatsheaf Inn
1 mile off Caerleon–Usk road
OS353929 ☎ (01633) 420468
11–3.30, 5.30–11; 11–11 Sat & summer

Gwent

Bass Worthington BB, Draught Bass; guest beer Ⓗ
Unspoilt, old village pub with a rare Rhymney Brewery huntsman figure in the bar. Excellent home-cooked lunches and speciality doorstep sandwiches; private dining room available. No food Sun. 🏰 Q ✿ ◁ ♣ P

Llanthony

Half Moon

200 yds beyond the priory
OS288279 ☎ (01873) 890611
11–3, 6–11
Bullmastiff Son of a Bitch; Hook Norton Best Bitter; guest beer (summer) Ⓗ
Small, basic and friendly pub, retaining its stone flagged floor. Situated in a tiny hamlet which has impressive monastic ruins and glorious walking for miles around. Remote, but a trip is rewarding.
🏰 Q ⌂ ◁ ▶ ♣ ◆ ⌕

Llantilio Crossenny

Hostry Inn

On B4233 ☎ (0160 085) 278
12–3, 6–11
Wye Valley Hereford Bitter, Brew 69 Ⓗ
15th-century village pub where visitors are welcomed. Large function room; folk music fortnightly on Thu. Good selection of food, with a choice of vegetarian dishes.
✿ ⌂ ◁ ▶ ♣ P ⑂

Llantrisant

Greyhound Inn

☎ (01291) 672505
11–3, 6–11
Marston's Pedigree; Morland Old Speckled Hen; Wadworth 6X; Whitbread Boddingtons Bitter, Flowers Original; guest beer Ⓗ
Rural, split-level, country inn catering for all tastes—with a restaurant, cocktail bar, lounge and a splendidly traditional bar. No access from A449.
🏰 Q ⌕ ✿ ◁ ▶ ◁ ♣ P

Magor

Golden Lion

The Square ☎ (01633) 880312
11–11
Hancock's HB; Ruddles County; Wadworth 6X Ⓗ
A golden lion guards the entrance to this pleasant village inn where a games room adjoins the public bar and the lounge includes a dining area. Plenty of stone and wood feature in the decor.

The menu includes popular home-made dishes. Beware the keg Scrumpy Jack cider on fake handpump. ✿ ◁ ▶ ◁ ♣

Monmouth

Green Dragon Inn

St Thomas Square
☎ (01600) 712561
11–11
Marston's Bitter, Pedigree; guest beers Ⓗ
Near the historic fortified bridge, a friendly, cosy pub embracing the traditions of its trade: good beer, good 'crack', and good food—the last very competitively priced. Superb cartoons in the loos. ◁ ◁ ♣

The Narth

Trekkers

OS525064 ☎ (01600) 860367
11–3.30, 6–11
Draught Bass; Felinfoel Bitter; Freeminer Bitter Ⓗ
Built in the style of a log cabin, this pub also doubles as the village post office. Excellent food is served in the dining area to one side of the central open fire. Friendly resident dogs; large garden with swings. 🏰 Q ✿ ◁ ▶ ◁ ♣ P

Newport

Hornblower Inn

126 Commercial Street
☎ (01633) 267575
11–11
Ansells Bitter, Mild; Ind Coope Burton Ale; Reckless Eric's Rejoice; Tetley Bitter Ⓗ
Loud, one-bar bikers' pub, part of the Reckless Eric's Brewing Co. (other Reckless Eric beers sometimes replace Rejoice). Motorbike photos are displayed on the wood-panelled walls. Wide range of music on the jukebox; occasional live music. ⇌

Ivy Bush

65 Clarence Place (near cenotaph) ☎ (01633) 267571
11–11
John Smith's Bitter Ⓗ
Traditional pub on the fringe of the town centre. The lounge bar has a high gantry and is the venue for popular karaoke eves. The public bar doubles as an excellent games room. Handy for Newport RFC.
✿ ⌕ ◁ ♣ ◆

St Julians

Caerleon Road
☎ (01633) 258663
11.30–11
Courage Best Bitter; Marston's Pedigree; Ruddles Best Bitter; John Smith's Bitter; guest beer Ⓗ

Firmly established outlet with a reputation for unusual guest ales. The food is cheap and popular (eve meals end at 8.30; no food Sun). An outdoor balcony offers picturesque views over the Usk. Skittle alley. ✿ ◁ ♣ P

Windsor Castle

19 Upper Dock Street
☎ (01633) 266819
11–3, 5–11; 11–11 Fri & Sat; 7–10.30 Sun, closed Sun lunch
Draught Bass; Hancock's HB Ⓗ
Popular, split-level, town-centre pub near the bus station. Friendly cross-section of locals during the week, but very busy at weekends. One of the last traditional pubs in an area that is being overrun with theme pubs. Wheelchair access at the side. ◁ ⌖ ⇌

Try also: Ale House, John Frost Sq (Carlsberg-Tetley)

Pantygelli

Crown Inn

Old Hereford Road
☎ (01873) 853314
11–3, 6–11
Draught Bass; Felinfoel Double Dragon Ⓗ
Large, open-plan pub with dining and separated drinking areas, in a small hamlet at the gateway to the Black Mountains. A good base for walkers or trekkers. Good views from the patio.
🏰 ✿ ◁ ▶ P

Parkhouse

Parkhouse Tavern

OS497029 ☎ (01600) 860224
12–2 (not Wed), 6.30–11
Draught Bass *or* **Wadworth 6X** Ⓖ
Isolated, but worth finding, hospitable village pub, where the hosts provide substantial home-cooked meals. Booking preferred for the traditional Sun lunch; no food Sun eve.
🏰 Q ✿ ◁ ▶ ♣ P

Penallt

Boat Inn

Lone Lane (off A466, access by footbridge from Redbrook)
OS536098 ☎ (01600) 712615
11–3, 6–11
Butcombe Bitter; Hook Norton Best Bitter, Old Hooky; S&N Theakston Old Peculier; Wadworth 6X; guest beers Ⓖ
Excellent riverside pub with a small bar and an adjoining room featuring stonework. Good value food from an imaginative menu. Live music Tue and Thu. Cider in

summer. The car park is in Redbrook.
🛏 🏵 🍴 ◑ P

Pontllanfraith

Crown
The Bryn (near A472/A4049 jct) ☎ (01495) 223404
12–3, 5–11; 12–11 Fri & Sat
Courage Best Bitter; Felinfoel Double Dragon; John Smith's Bitter; guest beer (summer) Ⓗ
Pub with a spacious lounge popular with diners (well-balanced menu; book for eve meals at weekends). The public bar has a pool table and a big TV. Good outdoor play area for children.
🏵 ◑ ▶ 🍴 ♣ P ✕

Pontypool

George
Commercial Street
☎ (01495) 764734
11.30–4, 7–11
John Smith's Bitter; guest beer Ⓗ
Smart, Edwardian-style bar with wooden floorboards and a gallery of pictures with a 'George' theme. Two round shelves, mounted on ornate lamp stands are other features. Popular upstairs restaurant. Handy for Pontypool Park. Book Sun lunch. ◑

Raglan

Ship Inn
High Street ☎ (01291) 690635
11–3, 5.30–11
Draught Bass; guest beers Ⓗ
Old coaching inn dating from the 16th century, with a cobbled forecourt and a water pump. At least two guest beers available. 🛏 Q 🏵 ◑ ▶ 🍴 ♣

Rhiwderin

Rhiwderin Inn
Caerphilly Road
☎ (01633) 893234
12–3, 5.30–11; 12–11 Sat
Draught Bass; Hancock's HB Ⓗ
Popular roadside inn with a comfortable lounge and a separate public bar. Well-known locally for formidable food portions (vegetarian options). No eve meals Sun.
🛏 Q 🏵 ◑ ▶ 🍴 ♣ P

Risca

Exchange Inn
52 St Mary Street (B4591)
☎ (01633) 612706
12–5, 7–11
Crown Buckley Best Bitter, SBB, Rev. James Ⓗ

Smart, colourful free house on the main road through the village. The traditional public bar is complemented by a comfortable lounge. Friendly regulars.
🏵 ◑ 🍴 ♣ P

Sebastopol

Open Hearth
Wern Road (off B4244)
☎ (01495) 763752
11–3, 6–11
Archers Golden; Draught Bass; Brains Dark, SA; guest beers Ⓗ
Welcoming canalside pub with a wide range of ales, which include local independents'. Cosy atmosphere throughout; good value food from an extensive menu, including occasional specials.
Q 🏵 ◑ ▶ 🍴 ♣ P

Shirenewton

Carpenters Arms
Usk Road (B4235)
☎ (01291) 641231
11–3, 6–11
Marston's Pedigree, Owd Rodger; Ruddles County; Wadworth 6X; Whitbread Boddingtons Bitter, Flowers IPA; guest beer Ⓗ
Very pleasant inn with seven rooms, featuring artefacts of past local industry. Superb home-cooked food, including occasional country specials.
🛏 Q 🏵 ◑ ▶ P

Talywain

Globe Inn
Commercial Road (main Abersychan–Varteg road)
☎ (01495) 772053
6 (11 Sat)–11
Brains Dark, Bitter; Crown Buckley Best Bitter; Hancock's HB; guest beers Ⓗ
Typical valleys pub, except for providing an excellent range of beers in a national brewers' domain. Separate pool room. Cider in summer.
🛏 🍴 ♣ ⌂

Tintern

Cherry Tree
Devauden Road (off A466)
OS526001 ☎ (01291) 689292
11–3, 6–11
Hancock's HB Ⓖ
This isolated pub is the centre of the village community, in scenic Wye valley countryside. A rare Toastmaster sign is displayed outside. In this guide every year since its inception. Limited parking.
🛏 Q 🏵 ♣ ⌂ P

Trellech Grange

Fountain Inn
Off B4293 OS503011
☎ (01291) 689303
12–3, 6–11
Wadworth 6X; guest beers Ⓗ
Traditional, 17th-century hostelry in the Wye valley. Unusually, a stream runs beneath the building itself. Excellent variety of meals, including vegetarian, plus children's portions.
🛏 🏵 🏠 ◑ ▶ ▲ ♣ P

Upper Llanover

Goose & Cuckoo
Off A4042, near Llanover
OS292073 ☎ (01873) 880277
11.30–3, 7–11
Bullmastiff Bitter; Wadworth 6X; guest beer (summer) Ⓗ
Pub situated at the end of a long, narrow lane rising up into the national park. Noted for its range of malts and vegetarian meals, as well as its beer. Beautiful views and excellent walks from the front door. Ring to check for eve meals in winter.
🛏 Q 🛏 🏵 ◑ ▶ ♣ P

Usk

Cardiff Arms
69 Bridge Street
☎ (01291) 672895
11–3, 6–11
Tetley Bitter; guest beers Ⓗ
Refurbished, corner local: a drinkers' pub—the only one in the town with a liquids-only menu. At least two guest beers, competitively priced.
♣

Greyhound Inn
1 Old Chepstow Road
☎ (01291) 672074
11.30–3, 6–11
Draught Bass; Hancock's HB; guest beer Ⓗ
Welcoming, single-roomed locals' pub just off the town square. A tastefully furnished lounge bar offers relaxing surroundings. Q 🏵 ◑ ▶

King's Head
Old Market Street
☎ (01291) 672963
11–11
Fuller's Chiswick; Marston's Pedigree; Whitbread Flowers Original; guest beer Ⓗ
Spacious pub with contrasting bars: a traditional public (popular with the young), and a comfortable lounge with an impressive fireplace. Appetising food. Separate dining/function room.
🛏 Q 🏠 ◑ ▶ 🍴 ♣ P

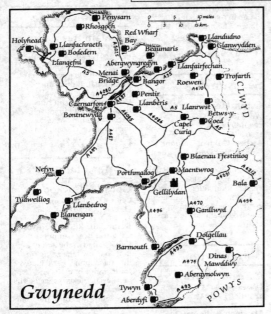

Gwynedd

 Snowdonia, Gellilydan

Aberdyfi

Penhelig Arms
☎ (01654) 767215
11–3, 6–11
**Tetley Walker Dark Mild,
Bitter; guest beers** Ⓗ
Bar overlooking the estuary,
popular with the yachting
fraternity. Good menu.
🏚 🛏 🌒 ▲ ≋ P

Abergwyngregyn

Aber Falls Hotel
☎ (01248) 680579
11–11 (midnight Thu–Sat)
**S&N Theakston Mild, Best
Bitter, XB** Ⓗ
Large pub in a small village,
close to the busy A55, soon to
be bypassed. It has a large
lounge and a conservatory
where meals are served
(families welcome).
🏚 Q ✿ 🛏 🌒 ▶ P

Abergynolwyn

Railway Inn
On B4405 ☎ (01654) 782279
12–3 (4 summer), 7 (6 summer)–11
**Ansells Mild; Draught Bass;
Felinfoel Double Dragon;
Greenalls Shipstone's Bitter;
Tetley Walker Bitter; guest
beer** Ⓗ
Friendly, three-roomed village
pub in a picturesque valley,
offering the widest selection of
beers for miles.
🏚 Q ✿ ✿ 🌒 ▶ ▲ ♣ P

Bala

Goat Inn
High Street ☎ (01678) 521189
11–11
**Banks's Mild; Marston's
Bitter, Pedigree** Ⓗ
Large, busy, two-roomed town
pub, recently modernised and
attracting all age groups.
🛏 🌒 ▲ ♣ P

Bangor

Harp
High Street ☎ (01248) 353888
12–11
**Marston's Bitter, Pedigree,
Owd Rodger** Ⓗ
Pub boasting a large bar room
with smaller areas, plus a pool
room upstairs. Very popular
with students, but it can be
smoky. Marston's Head
Brewer's Choice available. No
food Sun. 🏚 Q 🌒 ♣

Union Hotel
Garth Road ☎ (01248) 362462
11–11
**Burtonwood Bitter, Top
Hat** Ⓗ
A nautical theme in a pub with
lots of rooms, leading off a
single bar. Very friendly and

popular. No eve meals Tue.
Q ✿ 🛏 🌒 🔲 ▭ ≋ P

Barmouth

Tal y Don
High Street ☎ (01341) 280508
11–11
Burtonwood Mild, Bitter Ⓗ
Typical town pub, adorned
with brass, in a poorly-served
resort. 🏚 ✿ 🛏 🔲 ≋

Beaumaris

Olde Bull's Head
Castle Street ☎ (01248) 810329
11–11
**Bass Worthington BB,
Draught Bass; guest beers** Ⓗ
This is the Anglesey 'not to be
missed' pub, an historic Grade
II-listed building. Its past
guests include Dr Johnson and
Charles Dickens. The two bars
are full of antique weaponry
and china. No food Sun.
🏚 Q 🛏 🌒 P

Betws-y-Coed

Glan Aber
Holyhead Road
☎ (01690) 710325
11–11
**Felinfoel Double Dragon;
Tetley Walker Mild, Bitter** Ⓗ
Popular local of three rooms,
busy all year. Different bars
cater to different tastes. 🏚
Q ✿ ✿ 🛏 🌒 ▲ ≋ ♣ P

Miners Bridge Inn
Holyhead Road
☎ (01690) 710386
12–5, 6–11
**Bass Worthington BB; M&B
Mild; guest beers** Ⓗ
Three-roomed village pub
where a friendly welcome
awaits the traveller. Pool and
darts in the bar; meals in the
lounge. An additional lounge
opens for summer crowds,
leading onto the garden.
✿ 🛏 🌒 🔲 ▲ ≋ ♣ P

Blaenau Ffestiniog

Manod
Manod Road ☎ (01766) 830346
11–11
**S&N Theakston Mild, Best
Bitter, XB** Ⓗ
Traditional old town pub,
recently enlarged into the next
door house: a small smoke
room and a pleasant lounge.
Q ≋ ♣ P

Bodedern

Crown Hotel
☎ (01407) 740734
12–3.30, 6–11; 11–11 Sat & bank hols
Burtonwood Bitter Ⓗ

A good example of a village pub with letting bedrooms; an ideal base for exploring Anglesey. Three main rooms, a lounge bar and a darts room are complemented by a pool room, doubling as a children's room. Good food, good value.
🏠 ❀ 🛏 ◑ ♣ P

Bontnewydd

Newborough Arms
☎ (01286) 673126
11–3, 6–11; 11–11 Sat
Draught Bass; Ind Coope ABC Best Bitter, Burton Ale; Tetley Walker Mild, Bitter; guest beer Ⓗ
Lined glasses are used in this four-roomed local, which brims with atmosphere. The friendly landlord serves basic, good value food. Children welcome; wheelchair access is via the back entrance.
🏠 Q ❀ ◑ ♣

Caernarfon

Yr Goron Fach
Hole in the Wall Street
☎ (01286) 673338
11–11
Draught Bass; Cains Bitter; Tetley Walker Bitter; guest beers Ⓗ
Long and narrow pub with a bar in the middle. Partly stone walls and bench seating feature in the bar. The lounge is slightly quieter and more comfortable. Eve meals in summer only. No wheelchair access to ladies' WC.
❀ ◑ ♣

Capel Curig

Bryn Tyrch Hotel
☎ (0169 04) 223
12–11
Marston's Pedigree; Whitbread Flowers IPA, Castle Eden Ale Ⓗ
Old pub with a quiet room and a TV room, ideally located for Snowdonia and very popular with climbers (even in the middle of winter). Good varied meals all week.
🏠 Q ❀ 🛏 ◑ ♣ P

Cobden's Hotel
☎ (0169 04) 243
11–3, 6–11; 11–11 Sat
Greenalls Original; Ind Coope Burton Ale; Tetley Walker Bitter Ⓗ
Informal, fun, family-run hotel: a lounge, restaurant and a climbers' bar which features a natural rock face. Food is freshly prepared, with a local influence. Warm welcome.
🏠 Q ❀ 🛏 ◑ & ♣ P

Dinas Mawddwy

Red Lion
Off A470 ☎ (01650) 531247
11–3, 6–11; 11–11 Sat & summer
Bass Worthington BB, Draught Bass; Felinfoel Double Dragon Ⓗ
Friendly local with a large lounge, a popular meeting place. The public bar is full of brasses. 🏠 Q ☾ ❀ 🛏 ◑
◑ ⊟ & ▲ ♣ P

Dolgellau

Cross Keys
Mill Street ☎ (01341) 423342
11–11
Bass Worthington BB; Draught Bass Ⓗ
Unspoilt, welcoming, town pub; a real local. ⊟ ▲ ♣

Ganllwyd

Tyn y Groes
On A470 ☎ (01341) 402775
11–3, 7–11 (11–11 summer)
Tetley Walker Bitter; Whitbread Flowers IPA Ⓗ
Valley inn, set in a hillside forest. Good value food.
🏠 ☾ ❀ 🛏 ◑ ◑ ⊟ ▲ ♣ P

Glanwydden

Queen's Head
☎ (01492) 546570
11–3, 6–11
Ind Coope Burton Ale; Tetley Walker Bitter; guest beers Ⓗ
Country pub in a small village, one mile from the seafront. A warm welcome, but no children under 7. 🏠 Q ◑ ◑ P

Holyhead

Seventy Nine
79 Market Street
☎ (01407) 763939
11–3.30, 7–11
S&N Theakston XB; Whitbread Boddingtons Bitter; guest beers Ⓗ
Nicely furnished town pub on the edge of the shopping area. One long bar serves two comfortable lounge areas, with a dining room at one end. Frequent guest beers come mostly from independents and micro-breweries. Q ◑ ⇌

Llanbedrog

Ship Inn
Pig Street ☎ (01758) 740270
11–3.30, 5.30–11 (11–11 summer); closed Sun
Burtonwood Mild, Bitter Ⓗ
Cosy, friendly pub with a seafood restaurant. It boasts a new, unusually-shaped, no-smoking family room. 🏠
Q ☾ ❀ ◑ ◑ & ▲ ♣ P ⊬

Llanberis

Victoria Hotel
☎ (01286) 870253
11–3, 5.30–11; 11–11 Sat
Draught Bass; Felinfoel Double Dragon; Tetley Walker Bitter; Whitbread Boddingtons Bitter Ⓗ
Massive hotel on the southern outskirts of town, opposite Snowdon Mountain Railway. Typical hotel atmosphere.
Q ☾ ❀ 🛏 ◑ ◑ & P

Llandudno

Cottage Loaf
Market Street
☎ (01492) 870762
11–11
Courage Directors; Ruddles County; Webster's Yorkshire Bitter; guest beers Ⓗ
Pub built from ships' timbers on the site of an old bakehouse, with a stone and wood floor. Very popular for lunches. 🏠 Q ❀ ◑ & ⇌ P

Links Hotel
Conwy Road
☎ (01492) 879180
11–11
Lees GB Mild, Bitter Ⓔ
Large, two-room pub on a housing estate: a small public bar and a larger lounge bar with extra seating in the conservatory. An outside play area caters for children. Food is served all day.
Q ☾ ❀ 🛏 ◑ ◑ ⊟ & ♣ P

London Hotel
131 Upper Mostyn Street
☎ (01492) 876740
12–4, 7–11
Burtonwood Bitter, Forshaw's, Top Hat Ⓗ
Large, town-centre pub, recently refurbished, with a new bar. A working red phone box and London memorabilia feature. The family room opens lunchtimes. Folk club Sun; quiz Tue. ☾ 🛏 ◑ ♣

Llanengan

Sun
☎ (0175 881) 2260
11–11; closed Sun
Ind Coope Burton Ale; Tetley Walker Bitter Ⓗ**; guest beers** (summer)
Popular pub, near Hell's Mouth beach. Excellent food and safe gardens.
🏠 🛏 ◑ ◑ ⊟ ▲ ♣ P

Llanfachraeth

Holland Hotel
On A5025 ☎ (01407) 740252
11–3, 7–11 (11–11 summer)
Lees GB Mild, Bitter Ⓗ

Gwynedd

Friendly local with a traditional layout of several small rooms served from a single small bar. TV and pool room. Q ❀ 🛏 ◑ ◐ ♣ P

Llanfairfechan

Castle Hotel
Penmaenmawr Road
☎ (01248) 680719
11–11
Draught Bass [H]
Lively town pub, popular with the locals. Entertainment some eves in one of the two lounges.
Q 🛏 ▲ ≢ ♣ P

Pen-y-Bryn
Pen-y-Bryn Road
☎ (01248) 680017
11–11
Tetley Walker Dark Mild, Bitter [H]
Situated in an old village, with welcoming owners, this Welsh-speaking pub is friendly but often smoky.
♘ ≢

Llangefni

Railway
High Street ☎ (01248) 722166
11–3.30 (12–2 Mon–Thu), 6.30–11
Lees GB Mild, Bitter [H]
Friendly pub, just away from the noise and bustle of this busy market town. Close to the now defunct railway station, it retains a railway theme in its different rooms. Moonraker may be available in winter. Q ♣

Llanrwst

New Inn
12 Denbigh Street
☎ (01492) 640476
11–11
Banks's Mild; Marston's Bitter, Pedigree; guest beer [H]
One-roomed, town-centre pub, busy with young people (loud music and pool). Guests come from the Marston's list.
♛ ❀ ▲ ≢ ♣

Maentwrog

Grapes Hotel
☎ (01766) 85208
11–11
Bass Worthington BB, Draught Bass; guest beer [H]
13th-century hotel, family-run and very busy, overlooking the Vale of Ffestiniog. The basement restaurant enjoys a good reputation.
♛ ♘ ❀ 🛏 ◑ ◐ ⊞ ▲ ♣ P

Menai Bridge

Liverpool Arms
St George's Pier
☎ (01248) 712453
11.30–3, 5.30–11
Greenalls Bitter, Original [H]
Many-roomed pub with a community atmosphere. Good, home-made food comes in large portions and is good value (order by 8pm). Q ◑ ◐

Nefyn

Sportsman
Stryd Fawr ☎ (01758) 720205
12 (11 summer)–11; closed Sun
Bass Worthington BB, Draught Bass [H]
Friendly pub, popular with locals and tourists.
♛ Q ❀ ◑ ▲ ♣

Pentir

Vaynol Arms
Off B4366 ☎ (01248) 362896
12–3, 6–11; 12–11 Sat
S&N Theakston Old Peculier; Tetley Walker Bitter; guest beer [H]
Old village pub, refurbished, with a public bar, a pleasant, well-furnished lounge and a dining room. Good quality and value food. ♛ ❀ ◑ ◐ P

Penysarn

Bedol
Off A5025 ☎ (01407) 832590
12–11
Marston's Bitter, Pedigree; guest beers [H]
Fairly new pub, originally Greenalls, but now completely revitalised under Marston's. It offers regular entertainment.
♛ Q ❀ ◑ ◐ ⊞ ▲ ♣ P

Porthmadog

Ship
Lombard Street
☎ (01766) 512990
11–11; closed Sun
Ind Coope Burton Ale; Tetley Walker Mild, Bitter; guest beer [H]
Popular town pub overlooking a park, near the Ffestiniog Railway. It is known locally for the oriental cuisine in its upstairs restaurant. ♛ ♘ ❀ ◑ ◐ ⊞ ♿ ▲ ≢ ♣ P

Red Wharf Bay

Ship
Off A5025 ☎ (01248) 852568
11.30–3.30, 7–11 (11–11 summer)
Ind Coope Friary Meux Best Bitter; Tetley Walker Dark Mild, Bitter; guest beers [H]
The best pub site on Anglesey, with views across the bay to the surrounding hills. Full of character, it features stone walls, wooden beams and huge fireplaces. An award-winning food pub.
♛ Q ♘ ❀ ◑ ◐ ♣ P

Rhosgoch

Rhosgoch Hotel (Ring)
1 mile off B5111 OS409892
☎ (01407) 830720
5.30 (12 Fri & Sat)–11
Bass Worthington BB, Draught Bass; Stones Best Bitter [H]
Pub not very easy to find, but well worth the effort. Much improved in recent years, it has several different areas, all served from a central bar. Regular live entertainment.
♛ Q ❀ ◑ ◐ ♣ P

Roewen

Tŷ Gwyn Hotel
☎ (01492) 650232
12–11 (12–2, 5–11 winter)
Lees GB Mild, Bitter [H]
Village pub in an idyllic setting with a friendly atmosphere. Good garden.
♛ Q ♘ ❀ ◑ ◐ ⊞ ▲ ♣ P

Trofarth

Holland Arms
On B5113 ☎ (01492) 650777
12–2.30, 7–11
Ansells Mild; Tetley Walker Bitter [H]
18th-century coaching house offering a traditional, warm, Welsh welcome in the countryside; within sight of Snowdonia. Bar, lounge, and restaurant areas are all pleasantly furnished. Families are welcome until 9pm.
Q ❀ ◑ ◐ ♣ P

Tudweiliog

Lion Hotel
On B4417 ☎ (0175 887) 244
12–2, 7–11 (11–3, 6–11 summer); 11–11 Sat all year; closed Sun
Marston's Pedigree; S&N Matthew Brown Mild (summer)**, Theakston Best Bitter, XB** (winter)**; Whitbread Boddingtons Bitter** [H]
300-year-old inn near sandy beaches. Popular with holidaymakers; comfortable and friendly. Q ♘ ❀ 🛏 ◑ ◐ ⊞ ♿ ▲ ♣ P

Tywyn

Corbett Arms Hotel
High Street ☎ (01654) 710264
11–11
Draught Bass; Hancock's HB; Tetley Walker Bitter [H]
Hotel bar with a plush, pleasant lounge. Its dress code encourages older clients.
Q ❀ 🛏 ◑ ◐ ♿ ▲ ≢ P

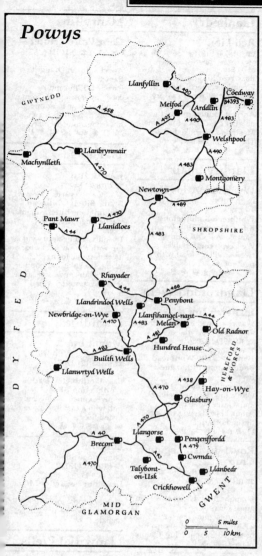

Powys

(Map showing Powys and surrounding areas: Gwynedd, Shropshire, Dyfed, Hereford & Worcs, Gwent, Mid Glamorgan. Locations marked include Llanfyllin, Coedway, Meifod, Arddlin, Welshpool, Llanbrynmair, Machynlleth, Montgomery, Newtown, Pant Mawr, Llanidloes, Rhayader, Llandrindod Wells, Penybont, Newbridge-on-Wye, Llanfihangel-nant-Melan, Old Radnor, Hundred House, Builth Wells, Llanwrtyd Wells, Hay-on-Wye, Glasbury, Llangorse, Pengenffordd, Brecon, Cwmdu, Talybont-on-Usk, Llanbedr, Crickhowell.)

Scale: 0 — 5 miles / 0 — 5 — 10 km

Old Boar's Head

Ship Street ☎ (01874) 622856
11–3, 5.30–11; 11–11 Tue, Fri & Sat
Brains SA; Crown Buckley Rev. James; Fuller's ESB; Hook Norton Best Bitter; Tetley Bitter; guest beer H
Old pub adjacent to the bridge over the River Usk: a characterful public bar, recently refurbished, and a spacious rear room with a pool table, popular with younger clientele. Live music monthly. Bar snacks always, but meals in summer only. Cask cider in summer. ❀ ◖ ⊟ ♣ ⌂ P

Try also **George Hotel**, George St (Free)

Builth Wells

Fountain Inn

Broad Street ☎ (01982) 553580
12–3, 7–11; 12–11 Sat
Wadworth 6X; Wood Special, Wonderful; Whitbread Flowers Original H
400-year-old inn reputed to be the oldest building in Builth, featuring oak beams, a large open fire and brass and copper jugs. ♨ ❀ A ♣

Coedway

Old Hand & Diamond

On B4393 ☎ (01743) 884379
11–11
Bass Worthington BB, Draught Bass; guest beers H
A plain exterior hides the immaculate, comfortable interior of this old pub of character: four rooms, including a restaurant with a good reputation.
♨ ❀ ◖ ◗ ⊟ A ♣ P

Crickhowell

Bear Hotel

On A40 ☎ (01873) 810408
11–3, 6–11
Draught Bass; Ruddles Best Bitter, County; Webster's Yorkshire Bitter; guest beers (occasional) H
Delightful, historic 15th-century coaching inn situated in the centre of town. A winner of many awards in recent years for its bar and cuisine. Popular with locals.
♨ Q ▓ ❀ ☺ ◖ ◗ P

White Hart Inn

Brecon Road (A40) ☎ (01873) 810473
12–3, 6–11; 11.45–11 Sat
Draught Bass; Brains Bitter; Hancock's HB; S&N Theakston XB H
15th-century former coaching inn and toll house (the tolls are still displayed on the wall

Arddlin

Horseshoe

On A483/B4392
☎ (0193 875) 318
12–3, 5.30–11
Bass Worthington BB; Marston's Pedigree H
Welcoming village pub: a traditional public bar, with a comfortable lounge/restaurant. Wide range of reasonably priced food. Children's play area in the garden. Three real ciders available.
♨ ❀ ◖ ◗ ⊟ ♣ ⌂ P

Brecon

Gremlin Hotel

48 The Watton
☎ (01874) 623829
12–3, 7–11 (12–11 during jazz festival)
Draught Bass; Brains Bitter H
Popular local with sub-medieval origins and a resident piano-playing ghost, close to S Wales Borderers' and Brecknock Museums. Comfortable bars with a wide range of competitively priced dishes on the menu. No eve meals Sun or Mon.
🛏 ◖ ◗ ⊟ ♣ P

Powys

outside). Two warm, friendly bars. Bar snacks and an à la carte restaurant menu available, with Welsh dishes a speciality. ❀ ◖ ▶ ▲ ♣ P

Cwmdu

Farmer's Arms
On A479, 6 miles S of Talgarth
☎ (01874) 730464
11–3, 6–11
Draught Bass; Brains Bitter; guest beers (summer) Ⓗ
Friendly country, roadside pub. Hearty, wholesome food at reasonable prices is the speciality.
🏠 Q ❀ ➾ ◖ ▶ ⊟ ▲ P

Glasbury

Harp Inn
On B4350, near A438 jct
☎ (01497) 847373
11–3, 6–11
Draught Bass; Robinson's Best Bitter; Whitbread Boddingtons Bitter, Flowers Original Ⓗ
Warm, welcoming inn bordering the River Wye, formerly a 17th-century cider house. Popular with locals and a good base for exploring the area. Excellent range of bar meals at reasonable prices.
🏠 Q ❀ ◖ ▶ ⊟ ♣ P

Hay-on-Wye

Blue Boar
Castle Street ☎ (01497) 820884
11–3, 6–11 (11–11 summer)
Draught Bass; Morland Old Speckled Hen; Wadworth 6X; Whitbread Flowers IPA, Original; guest beers Ⓗ
Traditional old pub close to the main car park, popular with locals and visitors to the capital of the second-hand book world. The panelled public bar has a real fire; children welcome in the dining room. Live music eves. No eve meals in winter.
🏠 Q ◖ ▶ ⊟

Try also: Kilvert's, Bull Ring (Free)

Hundred House

Hundred House Inn
On A481 ☎ (01982) 570231
11–3.30, 6.30–11
Bass Worthington BB; Hancock's HB; guest beers Ⓗ
Former drovers' pub set among fine upland scenery. No fewer than five rooms: a pool room, a farmer's bar, a lounge, a dining room and a garden bar. Families welcome.
🏠 Q ❀ ➾ ◖ ▶ ▲ ♣ P

Llanbedr

Red Lion
☎ (01873) 810754
12–2.30 (not Mon/Tue in winter), 7–11; 11–11 Sat
Bass Worthington BB; Freeminer Speculation; Wadworth Farmer's Glory; guest beer (occasional) Ⓗ
Ancient country pub in the heart of the Black Mountains. Mostly home-cooked food. The beer range may vary.
🏠 Q ➾ ❀ ◖ ▶ ▲ ♣ P ⅄

Llanbrynmair

Wynnstay Arms Hotel
On A470 ☎ (0165 03) 431
11–2.30, 6–11
Whitbread Boddingtons Bitter, Flowers IPA; Wood Sam Powell Old Sam Ⓗ
Well-kept, comfortable, two-bar village local with a pool room.
🏠 ❀ ➾ ◖ ▶ ⊟ ♣ P

Llandrindod Wells

Llanerch Inn
Waterloo Road (across station footbridge, 100 yds)
☎ (01597) 822086
11.30–2.30 (3 Sat), 6–11
Hancock's HB; Whitbread Boddingtons Bitter; guest beers Ⓗ
16th-century coaching inn with a low, beamed ceiling and a large stone hearth. Annual beer tasting week at the end of Aug.
Q ❀ ➾ ◖ ▶ ⇌ P

Royal British Legion Club
Tremont Road (by fire station)
☎ (01597) 822558
7–11; 12–3, 7–11 Fri; 11–11 Sat
Draught Bass; Hancock's HB; guest beers Ⓗ
Show this guide or your CAMRA membership card to be signed on to this club. Quoits played. ⇌ ♣ P

Try also Drovers Arms, Howey (Free)

Llanfihangel-nant-Melan

Red Lion
On A44 ☎ (0154 421) 220
11.30–3, 6.30–11 (10.30 Mon–Wed in winter)
Hook Norton Best Bitter Ⓗ
Comfortable and peaceful pub—an excellent refreshment halt. Radnor Forest provides a backdrop and the pub is popular with walkers.
🏠 Q ➾ ❀ ➾ ◖ ▶ ⊟ ▲ ♣ P

Try also Forest Inn (Bass)

Llanfyllin

Cain Valley Hotel
On A490 ☎ (01691) 648366
11–11
Ansells Bitter; Draught Bass Ⓗ
Excellent 17th-century coaching inn: a plush lounge with two basic bars, one serving as a games area. Imposing stone fireplace.
🏠 Q ❀ ➾ ◖ ▶ ⊟ ♣ P

Llangorse

Castle Inn
☎ (01874) 84225
12–2.30, 6–11 (extends in summer)
Brains Bitter; Whitbread Boddingtons Bitter (summer), Castle Eden Ale; guest beers Ⓗ
Friendly, 17th-century village inn with a good public bar and a comfortable lounge. Close to Llangorse Lake and popular with visitors and locals alike (busy in summer). Good meals.
🏠 Q ❀ ◖ ▶ ⊟ ▲ ♣ P

Llanidloes

Mount Inn
China Street (off A470)
☎ (0155 12) 2247
11–2.30, 5.30–11; 11–11 Sat
Bass Worthington Dark, Worthington BB Ⓗ
Many-roomed, 17th-century pub with a cast iron stove. Listed floor.
🏠 Q ➾ ◖ ▶ ⊟ ♣ P

Unicorn
Longbridge Street
☎ (01686) 413167
12–2.30, 6–11
Draught Bass; Tetley Mild, Bitter Ⓗ
A rare outpost for Tetley Mild in a town where all pubs sell real ale. ◖ ▶

Llanwrtyd Wells

Neuadd Arms Hotel
The Square (A483)
☎ (01591) 610236
11.30–11 (may close afternoons)
Bass Worthington Dark, Draught Bass; Felinfoel Double Dragon; Hancock's HB; guest beer Ⓗ
Imposing hotel in the centre of the smallest town in GB. The landlord organises a winter ale festival in Jan, and the Mid-Wales Beer Festival—with real ale rambles—in Nov. An excellent centre for outdoor activities in surrounding mountains and forests.
🏠 Q ❀ ➾ ◖ ▶ ⊟ ▲
⇌ (not winter Sun) ♣ P

Machynlleth

Skinners Arms
Main Street ☎ (01654) 702354
11–11
**Burtonwood Mild, Bitter,
Forshaw's** H
Wooden-beamed, town-centre
pub with a welcoming
atmosphere: a comfortable
lounge and a long, narrow
public bar. 🏰 ◖ ▶ ⊕ ⇌ ♣

White Horse
Maengwyn Street
11–11
Hancock's HB H
Popular public bar and a
lounge in an old coaching inn
displaying interesting old
photos. ◖ ▶ ⊕ & ⇌

Meifod

King's Head
On A495 ☎ (01938) 500265
12–3, 7–11
**Bass Worthington BB; guest
beer** H
Impressive, ivy-clad, stone-
built inn in the centre of the
village: a plush lounge with a
restaurant. ❀ ◖ ▶ ⊕ ♣ P

Montgomery

Dragon Hotel
Off B4385 ☎ (01686) 668359
11–11
**Felinfoel Double Dragon;
Wood Sam Powell Old Sam;
guest beer** H
Excellent, comfortable bar in a
hotel which was formerly a
coaching inn from the 1600s.
The stone and timber behind
the bar are reputed to have
come from the local castle. The
hotel has an indoor swimming
pool. Q ❀ 🛏 ◖ ▶ ♣

Newbridge-on-Wye

New Inn
At A470/B4358 jct
☎ (0159 789) 211
11–3, 7–11
**Whitbread Boddingtons
Bitter, Flowers Original; guest
beers** (summer) H
Formerly three 16th-century
cottages, but a hostelry since
around 1800.
Q ❀ 🛏 ◖ ▶ ▲ ♣ P

Newtown

Buck Inn
High Street ☎ (01686) 622699
11–11
**Banks's Mild, Bitter;
Camerons Strongarm** H
Comfortable, listed, town-
centre pub, with a large

inglenook. Courtyard for
outdoor drinking.
❀ ◖ ▶ ⇌ ♣

Sportsman
Severn Street (off A483)
☎ (01686) 625885
11–2.30, 5.30–11; 11–11 Fri & Sat
**Ind Coope Burton Ale; Tetley
Bitter; guest beers** H
Comfortable, friendly town-
centre local, attracting a wide
range of customers. Music jam
sessions every other Tue.
Q ❀ ◖ ▶ ⇌ ♣

Try also Pheasant, Market St
(Burtonwood); **Railway**, Old
Kerry Rd (Bass)

Old Radnor

Harp Inn
1 mile W of A44/B4362 jct
☎ (0154 421) 655
11–3, 6–11 (11–11 summer)
**Wood Special; Wye Valley
HPA; guest beers** (summer) H
15th-century inn beautifully
restored by the Landmark
Trust and featuring a flagged
floor, stone walls, a beamed
ceiling, antique furniture and
bric-a-brac. Memorable view
of Radnor Forest.
🏰 Q ⛺ ❀ 🛏 ◖ ▶ ▲ ♣ P

Try also Royal Oak, Gladestry
(Bass)

Pant Mawr

Glan Severn Arms
Hotel
On A44 ☎ (0155 15) 240
11–2, 6.30–11 (closed Sun before
Xmas–Dec 30)
**Bass Worthington Dark,
Draught Bass** H
Peaceful retreat on the road to
Aberystwyth, 1,050 feet above
sea level in the Wye valley.
Two impeccable bars, a hotel
and a restaurant. Restaurant
meals only (book eves and Sun
lunch; no food Sun eve).
Range of whiskies.
🏰 Q 🛏 P

Pengenffordd

Castle Inn
On A479, 3 miles S of Talgarth
☎ (01874) 711353
11–3, 7–11 (11–11 summer weekends
and bank hols)
**Greene King Abbot;
Wadworth 6X; guest beer**
(summer) H
Friendly country local,
popular with walkers, at the
summit of the mountain road
between Talgarth and
Crickhowell, with Castell
Dinas, the highest hillfort in
England and Wales, behind.
Beware the Scrumpy Jack cider
on fake handpump.
🏰 ❀ 🛏 ◖ ▶ ⊕ ▲ ♣ P

Penybont

Severn Arms Hotel
At A44/A488 jct
☎ (0159 787) 224
11–1.30, 6–11
**Bass Worthington BB,
Draught Bass; Tetley Bitter** H
Roadside inn with extensive
gardens sloping down to the
River Ithon (fishing rights).
Large public bar with an open
fire; games room, lounge bar
and a restaurant.
🏰 Q ❀ 🛏 ◖ ▶ & ▲
♣ P ⚲

Rhayader

Cornhill Inn
West Street ☎ (01597) 810869
7–11; 11–3, 7–11 Sat & summer
**Marston's Pedigree; Smiles
Best Bitter; Wood Wonderful;
Wye Valley Hereford Bitter;
guest beer** H
Friendly, low-beamed, 400-
year-old pub, reputedly
haunted: a single L-shaped
bar. 🏰 Q 🛏 ◖ ▶ ▲ ♣

Triangle Inn
Cwmdauddwr (off Bridge St,
B4518) ☎ (01597) 810537
12–3, 6.30–11; 11–11 Fri & Sat
Draught Bass; Hancock's HB H
Beautiful, little weatherboarded gem overlooking the
River Wye. The ceilings are so
low that customers have to
stand in a hole in the floor to
play darts. ❀ ◖ ▶ ♣

Talybont-on-Usk

Star Inn
On B4558, ¾ mile off A40
☎ (01874) 87635
11–3, 6–11; 11–11 Sat
**Draught Bass; Crown Buckley
Rev. James; Everards Tiger;
Freeminer Speculation;
Ruddles County; S&N
Theakston Old Peculier** H
Canalside pub with a real pub
atmosphere, very popular with
walkers and visitors. Up to 12
beers at most times, of which
the above list is a small
sample. Good bar food.
🏰 ❀ 🛏 ◖ ▶ ⊕ ▲ ♣ ♨

Welshpool

Royal Oak Hotel
Severn Street (off A483)
☎ (01938) 552217
11–3, 5.30–11; 11–11 Mon
**Bass Worthington BB,
Draught Bass; guest beers** H
Plush 300-year-old coaching
inn, once a manor house and
now a hotel which has been in
the same family for 60 years.
Two or more guest beers
available. Separate restaurant.
🏰 Q 🛏 ◖ ▶ & ⇌ P

Borders

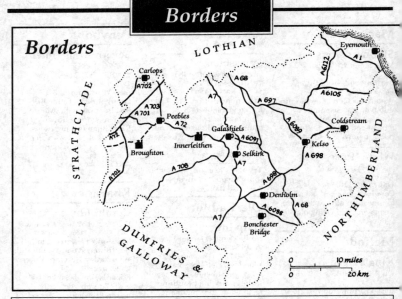

Borders

 Broughton, Broughton; **Traquair House**, Innerleithen

Bonchester Bridge

Horse & Hound Country Inn
On A6088 ☎ (0145 086) 645
11.30–2.30, 6 (5 Sat)–11 (midnight Fri & Sat); closed winter Tue; summer hours: 11–2.30, 6–11; 11–midnight Sat; 12.30–11 Sun
Caledonian Deuchars IPA, 80/-; Mitchell's Best Bitter; Orkney Dark Island; guest beer H
18th-century coaching inn with a cosy bar, lounge and restaurant. Ideal for hill walking, fishing or golfing.
🛏 ❀ 🍴 ◑ ▶ 🍺 ⚓ ♣ P

Carlops

Allan Ramsay Hotel
On A702 ☎ (01968) 60258
11 (12 Sun)–11 (midnight Fri & Sat)
Belhaven Sandy Hunter's Ale, 80/- H
Old coaching inn in a high village. Despite being knocked into a single eating/drinking area, its atmosphere has been retained by dark panelling and a log fire. Children welcome.
🛏 Q ❀ 🍴 ◑ ▶ P

Coldstream

Crown Hotel
Market Square (off A697)
☎ (01890) 882558
11 (12.30 Sun)–midnight (11.30 Sat & Sun)
Caledonian 80/- H
Pub on a quiet, residential

square. The bar is reached via a long corridor. Children welcome in summer.
🛏 ❀ 🍴 ◑ ♣

Denholm

Auld Cross Keys Inn
On A698 ☎ (0145 087) 305
11–2.30 (not Mon), 5–11; 11–midnight Thu & Sat; 11–1am Fri; 12.30–11 Sun
Broughton Greenmantle Ale; guest beer H
Picturesque, 17th-century pub in a quiet conservation village. The low-ceilinged bar has a pool table. The restaurant is worth booking (eve meals till 8.30; no lunches Sun). Award-winning high teas (busy Sun).
🛏 Q 🍴 ◑ ▶ 🍺 ♣ P

Eyemouth

Ship Hotel
Harbour Road
☎ (0189 07) 50224
11 (12.30 Sun)–midnight (11.30 Sat)
Caledonian 70/-, Deuchars IPA A
Small, family-run hotel on the harbour. The large public bar is warmed by a coal fire. Vast selection of rums. 🛏 🛏 ❀ 🍴 ◑ ▶ 🍺 ⚓ ♣ P

Galashiels

Ladhope Inn
33 High Buckholmside (A7, ½ mile N of centre)
☎ (01896) 2446
11 (12.30 Sun)–11 (midnight Thu–Sat)
Caledonian 80/-; guest beer H

Established in 1792, although much altered: a vibrant, comfortable locals' lounge. ♣

Kelso

Red Lion Inn
Crawford Street (just off town square) ☎ (01573) 224817
11 (12.30 Sun)–11 (1am Fri, midnight Sat)
Belhaven 80/-, St Andrew's Ale; guest beer H
An unusual beamed ceiling, an array of sherry casks, wood panelling and a mirrored canopy gantry all contribute character here. 🛏 🍺 🅰 ♣

Peebles

Green Tree Hotel
41 Eastgate (E end of High St, A72) ☎ (01721) 720582
11 (12 Sun)–midnight
Caledonian 80/-; guest beer H
Bustling hotel bar with interesting leaded windows. Very much a local in the front while the back room is more relaxed (children welcomed).
🛏 ❀ 🍴 ◑ ▶ 🍺 🅰 ⚓ ♣ P

Selkirk

Cross Keys Inn
Market Place ☎ (01750) 21283
11 (12.30 Sun)–11 (midnight Thu–Sat)
Caledonian 80/- H
Vibrant, wee, wood-panelled public bar which leads up to a comfortable lounge. Often packed. Award-winning meals (not Sat eve). 🛏 ◑ ▶ 🍺 ⚓ ♣

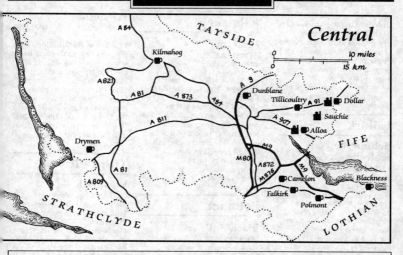

Central

 Harviestoun, Dollar; **Maclay,** Alloa; **Mansfield Arms,** Sauchie

Alloa

Crams Bar
8 Candleriggs
☎ (01259) 722019
11 (12.30 Sun)–11 (midnight Fri & Sat)
Maclay 80/- H
Friendly workingman's bar in a central location. Cheap beer.

Thistle
1 Junction Place
☎ (01259) 723933
11 (12.30 Sun)–11 (midnight Fri & Sat)
Maclay 80/-, Oat Malt Stout; guest beer H
Town-centre pub attached to Maclay's Brewery; a popular lounge and a sociable bar with a games room. The patio is open in summer.
No food Sun. Darts and pool played. ❀ ◖ ⌺ & ♣

Blackness

Blackness Inn
The Square (B903, off A904)
☎ (01506) 834252
11–3, 6–11; 12.30–11 Sun
Alloa Arrol's 80/- E; **Maclay 70/-; Whitbread Boddingtons Bitter** H
Typical country inn, nicely situated on the edge of the River Forth, near Blackness Castle. A warm welcome is assured, with real fires in both bars and award-winning, home-cooked food (fish a speciality).
🏶 ❀ 🛏 ◖ ▶ ⌺

Camelon

Rosebank
Main Street ☎ (01324) 611842
11–midnight (1am Fri & Sat); 11–11.30 Sun
Whitbread Boddingtons Bitter, Flowers Original; guest beers H
Pub opened in 1988 after a £1.5 million renovation of the former Rosebank Distillery bonded warehouse, which sits opposite the distillery on the Forth and Clyde Canal. Its unusual architecture and size dominates the crossroads on which it stands.
❀ ◖ ▶ ⌺ & P

Dollar

King's Seat
19 Bridge Street
☎ (01259) 742515
11–2.30, 5–midnight
Beer range varies H
Comfortable pub on the main street, offering a regularly changing selection of seven beers. A wide range of food is available in either the spacious restaurant or the cosy bar. Families welcome (children's certificate). 🏶 ◖ ▶ ▲

Lorne Tavern
17 Argyll Street
☎ (01259) 743423
11–2.30, 5–11 Mon; 5–11 Tue; 3–11 Wed; 3–midnight Thu; 11–1am Fri & Sat; 12.30–11 Sun
Greene King IPA, Abbot A; **Harviestoun Waverley 70/-, Original 80/-** H

Pub holding the oldest licence in Dollar (1850); ideal for a stop after a walk up Dollar Glen. You could meet the Harviestoun owner here sampling his own produce. Lunches Sat and Sun only; eve meals Thu–Sun. Children's certificate.
❀ ◖ ▶ ⌺ & ▲ ♣ P

Drymen

Clachan
The Square ☎ (01360) 60824
11–midnight; 12.30–midnight Sun
Belhaven St Andrew's Ale H
Friendly village local with meals available in a separate restaurant, lunchtime and eve. The landlord sometimes sells an alternative Belhaven cask ale. 🏶 &

Winnock Hotel
The Square ☎ (01360) 60245
11–midnight; 11–1am Fri & Sat; 12–midnight Sun
Draught Bass; Broughton Greenmantle Ale; Courage Directors; Ruddles Best Bitter; Webster's Yorkshire Bitter H
Large, 18th-century hotel at the centre of an attractive village. Ceilidhs held on summer Suns; petanque played. 🏶 Q ❀ 🛏 ◖ ▶ ⌺ P

Dunblane

Tappit Hen
Kirk Street ☎ (01786) 825226
11–11 (1am Fri & Sat)

Bass Worthington BB; Caledonian 80/-; Maclay Oat Malt Stout; guest beers H
Traditional local opposite the cathedral; recently renovated but kept traditional. Two guest beers are sold weekly, plus a good range of malt whiskies. Toasted sandwiches, tea and coffee all day.
≠ ♣

Falkirk

Behind the Wall (Eglesbrech Ale House)
14 Melville Street
☎ (01324) 633338
11.30–11 (midnight Wed, Thu & Sun, 12.45am Fri & Sat)
McEwan 80/-; Whitbread Flowers Original; Younger No. 3; guest beers H
Housed in a former Playtex bra factory, a pub with a cops and robbers theme, a large conservatory and an outdoor drinking area. Upstairs is the ale house which is a lot less noisy but which tends to get busy later in the eve. ❀ ◑ ▶ ≠ (Grahamston)

Kilmahog

Lade Inn
At A84/A821 jct
☎ (01877) 30152
12–11 (midnight Fri & Sat); 12–11 Sun (closed Mon & Tue, Dec–Feb)
Courage Directors; Ruddles County H
Owned and managed by Canadians, an inn on the main road to the Trossachs. Its location at the foot of Ben Ledi is often described as superb. Perfect for hill walkers. An Italian bistro is incorporated in the pub.
Q ❀ ⇔ ◑ ▶ ⅋ A P

Polmont

Black Bull
Main Street ☎ (01324) 716610
11–11 (midnight Fri, Sat & Sun)
Maclay 80/- H
Popular village local with a comfortable lounge. Look for the bull's head on the wall. Still the cheapest cask ale in the area.
◑ ▶ ⅋ ≠ P

Whyteside
Lewis Road ☎ (01324) 712394
11–11
Whitbread Boddingtons Bitter, Flowers Original; guest beers H
Imposing building set in a modern housing estate. Legend has it that Burke and Hare (the infamous grave robbers) stayed nearby when they worked as labourers on the Union Canal. The disabled facilities are superb. An ideal pub for a family outing.
◑ ▶ ⅋ ≠ P

Tillicoultry

Woolpack
Glassford Square (where main road crosses burn follow Tillicoultry Glen sign)
☎ (01259) 750332
11–midnight (1am Fri & Sat); 12.30–11 Sun
Beer range varies H
Welcoming bar handy for walkers coming from the glen or the Ochil Hills. Normally six ales are served, changed regularly. Lunches Fri–Sun; eve meals Fri and Sat only.
Q ◑ ▶ ♣

FAKING IT

The handpump is a sign of traditional beer (or cider). Customers who see it assume that whatever it serves will be unpasteurised and unfiltered, that it will not be chilled, and the product will not be full of gas. It should be a reasonable assumption to make. However, the marketing power of the handpump is so great that brewers and cider-makers use it to sell inferior, dead products ('real' products have a marketing advantage).

The apparent handpump may be simply fixed upright—when you ask for your pint, it comes from a keg tap behind the bar. Or the machine may be organised so that when the lever is depressed, a steady flow of cold, gassy keg beer or cider goes into your glass. In either case, the bar staff do not pump at the lever to produce the drink. Sometimes, a genuine handpump is adapted to dispense keg products. Whichever way, you are being conned. You will have seen the handpump and assumed that the product was real. You will have parted with good money for a dead drink. And you will have paid for it, and tasted it, and decided that you didn't like it, before you realised.

Pubs that use misleading dispense are no longer welcome in the Good Beer Guide. Any included in this edition will be encouraged to change their fake handpumps for standard keg fonts before the 1996 Guide. CAMRA will also campaign against brewers and cider manufacturers who promote fake handpumps. Perhaps the worst offender is Scrumpy Jack, a dead and fizzy cider, sold as if it was the real thing. This keg product also comes with a conventional keg tap, so we would urge publicans to request this instead of the deceptive 'handpump'.

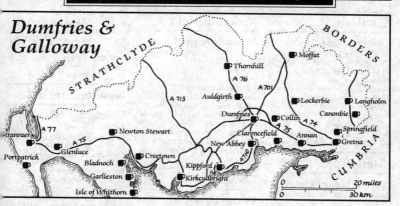

Dumfries & Galloway

Annan

Blue Bell Inn

High Street ☎ (01461) 202385
11 (12.30 Sun)–11 (midnight Thu–Sat)
S&N Theakston Best Bitter; guest beers H
Excellent, award-winning, traditional boozer with impressive wood panelling.
Q ❀ ♠ ≠ ♠

Auldgirth

Auldgirth Inn

Off A76, 7 miles N of Dumfries ☎ (01387) 74250
11–2.30, 5–11 (midnight Fri);
11–midnight Sat; 12.30–11 Sun
Draught Bass; Caledonian 80/- H
Quaint country inn bypassed by a road diversion. The comfortable lounge bar is decorated in Tudor style.
♨ Q ❀ ⇔ ◑ ▶ ◫ P

Bladnoch

Bladnoch Inn

A714, 6 miles S of Newton Stewart ☎ (01988) 402200
11 (12 Sun)–11 (midnight Fri & Sat)
S&N Theakston XB H
Friendly village local, popular with farmers, anglers and wildfowlers. Opposite Bladnoch Distillery (sadly out of production but maintaining a visitor centre). Two guest beers may replace the XB. Children's certificate.
♨ Q ♋ ❀ ⇔ ◑ ▶ P

Canonbie

Riverside Inn

☎ (0138 73) 71512
12–3, 6.30–11; 12–3, 7–10.30 Sun
(closed Sun lunchtime in winter; may vary)
Yates Bitter; guest beer H
Cosy, award-winning inn.
♨ Q ❀ ⇔ ◑ ▶ ⌣ P

Clarencefield

Farmers Inn

Main Street ☎ (01387) 87675
11–2.30, 6–11 (midnight Fri);
11–midnight Sat; 12.30–11 Sun; 11–11
bank hols
Caledonian 80/-; Tetley Bitter; guest beer H
Welcoming, 18th-century inn.
♨ ♋ ❀ ⇔ ◑ ▶ ◫ ♠ ♠ P

Collin

Squires Motel

3–5 Main Road
☎ (0138 75) 350
12 (12.30 Sun)–11 (midnight Fri & Sat)
(12–2, 6.30–11 Mon–Fri in winter)
Orkney Dark Island; guest beer H
Very friendly motel with a spacious function room. Large-screen TV.
❀ ⇔ ◑ ▶ ◫ ♠ P

Creetown

Barholm Arms Hotel

St John Street (off A75)
☎ (01671) 820553
12 (12.30 Sun)–3, 6–11
Caledonian 80/-; Courage Directors; guest beer H
Very friendly local in a village bypassed by the main Dumfries–Stranraer road. Close to the shore of Wigtown Bay and opposite a working farrier's. Meals in summer only. Children's certificate.
♨ ◑ ▶ ♠ P

Dumfries

Douglas Arms

Friars Vennel ☎ (01387) 56002
11 (12.30 Sun)–11 (midnight Thu & Sat)
Broughton Greenmantle Ale, Special, Oatmeal Stout; Jennings Cumberland Ale; guest beer H
Grand wee pub with a snug.
≠ ♠

Moreig Hotel

67 Annan Road
☎ (01387) 55524
11 (12 Sun)–11 (midnight Thu–Sat)
Courage Directors; John Smith's Bitter H
Friendly, comfortable hotel. Separate restaurant open at weekends. ♋ ◑ ▶ ≠ P

New Bazaar

38 Whitesands
☎ (01387) 68776
11–midnight (11 Tue & Wed);
12.30–11 Sun
Broughton Greenmantle Ale, Special; McEwan 80/-; Mitchell's ESB; guest beer H
Marvellous, old bar with Victorian fittings which overlooks the River Nith.
♨ ❀ ≠ ♠

Ship Inn

97 St Michael Street
☎ (01387) 55189
11–2.30, 5–11
Courage Directors; Fuller's London Pride; Greene King Abbot; Ind Coope Burton Ale; Marston's Pedigree; Morland Old Speckled Hen H
Superb, traditional, two-roomed pub—a gem not to be missed. Q ⊞ ≠ ♠

Tam O'Shanter

117 Queens Berry Street
☎ (01387) 54055
11–2.30, 5–11; closed Sun
Caledonian 60/-, Deuchars IPA, 80/-, Double Amber Ale, Golden Promise H
Excellent howff with several rooms. Another gem.
Q ≠ ♠

Troqueer Arms

Troqueer Road
☎ (01387) 54518
11–11 (midnight Thu, 1am Fri & Sat);
12.30–midnight Sun
Belhaven 80/-; Caledonian 80/-; Maclay 60/- H
Quiet and friendly local, near the Camera Obscura: a fine long bar, with views across the river. Q ❀ ♠ P

Dumfries & Galloway

Garlieston

Queens Arms Hotel
High Street ☎ (01988) 600652
11–3, 6–11; 11–11.30 Sat; 12–11 Sun
Whitbread Boddingtons Bitter; guest beer H
Traditional village hotel close to the seafront and harbour. Driftwood is used in the decor. The paddle steamer *Waverley* occasionally sails to the Isle of Man from Garlieston.
🏠 Q ➤ ❀ 🍴 ◁ ▷ 🌢 ♣

Glenluce

Kelvin House Hotel
Main Street ☎ (01581) 300303
11–11 (midnight Sat & Sun)
Alloa Arrol's 80/-; guest beer H
Small hotel at the head of Luce Bay, in a village now bypassed. Real ale may not be available Jan–Feb. Children's certificate.
Q ❀ 🍴 ◁ ▷ 🌢 ▲ ♣

Gretna

Solway Lodge Hotel
Annan Road ☎ (01461) 338266
11.45–11 (midnight Fri & Sat); 12–11 Sun (12–3 winter Sun)
Broughton Special; Tetley Bitter H
Friendly and welcoming hotel, with a comfortable lounge, in the wedding capital.
Q ❀ 🍴 ◁ ▷ ♿ P

Isle of Whithorn

Steam Packet Hotel
Harbour Row (A750)
☎ (01988) 500334
11 (12 Sun)–11
S&N Theakston XB H
Very attractive harbourside inn in a picturesque village, which is very popular with sailors in summer. The bar walls are stone-clad. The hotel has its own sailing and fishing boats.
🏠 Q ❀ 🍴 ◁ ▷ 🌢 ♿ ♣

Try also: Queens Arms Hotel, Main St (Bass)

Kippford

Mariner Hotel
Opp. pier ☎ (01556) 620206
12–2.30, 6–11 (12–11 Sat & Sun in summer)
Draught Bass; guest beers H
Hotel with a comfortable lounge bar affording beautiful views over the estuary to hills (breathtaking sunsets!); split-level bar. Children's play area and children's certificate.
🏠 ➤ ❀ 🍴 ◁ ▷ ♿ ▲ P

Try also: Anchor Hotel (S&N)

Kirkcudbright

Masonic Arms
19 Castle Street (opp. castle, near the harbour)
☎ (01557) 330517
11 (12.30 Sun)–midnight
Bass Worthington BB, Draught Bass; guest beer H
Interesting bar making use of barrels for the bar front, stools and tables, and displaying a selection of old bar mirrors. A friendly local in an attractive town famous for its artists.
🏠 ❀ 🌢

Langholm

Crown Hotel
High Street ☎ (0138 73) 80247
11 (12 Sun)–11 (midnight Thu–Sat)
Beer range varies H
Comfortable, 18th-century inn offering high teas 6–7pm (good value). Children's certificate.
🏠 ➤ 🍴 ◁ ▷ ▲ ♣

Try also: Langholm Guest House (Broughton)

Lockerbie

Somerton House Hotel
Carlisle Road
☎ (01576) 202583
11.30 (12 Sun)–11 (midnight Mon–Wed)
Broughton Greenmantle Ale, Merlin's Ale A
Deservedly popular, well-appointed hotel where friendly service is assured. Excellent meals. ❀ 🍴 ◁ ▷ P

Moffat

Balmoral Hotel
High Street ☎ (01683) 20288
11–11 (midnight Thu–Sat)
Broughton Greenmantle Ale, Oatmeal Stout; guest beer H
Friendly, traditional hotel, serving a guest beer from the Caledonian range.
➤ 🍴 ◁ ▷ ♿ ▲ P

Black Bull Hotel
Churchgate ☎ (01683) 20206
11–11 (midnight Thu–Sat)
McEwan 80/-; S&N Theakston Best Bitter; guest beers H
Historic, 16th-century hotel with a comfortable lounge and a traditional bar.
➤ ❀ 🍴 ◁ ▷ ♿ ▲ ♣

Try also: Star Hotel, High St (S&N Theakston)

New Abbey

Criffel Inn
On A710 ☎ (01387) 85305
12 (12.30 Sun)–2.30, 5.30 (6.30 Sun)–11
Broughton Special A
Traditional bar in a small hotel in a picturesque village near the ruins of Sweetheart Abbey. Old photos and timetables of local interest are displayed. Children's certificate.
🏠 Q ➤ ❀ 🍴 ◁ ▷ ♿ ♣

Newton Stewart

Creebridge House Hotel
Creebridge (old main road, E of river) ☎ (01671) 402121
11 (12.30 Sun)–2.30, 6 (7 Sun)–11 (11.30 Sat)
Beer range varies H
Country house hotel set in large garden grounds on the outskirts of Minnigaff (eastern part of the town). It has been reorganised internally, forming a larger lounge. Bar billiards played. Children welcome (certificate).
Q ➤ ❀ 🍴 ◁ ▷ ▲ ♣ P

Portpatrick

Harbour House Hotel
53 Main Street (on the harbour) ☎ (01776) 810456
11 (12.30 Sun)–11.15
Alloa Arrol's 80/- A
Open-plan lounge bar in a hotel looking onto a picturesque fishing port. No meals in winter. Children's certificate. 🏠 🍴 ◁ ▷ ▲ P

Springfield

Queens Head
Main Street ☎ (01461) 37173
12–2.30, 7–11 (midnight Thu–Sat)
McEwan 70/-, 80/-; S&N Theakston Mild, Best Bitter H
Refurbished, single-room local. Snacks available. ♣ P

Stranraer

Ruddicot Hotel
London Road (A75, 400 yds E of centre) ☎ (01776) 702684
12 (12.30 Sun)–2.30, 5 (6.30 Sun)–11
S&N Theakston XB *or* **guest beer** H
Small, family-run hotel, handy for ferry terminals and football and rugby grounds.
Q ❀ 🍴 ◁ ▲ ⚟ P

Thornhill

Buccleugh & Queensbury Hotel
112 Drumlanrig Street (A76)
☎ (01848) 330215
11–1am (midnight Sun)
Caledonian 80/- H
Comfortable lounge in a traditional hotel in the centre of the village. The 80/- may rotate with guest beers.
🏠 Q ➤ ❀ 🍴 ◁ ▷ ♿ ▲ ♣ P

Fife

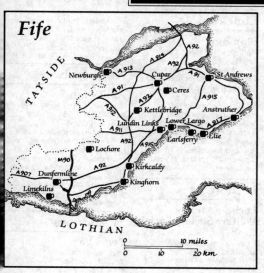

Irish painter whose works adorn the walls. Occasional live music. 🍴 ⇌ ♣

Earlsferry

Golf Tavern, 19th Hole
Links Road
☎ (01333) 330610
11–midnight (1am Fri; 11–2.30, 5–midnight Mon–Fri, Oct–Apr); 12.30–11 Sun
Caledonian Deuchars IPA; Maclay 80/-; guest beer Ⓗ
Unspoilt, traditional pub next to golf links. Golfing provides names for the 19th Hole Bar and the Bunker games room. Note the gas lighter on the bar. Children welcome until 8pm.
🏚 Q ☻ ◖ ▸ 🍴 ▲ ♣

Elie

Ship Inn
The Toft (follow signs for harbour) ☎ (01333) 330246
11–midnight; 12.30–11 Sun
Belhaven 80/-; Courage Directors; Whitbread Boddingtons Bitter Ⓗ
Renovated to a high standard, a bar boasting a stone-flagged floor and a beamed ceiling. The inn dates back to 1838 and now has three separate dining areas, with fine views over the sandy bay. Cricket and rugby matches played regularly. No keg beer available.
🏚 Q ☻ ❀ ◖ ▸ ♿ ▲ ♣

Kettlebridge

Kettlebridge Inn
9 Cupar Road
☎ (01337) 830232
11–2.30, 5–11; 11–midnight Fri & Sat; 12.30–11 Sun
Belhaven Sandy Hunter's Ale, 80/-, St Andrew's Ale; guest beers Ⓗ
A long-standing CAMRA favourite, twice voted *Best Pub* in NE Fife. The former lounge is now a restaurant. Eve meals end at 8.30pm; no eve meals Mon. Two guest beers.
🏚 Q 🛏 ◖ ▸ 🍴 ♿ ▲ ✂

Kinghorn

Auld Hoose
6–8 Nethergate (off A921)
☎ (01592) 891074
12 (12.30 Sun)–midnight
Broughton Greenmantle Ale Ⓐ; **guest beers** Ⓐ & Ⓗ
Busy side-street pub popular with locals and holidaymakers alike. The public bar has a pool table, while the lounge is relaxing and comfortable. Handily situated for the station and the nearby beach. Three guest beers.
Q ☻ 🛏 ⇌ ♣

Anstruther

Dreel Tavern
16 High Street
☎ (01333) 310727
11–midnight
Archibald Arrol's 80/-; Caledonian 80/-; guest beers Ⓗ
Stone-built pub at the side of an old ford over Dreel Burn. James V may have enjoyed a pint here before being carried over the burn. Popular with locals and visitors, who come for good atmosphere and excellent bar meals. 🏚 ◖ ▸

Ceres

Brands Inn
High Street
☎ (0133 482) 325
11.30–3, 5.30–midnight (1am Fri); 11–midnight Sat; 12.30–11.30 Sun
Caledonian 80/-; guest beers Ⓗ
Pub gradually being restored to its former bare stone interior; the mirrors are on display again in the bar. A separate games room welcomes children.
🏚 Q ☻ ❀ ◖ ▸ 🍴

Ceres Inn
The Cross ☎ (0133 482) 305
11–2.30, 5–midnight (11 Tue & Wed, 1am Thu & Fri)
Belhaven St Andrew's Ale Ⓗ
Welcoming local with an enormous collection of brass, mugs, etc. Restaurant downstairs. No eve meals Tue. The beer choice may vary.
❀ ◖ ▸ P

Cupar

Drookit Dug
43 Bonnygate (200 yds W of market cross)
☎ (01334) 55862
11–1am; 12.30–3, 6.30–11 Sun
Beer range varies Ⓗ
Lively town pub which has regular cut-price ale promotions and occasional beer festivals. ◖ ⇌

Dunfermline

City Hotel
(Cask & Barrel Bar)
18 Bridge Street
☎ (01383) 722538
11 (12.30 Sun)–11 (midnight Fri & Sat)
Courage Directors; Maclay 70/-, 80/-; guest beer Ⓗ
Originally a coaching inn, from around 1775, and now a prestigious town-centre hotel. The cask beers are in the ground floor bar, which is comfortable if a little lacking in atmosphere. Near the famous abbey and ruins of a royal palace as well as Pittencrieff Park.
🛏 ◖ ▸ 🍴 ♿ ⇌ P

Coady's
16 Pilmuir Street (near bus station and Kingsgate shopping centre)
☎ (01383) 723865
11–11.30; 12.30–11 Sun
S&N Theakston Best Bitter Ⓗ
Busy, street-corner locals' bar with bare wooden floorboards and a back sitting room. Pool room upstairs. Named after an

---

Fife

Ship Tavern

2 Bruce Street (A921)
☎ (01592) 890655
12 (11 Sat, 12.30 Sun)–midnight
Caledonian 80/-; guest beers H
Traditional wood-panelled gem where the public bar is decorated to a nautical theme. There is a fine bar counter and the gantry is quite ornate. The jug bar remains, too. One of the best surviving pub interiors in the kingdom. A most satisfying place for a pint. Meals in summer only.
🏚 Q ☺ 🏵 🕩 🍴 & ≉ ♣ P

Kirkcaldy

Betty Nicol's

297 High Street (E end of High St) ☎ (01592) 642083
11–midnight (11 Mon & Tue);
12.30–11 Sun (12.30–2.30, 6.30–11 winter Sun)
Alloa Arrol's 80/-; Ind Coope Burton Ale; Marston's Pedigree; Mitchell's Best Bitter; guest beer H
Town-centre ale house with some remaining vestiges of its former glory, sympathetically restored by the present management. The marvellous back room has a coal fire and can be used by families. Prices are rather high. No food Sun.
🏚 Q 🕩 🍴 & ♣

Harbour Bar

461–463 High Street
☎ (01592) 264270
11–2.30, 5–11; 11–midnight Fri & Sat
Belhaven St Andrew's Ale; guest beers H
Marvellous, unspoilt town boozer with lovely etched windows, and, rarely found today, a jug bar. Both lounge and public bars are wood-panelled. Watch out for the tricky step behind the louvred door into the gents'. Five guest beers. Its own brewery is planned.
Q 🕩

Limekilns

Ship Inn

Halkett's Hall (off A985)
☎ (01383) 872247
11 (12.30 Sun)–11 (midnight Thu–Sat)
Courage Directors; Belhaven Sandy Hunter's Ale, 80/-, St Andrew's Ale H
Small, but nonetheless comfortably appointed, one-room lounge bar with nautical bric-a-brac and fine views over the Firth of Forth. A warm and friendly welcome is assured. Children catered for. 🕩 & ♣

Lochore

Lochore Miners' Welfare Society Social Club

1 Lochleven Road (B920)
☎ (01592) 860358
12 (12.30 Sun)–3.30, 6 (6.30 Sun)–11
Maclay 70/- A
Large club, with a public bar, lounge, two dance halls and an upstairs games room, in what was once part of Fife's thriving coalfield. Non-members must be signed in but are made most welcome. Close to Loch Ore Meadows Country Park, reclaimed from pit wasteland. Bowling green. 🏵 & ♣

Lower Largo

Railway Inn

Station Wynd
☎ (0133 320) 239
11–midnight (including Sun)
Courage Best Bitter; Marston's Pedigree H
Locals' bar, underneath the viaduct in Robinson Crusoe's home village. Q 🏵 A ♣

Lundin Links

Coachman's (Old Manor Hotel)

Leven Road ☎ (0133 332) 0368
11–3, 5–11
Beer range varies H
Converted coachhouse where an excellent pint can wash down superb food in the attached Coachman's Grill. Children's certificate. Interesting beers. Q ☺ 🕩 ♪ P

Newburgh

Abbey Inn

East Port, Cupar Road
☎ (01337) 840761
11–11 (may extend)
Draught Bass; guest beers H
A go-ahead establishment on the east side of town, now a free house with a games room and a lounge. Good pub food (eve meals end at 8pm—no eve meals Tue). Cheap beer Sun afternoon. Two guest ales.
Q 🏵 🏡 🕩 ♪ 🏵 ♣

St Andrews

Bert's Bar

99 South Street
☎ (01334) 74543
11–midnight; 12–midnight Sun
Alloa Arrol's 80/-; Caledonian 80/-; Ind Coope Burton Ale; Taylor Landlord; guest beer H
Small, tastefully renovated bar: one of a small chain of Alloa-run Bert's Bars. Bar snacks available. & ♣

Cellar Bar

32 Bell Street ☎ (01334) 77425
11–3, 5–midnight; 11–11.45 Sat;
6.30–11 Sun
Belhaven 80/-; guest beers H
Below-street-level bar popular with students. Food is available in the upstairs wine bar. Three beers are available at any time; regular beer festivals held.

Whey Pat Tavern

1 Bridge Street
☎ (01334) 77740
11–11.30 (11.45 Fri & Sat); 12.30–2.30,
6.30–11.30 Sun
S&N Theakston XB; Younger No.3; guest beer H
Efficient service in a friendly bar, popular with students and locals. Its name derives from a pot used for heating whey. Bar snacks available. & ♣

OPENING HOURS

Permitted opening hours in England and Wales are 11–11, though not all pubs choose to take advantage of the full session and many close in the afternoons. Some pubs have special licences and there are sometimes special local arrangements for market days and other events. Standard Sunday hours are 12–3, 7–10.30. Scottish licensing laws are more generous and pubs may stay open longer.

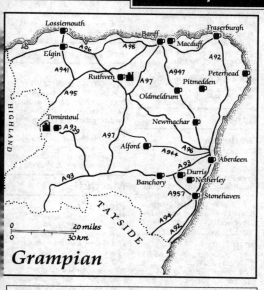

Grampian

 Borve, *Ruthven*; **Tomintoul**, *Tomintoul*

Aberdeen

Betty Burke's
45 Langstane Place
☎ (01224) 210359
11–midnight; 12.30–11 Sun
**Caledonian 80/-; Ind Coope
Burton Ale; Tetley Bitter** H
Very popular, city-centre bar
whose Drink the World
competition is ongoing and
features no less than 30 beers.
Always three guest beers
available. Very busy at
weekends. Opens 10am
Mon–Sat for coffee.
◖ ▶

Blue Lamp
121 Gallowgate
☎ (01224) 647472
11–midnight; 12.30–3, 6.30–11 Sun
**Caledonian Deuchars IPA;
McEwan 80/-; S&N Theakston
Best Bitter; Younger No.3;
guest beers** H
Large, modern, flagstoned
lounge and a smaller cosy bar,
popular with students. Guest
beers are sold in the bar only.
⊟

Bond Bar
Broad Street
☎ (01224) 623123
11–midnight; 12.30–11 Sun
**Orkney Dark Island; S&N
Theakston Best Bitter, Old
Peculier; Whitbread
Boddingtons Bitter, Castle
Eden Ale, Flowers Original;
guest beers** H

New split-level bar, created
partly in the cellar of the
original Bond, which closed 20
years ago. Bands play most
nights; take refuge in the
aptly-named Committee Room
4 (the pub is near the local
council HQ). 1930s and '50s
refurbished handpumps used.
Free monkey nuts provide
shells to scatter on the floor.
◖ ⇌

Camerons Inn
6 Little Belmont Street (off
Union St, by churchyard)
☎ (01224) 644487
11–11.45; 12.30–10.45 Sun
**Draught Bass; Orkney Dark
Island; Whitbread
Boddingtons Bitter; Younger
No.3; guest beer** H
Old coaching inn with a
lounge conversion to modern
taste, but leaving the original
public bar untouched. A guest
beer is available in the public
bar only (usually a rotation of
Caledonian beers). Attractive
snugs. Q ◖ ⊟ ⇌ ♠

Carriages
101 Crown Street
☎ (01224) 595440
11–2.30, 5–midnight; 6–11.30 Sun,
closed Sun lunch
**Caledonian Deuchars IPA;
S&N Theakston Best Bitter;
Whitbread Boddingtons
Bitter, Castle Eden Ale,
Flowers Original; Young's
Special; guest beers** H
Pub with a warm, welcoming
atmosphere, busy during the

week, but with excellent
service. Charity quiz Sun.
Q ⋈ ◖ ▶ ⇌ ♥ P

Cocky Hunters
504 Union Street
☎ (01224) 626720
11–midnight; 12.30–11 Sun
**S&N Theakston Best Bitter;
Whitbread Boddingtons
Bitter, Castle Eden Ale,
Flowers Original; guest
beers** H
Live music or entertainment
every night and a ceilidh on
Sun, plus a pensioner's happy
hour every day, in this
traditional, wooden-floored
pub with much bric-a-brac in
evidence. Major sporting
events shown on a big screen.
◖ ♿

Donview
2 Ellon Road, Bridge of Don
(A92) ☎ (01224) 703239
11–midnight; 12.30–11 Sun
**Ind Coope Burton Ale; Tetley
Bitter; guest beer** H
Popular pub with a restaurant,
in a picturesque spot on the
River Don estuary. It is handy
for riverside or coastal/beach
walks, and for buses. Good
food. ⋈ ♥ ◖ ▶ P

Ferryhill House
Bon Accord Street
☎ (01224) 590867
11–11; 11.30–midnight Fri & Sat
Caledonian 80/- H; **McEwan
80/-** A; **Taylor Landlord** H;
guest beers
The town's only hotel with a
garden drinking area,
currently being returned to its
former glory. A marvellous
place on sunny days (outside)
or snowy days (inside).
⋈ Q ❀ ◖ ▶ P

Mains of Scotstown
1 Jesmond Square East, Bridge
of Don (near Valentine
Rd/Jesmond Ave jct)
☎ (01224) 825222
11 (12.30 Sun)–11 (midnight Thu–Sat)
**Draught Bass; Whitbread
Boddingtons Bitter** H
Converted farmstead
comprising a public bar and a
restaurant (open daily).
◖ ▶ ⊟ P

Mill of Mundurno
Bridge of Don (B999, near A92
jct) ☎ (01224) 821217
11 (12.30 Sun)–11
**Marston's Pedigree;
Whitbread Boddingtons
Bitter, Flowers Original** H
A converted mill, modernised
in traditional style. Food is
available daily 11.30–10 in this
Brewers' Fayre pub with an
attached Travel Lodge.
Regular events; children's
playground. ⋈ ◖ ▶ ♿ P ✄

385

Grampian

Moorings

Trinity Quay ☎ (01224) 587602
11–midnight; 12.30–11 Sun
Draught Bass; Stones Best Bitter; guest beers Ⓗ
Hard rock and real ale—not a quaint fishing village pub. Sit back and enjoy the experience.
Ⓓ ⇌

Prince of Wales

5 St Nicholas Lane
☎ (01224) 640597
11 (12.30 Sun)–11.45 (10.45 Sun)
Draught Bass; Caledonian 80/-; Orkney Dark Island; S&N Theakston Old Peculier Ⓗ**; Younger No. 3** Ⓐ**; guest beers** Ⓗ
Popular, long bar with a quiet lounge area providing escape from the crowds at busy times. Formerly run-down, the area has been revitalised with new shops and flats. Good, wholesome lunches are served Mon–Sat. Occasional impromptu music sessions by local musicians. Q Ⓓ ⇌ ♣

Tilted Wig

55 Castle Street (opp. Court House) ☎ (01224) 583248
12–midnight; 7–11 Sun, closed Sun lunch
Alloa Arrol's 80/-; Caledonian 80/-; Ind Coope Burton Ale; Marston's Pedigree; Tetley Bitter; guest beers Ⓗ
Bright, bustling, busy and brimming with life: this smart bar stages regular quiz nights where Legal Eagles and their clients mix and match. Ⓓ ⇌

Alford

Vale Hotel

Main Street ☎ (0197 55) 62183
11–3, 5–11.45; 11–11.45 Sat; 11.30–11.45 Sun
Beer range varies Ⓗ
Good village local in a pleasant rural location. Cask beers are steadily increasing in popularity; there are normally two, changed regularly. Children are welcome in the lounge/restaurant. Excellent food. ❀ Ⓓ ▶ ⊟ ᴴ Ⓐ P

Banchory

Scott Skinners

Station Road (E side of town)
☎ (01330) 824393
11–11 (midnight Thu–Sat)
Draught Bass; Whitbread Castle Eden Ale; guest beers Ⓗ
Small, friendly local, with a games room and a garden play area for children.
♨ ❀ Ⓓ ▶ Ⓐ ♣ P

Tor-na-Coille Hotel

Inchmarlo Road (W side of town) ☎ (01330) 822242
11.30–2.30, 5–11.30

Banff

Castle Inn

47 Castle Street (off A98)
☎ (01261) 815068
11 (12.30 Sun)–midnight
Draught Bass; guest beer Ⓗ
Functional, but spartan public bar and a modern, airy lounge, in a friendly pub well worth a visit. Eve meals Sat; other days on request. Q Ⓓ ⊟ ᴴ Ⓐ ♣

Ship Inn

7–8 Deveronside (by harbour)
☎ (01261) 812620
11 (12.30 Sun)–midnight
Beer choice varies Ⓗ
Friendly, small pub established in 1710. *Local Hero* was partly filmed here. Designed as a clinker-built boat, it sports an unusual Archibald Arrol mirror. Lunches served Fri.
♨ ᴛ ▶ ⊟ Ⓐ ♣

Durris

Crofters Inn

Lochton of Durris (A957 Stonehaven–Crathes road)
☎ (01330) 844543
12–3, 6–10 (midnight Fri & Sat); 12.30–3, 5.30–11 Sun (closed Tue in winter)
Ind Coope Burton Ale Ⓗ
Remote country pub, enjoying an idyllic setting. The lounge is attractively furnished, while the bar remains basic. It is advisable to book for meals.
Q ᴛ ▶ ⊟ ᴴ ♣ P

Elgin

Thunderton House

Thunderton Place (off High St)
☎ (01343) 548769
11–11.30 (11.45 Fri & Sat)
Draught Bass; guest beers Ⓗ
Busy bar in an historic building, with links to Bonnie Prince Charlie. Very popular with all ages. Meals available until 7pm. ᴛ Ⓓ ▶ ᴴ ⇌

Fraserburgh

Crown Bar

Broad Street ☎ (01346) 514941
11–11.30; 12.30–11 Sun
McEwan 80/- Ⓗ
Unspoilt, but cosy, old-fashioned bar overlooking the

harbour. Note the old Guinness fount. A real gem in a real beer desert. ⊟ ♣

Lossiemouth

Clifton

Clifton Road ☎ (01343) 812100
11–2.30, 5–11 (11.45 Fri & Sat)
McEwan 80/-; S&N Theakston Old Peculier Ⓔ**; Whitbread Boddingtons Bitter** Ⓗ**; guest beer**
Comfortable bar on the road to the harbour. The local nautical and aeronautical links are self-evident. ♨ Ⓐ ♣ P

Macduff

Plough Inn

13–15 Skene Street (A98)
☎ (01261) 832270
10–midnight; 12.30–11 Sun
Ind Coope Burton Ale; guest beers Ⓗ
Pub comprising a small, wood-panelled public bar, with a pool room off, and a spacious, comfortable lounge. Real ale is sold in the public bar only, but staff will carry it through. ⊟ ♣ P

Netherley

Lairhillock

On B979 ☎ (01596) 30001
11–midnight (including Sun)
Courage Directors; Thwaites Craftsman; guest beers Ⓗ
Pub set in lovely Scottish countryside; look out for the word 'Inn' on the roof. The large lounge boasts a central fire. Families are welcome in the conservatory. The public bar has two fires and a welcoming atmosphere. Excellent food.
♨ Q ᴛ ❀ Ⓓ ▶ P

Newmachar

Beekies Neuk

Station Road (by A947)
☎ (01651) 862740
11–midnight (1am Fri, 11.45 Sat); 12.30–11.30 Sun
Courage Directors; guest beers Ⓗ
Friendly local with a small, attractive snug and a large, comfortable lounge where excellent food is served. Pool and darts are played.
♨ Ⓓ ▶ ⊟ ᴴ P

Oldmeldrum

Redgarth

Kirk Brae (off A947)
☎ (01651) 872353
11–2.30, 5–11 (11.45 Fri & Sat); 12.30–2.30, 5.30–11 Sun
Caledonian 80/-; guest beers Ⓗ

Large, single-room lounge which enjoys a wonderful view over the surrounding countryside. The superb food includes vegetarian dishes. Children welcome.
Q ❀ ◖ ▮ P

Peterhead

Grange Inn
West Road (A950 from centre)
☎ (01779) 473472
11–2.30, 5–11 (midnight Wed); 11–midnight Thu–Sat; 12.30–2.30, 6.30–midnight Sun
S&N Theakston XB; guest beer Ⓗ
Friendly pub on the outskirts of town. The comfortable lounge is being extended to add a function suite and dining area. The plain public bar features quaint bucket seats. Phone to check if meals are available. ❀ ◖ ▮ ⌂ P

Pitmedden

Linsmohr Hotel
Oldmeldrum Road (B999,

Tarves road, turn left at village) ☎ (01651) 842214
11–midnight (including Sun)
Beer range varies Ⓗ
Large old house set in a small village. The two bars extend a warm welcome (including to families in summer). The food is excellent.
Q ⌯ ❀ ◖ ▮ ⚅ ♣ P

Ruthven

Borve Brew House
Off A96, NE of Huntly
☎ (0146 687) 343
12.30–11 (11.45 Fri & Sat); 12.30–11 Sun
Borve Ale, Tall Ships IPA Ⓗ
Happiness is hand-pulled at this one-bar brew pub in a converted school. The distinctive ales are brewed by a master brewer.
🏠 Q ⚅ ♣ P

Stonehaven

Marine Hotel
Shorehead ☎ (0159 69) 62155

11–midnight; 12–11 Sun
Draught Bass; Taylor Landlord; guest beers Ⓗ
Popular village hotel beside a small, picturesque harbour. It gets crowded in summer, but you can sit on the harbour wall and relax in the sun. The family room is upstairs.
Q ⌯ ⊨ ◖ ▮ ⚅ ▲ ♣

Tomintoul

Glenavon Hotel
1 The Square
☎ (0180 74) 218
11.30–11.30 (including Sun)
Tomintoul Caillie and/or **Stag; guest beers** Ⓗ
Warm, friendly village pub, set in rolling Scottish countryside; used by walkers and skiers. The large, open bar has a real fire—cosy when snow is falling—lovely in summer. Try the home-cooked food. A family welcome.
🏠 ⊨ ◖ ▲ ♣

CAMRA's Aims

We aim to

 maintain consumer rights

 promote quality, choice and value for money

 support the public house

 and campaign for greater appreciation of traditional beers, ciders and perries

387

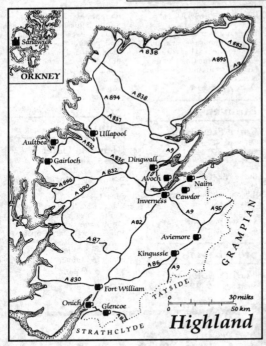

 Orkney, Sandwick, Orkney

Dingwall

National Hotel
High Street
☎ (01349) 62166
11–midnight (1am Fri, 11 Sun)
Alloa Arrol's 80/-; Caledonian 80/-; Ind Coope Burton Ale; Orkney Raven Ale, Dark Island; Tetley Bitter; guest beers H
Real ale is served in the friendly, comfortable but utilitarian bar in a modern extension to this 1930s-style hotel in the town centre. Occasional mini-beer fests, with up to 20 guest ales, in the winter.
❀ ⇋ ◑ ▶ ⇌ P

Fort William

Alexandra Hotel
The Parade (by roundabout at N end of town)
☎ (01397) 702241
11–11; 12.30–11 Sun
Caledonian Deuchars IPA, 80/- H
Bright, friendly lounge bar in the town's main hotel (AA 3-star). Whilst the hotel was built in the last century, the bar is modern but tasteful. Live music most nights. Good value food available next to the lounge; try the mixed grill.
➤ ❀ ⇋ ◑ ▶ ৬ ▲ ⇌ P

Gairloch

Old Inn
The Harbour
☎ (01445) 2006
11 (11.30 Sat)–midnight; 12.30–11 Sun
Beer range varies H
Small highland hotel in a picturesque setting, serving local customers all-year round, with a busy public bar and a quiet lounge. Popular with sailing, climbing and walking clients. Safe garden for children.
Q ❀ ⇋ ◑ ▶ ৬ ▲ ♣ P

Glencoe

Clachaig Inn
On old riverside road, to the rear of NT centre
☎ (0185 52) 252
11 (12.30 Sun)–11 (midnight Fri, 11.30 Sat)
Alloa Arrol's 80/-; Caledonian 80/-; Ind Coope Burton Ale H
Vibrant public bar with live folk and other music, attracting climbers, walkers and sundry others from all over Britain and beyond. CAMRA's Scottish *Pub of the Year* 1994. Beer festivals held.
⚒ ❀ ⇋ ◑ ▶ ▲ P

Aultbea

Drumchork Lodge Hotel
400 yds off A832 at southern edge of village, signed
☎ (01445) 731242
11–11 (1am Fri, 11.30 Sat); 12.30–11 Sun
Bateman XXXB; guest beers H
Popular holiday hotel with a splendid view over Loch Ewe of west coast sunsets. An old shooting lodge.
⚒ ❀ ◑ ▶ ⊡ ♣ P

Aviemore

Winking Owl
Grampian Road
☎ (01479) 810646
10.30–midnight; 12.30–11 Sun
Alloa Arrol's 80/-; Ind Coope Burton Ale; Tetley Bitter; Tomintoul Stag; guest beer H
A conversion from a farm building about 30 years ago, much patronised by skiers, hillwalkers and locals. The landlord is a member of the *Guild of Master Cellarmen*.
❀ ◑ ▶ ▲ ⇌ ♣ P

Avoch

Station Hotel
Bridge Street
☎ (01381) 620246
11–2.30, 5–midnight; 11–11.30 Sat & Sun
Beer choice varies H
Busy local in a pleasant Black Isle fishing village. Good walking, golfing and sailing nearby. Popular for its good value food (served all day Sat and Sun). Children's play area in the garden. The one beer is a guest. ❀ ◑ ▶ ৬ ♣ P

Cawdor

Cawdor Tavern
The Lane
☎ (01667) 404316
11–2.30, 5–11; 12.30–5, 6.30–11 Sun
Beer choice varies H
Pub close to the castle made famous by Shakespeare's *Macbeth*: a cosy, oak-panelled lounge with a log fire, and a public bar with a collection of stuffed and mounted animals. Set in a beautiful and tranquil village. Patio for outside drinking. Children's certificate till 9 in the lounge. Winter eve meals: Fri and Sat only.
⚒ Q ☻ ❀ ◑ ▶ P

Inverness

Gellions
10 Bridge Street
☎ (01463) 233648
9–11 (1am Wed–Fri, 11.45 Sat);
12.30–11 Sun
**Courage Directors; McEwan
80/-; Whitbread Flowers
Original; guest beer** H
Previously small, town-centre
hotel with two bars and an
upstairs wine bar. The cellar
was the original town jail.
Photographs of old Inverness
are on display in the lounge
bar. No real ale in the
public bar. Bar food in the
lounge; other meals in the
wine bar.
◨ 🍴 & 🗲 ♣

Heathmount Hotel
Kingsmills Road (up hill
from Eastgate shopping
centre)
☎ (01463) 235877
11–11 (12.30am Thu & Fri, 11.30 Sat);
12–11 Sun
**McEwan 80/-; Marston's
Pedigree; S&N Theakston
Best Bitter; guest beer** H
Busy lounge and public bar in
the midst of the B&B area.
Distinctive decor; imaginative,
good value menu; friendly and
efficient service.
🛏 ◨ 🍴 🗲 ♣ P

Lauders
16 Church Street
☎ (01463) 235909
11–11 (12.30am Thu & Fri, 11.45 Sat);
7–11 Sun
**Ind Coope Burton Ale; Tetley
Bitter; guest beer** H
Old, established town-centre
pub, recently refurbished to a
high standard in the modern
theme style. Popular with a
broad age group and crowded
at weekends. A defined eating
area serves home-cooked
meals made with local

produce (eve meals in summer
only). Children welcome.
◨ 🍴 & 🗲

Phoenix
108 Academy Street
☎ (01463) 233685
11–11 (12.30am Thu & Fri, 11.30 Sat);
12.30–2.30, 6.30–11 Sun
**Bass Worthington BB,
Draught Bass; Maclay 80/-;
guest beers** H
Traditional pub, 100 years old
in 1994, featuring sawdust on
the floor and white-aproned
staff. A rare example of an
island bar. No real ale in the
more spacious lounge bar but
no objections to taking it
through.
🛏 ◨ 🍴 🍺 & 🗲 ♣

Kingussie

Royal Hotel
High Street
☎ (01540) 661898
11–midnight (1am Thu–Sat);
12.30–midnight Sun
**Alloa Arrol's 80/-; Ind Coope
Burton Ale; Orkney Dark
Island; Robinson's Best
Bitter; Tetley Bitter; guest
beers** H
Large, extended hotel in the
centre of the village, formerly
a coaching house. Large
lounge bar; good value food.
Music often at weekends.
Guest beers (up to nine) are
frequently sold at special
prices.
🛏 ✿ 🛏 ◨ 🍴 & 🗲 ♣ P ⊬

Nairn

Claymore House Hotel
Seabank Road
☎ (01667) 453731
12–3, 5–11.30 (12.30am Thu & Fri)
**Whitbread Boddingtons
Bitter** H
Nicely decorated bar in a
recently refurbished hotel.

Situated in the west end of
town on the way to Nairn Golf
Club and not far from the sea
front. Children's licence till 9.
Live jazz on Mon. A popular
venue for bar suppers.
🍴 Q 🛏 ✿ 🛏 ◨ 🍴 P

Invernairne Hotel
Thurlow Road
☎ (01667) 452039
11–11.30 (12.30am Fri)
Beer choice varies H
Nice, friendly bar in a
Victorian seaside hotel, with
lovely wooden-panelling and a
superb fireplace. Panoramic
view of the sea; the beer
garden has a path leading to
the promenade and beach.
Children's certificate till 8pm.
🍴 🛏 ✿ 🛏 ◨ 🍴 P

Onich

Nether Lochaber
☎ (01855) 3235
11–2.30, 5–11; 12.30–2.30, 6.30–11
Sun
Draught Bass H
Nice, wee public bar situated
behind a family-owned hotel
at the eastern terminus of the
Corran ferry (gateway to
Morvern, Moidart and an
alternative route to Mull in the
summer).
Q ✿ 🛏 ◨ 🍴 🗲 P

Ullapool

Ferry Boat Inn
Shore Street
☎ (01854) 612366
11–11; 12.30–11 Sun
Beer range varies H
Small, friendly lounge bar on
the village waterfront, with
open views inland over Loch
Broom. Busy throughout the
summer months. Three
Scottish guest beers are sold.
🍴 Q 🛏 🛏 ◨ 🍴 🗲

THE SYMBOLS

🍴	real fire	&	easy wheelchair access
Q	quiet pub (at least one bar)	🗲	camping facilities at the pub
🛏	indoor room for children		or nearby
✿	garden or other outdoor drinking	⇌	near British Rail station
	area	⊖	near underground station
🛏	accommodation	♣	pub games
◨	lunchtime meals	⊙	real cider
▸	evening meals	P	pub car park
◨	public bar	⊬	no-smoking room or area

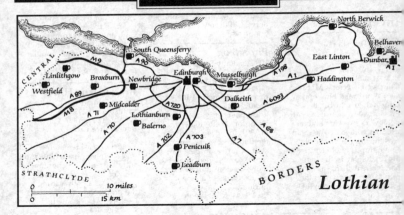

 Belhaven, *Dunbar*; **Caledonian, Physician & Firkin, Rose Street**, *Edinburgh*

Balerno

Grey Horse
Main Street (pedestrian precinct, off A70)
☎ (0131) 449 3092
11–2.30, 5–11; closed Sun
Belhaven Sandy Hunter's Ale, 80/- H
Traditionally run, busy wood-panelled village gem. A fine bank of handpumps dispenses the cheap beer. Collection of rare brewery mirrors.
Q 🍴 ♣

Johnsburn House
64 Johnsburn Road (off A70)
☎ (0131) 449 3847
12–3, 6.30–midnight; 12–midnight Sat; 12.30–11 Sun; closed Mon
S&N Theakston Best Bitter; guest beers H
Historic baronial mansion dating from 1760 and now Grade B-listed. Reputation for meals. The cosy bar has a convivial atmosphere. Four guest beers.
🏚 Q 🌳 🍴 ▶ P

Belhaven

Mason's Arms
High Street (A1087, ½ mile W of Dunbar)
☎ (01368) 863700
11–11 (1am Thu & Fri; midnight Sat); 12.30–4 Sun
Belhaven 80/- H
Plain village local, notable mainly for the aviary in the back yard and a fine view of the Lammermuir and Moorfoot Hills. Eve meals Thu–Sat.
Q 🍴 ▶ 🍴 ♣

Broxburn

Masonic Arms
Station Road (off E Main St)
☎ (01506) 856347
11 (12.30 Sun)–11 (midnight Fri & Sat)
Caledonian 80/- H
Wee gem of a pub on a street corner. A fine gantry, window screens, an old brewery mirror, wood-panelling and a floor which rolls and swells even when you're sober make this a must. 🍴 ♣

Dalkeith

Black Bull
1 Lothian Street (off A68, behind shopping precinct)
☎ (0131) 663 2095
11 (12.30 Sun)–11.30 (midnight Thu–Sat, 11.45 Sun)
Caledonian Deuchars IPA, 80/-, Double Amber Ale *or* **Orkney Dark Island** H
A good example of a 'Gothenburg', a busy pub with a spacious interior, fine arched windows and cornicework, along with a well-crafted gantry. 🍴 🍴 ♿ ♣

East Linton

Crown Hotel
27 Bridge Street (B1377)
☎ (01620) 860335
11–2.30, 5–11 (midnight Thu, 1am Fri); 11–midnight Sat; 12.30–midnight Sun
Belhaven 80/-; guest beer H
Down-to-earth village bar featuring lots of wood-panelling. Original Dudgeon windows contribute to the atmosphere.
🏚 Q 🍴 🍴 🍴 ♣

Drover's Inn
5 Bridge Street (B1377)
☎ (01620) 860298
11–2.30, 5–11; 12–11 Sun (11–11 summer; closed Mon Jan–Apr)
Beer range varies H
Formerly the Railway, tucked under the main line viaduct, this characterful bar has a dark, intimate feel. Interesting range of five beers downstairs; quality restaurant upstairs. Not cheap.
🏚 Q 🍴 ▶

Edinburgh

Bert's Bar
27 William Street (between Princes St and Haymarket)
☎ (0131) 225 5748
11–11 (midnight Thu–Sat); closed Sun
Alloa Arrol's 80/-; Caledonian 80/-; Ind Coope Burton Ale; guest beers H
Public bar with a snug and a sitting room off. A good example of modern pub architecture, using quality wood and tiling. Seven beers.
Q 🍴 🍴 ➤ (Haymarket)

Bow Bar
80 West Bow (between Royal Mile and Grassmarket)
☎ (0131) 220 1823
11–11.15; 7–11 Sun
Draught Bass; Caledonian 70/-, Deuchars IPA, 80/-, ERA; Taylor Landlord; guest beers A
Traditional one-room, stand-up bar with efficient, friendly service. Several extinct brewery mirrors and old cigarette ephemera cover the walls. Large selection of malts and 11 beers.
Q ➤ (Waverley)

Cask & Barrel

115 Broughton Street (between
Leith Walk and Canonmills)
☎ (0131) 556 3132
11 (12.30 Sun)–midnight (12.30
Thu–Sat)
**Draught Bass; Caledonian
Deuchars IPA, 80/-; guest
beers** Ⓗ
Spacious and extremely busy
suburban ale house with an
imposing horseshoe bar,
wooden floorboards and a
splendid cornice. Collection of
brewery mirrors. Ten
handpumps.
◁ Ⓓ & ≣ (Waverley)

Drew Nicol's (Coppers)

19 Cockburn Street
☎ (0131) 225 1441
11–11.45; closed Sun
**Mitchell's Best Bitter; guest
beers** Ⓗ
One-roomed pub for lovers of
the turf. Three guest beers; the
house beer is Alloa Arrol's
80/-. Can get extremely smoky
when busy.
Q Ⓓ ⊞ ≣ (Waverley)

Golden Rule

30 Yeaman Place,
Fountainbridge (off Dundee
St, near S&N factory)
☎ (0131) 229 3413
11 (12.30 Sun)–11.30 (11 Mon, Tue &
Sun)
**Draught Bass; Belhaven 80/-;
Caledonian Deuchars IPA,
80/-; Harviestoun 80/-; Maclay
Kane's Amber Ale; guest
beers** Ⓗ
Busy, split-level lounge bar in
a Victorian tenement building,
which can be smoky and hot.
⊞ ≣ (Haymarket)

Guildford Arms

1 West Register Street (behind
Burger King, E end of Princes
St, near bus station)
☎ (0131) 556 4312
11 (12.30 Sun)–11 (midnight Thu–Sat)
**Draught Bass; Belhaven 60/-;
Caledonian 80/-; Harviestoun
70/-, 80/-; Orkney Dark Island;
guest beers** Ⓗ
Pub where the majestic decor
combines ornate plasterwork
and ceilings, spectacular
cornices and friezes, window
arches and screens and a very
unusual, wood-panelled
gallery alcove overlooking the
busy main bar. Four guest
beers. Q ⊞ ≣ (Waverley)

Halfway House

24 Fleshmarket Close (between
Cockburn St and Waverley
station rear entrance)
☎ (0131) 225 7101
11 (10 Sat)–11.30 (midnight Wed, 1am
Thu–Sat); 12.30–11 Sun (7–11 winter
Sun)
**Belhaven 80/-, St Andrew's
Ale; guest beer** Ⓗ
Cosy, friendly, wee L-shaped

howff down an old town close.
Often crowded. The decor
features railway memorabilia.
⊞ ≣ (Waverley)

Holyrood Tavern

9 Holyrood Road
☎ (0131) 556 5044
12–midnight (1am Thu–Sat); 6–11 Sun
**Alloa Arrol's 80/-; Ansells
Mild; Caledonian 80/-; Ind
Coope Burton Ale; guest
beers** Ⓗ
Deceptively large, traditional
bar with a long, unspoilt
counter and gantry. Two
sitting rooms; the rear has a
large Ushers mirror. An
Edinburgh Festival Fringe
venue. Three guest beers. No
food Sun.
◁ ⊞ ≣ (Waverley) ✦

Kay's Bar

39 Jamaica Street (between
India St and Howe St)
☎ (0131) 225 1858
11–11.45; 12.30–11 Sun
**Belhaven 80/-; S&N
Theakston Best Bitter, XB;
guest beers** Ⓗ
Cosy, convivial, comfortable
new town bar featuring clever
and interesting furniture.
Good varied lunches. Three
guest beers and 50 single
malts.
🍴 Q ◁ ≣ (Waverley) ✦

Leslie's Bar

45 Ratcliffe Terrace (between
Newington and the Grange)
☎ (0131) 667 7205
11 (12.30 Sun)–11.15 (12.30am Fri,
11.45 Sat)
**Draught Bass; Belhaven 80/-;
Caledonian 70/-, Deuchars
IPA, 80/-; guest beer** Ⓗ
Superb Victorian pub with one
of the finest interiors in the
city. A snob screen separates
the saloon and snug from the
public bar. Permanently busy.
The cellarman has tended the
beers for over 60 years.
🍴 Q ⊞ ♣

Malt & Hops

45 The Shore, Leith
☎ (0131) 555 0083
12 (12.30 Sun)–11 (midnight Thu, 1am
Fri & Sat)
**Alloa Arrol's 80/-; Ind Coope
Burton Ale; Marston's
Pedigree; guest beers** Ⓗ
Dating from 1749, facing onto
the Water of Leith, a one-room
public bar with a large
collection of pump clips.
Haunted by the ghost of a
previous licensee, who
drowned when the cellar
flooded. No food Sun.
🍴 Q ◁ ≣ ♣

Oxford Bar

8 Young Street (between
George St and Queen St)
☎ (0131) 225 4262
11–1am; 12.30–late Sun

Belhaven 80/- Ⓐ**, St Andrew's
Ale; Courage Directors** Ⓗ
Tiny yet vibrant new town
drinking shop, retaining signs
of its original, early 19th-
century parlour arrangement.
Q ⊞ ≣ (Waverley)

Robbie's Bar

367 Leith Walk (A900 at Pilrig)
☎ (0131) 554 6850
12 (11 Sat)–midnight; 12.30–11 Sun
**Draught Bass; Caledonian
Deuchars IPA; guest beers** Ⓗ
Victorian-style workingman's
bar with interesting
woodwork, gantry and rare
mirrors. ⊞ & ≣

Royal Ettrick Hotel

13 Ettrick Road (behind
Merchiston Bowling and
Tennis Club)
☎ (0131) 228 6413
11 (12.30 Sun)–midnight
**Draught Bass; Caledonian
80/-; Maclay Kane's Amber
Ale; guest beers** Ⓗ
Built as a town house in 1875
and now a splendid family-
run hotel, set in leafy suburbs.
The lounge bar is comfortably
appointed and the restaurant
is bright and airy. Four guest
beers; excellent meals.
Q ✿ 🛏 ◁ Ⓓ ⌂ P

Southsider

3–5 West Richmond Street
(near Surgeons Hall)
☎ (0131) 667 2003
11–midnight (1am Fri); 12.30–11 Sun
**Maclay 60/-, 70/-, 80/-, Kane's
Amber Ale; guest beers** Ⓗ
Busy Southside lounge bar,
popular with discerning locals
and students. The public bar is
a handy refuge if the lounge
gets too smoky. Four guest
beers. ◁ Ⓓ ≣ (Waverley) ✦

Starbank Inn

64 Laverockbank Road,
Newhaven (between Leith and
Granton) ☎ (0131) 552 4141
11 (12.30 Sun)–11 (midnight Thu–Sat)
**Belhaven Sandy Hunter's Ale,
80/-, St Andrew's Ale; Taylor
Landlord; guest beers** Ⓗ
Pub transformed into a bright
and airy bare-floorboarded
house without a loss of
atmosphere. Three separate
areas. Fine views across the
Forth. Good value food.
Q ✿ ◁ ▶ ⊞ ✂

Winston's

20 Kirk Loan, Corstorphine
(off St John's Rd, A8)
☎ (0131) 539 7077
11–11.30; 12.30–3, 7–11 Sun
**Alloa Arrol's 80/-; Caledonian
70/-, Deuchars IPA, Double
Amber Ale; Ind Coope Burton
Ale** Ⓗ
Busy locals' lounge bar housed
in an ex-launderette, in a
western suburb. A modern

Lothian

one-roomed pub with a golfing and rugby theme. Q ⓖ

Try also: Cockburn, Jamaica St (Free)

Haddington

Pheasant
72 Market Street (off A1)
☎ (0162 082) 6342
11 (12.30 Sun)–11 (midnight Thu–Sat)
Caledonian 80/-; Ind Coope Burton Ale; Orkney Raven Ale; guest beer Ⓗ
Vibrant and often noisy pub attracting younger folk, especially at weekends. The long bar snakes through to the games area where Basil (a Norwegian Blue) holds court.
ⓖ ♣

Leadburn

Leadburn Inn
West Linton (at A703/A701/A6094 jct) ☎ (01968) 672952
11 (12.30 Sun)–midnight
Caledonian 80/-; guest beer Ⓗ
Large food-oriented hostelry where a converted railway coach serves as a restaurant. The public bar has two pot-bellied stoves and a picture window on the Pentland Hills. A conservatory links the bar to a plush lounge. Excellent menu: meals till 10pm.
🚲 Q ❀ 🛏 ⓓ ❙ 🍴 ♣ P ⟋

Linlithgow

Four Marys
High Street ☎ (01506) 842171
12–2.30, 5–11 (11.45 Fri); 12–11.45 Sat; 12.30–2.30, 7–11 Sun
Belhaven 70/-, 80/-, St Andrew's Ale; guest beers Ⓗ
Attractive lounge with antique furniture and items reflecting the town's history. Nine handpumps serve constantly changing guest beers; large choice of malts. Local CAMRA *Pub of the Year* 1994. No food Sun eve. ⓖ ❙ ≢

Red Lion
High Street ☎ (01506) 842348
11–11 (midnight Thu–Sat); 12.30–11 Sun
Greenalls Shipstone's Bitter; McEwan 80/-; Orkney Dark Island Ⓗ
Small, friendly bar offering reduced prices for pensioners.
❀ 🍴 & ≢ ♣

Lothianburn

Steading
118 Biggar Road (A702 near Hillend ski slope)
☎ (0131) 445 1128
11 (12.30 Sun)–11 (midnight Sat)

Draught Bass; Caledonian Deuchars IPA, 80/-, Double Amber Ale; Orkney Dark Island; Taylor Landlord; guest beer Ⓗ
Former stone cottages converted into an attractive bar and restaurant with a conservatory extension. A very popular eating establishment (till 10.30pm), but the drinking area has been preserved.
🚲 Q ❀ ⓓ ❙ & P

Midcalder

Torphichen Arms
Bank Street ☎ (01506) 880020
11 (12.30 Sun)–11 (midnight Thu–Sat)
Caledonian Deuchars IPA, 80/-; Greenalls Shipstone's Bitter; Ind Coope Burton Ale Ⓗ
Village local, originally several rooms, now one L-shaped bar, though retaining public and lounge areas. Live music Sun.
ⓓ ♣ P

Musselburgh

Levenhall Arms
10 Ravensheugh Road (off A199) ☎ (0131) 665 3220
11 (12.30 Sun)–11 (midnight Thu, 1am Fri & Sat)
Caledonian Deuchars IPA, 80/-; Ind Coope Burton Ale; guest beers Ⓗ
At the end of the racecourse; a busy public bar, popular with locals and racegoers. The separate lounge has occasional entertainment. Deservedly given the Burton Ale *Master Cellarman* award in 1993.
🍴 ♣ P

Volunteer Arms (Stagg's)
78–81 North High Street (behind Brunton Hall, Fisherrow) ☎ (0131) 665 6481
11–2.30, 5–11; 11–11 Thu; 11–midnight Fri & Sat; closed Sun
Draught Bass; Belhaven St Andrew's Ale; Caledonian Deuchars IPA, 80/-; guest beer Ⓗ
Very busy and friendly, traditional local with rare mirrors, fine panelling and a magnificent gantry. 🍴

Newbridge

Newbridge Inn
Bridge Street (near M8/M9 roundabout)
☎ (0131) 333 3220
11–2.30, 5–11; 11–11 Thu & Sat, 11–midnight Fri; 12.30–5, 6.30–11 Sun
Beer choice varies Ⓗ
Former coaching inn from 1683. The public bar is split into games and drinking areas; the lounge is at the rear. No food weekends. ⓓ 🍴 ♣

North Berwick

Dalrymple Arms
Quality Street ☎ (01620) 2969
11 (12.30 Sun)–11 (midnight Thu & Sat, 1am Fri)
Beer range varies Ⓗ
Popular local in the centre of town. The wood-panelled canopy and gantry give the feel of a village pub. Games room at the rear. Five guest beers; over 40 single malts.
🚲 ⓓ 🍴 ≢ ♣

Nether Abbey Hotel (Fly Half Bar)
20 Dirleton Avenue (A198 W of centre) ☎ (01620) 2802
12 (12.30 Sun)–11 (midnight Thu & Sat, 1am Fri)
Beer range varies Ⓐ
Basement bar and extension in a well-appointed, family-run Victorian hotel. Ideal for exploring the history of Lothian. Two guest beers; annual beer festival.
🛏 ⓓ ❙ ≢ P

Penicuik

Craigiebield House Hotel
50 Bog Road (off A766)
☎ (01968) 672557
11–3, 5–11.30 (12.30am Fri; 12–12.30am Sat); 12.30–11.30 Sun)
Caledonian Deuchars IPA, 80/-, Double Amber Ale; Taylor Landlord; guest beer Ⓗ
Handsome sandstone hotel on the outskirts of town. The small lounge is comfortable and decorated with humorous golfing prints. The restaurant enjoys a fine reputation for its Italian cuisine. Folk music Sun night. No-smoking upstairs lounge at weekends only.
🛏 ⓓ ❙ P ⟋

South Queensferry

Ferry Tap
High Street ☎ (0131) 331 2000
11 (12.30 Sun)–11 (midnight Thu–Sat)
Caledonian Deuchars IPA, 80/-; Orkney Raven Ale, Dark Island; guest beer Ⓗ
Well-appointed, friendly, one-roomer with an unusual barrel-vaulted ceiling. Can get busy at weekends. Live jazz Tue. No food Sun. ⓓ

Westfield

Logievale Inn
Main Street ☎ (01506) 56088
12–2.30, 5–11; 12–midnight Fri & Sat; 12.30–11 Sun
Belhaven 80/- Ⓗ**, Sandy Hunter's Ale** Ⓐ
Converted cottages, now a village local attracting passing trade. Best to book eve meals (good food). 🚲 ❀ ⓓ ❙ & P

Strathclyde

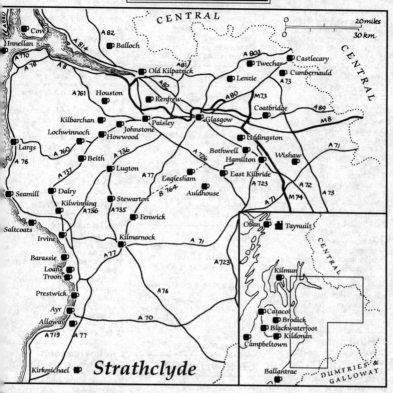

🏰 West Highland, Taynuilt

Note: licensing laws permit no entry after 11pm to pubs in the following locations: Houston, Howwood, Johnstone, Kilbarchan, Lochwinnoch, Paisley and Renfrew.

Alloway

Balgarth

Dunure Road (A719, at Doonfoot, S of Ayr)
☎ (01292) 442441
11 (12.30 Sun)–11 (midnight Fri & Sat)
Whitbread Boddingtons Bitter, Flowers Original H
Former country hotel opposite a popular garden centre, well-refurbished into a Brewers' Fayre pub/restaurant. The main bar features sporting activities. Children's certificate—families welcome. Food available all day. 🏚 Q ✿ 🕭 ◖ ▶ P

Bellisle House Hotel (Tam o' Shanter Bar)

Bellisle Park, Doonfoot Road (A719, S of Ayr)
☎ (01292) 442331
11–11 (6 winter)
Draught Bass H
A golfer's 19th hole attached to an hotel in a splendid country park with two golf courses, gardens and a pets corner. Photos of famous golfers adorn the walls. Meals available in the cafeteria or hotel.
🏚 ◖ P

Auldhouse

Auldhouse Arms

6 Langlands Road (from East Kilbride, right from Strathaven Rd, follow signs) OS624502
☎ (0135 52) 63242
12–2.30, 5–11; 12–midnight Fri & Sat; 12.30–11 Sun
Belhaven 80/- A
Traditional Scottish village pub—one of the last of a dying breed. Several rooms are warmed by well-fed fires. The handpump on the bar activates an air pressure pump. Phone to discover if food is available.
🏚 Q ✿ ◖ ▶ ♿ P

Ayr

Chestnuts Hotel

52 Racecourse Road (A719, S of centre) ☎ (01292) 264393
11 (12 Sun)–midnight
Draught Bass; Broughton Special; guest beers H
Comfortable lounge bar with a vaulted ceiling and a collection of over 300 water jugs. Excellent bar meals. Children's certificate. Two guest beers.
🏚 Q ✿ 🕭 🏚 ◖ ▶ ≉ P ♼

Geordie's Byre

103 Main Street (over river, towards Prestwick)
☎ (01292) 264925
11–11 (midnight Thu–Sat); 12.30–11 Sun
Caledonian Deuchars IPA, 80/-; guest beers A
Friendly, traditional local. The back lounge (open weekends) has an extensive collection of Victoriana and bric-a-brac.

Three guest beers from anywhere between Orkney and Cornwall. A regular venue for poets and pints nights. ⊞ ⅙ ⇌ (Newton-on-Ayr) ♣

Jonesy's

Nile Court, 154 High Street
☎ (01292) 288474
11 (12.30 Sun)–12.30 (midnight Sat & Sun)
Stones Best Bitter H
Open-plan, town-centre lounge: quiet during the day, but can be very loud and busy at weekends. A rock/blues music venue, with a rock/heavy metal disco upstairs (without real ale).
⅃ ⇌

Tam o' Shanter Inn

230 High Street
☎ (01292) 611684
11 (12.30 Sun)–midnight
Beer range varies H
Small, attractive, town-centre bar, recently returned to its original use after years as a Burns museum: traditional inside and out. The two beers are rotated on a regular basis. The music can be quite loud on occasions. ⅃ ⇌ ♣

Wellington's

17 Wellington Square (just behind the seafront)
☎ (01292) 262794
11–12.30; 12–midnight Sun
Draught Bass H
Basement lounge bar in a Georgian square near the beach. Regular Sun eve folk sessions. ⅃ ▶ ⇌

Try also: **Old Racecourse Hotel**, Victoria Pk (S&N Theakston)

Ballantrae

Kings Arms Hotel

40 Main Street (A77 coast road) ☎ (01465) 83202
11–12.30; 12–midnight Sun
Marston's Pedigree; guest beer H
Comfortable village hotel on the main route between central Scotland and Northern Ireland. Close to the seafront. Children's certificate.
♨ Q ☺ ⊛ ⊯ ⅃ ▶ ⊞ ♣ P

Balloch

Balloch Hotel

Balloch Road (right from station over river)
☎ (01389) 52579
11–11 (including Sun)
Alloa Arrol's 80/-; Ind Coope Burton Ale; guest beer H
Lounge bar which has been recently tastefully refurbished, with stone flooring around the

bar and the remainder neatly carpeted. The landlord was made a Burton *Master Cellarman* in 1993. Breakfast served to non-residents from 7.30am. ⊛ ⊯ ⅃ ▶ ⇌ P

Barassie

Tower Hotel

23 Beach Road (B748, seafront, N of Troon) ☎ (01292) 311142
11–midnight (including Sun)
Draught Bass; Caledonian 80/-; guest beers H
Attractive hotel on Troon's North Beach, offering a fine view over the Firth of Clyde to Arran. Real ale is available in both the lounge and public bars. Separate restaurant. Children welcome.
♨ Q ⊛ ⊯ ⅃ ▶ ⊞ ⅙ ⇌ ♣ P

Beith

Anderson Hotel

17 Eglinton Street (B7049, S of centre) ☎ (01505) 502034
11 (12.30 Sun)–midnight (1am Fri & Sat)
John Smith's Magnet H
Compact locals' hotel near the centre of a small town between Glasgow and the main population centres of Ayrshire. ♨ ⊯ ⅃ ⊞ ♣

Blackwaterfoot

Kinloch Hotel

☎ (01770) 860444
11.30–midnight (12.30am Thu–Sat);
12.30–midnight Sun
Courage Directors; S&N Theakston XB; Younger No.3 H
Prominent hotel on the seafront, with a swimming pool and other leisure facilities open to the public. Good views over to Campbeltown Loch. ⊯ ⅃ ▶ ⊞ ⅙ ▲ P

Bothwell

Camphill Vaults

1–3 Main Street
☎ (01698) 853526
11–11.45; 12.30–11.45 Sun
Draught Bass H
Traditional pub with sitting rooms and a modern lounge (children welcome till 8.30pm).
Q ⊞ ▲ ♣ P

Brodick

Brodick Bar

Alma Road (behind post office) ☎ (01770) 302169
11–11 (midnight Fri & Sat); closed Sun
Beer range varies H
Modern public and lounge bars in a single-storey building near the seafront. Two beers

from the S&N guest list served. ♨ ⅃ ▶ ⊞ ▲ P

Duncan's Bar (Kingsley Hotel)

Shore Road ☎ (01770) 302531
11–midnight (including Sun. Winter hours: 11–2.30; 11–2.30, 7.30–midnight Fri & Sat; closed Sun)
S&N Theakston XB; guest beer H
Large, comfortable bar to the side of a seashore hotel. The front garden enjoys an excellent view across the bay to Goat Fell. Regular folk and jazz nights in summer. Note the more restricted winter hours.
♨ Q ⏃ ⊛ ⊯ ⅃ ▶ ⅙ ▲ P

Campbeltown

Ardsheil Hotel

Kilkerran Road
☎ (01586) 552133
11–2.30, 5–midnight
McEwan 80/-; S&N Theakston XB H
Very popular, family-run hotel on the beautiful S Kintyre peninsula. Excellent home-cooking and a very wide range of malt whiskies served. Children welcome.
Q ⏃ ⊛ ⊯ ⅃ ▶ P

Commercial Inn

Cross Street ☎ (01586) 553703
11–1am; 12.30–1am Sun
Caledonian Deuchars IPA; guest beer H
Superb, friendly, family-run pub with an ever-increasing guest beer range. ⊞

Castlecary

Castlecary House Hotel

Main Street (off A80)
☎ (01324) 840233
11–11 (11.30 Fri & Sat); 11–2.30, 6–11.30 Sun
Draught Bass; guest beers H
Three separate drinking areas in a country hotel which stands near an impressive viaduct carrying the main Edinburgh to Glasgow railway. The village is on the site of one of the major Roman forts on the Antonine Wall.
⊛ ⊯ ⅃ ▶ ⊞ ⅙ P

Catacol

Catacol Bay Hotel

☎ (01770) 830231
11–midnight (11–1am Thu–Sat)
Ruddles Best Bitter; John Smith's Magnet; guest beer H
Originally built as a manse in the 19th century, a pub on the seafront with superb views to Kintyre. Food is always available. Next to the Twelve

Apostles, an unusual listed terrace of houses. Wheelchair access is via the garden.
🏛 ❀ 🛏 ◖ ▶ ⅃ ♿ P

Coatbridge

Carsons
4–6 Whifflet Street
☎ (01236) 422867
11–midnight; 12.30–midnight Sun
Belhaven Sandy Hunter's Ale *or* **St Andrew's Ale; Broughton Greenmantle Ale** Ⓗ
Family-run local, renovated in 1980 with interesting murals and old casks. It is much more accessible since Strathclyde Transport opened the railway station across the street.
◖ ▶ ⇌ (Whifflet) P

Cove

Knockderry Hotel
Shore Road (B833)
☎ (0143 684) 2283
11–midnight; 11–11 Sun
S&N Theakston Best Bitter, XB; guest beer Ⓗ
Architecturally rich, converted Victorian mansion, situated on the picturesque Rosneath peninsula. The magnificent wood-panelled lounge bar offers fine views over Loch Long. Good food. Local CAMRA *1993 Pub of the Year*.
🏛 ❀ 🛏 ◖ ▶ P

Cumbernauld

Smiddy Inn
Balloch loop road, Balloch
☎ (01236) 728419
11–11 (midnight Thu–Sat); 12.30–11 Sun
Broughton Greenmantle Ale; guest beer Ⓗ
Lively modern local next to a shopping centre in the Balloch housing estate. ◖ ⅃ P

Dalry

Greenbank Inn
97 New Street (A737, E of centre)
11–2.30, 5–11; 11–11 Fri & Sat; 12.30–2.30, 6.30–11 Sun
Beer choice varies Ⓗ
Friendly and comfortable bar and lounge near the railway station. One guest beer sold.
🍴 ⇌ ♣

Eaglesham

Cross Keys
Montgomery Street (B767)
☎ (0135 53) 2002
11 (12.30 Sun)–11 (11.30 Thu, midnight Fri, 11.45 Sat)
Belhaven St Andrew's Ale; Stones Best Bitter; Whitbread Flowers Original Ⓗ

A comfortable lounge contrasts with the traditional, stone public bar in this friendly village pub. The lounge is quiet, and the pub meals excellent. No food Sun.
◖ ▶ 🍴

Eglinton Arms Hotel
Gilmour Street
☎ (0135 53) 2631
11–2.30, 5–11, (midnight Thu–Sat)
McEwan 80/- Ⓐ
Typical S&N hostelry: popular, with a warm welcome guaranteed. Real ale is only served in the cocktail bar. 🛏 ◖ ▶ P

East Kilbride

Crooked Lum
Brunel Way ☎ (0135 52) 22809
11–11 (midnight Fri & Sat); 12.30–11 Sun
Morland Old Speckled Hen; Whitbread Boddingtons Bitter, Castle Eden Ale, Flowers Original Ⓗ
Large, recently-built pub, typical of the Beefeater chain, but a welcome addition to the former real beer desert of East Kilbride. Children's certificate and playground.
♿ ❀ ◖ ▶ ⅃ P

East Kilbride Sports Club
Torrance Avenue, Strathaven Road ☎ (0135 52) 36001
11–11; 12.30–11 Sun
Beer range varies Ⓗ & Ⓐ
Popular club with a commitment to real ale and three unusual guest beers—the chairman runs a beer agency. Show this guide or CAMRA membership in the members' lounge to be signed in. Annual beer festival. CAMRA Scotland *Club of the Year 1992*. Lunches not always available.
Q ❀ ◖ P

New Farm
Strathaven Road (near country park) ☎ (0135 52) 67177
11–11
Marston's Pedigree; Morland Old Speckled Hen; Whitbread Boddingtons Bitter, Flowers Original; guest beer Ⓗ
Typical Brewers' Fayre pub: good service and a family welcome. ❀ ◖ ▶ P

Fenwick

King's Arms
89 Main Road (B7061, just off A77) ☎ (01560) 600276
12.45–3, 5–midnight; 11–midnight Fri & Sat; 12.30–11.30 Sun
Beer choice varies Ⓗ
Fine village inn on the edge of moorland: a listed building

with an unusual exterior. Recently renovated but retaining original features, its new lounge is now a meals area. The bar features the work of a well-known local cartoonist. A bus service passes. Children's certificate.
♿ ◖ ▶ ♣ P

Glasgow

Allison Arms
720 Pollokshaws Road
☎ (0141) 423 1661
11–11 (midnight Fri & Sat); 12.30–11 Sun
Belhaven 80/-; guest beers Ⓐ
Friendly, unpretentious South-side local. Bottled Belgian beers sold.
⇌ (Queens Pk)

Athena Taverna
780 Pollokshaws Road (½ mile from Shawlands Cross)
☎ (0141) 424 0858
11–2.30, 5–11; closed Sun
Belhaven 80/-; guest beers Ⓐ
Café-style bar offering five guest ales and Belgian and German bottled beers. Can get very busy at weekends. The adjoining Greek restaurant serves high quality food.
◖ ▶ ⇌ (Queens Pk)

Babbity Bowster
16–18 Blackfriars Street, Merchant City (just off High St) ☎ (0141) 552 5055
11–midnight; 12.30–midnight Sun
Maclay 70/-, 80/-, Kane's Amber Ale; guest beer Ⓔ
Fine Merchant City pub with individual, distinctive decor, popular with the press and the legal profession, as well as students. Good food includes a barbecue on the outdoor patio in summer. Folk music Sun night. Friendly bar staff.
🏛 Q ❀ 🛏 ◖ ▶ ⇌ (High St) ⊖ (Buchanan St) ♣ ☕ P

Blackfriars
36 Bell Street (corner of Albion St, near City Halls)
☎ (0141) 552 5924
11–midnight; 12.30–midnight Sun
Alloa Arrol's 80/-; Ind Coope Burton Ale; Tetley Bitter; guest beers Ⓗ
Split-level, street-corner pub with a large bay window. Low lighting and candles feature in the eve when it is busy. Live jazz at weekends. Popular with all types, especially students. The food counter serves hot meals and salads. Belgian beers on draught and bottled; three guest ales.
◖ ▶ ⇌ (High St) ⊖ (St Enoch)

Bon Accord
153 North Street
☎ (0141) 248 4427
11–11.45; 12.30–11 Sun

Strathclyde

Beer range varies [H]
The best of Glasgow's recently refurbished T&J Bernard's pubs, selling six guest beers, with independent breweries well-represented.
☾ ◗ ♿ ⇌ (Charing Cross) ⌓

Brewery Tap
1055 Sauchiehall Street
☎ (0141) 339 8866
12–11 (midnight Fri & Sat); 12.30–11 Sun
Alloa Arrol's 80/-; Belhaven 60/-; Ind Coope Burton Ale; Tetley Bitter [A]**; guest beers** [A] **&** [H]
Pub situated close to the art gallery and transport museum, very busy most eves. Especially popular with the local students. Regular live music in one bar; friendly staff. Draught and bottled Belgian beers available.
❀ ☾ ⇌ (Exhibition Centre) ⊖ (Kelvinhall) ⌓

Macsorleys
42 Jamaica Street
☎ (0141) 221 8499
11–midnight; 3–midnight Sun
Draught Bass; Caledonian Deuchars IPA, 80/- [H]
Renovated pub near Central station and the River Clyde, with a mainly young clientele. Regular live music. ☾ ♿ ⇌ (Central) ⊖ (St Enoch)

Mitre
12 Brunswick Street (off Trongate) ☎ (0141) 552 3764
11–11 (midnight Fri & Sat); 12.30–8 Sun
Alloa Arrol's 80/-; Ind Coope Burton Ale; Tetley Bitter; guest beer [H]
Cosy and unspoilt pub with original (1866) decor, including a mini-horseshoe bar with dividing screens. Possibly the smallest bar in Glasgow, providing a friendly retreat from the busy Trongate. Selection of bottled Belgian beers; reasonably priced meals till 6pm. ☾ ◗ ⊞ ⇌ (Argyle St) ⊖ (St Enoch)

Station Bar
55 Port Dundas Road
☎ (0141) 332 3117
11–midnight; 12.30–midnight Sun
Draught Bass; Caledonian Deuchars IPA; guest beer [H]
Unpretentious, friendly, corner tenement gem, behind the Royal Concert Hall. The international Partick Thistle supporters' club HQ.
♿ ⇌ (Queens St) ⊖ (Cowcaddens)

Tennents
191 Byres Road
☎ (0141) 339 0649
11 (12.30 Sun)–11 (midnight Fri & Sat)
Draught Bass; Broughton Greenmantle Ale; Caledonian Deuchars IPA, 80/-; Jennings Cumberland Ale; Maclay Oat Malt Stout; Taylor Landlord; guest beers [H]
Large, one-room, late-Victorian pub with a rectangular bar which can get busy. Usually 12 beers are available, the range changing during its annual beer festival.
☾ ⊖ (Hillhead)

Three Judges
141 Dumbarton Road
☎ (0141) 337 3055
11–11 (midnight Fri & Sat); 12.30–11 Sun
Maclay 80/-, Oat Malt Stout; guest beers [H]
Lively, corner tenement bar which has sold over 350 different beers and farmhouse ciders in under two years (six guest ales at a time). Run by three-in-a-row winners of the local CAMRA's *Landlord of the Year* award. Beer festivals held. Not to be missed.
♿ ⇌ (Partick) ⊖ (Kelvinhall) ⌓

Ubiquitous Chip
12 Ashton Lane, Hillhead
☎ (0141) 334 5007
11 (12.30 Sun)–11 (midnight Fri & Sat)
Caledonian Deuchars IPA, 80/- [A]
Loft bar attached to one of Glasgow's better (though expensive and chip-free) restaurants, built in the former stable block of a coaching inn. Splendid food at all times.
♨ Q ☾ ◗ ⊖ (Hillhead) ⌓

Hamilton

George
18 Campbell Street (off Cadzow St, 100 yds from bottom cross)
☎ (01698) 424225
11–11.45; 6.30–11 Sun
Maclay 80/-, Oat Malt Stout; guest beer [H]
CAMRA's Lanarkshire *Pub of the Year* 1994: a small, family-run pub which is currently leading the way in watering Britain's worst remaining beer desert. Although in the town centre, it is difficult to find, but worth the effort.
☾ ⇌ (Central) ⚞

Houston

Fox & Hounds
Main Street ☎ (01505) 612248
11–midnight (11.45 Sat); 12.30–11 Sun
Broughton Greenmantle Ale; Maclay 70/- [A]
Pub where real ale is only available in the Huntsman Lounge and the separate upstairs restaurant. The mynah bird warning is still in effect! ☾ ◗ P

Howwood

Howwood Inn
Main Street ☎ (01505) 70 3119
11–11.45; 12.30–11 Sun
Caledonian Deuchars IPA [H]
200-year-old coaching inn, with a small, cosy bar and a large lounge. Entertainment at weekends. Parties and children welcome and well catered for. Watch out for the flying fish.
♞ ❀ ⛟ ☾ ♿ ♣ P

Innellan

Braemar Hotel
Shore Road (A815, 4 miles S of Dunoon) ☎ (0136 983) 792
12 (12.30 Sun)–midnight
S&N Theakston Best Bitter; guest beer [H]
Built in the 19th century as the superb seaside home of textile magnet JP Coates, with a splendid view over the Firth of Clyde from the large, outdoor seating area. Children's play area. ♞ ❀ ⛟ ☾ ◗ ♿ ♣ P

Irvine

Ship Inn
120–122 Harbour Street (harbourfront, next to Magnum leisure centre)
☎ (01294) 279722
11–2.30, 5–midnight (1am Fri); 11–1am Sat; 12.30–11 Sun
S&N Theakston Best Bitter; guest beer [H]
Interesting old harbourside pub, the oldest licensed premises in town. Old local scenes have been drawn in charcoal on the ceiling. Renowned for its well-cooked and good value meals, it is quiet at lunchtime and early eve, but rather lively later on at weekends. Children's certificate. Q ♞ ❀ ☾ ◗ ♿ ⇌

Turf Hotel
32–34 Eglinton Street (by mini-roundabout at N end of town) ☎ (01294) 275836
11–midnight (1am Fri & Sat); 12.30–11 Sun
S&N Theakston Best Bitter [H]
Totally unspoilt, traditional Scottish bar, with a separate lounge to the rear which has its own character. Quite cosmopolitan at lunchtime when quality lunches of amazing value are served; more of a local at night.
♨ ☾ ⊞ ⇌ ♣

Johnstone

Coanes
High Street ☎ (01505) 322925
11–11.30 (1am Fri, midnight Sat); 6.30–11 Sun

Draught Bass; Orkney Dark Island; Whitbread Boddingtons Bitter; guest beers H
Comfortable, town-centre pub, where the bar is wood-panelled, with a town house appearance, while the lounge is in the modern, open-plan style. Both drinking areas are decorated with period pictures and memorabilia. No food Sun. ◑ ⇌ ♣

Kilbarchan

Trust Inn
8 Low Barholm
☎ (01505) 72401
5 (11 Thu–Sat)–midnight
Ind Coope Burton Ale; Marston's Pedigree; guest beer H
Olde-worlde pub with an atmosphere to match, set in a village steeped in local history. The weaver's cottage is situated nearby. No food Sun. ◑ ▶ ⇌ (Miliken Pk)

Kildonan

Breadalbane Hotel
On loop road
☎ (01770) 820284
11–midnight (1am Thu–Sat)
Draught Bass H
Friendly seaside hotel in a quiet village off the beaten track, with views to Pladda and the Firth of Clyde.
🛏 ♨ ✿ 🍴 ◑ ▶ ♿ ♣ A P

Kilmarnock

Hunting Lodge
14–16 Glencairn Square (S of centre) ☎ (01563) 22920
11–3, 5–midnight; 11–midnight Thu–Sat; 12.30–midnight Sun
Draught Bass; Broughton Greenmantle Ale; guest beers H
Pub where real ale is sold in the recently refurbished and extended Malty Hop lounge, which has a no-smoking area. Interesting artefacts line the walls; good bar food. A venue for the local folk club (Thu). Occasional beer festivals and ceilidhs. Children's certificate.
🛏 ◑ ▶ 🍴 ⇌ ⚲

Tackity Bit
4a John Finnie Street (opp. main entrance to station)
☎ (01563) 72939
10 (12.30 Sun)–11 (midnight Fri & Sat)
Broughton Greenmantle Ale; Caledonian 80/-; Ind Coope Burton Ale; guest beers H
Charming, small, one-roomed modern conversion with interesting roof detail. Split into small raised areas, it has a fireside snug, prints adorn the

walls and genuine antiques sit on shelves. A quiet pub, except at weekends, with friendly staff and locals. Miss it at your peril. ⇌

Kilmun

Coylet Inn
Loch Eck (A815, 9 miles N of Dunoon) ☎ (0136 984) 426
11 (12.30 Sun)–2.30, 6.30–11 (5–midnight Fri & Sat)
Caledonian Deuchars IPA; McEwan 80/-; Younger No.3 E
Attractive and inviting, lochside bar where you can relax around the open fire after a day touring or walking in the hills. Good bar food. Caravan park nearby.
🛏 🛏 ✿ 🍴 ◑ ▶ A P

Kilwinning

Claremont Hotel
67 Byres Road (A738, by station) ☎ (01294) 558455
11–midnight (including Sun)
S&N Theakston Best Bitter; guest beer H
Small hotel completely refurbished following a fire: a public bar, in traditional Scottish style, and a comfortable lounge. The guest beer is in the lounge only. Children's certificate.
🛏 🍴 ◑ ▶ 🍴 ♿ ⇌ P

Kirkmichael

Kirkmichael Arms
3 Straiton Road
☎ (0165 55) 375
11 (12.30 Sun)–11 (winter hours: 11–2.30, 5–11 Fri & Sat)
Beer choice varies H
Rural gem with low ceilings, set in a conservation village with a comfortable lounge and a small bar, made cosy by a real fire. 🛏 🛏 ◑ ▶ 🍴 ♣

Largs

Clachan
14 Bath Street (B7025, just off A78) ☎ (01475) 672224
11 (12.30 Sun)–midnight (1am Thu–Sat)
Belhaven Sandy Hunter's Ale, 80/- A
Cheery, popular, single-bar pub in a side street just behind the seafront. Very busy at weekends with young people.
◑ ♿ ⇌

Lenzie

Carriages
Millersneuk Shopping Centre
☎ (0141) 777 7611
11–midnight (1am Fri); 12.30–midnight Sun

Broughton Greenmantle Ale A; **guest beer** H
Comfortable lounge bar in a modern shopping centre. Folk music Sun nights. Eve meals served till 8pm. ◑ ▶ ⇌

Loans

Bruce Inn
31–33 Main Street (A759)
☎ (01292) 315976
11 (12.30 Sun)–midnight (12.30am Fri)
Draught Bass; guest beer H
Traditional old inn at the centre of a small village close to Troon. A separate restaurant offers traditional fare at sensible prices. Real ale is available in both the restaurant and bar.
Q 🛏 🍴 ◑ ▶ ♿ ♣ P

Lochwinnoch

Mossend
Largs Road (A760)
☎ (01505) 842672
11–11
Marston's Pedigree; Whitbread Castle Eden Ale, Flowers Original; guest beers H
Typical Whitbread steakhouse, with excellent facilities for families. It benefits from convenient road and rail links, and the bird sanctuary and water sports centre nearby. Successful pub-based beer festivals held. The guest beers come from the Whitbread list.
🛏 ✿ ◑ ▶ ♿ ⇌ P

Lugton

Paraffin Lamp
1 Beith Road (A736/B777 jct)
☎ (01505) 850510
11 (12 Sun)–11
Whitbread Flowers Original; guest beer H
Brewers' Fayre country pub where food is available all day. It can be very busy at times but is difficult to reach by public transport. Popular with families (children's play area outside; toys inside). The guest beer is from the Whitbread range. 🛏 ✿ ◑ ▶ ♿ ♣ P

Oban

Caledonian Hotel
Station Square
☎ (01631) 63133
11–11 (including Sun)
Caledonian 80/- H
One of Oban's grand Victorian seafront hotels, next to the station and the islands ferry terminal. Tastefully modernised inside.
🍴 ◑ ▶ ♿ ⇌

Strathclyde

Lorne Hotel
Stevenson Street
☎ (01631) 66766
11–1am (including Sun)
McEwan 80/- Ⓐ**; S&N Theakston Best Bitter; guest beers** Ⓗ
Popular, one-room pub with an island bar in an aesthetically pleasing, modern interior. It can get very busy and lively; occasional live rock bands. Ⓓ ▶ & ⇌

Oban Inn
1 Stafford Street
☎ (01631) 62484
11–12.45am (including Sun)
McEwan 80/- Ⓐ
Harbourside pub which fully deserves its place as the town's best-known hostelry. The public bar has a nautical theme, while the upstairs lounge boasts some stained-glass panels. Ⓓ ▶ ⊞ ⇌

Old Kilpatrick

Ettrick
159 Dumbarton Road (A814)
☎ (01389) 72821
11–11.30 (midnight Thu–Sat); 12.30–11.30 Sun
S&N Theakston Best Bitter; Younger No. 3; guest beer Ⓗ
Traditional village local (est. 1893) in close proximity to Erskine Bridge. No smoking is allowed in the lounge during the day. ❀ Ⓓ &
⇌ (Kilpatrick) ♣ ⚲

Paisley

Abbey Bar
8 Lawn Street
☎ (0141) 889 8451
11–11 (1am Fri, 11.45 Sat)
McEwan 80/- Ⓗ
Small town tavern situated across from the magnificent Paisley Abbey, with a cosy, homely atmosphere and friendly bar staff. Live music Fri eve, plus other social events. Ⓓ ⇌ (Gilmour St)

Buddies
23 Broomlands Street
☎ (0141) 889 5314
11–11 (midnight Fri, 11.45 Sat)
Belhaven St Andrew's Ale Ⓗ
This fine corner pub epitomises all that is good about the Scottish social drinking environment. A good 'blether' in a warm atmosphere. Angling and chess clubs; larger lounge. ⊞

Gabriel's
33 Gauze Street (Silk St jct)
☎ (0141) 887 8204
11–midnight (1am Fri, 11.45 Sat); 12.30–11 Sun
Caledonian Deuchars IPA;

Orkney Dark Island; guest beers Ⓗ
Large, airy lounge with a raised dining area and an oval island bar. Inlaid stained-glass and empirical accoutrements on the walls serve as reminders of a bygone era. Enthusiastic and friendly staff; children's certificate held. Worth a visit.
ⓔ Ⓓ ▶ & ⇌ (Gilmour St)

Jay's Bar Diner
98 Causeyside Street
☎ (0141) 889 5522
11–midnight (1am Fri, 11.45 Sat)
Draught Bass Ⓗ
Pub with comfortable seating areas in the bar and split-level upstairs lounge, excellent for small private functions. A mirrored rosewood bar with chrome pillars is a feature. Friendly staff. Quiz night Wed. A great atmosphere for all ages. Ⓓ & ⇌ (Canal St)

RH Finlay's
33 Causeyside Street
☎ (0141) 889 9036
11–midnight (1am Fri, 11.45 Sat); 12–11 Sun
Draught Bass; guest beer Ⓗ
Two lounge bars furnished to a high standard in a central, attractive meeting place. Quality bar lunches served daily and at weekends. Friendly service.
Ⓓ & ⇌ (Gilmour St/Canal St)

Tannahills
100 Neilston Road (1 mile from centre) ☎ (0141) 889 2491
11–11 (midnight Thu & Fri, 11.45 Sat); 11–11 Sun
Caledonian Deuchars IPA Ⓐ
Olde-worlde-style pub with plenty of pictures of old Paisley and its poet, Robert Tannahill. Ⓓ

Waiting Room
42 Old Sneddon Street
☎ (0141) 889 5163
11–midnight (1am Fri, 11.45 Sat); 6.30–11 Sun
Belhaven Sandy Hunter's Ale; guest beers Ⓗ
Pub where total refurbishment makes use of previously hidden cornicing, storm shutters and a railway arch. Prints on the wall remind you to catch your train (one minute from the station). Spacious, L-shape lounge.
Ⓓ ▶ & ⇌ (Gilmour St)

Wee Howff
53 High Street
☎ (0141) 889 2095
11–11 (11.30 Fri & Sat); closed Sun
Ind Coope Burton Ale; Tetley Bitter; guest beers Ⓗ
Long, narrow bar with a mock Tudor interior; popular with students from the nearby

university. The publican was the first *Master Cellarman* in Scotland. Friendly and efficient bar staff. Occasional Sun opening for quizzes.
⇌ (Gilmour St) ♣

Prestwick

Parkstone Hotel
Central Esplanade (seafront; entrance on Ardayre Rd)
☎ (01292) 77286
11–12.30am; 12.30–midnight Sun
Belhaven 80/- Ⓗ
Comfortable lounge bar in a seafront hotel with views over to Arran. A long-established outlet for Belhaven. Children's certificate.
⌂ Q ⏟ ❀ ⋈ Ⓓ ▶ ⇌ P

Renfrew

Ferry Inn
2 Clyde Street
☎ (0141) 886 2104
11–midnight (11 Mon, 1am Fri, 11.45 Sat); 12.30–11 Sun
Caledonian Deuchars IPA Ⓗ
Riverside local displaying photographs of the Clyde's shipbuilding past and present. Biannual beer festivals. Cyclists, dogs, and radio presenters welcomed. ⌂

Tap & Spile
Terminal Building, Glasgow Airport ☎ (0141) 848 4869
10 (12.30 Sun)–11 (1am Fri, 11.45 Sun)
Alloa Arrol's 80/-; Broughton Greenmantle Ale; Caledonian 80/-; Mitchell's Best Bitter; guest beers Ⓗ
Modern, open-plan airport lounge bar, converted to a Tap & Spile in 1992, which has proved popular with travellers and the public alike. & P ⚲

Saltcoats

Hip Flask
13 Winton Street (road between Safeway and seafront) ☎ (01294) 465222
11–midnight (1am Thu–Sat)
Caledonian 80/-; guest beer Ⓗ
Small café-bar, well-placed for both the town centre and the beach. Friendly atmosphere. The raised seating area doubles as a small stage (and a Scalextric layout area on Tue eves!). Folk music Mon; quiz Wed; live bands Thu. Good value food. Children's certificate. ⏟ ❀ Ⓓ ▶ ⇌

Seamill

Waterside Inn
Ardrossan Road (A78 S end of village) ☎ (01294) 823238
11 (12.30 Sun)–11 (midnight Fri & Sat)

Marston's Pedigree; Whitbread Boddingtons Bitter; guest beers H
Former, run-down seaside hotel transformed into a Brewers' Fayre pub/restaurant, right on the beach with wonderful sea views. Regular quiz nights. Two guest beers; summer beer festival in a marquee. Food available all day.
🐴 ❀ ◖ ◗ P

Stewarton

Millhouse Hotel
8 Dean Street (B769, N of centre) ☎ (01560) 482255
11 (12.30 Sun)–midnight
Belhaven St Andrew's Ale A; guest beer H
Distinctive, stone-built, riverside hotel with a small wood-panelled bar, a comfortable lounge and a function suite where meals are served. Popular with local business people. Busy at weekends (when functions are on). Bus service nearby.
🐴 🛏 ◖ ◗ ⊟ ⇌ ♣ P

Troon

Anchorage Hotel
149 Templehill (B749 to harbour) ☎ (01292) 317448
12.30–12.30am (including Sun)
Broughton Greenmantle Ale; Maclay 80/-; Tetley Bitter; guest beers H
The oldest licensed premises in Troon, close to the harbour and marina. A nautical theme pervades. Petanque court to the rear. Children welcome till 9.30. Five guest beers.
♨ 🐴 🛏 ◖ ◗ ♿ ⇌ ♣ P

Harbour Bar
169 Templehill (B749 to harbour)
☎ (01292) 312668
11–12.30am; 12.30–midnight Sun
Broughton Greenmantle Ale; Ind Coope Burton Ale; Orkney Dark Island H
Friendly local with a lounge area and a games room served from the same bar. Near the marina with views over the Firth of Clyde. Nautical prints decorate the walls.
♿ ⇌ ♣ P

McKay's
69 Portland Street (A759)
☎ (01292) 311079
10.30–12.30am; 12.30–midnight Sun
Maclay 80/-; Mansfield Old Baily; Whitbread Boddingtons Bitter; guest beers H
Attractive bar in the centre of Troon. Quiet and relaxing through the week, it is busy at weekends when the music can be quite loud. Live bands occasionally on Sun. Two guest ales.
❀ ◖ ◗ ⇌

Piersland House Hotel
15 Craigend Road (B749, opp. Royal Troon golf course)
☎ (01292) 314747
11 (12.30 Sun)–midnight (12.30am Fri & Sat)
Broughton Greenmantle Ale; Courage Directors; guest beers H
Impressive, three-star hotel with a reputation for food and quality. A four-crown commended Scottish Tourist Board hotel with a lovely wood-panelled lounge. Bar prices tend to match the style of the hotel, but there are occasional reductions on guest beers.
♨ Q 🐴 ❀ 🛏 ◖ ◗ ♿ P

Twechar

Quarry Inn
Main Street ☎ (01236) 821496
11 (12.30 Sun)–11.30 (1am Fri)
Maclay 60/-, 70/-, 80/- H
Traditional, lively village pub in a former mining area. The bar is decorated with old brewery mirrors and warmed by pot-bellied stoves. Beer festivals. Petanque played. Good prices.
♨ ⊟ ♣ P

Uddingston

Rowan Tree
60 Old Mill Road (by Tunnocks bakery)
☎ (01698) 812678
11–11.45; 12.30–11 Sun
Maclay 80/- A
Vibrant community pub which hosts both a folk club and a chess club. Fine decor includes rare brewery mirrors. Lanarkshire's longest serving real ale outlet. Children welcome lunchtime if eating. No lunches Sun.
♨ Q ◖ ⊟ ♿ ⇌ P

Wishaw

Imperial (Tam Parks)
121 Main Street
☎ (01698) 372320
11–midnight; 12.30–11 Sun
McEwan 80/-; Younger No. 3 H
Auld-style pub with snug rooms. Note: no ladies' WC.
⇌

THE SYMBOLS

♨	real fire	♿	easy wheelchair access
Q	quiet pub (at least one bar)	⛺	camping facilities at the pub or nearby
🐴	indoor room for children	⇌	near British Rail station
❀	garden or other outdoor drinking area	⊖	near underground station
🛏	accommodation	♣	pub games
◖	lunchtime meals	⌓	real cider
◗	evening meals	P	pub car park
⊟	public bar	🚭	no-smoking room or area

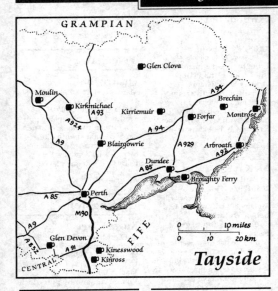

GRAMPIAN
Glen Clova
Moulin
Kirkmichael A93
Kirriemuir
A924
A9
Blairgowrie
A929
Brechin
Forfar
Montrose
A94
Arbroath
A92
Dundee
A85
Broughty Ferry
Perth
A85
M90
FIFE
A9
Glen Devon
A832
A91
Kinesswood
Kinross
CENTRAL
0   10 miles
0   10   20 km

Tayside

Arbroath

Victoria

15 Catherine Street
☎ (01241) 874589
11–2.30, 5–11; 11–midnight Fri & Sat;
12–2.30 Sun
**S&N Theakston Best Bitter;
guest beers** H
Friendly town-centre bar,
ideally situated for bus and
rail travellers. 🛱 🛦 ≠ ♣

Blairgowrie

Kintrae House Hotel

Balmoral Road, Rattray
☎ (01250) 872106
11–2.30, 5.30–11 (11.45 Fri & Sat);
12–3, 6.30–11 Sun
Beer range varies H
Comfortable lounge in a small
hotel. Extended opening hours
at weekends in summer.
🛏 Q 🛥 🕽 🕽 P

Stormont Arms

101 Perth Street
☎ (01250) 873142
11–3, 5–11; 11–11.45 Fri & Sat;
12.30–3, 6.30–11 Sun
**Belhaven Sandy Hunter's Ale,
St Andrew's Ale** H
Busy town pub: a traditional
bar with whisky mirrors and a
comfortable lounge. 🛱 ♣

Brechin

Dalhousie

Market Street
☎ (0135 662) 2096
11 (12.30 Sun)–11
Beer range varies H
Bright, popular town bar with
wood-panelling, a high ceiling
and lots of memorabilia. One
or two guest beers. 🛱 ♣

Broughty Ferry

Fisherman's Tavern

10 Fort Street (by lifeboat
station) ☎ (01382) 775941
11–midnight; 12.30–11 Sun
**Belhaven 60/-, 80/-, St
Andrew's Ale; Maclay 80/-;
Whitbread Boddingtons
Bitter; guest beers** H
1993 national CAMRA *Urban
Pub of the Year*, 21 years in the
Guide. Very busy on Fri/Sat
nights. Q 🛏 🛥 🕽 🛱 🕹 ≠

Dundee

Bert's Bar

141 Nethergate (by university)
☎ (01382) 26103
11–midnight; 12.30–11 Sun
**Alloa Arrol's 80/-; Ind Coope
Burton Ale; Marston's
Pedigree; Tetley Bitter; guest
beer** H
Cosy, welcoming bar with a
good mix of wood-panelling
and tiles; refurbished to a high
standard with a snug bar and
two rooms separated by a split
partition. Meals all day till
8pm. 🕽 🕽 🕹 ≠

Frews

117 Strathmartine Road (top of
Hilltown, opp. Coldside
library) ☎ (01382) 810975
11–11.45; 12.30–11 Sun
Draught Bass H
Friendly locals' pub retaining
its traditional decor and
atmosphere. Its proximity to
both football grounds ensures
a full pub on match days.
Worthington White Shield
sold. 🛱 🕹

Galleon Bar

2 Whitehall Crescent (near
City Sq, towards station)
☎ (01382) 24376
10–midnight; 12–11 Sun
**Caledonian 80/-; Ind Coope
Burton Ale; Orkney Dark
Island; guest beers** H
Large pub on two floors, with
an additional function room.
The walls and ceiling are
adorned with film/music and
other memorabilia. Regular
live music. Beer festivals in
spring and autumn. 🕽 🕽 🕹 ≠

Phoenix

103–105 Nethergate (near
university) ☎ (01382) 200014
11–midnight; 12.30–11 Sun
Beer range varies H
Popular Victorian-style pub
run by an enthusiastic
landlord. Busy Fri and Sat
nights. Local CAMRA *Pub of
the Year* 1993. Backgammon
played. 🕽 🕽 ≠

Planet Bar

161 South Road, Lochee (200
yds W of Lochee bypass)
☎ (01382) 623258
11–11.30 (midnight Fri & Sat);
12.30–11 Sun
**Orkney Dark Island; guest
beer** H
A large lounge and a public
bar in modern style in a
popular local with a convivial
atmosphere and friendly staff.
A wide range of sporting and
social events is organised by
regulars. The guest beer is
always from a Scottish
independent brewer. 🛱 🕹 P

Tavern

168–172 Perth Road
☎ (01382) 27135
11–2.30, 5–11.30; 11–11.30 Wed &
Thu; 11–midnight Fri & Sat; 7–11 Sun
**Draught Bass; Caledonian
80/-; guest beer** H
Cosy pub which can be very
busy when sport is on TV.
Friendly bar staff. Popular
with locals and students. Eve
meals end at 7pm. 🕽 🕽 🕹 ≠

Forfar

Osnaburg Bar

23 Osnaburg Street (off Main
St, between home-brew shop
and baths) ☎ (01307) 463380
11–midnight; 12.30–11 Sun
Belhaven 80/-; guest beers H
Pleasantly modernised,
welcoming bar with an
unusual inn sign. Snacks all
day. 🕽 🛱

Stag Hotel

140–144 Castle Street
☎ (01307) 462737
11–11 (midnight Sat); 12–midnight
Sun
**Marston's Pedigree; S&N
Theakston XB** H

Split-level, wood-panelled lounge with a small adjoining bar. The beer range may vary.
🏨 ◖ ▶ ⊟

Glen Clova

Clova Hotel
On B955, 15 miles N of Kirriemuir ☎ (01575) 550222
11–midnight; 12.30–11 Sun
Broughton Greenmantle Ale, Oatmeal Stout; Orkney Dark Island H
An outpost of good beer at the head of the Glen, popular with hill-walkers, pony trekkers and tourists. Spring beer festival.
🏨 ☎ ☺ 🏨 ◖ ▶ ⊟ ▲ P

Glen Devon

Tormaukin Hotel & Restaurant
☎ (01259) 781252
11–2.30, 5–11; 11–11 Fri & Sat; 12–11 Sun
Harviestoun 80/-; Ind Coope Burton Ale H
Comfortable, former coaching inn with a low, beamed ceiling in the bar area. Extensive range of home-cooked bar food available (all day Sun).
🏨 Q ☎ 🏨 ◖ ▶ ▲ P

Kinesswood

Lomond Country Inn
Main Street ☎ (01592) 840253
11–11 (midnight Fri & Sat)
Draught Bass; Belhaven Sandy Hunter's Ale; Jennings Bitter H
Pub situated in a quiet corner of Perthshire, near the border with Fife, with fine views over Loch Leven. 🏨 Q ☎ ☺ 🏨
◖ ▶ ▲ P ⅄

Kinross

Kirklands Hotel
20 High Street
☎ (01577) 863313
11.30–2.30, 5–11 (11.30 Fri & Sat); 12.30–11 Sun
Courage Directors; Maclay 80/-; guest beer H
Comfortable, traditional, small hotel offering bar meals in the lounge and separate

restaurant. Only one guest beer is available, but a wide range is covered. Children's certificate. High teas Sat and Sun. Q 🏨 ◖ ▶ ⊟ ▲ P ⅄

Muirs Inn
49 The Muirs (N of centre on Milnathort road)
☎ (01577) 862270
11–2.30, 5–11 (11.45 Fri); 11–11.45 Sat; 12.30–11 Sun
Belhaven 80/-; Caledonian ERA; Orkney Dark Island; guest beers H
Pub with a small, wood-panelled bar with rare brewery mirrors behind the gantry. Bar snacks available; meals served in the attached restaurant. Five guest beers.
Q ☺ 🏨 ⊟ ▲ P

Kirkmichael

Aldchlappie Hotel
At A924/B950 jct
☎ (01250) 881224
11–3 (not Mon), 5.30–11.45; 12–3, 6.30–11 Sun
Beer range varies H
Old country inn, pleasantly modernised, pioneering real ale and real food for walkers, skiers, golfers and hunters. Eve meals end at 8.45pm.
🏨 ☎ ☺ 🏨 ◖ ▶ ⊟ ▲ P

Kirriemuir

Roods Bar
10 Roods (off town centre, near car park)
☎ (01575) 572945
11–1am; 12.30–11 Sun
Beer choice varies H
Small, friendly local in a lane off the town centre. Robert Younger windows and an Aitken mirror are unusual features. The one beer changes regularly.

Thrums Hotel
Bank Street ☎ (01575) 572758
11 (12 Sun)–midnight
Caledonian 70/-, 80/-; Stones Best Bitter H
Black and white building named after Barrie's novel. A large, open-plan lounge offers a welcome and meals all day.
🏨 ◖ ▶ ♣

Montrose

George Hotel
22 George Street (1st left past steeple; by police station)
☎ (01674) 675050
11 (12 Sun)–11
Beer range varies H
Four ales in a bar-cum-restaurant with a no-smoking area.
☎ 🏨 ◖ ▶ ▲ ⇌ P ⅄

Moulin

Moulin Inn
11–13 Kirkmichael Road (¾ mile from Pitlochry on Braemar road)
☎ (01796) 472196
11 (12 Sun)–11 (11.45 Fri & Sat)
Alloa Arrol's 80/-; Ind Coope Burton Ale; Whitbread Boddingtons Bitter; guest beers H
Cosy, welcoming bar in a 100-year-old inn, now extended into an hotel but retaining original character. A haven for hill-walkers and thirsty tourists.
🏨 ☎ 🏨 ◖ ▶ ⊟ ▲ P

Perth

Greyfriars
15 South Street
☎ (01738) 633036
11 (12.30 Sun)–11 (11.45 Fri & Sat)
Ind Coope Burton Ale; Orkney Raven Ale; guest beers H
Small, cosy, city-centre pub with a friendly atmosphere. Only a short distance from the River Tay. Four guest ales.
◖ ▲ ⇌

Old Ship Inn
Skinnergate ☎ (01738) 24929
11–2.30, 5–11; 11–11 Fri & Sat; closed Sun
Alloa Arrol's 80/-; Caledonian Deuchars IPA; Ind Coope Burton Ale; guest beer H
Perth's oldest pub (established 1665). Ideal for a quiet drink. Regular dominoes nights held. Lunches served upstairs (eve meals Sat only).
Q ◖ ▲ ⇌ ♣

CAMRA BOOKS

The *Good Beer Guide* is not CAMRA's only publication. CAMRA Books offers a wide list of beer and pub related titles, from *Good Pub Food* to the *Good Beer Guide to Belgium and Holland*. Ask your bookseller, or see page 526 for details of how to order these post-free.

WATERING THE DESERT

Mark Hutchinson explains how cask beer is bouncing back in Northern Ireland.

T HE 1991 GOOD BEER GUIDE carried a report on the beer desert of Northern Ireland, providing firm evidence that, whilst real ale had boomed elsewhere in the UK, in the province at least, cask beer was still struggling to gain a foothold.

Four years on and things have begun to change in the six counties. The decision by Bass to reintroduce bottle-conditioned Worthington White Shield to Northern Irish bars in 1990 has proved to be a lifeline for discerning drinkers. Amidst a sea of keg stout, it has been used by local CAMRA activists to provide a 'foot in the door' at many dry pubs. The logic has been simple: with a bottle-conditioned ale on the shelves, it is only one step further to cask-conditioned ale. CAMRA Northern Ireland has used this approach to talk licensees into holding 'guest cask nights', which, in turn, have led to permanent cask beer sales. Consequently, the number of pubs in Northern Ireland which find their way into the *Good Beer Guide* has more than doubled in these past four years.

TRY ALSO

Another big brewer instrumental in bringing back real ale is Scottish & Newcastle. The company had pulled out when its depot was closed in 1986, but now its Theakston and Younger beers (whilst eschewed in many other parts of the UK) provide welcome variety. Bass, too, after much pressure from the local CAMRA branch, has pitched Draught Bass into a few outlets. So, in addition to the pubs listed opposite, try also The Elms in Belfast's University Street and the city's famous Victorian gin palace, the Crown Liquor Saloon. The Viscount of Clandeboye in Bangor is another convert and a few other cask Bass pubs are planned for Belfast. On the down side, though, Bass has queered the pitch to some degree by introducing Caffrey's Ale, a keg beer with a smoother texture, dispensed by mixed gas, and internal technical difficulties appear to have delayed some Bass cask installations.

THE WAY AHEAD

What for the future? It looks as though the province will continue to be a relative real ale desert for a number of years yet, as many pubs lack cellar facilities and the Guinness/Bass duopoly still holds sway. Locally, the only cask beer brewery is still Hilden at Lisburn, but most of its produce is consumed on the mainland, not in its home territory. However, progress has certainly been made and should continue.

Hopefully, the number of entries for Northern Ireland for *Good Beer Guide* 1996 will be higher still.

Mark Hutchinson is Chairman of CAMRA Northern Ireland.

Northern Ireland

Northern Ireland

0 ___ 10 miles
0 ___ 20 km

 Hilden, Lisburn

Ahoghill

Rowan Arms
The Diamond
☎ (01266) 871459
11.30–11; closed Sun
S&N Theakston Best Bitter H
Typical old-fashioned village
pub with friendly locals, pew
seating and local memorabilia.
NI CAMRA award-winner
1994. 🏠 Q ⊟ ♣ P

Ballyeaston

Carmichael's (Staffie's)
16 Ballyeaston Village
12–11; closed Sun
Worthington White Shield
Traditional, one-roomed
country pub with no draught
beer. Outside toilets are
'quaint'. A gem. 🏠 Q P

Bangor

Jenny Watts
High Street ☎ (01247) 270401
11.30–11; 12.30–2.30, 7–10.30 Sun
S&N Theakston Best Bitter H
Victorian-style, town-centre
bar offering good food and
music, especially Sun lunch.
🏠 Q ❀ ◖ ⇌ (NIR)

Belfast

Kings Head
829 Lisburn Road (A1, opp
King's Hall) ☎ (01232) 667805
12–11; 7–10 Sun, closed Sun lunch
S&N Theakston Best Bitter H
Multi-roomed, Victorian
building around a central

servery. Modern extension for
music (late nights weekends).
🏠 Q ❀ ◖ ⊟ ⇌ (Balmoral
NIR) P

Kitchen Bar & Parlour Bar
16 Victoria Square (corner of
Telfair St) ☎ (01232) 324901
11.30–11; usually closed Sun
**S&N Theakston Best Bitter;
guest beers** H
Award-winning favourite: a
long narrow bar and lounge
serving legendary lunches and
varied guest beers. In a
city-centre backwater, but it
attracts all types. Don't miss.
🏠 Q ◖ ⇌ (Central NIR)

Morrison's
21 Bedford Street (opp. BBC)
☎ (01232) 248458
11.30–11; 7–10, closed Sun lunch
S&N Theakston Best Bitter H
Large, two-storey, city-centre
pub, a recreation of a spirit
grocer, with snugs, counters
and memorabilia. Very
popular. The upstairs is
named after the old Linen Hall
bar. Music and late nights.
◖ & ⇌ (Botanic NIR)

Crosskeys

Crosskeys Inn
39 Grange Road, Toome (off
B52, 7 miles from
Randalstown) ☎ (01648) 50694
11–11; 7–10 Sun, closed Sun lunch
Worthington White Shield
A listed, thatched pub with
whitewashed stone walls and
a friendly owner. The quiet
room has a turf fire. Miss this

and you miss history.
🏠 Q ❀ ⊟ & P

Dromore

Old Brewery Inn
4 Meeting Street
☎ (01846) 692393
11.30–11; 7–10 Sun, closed Sun lunch
S&N Theakston Best Bitter H
Recently-opened pub. Friendly
staff. Restaurant to be added.
🏠 Q ◖ P

Glengormley

Crown & Shamrock
584 Antrim Road (A6, 1½
miles W of centre)
11.30–11
Worthington White Shield
Family-run, plain, panelled,
low-ceilinged pub adjoined by
an intimate sitting room.
Occasional draught beers.
Unspoilt. 🏠 Q ❀ ⊟ P

Whittley's
401 Ballyclare Road (B56, 2½
miles NW of centre)
☎ (01232) 832438
11.30–11; closed Sun
Worthington White Shield
Unspoilt, friendly public bar
with a low ceiling, a stone and
wood floor, a lounge and a
railway-themed restaurant.
Children catered for.
🏠 Q ⛄ ❀ ◖ ▶ ⊟ P

Hillsborough

Hillside Inn
Main Street ☎ (01846) 682765
12–11; 7–10 Sun, closed Sun lunch
**Hilden Ale; S&N Theakston
Best Bitter** H; **guest beers**
Long, narrow bar with nooks
and crannies in a comfortable
inn with a stone floor.
Excellent restaurant above.
Popular. 🏠 Q ❀ ◖ ▶ ⊟

Plough Inn
The Square ☎ (01846) 682985
11.30–11; 7–10 Sun, closed Sun lunch
S&N Theakston Best Bitter H
Comfortable, multi-roomed,
old village pub (est. 1758),
with wood-panelled seats,
ceiling beams, china and
memorabilia. Good restaurant.
Very popular. 🏠 Q ❀ ◖ ▶ P

Holywood

Bear Tavern
High Street ☎ (01232) 426837
11.30–11; 12.30–2.30, 7–10 Sun
Worthington White Shield
Long, cosy bar with a sloping
stone floor, mahogany fittings,
mirrors and glass. Paris
Docks-style upstairs bar.
Occasional draught beer.
🏠 ❀ ◖ & ⇌ (NIR)

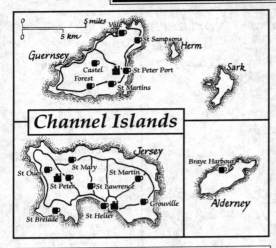

Channel Islands

 Ann Street, St Helier; **Guernsey, Randalls**, St Peter Port; **Tipsy Toad**, St Peter/St Helier

Alderney

Braye Harbour

Moorings Hotel
Braye Street
☎ (01481) 823558
10–midnight; 12–2, 8–midnight Sun
Guernsey Moorings Ale H
Light and airy bar overlooking Braye Bay, stocking a large selection of bottled beers from around the world. The house ale is a brewery blend of Braye and Sunbeam. Opposite is the terminus of the Alderney Railway. ✿ ⇔ ◑ ▶

Try also: Georgian House Hotel (Free)

Guernsey

Castel

Fleur du Jardin
Kings Mills ☎ (01481) 57996
11.30–11.45 (12–2, 7–10.30 Sun)
Guernsey Sunbeam H
Comfortable hotel in an attractive setting, renovated in keeping with its farmhouse origins. The garden has a play area. ✿ ⇔ ◑ ▶ ⊞ ♣ P

Forest

Venture Inn
Rue de la Villiaze (New Road)
☎ (01481) 63211
10–11.45; closed Sun
Randalls Best Bitter H
Well-run hostelry not far from the airport. A functional bar contrasts with the cosy lounge. The only outlet for cask Randalls.
Q ◑ ▶ ⊞ ♣ P

St Martins

Captains Hotel
La Fosse ☎ (01481) 38990
10.30–11.45; 6–10.30 Sun
Guernsey Sunbeam H
Attractive lounge bar boasting an impressive handpump. Moulin Huet Bay and Pottery are nearby.
✿ ⇔ ◑ ▶ P

Green Acres Hotel
Les Hubits
☎ (01481) 35711
11–2, 5.30–11.45; 12–2 Sun (for meals only)
Guernsey Sunbeam H
Comfortable hotel in the countryside with a relaxed atmosphere in the cosy bar and the long lounge overlooking the pool.
🏨 ✿ ⇔ ◑ P

L'Auberge Divette
☎ (01481) 38485
10.30–11.45; 12–3.30 Sun
Guernsey Braye, Sunbeam H
Well-run pub with a good atmosphere. Set on a cliff-bound peninsula, it boasts panoramic views from the lounge and suntrap garden, and easy access to cliff paths. No meals Thu eve.
🏨 ✿ ◑ ▶ ⊞ ♣ P

St Peter Port

Britannia Inn
Trinity Square
☎ (01481) 721082
10–11.45; closed Sun
Ann Street Old Jersey Ale; Guernsey Braye, Britannia, Sunbeam H
Single-roomed lounge bar in the old quarter of town. It sells no keg beer and is the only regular outlet for Old Jersey Ale in Guernsey. ♣

Drunken Duck
Charroterie
☎ (01481) 725045
11.30–2, 4.30–11.45; closed Sun
Fuller's London Pride, ESB; Ringwood Best Bitter, XXXX Porter, Fortyniner, Old Thumper G
Cosy, two-roomed pub with welcoming staff. Impromptu folk nights Tue; regular quiz nights. Cider in summer. ◔

Rohais Inn
Rohais ☎ (01481) 720060
10.30–2, 4.30–11.45; closed Sun
Guernsey Braye G
Unsophisticated local with one large bar and very limited parking. The only Guernsey house serving Braye on gravity dispense. Bar billiards played. ♣ P

Salerie Inn
La Salerie
☎ (01481) 724484
10.30–11.45; closed Sun
Guernsey Braye, Sunbeam H
Lively, single-roomed pub, opposite a public car park. The walls are decorated with nautical artefacts. ◑

Ship & Crown
North Pier Steps
☎ (01481) 721368
10–11.45; 12–3.30, 6–11 Sun
Ann Street Ann's Treat, Winter Ale; Guernsey Braye (summer), **Sunbeam** H
Busy single-bar town pub, opposite a marina for visiting yachts. The walls are covered with pictures of ships and local shipwrecks. Popular with yachtsmen and bankers at lunchtime. Local CAMRA *Pub of the Year* 1993. ◑

White Hart
The Pollet ☎ (01481) 723855
10–11.45; closed Sun
Guernsey Sunbeam H
Busy pub next to the main taxi rank. Popular with professional workers at lunchtime and the younger disco set eves. ◑

Try also: Foresters Inn (Guernsey)

St Sampsons

Pony Inn
Petites Capelles
☎ (01481) 44374
10.30–11.45; 12–2 summer Sun
Guernsey Braye (summer),
Sunbeam H
Popular local with three
different bars, handy for
Guernsey Candles and
Oatlands Craft Centre. Winter
eve meals on Fri and Sat only.
⚜ ◖ ▶ 🍴 ♣ P

Vale

Houmet Tavern
Grande Havre
☎ (01481) 43037
10.30–11.45; closed Sun
Guernsey Braye, Sunbeam
(summer) H
Busy pub with a lively bar and
a cosy lounge overlooking
Grande Havre bar. No eve
meals Sun, Mon or Thu; other
eves till 8.45pm. Bar billiards
table. ⚜ ◖ ▶ 🍴 ▲ ♣ P

Jersey

Grouville

Pembroke
Coast Road ☎ (01534) 855756
9am–11pm; 11–1, 4.30–11 Sun
**Draught Bass; Whitbread
Boddingtons Bitter; guest
beer** H
Pleasant family pub attracting
a broad spectrum of clientele.
Offering a good atmosphere
and good food, it stands next
to the golf course (west end).
No lunches Sun.
⚜ Q ⛲ ☸ ◖ ▶ 🍴 ♿ ♣ P

Seymour Inn
La Rocque ☎ (01534) 854558
9am–11pm; 11–1, 4.30–11 Sun
**Ann Street Old Jersey Ale,
Ann's Treat, Winter Ale;
Guernsey Sunbeam** H
Popular, friendly, coastal pub
with a separate real ale bar;
ask for real ale if this bar is
shut. Good food (not served
Sun). ⚜ ⛲ ☸ ◖ ▶ 🍴 ♿ ♣ P

St Brelade

Old Smugglers Inn
Ouaisne ☎ (01534) 41510
11–11; 11–1, 4.30–11 Sun
**Draught Bass; Ringwood
XXXX Porter; S&N Theakston
Old Peculier; guest beers** H
Converted, 17th-century
fisherman's cottage close to

the beach. Food-oriented (eve
meals till 8.45pm), it also offers
fast-changing guest beers. Live
folk and blues music Sun
night. ⚜ Q ⛲ ◖ ▶ ▲ ♣

**Try also: La Pulente Hotel,
Old Portelet Inn** (Randall
Vautier chain)

St Helier

Admiral
St James Street
☎ (01534) 30095
11–11; 11–1, 4.30–11 Sun
**S&N Theakston Old Peculier;
Whitbread Boddingtons
Bitter** H
Very popular, newly
refurbished, timbered town
pub. Very good quality,
reasonably priced food offsets
the slightly high beer prices.
⚜ ☸ ☸ ◖ ▶

Lamplighter
Mulcaster Street
☎ (01534) 23119
10–11; 11–1, 4.30–11 Sun
**Draught Bass; Whitbread
Boddingtons Bitter; guest
beers** H
Local CAMRA *Pub of the Year*
1993. This atmospheric, gas-lit
town pub boasts a notable
facade. No music, no TV; no
food Sun. Bulmers cider
served. Q ◖ ⊖

Pierson
Royal Square ☎ (01534) 22726
10–11; 11–1, 4.30–11 Sun
**Bass Worthington BB,
Draught Bass; Hancock's
HB** H
Historic town pub near the
seat of Government, serving
good value lunches (not Sun).
Named after the hero of the
Battle of Jersey in 1781; note
the bullet marks on the wall.
☸ ◖

Try also: Dog & Sausage,
Haskett St (Randall Vautier)

St Lawrence

British Union
Main Road (opp. parish
church) ☎ (01534) 861070
9.30am–11pm; 11–1, 4.30–11 Sun
**Ann Street Old Jersey Ale;
Guernsey Sunbeam** H
Very popular, friendly pub
with a rich local atmosphere.
Popular with families. Good
food. ⚜ Q ⛲ ☸ ◖ ▶ 🍴 ♣

St Martin

Anne Port Bay Hotel
☎ (01534) 852058

11–2.30 (1 Sun), 5 (4.30 Sun)–11;
11–11 Sat
**Draught Bass; Marston's
Pedigree; guest beers** G
Small hotel bar near the beach,
popular with the locals.
Q ☸ 🚐 ◖ ▲ P

Rozel Bay Inn
Rozel ☎ (01534) 863438
10–11; 11–1, 4.30–11 Sun
**Draught Bass; S&N
Theakston Old Peculier;
Whitbread Boddingtons
Bitter** H
Cosy pub, situated at the
bottom of a wooded valley,
near a picturesque harbour.
Roaring log fire in winter. No
food Sun. ⚜ Q ⛲ ☸ ◖ P

Try also: Royal (Randall
Vautier); **Trinity Arms**, Trinity
(Ann Street)

St Mary

St Mary's Country Inn
Opp. church ☎ (01534) 481561
11–11; 11–1, 4.30–11 Sun
**Bass Worthington BB,
Draught Bass; Hancock's
HB** H
Comfortable, rural pub. The
busy locals' bar (where patois
can still be heard) contrasts
with the smart lounge and
conservatory. Good food (not
served Sun; other eves till
8pm).
⚜ Q ⛲ ☸ ◖ ▶ ▲ P ✂

St Ouen

Moulin de Lecq
Greve de Lecq
☎ (01534) 482818
10–11; 11–1, 4.30–11 Sun
**Ann Street Ann's Treat,
Winter Ale; Guernsey Braye,
Sunbeam** H
Converted watermill which
features a moving drivewheel
behind the bar. Popular in
summer, it hosts outdoor
barbecues (no food Sun).
⚜ ⛲ ☸ ◖ ▶ P

St Peter

Star
La Route de Beaumont
☎ (01534) 485556
10–11; 11–1, 4.30–11 Sun
**Tipsy Toad Jimmy's Bitter,
Horny Toad; guest beers** H
Spacious, refurbished village
pub brewing its own beers.
Regular live music, good food,
and a children's play area.
⚜ ⛲ ☸ ◖ ▶ ♿ ♣ P

Protect your pleasure — Join CAMRA (see page 528)

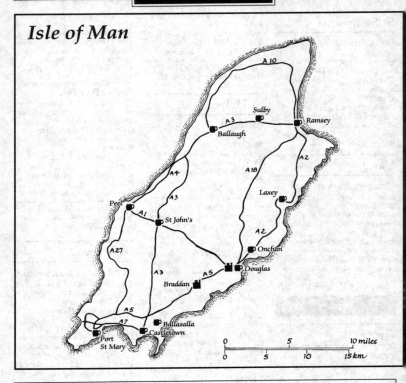

Isle of Man

🏰 **Bushy's**, *Braddan*; **Isle of Man**, *Douglas*

Sunday hours on the Isle of Man are 12–1.30, 8–10

Ballasalla

Whitestone Inn
☎ (01624) 822334
12–10.45
Okells Bitter H
Pub where the lounge is given over to catering at lunchtimes, serving a varied menu of reasonably-priced food. Convenient for all forms of transport, with the steam railway station about 100 yards away.
🍴 ⊟ ♿ ⇌ (IMR) P

Ballaugh

Raven
Main Road (on Ballaugh bridge) ☎ (01624) 897272
12–10.45
Marston's Pedigree; Okells Bitter; Whitbread Castle Eden Ale; guest beers H
Tastefully modernised pub on the TT course, offering four guest ales and lunchtime food. Ideal for all occasions.
❀ 🍴 ♣ P

Castletown

Castle Arms (Glue Pot)
Quayside ☎ (01624) 824673
12–10.45
Cains Mild, Bitter; Tetley Bitter H
On the harbour edge, in the shadow of Castle Rushen, this pub has a thriving lunchtime bar meal trade (not served Sun) as well as being a popular local. Its comfortable interior has a strong nautical theme. Outside drinking on the quay. ❀ ⊟ ⇌ (IMR)

Try also: Ship Inn (Okells)

Douglas

Albert
Chapel Row (50 yds from bus station) ☎ (01624) 673632
12–10.45
Okells Mild, Bitter H
Straightforward local; a good example of a typical Manx pub, and very popular. Note the pictures in the lounge.
⊟ ⇌ (IMR)

Foresters Arms
St George Street
☎ (01624) 676509
12–10.45
Okells Mild, Bitter H
Back-street pub, popular with locals, business people and post office workers from the nearby sorting office. Good social activities. Baps and toasties are available all day.
🎱 🍴 ⊟ ⇌ (IMR)

Old Market Inn
Chapel Row (50 yds from bus station) ☎ (01624) 675202
12–10.45
Bushy's Best Bitter; Okells Bitter H
Homely, back-street local with a good atmosphere; well worth a visit. 🎱 ⊟ ⇌ (IMR)

Samuel Webb
Marina Road (N end of shopping street)
☎ (01624) 625595
11–10.45
Draught Bass; Cains Mild, Bitter; Ind Coope Burton Ale; Okells Bitter; Tetley Bitter H

Very popular, town-centre pub attracting all age groups: a family-run pub serving good food at lunchtime.
Q ❀ ◑ ▶ ♣

Terminus Tavern

Strathallan Crescent, Queens Promenade ☎ (01624) 624312
11–10.30
Okells Mild, Bitter Ⓗ
A good range of food is served in this very popular pub, which is ideal for families, visitors and transport enthusiasts. The terminus refers to both horse trams and the electric railway. Well worth a visit.
🏚 Q ♨ ❀ ⋈ ◑ ▶ ⊟ ₼
≢ (MER) ♣ P

Tramshunters Arms

Harris Promenade
☎ (01624) 626011
12–10.45
Draught Bass; Okells Mild, Bitter; Whitbread Flowers Original; guest beers Ⓗ
Very popular town-centre pub, CAMRA IOM *Pub of the Year* 1993. Choose from 13 real ales and watch for £1-a-pint specials. Adjoining restaurant and hotel. Beef baps are a 'speciality'. ⋈ ◑ ₼ P

Try also: Bushy's Bar, Victoria St (Bushy's); **Rovers Return**, Church St (Bushy's); **Waterloo**, Strand St (Okells)

Laxey

Mines Tavern

On Laxey railway station
☎ (01624) 861484
12–10.45
Bushy's Best Bitter; Ind Coope Burton Ale Ⓗ
The former house of Captain Rowe, the one-time captain of the Laxey Mining Company, situated within easy walking distance of the world-famous Lady Isabella Water Wheel. The public bar has a replica of an MER Tram, while the theme for the lounge bar is based on mining traditions. The garden stands next to the station. Eve meals served during TT fortnight.
Q ❀ ◑ ₼ ▲ ≢ (MER) ♣ P

New Inn

New Road
☎ (01624) 861077
12–10.45

Okells Bitter; Whitbread Castle Eden Ale; guest beers (summer) Ⓗ
Popular local with a friendly clientele and a welcoming landlord. The generous bar meals offer good value (not served Sun) and guest beers are a regular feature in summer. Eve meals and accommodation available during TT fortnight.
Q ❀ ⋈ ◑ ≢ (MER) ♣ P

Try also: Glen Mona Hotel, Glen Mona (Free)

Onchan

Liverpool Arms

Whitebridge Road (Onchan–Laxey road)
☎ (01624) 674787
12–10.45
Okells Mild, Bitter Ⓗ
Typical Manx country pub, run by well-known licensees. This friendly local offers good food, and roaring coal fires in winter.
🏚 ♨ ❀ ◑ ⊟ ≢ (MER) P

Peel

Whitehouse

2 Tynwald Road
☎ (01624) 842252
11–10.45; 12–1.45, 8–10 Sun
Draught Bass; Bushy's Best Bitter; Marston's Pedigree; Okells Mild, Bitter; Whitbread Flowers Original Ⓗ
CAMRA IOM *Pub of the Year* 1992, a former coaching inn in the town-centre, popular with locals and visitors. Reduced prices for OAPs in the afternoons. Always six permanent and five guest beers available (gravity dispense on request). The landlord is a holder of S&N's *Cellarman* award.
🏚 Q ❀ ▲ ♣ P

Port St Mary

Albert

Athol Street (opp. harbour)
☎ (01624) 832118
12–10.45
Bushy's Best Bitter; Cains Mild, Bitter; Okells Bitter; Tetley Bitter Ⓗ
Fishermen's pub on the quayside; popular with sailors and locals. A typical Manx pub: note that the original bar

and shelves have been restored. A good, friendly atmosphere prevails and all food is home-cooked.
🏚 ◑ ▶ ⊟ ₼

Ramsey

Britannia

Waterloo Road (opp. MER station)
☎ (01624) 861547
12–10.45
Okells Mild, Bitter Ⓗ
Good, town-centre pub with a separate locals' bar. Ideal for railway enthusiasts.
◑ ⊟ ≢ (MER) ♣

Trafalgar

West Quay (near harbour swing bridge)
☎ (01624) 814601
12–10.45
Bushy's Best Bitter; Cains Bitter Ⓗ
Quayside pub, reopened after refurbishment, popular with locals and shoppers. Good food; separate dining room. Well worth a visit.
◑ ≢ (MER)

St John's

Farmers Arms

Station Road
☎ (01624) 801372
12–10.45
Cains Mild, Bitter; Ind Coope Burton Ale; Tetley Bitter; guest beers (summer) Ⓗ
Comfortable, old agricultural pub next to the cattle market and on the railway heritage trail. The Tynwald Ceremony takes place nearby every 5th July. The bar meals are substantial. Live music Sun and occasionally other nights. Formerly known as the Central. ❀ ◑ P

Sulby

Sulby Glen Hotel

Main Road (at crossroads)
☎ (01624) 897240
12–10.45
Bushy's Best Bitter; M&B Highgate Dark; Okells Bitter Ⓗ
Typical Manx pub on the TT course, displaying TT memorabilia: a very friendly pub where everyone is welcome. Good food.
🏚 ❀ ⋈ ◑ ▶ ⊟ ▲ ♣ P

Updates to the *Good Beer Guide* are published in CAMRA's newspaper, *What's Brewing*. Join CAMRA and receive a free copy each month.

THE BREWERIES

NEW BREWERIES are like the proverbial London buses: you don't see one for ages then three come along at once. Well, actually, thirty-five. The present boom in new micro-breweries has been little short of staggering. Throughout the 1970s and 1980s, we could expect perhaps one or two new companies a year. Now we are surprised if there are less than twenty. With the launch of the 1994 *Good Beer Guide* we triumphantly proclaimed the birth of some fifty new breweries in the previous two years. That number now stands at eighty-five in three years and we know of plenty more in the pipeline.

There is no question that one of the major reasons for the escalation in new brewers has been the guest beer market. The guest beer law, in force since 1 May 1990, permits tenants of brewers owning more than 2,000 pubs to stock a cask-conditioned (real) ale of their own choosing, in addition to any guest beer supplied by their controlling brewery. Micro-breweries have spotted opportunities to produce beer for enterprising local tenants and have sprung into action. However, the big brewers have fought back hard. By supplying their own list of guest beers to their tenants they have sought to hang onto control of the beers sold in their pubs, and, by discounting their own beers heavily in the free trade, they have tried to squeeze the smaller producers financially. Consequently, few of the new wave of breweries have expanded into major forces in the brewing world and several have not even managed to survive. In the last year, we have bidden a sad farewell to Lion's Original in Burnley, Trough in Bradford and the Atlas brewery in Preston. Others have had to be financially restructured, complete with new owners, like Hadrian, Banks & Taylor and Hull. But, on the plus side, there have not been so many interesting beers available in the UK for many, many years.

S&N ON THE MOVE

Another major development has been the emergence of Scottish & Newcastle as a truly national company. For years, S&N has been fostering its free trade accounts throughout the country, promoting Younger and Theakston brands in particular. However, in 1994, it purchased the Chef & Brewer division of managed pubs owned by Grand Metropolitan, and these 1,600, predominantly southern-based houses now give the company an estate which stretches down to the south coast. This also means that S&N now owns well over the 2,000 pub limit set by the Government for the guest beer law. S&N tenants can now sell a guest beer of their own choosing, over and above any supplied by the company itself.

The Chef & Brewer take-over also reminds us that national brewers are still concentrating control of the industry in their collective hands. It's a scenario which is likely to influence the European Union when it deliberates the tied house system in 1997. There is a very real threat that the EU may well abolish the tie. Whilst this may be welcomed as far the giant breweries are concerned, it would be disastrous for the rest of the British industry. Imagine the likes of Brakspear, Fuller's, Brains, St Austell, Joseph Holt, Vaux or Sam Smith's having to free their pubs of the tie, opening them up to complete competition in beer supply. With the discounting power of the nationals, we would be likely to see Draught Bass, Boddingtons Bitter, Courage Best and Tetley Bitter on sale in virtually every pub and our traditional regional breweries wiped out because they couldn't compete. Far from being a recipe for choice and genuine competition, it would be a green light for the biggest and the richest breweries to swallow up vast chunks of the market.

STOP SWANNING ABOUT

Until that time arrives, we can at least enjoy the new variety of ales in our pubs, although it has to be said that too many fine brews are being spoiled by inappropriate dispense. The offending equipment is the so-called swan neck and sparkler system. Developed as a means of re-creating the famous northern creamy head on beers, and intended for use on national brands originating in the North, like Tetley Bitter, John Smith's Bitter and Boddingtons Bitter, the swan neck is now being abused. Untrained staff and uncaring licensees are attaching these pumps to all manner of beers, many of which are best appreciated through conventional handpump dispense. Adnams Bitter, Wadworth 6X, Young's Special and the like are now being presented with a collar of foam the best part of an inch deep, instead of their light, bubbly heads. And it's not just a matter of looks. To create the thick head, the beer is violently agitated and compressed through tight sparkler holes which remove all condition from the body of the beer and transfer it into the head. Consequently, beneath the heavy froth, you find a rather flat pint which has had all its stuffing knocked out. The result is that Adnams, Wadworth and Young's do not taste like Adnams, Wadworth and Young's should. Our request is simple: use the swan neck on beers which have been brewed for that type of dispense, but let us enjoy other brews just as they should be, without the foam.

THE BREWERIES SECTION

Regular readers will instantly notice one major change this year. There are now only three parts to the breweries section: Independents, Nationals and Pub Groups. Brew pubs have been combined with Independents, as most of these pubs are now supplying beer to many other outlets as well as their own bars. However, all brew pubs are marked with the brew pub symbol for quick reference.

Such is the growth in the number of Pub Groups that we have only been able to list the very biggest (those running around thirty or more pubs). It is noticeable how few of these pub owning companies allow genuine free trade in their pubs. Most are tied to one or more of the nationals (often to the national the pubs were purchased or leased from), and give precious little exposure to smaller independent brewers.

The real ales produced by all the breweries are listed in ascending order of original gravity and most are accompanied by tasting notes provided by trained CAMRA tasting panels. Those not yet tasted are marked with an asterisk.

The tankard symbol, placed next to some beer names, indicates the Beers of the Year. They have been chosen by the tasting panels, by votes from CAMRA members and by the general public at our many beer festivals, and were all finalists in the Champion Beer of Britain contest held at the Great British Beer Festival at Olympia in August 1994. A full list of Beers of the Year can be found on page 273.

The Independents

ABC See Nationals, Carlsberg-Tetley

ABERYSTWYTH **Aberystwyth Ales, Tregynnan Isaf, Llanrhystud, Dyfed SY23 5DW. Tel./Fax. (01974) 202388**

Set up in a farm cowshed, using its own well water, this brewery went into production in March 1994, supplying 15 free trade outlets. Future plans include growing its own hops.

Dinas Dark Mild* (OG 1036, ABV 3.6%)

Dinas Draught* (OG 1038, ABV 3.6%)

Premium* (OG 1046, ABV 4.4%)

ABINGTON PARK **Abington Park Brewery Co., Wellingborough Road, Northampton NN1 4EY. Tel. (01604) 31240**

A Victorian-styled brew pub, opened in 1984 by Chef & Brewer and now owned by S&N Retail (Trent Inns Ltd.) Equipped with a five-barrel plant, the pub stores its beer in cellar tanks under CO_2 at atmospheric pressure. Beers: Cobblers Ale (OG 1037, ABV 3.3%), Becket (brewed with malt, wheat and maize, OG 1042, ABV 3.6%), Dark (OG 1044, ABV 3.6%), Extra (OG 1047, ABV 4.3%), Special (OG 1062, ABV 5%).

ADNAMS **Adnams and Company PLC, Sole Bay Brewery, Southwold, Suffolk IP18 6JW. Tel. (01502) 722424 Fax. (01502) 722740**

East Anglia's seaside brewery, established in 1890, whose local deliveries are still made by horse drays. Real ale is available in all its 115 pubs, and it also supplies almost 500 other outlets direct, with over 80% of beer production now sold outside the Adnams estate. Adnams Extra has been relaunched to make it more widely available. Occasional beer: Mayday (OG 1047, ABV 5%, May).

Mild (OG 1034, ABV 3.2%) A classic dark mild. The aroma is of malt with some fruit and sulphur, followed by a fine, subtle balance of roast malt, hops and fruit on a bittersweet base. Faint, dry finish.

Bitter (OG 1036, ABV 3.6%) A good session beer with a characteristic aroma of hops, fruit and some sulphur. Dry, hoppy flavour, with some fruit and malt, and a long, dry, hoppy finish.

Old (OG 1042, ABV 4.1%) A rich red/brown winter ale. A well-balanced blend of roast grain, malt and fruit, with a dry, bittersweet finish.

Extra (OG 1043, ABV 4.3%) An aroma of hops and citrus fruit leads through into a flavour of hops and bitter orange fruitiness. Very dry finish with some fruit and hops. *Champion Beer of Britain 1993.*

Broadside (OG 1049, ABV 4.4%) Robust and full-flavoured. Fruit and malt dominate but are balanced by a bitter hop base. Dry, fruity finish.

Tally Ho (OG 1075, ABV 6.2%) A rich winter brew with an aroma of malt and fruit. On the palate, the bittersweet fruit flavours linger through to the finish.

ALE HOUSE Leeds, W. Yorks.
Brewery closed

ALFORD ARMS **Alford Arms Brewhouse, Frithsden, Hemel Hempstead, Herts. HP1 3DD. Tel. (01442) 864480**

The Alford Arms started brewing again in September 1992 and expanded production in March 1993 to five barrels a week. It now supplies its malt extract beers to ten other outlets. Beers: Olde Frithsden (OG 1042, ABV 4.2%), Pickled Squirrel (OG 1045, ABV 4.5%), Alford Ale (OG 1048, ABV 5%, summer), Rudolf's Revenge (OG 1055, ABV 5.8%, winter).

ALL NATIONS

All Nations, Coalport Road, Madeley, Telford, Shropshire TF7 5DP. Tel. (01952) 585747

One of few brew pubs left before the new wave arrived, which has, in fact, been brewing for 200 years. Still known as Mrs Lewis's, the inn has been in the same family since 1934. Beer: Pale Ale (OG 1032, ABV 3%).

ALLIED BREWERIES

See Nationals, Carlsberg-Tetley

ALLOA

See Nationals, Carlsberg-Tetley

ANCIENT DRUIDS

Ancient Druids, Napier Street, Cambridge CB1 1HR. Tel. (01223) 324514

Brew pub set up in 1984 by Charles Wells. Malt extract is used and the beer range may be extended. Beer: Ellies SB (ABV 5–6%, varies with each brew).

ANN STREET

Ann Street Brewery, Ann Street, St Helier, Jersey JE1 1BZ. Tel. (01534) 31561 Fax. (01534) 67033

Brewery owning 50 pubs which started brewing cask beer again in 1992 after a break of 30 years. Since then it has increased its range to include a second beer, Ann's Treat, and a winter ale. Fourteen of its own pubs take the beers, and five other pubs are supplied direct. Two of Guernsey Brewery's beers (Braye and Sunbeam) are also available in Ann Street pubs.

Old Jersey Ale*

(OG 1035, ABV 3.6%)

Ann's Treat*

(OG 1050, ABV 5.2%)

Winter Ale*

(OG 1068, ABV 7.5%) Available November–March.

ANSELLS

See Nationals, Carlsberg-Tetley

ARCHERS

Archers Ales Ltd., Station Ind. Estate, London Street, Swindon, Wilts. SN1 5DY. Tel. (01793) 496789 Fax. (01793) 421598

A small brewery, set up in 1979, which has grown very successfully and now supplies 180 free trade outlets from Oxford to Bath (via wholesalers), plus three tied houses. A move to larger premises is on the cards.

Village Bitter

(OG 1035, ABV 3.6%) Dry and well balanced, with a full body for its gravity. Malty and fruity in the nose, then a fresh, hoppy flavour with balancing malt, and a hoppy, fruity finish.

Best Bitter

(OG 1040, ABV 4%) Slightly sweeter and rounder than Village, with a malty, fruity aroma and a pronounced bitter finish.

Black Jack Porter

(OG 1046, ABV 4.6%) A winter brew: a black beer with intense roast malt dominant on the tongue. The aroma is fruity and there is some sweetness on the palate, but the finish is pure roast grain.

Golden Bitter

(OG 1046, ABV 4.7%) A full-bodied, hoppy, straw-coloured brew with an underlying fruity sweetness. Very little aroma, but a strong bitter finish.

Old Cobleigh's*

(OG 1065, ABV 6.3%) Formerly Headbanger. Almost a barley wine in style, enjoying a full flavour. Sweet and powerful, with a pleasant, dry finish.

ARKELL'S

Arkell's Brewery Ltd., Kingsdown, Swindon, Wilts. SN2 6RU. Tel. (01793) 823026 Fax. (01793) 828864

Established in 1843 and now one of the few remaining breweries whose shares are all held by a family, with Managing Director, James Arkell, a great-great-grandson of founder John Arkell. A gradual expansion is taking place in the tied estate, mainly along the M4 corridor, and eight pubs were acquired from Whitbread in 1992. All 84 tied pubs serve real ale, which is also supplied direct to

220 free trade accounts. The Mild won a silver medal at the Brewing Industry's International Awards in 1994. A commemorative beer, Yeomanry Bicentenary Ale (OG 1045, ABV 4.5%), was produced in spring 1994, and may be maintained as a permanent offering (perhaps under a different name). A summer ale, a stout and a porter have also been planned. Occasional beer: Noel Ale (OG 1055, ABV 5.5%, Christmas).

2B (OG 1032, ABV 3.2%) Well-balanced, pale beer. Essentially bitter, but with a hint of fruit and honey. A most refreshing session or lunchtime beer with good body for its OG.

Mash Tun Mild (OG 1036, ABV 3.5%) A very dark, almost black mild ale with a predominantly malt/roast flavour and a similar faint aroma. There is bitterness and roast in the aftertaste. Hard to find on its home territory and available only in winter. The name may change.

3B (OG 1040, ABV 4%) An unusual bitter which is coloured by the use of crystal malt, giving a nutty flavour which persists throughout and combines with bitterness in the aftertaste.

Kingsdown Ale (OG 1052, ABV 5%) A darker, stronger version of 3B with which it is sometimes parti-gyled (derived from the same original brew). A distinct roast/fruit flavour persists with a lingering dry aftertaste.

ARUNDEL **Arundel Brewery, Ford Airfield Estate, Ford, Arundel, W. Sussex BN18 0BE. Tel. (01903) 733111 Fax. (01903) 733381**

Set up in 1992, the first brewery in this historic town for over 50 years, producing beers from authentic Sussex recipes, without the use of additives. Demand has steadily increased and the brewery now serves over 60 outlets, plus its single tied house, acquired in 1993 (the Swan in Arundel). Old Knucker was named after a legendary dragon, Knucker, who allegedly terrorised townsfolk before being slain by a local hero. Occasional beers: Old Conspirator (OG 1050, ABV 5%, November), Old Scrooge (OG 1060, ABV 6%, Christmas).

Best Bitter (OG 1040, ABV 4%) Pale tawny brew with a good hop and fruit aroma with underlying malt. Its dry, hoppy flavour is balanced by malt and fruit and leads through to a fruity, dry aftertaste.

Gold* (OG 1042, ABV 4.2%) Available in summer.

ESB* (OG 1045, ABV 4.5%) A new brew.

Stronghold (OG 1050, ABV 5%) Rich malt predominates in this brew, with a good balance of roast, fruit and hops on a bittersweet base.

Old Knucker (OG 1055, ABV 5.5%) Dark, full-bodied beer. The flavour is a complex blend of sweet fruit and caramel maltiness, which balances dry roast bitterness. This is mirrored in the aftertaste. In the aroma the roast malt is complemented by fruit, caramel and malt with some hops.

ASH VINE **Ash Vine Brewery Ltd., The White Hart, Trudoxhill, Frome, Somerset BA11 5DP. Tel./Fax. (01373) 836344**

Brewery set up in 1987 near Taunton, but moved to the White Hart pub in January 1989. Plans to increase its tied estate are going ahead, with the acquisition of a third pub in 1994 and more to follow. Some 30 free trade outlets are supplied locally and a 'charity' beer is brewed each month, always to a new recipe, for unusual fund-raising purposes.

Trudoxhill (OG 1034, ABV 3.3%) An amber beer, with a light floral hop aroma. A refreshing taste with good bitter dryness. A light beer retaining the distinctive Ash Vine taste.

Bitter (OG 1039, ABV 3.8%) A light gold bitter with a floral hop aroma. A powerful, bitter hoppiness dominates the taste and leads to a dry, and occasionally astringent finish. An unusual and distinctive brew.

Challenger	(OG 1043, ABV 4.1%) A mid-brown beer with a solid malt flavour balanced by a good hoppy bitterness and subtle citrus fruits.
Black Bess Porter	(OG 1044, ABV 4.2%) A dark copper-brown, bitter porter with roast malt, hops and a sweet fruitiness. Roast malt and hop nose; dry, bitter finish.
Tanker	(OG 1049, ABV 4.7%) A tawny-coloured beer with a complex balance of malt, bitter hops, fruit and notable sweetness. A hoppy aroma and a bitter, dry finish.
Hop & Glory	(OG 1058, ABV 5.5%) Copper-coloured with a malt, fruit and hop aroma. The taste is bittersweet, with hops in abundance and some citrus fruits. Similar finish. A complex, rich and warming winter ale.

ASTON MANOR

Aston Manor Brewery Company Ltd., 173 Thimblemill Lane, Aston, Birmingham, W. Midlands B7 5HS. Tel. (0121) 328 4336 Fax. (0121) 328 0139

Founded by ex-Ansells employees in 1983, Aston Manor moved very rapidly into the take-home trade, and discontinued brewing cask ale in 1986. Although still not its main income, the company resumed brewing real ale in 1990 under contract to Chandler's Brewery Company Ltd. It now has an off-licence at the brewery, selling draught ale, but most of its sales are via wholesalers.

Dolly's Dark Mild	(OG 1034, ABV 3.2%) A roast and hop-flavoured mild with a hint of bitterness and sweetness. Dry, bitter finish.
Old Deadlies*	(OG 1045, ABV 4.5%)
Organ Grinder*	(OG 1060, ABV 6%)

ATLAS — See Preston

AYLESBURY (ABC) — See Nationals, Carlsberg-Tetley

BALLARD'S

Ballard's Brewery Ltd., Unit C, The Old Sawmill, Nyewood, Rogate, Petersfield, Hants. GU31 5HA. Tel. (01730) 821301 Fax. (01730) 821742

Founded in 1980 at Cumbers Farm, Trotton, Ballard's has been trading at Nyewood (in West Sussex, despite the postal address) since 1988. The addition of a new copper has increased brewing capacity to 50 barrels a week, and around 60 free trade outlets are now supplied.

Midhurst Mild*	(OG 1034, ABV 3.5%) A dark mild.
Trotton Bitter	(OG 1035, ABV 3.6%) A well-flavoured session bitter, amber/tawny in colour. The good balance of malt and hops runs through from the aroma to the finish, with a slight fruitiness also present.
Best Bitter	(OG 1042, ABV 4.2%) Copper-red, with a malty aroma. Indeed, a notably malty beer altogether, but well-hopped and with a satisfying finish.
Wild*	(OG 1047, ABV 4.7%)
Wassail	(OG 1060, ABV 6%) A strong, full-bodied, fruity beer with a predominance of malt throughout, but also an underlying hoppiness. Tawny/red in colour.

BANKS & TAYLOR

B&T Brewery Ltd., The Brewery, Shefford, Beds. SG17 5DZ. Tel. (01462) 815080

Founded in 1981 in a small industrial unit, Banks & Taylor sadly fell into financial difficulties in spring 1994 and called in the receivers in April. In May, a new company, B&T Brewery Ltd.—with a new owner, Lewis Shepherd—acquired all the trading rights. Banks & Taylor men Martin Ayres and Mike Desquesnes,

The Independents

together with brewer John Waters, were retained by the new company, which continues to produce the same range of beers, including monthly special brews.

Shefford Bitter   (OG 1038, ABV 3.8%) A very drinkable, hoppy beer, with some malt and fruit flavours. Hoppy aroma and a bitter, hoppy aftertaste.

Shefford Mild   (OG 1038, ABV 3.8%) A dark beer with a well-balanced taste. Sweetish, roast malt aftertaste.

Dragonslayer*   (OG 1045, ABV 4.5%) A straw-coloured beer, dry, malty and lightly hopped.

Edwin Taylor's Extra Stout   (OG 1045, ABV 4.5%) A pleasant, bitter beer with a strong roast malt flavour.

Shefford Pale Ale (SPA)   (OG 1045, ABV 4.5%) A well-balanced beer, with hops, fruit and malt flavours. Dry, bitter aftertaste.

Shefford Old Dark (SOD)   (OG 1050, ABV 5%) SOS with caramel added for colour. Often sold under house names.

Shefford Old Strong (SOS)   (OG 1050, ABV 5%) A malty, fruity beer with a bitter aftertaste.

Black Bat   (OG 1060, ABV 6%) A powerful sweet, fruity and malty beer for winter. Fruity, nutty aroma; strong roast malt aftertaste.

2XS   (OG 1060, ABV 6%) A reddish beer with a strong, fruity, hoppy aroma. The taste is full-flavoured and the finish strong and sweetish.

Old Bat   (OG 1080, ABV 7%) Powerful-tasting, sweet winter beer, with bitterness coming through in the aftertaste. Fruit is present in both aroma and taste.

BANKS'S

The Wolverhampton & Dudley Breweries PLC, Park Brewery, Bath Road, Wolverhampton, W. Midlands WV1 4NY. Tel. (01902) 711811 Fax. (01902) 29136

Unspoilt by Progress

Wolverhampton & Dudley Breweries was formed in 1890 by the amalgamation of three local companies. Hanson's was acquired in 1943, but its Dudley brewery was closed in 1991 and Hanson's Mild is now brewed at Wolverhampton. The 150 Hanson's pubs keep their own livery. In 1992, W&D bought Camerons Brewery and 51 pubs from Brent Walker, bringing the tied estate for the whole group up to almost 1,000 houses, virtually all of them serving traditional ales, mostly through electric, metered dispense. Extensive free trade in pubs and clubs.

Hanson's Mild   (OG 1034, ABV 3.3%) A mid- to dark brown mild with a malty roast flavour and aftertaste.

Mild   (OG 1036, ABV 3.5%) A top-selling, amber-coloured, malty mild, with a hint of bitterness and touches of roast and caramel. Drinks like a dark bitter.

Bitter   (OG 1039, ABV 3.8%) A malty, pale brown, bittersweet beer with a dry, malty finish, with a touch of bitterness.

BARLEY   See Fox & Hounds

BARRY'S   See Snowdonia

BASS   See Nationals

BATEMAN   **George Bateman & Son Ltd., Salem Bridge Brewery, Mill Lane, Wainfleet, Skegness, Lincs. PE24 4JE. Tel. (01754) 880317 Fax. (01754) 880939**

A family-owned and -run brewery, established in 1874 by the present chairman's grandfather, then a bankrupt farmer, to serve local landworkers. In the mid-1980s a family dispute threatened the brewery's future, but, after a three-year battle, Chairman George Bateman secured the brewery's independence and is now steadily expanding its sales area to cover nearly the whole of the UK. All its 62 tied houses serve real ale, and around 220 free trade outlets are supplied direct.

Dark Mild   (OG 1033, ABV 3%) A yellow, creamy head tops the black/brown body of this mild. Roast malt and a slight fruitiness lead to a bitterness and hoppiness in the taste and finish. A beer that really looks and tastes the part.

XB (OG 1037, ABV 3.8%) Still a predominantly hoppy and bitter beer throughout, but also with some underlying malt. A satisfying ordinary bitter.

Valiant (OG 1043, ABV 4.3%) A worthy addition to the range with a nose of fruit and hops that lingers on in the taste. A bitter beer, in which malt joins fruitiness and hops in the aftertaste.

Salem Porter (OG 1049, ABV 5%) A fine, dark beer with a roasted malt nose and a fruit and nut taste. A very well-balanced porter, not as widely available as devotees would like.

XXXB (OG 1049, ABV 5%) Still as hoppy and bitter as ever. Apart from these predominant characteristics, some malt and fruit are present throughout. A classic beer of its type.

Victory Ale (OG 1059, ABV 6%) A fruity, powerful, strong beer. Malty and sweet to the taste, developing into a lighter, fruity, hoppy and bitter finish, that makes it dangerously drinkable for its strength.

BATHAM

Bathams (Delph) Ltd., Delph Brewery, Delph Road, Brierley Hill, W. Midlands DY5 2TN. Tel. (01384) 77229 Fax. (01384) 482292

Small brewery, hidden behind one of the Black Country's most famous pubs, the Vine (or the 'Bull & Bladder', as it is commonly known). Now in its fifth generation of family ownership, the firm has survived successfully since 1877 and currently supplies around 30 free trade outlets and nine tied houses. Occasional beer: XXX (OG 1064, ABV 6.3%, Christmas).

Mild Ale (OG 1037, ABV 3.5%) A well-balanced, dark brown, rich, malty mild with a hoppy, fruity finish.

Best Bitter (OG 1044, ABV 4.3%) A pale yellow, fruity bitter. Initial sweetness progresses to a complex, dry, hoppy taste.

BEER ENGINE

The Beer Engine, Newton St Cyres, Exeter, Devon EX5 5AX. Tel. (01392) 851282

Successful brew pub next to the Barnstaple branch railway line, hence the beer names. It owns one other pub, the Sleeper in Seaton, and serves a varying number of free trade outlets. Occasional beers: Porter (OG 1044, ABV 4.4%), Whistlemas (OG 1071, ABV 6.9%, Christmas).

Rail Ale (OG 1037, ABV 3.8%) Amber-coloured beer with a malty aroma and a fruity, sweet taste.

Piston Bitter (OG 1044, ABV 4.3%) Mid-brown, sweet-tasting beer with a pleasant bittersweet aftertaste.

Sleeper Heavy (OG 1054, ABV 5.4%) Red-coloured beer with a fruity, sweet taste and a bitter finish.

BELCHERS See Hedgehog & Hogshead

BELHAVEN

Belhaven Brewery Co. Ltd., Spott Road, Dunbar, Lothian EH42 1RS. Tel. (01368) 62734 Fax. (01368) 865411

With a tradition of brewing going back almost 800 years, Scotland's oldest brewery has had a chequered recent history. It was

The Independents

bought in 1989 by the London-based Control Securities PLC, but in 1993 its employees successfully engineered a management buy-out of the brewery. Despite all its ups and downs, it continues to produce award-winning beers, supplying 24 of its 61 houses, and a further 250 free trade outlets, with cask beer. The new management is strongly independent and aiming for expansion. Occasional beer: 90/- (OG 1071, ABV 8%).

60/- Ale*	(OG 1030, ABV 2.9%) Dark and malty.
70/- Ale*	(OG 1035, ABV 3.5%) Light and hoppy.
Sandy Hunter's Traditional Ale*	(OG 1038, ABV 3.6%)
80/- Ale*	(OG 1041, ABV 4.2%) Heavy, full-bodied ale.
St Andrew's Ale*	(OG 1046, ABV 4.6%)

BENSKINS   See Nationals, Carlsberg-Tetley

BENTLEY   See Nationals, Whitbread

BERROW   **Berrow Brewery, Coast Road, Berrow, Burnham-on-Sea, Somerset TA8 2QU. Tel. (01278) 751345**

Brewery founded in June 1982 and now supplying pubs and clubs locally (about ten free trade outlets).

Best Bitter (BBBB or 4Bs)   (OG 1038, ABV 4%) A pleasant, pale brown session beer, with a fruity aroma, a malty, fruity flavour and bitterness in the palate and finish.

Topsy Turvy (TT)   (OG 1055, ABV 6%) An excellent, straw-coloured beer. Its aroma is of malt and hops, which are also evident in the taste, together with sweetness. The aftertaste is malty. Very easy to drink. Beware!

BIG END   See Daleside

BIG LAMP   **Big Lamp Brewers, 1 Summerhill Street, Newcastle upon Tyne, Tyne & Wear NE4 6EJ. Tel. (0191) 261 4227**

Big Lamp was set up in 1982 and changed hands at the end of 1990. It currently supplies one tied house and a growing free trade (about 55 outlets), and, although there are no immediate plans to expand, the brewery has been working to full capacity for some time. Occasional beers: Old Genie (OG 1070, ABV 7.4%), Blackout (OG 1100, ABV 11%).

Bitter 🍺   (OG 1038, ABV 3.9%) A drinking bitter, with a complex and hoppy character and a smooth, satisfying mouthfeel.

Prince Bishop Ale   (OG 1044, ABV 4.8%) A light-coloured beer for its gravity with a straw hue and clean hoppiness. The aroma and taste are well-balanced, with malt and hop bitterness. Rounded and rich.

Summerhill Stout   (OG 1044, ABV 4.4%) Another beer with many features, including a rich roast aroma and a malty mouthfeel. Look for a light bitterness and some sweetness.

ESB   (OG 1046, ABV 5%) A complex beer with a red hue. Hops balance malt against a background fruitiness and a lingering bitterness. A distinctive and special bitter.

Winter Warmer   (OG 1048, ABV 5.2%) A strong bitter, fortified with roast character and rich maltiness. Try it for its mouthfeel and lasting bitterness.

BIRD IN HAND   **Paradise Brewery Ltd., Paradise Park, Hayle, Cornwall TR27 4HY. Tel. (01736) 753974**

Unusual brewery in a bird park, founded in 1980. Three other pubs are supplied, plus more in summer. Beers: Paradise Bitter (OG 1040, ABV 4.2%), Miller's Ale (OG 1045, ABV 4.7%), Artists Ale (OG 1055, ABV 5.4%), Victory Ale (OG 1070, ABV 7.5%, Christmas).

BISHOPS

Bishops Brewery, 2 Park Street, Borough Market, London SE1 9AB. Tel./Fax. (0171) 357 8343

Established in December 1993, by the former brewer at the Market Porter brew pub, Bishops is the latest addition to the capital's brewing scene. Malt extract is added to the mash. A second beer is planned.

Cathedral Bitter* (OG 1037, ABV 3.7%)

BLACKAWTON

Blackawton Brewery, Washbourne, Totnes, Devon TQ9 7UF. Tel. (01803) 732339 Fax. (01803) 732151

Situated just outside the village of Washbourne, this small family brewery was only founded in 1977 but is the oldest in Devon. It originated in the village of Blackawton, but moved to its present site in 1981 and, although changing ownership in 1988, retains a loyal local following. It serves around 50 free trade outlets, having no pubs of its own.

Bitter (OG 1037.5, ABV 3.8%) Tawny in colour, with a bitter/fruity taste and a bitter aftertaste.

Devon Gold* (OG 1040.5, ABV 4.1%) A summer brew, available April-October. A very pleasant, straw-coloured beer.

44 Special (OG 1044.5, ABV 4.5%) Tawny, fruity-flavoured bitter with a slightly sweet taste and finish.

Headstrong (OG 1051.5, ABV 5.2%) Mid-brown, strong, fruity beer, with a pleasant, fruity, sweet taste and finish.

BLACKBEARD See Freeminer and Hanby

BLACK BULL

Black Bull Brewery, Ashes Farm, Ashes Lane, Fenny Bentley, Ashbourne, Derbyshire D6 1LD. Tel. (0133 529) 581

Brewery opened by keen home brewer Michael Peach in a converted building on his own farm in April 1994. Half a dozen outlets currently take the beer.

Bitter* (OG 1040, ABV 4%) A dark ruby bitter.

BLACK HORSE See Solstice

BLACK HORSE & RAINBOW

The Liverpool Brewing Company Ltd., The Black Horse & Rainbow, 21–23 Berry Street, Liverpool, Merseyside L1 9DF. Tel. (0151) 709 5055 Fax. (0151) 709 9405

A five-barrel plant, set up in July 1990 to brew solely for the Black Horse & Rainbow pub, although a second pub is now being considered to take the brewery's excess capacity. The beer is stored in cellar tanks and the brewery can be viewed both from inside the pub and from the street. Beers: Black Horse Bitter (OG 1045, ABV 4.3%), Winter Ale (OG 1045, ABV 4.3%), Celebration Bitter (OG 1050, ABV 4.8%).

BLACK SHEEP

The Black Sheep Brewery PLC, Wellgarth, Masham, Ripon, N. Yorks. HG4 4EN. Tel. (01765) 689227 Fax. (01765) 689746

Set up in 1992 by Paul Theakston, a member of Masham's famous brewing family, in the former Wellgarth Maltings, Black Sheep is currently brewing 300 barrels a week, with all beer fermented exclusively in Yorkshire slate squares. Expansion is planned, to cater for the free trade, which now extends to some 200 outlets.

Best Bitter (OG 1039, ABV 3.8%) Subtle aroma of malt, with traces of fruit and hops. The flavour is malty with underlying faint fruit and hop bitterness. Dry finish but little depth of flavour.

Special Strong Bitter* (OG 1046, ABV 4.4%)

BLEWITTS See Ship & Plough

The Independents

BLUE ANCHOR 	**Blue Anchor, 50 Coinagehall Street, Helston, Cornwall TR13 8EL. Tel. (01326) 562821** Historic thatched brew pub, possibly the oldest in the UK, originating as a monks' resting place in the 15th century. It produces powerful ales known locally as 'Spingo' beers. Beers: Middle (OG 1050), Best (OG 1053), Special (OG 1066 summer, 1076 winter).
BODDINGTONS	See Nationals, Whitbread and Pub Groups
BODICOTE	See Plough Inn

BORDER

Border Brewery Company Ltd., The Old Kiln, Brewery Lane, Tweedmouth, Berwick-upon-Tweed, Northumberland TD15 2AH. Tel. (01289) 303303 Fax. (01289) 306115

Not to be confused with the Wrexham brewery taken over and closed by Marston's, this new operation opened in 1992 on the site of the town's original Border Brewery, which was established in the 17th century, but which lay idle for 50 years. A change of ownership took place in June 1994 and the brewery now supplies some 20–30 other outlets. Occasional beer: Rudolph's Ruin (OG 1067, ABV 7.1%, Christmas).

Old Kiln Bitter	(OG 1036, ABV 3.8%) A richly hoppy bitter, with strong mouthfeel and lasting maltiness. A bitter true to the Border style.
Old Kiln Ale	(OG 1038, ABV 4%) A light-tasting bitter with a hoppy and fruity character and lasting sweetness.
Noggins Nog	(OG 1042, ABV 4.2%) An unusual mix of roast and malt leaves an impressive chocolate character in the aftertaste of this solidly made beer.

BORVE

Borve Brew House, Ruthven, Huntly, Grampian AB54 4SR. Tel. (0146 687) 343

Borve moved from its original site on the Isle of Lewis in 1988, taking up residence in a former school on the mainland. The school is now a pub, with the brewhouse adjacent. A few free trade outlets are also supplied. Union Street (OG 1050, ABV 4.7%) was brewed as an anniversary ale, but may become a regular feature. All the other beers are also available bottle-conditioned. Beers: Borve Ale (OG 1040, ABV 3.9%), Tall Ships IPA (OG 1050, ABV 4.9%), Extra Strong (OG 1085, ABV 9.8%).

BRAINS

SA Brain & Co. Ltd., The Old Brewery, 49 St Mary Street, Cardiff, S. Glamorgan CF1 1SP. Tel. (01222) 399022 Fax. (01222) 383127

A traditional brewery which has been in the Brain family since Samuel Brain and his Uncle Joseph bought the Old Brewery in 1882. It supplies cask-conditioned beer to all its 119 pubs and over 500 free trade outlets, including many clubs. Its beers also feature as guests in many big brewers' outlets in South Wales and beyond, and the company still has interests in hotel, tourism and leisure projects in Wales and the West Country. MA (OG 1035, ABV 3.5%, a mix of Dark and Bitter) is only available at the Crown Hotel, Skewen, West Glamorgan.

Dark	(OG 1035, ABV 3.5%) A full-bodied, dark brown mild with traces of chocolate followed by a rounded, bittersweet finish.
Bitter	(OG 1035, ABV 3.7%) A distinctively bitter beer, pale and somewhat hoppy, with faint malt and a dry finish. Commonly known as 'Light'.
SA Best Bitter	(OG 1042, ABV 4.2%) A full-bodied, malty, hoppy, premium bitter; well-balanced, with a smooth, dry finish.

The pub sign indicates breweries which are also brew pubs, i.e. produce beer in part of a pub or in its grounds.

418

BRAKSPEAR

WH Brakspear & Sons PLC, The Brewery, New Street, Henley-on-Thames, Oxfordshire RG9 2BU. Tel. (01491) 573636 Fax. (01491) 410254

Brewing took place before 1700 on this Henley site, but the Brakspear family involvement only began in 1799, when Robert Brakspear formed a partnership with Richard Hayward. It was Robert's son, William Henry, who greatly expand the brewery and its trade. Brakspear today boasts many excellent, unspoilt pubs (though the estate is being rationalised) and all its 108 tied houses serve traditional ales. Around 350 free trade outlets are also supplied. Fermenting capacity has been increased to take the weekly output up to over 1,000 barrels, if required. Meanwhile, the Whitbread stake in the company has been sold on, leaving Brakspear free of big brewer connections.

Mild
(OG 1030, ABV 3.1%) Thin beer with a red/brown colour and a sweet, malty, fruity aroma. The well-balanced taste of malt, hops and caramel has a faint bitterness, complemented by a sweet, fruity flavour. The main characteristics extend through to the bittersweet finish.

Bitter
(OG 1035, ABV 3.5%) Amber in colour, with a good fruit, hop and malt nose. The initial taste of malt and the dry, well-hopped bitterness quickly dissolves into a predominantly bitter, sweet and fruity aftertaste.

Old Ale
(OG 1043, ABV 4.5%) Red/brown with good body. The strong, fruity aroma is well complemented by malt, hops and roast caramel. Its pronounced taste of malt, with discernible sweet, roast and caramel flavours, gives way to fruitiness. The aftertaste is of bittersweet chocolate, even though chocolate malt is not present.

Special
(OG 1043, ABV 4.5%) Tawny/amber in colour, its good, well-balanced aroma has a hint of sweetness. The initial taste is moderately sweet and malty, but is quickly overpowered by the dry bitterness of the hops, before a slightly sweet fruitiness. A distinct, dry, malty finish.

OBJ*
(OG 1051, ABV 5%)

BRANSCOMBE VALE

Branscombe Vale Brewery, Great Seaside Farm, Branscombe, Seaton, Devon EX12 3DP. Tel. (01297) 680511

Brewery set up in July 1992 in two cowsheds owned by the National Trust, by former dairy workers Paul Dimond and Graham Luxton, who converted the sheds and dug their own well. Nine local outlets take the beer regularly and 40 more are supplied on an occasional basis. There are plans to increase the brew length. A new own label 'house beer' (OG 1044, ABV 4.6%) is being produced, initially for six local pubs in East Devon. Occasional beer: Anniversary Ale (OG 1044, ABV 4.6%, December—to celebrate the brewery's birthday).

Branoc
(OG 1040, ABV 3.8%) Amber beer with a hoppy aroma, a distinct malty, bitter taste and a dry, bitter finish.

Olde Stoker
(OG 1055, ABV 5.4%) Dark brown with a hoppy aroma. Sweet-tasting, with a bittersweet aftertaste.

BREWERY ON SEA

The Brewery on Sea Ltd., Unit 24, Winston Business Centre, Chartwell Road, Lancing, W. Sussex BN15 8TU. Tel. (01903) 851482

Brewery established in 1993 by Jon Sale, whose Spinnaker beers had previously been brewed under contract by Premier/Pitfield. Beers are also brewed for East-West Ales—Tel. (01892) 834040—and the London Beer Company—Tel. (0171) 739 3701. Occasional brews: Spinnaker Porter (OG 1050, ABV 5%), Tidal Wave (OG 1068, ABV 7%).

Spinnaker Bitter*
(OG 1035, ABV 3.5%)

The Independents

Spinnaker Mild*   (OG 1035, ABV 3.5%)

Spinnaker Classic*   (OG 1040, ABV 4%)

Spinnaker Buzz*   (OG 1045, ABV 4.5%) A new beer, brewed with honey.

Special Crew*   (OG 1050, ABV 5.5%)

Black Rock*   (OG 1051, ABV 5.5%)

Spinnaker Ginger*   (OG 1055, ABV 5.5%)

Riptide*   (OG 1060, ABV 6.5%)

For East-West Ales:

Wicked Widget*   (OG 1046, ABV 4.7%)

For London Beer Company:

Pitfield Bitter*   (OG 1036, ABV 3.6%)

Hoxton Heavy*   (OG 1048, ABV 5.4%)

Dark Star*   (OG 1050, ABV 5.6%)

London Porter*   (OG 1058, ABV 5.7%)

BRIDGWATER

Bridgwater Brewing Company, Unit 1, Lovedere Farm, Goathurst, Bridgwater, Somerset TA5 2DD. Tel. (01278) 663996

Brewery established in spring 1993. Within the first 12 months, the equipment had been upgraded from a four- to a ten-barrel plant and the number of free trade outlets increased to 25. Occasional brews: Carnival Special Brew (OG 1035, ABV 3.5%, October-November), Bluto's Revenge (OG 1060, ABV 6%).

Blake's Bitter*   (OG 1035, ABV 3.4%)

Amber Ale*   (OG 1040, ABV 3.8%)

Coppernob*   (OG 1045, ABV 4.4%)

Sunbeam*   (OG 1052, ABV 5.4%)

BRISTOL BREWHOUSE

See Ross

BRITISH OAK

British Oak Brewery, Salop Street, Eve Hill, Dudley, W. Midlands DY1 3AX. Tel. (01384) 236297

British Oak began life as a family-run brew pub in May 1988, and now supplies 15 free trade outlets, as well as a second pub of its own. Traditional cider is also produced. Occasional beer: Castle Ruin (OG 1038, ABV 3.8%).

Oak Mild   (OG 1038, ABV 3.7%) A beer with a roast malt and pronounced malty caramel flavour.

Eve'ill Bitter   (OG 1042, ABV 4%) A delicious, medium-brown, creamy beer. Very malty, with a bittersweet aftertaste. Feels like a good wine in the mouth.

Colonel Pickering's Porter   (OG 1046, ABV 4.3%) Dark, fruity and bitter: a full-bodied, creamy, distinctive beer.

Dungeon Draught   (OG 1050, ABV 4.8%) A mid- to dark brown fruity ale with plenty of malt and hops. Smooth and fruity.

Old Jones   (OG 1062, ABV 6%) Available September-April: dark, sweet, rich and malty.

BROUGHTON

Broughton Brewery Ltd., Broughton, Biggar, Borders ML12 6HQ. Tel. (0189 94) 345 Fax. (0189 94) 474

Go-ahead brewery, founded in 1980 by former S&N executive David Younger to brew and distribute real ale in central and southern Scotland (to 250 outlets and a single tied house in Dumfries). While this remains the priority, a strong bottled beer trade (not bottle-conditioned) has developed nationwide.

Greenmantle Ale	(OG 1040, ABV 3.9%) A beer lacking aroma, but bittersweet in taste, with a hint of fruit, and a very dry finish.
Special Bitter*	(OG 1040, ABV 3.9%) A dry-hopped version of Greenmantle.
Scottish Oatmeal Stout*	(OG 1041, ABV 3.8%) Also sold by Jennings (see below).
Merlin's Ale*	(OG 1042, ABV 4.2%)
Old Jock	(OG 1070, ABV 6.7%) Strong, sweetish and fruity in the finish.
	For Jennings:
Oatmeal Stout*	(OG 1041, ABV 3.8%)

MATTHEW BROWN	See Nationals, Scottish & Newcastle

TOM BROWN'S	See Goldfinch

BRUNSWICK	**Brunswick Brewing Co. Ltd., 1 Railway Terrace, Derby DE1 2RU. Tel. (01332) 290677**

Purpose-built brewery attached to the Brunswick Inn, a famous railway hotel partly restored by the Derbyshire Historic Building Trust and bought by the present owners in 1987. Brewing began in 1991 and a viewing area allows pub-users to watch production. Occasional beers: Scrooge's Ale (OG 1054, ABV 5.4%, Christmas), Old Vicarage (OG 1074, ABV 7%). Bottle-conditioned beer: Old Vicarage (OG 1074, ABV 7%).

Recession Ale*	(OG 1033, ABV 3.3%)
First Brew*	(OG 1036, ABV 3.6%)
Pain I' T' Neck*	(OG 1039, ABV 3.9%)
150th Brew*	(OG 1042, ABV 4.2%)
Second Brew*	(OG 1042, ABV 4.2%)
Railway Porter*	(OG 1045, ABV 4.3%)
Festival*	(OG 1046, ABV 4.6%)
Old Accidental*	(OG 1050, ABV 5%)
Owd Abusive*	(OG 1066, ABV 6%)

BRYN ARMS	See Snowdonia

BUCKLEY	See Crown Buckley

BUFFY'S	**Buffy's Brewery, Mardle Hall, Rectory Road, Tivetshall St Mary, Norwich, Norfolk NR15 2DD. Tel. (01379) 676523**

Situated in a 15th-century house, Buffy's started life as Mardle Hall Brewery in November 1993, but was forced to change its name after a complaint from another brewery. About half the output is now sold to the take-home trade, with the rest going to some 20 pubs in the area.

Best Bitter*	(OG 1037, ABV 4%) A pale brown to amber, good, hoppy bitter. Refreshing and well-balanced, with a pleasant aftertaste. An enjoyable session beer.
Bitter*	(OG 1042, ABV 4.5%) Not as hoppy or bitter as the Best, but still well-balanced, with more maltiness coming through in the aftertaste.
Ale*	(OG 1050, ABV 5.5%) A full-bodied beer for its gravity. The rounded palate is smooth and complex, with plenty of malt, hop and fruit. Some bitterness also comes through in the aftertaste. Moreish.

The Independents

Strong Ale* (OG 1058, ABV 6.5%) Surprisingly dry for a beer of this strength. Much like the Ale in character, though fuller-bodied, with more fruit throughout, and bitterness and hop in the aftertaste.

BULLMASTIFF

Bullmastiff Brewery, 14 Bessemer Close, Leckwith, Cardiff, S. Glamorgan CF1 8DL. Tel. (01222) 665292

Small brewery set up in the Penarth docklands in 1987 and moved to larger premises in Cardiff in 1992. Bullmastiff now supplies about 30 outlets locally, but not on a regular basis, so the beers are rather hard to find on the brewery's home patch. Much of the production is sold in other parts of the country through wholesalers.

Bitter (OG 1036, ABV 3.5%) A pale brown, bitter beer, hoppy and malty with a dry finish. A popular session beer.

Ebony Dark (OG 1040, ABV 3.8%) As its name suggests, a very dark brown beer with a roast malt flavour and aroma. Very drinkable, with a rich, malt aftertaste.

Best Bitter (OG 1042, ABV 4%) A well-balanced, malty, bitter beer with a balanced, hoppy, fruity finish. Very drinkable.

Son of a Bitch (OG 1064, ABV 6%) A full-bodied, notably hoppy and malty, bitter beer. This premium bitter has a distinctive aroma and aftertaste.

BUNCES

Bunces Brewery, The Old Mill, Netheravon, Wilts. SP4 9QB. Tel. (01980) 70631

Tower brewery housed in a listed building on the Wiltshire Avon, established in 1984, but sold by Tony and Robin Bunce to new Danish proprietors in summer 1993. Its cask-conditioned beers are delivered to around 50 free trade outlets within a radius of 50 miles, and a number of wholesalers are supplied. Occasional beer: Rudolph (OG 1050, ABV 5%, Christmas).

Vice Beer* (OG 1033, ABV 3.2%) A wheat beer for summer.

Benchmark (OG 1035, ABV 3.5%) A pleasant, bitter ale of remarkable character, which maintains one's interest for a long time. The taste is malty, the aroma subtle and the very long finish is quite dry on the palate.

Pigswill* (OG 1040, ABV 4%) A beer first brewed for the Two Pigs at Corsham, now more widely available.

Best Bitter (OG 1042, ABV 4.1%) A first-rate beer. The piquant aroma introduces a complex, malty and bitter taste with a hint of fruit. Long, fresh, bitter aftertaste.

Old Smokey (OG 1050, ABV 5%) A delightful, warming, dark bitter ale, with a roasted malt taste and a hint of liquorice surrounding a developing bitter flavour. Very appealing to the eye.

BURTON BRIDGE

Burton Bridge Brewery, 24 Bridge Street, Burton upon Trent, Staffs. DE14 1SY. Tel. (01283) 510573

Established in 1982, with one tied outlet at the front of the brewery. Conversion of the adjoining premises into a new brewhouse has begun and the pub will eventually be extended into the old brewery buildings. Guest beers are supplied to around 250 outlets virtually nationwide, and Burton Bridge specialises in commemorative bottled beers to order. The brewery also brews for the Heritage Brewery Museum in Burton—Tel. (01283) 510246. Occasional beers: Battle Brew (OG 1050, ABV 5%, July-August), Hearty Ale (OG 1050, ABV 5%, Christmas). Bottle-conditioned beer: Burton Porter (OG 1045, ABV 4.6%).

Summer Ale* (OG 1038, ABV 3.8%) Only available during British Summer Time.

XL Bitter (OG 1040, ABV 4%) A golden/amber, malty drinking bitter, with a dry palate and finish. A faint hoppiness and fruitiness come through in the aroma and taste.

Bridge Bitter	(OG 1042, ABV 4.2%) Again, golden/amber in colour, robust and malty, with a hoppy and bitter palate and aftertaste. Though malt and hops are both present throughout, the dry, hoppy character dominates the finish. Some balancing fruitiness and sweetness.
Burton Porter	(OG 1045, ABV 4.5%) A dark, ruby-red, sweetish porter. The malty, slightly fruity aroma is followed by a roast malt and fruit flavour, and a malty and fairly bitter finish.
Knot Brown Ale*	(OG 1048, ABV 4.8%) An autumn beer.
Top Dog Stout*	(OG 1050, ABV 5%) A winter brew.
Burton Festival Ale	(OG 1055, ABV 5.5%) Strong, sweetish and full-bodied, copper-coloured beer. The nose is malty and slightly hoppy, and the palate has similar characteristics, with a pronounced fruitiness. A little cloying and heavy.
Old Expensive*	(OG 1065, ABV 6.7%) Winter only: a dark, warming beer, also known as OX.

For Heritage:

Thomas Sykes Old Ale*	(OG 1100, ABV 10%). Available in winter and spring. Also bottled-conditioned and sometimes sold as Christmas Ale.

BURTONWOOD

Burtonwood Brewery PLC, Bold Lane, Burtonwood, Warrington, Cheshire WA5 4PJ. Tel. (01925) 225131 Fax. (01925) 224562

A family-run public company established in 1867 by James Forshaw, who had learned his trade at Bath Springs Brewery in Ormskirk. In the 1980s, Burtonwood embarked on a £6 million extension plan and a new brewhouse was completed in 1990. Real ale is supplied to 350 of its 480 tied houses (138 of which are on long lease from Allied), and to 125 pubs in the free trade. Burtonwood also has a stake in the Paramount pub chain (see Pub Groups).

Mild	(OG 1032, ABV 3%) A smooth, dark brown, malty mild with a good roast flavour, some caramel and a hint of bitterness. Slightly dry finish.
Bitter	(OG 1036, ABV 3.8%) A well-balanced, refreshing and malty bitter, with good hoppiness and a little sweetness. Malty and bitter aftertaste.
James Forshaw's Bitter	(OG 1038, ABV 4%) A malty, hoppy and bitter beer. Fairly sweet, with a hint of fruit. More hoppy and characterful than the ordinary bitter.
Top Hat	(OG 1045, ABV 4.8%) Soft, nutty, malty and a little sweet. Fairly thin for its gravity, this beer is now available in an increasing number of outlets.

For Whitbread:

Chester's Best Bitter*	(OG 1033, ABV 3.6%)

BURTS

Mr Burt

Burts Brewery (Newport) Ltd., Dodnor Ind. Estate, Newport, Isle of Wight PO30 5FA. Tel./Fax. (01983) 528098

Brewery originally founded in 1840, but which went into receivership in 1992. The name and brands were bought by Hampshire soft drinks firm Hartridges, owners of Island Brewery, who now use the Burts name for all their brewing operations. From its modern and efficient base, Burts plans to add new beers and to attack mainland markets. Invasion Ale (OG 1049, ABV 5%) was brewed in 1994 to commemorate D-Day.

Nipper Bitter*	(OG 1038, ABV 3.8%)
Ventnor Premium Ale or VPA*	(OG 1041, ABV 4.2%)
Newport Nobbler*	(OG 1043, ABV 4.4%)

423

The Independents

Tanner Bitter*	(OG 1048, ABV 4.8%)
4X Old Ale*	(OG 1050, ABV 5%) A winter brew.
Vectis Venom*	(OG 1050, ABV 5.2%)

BUSHY'S

The Mount Murray Brewing Co. Ltd., Mount Murray, Castletown Road, Braddan, Isle of Man IM4 1JE. Tel. (01624) 661244 Fax. (01624) 611101

Set up in 1986 as Bushy's Brewpub, Bushy's moved to its present site in 1990, when demand outgrew capacity, and subsequently increased its range of beers (which are all brewed to the stipulations of the Manx Brewers' Act of 1874). The brewery has benefited from the closure of Castletown Brewery and the sale of pubs from Isle of Man Breweries' tied estate, which has widened its free trade market on the island (currently 15 outlets), but sales are also increasing on the mainland. Bushy's also runs four tied houses. Occasional beers: Piston Brew (OG 1045, ABV 4.5%, for the TT races in June and Manx Grand Prix in September), Lovely Jubbely Christmas Ale (OG 1060, ABV 6.2%).

Dark Mild

(OG 1035, ABV 3.7%) With a hoppy aroma, and notes of chocolate and coffee to the malty flavour, this rich, creamy, fruity, very dark brew is reminiscent of a porter.

Best Bitter

(OG 1038, ABV 3.7%) An aroma full of pale malt and hops introduces you to a beautifully hoppy, bitter beer. Despite the predominant hop character, malt is also evident. Fresh and clean-tasting.

Old Bushy Tail

(OG 1045, ABV 4.7%) An appealing reddish-brown beer with a pronounced hop and malt aroma, the malt tending towards treacle. Slightly sweet and malty on the palate, with distinct orangey tones. The full finish is malty and hoppy, with hints of toffee.

BUTCOMBE

Butcombe Brewery Ltd., Butcombe, Bristol, Avon BS18 6XQ Tel. (01275) 472240

One of the most successful of the new wave of breweries, set up in 1978 by a former Courage Western MD, Simon Whitmore. During 1992–93, the brewery virtually doubled in size (for the third time) allowing for an 80-barrel brew, and almost all the old plant was replaced. Real ale is supplied to its three houses and direct to over 300 other outlets, mostly within a 50-mile radius of the brewery, as well as further afield via wholesalers.

Bitter

(OG 1039, ABV 4.1%) An amber beer with a pleasant, malty, bitter taste, some hop and occasional fruit. It has a hoppy, malty aroma and a bitter finish, which can be very dry. A clean, crisp, refreshing beer.

BUTTERKNOWLE

Butterknowle Brewery, The Old School House, Lynesack, Butterknowle, Bishop Auckland, Co. Durham DL13 5QF Tel. (01388) 710109 Fax. (01388) 710373

Since its launch in August 1990, Butterknowle has continued to prosper and grow by producing award-winning ales. It now supplies 85 outlets on a regular basis, and over 100 others with guest beers from its impressive range, which is also available via wholesalers. The brewery is situated in Victorian buildings once home to the Lynesack National School.

Bitter

(OG 1036, ABV 3.6%) A good, hoppy bitter. Very drinkable, with a light bitterness and a malty aftertaste.

Festival Stout

(OG 1038, ABV 3.8%) Originally brewed for the sixth Darlington Spring Festival: a beer with a roast, slightly smoky flavour, a hoppy aroma and a sweetish aftertaste.

Conciliation Ale

(OG 1042, ABV 4.2%) Butterknowle's flagship brand, a strongly hoppy bitter, with an impressive balance of fruit and bitterness which is gaining national recognition. Light mouthfeel; dry and satisfying, hoppy aftertaste.

Black Diamond

(OG 1050, ABV 4.8%) Actually red-brown in colour. A richly pungent ale with a good body and sweet taste. Hop and bitter flavours are mild, leaving a grainy finish.

High Force 🍺

(OG 1060, ABV 6.2%) A smooth strong ale, well-hopped with some fruity sweetness. A good depth of flavour develops in the after-taste: a multi-dimensional beer.

Old Ebenezer

(OG 1080, ABV 8%) A splendid, rich and fruity, seasonal barley wine: liquid Christmas cake with a potent punch. Surprisingly moreish, if only in sips!

CAINS

The Robert Cain Brewery Ltd., Stanhope Street, Liverpool, Merseyside L8 5XJ. Tel. (0151) 709 8734 Fax. (0151) 708 8395

Robert Cain's brewery was first established on this site in 1850, but was bought out by Higsons in the 1920s, then by Boddingtons in 1985. Whitbread took control of the Boddingtons breweries in 1990 and closed the site, switching the brewing of Higsons to Sheffield (Higsons beers have subsequently moved again, to Castle Eden). The site was then bought by GB Breweries to brew canned beers, but with enthusiastic staff and CAMRA support, it soon moved on to cask ales. The Robert Cain name was revived and a tied house was opened in summer 1993, after an acclaimed refurbishment of a derelict pub. Further acquisitions are likely. The company is now a division of the brewery group Denmark A/S and supplies over 300 free trade outlets in Merseyside and the North-West. Occasional beer: Superior Stout (OG 1040, ABV 4.5%).

Dark Mild

(OG 1033, ABV 3.2%) Dry, roasty dark mild with some bitterness and hints of sweetness and fruit.

Traditional Bitter

(OG 1039, ABV 4%) Darkish full-bodied bitter, with a good, hoppy nose. Less malty than last year.

Formidable Ale (FA)

(OG 1048, ABV 5%) A hoppy and bitter beer with some fruit and a fairly dry aftertaste. Sharp, clean and dry.

CALEDONIAN

The Caledonian Brewing Company Ltd., 42 Slateford Road, Edinburgh, Lothian EH11 1PH. Tel. (0131) 337 1286 Fax. (0131) 337 2370

Described by Michael Jackson as a 'living, working museum of beer making', Caledonian (or Caley) operates from a Victorian brewhouse, using the last three direct-fired open coppers in Britain, one of which dates back to 1869, when the brewery was started by George Lorimer and Robert Clark. The site was taken over by Vaux of Sunderland in 1919, who continued to brew there until 1987, when, under threat of closure, it was acquired by a management buy-out team. It has no tied estate, but around 350 free trade outlets are supplied, and the beers are increasingly available South of the Border.

60/- Ale*

(OG 1032, ABV 3.2%) A flavoursome light ale.

70/- Ale*

(OG 1035, ABV 3.5%) Soft and malty in flavour.

Murrays Summer Ale*

(OG 1036, ABV 3.6%)

Deuchars IPA 🍺

(OG 1038, ABV 3.8%) A pale, golden beer with a malt and floral hop aroma. The taste is a delicate bittersweet balance, with hops, grain and hints of fruit. Bitterness comes through in the aftertaste.

Edinburgh Real Ale or ERA*

(OG 1041, ABV 4.1%)

80/- Ale*

(OG 1041, ABV 4.1%)

Porter*

(OG 1042, ABV 4.1%) Dry and nutty.

Murrays Heavy*

(OG 1044, ABV 4.3%)

Campbell, Hope & King's Double Amber Ale*

(OG 1046, ABV 4.6%)

Golden Promise*

(OG 1049, ABV 5%) An organic beer.

425

The Independents

Merman XXX* (OG 1050, ABV 5%) Dark, sweetish heavy beer, based on a Victorian recipe.

Edinburgh Strong Ale or ESA* (OG 1063, ABV 6.4%) Rich and deceptively strong.

CAMERONS

The Cameron Brewery Company, Lion Brewery, Hartlepool, Cleveland TS24 7QS. Tel. (01429) 266666 Fax. (01429) 868195

This major brewer of real ale, established in the late 19th century, went through a difficult period during the late 1980s when it was acquired by the ill-fated Brent Walker group. However, since being bought by Wolverhampton & Dudley Breweries in 1992, the future has looked much rosier. W&D has invested heavily in the brewery and pub refurbishments, successfully relaunching the beers in 1992. Real ale is now sold in 82 of the 95 local W&D tied houses, and Strongarm is taken in 150 W&D pubs in the West Midlands. Around 220 free trade outlets are also supplied.

Bitter (OG 1036, ABV 3.6%) A light bitter, but well-balanced, with hop and malt giving good drinking qualities.

Strongarm (OG 1042, ABV 4%) Recently revamped, and now more consistent in quality. Dark red in colour, with a full flavour of fruit and a complex balance of hoppiness, malt and bitterness. Dry, balanced aftertaste.

CANNON

Parker & Son Brewers Ltd., The Cannon, Cannon Street, Wellingborough, Northants NN8 4DL. Tel. (01933) 279629

Brewery founded in January 1993, in the old bottle store of the Cannon pub. A family-run business, it supplies the pub and ten other free trade outlets.

Light Brigade* (OG 1036, ABV 3.6%)

Pride* (OG 1042, ABV 4.2%)

Fodder* (OG 1055, ABV 5.5%)

Old Nosey* (OG 1060, ABV 6%)

CANNON ROYALL

Cannon Royall Brewery, The Fruiterer's Arms, Uphampton, Ombersley, Hereford & Worcester WR9 0JW Tel. (01905) 621161

This five-barrel plant was set up in 1993, in a converted cider house behind the Fruiterer's Arms pub, by the former brewer at the Fox & Hounds in Stottesdon. With around 30 free trade outlets supplied in 1994, there are plans to double this figure and increase the range of beers.

Arrowhead Bitter* (OG 1039, ABV 3.9%)

Buckshot Bitter* (OG 1045, ABV 4.5%)

Millward's Musket Mild* (OG 1046, ABV 4.6%)

Old Merrie* (OG 1060, ABV 6%)

CASTLE EDEN See Nationals, Whitbread

CASTLETOWN See Isle of Man Breweries

CHAINMAKER See United Breweries

CHALK HILL **Chalk Hill Brewery, Rosary Road, Thorpe Hamlet, Norwich, Norfolk NR1 4DA. Tel./Fax. (01603) 620703**

Run by former Reindeer brew pub owner Bill Thomas and his partners, Chalk Hill began production with a 15-barrel plant in December 1993 and now supplies a dozen outlets on a regular basis.

Tap Bitter	(OG 1036, ABV 3.6%) This beer's very faint aroma precedes a strongly bitter palate, which can surprise the unwary. Malt and hops provide balance, with bitterness again prominent in the long aftertaste.
CHB	(OG 1040, ABV 4.2%) A fairly well-balanced, mid-brown beer, not very strongly flavoured.
Old Tackle	(OG 1056, ABV 5.6%) A reddish brown beer with little aroma but a fairly full body and a full palate. The taste is complex, with mainly fruit and even hints of liquorice.

CHANDLER'S   See Aston Manor

CHARRINGTON   See Shepherd Neame and Nationals, Bass

CHERITON   **The Cheriton Brewhouse, Brandymount, Cheriton, Alresford, Hants. SO24 0QQ. Tel. (01962) 771166**

A purpose-built brewery, opened at Easter 1993 by Paul Tickner, licensee of the Flowerpots Inn next door, and two partners. With a ten-barrel plant, it now supplies around 40 free trade outlets, as well as a second pub recently bought by Paul, the Tally Ho! at Broughton, and the Watercress Line steam railway. Cheriton also produces occasional special brews.

Pots Ale*	(OG 1038, ABV 3.8%) Golden in colour and quite well-hopped.
Best Bitter*	(OG 1041, ABV 4.2%)
Diggers Gold*	(OG 1046, ABV 4.6%)
Old Grumblebelly Porter*	(OG 1053, ABV 5.4%) A winter beer.

CHESTER'S   See Burtonwood, Everards and Nationals, Whitbread

---

CHILTERN   **The Chiltern Brewery, Nash Lee Road, Terrick, Aylesbury, Bucks. HP17 0TQ. Tel. (01296) 613647 Fax. (01296) 612419**

Set up in 1980 on a small farm, Chiltern specialises in an unusual range of beer-related products, like beer mustards, Old Ale chutneys, cheeses and malt marmalade. These products are available from the brewery shop and also a dozen other retail outlets. Its latest venture is a small museum, and brewery tours are very popular. The beer itself is regularly supplied to around 20 free trade outlets (no tied houses). Bottle-conditioned beer: Bodgers Barley Wine (OG 1080, ABV 8.5%).

Ale*	(OG 1038, ABV 3.7%) A distinctive, tangy light bitter.
Beechwood Bitter*	(OG 1043, ABV 4.3%) Full-bodied and nutty.
Three Hundreds Old Ale*	(OG 1050, ABV 4.9%) A strong, rich, deep chestnut-coloured beer.

CHURCH END   **Church End Brewery Ltd., The Griffin Inn, Church Road, Shustoke, Warwickshire B46 2LP. Tel. (01675) 481567**

Brewery founded in autumn 1994 in an old stable and coffin workshop behind the Griffin Inn, with a four-barrel brewlength. Beer names were not available as we went to press but four ales were planned: a 3.6% ABV mild, a 4% bitter, a 4.5% porter and a 4.5–5% strong bitter.

WILLIAM CLARK   **William Clark Brewing Company, Unit 2, Beaconsfield Street, Scarborough, N. Yorks. YO12 4FI.**

Brewery which has also been known as North & East Riding Brewers and which, for a while, concentrated on supplying only its one regular outlet, the Highlander on Scarborough's Esplanade. It now aims to provide a range of short run beers of various strengths for the free trade.

Thistle Mild	(OG 1036) A thin and inoffensive mild with a malt nose and a nutty finish. Sweet and bitter at the end.

The Independents

EXB*   (OG 1040, ABV 4.1%)

Thistle Bitter   (OG 1040, ABV 4.1%) A bitter in the Scottish style. The faint hops in the aroma carry through to the finish.

Two Bays Best Bitter   (OG 1040, ABV 4.1%)

No. 68   (OG 1050, ABV 5.1%) A fruity, dark bitter with a bitter undertone, not sure if it is a bitter or a stout.

Triple X Pale Special*   (OG 1051, ABV 5.1%) Also sold as XXXPS, the same name as a former ordinary bitter. Scottish in style.

CLARK'S

HB Clark & Co. (Successors) Ltd., Westgate Brewery, Westgate, Wakefield, W. Yorks. WF2 9SW. Tel. (01924) 373328 Fax. (01924) 372306

The only brewery in Wakefield, founded in 1905, which ceased brewing during the keg revolution of the 1960 and 70s, although continuing to operate as a drinks wholesaler. It resumed cask ale production in 1982 and, within two months, Clark's Traditional Bitter was voted *Best Bitter* at the Great British Beer Festival in Leeds. It now has three tied houses and Clark's beers are widely available (including in Scotland) either supplied directly from the brewery or via beer agencies. Old Drovers Heavy is a house beer brewed for the Drovers Inn near Dunbar.

Traditional Bitter   (OG 1038, ABV 3.8%) An amber-coloured standard bitter with a pleasing, hoppy, fruity aroma. A fine hop flavour dominates in the palate, with malt and fruit. A good, clean-tasting bitter with a long, hoppy finish.

Festival Ale   (OG 1042, ABV 4.2%) A light-tasting, smooth, hoppy bitter, with balancing sweetness and malt, plus fruit notes. The finish is of hoppy bitterness and fruit, which is also evident in the aroma.

Burglar Bill   (OG 1044, ABV 4.5%) A good, hoppy aroma precedes an excellent, strong hop flavour, combined with rich malt and fruit. A long finish of hops and malt completes this full-bodied, strong bitter.

Rams Revenge   (OG 1046, ABV 4.7%) A dark brown beer with a reddish hue and a taste dominated by roast malt and caramel. The aroma is fruity, with roast malt, and the finish is dry and malty but short.

Hammerhead   (OG 1055, ABV 5.5%) Rich malt in the mouth, but with hop flavour and bitterness to balance. The malty, hoppy aroma is faint, but the finish is long, malty and dry. A robust, strong bitter.

Winter Warmer   (OG 1060, ABV 6.3%) A dark brown, powerful strong ale. A strong mouth-filling blend of roast malt, hop flavour, sweetness and fruit notes concludes with a satisfying finish of bittersweet roast malt.

Dreadnought*   (OG 1080, ABV 9.5%)

COACH HOUSE

The Coach House Brewing Company Ltd., Wharf Street, Howley, Warrington, Cheshire WA1 2DQ. Tel. (01925) 232800 Fax. (01925) 232700

Founded in 1991 and run mainly by ex-Greenall Whitley employees, Coach House has quickly established itself and has now extended its trading area into northern Scotland and southern England via the Tap & Spile chain. It currently supplies some 300 outlets directly and a tied estate is being considered, as the beers are still hard to find locally. Coach House also produces specially commissioned beers. Occasional beers: Bootleg Valentines Ale (OG 1050, ABV 5%, February), Burns Auld Sleekit (OG 1055, ABV 5.5%, January), Anniversary Ale (OG 1060, ABV 6%, July), Three Kings Christmas Ale (OG 1060, ABV 6%).

Coachman's Bitter   (OG 1037, ABV 3.7%) A well-hopped, malty bitter, moderately fruity with a hint of sweetness and a peppery, hop nose. A refreshing beer.

Gunpowder Mild
(OG 1037, ABV 3.8%) Full-bodied and roasty dark mild with hints of pepper, fruit and liquorice, and chocolate overtones. Malty aroma and full finish.

Ostlers Summer Pale Ale
(OG 1038, ABV 3.9%) Light, refreshing and very bitter, with a hint of pepper and a very dry finish. German hops are used.

Squires Gold Spring Ale
(OG 1042, ABV 4.2%) A golden beer. New Zealand hops give intense bitterness which is followed by a strong chocolate flavour from amber malt. Bitterness mellows in older samples. Uncompromising and characterful.

Innkeeper's Special Reserve
(OG 1045, ABV 4.7%) A darkish, full-flavoured bitter. Quite fruity with a strong, bitter aftertaste.

Posthorn Premium Ale
(OG 1050, ABV 5%) Well-hopped and very fruity, with bitterness and malt also prominent. Hoppy aroma; fruity aftertaste.

Taverners Autumn Ale
(OG 1050, ABV 5%) Fruity and bitter; golden in colour. Slightly dry aftertaste. A warming, autumnal ale.

Blunderbus Old Porter
(OG 1055, ABV 5.5%) A super winter beer. The intense roast flavour is backed up by coffee, chocolate and liquorice, and hints of spice and smoke. Very well-hopped; massive mouthfeel. An intense, chewy pint which is surprisingly refreshing and moreish.

COMMERCIAL

Commercial Brewing Co. Ltd., Worth Brewery, Worth Way, Keighley, W. Yorks. BD21 5LP. Tel. (01535) 611914 Fax. (01535) 690705

Set up in a former garage, this ambitious brewery's first beer was produced in February 1992, but the beers have changed considerably over the last two years. Its direct free trade extends to around 50 outlets. The brewing plant is also sublet to Pennine Brewing (see separate entry), whilst Commercial itself is in the throes of setting up a visitor centre in conjunction with the local tourist board. Occasional beers: Beckside (OG 1034, ABV 3.5%, May), Hi Summer (OG 1035, ABV 3.4%, June-July), Rampant Spring (OG 1048, ABV 4.8%, March-April), Winter Blues (OG 1052, ABV 5.2%, January-February), Neat Wheat Mate (OG 1054, ABV 5.8%, to order), Harvest Festival (OG 1055, ABV 5.5%), Ruggy's Russet Nectar (OG 1070, ABV 7%, October-November), Santa's Toss (OG 1088, ABV 8%, Christmas). Bottle-conditioned beers: Alesman (OG 1036, ABV 3.7%), Worth Bitter (OG 1045, ABV 4.5%), Porter (OG 1045, ABV 4.6%), Old Toss (OG 1065, ABV 6.5%), Master James (OG 1080, ABV 8%), Santa's Toss (OG 1080, ABV 8%).

Alesman Traditional Bitter*
(OG 1036, ABV 3.7%)

Keighlian Bitter
(OG 1036, ABV 3.7%) Clean, fruity beer with a pungent hop/citrus fruit character on the nose. Bitter fruit aftertaste.

Neary's Stout*
(OG 1040, ABV 4%)

Worth Best Bitter*
(OG 1045, ABV 4.5%)

Worth Porter*
(OG 1045, ABV 4.6%)

Old Toss*
(OG 1065, ABV 6.5%)

CONCERTINA

The Concertina Brewery, The Mexborough Concertina Band Club, 9a Dolcliffe Road, Mexborough, S. Yorks. S64 9AZ. Tel. (01709) 580841

Brewery in the cellar of a club, which began production in 1993, brewing eight barrels a week and supplying about 25 occasional outlets. The partners hope to expand and possibly acquire a pub. Bottle-conditioned beer: APA Strong (OG 1048, ABV 5.2%).

Best Bitter
(OG 1038, ABV 4%) A mid-brown bitter with a light hop and fruit aroma, and subtle malt and hoppiness in the mouth. Dry aftertaste.

Old Dark Attic*
(OG 1038, ABV 4%)

The Independents

Hackett VC
(OG 1040, ABV 4.2%) A well-balanced, malty ale with a hop underlay and even coffee tastes, though the finish has a bitter edge. Mid-brown to amber in colour.

KW Special Pride ⊞
(OG 1042, ABV 4.5%) A smooth, medium-bodied premium bitter with a fine mixture of grain, fruit and hop in the mouth, followed by a balanced, mellow aftertaste. Easy drinking for a beer of its strength.

Fitzpatricks Stout*
(OG 1043, ABV 4.5%)

IPA*
(OG 1043, ABV 4.5%)

Bandsman Strong Ale
(OG 1048, ABV 5.2%)

COOK'S

The Cook Brewery Co., 44 Burley Road, Bockhampton, Christchurch, Dorset BH23 7AJ. Tel. (01425) 673721

After 15 years as a brewing plant engineer, Nigel Cook started small scale brewing in Twickenham in 1988, then moved to Dorset in 1989 with plant from the ex-Swannell's brewery in Hertfordshire, beginning production in May 1991. Free trade outlets have increased in the last year, to 50, and the number of beers has risen accordingly. Both the new brews were originally one-offs, but have continued on a permanent basis.

Priory 900 Ale*
(OG 1039, ABV 3.8%)

New Forest Gold Bitter*
(OG 1043, ABV 4.1%)

Yardarm Special Bitter*
(OG 1052, ABV 5.2%) A hoppy premium bitter.

CORNISH
See Nationals, Whitbread, and Pub Groups, Greenalls

COTLEIGH
Cotleigh Brewery, Ford Road, Wiveliscombe, Somerset TA4 2RE. Tel. (01984) 624086 Fax. (01984) 624365

Continued growth has taken this brewery a long way from its first home, a stable block at Cotleigh Farmhouse in 1979. In 1985, a purpose-built brewhouse was completed and there was further expansion in 1991 and 1993 with the installation of new plant, effectively doubling capacity. Cotleigh now serves some 120 outlets, mostly in Devon and Somerset, although the beers are also available across the country via wholesalers. Occasional beers (made available to customers on a monthly guest beer rota): Swift (OG 1030, ABV 3.2%), Nutcracker Mild (OG 1036, ABV 3.6%), Hobby Ale (OG 1042, ABV 4.2%), Peregrine Porter (OG 1045, ABV 4.4%), Golden Eagle (OG 1045, ABV 4.5%), Snowy Ale (OG 1050, ABV 5%), Red Nose Reinbeer (OG 1060, ABV 5.6%, Christmas). Cotleigh also brews for the Kent wholesalers, East-West Ales Ltd.—Tel. (01892) 834040

Harrier SPA
(OG 1035, ABV 3.6%) A straw-coloured beer with a very hoppy aroma and flavour, and a hoppy, bitter finish. Plenty of flavour for a light, low gravity beer.

Tawny Bitter
(OG 1038, ABV 3.8%) A mid-brown-coloured, very consistent beer. A hoppy aroma, a hoppy but quite well-balanced flavour, and a hoppy, bitter finish.

Barn Owl Bitter*
(OG 1045, ABV 4.5%) Brewed for the Hawk & Owl Trust charity.

Old Buzzard
(OG 1048, ABV 4.8%) Dark ruby-red beer, tasting strongly of roast malt, balanced with hops. Roast malt again in the finish, with bitterness. Very drinkable once the taste is acquired.

For East-West Ales:

Aldercote Ale*
(OG 1042, ABV 4.2%)

Aldercote Extra*
(OG 1046, ABV 4.7%)

COTTAGE

Cottage Brewing Company, Little Orchard, West Lydford, Somerset TA11 7DQ. Tel. (01963) 240551 Fax. (01963) 240383

Brewery founded in 1993 by Chris Norman, a former airline pilot, and his wife, Helen. The beers are served in about 40 outlets locally, and distributed further afield via wholesalers. The names mostly follow a steam railway theme. A porter is also planned.

Southern Bitter*

(OG 1038, ABV 3.7%)

S&D Bitter*

(OG 1044, ABV 4.4%) Named after the Somerset & Dorset Railway: a well-hopped, malty brew, with a deep red colour.

GWR*

(OG 1054, ABV 5.4%) Similar to S&D but stronger and darker, with a full-bodied maltiness.

Norman's Conquest*

(OG 1066, ABV 7%) A dark strong ale, with plenty of fruit flavour and a touch of bitterness.

COURAGE

See Nationals

CROPTON

Cropton Brewery Co., The New Inn, Cropton, Pickering, N. Yorks. YO18 8HH. Tel. (01751) 417330

Set up in 1984 just to supply the New Inn, this brewery was expanded in 1988 and now supplies its additive-free beers to around 30 local free trade outlets, as well as pubs further afield via wholesalers. Plans have been accepted to build a new brewery and work should soon be underway.

King Billy Bitter

(OG 1036, ABV 3.6%) Initially brewed for the King William pub in Hull: a gold-coloured, beautifully clean, hoppy bitter, light on the palate but with strong hop flavour and bitterness. Long, hoppy and bitter finish, but only a slight aroma.

Two Pints Best Bitter

(OG 1040, ABV 4%) A hop aroma precedes a powerful, flowery hop character with some malt and bitterness. Long, smooth, hoppy and sweet finish. A fine, distinctive bitter.

Scoresby Stout

(OG 1042, ABV 4.2%) A rich assault of predominantly roast malt and bitterness, moving to a long bitter finish of roast malt and chocolate. Jet black, and a stout in every sense.

Special Strong Bitter*

(OG 1060, ABV 6.2%) A powerful ale, produced all year but popular at Christmas.

CROUCH VALE

Crouch Vale Brewery Ltd., 12 Redhills Road, South Woodham Ferrers, Chelmsford, Essex CM3 5UP. Tel. (01245) 322744 Fax. (01245) 329082

Founded in 1981 by two CAMRA enthusiasts, Crouch Vale has expanded slowly but surely. Recent growth in the guest beer and wholesale markets has resulted in the building of new offices and the installation of new brewing plant. The brewery's single tied house, the Cap & Feathers at Tillingham, was the CAMRA national *Pub of the Year* in 1989. Crouch Vale currently delivers its wares by liveried dray to over 250 free trade outlets in Suffolk, Essex and Greater London. Occasional beers: Best Mild (OG 1035, ABV 3.6%), FPA or Fine Pale Ale (OG 1059, ABV 5.9%).

Woodham IPA

(OG 1036, ABV 3.6%) An amber beer with a fresh, hoppy nose with slight fruitiness. A good session bitter with a well-balanced taste leading to a fruit and hop finish.

Best Bitter

(OG 1040, ABV 4%) The fruity aroma of this red/brown brew invites drinkers into a splendid taste of malt and fruit, with some hops, leading to a bitter finish.

Millennium Gold

(OG 1042, ABV 4.2%) A golden beer featuring a strong, hoppy nose with maltiness. A powerful mixture of hops and fruit combines with pale malt to give a final sharp, bitter flavour with malty undertones.

431

The Independents

Strong Anglian Special or SAS
(OG 1048, ABV 4.8%) A tawny-coloured beer with a fruity nose. Well-balanced, full-bodied and sharply bitter, with a dry aftertaste.

Essex Porter
(OG 1049, ABV 4.9%) Dark brew with a complex aroma followed by a flavour that is fruity and slightly nutty on a sweet base. Balanced sweet finish. This beer can be difficult to find.

Santa's Revenge
(OG 1057, ABV 5.7%) A Christmas ale, also sold throughout the year under house names. Despite its strength, it is dry and winey, not sweet.

Willie Warmer
(OG 1065, ABV 6.4%) A meal in a mug! This very dark red ale brims with malt and fruit aromas. Sweet fruitiness fills the taste, offset by roast malt and hops.

CROWN BUCKLEY

Crown Brewery, Cowbridge Road, Pontyclun, Mid Glamorgan CF7 9YG. Tel. (01443) 225453 Fax. (01443) 237096

Following several take-overs, Buckley, the oldest brewery in Wales (est.1767) merged with Crown Brewery (the former United Clubs Brewery) in 1989, with Harp financial backing. This ultimately meant that the new company was owned by Guinness but represented a genuine lifeline for the company. Crown Buckley subsequently underwent heavy rationalisation and restructuring, before a management buy-out in June 1993 ensured its true independence once more. Today, all beer production is carried out at the Llanelli (Buckley) site, with kegging and bottling taking place at Pontyclun (the old Crown brewery). A tied estate (actually Harp houses) of 76 pubs, and a free trade of around 400 outlets, are supplied direct from the brewery. The clubs trade is still important, too. Special beers (OG 1041, ABV 4.1%) are occasionally brewed for festivals.

Buckley's Dark Mild
(OG 1034, ABV 3.4%) A very dark, malty mild, fairly sweet with traces of chocolate, followed by a nutty, bitter finish. Very drinkable.

Buckley's Best Bitter
(OG 1037, ABV 3.7%) A well-balanced, medium gravity bitter which has a rather sweet, malty flavour and a pleasant, bitter finish.

Special Best Bitter (SBB)
(OG 1037, ABV 3.7%) Distinctively malty and clean-tasting, with a pronounced bitter flavour and a rather dry aftertaste.

The Reverend James Original Ale
(OG 1045, ABV 4.5%) A malty, full-bodied bitter with hoppy and fruity overtones, followed by a bittersweet aftertaste.

CROWN HOTEL   See Scott's

CYDER HOUSE INN

Cyder House Inn, Shackleford Brewery Co., Peperharow Lane, Shackleford, Godalming, Surrey GU8 6AN. Tel. (01483) 810360

Full mash brewery set up in 1992, which also supplies beer to its second pub, the Thurlow Arms at Cranleigh, acquired in 1993. However, brewing was suspended for a while in 1994, owing to mechanical problems. Beers: Piston Broke (OG 1040, ABV 4%), Old Shackle (OG 1048, ABV 4.7%), Ted's Tipple (OG 1058, ABV 5.8%).

DALESIDE

Daleside Brewery, Camwal Road, Starbeck, Harrogate, N. Yorks. HG1 4PT. Tel. (01423) 880041

Formerly Big End brewery, founded in 1988 by Bill Witty and now run with his son, Craig. The move to new premises and a change of company name in the spring of 1992 also brought an improvement in quality and character to the beers. Daleside now supplies some 200 outlets within a 100-mile radius.

Bitter
(OG 1038, ABV 3.7%) Pale brown bitter with a strong, fruity aroma. The clean, fruity taste with balancing malt and bitterness, is finished with a long bitter, fruit aftertaste. It may be sold under house names.

432

Country Stile*	(OG 1042, ABV 4.1%) Also sold as Old Legover.
Dalesman Old Ale	(OG 1042, ABV 4.1%) Satisfying, dark brown, strong bitter, with rich malt and roast in the mouth, complemented by fruit and hop flavour. Light hop and roast malt finish. It can also have house names.
Monkey Wrench	(OG 1056, ABV 5.3%) A strong aroma of fruit leads to a rich assault of malt/roast and a strong fruit flavour with balancing bitterness, ending in a long, fruity, malty and bitter finish. Some sweetness throughout. A powerful strong ale, dark ruby/brown in hue, but it can be difficult to find.

DARLEY	See Wards

DAVENPORTS	See Nationals, Carlsberg-Tetley, and Pub Groups, Greenalls

DENT   **Dent Brewery, Hollins, Cowgill, Dent, Cumbria LA10 5TQ. Tel./Fax. (01539) 625326**

Brewery set up in a converted barn in the Yorkshire Dales in March 1990, originally to supply just three local pubs. It now has two tied houses and supplies 12 free trade outlets directly. Its own distribution company, Flying Firkin Distribution, delivers all over northern England and is making some inroads into the South, too. All Dent's beers are brewed using the brewery's own spring water.

Bitter*	(OG 1036, ABV 3.7%)
Ramsbottom Strong Ale*	(OG 1046, ABV 4.5%)
T'Owd Tup*	(OG 1058, ABV 6%)

DEVENISH	See Pub Groups, Greenalls, and Nationals, Whitbread

DONNINGTON   **Donnington Brewery, Stow-on-the-Wold, Gloucestershire. GL54 1EP. Tel. (01451) 830603**

Possibly the most attractive brewery in the country, set in a 13th-century watermill in idyllic surroundings. Bought by Thomas Arkell in 1827, it became a brewery in 1865, and is still owned and run by the family. Donnington currently supplies 15 tied houses, and 12 free trade outlets, though XXX is only available in a few pubs.

BB	(OG 1036, ABV 3.5%) Little aroma, but a pleasing, bitter beer, with a good malt/hop balance. Not as distinctive as it used to be.
XXX	(OG 1036, ABV 3.5%) Again, thin in aroma, but flavoursome. More subtle than others in its class. Some fruit and traces of chocolate and liquorice in the taste, with a notably malty finish.
SBA	(OG 1046, ABV 4%) Malt dominates over bitterness in the flavour of this premium bitter, which is subtle, with just a hint of fruit and a dry, malty finish. Faintly malty aroma.

DUNN PLOWMAN	See Solstice

DYFFRYN CLWYD   **Bracdy Dyffryn Clwyd Brewery, Chapel Place, Denbigh, Clwyd LL16 3TJ. Tel. (01745) 815007**

Brewery founded by local pub landlord Ioan Evans, with the first barrels of beer rolling out in summer 1993. The beers have bilingual pump clips and are sold in about 20 local outlets, as well as through wholesalers. Two bars in France's Loire Valley are also supplied.

Cysur or Comfort Bitter	(OG 1036, ABV 3.6%) A sharp, clean and fruity bitter with good hop character. Fairly dry finish.
Druid	(OG 1039, ABV 3.9%) Dry, darkish bitter with hints of coffee and roast. A blend of Cysur and Castell.

433

The Independents

Cwrw Castell or Castle Bitter	(OG 1042, ABV 4.2%) Darkish, smooth bitter, with good hop character. Fairly fruity, with some roast flavour. A complex bitter.
Pedwar Bawd or Four Thumbs*	(OG 1045, ABV 4.8%) A new premium beer, light and golden.

EARL SOHAM

Earl Soham Brewery, The Victoria, Earl Soham, Woodbridge, Suffolk IP13 7RL. Tel. (01728) 685758

Brewery established in April 1985 to supply its own pub, the Victoria, and a few years' later acquiring a second pub, the Tram Depot in Cambridge, which has since been sold to Everards. A few other free trade outlets take the beer.

Gannet Mild	(OG 1032, ABV 3%) Unusual ale, more like a light porter than a mild, given the bitter finish and roast flavours which compete with the underlying maltiness.
Victoria	(OG 1036, ABV 3.5%) A characterful, well-hopped, malty beer whose best feature is the superbly tangy, hoppy aftertaste.
Albert Ale	(OG 1044, ABV 4.3%) Hops predominate in every aspect of this beer but especially in the finish, which some will find glorious, others astringent. A truly extreme brew.
Jolabrugg	(OG 1060, ABV 5.4%) The recipe for this winter brew tends to change from batch to batch, but expect something rich, smooth and fruity with a bittersweet aftertaste.

EAST-WEST ALES See Brewery on Sea and Cotleigh

EASTWOOD'S

Eastwood's Brewery, Unit A2A, Commercial Mill, Savile Street, Milnsbridge, Huddersfield, W. Yorks. HD3 4PG. Tel. (01484) 656024

Brewery established by John Eastwood, former licensee of the Dusty Miller pub in Huddersfield, in April 1993. The Best has been joined by two other regular brews, and a barley wine (around 1070 OG) is on the cards. Some 25 free trade outlets are supplied.

Best Bitter*	(OG 1038, ABV 3.8%)
Black Stump*	(OG 1050, ABV 5.1%) A new porter.
Nettlethrasher*	(OG 1050, ABV 5.1%)

ELDRIDGE POPE

Eldridge, Pope & Co. PLC, Weymouth Avenue, Dorchester, Dorset DT1 1QT. Tel. (01305) 251251 Fax. (01305) 258300

Charles and Sarah Eldridge started the Green Dragon Brewery in Dorchester in 1837. By 1880, Edwin and Alfred Pope had bought into the company and it had moved to its present site, next to the railway, with its first pubs situated along the line. The brewery is still run by the Pope family, owning some 200 pubs and producing award-winning ales, with Thomas Hardy's Ale long notable as the strongest naturally-conditioned bottled beer available in the UK. Free trade extends as far as London, Bristol and Exeter, and the brewery also brews under contract for Ross and the Liquid Assets wholesaler—tel. (0161) 864 5000. Bottle-conditioned beers: Thomas Hardy Country Bitter (OG 1040, ABV 4.2%), Thomas Hardy's Ale ⊞ (OG 1125, ABV 12%).

Dorchester Bitter	(OG 1032, ABV 3.3%) A light session beer which is hoppy and bitter throughout, with some balancing malt.
Best Bitter	(OG 1036, ABV 3.8%) A mixture of malt and hop, with a hint of fruit. Difficult to find in cask-conditioned form.
Blackdown Porter	(OG 1040, ABV 4%) A dark beer with an intense roast malt aroma. There are traces of coffee, chocolate and blackcurrant in the taste, leading into a dry, bitter finish. Deliberately served chilled in some outlets.

Thomas Hardy Country Bitter

(OG 1040, ABV 4.2%) A dry, hoppy beer, with faint undertones of malt and fruit. The taste is smooth despite a bitter edge which continues into the aftertaste.

Royal Oak

(OG 1048, ABV 5%) A full-bodied beer with a distinctive banana aroma and a mainly sweet, fruity taste. This is balanced by malt and some hop, and there is a fruity finish to this smooth, well-rounded brew.

For Liquid Assets:

Potter's Pride*

(ABV 3.8%)

For Ross:

Bottle-conditioned beer: Saxon Strong Ale (OG 1050, ABV 5%)

ELGOOD'S

Elgood & Sons Ltd., North Brink Brewery, Wisbech, Cambs. PE13 1LN. Tel. (01945) 583160 Fax. (01945) 587711

From its classical Georgian, riverside premises (converted in the 1790s from a mill and granary and acquired by Elgood's in 1878), this brewery supplies real ale to all but two of its 47 tied houses, and to a free trade of around 200 outlets. In addition, a mini-brewery produces a variety of beers in small volumes for sale as guests. To celebrate the brewery's bicentenary in 1995, a visitors' centre and brewery museum have been opened.

Black Dog Mild*

(OG 1036, ABV 3.6%) A seasonal brew for the spring.

Cambridge Bitter

(OG 1037, ABV 3.8%) A good balance of malt and hops on the palate combines with a sharp pungent bitterness. Malt in the aroma is often accompanied by sulphury hoppiness.

Barleymead*

(OG 1048, ABV 4.8%) A seasonal, autumn brew.

Greyhound Strong Bitter or GSB

(OG 1049, ABV 5.2%) Still rare, but improving all the time. An aroma of malt and fruit leads into a robust flavour of malt and fruit on a bittersweet base. Bitter finish.

North Brink Porter ⊕

(OG 1055, ABV 5%) Sir Henry's Porter renamed. A rich and complex blend of roast malt and fruit is present in the aroma and on the palate, moving through to a bittersweet finish. Highly drinkable.

Wenceslas Winter Warmer

(OG 1075, ABV 7.5%) A red/brown winter ale, with a robust combination of chocolate, roast malt and fruit, and a warming, wine-like mouthfeel. A rich, fruit/malt aroma and a bitter fruit finish.

ENVILLE

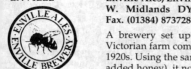

Enville Ales, Enville Brewery, Cox Green, Enville, Stourbridge, W. Midlands DY7 5LG. Tel. (01384) 873770/872280 (sales) Fax. (01384) 873728

A brewery set up by a beekeeper in 1993, on a picturesque Victorian farm complex, in a village where brewing ceased in the 1920s. Using the same water source as the original brewery (with added honey), it now serves around 60 free trade outlets. Enville also runs the Victoria Pub Co. for which it brews Enville Bitter (OG 1037, ABV 3.8%) and plans are now underway for a tied house of its own. Enville is in Staffordshire, despite the postal address.

White

(OG 1041, ABV 4.2%) A clean, refreshing beer, with no dominant flavours, but appealing nevertheless.

Ale

(OG 1045, ABV 4.5%) A pale gold, bittersweet, medium-bodied bitter. Light hops and fruitiness are present in the taste, with the added honey noticeable in the finish.

Gothic Ale

(OG 1051, ABV 5.2%) Roast malt, hops and caramel flavours all combine in this dry, stout-like black beer. Complex and well-balanced, with lurking hints of honey.

The Independents

EVERARDS

Everards Brewery Ltd., Castle Acres, Narborough, Leicester LE9 5BY. Tel. (0116) 2630900 Fax. (0116) 2827270

A small, family-owned brewery, established in Leicester in 1849, by the great-great-grandfather of the current chairman, Richard Everard. Over the years its beers were brewed in both Leicester and Burton upon Trent, until all production was transferred to Castle Acres in 1991. Most of its 144 tied houses sell real ale, but some use cask breathers. Many offer guest beers. Everards also services some 500 free trade accounts. The new winter warmer is the latest addition to the range.

Mild*
(OG 1036, ABV 3.3%) Increasingly rare, and, when it is available, it is often on cask breather.

Beacon Bitter ⊞
(OG 1036, ABV 3.8%) Light and refreshing, with a gentle aroma of malt, fruit and hops. Well-balanced, with a hoppy, malty flavour and a pleasant, lingering bitterness.

Tiger Best Bitter
(OG 1041, ABV 4.2%) A satisfying aroma of malt, hops and fruit, with more than a dash of sulphur leads to a soft, malty palate with a good balance, and a finish that is bitter and hoppy. A good, medium-bodied bitter.

Old Original
(OG 1050, ABV 5.2%) A beer with a smooth, distinctive palate and a fruity, faintly hoppy aroma. A well-balanced, complex beer, fruity, hoppy and sweetish, with an equally complex bitter finish.

Daredevil Winter Warmer
(OG 1070, ABV 7.1%) Brewed December-January, a splendid, full-flavoured and fruity beer, with an aroma of malt and fruit, preceding a sweetish, powerful blend of hops, malt and fruit. Hops and liquorice linger on the palate.

For Whitbread:

Chester's Best Mild*
(OG 1032, ABV 3.5%)

EVESHAM

Evesham Brewery, Oat Street, Evesham, Hereford & Worcester WR11 48J. Tel./Fax. (01386) 443462

Brewery based in the old bottle store at the Green Dragon Inn in Evesham. The owner and licensee, Steve Murphy, who also owns another pub, currently supplies some 20 other outlets, and aims to expand quickly into the commercial market. 'Asum' is the local pronunciation of Evesham.

Asum Ale*
(OG 1038, ABV 3.8%)

Asum Gold*
(OG 1050, ABV 5.2%)

EXE VALLEY

Exe Valley Brewery, Land Farm, Silverton, Exeter, Devon EX5 4HF. Tel. (01392) 860406

Founded as Barron Brewery in 1984, by Richard Barron, this company's name changed when Richard was joined as partner by Guy Sheppard. It operates from an old barn (using the farm's own spring water), and new plant was installed in 1993, to treble capacity. Some 40 local free trade outlets within a 25-mile radius are supplied on a regular basis, and the beers are available nationally via wholesalers.

Bitter
(OG 1038, ABV 3.7%) Tawny-coloured beer, with a distinct fruity aroma and taste. The aftertaste is slightly sweet, yet fruity.

Dob's Best Bitter
(OG 1040, ABV 4.1%) Pale brown bitter with a strong fruit and hop aroma and taste. Smooth, fruity, bittersweet finish.

Devon Glory
(OG 1047, ABV 4.7%) A tawny-coloured beer with malt and fruit running through from the aroma to the finish.

Exeter Old Bitter
(OG 1047, ABV 4.8%) Tawny-coloured, with a fruity aroma and taste, and a hoppy finish.

436

The Independents

EXMOOR

Exmoor Ales Ltd., Golden Hill Brewery, Wiveliscombe, Somerset TA4 2NY. Tel. (01984) 23798 Fax. (01984) 624572

Somerset's largest brewery was founded in 1980 in the old Hancock's brewery, which had been closed since 1959. It quickly won national acclaim, as its Exmoor Ale took the *Best Bitter* award at CAMRA's Great British Beer Festival, the first of many prizes. Brewing capacity is being increased all the time to meet demand from the 200 pubs in the South-West that are supplied directly, and wholesalers and pub chains nationwide. Occasional beers: Dark (OG 1042, ABV 4.1%), Stoat (OG 1044, ABV 4.2%), Exmas (OG 1058, ABV 6%, Christmas).

Ale

(OG 1039, ABV 3.8%) A pale brown beer with a malty aroma, a malty, dry taste and a bitter and malty finish. Very drinkable.

Gold

(OG 1045, ABV 4.5%) Yellow/golden in colour, with a malty aroma and flavour, and a slight sweetness and hoppiness. Sweet, malty finish.

Stag

(OG 1050, ABV 5.2%) A pale brown beer, with a malty taste and aroma, and a bitter finish. Slightly sweet. Very similar to Exmoor Ale and drinks as easily.

Beast*

(OG 1066, ABV 6.6%) A winter brew, available October-March.

FARMERS ARMS

Mayhem's Brew House, Ledbury Road, Apperley, Gloucestershire. GL19 4DR. Tel. (01452) 780172 Fax. (01452) 780307

Brewery opened in 1992 in the grounds of the Farmers Arms, which also produces its own cider. The beers are stored in cellar tanks and are only available at the pub. Beers: Odda's Light (OG 1038, ABV 3.8%), Sundowner (OG 1044, ABV 4.5%).

FEATHERSTONE

Featherstone Brewery, Unit 2, King Street, Enderby, Leicester. Tel. (0116) 2750952

Small brewery which has moved site several times but specialises in supplying custom beers to pubs for sale under house names. A few local outlets take the beers regularly.

Howes Howler*

(OG 1036, ABV 3.6%)

Best Bitter*

(OG 1042, ABV 4.2%)

Vulcan Bitter*

(OG 1049, ABV 5.1%)

ESB*

(OG 1062, ABV 6%)

FEDERATION

Northern Clubs Federation Brewery Ltd., Lancaster Road, Dunston, Tyne & Wear NE11 9JR. Tel. (0191) 460 9023 Fax. (0191) 460 1297

A co-operative, founded in 1919 to overcome the post-war beer shortage, which expanded to supply pubs and clubs through its own depots and wholesalers. It moved to John Buchanan's Brewery in 1930, but was forced to expand again in 1980 to a green field site at Dunston. The brewery is still owned by local clubs, and their business accounts for the majority of the brewery's trade. Cask beers were reinstated in 1986, but only since the introduction of the Buchanan range in 1991 have sales taken off. However, real ales still only amount to a small percentage of the brewery's output.

Buchanan's Best Bitter

(OG 1034, ABV 3.6%) Very difficult to find, especially on top form, when it has a pleasant aroma, a bitter flavour and a well-balanced aftertaste, with a hint of fruit throughout. Really an ordinary bitter, not a best.

Buchanan's Special

(OG 1040, ABV 4%) A clean, hoppy and bitter ale, finishing dry with fruit and hop also lingering.

Buchanan's Original

(OG 1042, ABV 4.4%) A creamy tasting bitter, with a rich mouth-feel and soft bitterness, allowing the malt character to dominate.

The Independents

FELINFOEL

Felinfoel Brewery Co. Ltd., Farmers Row, Felinfoel, Llanelli, Dyfed SA14 8LB. Tel. (01554) 773357 Fax. (01554) 752452

This renowned Welsh brewery was built in 1878, when the village brew pub could no longer keep up with demand. In the 1930s, Felinfoel became famous as the first British brewer to can beer, and, despite recent predators, it is still managing to hang on to its independence. For a while Crown Buckley held a considerable stake but, after investment in the latter company by Guinness, the Lewis family trust which runs Felinfoel was able to buy back all Felinfoel shares. It now supplies draught ale to all but one of its 87 houses (though some use top pressure) and serves roughly 300 free trade outlets.

Bitter

(OG 1032, ABV 3.2%) A hoppy and slightly malty session beer. Refreshing.

Dark

(OG 1032, ABV 3.2%) A dark brown/red mild, rather thin with a slightly bitter flavour and aftertaste.

Double Dragon

(OG 1040, ABV 4.2%) A fine, well-balanced, rich bitter with a nutty malt flavour, a fruity nose and a rounded, bittersweet finish. It is now back at its lower strength after a time at 5%.

FELLOWS, MORTON & CLAYTON

Fellows, Morton & Clayton Brewhouse Company, 54 Canal Street, Nottingham NG1 7EH. Tel. (0115) 9506795 Fax. (0115) 9241937

This pub, leased from Whitbread, began brewing in 1980 and still uses malt extract. Beers: Samuel Fellows Bitter (OG 1038, ABV 4%), Matthew Clayton's Original Strong Ale (OG 1048, ABV 5%). Seasonal strong ales (OG 1060, ABV 6%) are also produced.

FIRKIN

The Firkin Brewery, 77 Muswell Hill, London N10 3PH. Tel. (0181) 365 2823 Fax. (0181) 442 2000

Pub brewery chain founded by David Bruce in 1979, relaunching the brew pub concept in what used to be run-down national brewers' houses. The pubs were refurbished in a back-to-basics fashion and were given in-house breweries, tucked away behind viewing windows. The Bruce's Brewery chain rapidly grew in number until 1988, when he sold all the pubs to Midsummer Leisure (later European Leisure), who, in turn, sold them to Stakis Leisure in 1990. Since 1991, the chain has been owned by Allied-Lyons, through its subsidiaries Taylor Walker, Ind Coope Retail, Ansells Retail, Tetley Pub Co. and Alloa. Much expansion has taken place, with new sites opened in university towns. The estate currently runs to 44 pubs, but only 19 of them brew. The remainder are supplied by the brew pubs (mainly the Falcon & Firkin in London), so only the actual brew pubs are listed here. Four basic brews are available, usually sold under house names, a 1034 OG/3.4% ABV mild, 1036 OG/3.5% ABV bitter, a stronger bitter at 1043/4.3%, and Dogbolter (OG 1056, ABV 5.6%). Some pubs offer extra one-off brews, including summer and winter ales. All the brews are full mash and most pubs now offer some cask-conditioned beer with no additional gas applied. However, cellar tanks with mixed gas breathers are still used in some outlets. The Flamingo & Firkin in Kingston now belongs to Saxon Inns (see Flamingo).

Current brew pubs:
Falcon & Firkin, 360 Victoria Park Road, Hackney, London E9 7BT. Tel. (0181) 985 0693
Ferret & Firkin, 114 Lots Road, Chelsea, London SW10 0RJ. Tel. (0171) 352 6645
Fiddler & Firkin, 14 South End, Croydon, London CR0 1DL. Tel. (0181) 680 9728

The tankard symbol indicates the *Good Beer Guide Beers of the Year*, finalists in the *Champion Beer of Britain* contest held at the *Great British Beer Festival* at Olympia in August 1994.

Fielder & Firkin, 346 Sutton High Street, Sutton, Gtr. London SM1 1PR. Tel. (0181) 642 9018

Finch & Firkin, 487 Smithdown Road, Liverpool, Merseyside L15 5AE. Tel. (0151) 733 2403

Flamingo & Firkin, 1–7 Becket Street, Derby DE1 1HT. Tel. (01332) 45948

Flea & Firkin, 137 Grosvenor Street, Manchester M1 7BZ. Tel. (0161) 274 3682

Flicker & Firkin, 1 Duke Street, Richmond, London TW9 1HP.

Flounder & Firkin, 54 Holloway Road, Holloway, London N7 8JP. Tel. (0171) 609 9574

Forrester & Firkin, 3 Eastgate Street, Stafford, ST16 2NQ. Tel. (01785) 223742

Fowl & Firkin, 1–2 The Butts, Coventry, W. Midlands CV1 3GR. Tel. (01203) 221622

Fox & Firkin, 316 Lewisham High Street, Lewisham, London SE13 3HL. Tel. (0181) 690 8925

Friar & Firkin, 120 Euston Road, Euston, London NW1 2AL. Tel. (0171) 387 2419

Friesian & Firkin, 87 Rectory Grove, Clapham, London SW4 0DR. Tel. (0171) 622 4666

Phantom & Firkin, Leicester Road, Loughborough, Leics. LE11 2AG. Tel. (01509) 263226

Pharoah & Firkin, 88–89 Fulham High Street, Fulham, London SW6 3LF.

Philanthropist & Firkin, Victoria Street, St Albans, Herts. Tel. (01727) 847021

Phoenix & Firkin, 5 Windsor Walk, Camberwell, London SE5 8BB. Tel. (0171) 701 8282

Physician & Firkin, 58 Dalkeith Road, Edinburgh, Lothian EH16 5AD. Tel. (0131) 667 1816

FIRST IN, LAST OUT	**FILO Brewery, 14–15 High Street, Old Town, Hastings, E. Sussex TN34 3EY. Tel. (01424) 425079 Fax. (01424) 420802**

The First In, Last Out began brewing in 1985, but the establishment changed hands three years later. Its current proprietor, Mike Bigg, now brews once a week (five barrels) and all the beer is sold through the pub. Beers: Crofters (OG 1040, ABV 4%), Cardinal (OG 1042, ABV 4.2%).

FLAMINGO	**Flamingo Brewery Company, 88 London Road, Kingston upon Thames, Gtr London KT2 6PX. Tel. (0181) 541 3717**

Previously part of the Firkin chain, now owned by Saxon Inns, this five-barrel brewhouse is situated behind the Flamingo & Firkin pub. Some of the beer is stored under mixed gas in cellar tanks. Beers: Fairfield Bitter (OG 1035, ABV 3.4%), Royal Charter (OG 1042, ABV 4.2%), Coronation (OG 1057, ABV 5.8%), Rudolph's Revenge (OG 1070, ABV 7%, Christmas).

FLOWERPOTS INN	See Cheriton.

FLOWERS	See Nationals, Whitbread.

FORBES	See Green Jack.

The Independents

FOX & HOUNDS

Barley Brewery, Barley, Royston, Herts. SG8 8HU. Tel. (01763) 848459

An early member of the pub brewing revival, using a 19th-century brewhouse at what used to be the Waggon & Horses before changing its name. Beers: Nathaniel's Special (OG 1038, ABV 3.5%), Flame Thrower (OG 1043, ABV 4.1%), Old Dragon (OG 1048, ABV 4.6%), Rudy's Revenge (OG 1055, ABV 5.3%, Christmas).

FOX & HOUNDS

Woody Woodward's Brewery, The Fox & Hounds, High Street, Stottesdon, Kidderminster, Hereford & Worcester DY14 8TZ. Tel. (0174 632) 222

Shropshire Pub (despite the postal address) which started brewing in 1979 and which had two owners before the present landlord. After some experimentation, he has consolidated the beer range, and hopes to increase the free trade from the three or four outlets currently supplied. 'Wust' and 'Bostin' are Black Country expressions meaning worst and best. Beers: Wust Bitter (OG 1038, ABV 3.7%), Wust Mild (OG 1042, ABV 4.1%), Bostin Bitter (OG 1043, ABV 4.2%), Gobstopper (OG 1070, ABV 7%, winter).

FOX & NEWT

9 Burley Street, Leeds, W. Yorks. LS9 1LD. Tel. (0113) 2432612

Brew pub which has resumed production and now produces four beers. Beers: Billy's Special (ABV 3.8%), Cushtie (ABV 4.2%), Ghostbuster (ABV 5.1%), The Bitch (ABV 6.5%).

FOXLEY

Foxley Brewing Company Ltd., Unit 3, Home Farm Workshops, Mildenhall, Marlborough, Wilts. SN8 2LR. Tel. (01672) 515000

Rob Owen and Neil Collings, both keen home brewers, started this, their first commercial venture, in June 1992. Production increased steadily and the range was quickly extended to four beers. Foxley now directly supplies around 80 free trade outlets within a 50-mile radius, and pubs further afield via wholesalers.

Best Bitter*	(OG 1038, ABV 3.8%)
Barking Mad*	(OG 1043, ABV 4.3%)
Dog Booter*	(OG 1046, ABV 4.6%)
Strong Bitter*	(OG 1048, ABV 4.8%)

FRANKLIN'S

Franklin's Brewery, Bilton Lane, Bilton, Harrogate, N. Yorks. HG1 4DH. Tel. (01423) 322345

A brewery set up in 1980 by Sean Franklin, who devised a beer to copy the bouquet of the wines in which he specialised. It is now run by Leeds CAMRA founder-member Tommy Thomas and around ten free trade outlets, plus beer festivals, are supplied.

Bitter — (OG 1038, ABV 3.9%) A tremendous hop aroma precedes a flowery hop flavour, combined with malt. Long hop and bitter finish. A fine, unusual amber bitter.

Summer Blotto* — (OG 1055, ABV 4.7%) Seasonal.

Winter Blotto* — (OG 1055, ABV 4.7%) Seasonal.

FREEMINER

Freeminer Brewery Ltd, Sling, Coleford, Gloucestershire. GL16 8JJ. Tel./Fax. (01594) 810408

Established at the edge of the Forest of Dean in November 1992 by partners Don Burgess and Chris Lewis (formerly with the Firkin chain), Freeminer currently has one tied house (the Miners Arms in Sling). It supplies 30 free trade outlets directly, including several in Manchester, plus others nationwide via wholesalers. Bottle-conditioned beer: Deep Shaft (OG 1060, ABV 6.2%). Beers are also brewed under contract for the Blackbeard wholesaling company— Tel. (01584) 872908.

Bitter*	(OG 1038, ABV 4%)
Speculation Ale*	(OG 1047, ABV 4.8%)
Slaughter Porter*	(OG 1055, ABV 5.2%)
Deep Shaft Stout*	(OG 1060, ABV 6.2%)

	For Blackbeard:
Dead Ringer*	(OG 1048, ABV 4.8%)
Stairway to Heaven*	(OG 1050, ABV 5%)
Low Rider*	(OG 1060, ABV 6%)

FREETRADERS See King & Barnes

FREMLINS See Nationals, Whitbread

FRIARY MEUX See Nationals, Carlsberg-Tetley

FROG & PARROT **Frog & Parrot, 64 Division Street, Sheffield, S. Yorks. S1 4SG. Tel. (0114) 2721280**

Whitbread malt extract brew pub whose Roger & Out has been listed in the *Guinness Book of Records* as the world's strongest beer at an ABV of 16.9%, although this has now been reduced. Beers are kept under a nitrogen blanket in casks and are sometimes available in a handful of other pubs. Beers: Old Croak (OG 1036, ABV 3.5%), Reckless (OG 1045, ABV 4.5%), Conqueror (OG 1066, ABV 6.9%), Roger & Out (OG 1125, ABV 12.5%).

FROMES HILL See Wheatsheaf Inn

FRUITERER'S ARMS See Cannon Royall

FULLER'S **Fuller, Smith and Turner PLC, Griffin Brewery, Chiswick Lane South, Chiswick, London W4 2QB. Tel. (0181) 994 3691 Fax. (0181) 995 0230**

Beer has been brewed on the Fuller's site for over 325 years, John Fuller being joined by Henry Smith and John Turner in 1845. Descendants of the original partners are still on the board today. The brewery recently completed a £1.6 million brewhouse redevelopment to cope with growing demand, and the installation of new mash tuns in 1993 has meant an increase in capacity of 50%. It owns 196 pubs and all but three serve real ale. Occasional beer: Golden Pride (OG 1089, ABV 9.2%, Christmas).

Hock	(OG 1033, ABV 3.2%) A reddish brown, malty mild with a pleasant, dry finish. Now brewed all year.
Chiswick Bitter	(OG 1034, ABV 3.5%) A distinctively hoppy, refreshing beer, with a moderate maltiness and a faint fruity character. Finishes with a lasting bitterness. *Champion Beer of Britain* 1989.
Summer Ale*	(OG 1037, ABV 3.9%) A new seasonal brew.
London Pride	(OG 1040, ABV 4.1%) An excellent beer with a strong, malty base and a rich balance of well-developed hop flavours.
Mr Harry*	(OG 1048, ABV 4.8%) Available November-February.
ESB	(OG 1053, ABV 5.5%) Strong and aromatic, this beer has great character. A full-bodied maltiness and a rich hoppiness are immediately evident and develop into a deep fruitiness.

FURGUSONS See Nationals, Carlsberg-Tetley

GALE'S **George Gale & Co. Ltd., The Hampshire Brewery, Horndean, Hants. PO8 0DA. Tel. (01705) 571212 Fax. (01705) 598641**

Hampshire's major brewery, Gale's was founded in 1847. The original building was largely destroyed by fire and a new, enlarged brewery was built on the site in 1869. Still family owned, it has grown slowly and steadily during the early 20th century,

The Independents

George Gale & Co.Ltd.
THE HAMPSHIRE BREWERY
ESTABLISHED 1847
George Gale & Cube

taking over other small local breweries along the way. It has now sold off 13 of its pubs to Maritime Taverns, but all the remaining 131 tied houses, which include some very attractive old inns, serve real ale. Gale's also supplies around 300 free trade outlets directly, and other pubs via the big breweries. Licensees who join the Gale's Beer Club can take a series of special one-off brews, in a similar scheme to Marston's Head Brewer's Choice. Portsmouth 800 and D-Day (both OG 1062, ABV 6.2%) were commemorative beers produced in 1994, available also bottle-conditioned. Bottle-conditioned beer: Prize Old Ale ⊞ (OG 1094, ABV 9%).

XXXD*	(OG 1031, ABV 2.9%)
BBB or Butser Brew Bitter	(OG 1035, ABV 3.4%) Golden brown in colour, with little aroma. Fairly sweet-tasting, with the sweetness not appearing to come entirely from malt. Some grain and maltiness are also present, with some bitterness and hop flavour to finish.
Best Bitter	(OG 1040, ABV 3.8%) Probably the best-balanced beer of the Gale's range: sweet and malty, with some fruit leading to a malty finish with some hop character. A reddish brown brew.
Gold*	(OG 1040, ABV 4%) A new straw-coloured beer, served a few degrees cooler than most ales.
5X	(OG 1044, ABV 4.2%) Available October-March. A very fruity beer, occasionally with liquorice and aniseed flavours, too. There is a winey fruitiness to the nose and some bitterness in the finish.
HSB	(OG 1050, ABV 4.8%) Too sugary-sweet for some palates. A deep-brown beer with little aroma but a flavour of malt grain and mixed fruit (apples, bananas and damson), leading to a dry, hoppy finish.
Festival Mild*	(OG 1051, ABV 4.8%) A dark, strong mild.

For Whitbread:

Pompey Royal	(OG 1043, ABV 4.5%) A brown beer with a hint of red. Low in aroma, with the flavour dominated by sweetness and pear fruit. The finish can be a little cloying.

GASTONS	See Little Avenham

GIBBS MEW	**Gibbs Mew PLC, Anchor Brewery, Gigant Street, Salisbury, Wilts. SP1 2AR. Tel. (01722) 411911 Fax. (01722) 410013**

Gibbs Mew was established in 1898 by the amalgamation of Salisbury brewers Bridger Gibbs & Sons and Herbert Mew & Co. Charrington bought a stake in the company in the 1960s, which the Gibbs family bought back in 1972, and, in 1992, with CAMRA support, it saw off new predators, Brierly Investments. The tied estate has grown considerably in the last ten years, and more acquisitions are being sought. Real ale is now supplied to all 124 pubs, as well as a growing free trade in southern and south-western England. Overlord (OG 1037, ABV 3.6%) was produced to commemorate D-Day in 1994 and may be continued.

Timothy Chudley Local Line	(OG 1036, ABV 3.6%) A clean-tasting bitter to be savoured. Moderately-hopped and slightly fruity. An ideal lunchtime ale.
Wiltshire Traditional Bitter	(OG 1036, ABV 3.6%) A beer with a pleasant enough flavour of malt and hops, and a dry finish.
Salisbury Best Bitter	(OG 1042, ABV 4%) A rather chewy, sweet ale, decidedly lacking in bitterness. All the same, a pleasant beer.
Wake Ale*	(OG 1050, ABV 5%) A new winter beer.
Deacon	(OG 1051, ABV 5%) A pale, golden beer with a faint orange aroma, an initial bitter taste, and a lingering, dry aftertaste.
The Bishop's Tipple ⊞	(OG 1066, ABV 6.5%) Weaker than the average barley wine, but not lacking in flavour. The full-bodied taste is marvellously malty with a kick that leaves the brain rather less clear than the beer.

GLENNY	See Wychwood

GOACHER'S

P&DJ Goacher, Unit 8, Tovil Green Business Park, Tovil, Maidstone, Kent ME15 6TA. Tel. (01622) 682112

Kent's most successful small independent brewer, set up in 1983 by Phil and Debbie Goacher, producing all-malt ales with Kentish hops for about 30 free trade outlets in the Maidstone area. It acquired its first tied house in 1992. Special, a 75%/25% mix of Light and Dark, is also available to pubs for sale under house names.

Real Mild Ale* (OG 1033, ABV 3.4%) A full-flavoured malty ale with a background bitterness.

Fine Light Ale* (OG 1036, ABV 3.7%) A pale, golden brown bitter ale with a strong, hoppy aroma and aftertaste. A very hoppy and moderately malty session beer.

Best Dark Ale (OG 1040, ABV 4.1%) An intensely bitter beer, balanced by a moderate maltiness, with a complex aftertaste. Lighter in colour than it once was, but still darker than most bitters.

Gold Star* (OG 1050, ABV 5.1%) A summer pale ale.

Maidstone Porter* (OG 1050, ABV 5.1%) A dark ruby winter beer with a roast malt flavour.

Old 1066 Ale* (OG 1066, ABV 6.7%) Black, potent old ale, produced in winter only.

GODDARD'S

Goddard's Brewery, Barnsley Farm, Bullen Road, Ryde, Isle of Wight PO33 1QF. Tel./Fax. (01983) 616833

Farm-based brewing company formed in 1993 and currently supplying around 30 outlets.

Special Bitter* (OG 1039, ABV 4%)

Winter Warmer* (OG 1050, ABV 5.2%)

GOLDFINCH

Goldfinch Brewery, 47 High East Street, Dorchester, Dorset DT1 1HU. Tel. (01305) 264020

Brewery established in 1987 at Tom Brown's Public House, whose theme is broadly based on *Tom Brown's Schooldays*. It has expanded from a one-barrel to a four-barrel plant and has plans for future growth. It supplies Tom Brown's (which is run as a free house) and nine other free trade outlets.

Tom Brown's Best Bitter (OG 1039, ABV 4%) A pale-coloured bitter which is fruity in both aroma and taste, with hop and some malt. The bittersweet taste gives way to a predominantly bitter finish.

Flashman's Clout Strong Ale (OG 1043, ABV 4.5%) A beer with an attractive, honeyed aroma, and, again, a bittersweet taste with malt and some hop. Tawny/mid-brown in colour, with hoppiness coming through to give a bitter edge to the aftertaste.

Midnight Blinder (OG 1050, ABV 5%) A ruby red-coloured beer with an intense fruit aroma. Malt, hop and fruit combine to give the familiar bittersweet taste of Goldfinch beers, leading into a marvellous hoppy, bitter finish.

DOROTHY GOODBODY	See Wye Valley

GOOSE EYE

Goose Eye Brewery, Ingrow Bridge, South Street, Keighley, W. Yorks. BD21 5AX. Tel. (01535) 605807

After an absence of four years from the brewing scene, Goose Eye was re-opened in 1991 in a converted carpet warehouse by Bryan Eastell, with a new partner, Jack Atkinson, who went on to become the sole proprietor in 1993. The brewery supplies 30 free trade outlets, and is still expanding.

The Independents

Black Goose Mild*	(OG 1036, ABV 3.5%)
Bitter*	(OG 1038, ABV 3.8%)
Wharfedale*	(OG 1045, ABV 4.5%)
Pommie's Revenge*	(OG 1052, ABV 5.2%)

GRAND METROPOLITAN — See Nationals, Courage, and Pub Groups, Inntrepreneur

---

GREENALLS — See Pub Groups and Nationals, Carlsberg-Tetley

GREEN DRAGON

Green Dragon, Broad Street, Bungay, Suffolk, NR35 1EE. Tel. (01986) 892681

The Green Dragon was purchased from Brent Walker in 1991 and the buildings at the rear converted to a brewery. Since then, its capacity has increased from three to five barrels and the brewery is likely to move into a converted barn on the same premises, to allow for further expansion (mostly catering for in-house demand, but also to supply a few other outlets). Beers: Chaucer Ale (OG 1036, ABV 3.6%), Bridge Street Bitter (OG 1045, ABV 4.5%), Dragon (OG 1055, ABV 5.5%).

GREEN DRAGON — See Evesham

GREEN JACK

Green Jack Brewing Co. Ltd., Oulton Broad Brewery, Harbour Road Ind. Estate, Oulton Broad, Suffolk NR32 3LZ. Tel. (01502) 587905

Green Jack opened in November 1993, on the site of the Forbes Brewery (which closed in February the same year), with new owners in charge. It has already acquired a tied house and also supplies one other pub nearby with its range of five beers.

Bitter — (OG 1036, ABV 3.5%) Pleasant, light-coloured bitter with plenty of body. Distinctively fruity, with an intense underlying bitterness. Good fruit and hop aroma.

Best Bitter* — (OG 1042, ABV 4.1%)

Golden Sickle* — (OG 1050, ABV 5%) A pale, strong ale.

Norfolk Wolf Porter — (OG 1052, ABV 5%) A truly intense, black beer with substantial body. The chocolate/roast flavour is dominant, but balancing malt, fruit and hops are also present. Bitter chocolate finish.

Lurcher — (OG 1060, ABV 6%) A beer dominated by fruity malt, with a toffee edge. The aftertaste is clean with some bitterness to counter the malt. Hops and malt are present in the aroma of this red/brown ale.

GREENE KING

Greene King PLC, Westgate Brewery, Westgate Street, Bury St Edmunds, Suffolk IP33 1QT. Tel. (01284) 763222 Fax. (01284) 706502

East Anglia's largest regional brewery (established 1799), producing cask-conditioned beers at Bury (its Biggleswade brewery is entirely given over to lager production). In May 1992, Greene King bought up the Whitbread Investment Company's stake in Morland, but its bid to take full control (and close the Abingdon brewery) flopped disastrously. Having recently acquired 85 new pubs from Bass, its tied estate now amounts to 900 pubs (90% of which take cask ale), stretching from East Anglia down into London, Kent, Surrey and Sussex. The majority of pubs have a cask breather device fitted in the cellar, but, thankfully, some licensees choose not to use it. Extensive free trade.

XX Dark Mild — (OG 1035, ABV 3%) The recipe of this beer was changed in summer 1994, making it fuller-bodied and sweeter, with a longer finish. Hopefully, these changes will help this fine beer survive.

IPA (OG 1036, ABV 3.6%) A good session bitter, hoppy on the nose with hop and bitterness ending in an intense bitter finish.

Rayments Special Bitter (OG 1040, ABV 4%) Very different to the other Greene King beers: predominantly malty and sweet, with a complex bitterness and hops lingering in the aftertaste.

Abbot Ale (OG 1049, ABV 5%) A complex, satisfying strong ale, with a good balance of malt, fruit and hops. However, some still find the hop oils intrusive.

Winter Ale (OG 1063, ABV 6.4%) Available November-January and usually served from polypins on the bar. A dark red/brown old ale of substance, like a good wine in many ways. A predominantly fruity nose with some chocolate leads through to a rich blend of fruit, roast malt and some sweetness in the taste. A surprisingly dry aftertaste rounds off this warming brew.

GREYHOUND

Greyhound Brewery Company Ltd., 151 Greyhound Lane, Streatham Common, London SW16 5NJ. Tel. (0181) 677 9962

Set up in 1984, the Greyhound brew pub was acquired by Scottish & Newcastle in November 1993. S&N intends to develop the brewery and improvements to the plant began in 1994. Cellar tanks, with a blanket of CO_2, are used at the pub. Beers: Special (OG 1038, ABV 3.6%), Streatham Strong (OG 1048, ABV 4.3%), Dynamite (OG 1055, ABV 5%).

GRIBBLE

Gribble Inn, Oving, Chichester, W. Sussex PO20 6BP. Tel. (01243) 786893

Brew pub owned by Hall & Woodhouse and sometimes supplying other Hall & Woodhouse pubs. Black Adder II is not to be confused with the 1991 *Champion Beer of Britain* from Mauldons, nor Pig's Ear with the brew from Uley. The pub continues to experiment with new beers and plans to install a new brew vessel to keep up with demand. Beers: Harvest Pale (OG 1030, ABV 2.7%, summer), Gribble Ale (OG 1043, ABV 4.1%), Porter (OG 1045, ABV 4%, winter), Reg's Tipple (OG 1055, ABV 5%), Plucking Pheasant (OG 1055, ABV 5.2%), Black Adder II (OG 1060, ABV 5.8%), Pig's Ear Old Ale (OG 1060, ABV 6%), Wobbler (OG 1080, ABV 7.2%, Christmas).

GRIFFIN INN See Church End

GUERNSEY

The Guernsey Brewery Co. (1920) Ltd., South Esplanade, St Peter Port, Guernsey GY1 1BJ. Tel. (01481) 720143 Fax. (01481) 710658

One of two breweries on this Channel Isle, serving its stronger than average real ales in 12 of its 33 tied houses. Originally opened as the London Brewery in 1865, it became a Guernsey registered company in 1920 upon the introduction of income tax on the mainland. It was taken over by Jersey's Ann Street Brewery in 1988 and Guernsey real ale is still available in selected Ann Street houses. Britannia Bitter is often sold under house names. Sadly, more beer is now being sold as keg dispensed with mixed gas. Seven free trade outlets in the Channel Isles are supplied with the real thing.

Braye Ale (OG 1037, ABV 3.7%) Formerly LBA Mild: copper-red in colour, with a complex aroma of malt, hops, fruit and toffee. The rich, mellow flavour combines malt, fruit, hops and butterscotch, whilst the finish has malt and hops. Full-flavoured and surprisingly dry.

Britannia Bitter (OG 1040, ABV 4%) Amber/tawny in colour, with an aroma of malt, fruit and toffee. Very malty on the palate and again in the finish. Full-bodied and satisfying.

Sunbeam Bitter (OG 1045, ABV 4.2%) Formerly Real Draught Bitter: golden in colour, with a fine malt aroma. Malt and fruit are strong on the palate and the beer is quite dry for its strength. Excellent, dry malt and hop finish.

The Independents

GUINNESS	See Nationals
HP&D	See Nationals, Carlsberg-Tetley

HADRIAN

Hadrian Brewery Ltd., Unit 10, Hawick Crescent Ind. Estate, Newcastle upon Tyne, Tyne & Wear NE6 1AS. Tel. (0191) 276 5302

Brewery started with a five-barrel plant in 1987. It grew steadily, and was forced to move to new premises at the end of 1991 in order to expand. Financial problems followed, but the brewery was saved from receivership and now supplies 40 free trade outlets. Beer is also brewed for the Village Brewer, a wholesale operation based near Richmond, North Yorkshire—Tel. (01325) 374887. Occasional beer: Yule Fule (OG 1060, ABV 4.2%, Christmas).

Gladiator Bitter
(OG 1039, ABV 4%) Renowned as a fresh-tasting, full-flavoured premium bitter. Hoppiness dominates, to accompany a lasting bitterness and a dry finish.

Centurion Best Bitter ᗡ
(OG 1045, ABV 4.5%) Excellently-balanced beer with a prolonged malt and bitter character, balancing a lingering hoppiness.

Emperor Ale ᗡ
(OG 1050, ABV 5%) A beautiful old ale, well-crafted, to give a good match for the style. Highly-hopped, and with a good balance of fruit and bitterness, finishing rich but dry.

For Village Brewer:

Zetland Best Bitter*
(OG 1042, ABV 4.2%)

HALL & WOODHOUSE

BADGER

Hall & Woodhouse Ltd., The Brewery, Blandford St Mary, Blandford Forum, Dorset DT11 9LS. Tel. (01258) 452141 Fax. (01258) 454700

Founded as the Ansty Brewery in 1777 by Charles Hall, whose son, Robert, took Mr GEI Woodhouse into partnership in 1847. More usually known as 'Badger's', the brewery serves cask beer in all of its 155 houses (although an increasing number now use cask breathers), as well as around 500 free trade outlets in southern England. The brewery also owns the Gribble Inn brew pub in Oving, West Sussex, and sometimes sells its beers in other Badger pubs (see Gribble).

Badger Best Bitter
(OG 1041, ABV 4%) A fine best bitter whose taste is strong in hop and bitterness, with underlying malt and fruit. A hoppy finish with a bitter edge.

Hard Tackle
(OG 1045, ABV 4.5%) A well-balanced, tawny-coloured beer. The nose is fruity and hoppy with some malt, and the palate has similar characteristics. A mainly bitter aftertaste.

Tanglefoot
(OG 1048, ABV 5%) A pale-coloured beer with a full fruit character throughout. Some malt and hop are also present in the palate, whilst the finish is bittersweet. Dangerously drinkable.

HALLCROSS	See Stocks
HALLS	See Nationals, Carlsberg-Tetley

HAMBLETON

Hambleton Ales, Holme-on-Swale, Thirsk, N. Yorks. YO7 4JE. Tel. (01845) 567460

Brewery set up in March 1991 in a Victorian barn on the banks of the River Swale. The production target of 20 barrels a week was quickly achieved and demand for its beers has increased to such an extent that relocation has become essential. Hambleton now supplies over 100 free trade outlets and brews three beers under contract for the Village Brewer wholesale company—Tel. (01325) 374887.

Bitter	(OG 1036, ABV 3.6%) A crisp, satisfying bitter, with early malt character and final dryness. A solid body gives good support to a hoppy and fruity aroma.
Goldfield	(OG 1041, ABV 4.2%) Light amber bitter with good hop character and increasing dryness. A fine blend of malts gives a smooth overall impression.
Stallion	(OG 1041, ABV 4.2%) A premium bitter, with strong fruit flavours. Excellently hoppy and richly balanced with bitterness. Note the lasting dry mouthfeel and fruity finish.
Nightmare ⊟	(OG 1048, ABV 5%) Roast malt rears out of this complex mixture to balance a rich creamy sweetness and a lingering dry aftertaste. Available in winter.
Thoroughbred*	(OG 1048, ABV 5%) Available in summer.

For Village Brewer:

White Boar	(OG 1036, ABV 3.7%) Light, dry bitter, with a sharp aftertaste, leaving a dry mouthfeel.
Bull*	(OG 1039, ABV 4%)
Old Raby	(OG 1046, ABV 4.8%) A full-bodied beer with a pleasing, fruity aroma and a powerful maltiness. Excellently-balanced, to leave a lasting impression.

HAMPSHIRE

Hampshire Brewery, 5 Anton Trading Estate, Andover, Hants. SP10 2NJ. Tel. (01264) 336699 Fax. (01264) 332338

Brewery set up in 1992 with a purpose-built, 25-barrel plant. The first brew was named after Alfred the Great, whose parliament resided in Andover, and the business has since expanded to supply more local outlets, as well as regional wholesalers throughout the UK.

King Alfred's	(OG 1038, ABV 3.8%) A good session beer. The well-hopped, fruity, slightly perfumed flavour has a lingering bitter finish.
Lionheart*	(OG 1042, ABV 4.2%)
Pendragon*	(OG 1048, ABV 4.8%)
1066*	(OG 1066, ABV 6.3%)

HANBY

Hanby Ales Ltd., New Brewery, Aston Park, Soulton Road, Wem, Shropshire SY4 5SD. Tel. (01939) 232432

Following the closure of Wem Brewery by Greenalls in 1988, the former head brewer, Jack Hanby, set up his own brewery with a partner, Peter Simmonds. Brewing commenced the following spring and by February 1990 they had moved into a new, larger brewhouse, which was altered and expanded again in 1991. The business is growing steadily, supplying pubs directly and via wholesalers. Hanby also acts as a wholesaler for other breweries and brews for Blackbeard Trading—Tel. (01584) 872908. A subsidiary company, Hanby Taverns Ltd., has been formed, and its first pub opened in summer 1994.

Pale Ale	(OG 1030, ABV 3%) A light session beer sold to the free trade as a house beer. Worth seeking out in its own right.
Black Magic Mild	(OG 1033, ABV 3.3%) A dark, reddish brown mild, which is dry and bitter with a roast malt taste.
Drawwell Bitter	(OG 1039, ABV 3.9%) A splendid hoppy beer with excellent bitterness, both in taste and aftertaste. Beautiful amber colour.
Shropshire Stout	(OG 1045, ABV 4.4%) Full-bodied, rich ruby stout, with a very distinctive, chocolate malt, dry flavour.
Treacleminer Bitter	(OG 1046, ABV 4.6%) A pale brown beer which is sweeter and fruitier than the beers above. Slight malt and hop taste.

The Independents

Nutcracker Bitter	(OG 1060, ABV 6%) A warming, smooth, mid-brown beer, with malt and hops coming through. Definitely more bitter than sweet.
Cocklewarmer Bitter	(OG 1080, ABV 8%) A strong, heavy winter brew.
	For Blackbeard:
Happy Jack*	(OG 1030, ABV 3%)
Black Betty*	(OG 1045, ABV 4.4%)
Cherry Bomb*	(OG 1060, ABV 5.9%)
Joy Bringer*	(OG 1060, ABV 5.9%)
Queen Ann's Revenge*	(OG 1080, ABV 7.6%)

HANCOCK'S — See Nationals, Bass

HAND IN HAND — See Kemptown

HANSEATIC — See McMullen

HANSON'S — See Banks's

HARDINGTON

Hardington Brewery, Albany Buildings, Dean Lane, Bedminster, Bristol, Avon BS3 1BT. Tel. (0117) 9636194

Set up in April 1991, Hardington, however, has no connection with the old Somerset brewery of the same name. Demand for its beers continues to grow and it now serves 150 outlets as well as a single tied house, acquired in 1992. Occasional beer: Rocket Best Bitter (OG 1040, ABV 4%).

Special Pale — (OG 1037, ABV 3.75%) A golden pale ale, with malt and a touch of hops and citrus fruit in the aroma. The taste is delicate and creamy, with a dry bitterness. Refreshing.

Traditional Bitter ⊕ — (OG 1037, ABV 3.7%) An amber, clean, refreshing beer with a floral hop and citrus fruit aroma and taste, balanced by malt and a little sweetness. Long, dry, bitter finish.

Best Bitter — (OG 1042, ABV 4.2%) A crisp, refreshing amber beer with a malty, slightly sweet, bitter taste, and a dry finish. Floral hop and citrus fruit aroma. Moreish.

Jubilee — (OG 1050, ABV 5%) A mid-brown, smooth, complex, fruity and warming beer. Beautifully-balanced throughout.

Moonshine — (OG 1050, ABV 5%) A yellow/gold beer, with a wheaty malt and slight citrus fruit aroma. A smooth, sweetish taste of pale malt, with hints of fruit and spice, and a dry, bitter finish. Enigmatic.

Old Lucifer — (OG 1060, ABV 6%) A smooth, powerful and distinctive, pale brown beer, sweet, fruity and warming. A complex malt and hop balance with pleasant bitterness in a superb, full-bodied, warming ale.

Old Ale — (OG 1065, ABV 6.5%) A rich, copper-red, full-bodied, warming ale. Well-balanced, with a fruity, hoppy, roast malt aroma and a similar bittersweet, vinous taste with fruit undertones. Complex finish. A powerful, well-crafted old ale.

HARDYS & HANSONS

Hardys & Hansons PLC, Kimberley Brewery, Kimberley, Nottingham NG16 2NS. Tel. (0115) 9383611 Fax. (0115) 9459055

Established in 1832 and 1847 respectively, Hardys and Hansons were two competitive breweries until a merger in 1930 produced the present company. Nottingham's last independent brewery is today controlled by descendants of the original Hardy and Hanson families, who are committed to keeping it that way. Its good value real ales are supplied to roughly 200 of its 250 tied houses but there is still a tendency to spoil them with top pressure (though never used on the strong Kimberley Classic). The brewery supplies around 70 other free trade outlets.

Best Mild
(OG 1035, ABV 3.1%) A dark, sweetish mild, slightly malty. Can have fruity notes.

Best Bitter
(OG 1039, ABV 3.9%) Golden/straw-coloured, distinctive, faintly fruity beer. Subtle in aroma; malt is more prominent than hop character and balancing bitterness in the taste.

Kimberley Classic*
(OG 1047, ABV 4.8%) A light-coloured, deceptively strong beer.

HARTLEYS　　See Robinson's

HARVEYS
Harvey & Son (Lewes) Ltd., The Bridge Wharf Brewery, 6 Cliffe High Street, Lewes, E. Sussex BN7 2AH. Tel. (01273) 480209 Fax. (01273) 483706

Established in the late 18th century by John Harvey, on the banks of the River Ouse, this Georgian brewery was partly rebuilt in 1880 and the Victorian Gothic tower and brewhouse remain a very attractive feature in the town centre. Still a family-run company, it is slowly building up its tied estate, supplying real ale to all its 35 pubs and about 300 free trade outlets in Sussex and Kent. One of the first breweries to introduce seasonal ales, it also frequently produces commemorative beers, which are sometimes available on draught. Occasional beers: Tom Paine (OG 1055, ABV 5.5%, July), Elizabethan (OG 1090, ABV 8.3%, December). Bottle-conditioned beer: 1859 Porter (OG 1048, ABV 4.8%).

XX Mild Ale
(OG 1030, ABV 3%) A dark, malty brew with some roast in the aroma. The flavour also sees some fruity sweetness. Roast malt finish.

Sussex Pale Ale
(OG 1035, ABV 3.5%) An amber ale with a hoppy, fruity aroma and some malt. This leads through to a refreshing hop and fruit flavour on a bitter base, with some malt, too. Good dry finish.

Sussex Best Bitter
(OG 1040, ABV 4%) Fruit and hops are prominent all the way through this drinkable southern bitter. The bitter palate also has some caramel maltiness. Bitter hop/fruit finish.

XXXX or Old Ale
(OG 1043, ABV 4.3%) Brewed October-May: a rich, dark beer with a good malty nose, with some undertones of roast, hops and fruit. The flavour is a complex blend of roast malt, grain, fruit and hops with some caramel. Malty caramel finish with roast, too.

Armada Ale
(OG 1046, ABV 4.5%) Full-bodied brew with a good bitter-fruit and hoppy finish. This balance of hops and fruit is present throughout, with some grain and malt. The bitterness in the flavour makes it very drinkable.

HARVIESTOUN
Harviestoun Brewery Ltd., Devon Road, Dollar, Clackmannan-shire, Central FK14 7LX. Tel. (01259) 742141

Hand-built in a 200-year-old stone byre by two home-brew enthusiasts in 1985, this small brewery operates from a former dairy at the foot of the Ochil Hills, near Stirling. Harviestoun is enjoying continued growth and currently serves some 70 outlets in central Scotland. Occasional brew: Nouveau (OG 1095, ABV 9.5%, a barley wine brewed for Christmas and the New Year, with the OG increasing in accordance with the date).

Waverley 70/-*
(OG 1037, ABV 3.7%) A light session beer with hints of roast in the aftertaste.

Original 80/-*
(OG 1041, ABV 4.1%) A malty brew with hop flavour.

Montrose*
(OG 1042, ABV 4.2%) The latest addition to the range.

Ptarmigan 85/-*
(OG 1045, ABV 4.5%) The first known 85/- ale, brewed with Bavarian hops and Scottish malt.

Old Manor*
(OG 1050, ABV 5%) A dark beer with a roast malt flavour.

The Independents

HEDGEHOG & **HOGSHEAD** 	Belchers Brewery, 100 Goldstone Villas, Hove, E. Sussex BN3 3RX. Tel. (01273) 324660; 163 University Road, Highfield, Southampton, Hants. SO2 1TS. Tel. (01703) 581124

Two brew pubs set up in 1990 by David Bruce (of Firkins fame), then sold in March 1994 to Grosvenor Inns for shares, with Bruce taking a seat on the Grosvenor board (see Pub Groups). The beers are stored in cellar tanks and a cask breather is used on slower sellers. A third Hedgehog & Hogshead in Essex Street, London WC2 does not brew. Beers: Belchers Original (OG 1038, ABV 3.8%), Belchers Best Bitter (OG 1042, ABV 4.2%), Blackleg Porter (OG 1052, ABV 5.2%), Bootleg Bitter (OG 1052, ABV 5.2%), Hogbolter (OG 1057, ABV 5.6%).

HERITAGE See Burton Bridge and Lloyds

HESKET **NEWMARKET** 	**Hesket Newmarket Brewery, Old Crown Barn, Hesket Newmarket, Cumbria CA7 8JG. Tel. (0169 74) 78288**

Brewery set up in a barn behind the owners' pub in an attractive North Lakes village. Most of the beers are named after local fells. Sixty per cent of the brewery's production goes to the free trade: 12 pubs in the North, plus a further 30 or so outlets from Edinburgh down to Kent on an occasional or guest beer basis. A new beer has just been produced: at 1052 OG, ABV 4.9%, it was unnamed as we went to press. Occasional beer: Ayala's Angel (OG 1080, ABV 7%, Christmas).

Great Cockup Porter*	(OG 1035, ABV 2.8%) A refreshing, chocolate-tasting beer.
Blencathra Bitter*	(OG 1035, ABV 3.1%)
Skiddaw Special Bitter*	(OG 1035, ABV 3.7%) A golden session beer, despite its name.
Doris's 90th Birthday Ale*	(OG 1045, ABV 4.3%) A fruity premium ale.
Old Carrock Strong Ale*	(OG 1065, ABV 5.6%) A dark red, powerful ale.

HEXHAMSHIRE 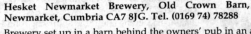	**Hexhamshire Brewery, Ordley, Hexham, Northumberland NE46 1SX. Tel. (01434) 673031**

Brewery set up in a redundant farm building in November 1992 by the owner of the Dipton Mill Inn with two partners, using equipment manufactured from former milk tanks. No adjuncts are used in the beers, which are produced for the inn and over 25 other local outlets. Occasional beer: Blackhall Stout (OG 1043, ABV 4.3%).

Low Quarter Ale	(OG 1035, ABV 3.5%) Nice, full-bodied, hoppy ale, with low bitterness and a golden hue.
Shire Bitter	(OG 1037, ABV 3.8%) Thicker than expected: a more bitter beer than its companion, but keeping a malty overtone.
Devil's Water	(OG 1041, ABV 4.1%) A beer of mixed character and an unexpected range of flavours. Malt dominates and bitterness gradually declines, giving a strong, sweet finish.
Whapweasel or Strong	(OG 1048, ABV 4.8%) This malty bitter has a lasting hoppiness and a smooth mouthfeel.

HIGHGATE See Nationals, Bass

HIGHLANDER See William Clark

HIGH PEAK See Lloyds

HIGSONS See Cains and Nationals, Whitbread

HILDEN

Hilden Brewery, Hilden House, Lisburn, Co. Antrim BT27 4TY. Tel. (01846) 663863

Mini-brewery beside a Georgian country house, set up in 1981 to counter the local all-keg Guinness/Bass duopoly. Presently the only real ale brewery in Northern Ireland, supplying Hilden Ale to just a single pub there, and the full range to some pubs in England.

Ale
(OG 1038) An amber-coloured beer with an aroma of malt, hops and fruit. The balanced taste is slightly slanted towards hops, and hops are also prominent in the full, malty finish. Bitter and refreshing.

Great Northern Porter
(OG 1039) A beer with a rich, tawny colour and a pronounced malty aroma. Crystal malt is dominant in both the flavour and aftertaste.

Special Reserve
(OG 1040) Dark red/brown in colour and superbly aromatic—full of dark malts, producing an aroma of liquorice and toffee. Malt, fruit and toffee on the palate, with a sweet, malty finish. Mellow and satisfying, but not always available.

HOBSONS

Hobsons Brewery & Co., The Brewery, Cleobury Ind. Estate, Cleobury Mortimer, Kidderminster, Hereford & Worcester DY14 8DP. Tel. (01299) 270837

Opening at Easter 1993 in a former sawmill, Hobsons is run by Nick Davies and his parents, supplying their own pub and 80 other outlets within an hour's drive. The brewery is actually in Shropshire, despite the postal address.

Best Bitter
(OG 1038, ABV 3.8%) A pale brown to amber, medium-bodied beer with strong hop character all through. Consequently bitter, but with malt discernible in the taste.

Town Crier*
(OG 1043, ABV 4.5%) A new straw-coloured bitter.

Old Henry*
(OG 1050, ABV 5.2%)

HOGS BACK

Hogs Back Brewery, Manor Farm, The Street, Tongham, Surrey GU10 1DE. Tel. (01252) 783000 Fax. (01252) 782328

This purpose-built brewery was set up in a restored farm building (circa 1768) in August 1992. The business began by supplying guest beers and bottled foreign beers to local pubs, but now its own beers are regularly sold to almost 200 outlets. There is also a well-stocked shop/off-licence on site, offering a wide range of English and Belgian bottled beers. Plans include the acquisition of a tied house and a small specialised bottling plant. Occasional beer: Santa's Wobble (OG 1077, ABV 7.5%, Christmas and sometimes in summer under the name of Still Wobbling). Bottle-conditioned beers: Brewsters Bundle (OG 1076, ABV 7.45%), A over T (OG 1091, ABV 9%).

Dark Mild
(OG 1036, ABV 3.4%) A reddish brown, malty mild with an underlying fruitiness and a bitter finish.

APB or A Pinta Bitter*
(OG 1037, ABV 3.7%)

TEA or Traditional English Ale
(OG 1044, ABV 4.2%) Tawny/brown, malty bitter with balancing hoppiness. Slightly fruity.

Blackwater Porter*
(OG 1046, ABV 4.4%)

Hop Garden Gold*
(OG 1048, ABV 4.6%)

Ripsnorter*
(OG 1052, ABV 5%) A strong special bitter.

OTT or Olde Tongham Tasty*
(OG 1066, ABV 6.5%) A winter ale.

A over T or Aromas over Tongham*
(OG 1091, ABV 9%)

The Independents

HOLDEN'S

Holden's Brewery Co. Ltd., Hopden Brewery, George Street, Woodsetton, Dudley, W. Midlands DY1 4LN. Tel. (01902) 880051 Fax. (01902) 665473

A fourth generation of the Holden family has now joined this long-established Black Country brewery, which started as a brew pub at the Park Inn (now the brewery tap) in 1916. It produces a good range of real ales for its 21 pubs and around 60 free trade customers, and also bottles its own beers and others under contract at the only remaining bottling hall in the Black Country. Occasional beer: Stout (OG 1036, ABV 3.6%).

Mild

(OG 1037, ABV 3.7%) A smooth, medium-bodied blend of malt, hops, roast and fruitiness, which drinks with the body of a much stronger beer.

Bitter

(OG 1039, ABV 3.9%) A golden ale combining malt and hops and a dry, crisp, bittersweet finish.

Lucy B or XB

(OG 1042, ABV 4.1%) Previously sold under names peculiar to each Holden's pub, this is a sweeter, fruitier, fuller version of the bitter.

Special Bitter

(OG 1051, ABV 5%) A strong, sweet and malty amber ale, full-bodied, with a bittersweet aftertaste.

XL*

(OG 1072, ABV 6.9%) A winter brew.

HOLT

EST. 1849

Joseph Holt PLC, Derby Brewery, Empire Street, Cheetham, Manchester M3 1JD. Tel. (0161) 834 3285 Fax. (0161) 834 6458

Successful family brewery, founded in 1849 (not to be confused with Carlsberg-Tetley's Midlands company Holt, Plant & Deakin). All 109 tied houses serve real ale, most of them taking hogsheads (54-gallon casks), because their low prices result in a high turnover. The beers are popular as guests and, with a free trade of around 80 outlets (plus another 40 or so via an agent), the brewery was extended in 1992 to cope with growing demand.

Mild

(OG 1032, ABV 3.2%) Very dark beer with a complex aroma and taste. Roast malt is prominent, but so are hops and fruit. Strong in bitterness for a mild, with a long-lasting, satisfying aftertaste.

Bitter

(OG 1039, ABV 4%) Tawny beer with a good hop aroma. Although balanced by malt and fruit, the uncompromising bitterness can be a shock to the unwary. It has gained a little sweetness recently.

HOLTS

See Nationals, Carlsberg-Tetley

HOME

See Nationals, Scottish & Newcastle

HOOK NORTON

The Hook Norton Brewery Co. Ltd., Hook Norton, Banbury, Oxfordshire OX15 5NY. Tel. (01608) 737210 Fax. (01608) 730294

Built by John Harris on the family farm in 1850, Hook Norton remains one of the most delightful traditional Victorian tower breweries in Britain. It retains much of its original plant and machinery, the showpiece being a 25-horsepower stationary steam engine which still pumps the Cotswold well water used for brewing. The brewery boasts some fine old country pubs, with all 34 of its tied houses serving real ale, and some 400 free trade outlets also supplied. Occasional beer: Twelve Days (OG 1058, ABV 5.4%, Christmas).

Best Mild

(OG 1032, ABV 3%) A dark, red/brown mild with a malty aroma and a malty, sweetish taste, tinged with a faint hoppy balance. Malty in the aftertaste. Splendid and highly drinkable.

Best Bitter

(OG 1036, ABV 3.4%) An excellently-balanced, golden bitter. Malty and hoppy on the nose and in the mouth, with a hint of fruitiness. Dry, but with some balancing sweetness. A hoppy bitterness dominates the finish.

Old Hooky — (OG 1049, ABV 4.6%) An unusual, tawny beer with a strong fruity and grainy aroma and palate, balanced by a hint of hops. Full-bodied, with a bitter, fruity and malty aftertaste.

HOP BACK — **Hop Back Brewery PLC, Unit 22, Batten Road Ind. Estate, Downton, Salisbury, Wilts. SP5 3HU. Tel. (01725) 510986 Fax. (01725) 513116**

Originally a brew pub, the Wyndham Arms, set up in 1987 with a five-barrel plant, Hop Back switched most of its production to a new brewery at Downton in 1992 to cope with increased demand. However, the brewery at the pub is still used for trial and speciality beers. There are plans to further expand its tied estate, after two new pubs were added during 1994 to the two leased houses it already supplied. Hop Back also sells directly to 60 free trade outlets and brews monthly beers to different recipes under contract for wholesaler Westbury Ales (the former Miners Arms brewery)—tel. (01749) 870719.

Mild — (OG 1032, ABV 3.2%) A dark, well-balanced, very tasty mild, with bags of chocolate malt. Dry, clean-tasting and well-hopped. A very quaffable session ale.

GFB — (OG 1035, ABV 3.5%) Golden, with the sort of light, clean, tasty quality which makes an ideal session ale. Hoppy aroma and taste, leading to a good dry finish. Refreshing.

Special — (OG 1042, ABV 4%) A medium bitter. Slightly sweet, but with a good balance of malt and hops and a long finish.

Alternative Wilt* — (OG 1042, ABV 4%) A light, straw-coloured, crisp, clean-tasting best bitter, with a fine aroma and taste of honey. Well-hopped for bitterness, which lasts.

Stout — (OG 1042, ABV 4.5%) A rich dark stout with a strong roasted malt flavour and a long, sweet and malty aftertaste. A vegan beer.

Summer Lightning ⊲ — (OG 1050, ABV 5%) A very pleasurable pale bitter with a good, fresh, hoppy aroma and a malty, hoppy flavour. Finely balanced, it has an intense bitterness leading to a long, dry finish. Strong, but it still tastes like a session ale.

Wheat Beer — (OG 1050, ABV 5%) Very pale in colour. Full-bodied, with a rich, fruity taste and a dry, clean apricot finish. Very moreish.

HOPE & ANCHOR — **The Lucifer Live Beer Brewing Company, Hope & Anchor, 38 Jacob's Well Road, Clifton, Bristol, Avon BS8 1DR. Tel./Fax. (0117) 9292987**

The former Raisdale Sparging and Brewing Company of Penarth (which closed in the late 1980s) refurbished the Hope & Anchor in December 1993 and installed a brewery. The beers (produced from a hybrid full mash/malt extract system) are stored in cellar tanks under a blanket of CO_2. A 'live lager' is planned. Beers: Jack High (OG 1036, ABV 3.2%), Eight Bore Special (OG 1044, ABV 4.2%), O'Hooligan's Revolt (OG 1056, ABV 5.2%, a stout).

HORSEBRIDGE — See Royal Inn

HOSKINS — **T Hoskins Ltd., Beaumanor Brewery, 133 Beaumanor Road, Leicester LE4 5QE. Tel. (0116) 2661122 Fax. (0116) 2610150**

Established in 1877 and now the smallest remaining tower brewery in the country, Hoskins was family-owned until 1983, when it was acquired and expanded by TRD Estates Ltd. Following the sale of eight pubs to Wolverhampton & Dudley in 1992, the brewery itself was taken over by the present owners, Halkin Holdings, in 1993. It now has only six tied houses (all serving real ale), but purchases are planned. Its beers are supplied to a growing list of wholesalers, as well as to 20 outlets directly.

The Independents

Bitter	(OG 1039, ABV 3.7%) A beer dominated by astringent hoppiness.
Penn's Ale	(OG 1045, ABV 4.6%) Once golden in colour, this beer has now evolved into a reddish-coloured, medium-bodied brew. A hoppy bitterness predominates, but there is more than a hint of fruit cake in the palate.
Premium	(OG 1050, ABV 4.9%) For its gravity, this beer lacks flavour, and is noted for a yeasty aftertaste.
Old Nigel	(OG 1060, ABV 5.8%) A distinctive, full-bodied, fruity winter brew, somewhat sulphurous and astringent.

HOSKINS & OLDFIELD — **Hoskins & Oldfield Brewery Ltd., North Mills, Frog Island, Leicester LE3 5DH. Tel. (0116) 2510532**

Brewery set up by two members of Leicester's famous brewing family, Philip and Stephen Hoskins, in 1984, after the sale of the old Hoskins Brewery. A wide range of beers is produced for a small but increasing number of regular outlets, plus wholesalers. The range has been enlarged again this year and is supplemented by seasonal, fruit-flavoured ales. Occasional beer: Tom Kelly's Christmas Pudding Porter* (OG 1052, ABV 5%, Christmas).

HOB Mild ⌑	(OG 1036, ABV 3.5%) A dark, almost black, mild with a rich aroma and complex flavour. Dry and stout-like, there are overtones of fruit, chocolate and liquorice. Heavy and creamy, with a long finish. A classic.
Brigadier Bitter	(OG 1036, ABV 3.6%) A pleasant ordinary bitter. Fruity, but somewhat lacking in balancing bitterness.
HOB Bitter	(OG 1041, ABV 4%) Golden in colour, with an aroma of pear drops. It has a good balance of malt and hops throughout, with a long, bitter, hoppy aftertaste, with hints of sweetness.
Little Matty	(OG 1041, ABV 4%) Very complex brown/red beer. Hops and fruit blend with malt for an almost 'nuts and raisins' aroma. The flavour is a good balance of hops and bittersweet citrus fruits. Long, dry aftertaste.
White Dolphin*	(OG 1041, ABV 4%) A wheat beer, spiced with orange and coriander.
Tom Kelly's Stout	(OG 1043, ABV 4.2%) A satisfying stout, dark in colour, with an attractive, golden, creamy head and an aroma of malt and fruit. The flavour is exceedingly bitter but malty, and the finish is dry and chocolatey.
Supreme*	(OG 1045, ABV 4.4%) Very light gold, best bitter.
Tom Hoskins Porter*	(OG 1050, ABV 4.8%) Brewed using honey and oats.
EXS Bitter*	(OG 1051, ABV 5%)
Ginger Tom*	(OG 1053, ABV 5.2%) A ginger beer.
Old Navigation Ale	(OG 1071, ABV 7%) Ruby/black beer, with an aroma reminiscent of sherry. Sweet and fruity, with a stout-like malt flavour.
Christmas Noggin	(OG 1100, ABV 10%) Russet-coloured beer with a spicy, fruity aroma. The taste is of malt and fruit, and the finish balances malt and hops. Sweet but not cloying. Available throughout the year.

HP&D — See Nationals, Carlsberg-Tetley

SARAH HUGHES — **Sarah Hughes Brewery, Beacon Hotel, 129 Bilston Street, Sedgley, Dudley, W. Midlands DY3 1JE. Tel. (01902) 883380**

Brewery re-opened in 1988 after lying idle for 30 years. It initially served just the village pub and a few other outlets, but now also produces for the free trade. A Victorian-style conservatory acts as a reception area for brewery visits. Plans for bottling have still not materialised.

Sedgley Surprise

(OG 1048, ABV 5%) A sweet and malty pale ale that tastes lighter than its gravity. Indistinctly bittersweet and malty with underlying fruitiness.

Original Dark Ruby Mild 🍺

(OG 1058, ABV 6%) A wonderful rich ruby ale, sweet, malty and fruity in the mouth with a lingering hoppy and malty finish.

HULL

The Hull Brewery Co. Ltd., 144-148 English Street, Hull, Humbs. HU3 2BT. Tel. (01482) 586364 Fax. (01482) 586365

Hull Brewery was resurrected in 1989 after a 15-year absence, and was taken over by new owners in March 1994. From early beginnings as a mild-only operation, it now brews three regular beers, as well as special brews. Around 200 free trade outlets are supplied. Occasional beers: Kingston Pale Ale (OG 1047, ABV 4.6%), Hearthrob (OG 1048, ABV 4.8%), March Madness (OG 1051, ABV 5%), Rudolph's P-ss (OG 1054, ABV 5.2%, Christmas).

Traditional Dark Mild*

(OG 1033, ABV 3.1%)

Bitter*

(OG 1036, ABV 3.6%)

Governor Strong Ale*

(OG 1046, ABV 4.4%)

HYDES' ANVIL

Hydes' Anvil Brewery Ltd., 46 Moss Lane West, Manchester M15 5PH. Tel. (0161) 226 1317 Fax. (0161) 227 9593

Family-controlled traditional brewery, first established at the Crown Brewery, Audenshaw, Manchester in 1863 and on its present site, a former vinegar brewery, since the turn of the century. The smallest of the established Manchester breweries, it supplies cask ale to all its 61 tied houses and 20 free trade outlets. It also brews Harp lager under contract.

Mild

(OG 1032, ABV 3.5%) A light, refreshing and quite fruity drink, with a short, dry aftertaste. This mid-brown beer has a fruity and malty aroma.

Dark Mild*

(OG 1034, ABV 3.5%) A mild with a caramel and fruit aroma. Quite sweet and fruity with a pleasant aftertaste. Sold mainly in the company's Welsh pubs, but rare in the Manchester area.

Light 🍺

(OG 1034, ABV 3.7%) A lightly-hopped session beer, with malt and a refreshing fruitiness dominating before a brief but dry finish.

Bitter

(OG 1036, ABV 3.8%) A good-flavoured bitter, with a malty and hoppy nose, fruity background and malt and hops in the finish. A hint of bitterness and astringency throughout.

IND COOPE

See Nationals, Carlsberg-Tetley

ISLAND

See Burts

ISLE OF MAN

Isle Of Man Breweries Ltd., Kewaigue, Douglas, Isle of Man IM2 1QG. Tel. (01624) 661120 Fax. (01624) 612746

The main brewery on the island, having taken over and closed the rival Castletown brewery in 1986. Production of Castletown beers ceased completely in 1992 after a period at the Victorian Falcon Brewery, which itself was closed in 1994, when production moved to a new, purpose-built brewery at Kewaigue. All beers are produced under the unique Manx Brewers' Act 1874 (permitted ingredients: water, malt, sugar and hops only). The company has 58 pubs and all but one sell real ale. Ten free trade outlets are also supplied.

Okells Mild

(OG 1034, ABV 3.4%) A genuine, well-brewed mild ale, with a fine aroma of hops and crystal malt. Reddish-brown in colour, this beer has a full malt flavour with surprising bitter hop notes and a hint of blackcurrants and oranges. Full, malty finish.

The Independents

Okells Bitter	(OG 1035, ABV 3.7%) Golden, malty and superbly hoppy in aroma, with a hint of honey. Rich and malty on the tongue, with a wonderful, dry malt and hop finish. Complex but rewarding.

JENNINGS

Jennings Bros PLC, Castle Brewery, Cockermouth, Cumbria CA13 9NE. Tel. (01900) 823214 Fax. (01900) 827462

Brewery founded in 1828 and moved to its present site in 1874, where the beer is brewed using water from a spring first used in Norman times. Jennings gradually expanded over the years, particularly during the 1920s, by taking over other smaller breweries and their pubs. It has seen rapid growth again since 1989, with over 450 free trade outlets now supplied from its own Leyland and Newcastle depots, and many more via a network of wholesalers throughout the UK. Real ale is also available at 88 of the 96 tied houses. Oatmeal Stout (OG 1041, ABV 3.8%) is brewed for Jennings by Broughton.

Dark Mild*	(OG 1031, ABV 3.1%) A dark, mellow mild.
Bitter	(OG 1035, ABV 3.5%) An excellent, distinctive, red/brown brew with a hoppy, malty aroma. A good, strong balance of grain and hops in the taste, with a moderate bitterness, develops into a lingering, dry, malty finish.
Cumberland Ale*	(OG 1040, ABV 4%) A hoppy, golden bitter.
Sneck Lifter*	(OG 1055, ABV 5.1%) A dark, strong warmer.

JOHN THOMPSON INN

John Thompson Brewery, Ingleby, Derbyshire DE73 1HW. Tel. (01332) 862469

Fifteenth-century farmhouse, converted to a pub in 1969. It has brewed since 1977, with most of the production supplied to the free trade through Lloyds Country Beers (see Lloyds), a separate enterprise. Beers (on sale here): Summer Gold (OG 1040, ABV 4%), JTS XXX (OG 1042, ABV 4.1%, sold elsewhere as Lloyds Derby Bitter), JTS Rich Porter (OG 1045, ABV 4.3%, winter).

JOLLY ROGER

Jolly Roger Brewery, 31-33 Friar Street, Worcester, Hereford & Worcester WR1 2NA. Tel. (01905) 22222 Fax. (01905) 20977

Founded as a brew pub in Upton upon Severn in 1982, Jolly Roger made its new home in Worcester in 1985 and expanded quickly thereafter. However, a few setbacks in 1993 led to changes in control and a scaling down of operations. It now supplies four of its own outlets and five local free trade outlets. Two brews are produced exclusively for the Brewery Tap in Lowesmoor, Worcester, a former brew pub: Quaff (OG 1039, ABV 3.9%), Old Lowesmoor (OG 1056, ABV 5.6%), whilst the Jolly Roger brew pub in Hereford has now been sold to Wye Valley and no longer brews. Bottle-conditioned beer: Winter Wobbler (OG 1094, ABV 9%, the OG increasing with each year).

Ale*	(OG 1038, ABV 3.8%)
Broadsword*	(OG 1039, ABV 3.9%)
Shipwrecked*	(OG 1040, ABV 4%)
Goodness Stout*	(OG 1042, ABV 4.2%)
Flagship*	(OG 1052, ABV 5.2%)
Winter Wobbler*	(OG 1094, ABV 11%) A winter ale.

JUDGES

Judges Brewery, Unit 5, Church Lawford Business Centre, Church Lawford, Warwickshire CV23 9HD. Tel. (01203) 545559

Brewery set up by Graham and Anne Judge in May 1992 in a sleepy Warwickshire village. It fills the gap in Warwickshire brewing left by the demise of Thornley's in 1968. Some 90% of production is sold within 20 miles of the brewery. Occasional beer: Santa's Surprise (OG 1052, ABV 5%, a Christmas porter).

Barristers Bitter ⊟ (OG 1038, ABV 3.5%) A well-balanced, pale-coloured session beer; light and easily drinkable.

Old Gavel Bender (OG 1050, ABV 4.8%) Full-bodied, with a caramel aroma and taste. Good, dry, sharp aftertaste.

Solicitor's Ruin (OG 1056, ABV 5.6%) A full-flavoured new beer, full of malt and fruit. Smooth, with a dry finish.

KELHAM ISLAND **Kelham Island Brewery, 23 Alma Street, Sheffield, S. Yorks. S3 8SA. Tel. (0114) 2781867 Fax. (0114) 2786850**

Brewery opened in 1990 at the Fat Cat pub, using equipment purchased from the former Oxford Brewery and Bakehouse, serving free trade outlets in Derbyshire, Nottinghamshire and South Yorkshire. Bottle-conditioned beers: Golden Eagle (OG 1042, ABV 4.2%), Wheat Beer (OG 1050, ABV 5%), Pale Rider (OG 1052, ABV 5.2%), Bête Noire (OG 1055, ABV 5.4%).

Bitter (OG 1038, ABV 3.8%) A strong floral nose leads into a hoppy taste, tinged with citrus notes. The short bitter aftertaste is overtaken by a slightly cloying sweetness. A different brew, worth trying.

Golden Eagle* (OG 1042, ABV 4.2%)

Wheat Beer* (OG 1050, ABV 5%)

Pale Rider* (OG 1052, ABV 5.2%)

Bête Noire (OG 1055, ABV 5.4%) A beer with a thin aroma with hints of coffee. Malt and caramel chocolate in the mouth, developing into plum notes and a sweet, yet dry aftertaste.

KEMPTOWN **The Kemptown Brewery Co. Ltd., 33 Upper St James's Street, Kemptown, Brighton, E. Sussex BN2 1JN. Tel. (01273) 699595**

Brewery established in 1989, built in the 'tower' tradition behind the Hand in Hand pub. It takes its name and logo from the former Charrington's Kemptown Brewery situated 500 yards away, which closed in 1964. With now over 12 outlets supplied direct, expansion in capacity is planned. Occasional beer: Mild (OG 1038, ABV 3.8%).

Budget Bitter* (OG 1035, ABV 3.5%)

Best Bitter* (OG 1041, ABV 4%)

Crewsaver* (OG 1045, ABV 4.5%) Brewed to benefit the Brighton Marina Lifeboat.

Celebrated Staggering Ale* (OG 1050, ABV 5%)

Staggering in the Dark (SID)* (OG 1052, ABV 5.2%)

Old Grumpy* (OG 1060, ABV 6%) Available November-February.

KING & BARNES **King & Barnes Ltd., The Horsham Brewery, 18 Bishopric, Horsham, W. Sussex RH12 1QP. Tel. (01403) 270470 Fax. (01403) 270570**

Long-established brewery, dating back almost 200 years and in the present premises since 1850. It is run by the fifth generation of the King family, having united with the Barnes family brewery in 1906. Its 'Fine Sussex Ales' are served in all 58 country houses and to some 250 free trade outlets, mostly within a radius of 40 miles. Twelve Bore Bitter is produced for the Freetraders Group wholesalers—Tel. (0181) 965 0222. Occasional beers: Summer Ale (OG 1035, ABV 3.8%), Harvest Ale (OG 1045, ABV 4.5%), Easter Ale (OG 1048, ABV 4.5%), Christmas Ale (OG 1075, ABV 8%). Bottle-conditioned beer: Festive ⊟ (OG 1050, ABV 5.3%), Old Porter (OG 1055, ABV 5.5%).

Mild Ale (OG 1034, ABV 3.5%) A smooth, malty, dark brown mild, with a bittersweet finish and a fruity, malty aroma. Tends to be displaced by Old Ale in winter.

The Independents

Sussex	(OG 1034, ABV 3.5%) A hoppy, tawny-coloured bitter, with good malt balance and a dry finish.
Broadwood	(OG 1040, ABV 4.2%) A malty aroma leads to a good marriage of malt and hops in the taste, with malt slightly dominating. There is an underlying fruitiness throughout.
Old Ale	(OG 1046, ABV 4.5%) A classic, almost black old ale. A fruity, roast malt flavour, with some hops, leads to a bittersweet, malty finish. Lovely roast malt aroma. Available October-Easter.
Festive	(OG 1050, ABV 5%) Tawny/red with a fruity, malt aroma. The flavour is also fruity and malty, with a noticeable hop presence. Malt dominates the finish.

For Freetraders:

Twelve Bore Bitter	(OG 1035, ABV 3.7%) Thin, mid-brown bitter, with a clean finish. A good balance of malt and hops throughout.

KING'S HEAD

King's Head Ale House and Brewery, 21 Bretonside, Plymouth, Devon PL4 0BB. Tel. (01752) 665619

Brewery founded in January 1994 to supply the King's Head and the Little Mutton Monster (the owners' other pub). A few other outlets also take the beer. Beers: King's Ransom (OG 1041, ABV 4%), Old Monk (OG 1050, ABV 5%).

LAKELAND   See Masons Arms

LARKINS

Larkins Brewery Ltd., Chiddingstone, Edenbridge, Kent TN8 7BB. Tel. (01892) 870328

Larkins brewery was founded in 1986 by the Dockerty family, who are farmers and hop-growers, with the purchase of the Royal Tunbridge Wells Brewery. Brewing was transferred to a converted barn at the family farm in 1990 and an additional copper and fermenter were acquired in 1991 to keep up with the growing local free trade. The additive-free beers can now be found in around 85 pubs and tourist venues in the South-East. Only Kent hops are used, some from the farm itself.

Traditional Bitter*	(OG 1035, ABV 3.5%) A tawny-coloured beer.
Sovereign	(OG 1040, ABV 4%) A malty and slightly fruity, bitter ale, with a very malty finish. Copper-red in colour.
Best Bitter	(OG 1045, ABV 4.7%) Full-bodied, slightly fruity and unusually bitter for its gravity. Dangerously drinkable!
Porter	(OG 1053, ABV 5.5%) Each taste and smell of this potent black winter beer reveals another facet of its character. An explosion of roasted malt, bitter and fruity flavours leaves a bittersweet aftertaste.

LASS O'GOWRIE

Lass O'Gowrie, 36 Charles Street, Manchester M1 7DB. Tel. (0161) 273 6932

Victorian pub, revamped and re-opened as a Whitbread malt extract brew pub in 1983. The brewery in the cellar is visible from the bar. The beer is stored in tanks without a blanket of gas. Beers: LOG 35 (OG 1035, ABV 3.6%), LOG 42 (OG 1042, ABV 4%). Occasional beers: LOG 52 (OG 1052, ABV 4.2%), LOG 56 (OG 1056, ABV 4.5%).

LASTINGHAM

Lastingham Brewery Co. Ltd., Unit 5, Westgate Carr Road, Pickering, N. Yorks. YO18 8LX. Tel. (01751) 477628

Though only set up in May 1993, this brewery has quickly expanded, despite the setback of having to move premises in its first year. It has one tied house in the village of Lastingham and is seeking a second. A free trade of around 30 outlets is also supplied. A stout and a mild are planned as occasional brews.

Church Bitter*	(OG 1038, ABV 3.7%)
Celtic Ale*	(OG 1042, ABV 4.2%)
Curate's Downfall*	(OG 1044, ABV 4.3%)
Amen*	(OG 1055, ABV 5.4%)

LEES

JW Lees & Co. (Brewers) Ltd., Greengate Brewery, Middleton Junction, Manchester M24 2AX. Tel. (0161) 643 2487 Fax. (0161) 655 3731

Family-owned brewery, founded in 1828 by John Willie Lees, a retired cotton manufacturer, and now run by two brothers, Richard and Christopher Lees-Jones. The existing brewhouse dates from 1876 but recent demand has led to expansion and modernisation, including the installation of a new copper to enable the bitter to be an all-malt brew. All the brewery's 175 pubs, mostly in northern Manchester, serve real ale. Free trade in the North-West extends to about 150 outlets, of which about 60 take real ale.

GB Mild — (OG 1032, ABV 3.5%) Malty and fruity in aroma. The same flavours are found in the taste, but do not dominate in a beer with a rounded and smooth character. Dry, malty aftertaste.

Bitter — (OG 1037, ABV 4%) Pale beer with a malty, fruity aroma and a distinctive, malty, dry and slightly metallic taste. Clean, dry Lees finish.

Moonraker — (OG 1075, ABV 7.3%) Reddish-brown in colour, having a strong, malty, fruity aroma. The flavour is rich and sweet, with roast malt, and the finish is fruity yet dry. Only available in a handful of outlets.

LICHFIELD

Lichfield Brewery, 3 Europa Way, Boley Park, Lichfield, Staffs. WS14 9TZ. Tel. (01543) 419919

Two CAMRA members began brewing at Lichfield in 1992, bringing production back to the city after 60 years. Its capacity has doubled in the first two years, and a third beer, Steeplejack, was added in the summer of 1993. A dozen local outlets regularly take the beers, which are also becoming popular as guest ales around the Midlands. Occasional beer: Mincespired (OG 1060, ABV 6%, Christmas).

Inspired — (OG 1040, ABV 4%) Dark and malty, with a proper bitter aftertaste.

Steeplejack — (OG 1045, ABV 4.5%) Refreshing, pale brown, hoppy beer, with a bitter finish.

Xpired — (OG 1050, ABV 5%) A dark bitter, with malt and chocolate flavours.

LINCOLNSHIRE STEAM

Lincolnshire Steam Beer Co., The Maltings Brewery, St Peter's Road, Bourne, Lincs. PE10 9NF. Tel. (01778) 394422 Fax. (01778) 393399

Brewing ceased in Bourne in the 1930s, but it was revived in summer 1994, with the founding of the Lincolnshire Steam Beer Co. and the installation of a 120-barrel system and two steam generating plants on the site of the old Bourne Brewery.

John Barleycorn*	(OG 1039, ABV 3.8%)
Russett Gold*	(OG 1043, ABV 4.2%)
Victualler's Choice*	(OG 1048, ABV 5%)
Rum Sugar*	(OG 1052, ABV 5.4%)

The Independents

LINFIT

Linfit Brewery, Sair Inn, Lane Top, Linthwaite, Huddersfield, W. Yorks. HD7 5SG. Tel. (01484) 842370

A 19th-century brew pub which recommenced brewing in 1982, producing an impressive range of ales for sale at the Sair Inn and in the free trade as far away as Manchester (seven regular outlets). New plant installed in 1994 has almost doubled its capacity. It also brews West Riding Bitter for the West Riding Licensed Refreshment Rooms in Dewsbury, as well as special occasional beers. Bottling of English Guineas Stout has been so successful that an in-house bottling line is being set up, and other beers will soon be bottled from time to time. Occasional beer: Xmas Ale (OG 1082, ABV 8.6%).

Mild
(OG 1032, ABV 3%) Roast malt dominates in this straightforward dark mild. Some hop aroma; slightly dry flavour. The finish is malty.

Bitter
(OG 1035, ABV 3.7%) Good session beer. A dry-hopped aroma leads to a clean-tasting, hoppy bitterness, balanced with some maltiness. The finish is well-balanced, too, but sometimes has an intense bitterness.

Special
(OG 1041, ABV 4.3%) Dry-hopping again provides the aroma for this rich and mellow bitter. Very soft profile and character: it fills the mouth with texture rather than taste. Clean, rounded finish.

Autumn Gold*
(OG 1045, ABV 4.7%) The latest addition to the range.

English Guineas Stout
(OG 1050, ABV 5.3%) A fruity, roasted aroma preludes a smooth, roasted, chocolatey flavour which is bitter but not too dry. Excellent appearance; good, bitter finish.

Old Eli
(OG 1050, ABV 5.3%) Excellent, well-balanced premium bitter with a dry-hopped aroma and a fruity, bitter finish.

Leadboiler
(OG 1063, ABV 6.6%) Flowery and hoppy in aroma, with a very moreish, strong bitter flavour which is well-balanced by a prominent maltiness. Rounded, bitter finish.

Enoch's Hammer
(OG 1080, ABV 8.6%) Straw-coloured, vinous bitter with no pretensions about its strength or pedigree. A full, fruity aroma leads on to a smooth, alcoholic-tasting, hoppy, bitter flavour, with an unexpectedly bitter finish.

LION'S

Lion's Original Brews Ltd., Burnley, Lancs.

Brewery closed in June 1994.

LIQUID ASSETS

See Eldridge Pope

LITTLE AVENHAM

The Little Avenham Brewery, 30 Avenham Street, Preston, Lancs. PR1 3BN. Tel. (01772) 251380

After winning a local CAMRA *Pub of the Year* award for their pub, Gastons Real Ale and Fine Wine Pub, the owners and licensee decided to brew their own beer. The first brew was produced in 1992 and proved so popular that they began to supply other outlets (currently around 70), as well as a second tied house. Experimental brews are planned, including a fruit beer flavoured with bananas. Occasional beer: Hedgerow Bitter (ABV 1038, ABV 4%, autumn, using wild hops and nettles).

Arkwright Mild
(OG 1035, ABV 3.5%) A dark mild with intense fruit flavours and a dry aftertaste.

Arkwright Ale
(OG 1035, ABV 3.6%) A mid-brown session beer with a gentle aroma but strong fruit and hop flavours which continue through to the aftertaste. A sourness and wine-like tartness are not unpleasant.

Clog Dancer
(OG 1038, ABV 4%) A golden yellow, distinctive bitter. Though well-balanced, complex fruit and hop flavours make it rich and moreish.

Porter	(ABV 4%) An excellent dark beer with hints of ruby red. Thinner than you would expect from its colour, but very satisfying. Chocolate and roast malt flavours are prominent, with a slight hoppiness and a dry aftertaste.
Pickled Priest	(OG 1043, ABV 4.3%) A pale, thin and tart bitter in which fruit flavours give way to a lasting dryness in the finish. Stronger than last year (3.5%).
Torchlight	(OG 1050, ABV 5%) A dark to mid-brown premium ale. Malt and fruit are prominent in the aroma and flavour. Enjoyable and distinctive, it is mild and complex in the mouth, with some sweetness.
Stocking Filler*	(OG 1060, ABV 6%) A winter porter.
Pierrepoints Last Drop	(OG 1063, ABV 7%) A pale, strong ale with prominent fruit flavours and a dry aftertaste.

LIVERPOOL	See Black Horse & Rainbow

LLOYDS	**Lloyds Country Beers Ltd., John Thompson Brewery, Ingleby, Derbyshire DE7 1HW. Tel. (01332) 863426**
	Lloyds is the separate business set up to supply the beers brewed at the John Thompson Inn (see separate entry) to the free trade. It currently has over 150 outlets, mainly in the Midlands and the company may soon acquire a pub of its own. Lloyds also provides beer for the Heritage Brewery Museum in Burton—Tel. (01283) 510246—and the fledgling High Peak brewery in Chinley, Derbyshire, which is yet to go into production. The High Peak beers have included Bagman's Bitter (OG 1045, ABV 4.3%) and Cracken (OG 1049, ABV 4.9%, Christmas), as well as a 3.8% bitter. Lloyds occasional beers: Derby Mild (OG 1037, ABV 3.6%), Skullcrusher (OG 1065, ABV 6.5%, Christmas).
Classic*	(OG 1034, ABV 3.6%)
Gold*	(OG 1040, ABV 4%) Brewed mainly in summer.
Derby Bitter or Country Bitter or JTS XXX*	(OG 1042, ABV 4.1%) Full and fruity.
Vixen Velvet*	(OG 1045, ABV 4.2%) A porter, mainly a winter beer.
VIP (Very Important Pint)*	(OG 1048, ABV 4.8%) Heavier, darker version of the bitter.
Overdraught*	(OG 1070, ABV 7%) A winter beer.
	For Heritage:
Dark Amber*	(OG 1045, ABV 4.2%)

LONDON BEER COMPANY	See Brewery on Sea

LONGSTONE	**Longstone Brewery, Station Road, Belford, Northumberland NE70 7DT. Tel (01668) 213031**
	Brewery operational since 1991, the first in Northumberland for many years. A second, stronger beer (ABV 4.9%) is planned. Longstone currently supplies 16 free trade outlets regularly in the North, and others further afield via beer agencies.
Bitter	(OG 1039, ABV 4%) An imaginative beer with pungent and sometimes undefinable flavours. Hop character dominates but notice also the underlying fruit, a solid body and lasting sweetness.

LORIMER & CLARK	See Vaux and Caledonian

LUCIFER	See Hope & Anchor

The Independents

LUNDY

Lundy Company, Marisco Tavern Brewery, Lundy Island, Bristol Channel EX39 2LY. Tel. (01237) 431831 Fax. (01237) 431832

Brewery opened in 1984 but closed and relocated in 1992. Recommencing brewing in autumn 1994, it produces beer from malt extract for visitors to the island's pub. Beer: Old Light Bitter (OG 1055).

McEWAN

See Nationals, Scottish & Newcastle

THOMAS McGUINNESS

Thomas McGuinness Brewing Company, Cask & Feather, 1 Oldham Road, Rochdale, Gtr. Manchester. OL16 1UA. Tel. (01706) 711476

Brewery established in 1991 behind the Cask & Feather pub, by Thomas McGuinness and brewer, Eric Hoare. Sadly, Tom died in 1993, but the brewery is continuing under the guidance of his wife, Jackie, who plans to expand and double production. It supplies real ale to its own three pubs, and to around 20 free trade outlets.

Dark Mild*
(OG 1034, ABV 3.4%) Dark brown beer, with roast malt dominant in the aroma and taste, and a touch of bitterness.

Best Bitter
(OG 1038, ABV 3.8%) Gold in colour with a hoppy aroma: a clean, refreshing beer with a balance of hops and grainy malt, which extends to the aftertaste. A hint of grapefruit comes through in the flavour.

Special Reserve Bitter
(OG 1040, ABV 4%) A tawny beer, sweet and malty, with underlying fruit and bitterness, and a bittersweet aftertaste.

Junction Bitter*
(OG 1042, ABV 4.2%)

Tommy Todd Porter
(OG 1050, ABV 5.2%) A winter warmer, with a fruit and roast aroma, leading to a balance of malt and roast malt flavours, with a touch of chocolate. Not too sweet for its gravity.

MACLAY

Maclay & Co. Ltd., Thistle Brewery, East Vennel, Alloa, Clackmannanshire, Central FK10 1ED. Tel. (01259) 723387 Fax. (01259) 216511

Founded in 1830 and moved to the present Victorian tower brewery in 1869, Maclay's still uses traditional brewing methods and direct-fired coppers, with the beers produced using only bore-hole water (the only Scottish brewery to do so) without any adjuncts. Until three years ago, the company had always been run by descendants of the founder, James Maclay, but is now owned by the family of the present chairman, Evelyn Matthews. All but five of its 30 tied houses offer real ale, which is also supplied to 100 other outlets. Occasional beer: Old Alloa Ale (OG 1065, ABV 6.5%, Christmas).

60/- Ale*
(OG 1034, ABV 3.4%) A flavoursome, dark session beer.

70/- Ale*
(OG 1036, ABV 3.6%) A well-hopped, quenching beer.

Porter*
(OG 1036, ABV 4%)

80/- Export*
(OG 1040, ABV 4%) Well-balanced and rich.

Kane's Amber Ale*
(OG 1040, ABV 4%)

Oat Malt Stout*
(OG 1045, ABV 4.5%)

McMULLEN

McMullen & Sons Ltd., The Hertford Brewery, 26 Old Cross, Hertford SG14 1RD. Tel. (01992) 584911 Fax. (01992) 553395

Hertfordshire's oldest independent brewery, founded in 1827 by Peter McMullen. The Victorian tower brewery, which houses the original oak and copper-lined fermenters still in use today, was built on the site of three wells. In April 1993, the company launched a new initiative, McMullen Special Reserve, a series of seasonal cask-conditioned ales for sale through selected McMullen and free trade pubs for a limited period. Real ale is served in all

The Independents

McMullen's 145 pubs in Hertfordshire, Essex and London, and also supplied to around 180 free trade outlets. The company also brews bottle-conditioned beers for Hanseatic Trading Company— Tel. (01778) 560662—which sells them largely through Oddbins off-licences.

Original AK
(OG 1033, ABV 3.7%) A light bitter with a hoppy aroma. A sweetish beer with hop and malt flavours. Distinctive, dry aftertaste.

Country Best Bitter
(OG 1041, ABV 4.3%) A beer with a hoppy, fruity aroma, a well-balanced flavour and a dry, hoppy aftertaste.

Stronghart
(OG 1070, ABV 7%) A sweet, rich, dark beer, a single brew for the winter months. It has a malty aroma, with hints of hops and roast malt which carry through to the taste.

For Whitbread:

Wethered Bitter*
(OG 1035, ABV 3.9%)

For Hanseatic:

Bottle-conditioned beers: BCA (OG 1045, ABV 4.5%), IPA (OG 1045, ABV 4.5%), Vassilenski's Black Russian (OG 1048, ABV 4.8%)

MALTON

Malton Brewery Company Ltd., Crown Hotel, Wheelgate, Malton, N. Yorks. YO17 0HP. Tel. (01653) 697580

Malton began brewing in 1985 in a stable block at the rear of the Crown Hotel, where the former Grand National winner Double Chance was once stabled, hence the name of the bitter. Steady growth in the sales of its additive-free beers and occasional special brews led to the installation of more fermenting vessels. Malton now supplies around 20 free trade outlets directly and pubs further afield via wholesalers.

Pale Ale
(OG 1034, ABV 3.6%) Do not be fooled by either the gravity or the body of this light, fresh, golden brew, which has a hoppy nose that develops into a bitter taste and a delicate, dry finish.

Double Chance Bitter
(OG 1038, ABV 4.1%) Strong hop aroma and taste with hints of malt and fruit on the palate. Perhaps less malty this year, and a bit thinner, with the bitter, dry aftertaste accompanied by some fudgy sweetness.

Pickwick's Porter
(OG 1042, ABV 3.9%) Lots of roast and malt in the nose and mouth, with a dry balance of tart fruit and plain chocolate. A dry and nutty, yet sticky, finish. A bit thinner this year, and more stout-like.

Owd Bob 🍺
(OG 1055, ABV 5.8%) A rich, warming, beautifully complex arrangement of hop and roast characters, floral fruit and chocolate tastes, plus a slightly sweet, yet still bitter, finish. Dark brown with red hints.

MANSFIELD

Mansfield Brewery PLC, Littleworth, Mansfield, Notts. NG18 1AB. Tel. (01623) 25691 Fax. (01623) 658620

Founded in 1855, and now one of the country's leading regional brewers, Mansfield stopped brewing cask beer in the early 1970s. It resumed real ale production in 1982 as an experiment and has not looked back since. Its award-winning ales are all fermented in traditional Yorkshire squares and have enjoyed steadily rising sales, aided in 1991 by the acquisition of a substantial number of pubs from Courage, and another dozen from S&N in 1993. Now most of its 480 pubs serve cask beer. An extensive free trade (particularly East Midlands clubs) is also supplied and Mansfield enjoys a reciprocal trading arrangement with Charles Wells. Occasional beer: Deakin's Yule Brew (OG 1056, ABV 6%, Christmas).

Old Shilling*
(OG 1030, ABV 3.1%) Primarily a brew for the Boddingtons Pub Company, now sold in the Mansfield estate.

463

The Independents

Riding Mild	(OG 1035, ABV 3.5%) Dark ruby-coloured and quite rich for a mild, with a complex aroma of malt, roast and fruit. The dry, roasty flavour, with traces of bittersweet fruit, follows through into a dry aftertaste.
Riding Bitter	(OG 1035, ABV 3.6%) Pale brown, with a malty, hoppy nose. A firm malt background is overlaid with a good bitter bite and hop flavours.
Bitter*	(OG 1038, ABV 3.9%) A long-established keg beer, now available in cask form.
Old Baily	(OG 1045, ABV 4.8%) A beer which resembles a Scottish heavy, but with a fine balance of hop, malt and fruit flavours. Dark copper-red in colour, with an aroma of malt and fruit.

For Scottish & Newcastle:

Home Mild*	(OG 1036, ABV 3.6%)

MANSFIELD ARMS

Mansfield Arms, 7 Main Street, Sauchie, Alloa, Central. Tel. (01259) 722020 Fax. (01259) 218409

Brew pub established in spring 1994, brewing around 12 barrels a week. Beers: Devon Original (OG 1038, ABV 3.8%), Devon Thick Black (OG 1042, ABV 4%).

MARISCO TAVERN

See Lundy

MARSTON MOOR

Marston Moor Brewery, Crown House, Kirk Hammerton, York, N. Yorks. YO5 8DD. Tel. (01423) 330341

Small, but expanding brewery, set up in 1983 and moved to the rear of its first tied house, the Crown, in 1988. This pub was closed in December 1993 after the acquisition of the Beer Exchange at Woodhouse in Leeds, but more pubs are being sought. The company currently produces 1,000 barrels a year and supplies around 40 free trade outlets. It also sells brewing plants to mini-brewers. Occasional beer: Black Tom Stout (OG 1045, ABV 4.5%, winter).

Cromwell Bitter*	(OG 1036, ABV 3.6%) A distinctive, bitter beer.
Brewers Pride*	(OG 1041, ABV 4.2%) An amber-coloured, premium beer.
Porter*	(OG 1041, ABV 4.2%) A seasonal brew (October-May), ruby-coloured and stout-like.
Merrie Maker*	(OG 1045, ABV 4.5%) A new premium bitter.
Brewers Droop*	(OG 1050, ABV 5.1%) A potent, straw-coloured ale.
Trooper*	(OG 1050, ABV 5.1%)

MARSTON'S

Marston, Thompson & Evershed PLC, Shobnall Road, Burton upon Trent, Staffs. DE14 2BW. Tel. (01283) 531131 Fax. (01293) 510378

The only brewery still using the Burton Union system of fermentation (for its stronger ales), Marston's commitment to this method was reinforced in 1992 with a £1 million investment in a new Union room. Real ale is available in most of the company's 882 pubs, stretching from Yorkshire to Hampshire, and the enormous free trade is helped by trading agreements with Wolverhampton & Dudley and the fact that many national brewers' houses now stock Pedigree Bitter. It has reduced its regular range to just three beers (with Merrie Monk now discontinued), but operates a Head Brewer's Choice scheme for selected houses, offering new brews for two weeks at a time. Banks's Mild is also available in Marston's pubs.

Bitter	(OG 1038, ABV 3.8%) Formerly Burton Best Bitter. An amber/tawny session beer which can often be markedly sulphury in the

aroma and taste. At its best, a splendid, subtle balance of malt, hops and fruit follows a faintly hoppy aroma and develops into a balanced, dry aftertaste.

Pedigree (OG 1043, ABV 4.5%) Variable; it can be excellent, but is often spoilt by swan-necked dispense which removes the unique sulphury flavour and dominant aroma. When on form, it can have a good hop flavour with some malt and a bitter finish.

Owd Rodger ⊈ (OG 1078, ABV 7.6%) A dark, ruby-red barley wine, with an intense fruity nose before a deep, winey, heavy fruit flavour, with malt and faint hops. The finish is dry and fruity (strawberries). Misunderstood, moreish and strong.

MASONS ARMS **Lakeland Brewing Co., Strawberry Bank, Cartmel Fell, Cumbria LA11 6NW. Tel. (0153 95) 68686**

Famous pub, known for its large selection of bottled beers, which began brewing in May 1990. Beer names are based on books by local author Arthur Ransome. Beers: Amazon Bitter (OG 1038, ABV 4%), Great Northern (OG 1047, ABV 5%), Big Six (OG 1064, ABV 6%), Damson Beer (OG 1070, ABV 7%). Bottle-conditioned beers: Great Northern (OG 1047, ABV 5%), Big Six (OG 1064, ABV 6%), Damson Beer (OG 1070, ABV 9%).

MAULDONS **Mauldons Brewery, 7 Addison Road, Chilton Ind. Estate, Sudbury, Suffolk CO10 6YW. Tel. (01787) 311055**

Company set up in 1982 by former Watney's brewer Peter Mauldon, whose family once had its own brewery. Its extensive beer list changes frequently and is supplied to 150 free trade outlets in East Anglia and Hertfordshire, as well as pubs further afield via wholesalers. It produces one-off beers for special occasions, e.g. Broomstick Bitter for Hallowe'en, and provides house beers for local pubs. Occasional beer: Christmas Reserve (OG 1065, ABV 6.6%).

FA Mild (OG 1034, ABV 3.4%) A mild with well-balanced malt and roast flavours, and a dry aftertaste.

Bitter (OG 1037, ABV 3.8%) A well-balanced session beer with a crisp, hoppy bitterness balancing sweet malt.

Original Porter (OG 1042, ABV 3.8%) A black beer with malt and roast flavours dominating. Some hop in the finish.

Old XXXX (OG 1042, ABV 4%) A winter ale with a reddish brown appearance. The taste is complex, with fruit, malt, caramel, hop and bitterness all present.

Squires Bitter (OG 1044, ABV 4.2%) A best bitter with a good, malty aroma and a reasonably balanced flavour, tending towards malt. Somewhat fruity, with a moderate, dry aftertaste.

Special (OG 1045, ABV 4.2%) By far the most hoppy of the Mauldons beers, with a good, bitter finish. Some balancing malt.

Suffolk Punch (OG 1050, ABV 4.8%) A full-bodied, strong bitter. The malt and fruit in the aroma are reflected in the taste and there is some hop character in the finish. Deep tawny/red in colour.

Black Adder (OG 1055, ABV 5.3%) A dark stout. Roast malt is very strong in the aroma and taste, but malt, hop and bitterness provide an excellent balance and a lingering finish. *Champion Beer of Britain* 1991.

White Adder (OG 1055, ABV 5.3%) An amber beer full of citrus spiciness, with a hoppy/fruitiness dominating the aroma and the flavour. Clean, dry finish.

Suffolk Comfort (OG 1065, ABV 6.6%) A clean, hoppy nose leads to a predominantly malty flavour in this full-bodied beer. Dry, hoppy aftertaste.

The Independents

MAYHEM'S	See Farmers Arms
MILDMAY	**The Mildmay Brewery, Holbeton, Plymouth, Devon PL8 1NA. Tel. (01752) 830248 Fax. (01752) 830540** Mildmay started brewing in November 1993, with the first brew available on its single pub's bar on Christmas Day. Sales have increased since then to around ten free trade outlets, and there are plans for further expansion.
Colours Best*	(OG 1040, ABV 3.8%)
SP or Starting Price*	(OG 1045, ABV 4.5%)
50/1*	(OG 1050, ABV 5.1%)

MILL	**Mill Brewery, 18c Bradley Lane, Newton Abbot, Devon TQ12 4JW. Tel. (01626) 63322** Brewery founded in 1983 on the site of an old watermill and run on a part-time basis until changing hands in March 1994. The new owners, brewing full-time, have kept the original beer names, 'Janner' being the local term for a Devonian. Occasional beer: Janner's Christmas Ale (OG 1050, ABV 5.5%). More occasional beers are planned.
Janner's Ale	(OG 1038, ABV 3.8%) A pale brown beer, with a fruity aroma and a bitter taste and aftertaste.
Janner's Old Original*	(OG 1048, ABV 5%) A golden beer with plenty of fruit and hops present in both aroma and flavour. Not tasted since the brewery changed hands.

MINERS ARMS	See Hop Back
MINERVA	**Minerva Hotel, Nelson Street, Hull, Humbs. HU1 1XE. Tel. (01482) 26909** Joshua Tetley full mash brew pub, set up in 1983 and storing its beer under blanket pressure in cellar tanks. It produces special brews all year round. Beer: Pilots Pride (OG 1039, ABV 4.1%).
MIN PIN INN	**North Cornwall Brewers, Tregatta Corner, Tintagel, Cornwall PL34 0DX. Tel. (01840) 770241** Converted farmhouse with possibly the only entirely female-operated brewery (malt extract) in the country (est. 1985). However, brewing was suspended in spring 1994 and may not resume. Beers: Legend Bitter (OG 1035, ABV 3.6%), Brown Willy Bitter (OG 1055, ABV 4.3%).

MITCHELL'S	**Mitchell's of Lancaster (Brewers) Ltd., 11 Moor Lane, Lancaster, Lancs. LA1 1QB. Tel. (01524) 63773** The only surviving independent brewery in Lancaster (est. 1880), wholly owned and run by direct descendants of founder William Mitchell. The company is very traditional: many of the casks are still wooden and its award-winning beers are brewed with natural spring well water. Real ale is sold in all but four of its 53 pubs and is available virtually countrywide in the free trade. The company is now building a reputation as a supplier of guest ales in the North-West.
Best Bitter	(OG 1036, ABV 3.5%) A golden bitter with a malty aroma and a superb, dry, malty flavour, with a faint balance of hops. The delicate bitter aftertaste usually demands more of the same.
Lancaster Bomber*	(ABV 4.4%)
Old Clog*	(OG 1045, ABV 4.2%)
ESB	(OG 1050, ABV 5%) Creamy in texture; malty in aroma. The flavour is also malty and fruity, with a hoppy finish.

Single Malt (OG 1064, ABV 7.2%) A winter brew, mid-brown in colour and suggestive of malt whisky in aroma and flavour. Strongly malty throughout, with a subtle bittersweet, hoppy balance in the taste.

MITCHELLS & BUTLERS (M&B) See Nationals, Bass

MOLE'S

Mole's Brewery (Cascade Drinks Ltd.), 5 Merlin Way, Bowerhill, Melksham, Wilts. SN12 6TJ. Tel. (01225) 704734 Fax. (01225) 790770

Brewery established in 1982 and run on very traditional lines by former Ushers brewer Roger Catté (the brewery name came from his nickname). The business continues to grow, with 16 tied houses and some 60-70 free trade outlets supplied direct, while other parts of the country are serviced via beer agencies. To keep up with demand, plans are in hand for a new brewery on the same site. Mole's also acts as a distributor for other members of the Small Independent Brewers Association (SIBA).

Tap Bitter (OG 1035, ABV 3.5%) Formerly called IPA. A pale brown beer with a trace of maltiness in the aroma and a thin, malty dry flavour with little aftertaste.

Best Bitter (OG 1040, ABV 4%) A pale brown/golden-coloured beer with a light malt aroma and a clean, dry, malty taste, with some bitterness and delicate floral hop flavour. A well-balanced, light, subtle malt ale. Formerly called Cask Bitter.

Landlords Choice* (OG 1045, ABV 4.5%) A dark bitter, not widely available.

Brew 97 (OG 1050, ABV 5%) A mid-brown, full-bodied beer with a gentle malt and hop aroma. The rich flavour is malty, with fruit, hop and traces of vanilla. A wonderfully warming, malty ale.

XB* (OG 1060, ABV 6%) A winter brew.

MOORHOUSE'S

Moorhouse's Brewery (Burnley) Ltd., 4 Moorhouse Street, Burnley, Lancs. BB11 5EN. Tel. (01282) 422864 Fax. (01282) 838493

Long-established (1865) producer of hop bitters, which in 1978 began brewing cask beer. The business developed slowly until it was boosted by winning the Silver Award at the 1982 International Beer Festival. The present owner, Bill Parkinson, took over in 1985 and invested in a new brewhouse to meet increased demand. The brewery is continuing to build up its tied estate (currently six pubs, all offering real ale), and it also supplies around 150 free trade outlets.

Black Cat Mild* (OG 1034, ABV 3.2%)

Premier Bitter (OG 1036, ABV 3.7%) Pale brown in colour but not in character, this brew has a superb hop flower aroma, with some fruit and malt. On the palate, citrus flavours are balanced by malt and hoppy bitterness. Dry, hoppy finish.

Pendle Witches Brew 🍺 (OG 1050, ABV 5.1%) A good hoppy aroma leads through to a full-bodied, malty sweetness, with a trace of hop bitterness. Bittersweet aftertaste.

Owd Ale* (OG 1056, ABV 6%) A winter brew, available November-March.

MORLAND

Morland & Co. PLC, PO Box 5, Ock Street, Abingdon, Oxfordshire OX14 5DD. Tel. (01235) 553377 Fax. (01235) 529484

Established in 1711, Morland is the second oldest independent brewer in the UK and has been on its present site since 1861. It took over several other local breweries in the inter-war years, but, in 1992, Morland itself survived a take-over bid by Greene King. The East Anglian giant, after buying Whitbread Investment Company's 43.4% stake, tried (but failed) to pick up a further 6.7% to take overall control and close the Abingdon brewery. Nearly all Morland's 370 pubs serve real ale, but in many cases the licensee uses a cask-breather. The company also supplies an extensive free trade (with Old Speckled Hen particularly prominent). To keep up with demand, a new distribution depot has been opened, and a new beer, Independent IPA, was launched in April 1994, after trials of a beer called Ock Lea Bitter. Morland also brews under contract for Courage.

Original Bitter — (OG 1035, ABV 4%) A light amber beer with malty, hoppy nose with a hint of fruitiness. The distinct, but lightish malt and hops carry over to the flavour and leave a sweet but dry, hoppy aftertaste.

Independent IPA* — (OG 1037, ABV 3.4%)

Old Masters — (OG 1040, ABV 4.6%) A well-balanced tawny/amber beer with not outstandingly strong flavours. The initial aroma of malt and hops leads to a moderately malty, but dry and hoppy flavour, with a hint of fruit which can be faintly sulphurous. Dry, bitter finish.

Old Speckled Hen — (OG 1050, ABV 5.2%) Morland's most distinctive beer, deep tawny/amber in colour. A well-balanced aroma of roasted malt and hops is complemented by a good hint of caramel. An initial sweet, malty, fruity, roast caramel taste soon allows the dry hop flavour through, leaving a well-balanced aftertaste.

For Courage:

Wilson's Original Mild* — (OG 1032, ABV 3%)

MORRELLS — **Morrells Brewery Ltd., The Lion Brewery, St Thomas' Street, Oxford OX1 1LA. Tel. (01865) 792013 Fax. (01865) 791868**

1782
MORRELLS BREWERY
Oxford

The oldest brewery in Oxford is run by the Morrell family, as it has been since 1782. Of its 138 pubs, over 50 are within the city limits and all but four of the outlets serve real ale, though some employ blanket pressure. Over 50 free trade outlets stock Morrells beers. Occasional beer: College Ale (OG 1073, ABV 7.4%, November).

Bitter — (OG 1036, ABV 3.7%) Golden in colour and light in body, but not in flavour, with a good aroma of hops complemented by malt and fruitiness. An initial dry hop bitterness is well balanced by malt, which gives way to a refreshing, slightly sweet fruitiness, with a hint of roast caramel. A bittersweet, hoppy finish.

Mild* — (OG 1037, ABV 3.7%)

Varsity — (OG 1041, ABV 4.3%) A tawny/amber beer. Malt, hops and fruit are the main features in both aroma and taste, but are well-balanced. The slightly sweet, malty, fruity start fades away to a distinctive, bittersweet finish.

Graduate — (OG 1048, ABV 5.2%) An intense malt and roast aroma is complemented by a moderate hoppiness in the taste. Pleasant, bitter finish.

For Whitbread:

Strong Country Bitter* — (OG 1037, ABV 3.9%)

MUNDANE — **Mundane Ales, Burton upon Trent, Staffs.**
A beer wholesaler which no longer brews.

NENE VALLEY — **Nene Valley Brewery, Unit 1, Midland Business Centre, Midland Road, Higham Ferrers, Northants. NN9 8PN. Tel. (01933) 412411**

A brewery which opened with a single-barrel outfit in April 1992 before moving to its present site in October that year with a five-barrel plant. It has now acquired its first tied house and also supplies over 20 free trade outlets. Occasional beer: Santa's Tipple (OG 1130, ABV 12.8%, Christmas).

Union Bitter*	(OG 1036, ABV 3.6%)
Trojan Bitter	(OG 1038, ABV 3.8%) A well-presented beer, but with little depth of flavour. Clean and dry, with a dried grass hop character and a palate-cleansing dry finish.
Shopmates Ale*	(OG 1044, ABV 4.4%)
Old Black Bob*	(OG 1047, ABV 4.7%) A new stout.
Rawhide*	(OG 1050, ABV 5.1%)
Medusa Ale*	(OG 1080, ABV 7.8%)

NETHERGATE

Nethergate Brewery Co. Ltd., 11-13 High Street, Clare, Suffolk CO10 8NY. Tel. (01787) 277244 Fax. (01787) 277123

Small brewer of award-winning beers, set up in 1986, which continues to use traditional methods, adding no sugars, no colourings and no hop extracts. The brewing capacity was increased to 180 barrels a week in 1993. Some 140 free trade outlets are now supplied, mostly in East Anglia.

IPA	(OG 1036, ABV 3.6%) A splendid session beer, apple crisp and refreshing, with balanced malt and hops and a lingering, bitter aftertaste.
Special Coriander Ale*	(OG 1038.5, ABV 3.8%) A new beer, building on the success of the Old Growler variation listed below.
Bitter 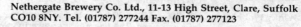	(OG 1039, ABV 4%) A dark bitter with delightful malt and hop aromas giving way to a well-balanced palate. Rich malts and powerful bitterness dominate the flavour, ending in a strong, bitter finish.
Old Growler	(OG 1055, ABV 5.5%) A complex and satisfying porter, smooth and distinctive. Sweetness, roast malt and fruit feature in the palate, with bitter chocolate lingering. The finish is typically Nethergate: powerfully hoppy.
Old Growler With Coriander*	(OG 1055, ABV 5.5%) Launched as a Christmas special and now a permanent feature. Old Growler wort is percolated through coriander seeds.

NEWALE

Newale Brewing Company, 6 Viscount Court, Walworth Ind. Estate, Andover, Hants. SP10 5NW. Tel. (01264) 336336 Fax. (01264) 333310

Five-barrel plant set up in September 1993 by Phil Newton, owner of an air-conditioning company, with which the premises are shared. Around 30 outlets are presently supplied.

Anna Valley Ale*	(OG 1038, ABV 4%)
Balksbury Bitter*	(OG 1044, ABV 4.5%)
Clatford Clout*	(OG 1050, ABV 5%)

NICHOLSON'S — See Nationals, Carlsberg-Tetley

NIX WINCOTT

Nix Wincott Brewery, Three Fyshes Inn, Bridge Street, Turvey, Beds. MK43 8ER. Tel. (01234) 881264 Fax. (01234) 881310

Brew pub, founded in 1987, which quickly doubled its capacity to meet demand from the local free trade and wholesalers, then doubled again in 1993, with the addition of a new fermenting room. It now produces seven real ales on a regular basis, supplying 16 free trade outlets locally, as well as the Three Fyshes. Occasional beer: Winky's Winter Warmer (OG 1058, ABV 6.1%, Christmas).

Old Cock Up*	(OG 1032, ABV 3.4%) The latest addition to the range.
Turvey Bitter	(OG 1032, ABV 3.4%) An unusual toffee aroma leads through into a toffee malt flavour with a hint of hops. Clean, slightly astringent, dry aftertaste.

The Independents

Two Henrys Bitter (OG 1037, ABV 3.9%) A dry, fruity beer with some malt in the flavour and a very bitter, slightly hoppy aftertaste. Hops, malt and some fruit in the nose.

THAT (OG 1046, ABV 4.8%) Fruit is present throughout in this mid-brown brew. A flavour of malt, hops and fruit on a bitter base leads through into a bitter fruit finish. 'THAT' stands for Two Henrys Alternative Tipple.

Old Nix (OG 1058, ABV 6%) This pungent, almost wine-like beer has an overwhelming fruit and malt aroma, characteristics carried through to the flavour which also has a bitter, slightly hoppy base. Dry, fruity finish.

Winky Wobbler (OG 1069, ABV 7.3%) A potent winter brew that has an aroma of fruit and wine. The flavour is a powerful combination of bitter-sweet malt, fruit, roast and some hops. Dry, fruity aftertaste.

NORTH & EAST RIDING See William Clark

NORTH CORNWALL See Min Pin Inn

NORTH YORKSHIRE **North Yorkshire Brewing Co., 80-84 North Ormesby Road, Middlesbrough, Cleveland TS4 2AG. Tel. (01642) 226224 Fax. (01642) 226225**

Company started in March 1990 with a purpose-built brewery, but demand was such that the capacity had to be increased in 1992. Two tied houses and over 100 free trade outlets are currently supplied. Occasional beer: Xmas Herbert (OG 1040, ABV 4.1%).

Best Bitter (OG 1036, ABV 3.6%) Light and very refreshing. Surprisingly full-flavoured for a pale, low gravity beer, with a complex, bitter-sweet mixture of malt, hops and fruit carrying through into the aftertaste.

Yorkshire Brown (OG 1040, ABV 3.8%) A ruby-red beer with a soft, malty taste and a hoppy aftertaste. Dry finish.

Yorkshire Porter (OG 1040, ABV 3.8%) A very dark brew with good burnt malt and liquorice flavours and a burnt, dry finish.

Fools Gold* (OG 1044, ABV 4.6%) A well-hopped, lightly malted, golden premium bitter, using Styrian and Goldings hops.

Erimus Dark (OG 1046, ABV 4.5%) A dark, full-bodied, sweet brew with lots of roast malt and caramel flavour, and an underlying hoppiness. At its best, it is very smooth indeed, with a tight, creamy head and a sweet, malty finish.

Flying Herbert (OG 1048, ABV 4.8%) A refreshing, red/brown beer with a hoppy aroma. The flavour is a pleasant balance of roast malt and sweetness which predominates over the hops. The malty, bitter finish develops slowly.

Dizzy Dick (OG 1080, ABV 7.7%) A smooth, strong, dark, aromatic ale with an obvious bite, although too sweet for some. The very full, roast malt and caramel flavour has hints of fruit and toffee. The malty sweetness persists in the aftertaste.

OAK **Oak Brewing Company Ltd., Phoenix Brewery, Green Lane, Heywood, Gtr. Manchester OL10 2EP. Tel. (01706) 627009**

Brewery established in 1982 in Ellesmere Port which moved in 1991 to Heywood and now supplies over 60 free trade outlets, from West Cheshire to West Yorkshire. In 1994, the company introduced a series of beers associated with classic British motorcycles. Further 'theme' beers are planned. Occasional beer: March Hare (OG 1042, ABV 4.2%, March).

Hopwood Bitter* (OG 1035, ABV 3.5%)

Best Bitter
(OG 1038, ABV 3.9%) A tawny, hoppy session beer with some balancing malt in the aroma and taste. Strong, dry and hoppy finish.

Tyke Bitter*
(OG 1042, ABV 4.3%) Originally brewed for the West Riding Brewery (currently inoperative), but available throughout Oak's free trade.

Midsummer Madness*
(OG 1044, ABV 4.4%) Available June-September.

Old Oak Ale
(OG 1044, ABV 4.5%) A well-balanced, brown beer with a multitude of mellow fruit flavours. Malt and hops balance the strong fruitiness in the aroma and taste, and the finish is malty, fruity and dry.

Double Dagger
(OG 1050, ABV 5.1%) A pale brown, malty brew, more pleasantly dry and light than its gravity would suggest. Moderately fruity throughout and a hoppy bitterness in the mouth balances the strong graininess.

Porter
(OG 1050, ABV 5.1%) The roast malt promised by the aroma is joined in the taste by malt, caramel and hops. Long and pleasant aftertaste.

Wobbly Bob
(OG 1060, ABV 6.1%) A red/brown beer with a malty, fruity aroma. Strongly malty and quite hoppy, with the sweetness yielding to a dryness in the aftertaste.

Humbug*
(OG 1064, ABV 6.5%) Available November-January.

OAKHAM
Oakham Ales, 12-13 Midland Court, Station Approach, Oakham, Rutland, Leics. LE15 6QW. Tel. (01572) 755338

This new brewery was set up in October 1993 in industrial units on a trading estate, with a custom-built, ten-barrel plant. A one-man business, it currently supplies over 30 free trade outlets, within a 30-mile radius of Oakham.

Jeffrey Hudson Bitter or JHB
(OG 1038, ABV 3.8%) Very hoppy and fruity, with a sharp, hoppy aftertaste.

Old Tosspot
(OG 1052, ABV 5.2%) A full-flavoured, fruity new brew.

OAKHILL
Oakhill Brewery, High Street, Oakhill, Bath, Avon BA3 5AS. Tel. (01749) 840134 Fax. (01749) 880503

Situated high in the Mendip Hills in Somerset (despite the Avon address), this brewery was set up by a farmer in 1984 in an old fermentation room of the original Oakhill Brewery (est. 1767, but burnt down in 1924). However, a move to new premises, the old Maltings building in Oakhill, is planned. The brewery currently supplies real ale to two tied houses and around 100 other outlets.

Somer Ale
(OG 1035, ABV 3.5%) An amber, light and refreshing, fruity pale ale, with a pleasant, dry, bitter finish. An excellent summer brew.

Best Bitter
(OG 1039, ABV 4%) A clean-tasting, tangy bitter, with a good hop content and citrus fruit and malt balance. Dry finish; light hop aroma. Very quenching.

Black Magic ⊟
(OG 1044, ABV 4.5%) A black/brown bitter stout with roast malt and a touch of fruit in the nose. Smooth roast malt and bitterness in the taste, with mellow coffee and chocolate.

Yeoman Strong Ale
(OG 1049, ABV 5%) A strong, pale brown, full-bodied bitter, with a floral hop palate with notable fruitiness. Dry, bitter, lasting finish.

OKELLS
See Isle of Man Breweries

OG stands for Original Gravity, the reading taken before fermentation of the amount of fermentable material in the brew. It is a rough indicator of strength. More reliable is the ABV (Alcohol by Volume) rating, which gives the percentage of alcohol in the finished beer.

The Independents

OLD BEAR

The Old Bear Brewery, The Old White Bear, 6 Keighley Road, Cross Hills, Keighley, W. Yorks. BD20 7RN.
Tel. (01535) 632115

Brewery founded by Bryan Eastell, former owner of Goose Eye Brewery. Production began in summer 1993 but sales were confined to within the pub until summer 1994. Old Bear is now looking to expand into the free trade. Beers: Bitter (OG 1037, ABV 3.9%), Ursa Minor (OG 1045, ABV 4.7%), Ursa Major (OG 1054, ABV 5.7%).

OLDHAM

See Nationals, Whitbread, and Pub Groups, Boddingtons

OLD LUXTERS

Barn Ale

Old Luxters Farm Brewery, Hambleden, Henley-on-Thames, Oxfordshire RG9 6JW. Tel. (01491) 638330 Fax. (01491) 638645

Brewery set up in May 1990 in a 17th-century barn by David Ealand, owner of Chiltern Valley Wines. Apart from the brewery and vineyard, the site also houses a fine art gallery and a cellar shop. Extra fermentation tanks have increased the brewery's capacity and it now supplies some 30 free trade outlets. Note: Hambleden is in Buckinghamshire, despite the brewery's postal address. Bottle-conditioned beer: Barn Ale (OG 1052, ABV 5.4%).

(OG 1042, ABV 4.4%) Predominantly malty, fruity and hoppy in taste and nose, and tawny/amber in colour. Fairly rich and strong in flavours: the initial, sharp, malty and fruity taste leaves a dry, bittersweet, fruity aftertaste, with hints of black cherry. Can be slightly sulphurous.

OLD MILL

Old Mill Brewery Ltd., Mill Street, Snaith, Goole, Humbs. DN14 9HS. Tel. (01405) 861813

Small brewery, started in 1983 in a 200-year-old former malt kiln, that had been used to manufacture clog soles until 1946! The purpose-built brewing plant was expanded in 1992 when new equipment was installed to increase capacity by 50%. Since then new offices and a warehouse have also been added, with one more pub acquired in the last year to bring the tied estate to a total of 11 houses. Some 150 free trade outlets are also supplied.

Traditional Mild

(OG 1034, ABV 3.4%) A thin dark brown/red beer, that is now rare in the free trade. A malty aroma leads to roast and chocolate in the taste, which permeate to the finish, where they are joined by a slight dry and nutty flavour.

Traditional Bitter

(OG 1037, ABV 3.9%) Although still a bit thin, this beer has more body this year. Hops are dominant in the lingering finish, though malt takes initial control in the nose and taste. Improving, though residual sweetness persists.

Bullion

(OG 1044, ABV 4.7%) A beer with malty and hoppy aroma, malt, hop and fruit in the mouth and a finish of hoppy bitterness, amidst a nutty sweetness. Usually dark brown with amber hints, though red notes have been detected.

Traditional Porter

(OG 1050, ABV 5%) Not a porter: perhaps a finer mild than the real one? A complex beer, despite the thin consistency and the sweet overlay that belies its strength. A winter brew worth development.

ORANGE BREWERY

Orange Brewery, 37-39 Pimlico Road, Pimlico, London SW1W 8NE. Tel. (0171) 730 5984

Brewery opened in 1983, which, like its fellow brew pubs, the Greyhound and the Yorkshire Grey, has now been acquired by Scottish & Newcastle. The full mash brews are stored in cellar tanks and are kept under blanket pressure. Orange also brews a lager. Beers: Pimlico Light (OG 1032, ABV 3%), SW1 (OG 1040, ABV 4%), Pimlico Porter (OG 1045, ABV 4.2%), SW2 (OG 1050, ABV 5%). Occasional beers: Resurrection Ale (OG 1056, ABV 5.3%, Easter), Something Wicked (OG 1073, ABV 7%, Hallowe'en), Angels Downfall (OG 1082, ABV 7.6%, Christmas). Pimlico Passport, a summer wheat beer, refermented with raspberries, is also scheduled.

ORKNEY

The Orkney Brewery, Quoyloo, Orkney KW16 3LT.
Tel. (01856) 84802 Fax. (01856) 84754

The Orkney's first brewery in living memory, set up in 1988 by former licensee Roger White. Initially only brewing keg beer for local outlets, Roger's personal commitment to real ale has resulted in cask ales now representing 90% of sales (mostly to central Scotland).

Raven Ale

(OG 1038, ABV 3.8%) Still mainly keg on the island, but worth seeking out when in 'real' form. Smooth, mellow and malty, with a distinctive aroma and finish.

Dragonhead Stout*

(OG 1040, ABV 4%)

Dark Island*

(OG 1045, ABV 4.6%)

Skullsplitter*

(OG 1080, ABV 8.5%)

OTTER

Otter Brewery, Mathayes, Luppitt, Honiton, Devon EX14 0SA.
Tel. (01404) 891285

Otter began brewing in November 1990 and has grown steadily, recently increasing its capacity to a 60-barrel brew length. Some 40 pubs now take the beers, which are produced using local malt and the brewery's own spring water.

Bitter

(OG 1036, ABV 3.6%) Pale brown-coloured beer, with a pleasantly malty aroma, a complex taste and a bitter finish.

Bright*

(OG 1039, ABV 4.3%) A new summer beer.

Ale 🍺

(OG 1043, ABV 4.5%) Tawny-coloured, well-balanced beer: a malty aroma and a hoppy, bitter taste (with a hint of apple) and aftertaste.

Head

(OG 1054, ABV 5.8%) Mid-brown-coloured beer with a hoppy nose, a sweet, roast malt taste and a smooth, bitter, fruity finish.

PALMERS

JC & RH Palmer Ltd., The Old Brewery, West Bay Road, Bridport, Dorset DT6 4JA. Tel. (01308) 422396 Fax. (01308) 421149

Britain's only thatched brewery is situated by the sea in former mill buildings. The company, which is managed by the great-grandsons of the founder, JC Palmer, celebrated its bicentenary in 1994 by launching its first new draught ale for many years. It is still slowly developing its tied estate (presently 64 houses) with very selective acquisitions. All its pubs serve real ale, although top pressure and cask breathers are widely in use. About 50 free trade outlets are serviced directly, but Palmers' beers are reaching a wider audience throughout the South via wholesalers.

Bridport Bitter or BB

(OG 1032, ABV 3.2%) A light beer with a hoppy aroma, a bitter, hoppy taste with some malt, and a bitter aftertaste.

Best Bitter or IPA

(OG 1040, ABV 4.2%) A beer that is hoppy and bitter throughout. Fruit and malt undertones give some balance to the aroma and taste, and there is a lingering bitter aftertaste. A return to its true form.

Tally Ho!

(OG 1046, ABV 4.7%) A dark and complex brew with a mainly malty aroma. The nutty taste is dominated by roast malt and the aftertaste is malty and bitter. Limited availability in winter.

200*

(OG 1054, ABV 5%) The anniversary ale, now a permanent feature.

PARADISE

See Bird in Hand

PARISH

Parish Brewery, The Old Brewery Inn Courtyard, Somerby, Leics. LE14 2PZ. Tel. (01664) 454781

The first brewery to be established in Somerby since the 16th century, Parish started life at the Stag & Hounds, Burrough on the Hill, in 1983. It moved in 1991, acquiring a new 20-barrel plant to keep up with demand for the beers, which are now supplied to around 20 free trade outlets, as well as the Old Brewery Inn (which is a free house).

Mild (OG 1035, ABV 3.3%) A thin, dark brew with a faint, malty aroma. The palate features caramel and fruit, with a dry roast finish.

Special Bitter or PSB (OG 1038, ABV 3.5%) A tasty, thin-bodied, pale brown, well-balanced bitter, with hops predominating throughout. Refreshing, bitter aftertaste.

Somerby Premium (OG 1040, ABV 4%) Though tawny in colour, this medium-bodied beer has a pronounced orange marmalade taste superimposed on its hoppy flavour and dry finish.

Porter* (OG 1048, ABV 4.5%) A winter beer.

Poachers Ale (OG 1060, ABV 5.5%) A complex full-flavoured ale which encompasses malt, hops, fruit and acidity. It has a dark ruby colour, with hints of yeast on the palate.

Baz's Bonce Blower or BBB ⊈ (OG 1110, ABV 10%) A robust and vigorous Christmas pudding of a beer, black in colour with a caramel taste but chocolate finish. There are some pronounced liquorice notes hidden in its rich palate.

PARKER See Cannon

PASSAGEWAY **Passageway Brewery Company, Unit G8, Queen's Dock Storage Yard, Norfolk Street, Liverpool, Merseyside L1 0BG. Tel. (0151) 708 0730 Fax. (0151) 709 0925**

Brewery established in May 1994 after a few years of planning permission difficulties. Its two founders, Steve Dugmore and Phil Burke, painstakingly researched the history of St Arnold, the Belgian patron saint of brewing, before beginning production. Their one beer uses yeast from a Trappist monastery, and about 150ml of water from St Arnold's holy spring is added to the copper before each mash. The result is an individual distinctive brew.

St Arnold* (OG 1050, ABV 5%) Dark and flavoursome.

PEMBROKE **Pembroke Brewery Company, Eaton House, 108 Main Street, Pembroke, Dyfed SA71 4HN. Tel. (01646) 682517 Fax. (01646) 682008**

Brewery founded in May 1994 in historic old stables behind the proprietors' house. About 20 outlets are supplied locally.

Main Street Bitter* (OG 1040, ABV 4.1%)

Gold Hill Bitter* (OG 1046, ABV 4.5%) A light-coloured bitter.

PENNINE **Pennine Brewing Company, Worth Brewery, Worth Way, Keighley, W. Yorks. BD21 5LP. Tel. (01535) 611914 Fax. (01535) 690705**

A company sharing the Worth Brewery premises of Commercial Brewery.

Golden Promise* (OG 1035, ABV 3.5%)

Golden Bitter* (OG 1039, ABV 3.7%)

Premium Gold* (OG 1050, ABV 5%)

Liquid Gold* (OG 1055, ABV 5.5%)

PILGRIM **Pilgrim Brewery, West Street, Reigate, Surrey RH2 9BL. Tel. (01737) 222651 Fax. (01737) 225785**

Set up in 1982, and moved to Reigate in 1985, Pilgrim's capacity has gradually increased and its beers have won both local and national awards, although sales are mostly concentrated in the Surrey area. The brewery has gained a new admin block in the past year and a laboratory is planned. Brewery tours are available on the last Friday of the month in summer. Occasional beers: Saracen Stout (OG 1047, ABV 4.7%), Conqueror (OG 1070, ABV 6.5%, November, brewed with spices).

Surrey Pale Ale

(OG 1037, ABV 3.7%) A well-balanced bitter with an underlying fruitiness. Hop flavour comes through in the finish. A good session beer.

Porter

(OG 1041, ABV 4%) A dark brown beer with a roast malt flavour. The finish is balanced by a faint developing hoppiness.

Progress Best Bitter

(OG 1041, ABV 4%) Reddish-brown in colour, with a predominantly malty flavour and aroma, although hops are also evident in the taste.

Talisman

(OG 1048, ABV 4.8%) A strong ale with a dark red colour, a fruity, malt flavour and roast overtones. More commonly available in winter.

Crusader Premium

(OG 1048, ABV 4.9%) Light, golden beer with a malty bitterness, and an underlying fruitiness. A very drinkable summer brew.

PIONEER

See Rooster's

PITFIELD

See United Breweries and Brewery on Sea

PLASSEY

Plassey Brewery, The Plassey, Eyton, Wrexham, Clwyd LL13 0SP. Tel. (01978) 780922 Fax. (01978) 780019

Brewery founded in 1985 by former Border brewer, Alan Beresford. Following his death in 1989, it was taken over by another ex-Border man, Ian Dale, in partnership with Tony Brookshaw, owner of the estate on which the brewery is sited. The estate also includes a touring caravan park, craft centres, a new golf course and three licensed outlets for Plassey's ales. There are plans to build a new brewery, to increase the supply of beer to the free trade (mainly via wholesalers), and to bottle-condition some beers.

Bitter

(OG 1038, ABV 3.8%) A well-hopped, straw-coloured beer, with blackcurrant fruitiness. Less malty than previously.

Cwrw Tudno

(OG 1047, ABV 5%) More malty and sweet and less bitter than the bitter, but with a fairly dry aftertaste.

Dragon's Breath

(OG 1060, ABV 6%) A fruity, strong bitter, smooth and quite sweet, though not cloying, with an intense, fruity aroma. A dangerously drinkable winter warmer.

PLOUGH INN

Bodicote Brewery, Plough Inn, Bodicote, Banbury, Oxfordshire OX15 4BZ. Tel. (01245) 262327

Brewery founded in 1982 at the Plough, No. 9 High Street (hence the beer name), which has been in the same hands since 1957. Two other outlets are also supplied with its full mash beers. Beers: Bitter (OG 1035, ABV 3.3%), No. 9 (OG 1045, ABV 4.2%), Old English Porter (OG 1045, ABV 4.3%), Triple X (OG 1050, ABV 5.1%).

POOLE

The Brewhouse Brewery, 68 High Street, Poole, Dorset BH15 1DA. Tel. (01202) 682345

Brewery established in 1981, two years before the Brewhouse pub/brewery was opened. When an extension to the Brewhouse was completed in 1990, the entire brewing operation was transferred there and further expansion has now taken place. The Brewhouse pub keeps the beer under blanket pressure, but 15 other outlets also take Poole products, and it brews Ansty Ale (OG 1080, ABV 8.5%) for the Fox at Ansty.

Poole Best Bitter or Dolphin*

(OG 1038, ABV 3.8%) An amber-coloured, balanced bitter.

Bosun Bitter*

(OG 1045, ABV 4.6%) Amber and rich.

The Independents

PORTER $\stackrel{\textstyle\bullet}{\textbf{\textsf{Q}}}$	**Porter Brewing Co. Ltd., Rossendale Brewery, The Griffin Inn, Haslingden, Lancs. BB4 5AF. Tel./Fax. (01705) 214021** When keen home brewer David Porter bought the Griffin Inn in Haslingden, he saw the possibility of founding a brewery. The pub opened (complete with microbrewery) in March 1994, and after just a few weeks was supplying its full mash beers to four other free trade outlets. It also brews Black Syke Bitter for the Farmers Arms in Holmfirth.
Dark Mild*	(OG 1033, ABV 3.3%)
Bitter*	(OG 1038, ABV 3.8%)
Sunshine*	(OG 1048, ABV 5%)
Porter*	(OG 1049, ABV 5%)
POWELL	See Wood
PREMIER	See United Breweries
PRESTON	**The Preston Brewing Co., The Atlas Brewery, Preston, Lancs.** Brewery closed and planning to relocate.
QUEENS HEAD	See Solstice
RCH	**RCH Brewery, West Hewish, Weston Super Mare, Avon BS24 6RR. Tel. (01934) 834447 Fax. (01934) 834167** Brewery originally installed in the early 1980s behind the Royal Clarence Hotel at Burnham-on-Sea, but, since January 1993, RCH has been brewing on a commercial basis, from a new site. New beers have been added to the range and the products are supplied to around 50 free trade outlets by the company's own beer agency, and nationwide via wholesalers. Occasional beer: Santa F (OG 1074, ABV 7.3%, Christmas).
PG Steam*	(OG 1039, ABV 3.9%)
Pitchfork*	(OG 1043, ABV 4.3%)
Old Slug Porter*	(OG 1045, ABV 4.5%)
East Street Cream*	(OG 1050, ABV 5%)
Firebox*	(OG 1060, ABV 6%)
RANDALLS 	**RW Randall Ltd., Vauxlaurens Brewery, St Julian's Avenue, St Peter Port, Guernsey GY1 3JG. Tel. (01481) 720134 Fax. (01481) 713233** The smaller of Guernsey's two breweries, which was purchased by RH Randall from Joseph Gullick in 1868. Successive generations have continued to run the business, except during the period of the German occupation, when brewing ceased until after the war. It currently owns 16 houses, but only four serve real ale. Eight other free trade outlets are supplied. Do not confuse with Randalls Vautier of Jersey, which no longer brews but which still runs 29 pubs on that island.
Best Mild	(OG 1035, ABV 3.8%) Copper-red, with a malty and fruity aroma and a hint of hops. The fruity character remains throughout, with a sweetish, malty undertone.
Best Bitter	(OG 1046, ABV 5%) Amber in colour, with a hoppy aroma. Bitter and hoppy both in the palate and finish. A beer which has changed substantially.
RAYMENTS	See Greene King

Beers marked with an asterisk have not been tasted by official CAMRA tasting panels. However, some of these beers do carry brief descriptions derived from limited samplings or other sources, and can be used for rough guidance.

REBELLION

REBELLION BEER CO.

Rebellion Beer Company, Unit J, Rose Ind. Estate, Marlow Bottom Road, Marlow, Bucks. SL7 3ND. Tel. (01628) 476594 Fax. (01628) 482354

Opened in 1993, Rebellion hopes to fill the gap left in Marlow by Wethered, and is in fact discussing the possibility of taking over part of the old Wethered site, closed by Whitbread in 1988. At present, the brewery water is being 'Marlowised', i.e. treated to recreate the mineral composition of the water used by the old brewery. Already expanding, its second beer, introduced in late 1993, has proved popular, and a third beer may soon be launched.

IPA* (OG 1037, ABV 3.9%)

ESB* (OG 1046, ABV 4.5%)

RECKLESS ERIC'S

Reckless Brewing & Supply Co. Ltd., Unit 4, Albion Ind. Estate, Cilfynydd, Pontypridd, Mid Glamorgan CF37 4NX. Tel. (01443) 409229

A new, small brewery, opened in late 1993. The company runs a few pubs in the area which it supplies along with some 55 free trade outlets much further afield. The brewing formulae are still under review (hence no tasting notes).

Retribution* (OG 1039, ABV 3.8%)

Renown* (OG 1040, ABV 4%)

Retaliation* (OG 1049, ABV 4.8%)

'Recked 'Em* (OG 1052, ABV 5.2%)

Rejoice* (OG 1060, ABV 6%) A stout.

RED CROSS

Red Cross Brewery, Perryfields, Bromsgrove, Hereford & Worcester B61 8QW. Tel. (01527) 871409

After battling for two years with planning problems, this brewery opened in October 1993 in the old bull pen of Red Cross Farm, a 17th-century yeoman farmhouse. Initially just brewing for its tied house, the Hop Pole Inn in Bromsgrove, there are plans to expand into the free trade. Beer: Nailers OBJ* (OG 1046, ABV 4.5%).

REDRUTH

Redruth Brewery Ltd., The Brewery, Redruth, Cornwall TR15 1AT. Tel. (01209) 212244

The old Cornish Brewery, originally founded in 1792 and now back under its original name, following a management buy-out from Devenish in July 1991. The only real ale brewed is Cornish Original, for Whitbread to supply to Greenalls/Devenish. With no tied estate and most local pubs being tied to other breweries, Redruth has few outlets for beers of its own and therefore concentrates on contract packaging and brewing.

For Whitbread:

Cornish Original Bitter* (OG 1036, ABV 3.4%)

REEPHAM

Reepham Brewery, Unit 1, Collers Way, Reepham, Norfolk NR10 4SW. Tel. (01603) 871091

Family brewery, founded in 1983 by a former Watney's research engineer with a purpose-built plant in a small industrial unit. The company was launched on a single beer, Granary Bitter, but now produces quite a range, which varies from year to year and includes some award-winners. Reepham now has a brewery tap (the Crown—by agreement with the owners) and 20 other local outlets are supplied directly.

Granary Bitter (OG 1038, ABV 3.8%) An amber beer which is well-balanced and makes easy drinking. The malt and hops are complemented by a pleasing amount of bitterness and hints of fruit.

The Independents

Dark*	(OG 1039, ABV 3.9%) A strong mild.
Rapier Pale Ale	(OG 1042, ABV 4.2%) A beer which appears to be slightly more attenuated than before. It still possesses a flowery hop aroma, and maltiness in the taste on a fruit and hop background, but it has lost some of its clean edge and a little body.
Summer Velvet*	(OG 1042, ABV 4.2%)
Velvet Stout	(OG 1043, ABV 4.2%) The fruity, malt aroma of this darkish brown beer gives way to a sweet, mellow taste explosion of malt, roast, fruit and hops. This subsides to a pleasant aftertaste with hints of liquorice.
Old Bircham Ale	(OG 1046, ABV 4.6%) An amber/tawny beer with good body for its gravity. The fruity aroma precedes a complex, malty, hoppy palate, which also has a sweetness that dies away in the malty, dry finish. A winter brew.
Brewhouse*	(OG 1055, ABV 5%) A strong winter ale.
Anniversary Ale*	(OG 1076, ABV 7.3%)

REINDEER

Reindeer Trading Company Ltd., 10 Dereham Road, Norwich, Norfolk NR2 4AY. Tel. (01603) 666821 Fax. (01603) 666872

Brew pub which opened in 1987 and has progressed in leaps and bounds since. Half its weekly output of 40 barrels goes to the pub and to 20 local free trade outlets. The rest is sold nationwide through East-West Ales wholesalers. At the pub, most of the beers are now kept in casks, but Reindeer, Red Nose and Bevy are still kept under blanket pressure. Occasional beers: Mosel Magic (OG 1043, ABV 4.5%, twice-yearly for the RAF), Sanity Clause (OG 1065, ABV 7%, Christmas). Norvic Old Ale (OG 1046, ABV 4.7%) was brewed in 1994 for the Royal Charter of Norwich celebrations.

Moild	(OG 1034, ABV 3.5%) Full-bodied (for a mild) and definitely full-flavoured. The palate has a malt and roast base with hops, sweetness and some bitterness. Usually a dry mild, but can be initially quite fruity. Not your average mild.
Pale Ale or RPA	(OG 1034, ABV 3.5%) An amber-coloured, simple and unpretentious session beer, with malt and hops well-balanced throughout and variable degrees of sweetness and bitterness.
Bevy	(OG 1037, ABV 3.9%) A stronger session beer than the RPA, with a bias towards hoppiness in the nose and palate, and a little less sweetness.
Gnu Bru	(OG 1043, ABV 4.5%) A fairly full-bodied beer for its strength, well-balanced throughout. Hops and malt feature in the taste, with some fruit.
Bitter	(OG 1047, ABV 5%) A full-bodied beer which is complex and flavoursome: fruity, hoppy and malty throughout, with some lingering hop bitterness.
Red Nose	(OG 1057, ABV 6%) A dark red/brown, very full-bodied beer. Mainly fruity and malty, it is a rich, complex brew, good for cold evenings, although some may find it a touch cloying.
Sledgehammer	(OG 1076, ABV 7.5%) Not a subtle beer. A dark reddish brown beer with lots of body and strength. Fruit and malt predominate, but there is also plenty of sweetness and very little bitterness.

RIDLEYS

TD Ridley & Sons Ltd., Hartford End Brewery, Hartford End, Chelmsford, Essex CM3 1JZ. Tel. (01371) 820316 Fax. (01371) 821216

Ridleys was established by a miller, Thomas Dixon Ridley, on the banks of the picturesque River Chelmer in 1842. A range of seasonal ales has successfully been launched since the last edition of this guide, and a bottle-conditioned beer is planned. A programme of improvement is still underway in the tied estate and all 63 pubs sell real ale. Around 300 other outlets are also supplied, at some of the lowest prices in the South-East.

IPA Bitter (OG 1034, ABV 3.5%) A refreshing, hoppy bitter, well-balanced by malt in the flavour and delicate fruit in the finish, with lingering bitterness.

Mild (OG 1034, ABV 3.5%) A very dark mild with a light aroma of roast and caramel. Quite bitter for a mild, with roast malt flavours. The finish has hops, roast and caramel, with none dominant.

ESX Best Bitter (OG 1045, ABV 4.3%) Harmonious malt and hops dominate the taste of this long overdue best bitter, with a hint of fruit. Hops just gain over malt in the finish.

Witchfinder Porter (OG 1045, ABV 4.3%) A very dark red, sweet brew, not too heavy. Malt is much in evidence in the aroma, taste and finish, with a careful hoppiness.

Spectacular* (OG 1048, ABV 4.6%) A summer beer, available May-October.

Winter Ale (OG 1055, ABV 5%) A seasonal soup! This has it all, but mostly at the malty end of the palate, with fruit and roast flavours in support, underscored by some hoppiness.

RINGWOOD **Ringwood Brewery Ltd., 138 Christchurch Road, Ringwood, Hants. BH24 3AP. Tel. (01425) 471177 Fax. (01425) 480273**

Hampshire's first new brewery in the real ale revival, founded in 1978 and housed in attractive 18th-century buildings, formerly part of the old Tunks brewery, although work on a new brewhouse should soon be completed. Famous for its award-winning Old Thumper, it has two tied houses and around 340 free trade accounts, from Weymouth to Chichester and across to the Channel Isles.

Best Bitter (OG 1038, ABV 3.8%) A golden brown, moreish beer, with flavours for all. The aroma has a hint of hops and leads to a malty sweetness, which becomes dry, with a hint of orange. Malt and bitterness in the finish.

XXXX Porter (OG 1048, ABV 4.7%) Sadly only available October-March: a rich, dark brew with a strong aroma of roasted malt, hops and fruit. Rich in flavour, with coffee, vanilla, damsons, apples and molasses evident. The overall roast maltiness continues into the drying, hoppy, bitter finish.

Fortyniner (OG 1048, ABV 4.8%) A good premium beer, with malt and hops in good balance. The flavours slowly increase to a fruity finish.

Old Thumper (OG 1058, ABV 5.8%) A golden beer with a surprisingly bitter aftertaste, which follows a middle period tasting of various fruits. May be a little sweet for some.

RISING SUN **The Rising Sun Inn, Shraley Brook, Audley, Stoke-on-Trent, Staffs. ST7 8DS. Tel. (01782) 720600**

Brewing began in June 1989 at the Rising Sun and the brewery now supplies the busy pub and a thriving free trade (20 outlets). A new conditioning tank has been acquired to keep up with demand. Bottle-conditioned beer: Solar Flare (OG 1100, ABV 11.5%).

Dark Mild* (OG 1034, ABV 3.5%)

Sunlight* (OG 1036, ABV 3.5%) Summer only.

Rising (OG 1040, ABV 3.9%) A lightly-flavoured, easy-drinking amber beer, tasting fruity and hoppy with a little malt. Bittersweet aftertaste; slight aroma of hops.

Setting (OG 1045, ABV 4.4%) The faint aroma implies fruit and hops. This bittersweet, dark brown, medium-flavoured ale has fruit, hops and largely malt characteristics.

The Independents

Sun Stroke	(OG 1056, ABV 5.6%) A dark, red/brown, medium-bodied ale. The aroma has roast malt and some hops, whilst the taste is bittersweet with a dominating maltiness and the aftertaste sees malt, roast and hops coming through.
Total Eclipse*	(OG 1072, ABV 6.9%)
Solar Flare*	(OG 1100, ABV 11.5%) Winter only.

ROBINSON'S

Frederic Robinson Ltd., Unicorn Brewery, Lower Hillgate, Stockport, Cheshire SK1 1JJ. Tel. (0161) 480 6571 Fax. (0161) 476 6011

Major Greater Manchester family brewery, founded in 1838. Robinson's took over Hartleys of Ulverston in 1982, but closed that brewery in October 1991 and is now planning to demolish some of the buildings (including a listed chimney). Only Hartleys XB is still brewed (at Stockport). The brewery supplies real ale to most of its 412 tied houses (70 from the Hartleys Cumbrian estate, but most in southern Manchester and Cheshire).

Dark Best Mild	(OG 1033, ABV 3.3%) Toffee/malt-tasting, with a slight bitterness. A very quaffable beer with a fruity malt aroma and a dry finish. A very rare find.
Hatters Mild	(OG 1033, ABV 3.3%) Formerly Best Mild. A pale brown, well-balanced beer, with a sweet aftertaste. A good, refreshing drink.
Bitter	(OG 1035, ABV 3.5%) A beer with a refreshing, malty and fruity taste, a characteristic fruity aroma, with a touch of sulphur, and a short, dry finish. Sold in very few outlets and may be renamed.
Hartleys XB	(OG 1040, ABV 4%) Little aroma, but malty with some hop bitterness in the taste, with a dry finish.
Best Bitter	(OG 1041, ABV 4.2%) An amber beer with a malty, hoppy nose. A well-balanced taste precedes a slight, bitter finish.
Frederic's*	(OG 1050, ABV 5%) The latest addition to the range.
Old Tom ⊞	(OG 1079, ABV 8.5%) A full-bodied, dark, fruity beer. The aroma is fruity and mouth-watering; the aftertaste is bittersweet, with an alcoholic kick. A beer to be sipped by a roaring winter fire.

ROBINWOOD

Robinwood Brewers & Vintners, Todmorden, W. Yorks.

Brewery no longer in operation.

ROOSTER'S

Rooster's Brewery, Unit 20, Claro Court, Claro Business Centre, Claro Road, Harrogate, N. Yorks. HG1 4BA. Tel. (01423) 561861

Brewery set up in 1992 by Sean Franklin, formerly of Franklin's Brewery. Rooster's is now successfully building up its business and handles some 70 free trade accounts. Apart from the regular beers, it now runs a second label, called the Pioneer Brewing Co., producing a different beer each month for the guest beer market. Bottle-conditioned beer: Rooster's (OG 1047, ABV 4.7%). Yankee and Nectar may also become available in bottle-conditioned form.

Mayflower II*	(OG 1037, ABV 3.7%)
Jak's*	(OG 1039, ABV 3.9%)
Special*	(OG 1039, ABV 3.9%)
Yankee	(OG 1043, ABV 4.3%) A straw-coloured beer with a delicate aroma. The flavour is an interesting mix of malt and hops, with a gentle sweetness and a bite of orange peel, leading to a short, pleasant finish.
Rooster's	(OG 1047, ABV 4.7%) A light amber beer with a subtle, sweet, slightly hoppy nose. Intense malt flavours, reminiscent of treacle toffee with chocolate and orange undertones, precede an unexpected hoppy finish.
Nectar*	(OG 1058, ABV 5.8%)

The Independents

ROSE STREET

Rose Street Brewery, 55 Rose Street, Edinburgh, Lothian EH2 2NH. Tel. (0131) 220 1227

Brew pub founded in 1983 and run by Alloa Brewery, supplying six other Alloa outlets with beers produced from malt extract. Beers: Auld Reekie 80/- (OG 1043, ABV 4.1%), Auld Reekie 90/- (OG 1055, ABV 5.2%).

ROSS

Ross Brewing Company, The Bristol Brewhouse, 117-119 Stokes Croft, Bristol, Avon BS1 3RW. Tel. (0117) 9420306 Fax. (0117) 9428746

Set up in Hartcliffe in 1989, Ross was the first brewery to brew with organic Soil Association barley, initially producing bottle-conditioned beers only. The brewery has now moved to the Bristol Brewhouse pub and the one remaining bottled beer, Saxon Strong Ale, is now brewed under contract by Eldridge Pope (see Eldridge Pope). Ross instead now brews cask beers for consumption in the pub and in a very limited free trade. It also produces the world's strongest beer, Uncle Igor's, and is launching a new range of strong ales to be sold in one-third pint glasses.

Picton's Pleasure*   (OG 1042, ABV 4.2%)

Hartcliffe Bitter   (OG 1045, ABV 4.5%) A pale brown, malty beer with a balancing bittersweetness, little aroma and a dry, malt finish.

Porter*   (OG 1053, ABV 5%) A winter brew.

SPA*   (OG 1055, ABV 5.5%)

Numbskull*   (OG 1063, ABV 6%) Another winter offering.

Uncle Igor's*   (OG 1200, ABV 21%) Brewed only in very small quantities.

ROSSENDALE   See Porter

ROTHER VALLEY   **Rother Valley Brewing Company, Gate Court, Northiam, Rye, E. Sussex TN31 6QT. Tel. (01797) 252444 Fax. (01797) 252757**

Founded jointly by a hop farmer and a publican, this new outfit began brewing part-time in August 1993. Using their own yeast strain and local hops, the partners currently supply 12 free trade outlets, from Maidstone to the south coast.

Level Best*   (OG 1040, ABV 4%)

ROYAL CLARENCE   See RCH

ROYAL INN

Royal Inn & Horsebridge Brewery, Horsebridge, Tavistock, Devon PL19 8TJ. Tel. (0182 287) 214

Fifteenth-century country pub, once a nunnery, which began brewing in 1981. After a change of hands, and a period of inactivity, the single-barrel plant recommenced brewing in 1984. Beers: Tamar (OG 1039, ABV 3.9%), Horsebridge Best (OG 1045, ABV 4.5%), Heller (OG 1060, ABV 6%).

RUDDLES

Ruddles Brewery Ltd., Langham, Oakham, Leics. LE15 7JD. Tel. (01572) 756911 Fax. (01572) 756116

Famous real ale brewery, founded in 1858, which lost its independence when it was taken over by Grand Metropolitan in 1986. Ruddles beers subsequently became national brands. The brewery is now in the hands of Dutch lager giants Grolsch, who purchased the business from Courage in 1992.

Best Bitter   (OG 1037, ABV 3.7%) Medium-bodied, tawny bitter with an aroma of sulphur and hops leading to a bitter, hoppy flavour and dry finish.

County   (OG 1050, ABV 4.9%) Hoppy bitterness, softened by malt, characterises this mid-brown, good-bodied beer.

481

The Independents

RUDGATE

Rudgate Brewery Ltd., 2 Centre Park, Marston Business Park, Rudgate, Tockwith, York, N. Yorks. YO5 8QF. Tel. (01423) 358382

Brewery founded in April 1992, which was bought by two former Bass executives in November that year. It operates from an old armoury building on the edge of Tockwith's disused airfield and now supplies 60 regular outlets, from Tyneside to Nottingham. Rudgate itself lies on an old Viking road, hence the beer names. Occasional beers: Easter Special (OG 1052, ABV 5%), Rudolf's Ruin (OG 1060, ABV 6%, Christmas).

Viking*	(OG 1039, ABV 3.8%)
Battleaxe*	(OG 1044, ABV 4.2%)
Pillage Porter*	(OG 1048, ABV 4.5%) Brewed only in the autumn.
Thor's Hammer*	(OG 1055, ABV 5.5%)

RYBURN

Ryburn Brewery, Mill House, Mill House Lane, Sowerby Bridge, Halifax, W. Yorks. HX6 3LN. Tel./Fax. (01422) 835413

Brewery founded with a tiny, two-barrel plant in a former dye works, in 1990. The growing popularity of the beers called for new plant early in 1993 and Ryburn acquired its first tied house, the Rams Head in Sowerby Bridge, at the end of that year. Now supplying 20 free trade outlets, it also produces occasional special brews and a number of pub house beers. Occasional beer: Porter (OG 1044, ABV 4.2%, Christmas).

Best Mild (OG 1033, ABV 3.3%) Stout-like in taste and colour, with a rich roast malt flavour and balancing bitterness, which is reflected in the finish and aroma.

Best Bitter* (OG 1036, ABV 3.8%)

Rydale Bitter* (OG 1044, ABV 4.2%) Mid-brown in colour with little aroma. A smooth, malty bitter with hop character and bitterness, plus some fruit notes. Long, malty and bitter finish.

Old Stone Troff Bitter* (OG 1047, ABV 4.7%)

Luddite* (OG 1050, ABV 5%) A dark beer.

Stabbers Bitter (OG 1050, ABV 5.2%) A malty aroma leads to a rich maltiness in the mouth with bittersweet, fruity elements, concluding in a malty and bitter finish. A mid-brown, powerful strong ale.

Coiners* (OG 1060, ABV 6%)

ST AUSTELL

St Austell Brewery Co. Ltd., 63 Trevarthian Road, St Austell, Cornwall PL25 4BY. Tel. (01726) 74444 Fax. (01726) 68965

Brewing company set up in 1851 by maltster and wine merchant Walter Hicks. It moved to the present site in 1893 and remains a family business, with many of Hicks's descendants employed in the company. It owns 140 pubs, spread right across Cornwall. Most of these serve traditional ale, and some 350 free trade outlets are also supplied. The recently-opened visitors' centre is proving to be a success.

Bosun's Bitter (OG 1034, ABV 3.4%) A refreshing session beer, sweetish in aroma and bittersweet in flavour. Lingering, hoppy finish.

XXXX Mild (OG 1037, ABV 3.6%) Little aroma, but a strong, malty, caramel-sweetish flavour is followed by a good, lingering aftertaste, which is sweet but with a fruity dryness. Very drinkable.

Tinners Ale (OG 1038, ABV 3.7%) A deservedly-popular, golden beer with an appetising malt aroma and a good balance of malt and hops in the flavour. Lasting finish.

Hicks Special Draught or HSD	(OG 1050, ABV 5%) An aromatic, fruity, hoppy bitter which is initially sweet and has an aftertaste of pronounced bitterness, but whose flavour is fully-rounded.
Winter Warmer*	(OG 1060, ABV 6%) Available November-February.

SCOTT'S

Scott's Brewing Company, Crown Hotel, 151 High Street, Lowestoft, Suffolk NR32 1HR. Tel. (01502) 537237

Brewery founded in 1988, in the former stables at the rear of the Crown Hotel, the site of a brewery owned by William French 400 years ago. It supplies real ales to its own four pubs (none of which are tied) and around 30 local free trade outlets. Viking Brew (ABV 3.75%) and Viking Strong (ABV 5%) are brewed for the Viking Hotel in Lowestoft.

Golden Best Bitter	(OG 1033, ABV 3.4%) A golden beer which is not at all strong tasting. The flavour is a reasonable balance of malt and (pungent) hop and the latter dominates the aftertaste.
Blues and Bloater	(OG 1036, ABV 3.7%) This pleasant, malty, fruity beer lacks bitterness in the taste which is light and a bit cloying. More of a light mild than a bitter.
William French	(OG 1048, ABV 5%) A full and beautifully-balanced beer. A faint, malty aroma leads into a palate with strong malt and hop flavours, and considerable fruitiness. A full and balanced aftertaste, too.
Dark Oast	(OG 1049, ABV 5%) A winter beer, red/brown in colour, with less body than its gravity would suggest. The taste has roast malt as its main characteristic, with hoppiness prominent in the aftertaste.

SCOTTISH & NEWCASTLE	See Nationals

SELBY

Selby (Middlesbrough) Brewery Ltd., 131 Millgate, Selby, N. Yorks. YO8 0LL. Tel. (01757) 702826

Old family brewery which resumed brewing in 1972 after a gap of 18 years and is now mostly involved in wholesaling. Its single real ale is brewed once a year in November and is available, while stocks last, primarily through its Brewery Tap off-licence in Selby, and not at the company's single pub.

Old Tom	(OG 1065, ABV 6.5%) Deceptively strong, tawny-hued ale, with mouthfilling malt, roast and tangy hop on the palate, and a distinctive 'smoky' character. Hoppy and malty finish, but the aroma is not marked.

SHACKLEFORD	See Cyder House Inn

SHARDLOW

Shardlow Brewery Ltd., Ground Floor, Kiln Warehouse, British Waterways Yard, Cavendish Bridge, Leics. DE72 2HL. Tel. (01332) 799188

This new brewery opened in October 1993 on the site of the maltings of the original Cavendish Bridge Brewery, which closed in the 1920s. It stands on the River Trent, opposite Shardlow Marina. Portland Bitter (OG 1040, ABV 4%) is brewed exclusively for the Portland Hotel in Derby, whilst the other brews are supplied to almost 40 free trade outlets.

Session*	(OG 1036, ABV 3.5%)
Bitter*	(OG 1042, ABV 4.1%)
Cavendish 47 Bridge*	(OG 1047, ABV 4.5%)
Sleighed*	(OG 1058, ABV 5.5%) A winter brew, available October-March.

The pub sign indicates breweries which are also brew pubs, i.e. produce beer in part of a pub or in its grounds.

The Independents

SHARP'S	**Sharp's Brewery, Rock, Wadebridge, Cornwall PL27 6NU. Tel. (01208) 862121**
	Brewery established in an industrial unit in summer 1994 by silversmith Bill Sharp.
Cornish Coaster*	(OG 1038, ABV 3.6%)
Own Cornish*	(OG 1043, ABV 4.4%)

SHEPHERD NEAME

Shepherd Neame Ltd., 17 Court Street, Faversham, Kent ME13 7AX. Tel. (01795) 532206 Fax. (01795) 538907

Shepherd Neame is believed to be the oldest continuous brewer in the land (since 1698) and operates from a fine old brewery retaining many original features. Steam engines have recently been brought back into use and the mash is produced in two teak tuns which date from 1910. A visitors' reception centre is housed in a restored medieval hall. Its tied estate of 382 pubs are mostly in Kent, but acquisitions are being made across Surrey, Sussex, Essex and London. Most sell cask ale, but tenants are encouraged to keep beers under blanket pressure if the cask is likely to be on sale for more than three days. Some 300 free trade outlets are supplied directly by the brewery, while Spitfire and Bishops Finger are available nationwide via wholesalers. Shepherd Neame now also brews Charrington IPA under licence for Bass. Bottle-conditioned beer: Spitfire ⊟ (OG 1047, ABV 4.7%).

Masons Pale Ale*	(ABV 3.3%) A summer beer.
Master Brew Bitter	(OG 1037, ABV 3.7%) A very distinctive bitter, mid-brown in colour, with a very hoppy aroma. Well-balanced with a nicely aggressive bitter taste from its hops, leaving a hoppy/bitter finish, tinged with sweetness.
Best Bitter	(OG 1041, ABV 4.1%) Mid-brown, with less marked characteristics than the bitter. However, the nose is very well-balanced and the taste enjoys a malty, bitter smokiness. A malty, well-rounded finish.
Spitfire Ale*	(OG 1047, ABV 4.7%) A commemorative brew (Battle of Britain) for the RAF Benevolent Fund's appeal, now a permanent feature.
Bishops Finger*	(OG 1052, ABV 5.2%) A well-known bottled beer, introduced in cask-conditioned form in 1989.
Original Porter	(OG 1052, ABV 5.2%) Rich, black, full-bodied, winter brew. The good malt and roast aroma also has a fine fruit edge. The complex blend of flavours is dominated by roast malt, which is also present in a very dry aftertaste.
	For Bass:
Charrington IPA*	(OG 1036, ABV 3.4%)

SHIP & PLOUGH

Blewitts Brewery, Ship & Plough, The Promenade, Kingsbridge, Devon TQ7 1JD. Tel./Fax. (01548) 852485

Brewery started in 1991 which may expand to serve other pubs. Beers: Blewitts Nose (OG 1040, ABV 3.8%, occasional), King's Ale (OG 1040, ABV 4%, occasional), Blewitts Best (OG 1042, ABV 4%), Blewitts Black Balls (OG 1046, ABV 4.5%, occasional), Blewitts Head Off (OG 1048, ABV 5%), Blewitts Brains Out (OG 1060, ABV 6%, occasional).

SHIPSTONE'S	See Nationals, Carlsberg-Tetley and Pub Groups, Greenalls

SMILES

Smiles Brewing Co. Ltd., Colston Yard, Colston Street, Bristol, Avon BS1 5BD. Tel. (0117) 9297350 Fax. (0117) 9258235

Brewery established in 1977 to supply a local restaurant and which began full-scale brewing early in 1978. It changed ownership in 1991. Noted for its quality ales and good pubs (winners of

CAMRA's *Pub Design* awards), the brewery now supplies 11 managed houses and 200 free trade outlets, and is looking to acquire more houses through its separate pub company.

Bitter

(OG 1037, ABV 3.7%) A golden/amber, light beer. Its slightly sweet, fruit palate is followed by a pleasant, bitter, dry finish. Light, fruity nose.

Best Bitter

(OG 1041, ABV 4.1%) A mid-brown, fruity beer with some malt and hops in both nose and taste. Slightly sweet, but a well-rounded beer with a bitter, dry finish.

Bristol Stout

(OG 1047, ABV 4.7%) A dark, red/brown stout with a roast malt and coffee aroma. The predominantly rich roast malt taste features some hops and fruit. Roast, bitter, dry finish. Available September-March.

Exhibition Bitter

(OG 1052, ABV 5.2%) A deep copper-brown beer with a pronounced malt, hop and fruit taste, with hints of roast, turning to a dry, bitter finish.

JOHN SMITH'S

See Nationals, Courage

SAMUEL SMITH

Samuel Smith Old Brewery (Tadcaster), Tadcaster, N. Yorks. LS24 9SB. Tel. (01937) 832225 Fax. (01937) 834673

Small company operating from the oldest brewery in Yorkshire, dating from 1758 and once owned by John Smith. Although John Smith's is now Courage-owned, 'Sam's' remains family-owned and firmly independent. Beers are brewed from well water without the use of any adjuncts and all cask beer is fermented in Yorkshire stone squares and racked into wooden casks provided by the brewery's own cooperage. Real ale is served in the majority of its 200-plus tied houses, which include 27 in London, representing good value for the capital. Some free trade is also supplied.

Old Brewery Bitter (OBB)

(OG 1040, ABV 4%) Malt dominates the nose, the taste and aftertaste, although this is underscored at all stages by a gentle hoppiness. A 'big' beer with loads of flavour, complemented by an attractive amber colour.

Museum Ale

(OG 1049, ABV 5%) Deep amber in colour, which gives some idea of the fruitiness to be found in the nose, taste and finish. A sweet beer with winey flavours, despite no sugar being used in the brewing process.

SNOWDONIA

Snowdonia Brewing Co. Ltd., c/o The Bryn Arms, Gellilydan, Gwynedd LL41 4EH. Tel. (01766) 590379

Beginning as a brew pub, Barry's Brewery at the Bryn Arms has since changed its name. With the beer range now established, there are plans to expand by acquiring a five-barrel plant and moving into an industrial unit. Other plans include producing more bottle-conditioned beers. Brewing only at weekends, it currently serves the Bryn Arms and some 20-40 free trade outlets. Bottle-conditioned beer: Celt (OG 1074, ABV 8%).

Mêl y Moelwyn Bitter*

(OG 1037, ABV 3.5%) A beer whose recipe has changed in the last year.

Choir Porter*

(OG 1045, ABV 4.5%) Again, the recipe of this beer has changed in the last year.

Merion Premium Bitter

(OG 1046, ABV 4.5%) Well-balanced and bitter. More fully-flavoured than the Mêl y Moelwyn.

Snowdon Strong Bitter

(OG 1050, ABV 5.2%) A well-hopped, fruity and bitter strong beer. Quite sweet, but not cloying, with a fairly dry finish. Very drinkable.

Wheat Dragon*

(OG 1055, ABV 5%) A new wheat beer.

Celt

(OG 1074, ABV 8%) A complex strong ale. Fruity and bitter, but not too sweet, with hints of smoke.

The Independents

SOLSTICE

Solstice Brewing Company, The Brew House, Queens Head, Bridge Street, Kington, Hereford & Worcester. Tel. (01568) 610063

Formerly the Dunn Plowman, this brewery was renamed when two new partners joined the company in December 1993. It also expanded into new premises at the rear of the Queens Head, but still brews a range of Dunn Plowman beers for the Black Horse in Leominster, where it was founded: Black Horse Bitter (OG 1038, ABV 3.8%), Woody's Crown (OG 1045, ABV 4.5%), Shire Horse Ale (OG 1050, ABV 5%), Muletide (OG 1072, ABV 7.2%). It also supplies a dozen other free trade outlets, and plans to produce special seasonal brews. Bottle-conditioned beers: Capstone (OG 1050, ABV 5%), Druid's Revenge (OG 1072, ABV 7.2%).

Golden Torc* (OG 1038, ABV 3.8%) A straw-coloured, hoppy ale.

Talisman* (OG 1045, ABV 4.5%) A tawny brown, fruity beer.

Capstone* (OG 1050, ABV 5%) A dark ruby-coloured, full-bodied, fruity ale.

Druid's Revenge* (OG 1072, ABV 7.2%) A dark and sweet winter warmer.

SOLVA

The Solva Brewing Co. Ltd., Panteg, Solva, Haverfordwest, Dyfed SA62 6TL. Tel. (01437) 720040

Only in operation since late 1993, this brewery plans to add to the beer range, with a second regular brew and some specialist beers. The beer can be currently found in three free trade outlets in Pembrokeshire, as well as in The Ship, home of the brewery. Beer: Ramsey Bitter (OG 1040, ABV 4.1%).

SOUTH YORKSHIRE

South Yorkshire Brewing Co.

South Yorkshire Brewing Co., Elsecar Workshops, Wath Road, Elsecar, Barnsley, S. Yorks. S74 8HJ. Tel. (01226) 741010

Commissioned in March 1994, with a 20-barrel plant, this new brewery uses old yeast: the culture dates back to 1960 and comes from the old Oakwell Brewery in Barnsley. There are plans to expand fermenting capacity in 1995. Currently 20 free trade outlets are supplied.

Barnsley Bitter* (OG 1037, ABV 3.8%)

Heritage Bitter* (OG 1040, ABV 4.2%)

SPRINGFIELD See Nationals, Bass

SPRINGHEAD

Springhead Brewery, Main Street, Sutton on Trent, Newark, Notts. NG23 6PE. Tel. (01636) 821000

Possibly the smallest brewery in the country, occupying a mere 12 square yards of floor space. It began production in 1990 and has expanded from a single-barrel to a seven and a half-barrel plant. Now working to capacity, it plans to expand again and a brewery move may be necessary. A second beer has been launched and free trade outlets have increased to 65.

Bitter* (OG 1039, ABV 4%)

The Leveller* (OG 1045, ABV 4.8%)

Roaring Meg* (OG 1054, ABV 5.5%)

STANWAY

Stanway Brewery, Stanway, Cheltenham, Gloucestershire GL54 5PQ. Tel. (01386) 584320

Small brewery founded in March 1993 with a five-barrel plant, which confines its sales to the Cotswolds area.

Stanney Bitter* (OG 1042, ABV 4.5%)

Old Eccentric* (OG 1052, ABV 5.5%) A winter beer.

STAR & TIPSY TOAD See Tipsy Toad

STEAM PACKET

The Steam Packet Brewery, The Bundles, Racca Green, Knottingley, W. Yorks. WF11 8AT. Tel. (01977) 674176 Fax. (01977) 674176

Brewery which began producing beers for the Steam Packet pub in November 1990, but which has expanded to supply 50 outlets regularly (and more on an occasional basis), mainly in the North-West. New brews are regularly added to its already substantial range of beers.

Summer Lite*
(OG 1030, ABV 3.5%) Summer only.

Mellor's Gamekeeper Bitter*
(OG 1036, ABV 3.6%) A malty brew, with a dry, malty initial taste, but it can be very weak in aftertaste. Light brown in colour.

Chatterley
(OG 1038, ABV 3.7%) A wheat malt brew, with a light golden colour and a quite fruity, hoppy taste. A really good session beer with a lemon aftertaste.

Foxy
(OG 1039, ABV 3.9%) A new, russet-coloured beer with a small amount of wheat malt. The very well-balanced malt and hop flavour is also fruity, with a slight lemon flavour in the aftertaste.

Bit o Black
(OG 1040, ABV 4%) A dark, malty brew with a well-balanced taste of malt and a lightly vinous nose and aftertaste. Like a good, dark strong mild.

Brown Ale*
(OG 1045, ABV 4.5%)

Packet Porter*
(OG 1045, ABV 4.5%)

Bargee
(OG 1048, ABV 4.8%) A splendid Belgian-style beer of a slightly darker colour than Foxy, with a very malty initial taste which bursts into a fruity aftertaste.

Poacher's Swag
(OG 1050, ABV 5%) A pale-coloured, strong, dry beer with a real taste of alcohol. Dry in the aftertaste.

Giddy Ass
(OG 1080, ABV 8%) A beer with a winey taste and no hint of sweetness. Dangerously drinkable.

STOCKS

Stocks Brewery, The Hallcross, 33-34 Hallgate, Doncaster, S. Yorks. DN1 3NL. Tel. (01302) 328213

Brewery founded in December 1981 as a brew pub in a former baker's shop. It now runs two other tied houses. The free trade is expanding and includes Tap & Spile outlets, as well as 12 local outlets which are supplied directly.

Best Bitter
(OG 1037, ABV 3.9%) A clean and thin session beer, which is really an ordinary, rather than a best bitter. A malt and hoppy, bitter taste, with a short aftertaste and dryness. Dark/mid-brown colour, with little depth.

Select
(OG 1044, ABV 4.3%) A smooth and nicely-balanced drinking beer that has a light aroma and mouthfeel, with malt on the tongue and a short, bitter finish, with a touch of plain chocolate thrown in. Mid-brown in colour with red hints.

St Leger Porter
(OG 1050, ABV 5.1%) A fine beer, but more like a thin stout than a true porter. Black, with a red/brown hue, it has a strong roast aroma and taste touched with hints of bitterness and chocolate, yet it lacks sweetness everywhere.

Old Horizontal
(OG 1054, ABV 5.3%) Despite being thinner this year, this remains a rich and deep beer, with fruit, roast and chocolate tastes on a malty background. A dry, nutty but short finish to a dark brown beer with ruby red hints.

STONES

See Nationals, Bass

STRONG

See Morrells and Nationals, Whitbread

The Independents

SUMMERSKILLS

Summerskills Brewery, Unit 15, Pomphlett Farm Ind. Estate, Broxton Drive, Billacombe, Plymouth, Devon PL9 7BG. Tel. (01752) 481283

Summerskills was initially set up in 1983 in a vineyard, but was only operational for two years. It was relaunched by new owners in 1990, with plant from the old Penrhos brewery, and production has grown at a steady rate. It currently supplies around 20 free trade outlets directly, and others nationally via wholesalers. The brewery logo comes from the ship's crest of HMS Bigbury Bay.

Best Bitter

(OG 1042, ABV 4.3%) A mid-brown beer, with plenty of malt and hops through the aroma, taste and finish. A good session beer.

Whistle Belly Vengeance*

(OG 1046, ABV 4.7%) Mid-brown in colour, with a fruity aroma and a complex malt, fruit and hop taste, with a sweet, fruity finish.

Ninjabeer

(OG 1049, ABV 5%) A dark beer, with a strong, fruity aroma and a predominantly fruity taste and aftertaste. Very drinkable.

Indiana's Bones

(OG 1056, ABV 5.6%) A mid-brown, fruity beer, well-balanced and full-bodied, with a fruity malt taste and finish.

SUTTON

Sutton Brewing Company, 31 Commercial Road, Plymouth, Devon PL4 0LE. Tel. (01752) 255335 Fax. (01752) 672235

This new brewery was built alongside the Thistle Park Tavern, near Plymouth's Sutton Harbour, in 1993. It went into production the following year to supply that pub and the free trade. Such was the demand (currently 35 outlets) that additional fermenters and a redesign of the plant were quickly needed. Draught Commemoration Ale was brewed especially for the D-Day celebrations in 1994, with just 500 (numbered and signed) bottles of this bottle-conditioned beer produced.

Plymouth Pride*

(OG 1039, ABV 3.8%)

XSB

(OG 1042, ABV 4.2%) A mid-brown beer with a malty aroma, bitter taste and a hoppy, bitter finish.

Eddystone Light*

(OG 1052, ABV 5%)

Plymouth Porter*

(OG 1055, ABV 5.5%) A winter brew.

TALLY HO

Tally Ho Country Inn and Brewery, 14 Market Street, Hatherleigh, Devon EX20 3JN. Tel. (01837) 810306

The Tally Ho recommenced brewing at Easter 1990, reviving the tradition of the old New Inn brewery on the same site. Its beers are produced from a full mash, with no additives, but no other pubs are supplied at present, because of the limited genuine free trade in the locality. The pub was placed on the market in summer 1994. Beers: Dark Mild (OG 1034, ABV 2.8%), Potboiler's Brew (OG 1038, ABV 3.5%), Tarka Tipple (OG 1042, ABV 4%), Nutters (OG 1048, ABV 4.6%), Thurgia (OG 1056, ABV 5.7%), Janni Jollop (OG 1066, ABV 6.6%, winter). Bottle-conditioned beers: Tarka Tipple (OG 1048, ABV 4.6%), Thurgia (OG 1056, ABV 5.7%).

TAYLOR

Timothy Taylor & Co. Ltd., Knowle Spring Brewery, Keighley, W. Yorks. BD21 1AW. Tel. (01535) 603139 Fax. (01535) 691167

Timothy Taylor began brewing in Keighley in 1858 and moved to the site of the Knowle Spring in 1863. The business was continued by his sons and remains an independent family-owned company to this day. Its prize-winning ales are served in all 29 of the brewery's pubs as well as a wide free trade.

Golden Best

(OG 1033, ABV 3.5%) A soft and smooth, slightly sweet, malty taste follows a light malt and hop aroma. There is a hint of bitterness in the delicate finish, which is short and malty, and laced with hops. Golden colour, tinged with amber.

Dark Mild	(OG 1034, ABV 3.5%) Dark brown with red hints, the caramel conceals the Golden Best it is based on until the finish, when a short, light and dry aftertaste emerges from this relatively thin brew.
Best Bitter	(OG 1037, ABV 4%) Not as multilayered as before, but still enjoying a floral nose, with fruit and malt also present. A bitter taste leads to a short and dry finish. A fine drinker's bitter that lacks its old depth, somehow.
Porter	(OG 1041, ABV 3.8%) Roast malt and caramel dominate the whole drink until the aftertaste, when sweetness wins through. In an age of new, true porters, this brew looks lost. Perhaps that is why it is increasingly difficult to find.
Landlord ⊈	(OG 1042, ABV 4.3%) A strong assault of fruit and hops on the nose, followed by a hoppy bitterness at all stages. Less complex than before but still better than most brews.
Ram Tam (XXXX)	(OG 1043, ABV 4.3%) The caramel is not as daunting as previously, so that the dry hop bitterness in the taste and finish manages to come through. Quite rounded, yet it has a harsh hop edge contrasted by a gentle sweetness.

TAYLOR WALKER	See Nationals, Carlsberg-Tetley

TEIGNWORTHY	**Teignworthy Brewery, Tuckers Maltings, Teign Road, Newton Abbot, Devon TQ12 4AA. Tel. (01626) 332066**
	Brewery founded in June 1994 with a 15-barrel plant by former Oakhill and Ringwood brewer John Lawton, using part of the Tuckers Maltings site.
Reel Ale*	(OG 1039, ABV 4%)

TENNENT CALEDONIAN	See Nationals, Bass

JOSHUA TETLEY	See Nationals, Carlsberg-Tetley

THEAKSTON	See Nationals, Scottish & Newcastle

THOMPSON'S	**Thompson's Brewery, Unit 4, Exhibition Way, Pinhoe Trading Estate, Exeter, Devon EX4 8HX. Tel. (0345) 626588 Fax. (01392) 464760**
	Brewery which began operation in 1981 by brewing for its own pub, the London Inn in Ashburton, which has since been joined by a second tied house, the Mytton & Mermaid in Shrewsbury. Thompson's office moved to new premises in Exeter in 1993, but the brewery remains in Ashburton.
Best Bitter	(OG 1040, ABV 4.1%) A pale brown beer with a hoppy aroma and taste. Bitter finish.
Black Velvet Stout*	(OG 1040, ABV 4.2%)
Celebration Porter*	(OG 1040, ABV 4.2%)
IPA	(OG 1044, ABV 4.8%) A mid-brown-coloured ale with a distinct hoppy aroma and a bitter taste and finish.

The tankard symbol indicates the *Good Beer Guide Beers of the Year*, finalists in the *Champion Beer of Britain* contest held at the *Great British Beer Festival* at Olympia in August 1994.

The Independents

Man of War	(OG 1050, ABV 4.9%) A golden, summer beer with a fruity sweet taste and aftertaste.
Figurehead	(OG 1050, ABV 5.2%) A dark brown, full-bodied winter beer with a malty nose and a roasty, bitter taste and finish.

THREE FYSHES INN — See Nix Wincott

THREE TUNS

The Three Tuns Brewery, Salop Street, Bishop's Castle, Shropshire SY9 5BW. Tel. (01588) 638797

Historic brew pub which first obtained a brewing licence in 1642. The tower brewery was built in 1888 and is still in use, but the pub and brewery are up for sale. Beers: Mild Light (OG 1035, ABV 3.5%), XXX (OG 1042, ABV 4.3%), Jim Wood's Porter (OG 1058, ABV 5.8%).

THWAITES

Daniel Thwaites PLC, PO Box 50, Star Brewery, Blackburn, Lancs. BB1 5BU. Tel. (01254) 54431 Fax. (01254) 681439

Lancashire brewery, founded by excise officer Daniel Thwaites in 1807 and now run by his great-great grandson. It still uses shire horse drays and nearly all its 413 pubs serve real ale. A substantial free trade is also supplied. However, only one mild is now available, the ordinary mild having been discontinued.

Best Mild — (OG 1034, ABV 3.3%) A rich, dark mild presenting a smooth, malty flavour and a pleasant, slightly bitter finish.

Bitter — (OG 1036, ABV 3.6%) A gently-flavoured, clean-tasting bitter. Malt and hops lead into a full, lingering, bitter finish.

Craftsman* — (OG 1042, ABV 4.5%)

TIPSY TOAD

The Tipsy Toad Brewery, St Peter, Jersey JE3 7AA. Tel. (01534) 485556 Fax. (01534) 485559; The Tipsy Toad Townhouse and Brewery, 57-59 New Street, St Helier, Jersey JE2 3RB. Tel. (01534) 615002 Fax. (01534) 615003

Following a £½ million pound refurbishment of the old Star pub, brewing began on the premises in spring 1992. Two other outlets are now supplied on regular basis with the full mash brews and, at the pub itself, the ales are properly cask-conditioned, with no extraneous gases now applied in the cellar. A porter may be added to the range. Beers: Jimmy's Bitter (OG 1040, ABV 4%), Horny Toad (OG 1050, ABV 5%), Star Drooper (OG 1060, ABV 6%, winter). The brewery has also opened a brew pub-cum-real ale shop in St Helier, The Tipsy Toad Townhouse and Brewery. Beers: Golden Toad (OG 1038, ABV 3.7%, the name may change), Jimmy's Bitter (OG 1040, ABV 4%).

TITANIC

Titanic Brewery, Unit G, Harvey Works, Lingard Street, Burslem, Stoke-on-Trent, Staffs. ST6 1ED. Tel. (01782) 823447 Fax. (01782) 812349

This brewery, named in honour of the Titanic's Captain Smith, who hailed from Stoke, was founded in 1985 but fell into difficulties until rescued by the present owners. A move to larger premises took place in 1992, and the brewery now supplies some 200 free trade outlets, as well as two pubs of its own (which also sell other Independents' guest beers). Occasional beer: Anniversary Ale (OG 1050, ABV 4.8%). Bottle-conditioned beers: Stout (OG 1046, ABV 4.5%), Christmas Ale (OG 1080, ABV 7.8%).

Best Bitter — (OG 1036, ABV 3.5%) A refreshing, clean-drinking, hoppy, amber/gold bitter. Fruit, malt and predominantly hops carry through to the aftertaste.

Lifeboat Ale — (OG 1040, ABV 3.9%) A fruity and malty, red/brown, bittersweet beer, with a slight caramel character. The finish is dry and fruity.

Premium Bitter (OG 1042, ABV 4.1%) An impressive pale brown beer with a strong fruit and hops aroma. The taste is bitter and very hoppy, but known to change with hop yield. Bitter hops in the aftertaste.

Stout (OG 1046, ABV 4.5%) A dark combination of malt and roast with some hops. Strongly flavoured and well-balanced.

Captain Smith's Strong Ale (OG 1050, ABV 4.8%) A red/brown, full-bodied beer, hoppy and bitter with a malty sweetness and roast malt flavour, and a good finish.

Wreckage (OG 1080, ABV 7.8%) A dark winter brew, full-flavoured with a rich bittersweet finish.

TOLLY COBBOLD

Tollemache & Cobbold Brewery Ltd., Cliff Road, Ipswich, Suffolk IP3 0AZ. Tel. (01473) 231723 Fax. (01473) 280045

TOLLY·COBBOLD

One of the oldest breweries in the country, founded by Thomas Cobbold in 1723 at Harwich, which survived several changes in ownership until the Brent Walker take-over in 1989, when the Cliff Brewery was closed and production transferred to Camerons in Hartlepool. However, a management buy-out, led by former Tolly directors Brian Cowie and Bob Wales, saved the day and Tolly Cobbold Ipswich-brewed ales were back on sale in September 1990. The new company acquired no pubs from Brent Walker, but secured a five-year trading agreement, supplying a total of 550 pubs. It opened a brewery tap, the only tied house, in June 1992.

Mild (OG 1032, ABV 3.2%) A dark mild with a predominantly malty aroma. Fruit and malt come through initially, but the finish is dryish and hoppy.

Bitter (OG 1035, ABV 3.5%) A malty, mid-brown-coloured beer with a light malt and hop nose. Malty palate, with very little balancing bitterness.

Original Best Bitter (OG 1038, ABV 3.8%) A slightly stronger bitter with assertive hop character throughout. The finish is bitter, but with a good balancing maltiness. A tendency to serve this beer through a sparkler reduces the hop character.

Beano Stout (OG 1045, ABV 4.1%) A beer with roast and chocolate flavours well-defined, but perhaps lacking a little body for a true stout.

Old Strong Winter Ale (OG 1047, ABV 4.5%) Available November-February. A dark winter ale with plenty of roast and malt in the aroma. These characteristics are also evident in the initial flavour, although the finish is bittersweet.

Tollyshooter (OG 1052, ABV 5%) A reddish premium bitter with a pleasant aroma of fruit and malt. The taste combines both these characteristics, with sweetness offset by some hops. Fruity and hoppy finish, with little bitterness. Named after the Sir John Harvey-Jones TV series, *Troubleshooter*, in which Tolly featured.

TOMINTOUL

Tomintoul Brewery Co. Ltd., Mill of Auchriachan, Tomintoul, Ballindalloch, Grampian AB37 9EQ. Tel. (01807) 580333 Fax. (01807) 580358

Brewery opened in November 1993 in an area better known for malt whisky and snow-blocked roads, plugging a huge gap in the brewery map of Britain. A winter ale, bottled beers and a visitor centre are all planned. Around half-a-dozen outlets are currently supplied.

Caillie* (OG 1035, ABV 3.6%)

Stag* (OG 1039.5, ABV 4.1%)

The Independents

TOMLINSON'S

Tomlinson's Old Castle Brewery, Unit 5, Britannia Works, Skinner Lane, Pontefract, W. Yorks. WF8 1HU. Tel. (01977) 780866

Marking a return to brewing in Pontefract after over 60 years, Tomlinson's was built and is run by a former pipe fitter and fabricator. The first brew went out on Boxing Day 1993 and the beers have already begun to win beer festival awards. They take their names from local historical connections: 'Down With It!' was the cry of the people when asked by Cromwell if the town's castle should stand, Fractus comes from the Latin Pontus Fractus, meaning broken bridge and the source of the name Pontefract, and Richard's Defeat refers to Richard II, who died at Pontefract Castle. Some 25 outlets are now supplied.

Down With It!*	(OG 1040, ABV 4%) A bitter.
Fractus XB*	(OG 1045, ABV 4.5%) A best bitter.
Richard's Defeat*	(OG 1050, ABV 5%) A porter.

TOWNES

Townes Brewery, Bay 9, Suon Buildings, Lockoford Lane, Chesterfield, Derbyshire S41 7JJ. Tel. (01246) 277994

Brewery established in an old bakery in May 1994 by photographer Alan Wood, bringing brewing back to Chesterfield. A dark winter beer is planned.

Best Lockoford Bitter*	(OG 1040, ABV 4%)
Double Bagger*	(OG 1050, ABV 5%)

TRAQUAIR

Traquair House Brewery, Innerleithen, Peeblesshire, Borders EH44 6PW. Tel. (01896) 830323 Fax. (01896) 830639

This 18th-century brewhouse is situated in one of the wings of Traquair House (over 1,000 years old) and was rediscovered by the 20th Laird, Peter Maxwell Stuart, in 1965. He began brewing again using all the original equipment (which remained intact, despite having lain idle for over 100 years). Today the bottled product, Traquair House Ale (not bottle-conditioned), is exported worldwide, although production is only set at around 5,000 gallons a year. This beer is available on draught only at the White Horse in Parsons Green, London, but four outlets are supplied with the cask-conditioned Bear Ale. The brewery passed to Catherine Maxwell Stuart in 1990.

Bear Ale*	(OG 1050, ABV 5%) A strong bitter.
Traquair House Ale*	(OG 1070, ABV 7.2%) Dark and potent.

TRING

Tring Brewery Company Ltd., 81-82 Akeman Street, Tring, Herts. HP23 6AF. Tel. (01442) 890721 Fax. (01442) 890740

Established in December 1992, brewing the first beer in the town for almost 60 years, Tring has been so successful that expansion has already been considered (almost 50 outlets are now supplied). Occasional beer: Death or Glory Ale (OG 1068, ABV 7.2%, brewed on October 25 to commemorate the Charge of the Light Brigade in 1854). Bottle-conditioned beer: Death or Glory Ale (OG 1068, ABV 7.2%).

The Ridgeway Bitter	(OG 1039.5, ABV 4%) A hoppy, bitter beer with a bitter aftertaste.
Old Icknield Ale	(OG 1050, ABV 5%) A beer with a hoppy aroma, a sweetish, hoppy taste and a sweet, hoppy aftertaste.

The pub sign indicates breweries which are also brew pubs, i.e. produce beer in part of a pub or in its grounds.

TROUGH

Trough Brewery Ltd., Idle, Bradford, W. Yorks.
Brewery which ceased operation early in 1994.

ULEY

Uley Brewery Ltd., The Old Brewery, Uley, Dursley, Gloucestershire. GL11 5TB. Tel. (01453) 860120

Brewing at Uley began in 1833, but Price's Brewery, as it was then, remained inactive for most of this century. Work commenced on restoring the premises in 1984 and Uley Brewery was reborn in 1985. The brewery has no pubs of its own but now serves 50 free trade outlets in the Cotswolds area.

Bitter or Hogshead or UB40

(OG 1040, ABV 3.8%) Copper-coloured beer with malt, hops and fruit in the aroma and a malty, fruity taste, underscored by a hoppy bitterness. The finish is dry, with a balance of hops and malt.

Old Spot Prize Ale

(OG 1050, ABV 4.8%) A fairly full-bodied, red/brown ale with a fruity aroma, a malty, fruity taste (with a hoppy bitterness), and a strong, balanced aftertaste.

Pig's Ear Strong Beer

(OG 1050, ABV 4.8%) A pale-coloured, light beer, deceptively strong. Notably bitter in flavour, with a hoppy, fruity aroma and a bitter finish.

Pigor Mortis

(OG 1060, ABV 6%) A winter brew, another beer which belies its strength. No distinct aroma, but a sweet, smooth flavour, with hints of fruit and hops. Dry finish.

UNITED BREWERIES

United Breweries PLC, Tingewick Road, Buckingham, MK18 1AN. Tel. (01280) 822663 Fax. (01280) 823728

The UB Group (United Breweries of India), owner of the Chainmaker Beer Company, which produced the former Premier/Pitfield beers and the Wiltshire Brewery brands, is not currently brewing. There are plans to contract out production of Wiltshire Stonehenge Bitter (OG 1036, ABV 3.6%), but the Pitfield brands are now brewed by Brewery on Sea for the London Beer Company.

USHERS

Ushers of Trowbridge PLC, Directors House, 68 Fore Street, Trowbridge, Wilts. BA14 8JF. Tel. (01225) 763171
Fax. (01225) 753661

This famous West Country brewery was founded in 1824, but lost its identity after being swallowed up by Watney (later Grand Met) in 1960. A successful management buy-out from Courage in 1991 gave Ushers back its independence. It has since invested in pubs and plant, with over £2 million spent on the brewery, and a new seasonal beer project was launched in 1994. Four Seasons Ales offers a range of short-term cask beers which aims to reflect the season and the cereals harvested at that time. The first brew was Spring Fever (OG 1035.5, ABV 3.4%), produced from malted oats. Ushers supplies real ale to 440 of its 460 houses and to Courage/Grand Met Inntrepreneur pubs.

Best Bitter

(OG 1038, ABV 3.8%) A dry bitter with a grainy malt character, a faint hop aroma and palate, and a malty, dry finish.

Founders Ale

(OG 1046, ABV 4.5%) A pale brown beer with a bitter hop taste, balanced by sweet maltiness and faint citrus fruit. Predominantly bitter finish.

1824 Particular

(OG 1064, ABV 6.2%) This winter beer has a light malt and caramel aroma and taste, balanced by some bittersweetness in the flavour and finish.

VAUX

Vaux Breweries Ltd., The Brewery, Sunderland, Tyne & Wear SR1 3AN. Tel. (0191) 567 6277 Fax. (0191) 514 0422

First established in 1837 and now one of the country's largest regional brewers, Vaux remains firmly independent. It owns Wards of Sheffield, but sold off Lorimer & Clark in Edinburgh to Caledonian in 1987. Real ale is sold in over 300 of its 700 tied houses (which include those run by Wards and Vaux Inns Ltd.) and is also provided to 10% of its 700 free trade customers. It is looking to increase its tied estate, buying pubs in Yorkshire, the North-West and elsewhere from national brewers. A new Vaux Extra Special (OG 1047, ABV 5%) is produced at Wards (see Wards) and takes the place of not only the old Extra Special but also Wards Kirby Strong Ale and Vaux Durham Celebration Ale, which was available for a while. Meanwhile, Vaux Mild is Wards Mild rebadged.

Lorimer's Best Scotch
(OG 1036, ABV 3.6%) A replica of the original Scottish Scotch. Aroma is often lacking, but, when fresh, there can be a subtle hop character to balance a sweet and malty taste.

Bitter
(OG 1036, ABV 3.9%) A light and drinkable bitter with low bitterness and some fruit evident. Aroma is easily lost, but can be hoppy.

Samson
(OG 1041, ABV 4.1%) A very light bitter with a grainy aftertaste, and a sulphury aroma when fresh. Bitterness is moderate and sweetness may persist in the taste.

Double Maxim
(OG 1044, ABV 4.2%) A smooth brown ale, rich and well-balanced, with lasting fruit and good body.

VILLAGE BREWER
See Hadrian and Hambleton

WADWORTH

Wadworth & Co. Ltd., Northgate Brewery, Devizes, Wilts. SN10 1JW. Tel. (01380) 723361 Fax. (01380) 724342

Delightful market town tower brewery set up in 1885 by Henry Wadworth. Though solidly traditional (with its own dray horses), it continues to invest in the future, with the emphasis on quality control. The brewery continues to expand, and is producing up to 2,000 barrels a week to supply a wide-ranging free trade in the South of England, as well as its own 200 tied houses (a figure which it is always looking to increase). All the pubs serve real ale and 6X remains one of the South's most famous beers. Occasional beers: Easter Ale (OG 1044, ABV 4.5%), Malt & Hops (OG 1044, ABV 4.5%, September), Summersault (OG 1044, ABV 4.5%, July-August).

Henry's Original IPA
(OG 1034, ABV 3.8%) A golden brown-coloured beer with a gentle, malty and slightly hoppy aroma, a good balance of flavours, with maltiness gradually dominating, and then a long-lasting aftertaste to match, eventually becoming biscuity. A good session beer.

6X
(OG 1040, ABV 4.3%) Mid-brown in colour, with a malty and fruity nose and some balancing hop character. The flavour is similar, with some bitterness and a lingering malty, but bitter finish. Full-bodied and distinctive.

Farmer's Glory
(OG 1046, ABV 4.5%) This dark beer can be delightfully hoppy and fruity. The aroma is of malt and it should have a dryish, hoppy aftertaste.

Old Timer
(OG 1055, ABV 5.8%) Available from October to March only: a rich, copper-brown beer with a strong, fruity, malty aroma. The flavour is full-bodied and complete, with hints of butterscotch and peaches, beautifully balanced by a lasting, malty, dry finish. A classic beer.

PETER WALKER
See Nationals, Carlsberg-Tetley

WARDS

SH Ward & Co. Ltd., Sheaf Brewery, Ecclesall Road, Sheffield, S. Yorks. S11 8HZ. Tel. (0114) 2755155 Fax. (0114) 2751816

Established in 1840 by Josiah Kirby, Wards has been a subsidiary of Vaux of Sunderland since 1972. Since the closure of the neighbouring Thorne brewery in 1986, it has also produced Darley's beers. Real ale is available in about half of the brewery's 240 tied houses and over 100 free trade outlets are supplied directly. Kirby Strong Ale has been discontinued in favour of a new version of Vaux Extra Special.

Mild or Darley's Dark Mild	(OG 1032, ABV 3.4%) Also sold as Vaux Mild. This beer's rich dark brown and red hue promises more than is delivered. A strong malt nose precedes a roast malt taste, with hints of chocolate. The dry finish can be tinged with sweetness, if it lasts long enough.
Thorne Best Bitter	(OG 1038, ABV 3.8%) A soft session brew. The thin, hoppy air does not hide the malty base or the mellow, dry finish. Not very challenging, but it can be very tasty. The dry hopping can be unsubtle.
Best Bitter	(OG 1040, ABV 4%) Formerly Sheffield Best Bitter. An unmistakable malt aroma opens into a full malt taste, with a hoppy edge. It often feels thin, but has a clean tone and is seldom cloying. Short, bittersweet finish.
	For Vaux:
Extra Special Bitter*	(OG 1047, ABV 5%)

WATNEY — See Nationals, Courage

WEBSTER'S — See Nationals, Courage

WEETWOOD

Weetwood Ales Ltd., Weetwood Grange, Weetwood, Tarporley, Cheshire CW6 0NQ. Tel. (01829) 752377

Brewery set up at an equestrian centre in 1993, by an ex-brewer and a former pig farmer, with their first brew on sale in March of that year. Over 20 regular customers are now supplied and more beers are planned.

Best Bitter — (OG 1039, ABV 3.8%) A clean, dry and fruity bitter, well-balanced and consistent.

WELLS

CHARLES WELLS

Charles Wells Ltd., The Eagle Brewery, Havelock Street, Bedford, MK40 4LU. Tel. (01234) 272766 Fax. (01234) 279000

Successful, family-owned brewery, established in 1876 and still run by descendants of the founder. The brewery has been on this site since 1976 and now all but 20 of its 330 tied pubs serve cask ale, though about 50% apply cask breathers. Wells also supplies around 350 other outlets direct and owns the Ancient Druids brew pub in Cambridge (see Ancient Druids).

Eagle IPA — (OG 1035, ABV 3.6%) A well-balanced, hoppy session beer, with hop character often lending refreshing citrus notes to the aroma and flavour. Very dry finish.

Bombardier Best Bitter — (OG 1042, ABV 4.3%) A beer with a complex, but well-balanced flavour of malt, fruit and hops on a bittersweet base. Bitter fruit finish; hops and some fruit in the aroma.

WELSH BREWERS — See Nationals, Bass

WESTBURY ALES — See Hop Back

WEST COAST

West Coast Brewing Co. Ltd., Justin Close, Chorlton-on-Medlock, Gtr. Manchester M13 9UX. Tel. (0161) 274 4344 Fax. (0161) 273 6366

Enterprising brewery set up in 1989 by consultant brewer Brendan Dobbin to serve his own pub, the Kings Arms. Outside demand grew (it currently stands at around 20 free trade outlets) and led to the moving of the brewery a few hundred yards to new premises in 1993. The already extensive beer range is often added to by one-off, humorously-titled brews. Occasional beer: DNC Old Soporific (OG 1084, ABV 9.5%, winter). Bottle-conditioned beers: DNC Guiltless Stout (OG 1039, ABV 3.8%), DNC Ginger Beer (OG 1045, ABV 4.6%), DNC Yakima Grande Pale Ale (OG 1050, ABV 5.5%).

The Independents

Dobbin's North Country (DNC) Dark Mild	(OG 1032, ABV 3.2%) Very full-flavoured for its gravity; dark and rather fruity.
DNC Best Bitter	(OG 1038, ABV 3.7%) A pale beer with malt, hops and fruit in the aroma and taste and a fresh, clean taste, hoppy and bitter, with some malt and a dry finish.
DNC Guiltless Stout	(OG 1039, ABV 3.8%) Very dark in colour, with roast malt predominant in the aroma and taste. Long, dry aftertaste. It also appears in keg form, with nitrogen/CO_2 dispense.
DNC Kangaroo XXXX Pale Ale*	(OG 1042, ABV 4%) A hoppy, light-coloured premium bitter, brewed only in summer.
DNC Big Heavy Jimmie*	(OG 1045, ABV 4.1%) A pale beer with a greater malt emphasis than is usual for the brewery. A recreation of an old-style Scottish heavy, brewed in autumn and winter only.
DNC Ginger Beer*	(OG 1045, ABV 4.6%) Originally brewed as a strong summer 'refresher', its popularity has led to year-round production.
DNC Yakima Grande Pale Ale	(OG 1050, ABV 5.5%) A pale beer with a strong, hoppy nose. Hops are also very evident in the flavour. A well-attenuated beer, making it strong and very dry.
DNC Yakima Grande Porter	(OG 1050, ABV 5.5%) A winter beer with a roast malt and fruit aroma. The complex taste is bittersweet, with malt, chocolate, fruit and hops all present. Long aftertaste.
DNC Extra Special Bitter	(OG 1060, ABV 6.5%) A powerful, mid-brown beer with a strong, complex aroma, malt and hops on the tongue (with sweetish, fruity undertones), and a full, predominantly bitter, hoppy finish.

WEST HIGHLAND

West Highland Brewers, Old Station Brewery, Taynuilt, Argyll, Strathclyde PA35 1JB. Tel. (0186 62) 246

Brewery constructed in November 1989 in listed buildings, part of the last remaining station of the Callander and Oban Railway. It has one tied house, the station tap, and supplies roughly 12 free trade outlets. The brewery is open to the public, grows its own hops (sufficient for one brew) and also acts as an informal tourist office.

Highland Heavy*	(OG 1038, ABV 3.8%)
Old Station Porter*	(OG 1041, ABV 4.2%)
Highland Severe*	(OG 1050, ABV 4.8%)

WETHERED See McMullen and Nationals, Whitbread

WHEATSHEAF INN

Fromes Hill Brewery, Fromes Hill, Ledbury, Hereford & Worcester HR8 1HT. Tel. (01531) 640888

Brewery founded in April 1993, using local hops for its one bitter. A stronger beer may be added. One other outlet is also supplied. Beers: Buckswood Dingle (OG 1036, ABV 3.6%), Overture (OG 1042, ABV 4%), IDK (OG 1050, 4.8%).

WHIM

Whim Ales, Whim Farm, Hartington, Buxton, Derbyshire SK17 0AX. Tel. (01298) 84702

Brewery opened in December 1993 in redundant outbuildings at Whim Farm. Old Izaak is named after Dovedale's Father of Fishing, Izaak Walton. A wheat beer may be added and about 30 outlets are currently supplied. Occasional beer: Black Christmas (OG 1058, ABV 5.8%).

Hartington Bitter*	(OG 1037, ABV 3.8%) A well-hopped ordinary bitter.
Special*	(OG 1043, ABV 4.4%)
Old Izaak*	(OG 1048, ABV 4.8%) A strong mild.

WHITBREAD	See Nationals

WHITBY'S — **Whitby's Own Brewery Ltd., St Hilda's, The Ropery, Whitby, N. Yorks. YO22 4ET. Tel. (01947) 605914**

Brewery opened in a former workhouse in 1988 and moved 50 yards in 1992 into newer, larger premises. Free trade (mostly as guest beers) extends from Newcastle upon Tyne to Huddersfield and takes in roughly 40 outlets, but the brewery is still looking for a first pub of its own.

Golden Pale Bitter* — (OG 1033, ABV 3.3%)

Merryman's Mild* — (OG 1036, ABV 3.5%) A dark mild.

Wallop — (OG 1038, ABV 3.6%) Formerly known as Ammonite Bitter. A light, refreshing beer, pleasant and fruity, with a hoppy aftertaste. Difficult to track down, but well worth the effort.

Woble — (OG 1045, ABV 4.5%) A copper-red, full-bodied, malty bitter, with a burnt roast flavour and a dry, hoppy finish.

Force Nine — (OG 1055, ABV 5.5%) Strong and dark, with a well-balanced blend of contrasting flavours: sweet and fruity, dry and malty, with a strong, bitter finish. A beer of the winter ale type, excellent in its class.

WHITWORTH HALL — **Whitworth Hall Brewery, Whitworth Lane, Spennymoor, Co. Durham DL16 7QX. Tel. (01388) 817419**

A small brewery set up mainly to supply the Whitworth Hall tearoom, catering for visitors to the house and grounds. Outside sales have been limited by the brewery's lack of small casks. Occasional beer: Plum Beer (ABV 8%, Bobby Shafto further fermented with plum juice). Bottle-conditioned beer: Bobby Shafto Wheat Beer (ABV 5%).

Bonnie Bobby Shafto — (OG 1062, ABV 6%) A Belgian-styled brown ale with an unusual spicy character and strong hoppiness.

WICKWAR — **The Wickwar Brewing Co., The Old Cider Mill, Station Road, Wickwar, Avon GL12 8NB. Tel. (01454) 294168**

WICKWAR BREWING CO
NOTED BEERS

Brewery launched on the 'Glorious First of May 1990' (guest beer law day) by two Courage tenants, Brian Rides and Ray Penny, with the aim of providing guest ales for their three tenancies. The business proved so successful that they dropped the pubs to concentrate on supplying their other regular outlets (now totalling around 55). The brewery operates from an old cider mill, originally the site of the Arnold, Perrett & Co. Ltd. brewery.

Coopers WPA — (OG 1035, ABV 3.5%) A yellow/gold, well-balanced, light, summer brew with hops, citrus fruit and a delicate, sweet maltiness.

Brand Oak Bitter — (OG 1039, ABV 4%) A distinct blend of hops, malt and citrus fruits. The slightly sweet taste turns into a fine, dry bitterness with a similar lasting finish. Known locally as 'Bob'.

Olde Merryford Ale — (OG 1049, ABV 5.1%) A pale brown, full-flavoured, well-balanced beer, with malt, hops and fruit elements throughout. Slightly sweet, with a long lasting, malty, dry finish.

Station Porter — (OG 1061, ABV 6.1%) A smooth, warming, dark copper-brown ale with a roast malt, coffee and rich fruit aroma. It has a similarly complex, rich, bittersweet taste and a long, smooth, roast finish. An excellent strong porter, almost an old ale, brewed in winter.

The Independents

WILLY'S

Willy's, 17 High Cliff Road, Cleethorpes, Humbs. DN35 8RQ. Tel. (01472) 602145 Fax. (01472) 603578

Brewery opened in May 1989 to supply a seafront pub and some free trade. Some 60% of production is now sold outside the pub and Old Groyne is particularly popular as a guest beer through wholesalers. Another outlet, SWIGS (Second Willy's In Grimsby), was bought in December 1989.

Original Bitter*	(OG 1038, ABV 3.7%)
Burcom Bitter*	(OG 1044, ABV 4.2%) Known locally as Mariner's Gold.
Coxswains Special Bitter*	(OG 1049, ABV 4.9%)
Old Groyne*	(OG 1060, ABV 6.2%).

WILSONS   See Morland, and Nationals, Courage

WILTSHIRE   See United Breweries

WOLVERHAMP-TON & DUDLEY   See Banks's and Camerons

WOOD

The Wood Brewery Ltd., Wistanstow, Craven Arms, Shropshire SY7 8DG. Tel. (01588) 672523 Fax. (01588) 673939

A village brewery, founded by the Wood family in 1980, which has enjoyed steady growth in recent years. It still owns just one house, the Plough next to the brewery, but it is considering further acquisitions. Around 200 other outlets are also supplied and the brewery specialises in producing commemorative bottled beers. Sam Powell beers have been brewed here since the Powell brewery in Newtown went into receivership in 1991. Occasional beers: Anniversary Ale (OG 1050, ABV 5%, April), Christmas Cracker (OG 1060, ABV 6%).

Wallop*	(OG 1034, ABV 3.4%)
Sam Powell Original Bitter*	(OG 1038, ABV 3.7%)
Parish Bitter	(OG 1040, ABV 4%) A blend of malt and hops with a bitter aftertaste. Pale brown in colour.
Special Bitter	(OG 1043, ABV 4.2%) A tawny brown bitter with malt, hops and some fruitiness.
Sam Powell Old Sam*	(OG 1048, ABV 4.6%)
Wonderful	(OG 1050, ABV 4.8%) A mid-brown, fruity beer, with a roast and malt taste.

WOODFORDE'S

WOODFORDE'S
Norfolk Ales

Woodforde's Norfolk Ales (Woodforde's Ltd.), Broadland Brewery, Woodbastwick, Norwich, Norfolk NR13 6SW. Tel. (01603) 720353 Fax. (01603) 721806

Founded in late 1980 in Norwich, to bring much-needed choice to a long Watney-dominated region, Woodforde's moved to a converted farm complex, with greatly increased production capacity, in the picturesque Broadland village of Woodbastwick in 1989. It brews an extensive range of beers and runs two tied houses, with some 200 other outlets supplied on a regular basis. Bottle-conditioned beer: Norfolk Nips (OG 1085, ABV 8.6%) sometimes also on draught.

Broadsman Bitter	(OG 1035, ABV 3.5%) A session beer which is a straightforward combination of malt and hops, with hints of sweetness and fruit. Hops and bitterness dominate the aftertaste.
Mardler's Mild	(OG 1035, ABV 3.5%) A red/brown mild which is smooth and malty, and well-balanced with some subtle fruitiness. The aftertaste is pleasant but short. Enjoyable.

498

Wherry Best Bitter (OG 1038, ABV 3.8%) This award-winning, amber beer has a distinctly hoppy nose and a well-balanced palate with pronounced bitterness and, usually, a flowery hop character. A long-lasting, satisfying, bitter aftertaste.

Norfolk Porter (OG 1043, ABV 4.1%) A red/brown beer with a gentle but complex aroma and an equally complex but fuller palate. Little aftertaste, though. Thinner and easier drinking than one might expect for a dark beer of this strength.

Old Bram* (OG 1043, ABV 4.1%)

Great Eastern Ale* (OG 1043, ABV 4.3%)

John Browne's Ale* (OG 1043, ABV 4.3%) Malt is the most noticeable component of this beer, particularly in the aftertaste. Little bitterness, but the hop and fruitiness (neither very strong) help make this a complex beer for its strength.

Nelson's Revenge (OG 1045, ABV 4.5%) This premium bitter has quite a strong, pleasant, malty, fruity, hoppy aroma which the rounded and complex, malty palate doesn't quite live up to. The hoppiness and bitterness come through more distinctly at the end to give a good, lasting aftertaste.

Norfolk Nog (OG 1049, ABV 4.6%) A full-bodied red/brown beer with plenty of flavour and aroma. Roast malt balances the sweeter components of the palate. A very good, dark winter brew. *Champion Beer of Britain 1992*.

Baldric (OG 1052, ABV 5.6%) Much changed. Now an amber/golden, light beer, with almost delicate hopping. A pleasing combination of malt, hops and fruit, with some sweetness in the palate and bitterness in the finish.

Headcracker ⊞ (OG 1069, ABV 7%) This fairly pale brown barley wine is full-bodied and fruity throughout. The sweetness in the palate is balanced by the hoppiness and bitterness, and the aftertaste is warming.

WOODY WOODWARD'S See Fox & Hounds

WORLDHAM **Worldham Brewery, Smith's Farm, East Worldham, Alton, Hants. GU34 3AT. Tel. (01420) 83383 Fax. (01420) 83600**

It took 18 months for Worldham to convert a hop kiln into a ten-barrel brewery, using plant acquired from a number of different breweries, and it eventually launched its first beer at the 1991 CAMRA Farnham Beerex. It now serves around 50 free trade outlets and two new brews have been introduced in the last year (Session and Barbarian).

Session Bitter* (OG 1037, ABV 3.6%) Quaffable bitter with a clean, hoppy finish.

Old Dray Bitter (OG 1043, ABV 4.4%) Mid- to deep brown beer, low in aroma and with a dry flavour with some grain. Strong on hops in the slightly cloying finish.

Barbarian Bitter* (OG 1052, ABV 5.2%) A well-hopped premium bitter.

WORTH See Commercial

WORTHINGTON See Nationals, Bass

WORTLEY **Wortley Brewery, Wortley Arms Hotel, Halifax Road, Wortley, Sheffield, S. Yorks. S30 7DB. Tel. (0114) 2882245**

Brewery opened in December 1991 in the cellar of the Wortley Arms Hotel, initially to produce beer for the pub. It survived a brief closure in April 1992 during which all brewing equipment was removed, but now it supplies more than ten other outlets regularly.

The Independents

Bitter	(OG 1036, ABV 3.6%) A light, malty and hoppy-nosed beer that has suffered from change this year. A hoppy, bitter taste, but less malty than of old, with an aftertaste that can be extremely gentle.
Earls Ale	(OG 1044, ABV 4.2%) The hops are more evident this year than last. The aftertaste remains clean and dry, but the malty base has been eroded, although fruit remains in the nose and lingers in the mouth. A brew that needs stability.
Countess Ale*	(OG 1055, ABV 5.8%)

WYCHWOOD

Wychwood Brewery Ltd., Eagle Brewery, The Crofts, Witney, Oxfordshire. Tel. (01993) 702574 Fax. (01993) 772553

Formerly Glenny Brewery, set up in 1983 in the old maltings of the extinct Clinch's brewery, and moved to its own premises in 1987. The brewery was radically revamped during 1992, and nine pubs were acquired (leased from Allied or Inntrepreneur). Since then eight more pubs have been taken on, in various towns across the South and South-West, all revamped in the bare boards and breweriana idiom, most renamed Hobgoblin and all taking real ale, which is also supplied to 70 other outlets. As a consequence of the extra demand, another brewery move has taken place—back to the old Clinch's site.

Shires Bitter	(OG 1034, ABV 3.4%) A pleasantly hoppy and malty, light brown session beer, with a roast malt and fruit aroma.
Fiddlers Elbow*	(OG 1040, ABV 4%) Brewed May-October, from a mixture of barley and wheat malts.
Best	(OG 1042, ABV 4.2%) Mid-brown, full-flavoured premium bitter. Moderately strong in hop and malt flavours, with pleasing, fruity overtones which last through to the aftertaste.
Blackwych Stout*	(OG 1050, ABV 5%)
Dr Thirsty's Draught*	(OG 1050, ABV 5.2%) Primarily aimed at the guest beer market.
Hobgoblin	(OG 1058, ABV 6%) Powerful, full-bodied, copper-red, well-balanced brew. Strong in roasted malt, with a moderate, hoppy bitterness and a slight fruity character.
The Dog's Bollocks*	(OG 1062, ABV 6.5%) A golden, fruity beer.

WYE VALLEY

Wye Valley Brewery, 69 St Owen Street, Hereford, Hereford & Worcester HR1 2JQ. Tel. (01432) 342546 Fax. (01432) 274998

Brewery which started production in March 1985 and moved to its present address in October 1986. New plant was installed in 1992 to increase capacity and cater for a rapidly growing free trade (currently 58 outlets). The company now also has two pubs of its own. The following seasonal beers have been produced under the Dorothy Goodbody name: Springtime Ale (OG 1037, ABV 3.6%, April-June), Golden Summertime Ale (OG 1042, ABV 4.2%, July-Sept), Wholesome Stout (OG 1046, ABV 4.6%, January-March), Wintertime Ale (OG 1055, ABV 5.6%, October-November), Father Xmas Ale (OG 1080, ABV 8.5%, December).

Hereford Bitter	(OG 1036, ABV 3.5%) Very little nose, but a crisp, dry and truly bitter taste, with a balancing malt flavour. The initial bitter aftertaste mellows to a pleasant, lingering malt.
Hereford Pale Ale or HPA	(OG 1040, ABV 4%) Beer with a distinctive colour of old pine and a malty nose. On the tongue, it is malty, with some balancing bitterness and a hint of sweetness. Good, dry finish.
Hereford Supreme	(OG 1043, ABV 4.3%) This rich, copper-red beer has a good malty, fruity aroma. In the complex variety of flavours, the malt, fruit and bitterness are distinctive. The finish has bitterness but can be cloyingly malty.

Brew 69

(OG 1055, ABV 5.6%) A pale beer which disguises its strength. It has a well-balanced flavour and finish, without the sweetness which normally characterises beer of this strength.

YATES

Yates Brewery, Ghyll Farm, Westnewton, Aspatria, Cumbria CA5 3NX. Tel. (0169 73) 21081

Small, traditional brewery set up in 1986 by Peter and Carol Yates in an old farm building on their smallholding, where a herd of pedigree goats makes good use of the brewery's by-products. Brewing award-winning beers to their capacity of 34 barrels a week during summer and other peak times, they also serve 25 free trade outlets and now own one hotel.

Bitter

(OG 1035, ABV 3.7%) A fruity, bitter, straw-coloured ale with malt and hops in the aroma and a long, bitter aftertaste.

Premium

(OG 1048, ABV 5.5%) Available at Christmas and a few other times of the year. Straw-coloured, with a strong aroma of malt and hops, and full-flavoured, with a slight toffee taste. The malty aftertaste becomes strongly bitter.

Best Cellar

(OG 1052, ABV 6%) Brewed only in winter and the strength changes from year to year. An excellent, red/brown beer with a fruity aroma and a sweet, malty flavour, contrasted by a hoppy bitterness. The finish is a bittersweet balance, with grain and some hops.

YORKSHIRE GREY

Yorkshire Grey, 2-6 Theobalds Road, Holborn, London WC1X 8PN. Tel. (0171) 405 2519

Malt extract brew pub on the corner of Gray's Inn Road, now owned by S&N. A CO_2 blanket is applied to the cellar tanks. Beers: Headline Bitter (OG 1037, ABV 3.3%), Chancery Best Bitter (OG 1040, ABV 4.1%), Holborn Best Bitter (OG 1047, ABV 4.4%).

YOUNGER

See Nationals, Scottish & Newcastle

YOUNG'S

Young & Co.'s Brewery PLC, The Ram Brewery, High Street, Wandsworth, London SW18 4JD. Tel. (0181) 870 0141 Fax. (0181) 870 9444

Brewery founded in 1675 by the Draper family, and bought by Charles Young and Anthony Bainbridge in 1831. Their partnership was dissolved in 1884 and the business was continued by the Young family. Though a public company since 1898, Young's is still very much a family affair and was the only London brewer not to join the keg revolution in the 1970s. It still brews award-winning beers in the traditional manner, with some of its pub deliveries made by horse-drawn drays. Around 600 free trade outlets are supplied, mostly within the M25 ring, though the brewery's presence is extending westward, and the brewery's tied estate has now increased to 180 houses. The Bill Bentley's wine bar chain is also now part of the business.

Bitter

(OG 1037, ABV 3.7%) A light and distinctive bitter with well-balanced malt and hop characters. A strong bitterness is followed by a delightfully astringent and hoppy, bitter aftertaste.

Porter

(OG 1040, ABV 4%) An almost black beer with a roasted grain aroma leading to a fruity malt flavour and a sweet finish. It tends to be displaced by Winter Warmer when available.

Special ◫

(OG 1046, ABV 4.6%) A strong, full-flavoured, bitter beer with a powerful hoppiness and a balancing malt flavour. Hops persist in the aftertaste.

Winter Warmer ◫

(OG 1055, ABV 5%) A dark reddish-brown ale with a malty, fruity aroma, a fruity flavour, with roast malt, and a bittersweet finish, including some lingering malt.

BASS

Bass Brewers Ltd., 137 High Street, Burton upon Trent, Staffs. DE14 1JZ Tel. (01283) 511000 Fax. (01283) 513256

Britain's biggest brewer, founded by William Bass in 1777. Today it commands some 23% of all beer production in the UK, with two of the company's ale brands (Stones Best Bitter and Worthington Best Bitter) featuring amongst the top five sellers, and Draught Bass the biggest-selling premium cask ale. Following the closures of the breweries in Edinburgh (Heriot), Sheffield (Hope) and Wolverhampton (Springfield), Bass now brews at just nine sites, with those at Alton, Glasgow, Belfast and Tadcaster producing only keg beer.

Bass continues to promote its leading brands. Both Stones and Worthington Best Bitter have been supported by extensive advertising campaigns, to the detriment of Springfield Bitter (now discontinued) and Charrington IPA, in particular. The latter, originally from London, but brewed in Birmingham until recently, has been contracted out to Shepherd Neame. Worthington Best, meanwhile, is now brewed at Sheffield, as well as at Cardiff, such is demand. The resurgence in darker beers has given a boost to Highgate Mild, now renamed Highgate Dark, which is readily available in the South-East as well as its native Midlands.

On the pub side, Bass Taverns controls 4,200 houses (74% cask). The remaining 1,350 pubs, excluding 200 Toby Restaurants, are operated by the Bass Lease Company. Many pubs still bear the liveries of former Bass trading divisions like Charrington, Tennents, M&B and Welsh Brewers. Overall, Bass has sold about 2,730 pubs to comply with the DTI Orders, although many of these have been to new pub chain companies which have also agreed to take their beer from Bass. Free trade represents some 49% of sales; the tied estate accounts for 31%, and the balance comes from the take-home trade.

BURTON	**Burton Brewery, Station Street, Burton upon Trent, Staffs. DE14 1JZ. Tel. (01283) 513578**

The original home of Bass, producing one of Britain's most famous ales, available throughout its estate and the free trade.

Draught Bass (OG 1043, ABV 4.4%) Can be a classic, but swan neck and sparkler dispense reduces aroma, taste and aftertaste to minimal levels. At its best, it is malty with underlying hops and a dry finish.

BIRMINGHAM	**Cape Hill Brewery, PO Box 27, Smethwick, Birmingham, W. Midlands B16 0PQ. Tel. (0121) 558 1481**

One of the largest cask beer production centres in the country, subject of a £60 million investment programme in the past year. The 'Cape 94' project has included an extension to the brewhouse and a new packaging hall. Despite all this, Charrington IPA has now been farmed out to Shepherd Neame for contract brewing. Bottle-conditioned beer: Worthington White Shield ⊕ (OG 1050.5, ABV 5.6%)

M&B Mild (OG 1034.5, ABV 3.2%) A dark brown quaffing mild with roast and malt flavours. Dry, slightly bitter finish.

M&B Brew XI (OG 1039.5, ABV 3.9%) A sweet, malty beer with a hoppy, bitter aftertaste.

WALSALL	**Highgate Brewery, Sandymount Road, Walsall, W. Midlands WS1 3AP. Tel. (01922) 23168**

Built in 1895 and now a listed building, the Highgate Brewery is the smallest in the Bass group and has remained unchanged for many years. Springfield Bitter, however, has now been discontinued.

M&B Highgate Dark ⊟ (OG 1034.5, ABV 3.2%) A classic Black Country dark mild, increasingly being shared with the rest of the country. Smooth, dry and nutty, with well-balanced hints of fruit, roast and bittersweet maltiness.

M&B Highgate Old Ale (OG 1053.5, ABV 5.1%) November-January only: a dark brown/ruby-coloured old ale. A full-flavoured, fruity, malty ale with a complex aftertaste, with touches of malt, roast, hops and fruit.

SHEFFIELD **Cannon Brewery, 43 Rutland Road, Sheffield, S. Yorks. S3 8BE. Tel. (0114) 2720323**

The original home of William Stones Ltd., dating from at least 1860. It was taken over by Bass in 1968.

Mild (OG 1032, ABV 3.1%) Formerly XXXX Mild. A pleasant, smooth, dark mild with a faint aroma of caramel, which leads to a caramel and roast rich taste, with complementing sweetness and bitterness. A good, long, satisfying, roast malt and caramel-sweet finish.

Light (OG 1032, ABV 3.2%) An amber-coloured mild: a lightly-flavoured blend of malt, sweetness and bitterness. At its best, it has a delicate, pleasing, flowery taste but a disappointing, short, sweetish finish and little aroma. Also known as Toby Light.

William Butler's Black Country Ale* (OG 1032, ABV 3.5%)

Special Bitter (OG 1034, ABV 3.4%) Certainly not special. Pale brown in hue, with little aroma. The generally bland taste has sweetness, malt and a slight bitterness. The poor, sweet and dryish finish can be cloying. Unexciting.

Worthington Best Bitter* (OG 1038, ABV 3.6%) A recent addition to supplement supplies from the Cardiff brewery.

Stones Best Bitter (OG 1039, ABV 3.9%) A fine mixture of malt, hop and fruit in the nose extends into delicate malt and hop tastes in the mouth, ending in a light, clean yet mellow and bitter finish. More often golden in colour now than its famous straw.

CARDIFF **The Brewery, Crawshay Street, Cardiff, S. Glamorgan CF1 1TR. Tel. (01222) 233071**

The Hancock's brewery (founded in 1884) which was taken over by Bass Charrington in 1968.

Worthington Dark (OG 1034.5, ABV 3%) A dark brown, creamy mild with a somewhat malty flavour, followed by a sweet finish. Very popular in the Swansea area.

Hancock's HB (OG 1038, ABV 3.6%) A slightly malty, bitter beer, with a bittersweet aftertaste. The brewery's quality control is of a high standard.

Worthington Best Bitter (OG 1038, ABV 3.6%) A faintly malty, light brown beer, with a somewhat bitter finish. A consistent national brand.

CARLSBERG-TETLEY

Carlsberg-Tetley Brewing Ltd., 107 Station Street, Burton upon Trent, Staffs. DE14 1BZ. Tel. (01283) 531111 Fax. (01283) 502053

The company formed by the merger of Allied Breweries with Danish giant Carlsberg. Allied was established in 1961 with the amalgamation of Ansells, Tetley Walker and Ind Coope. Carlsberg has long been a world-famous brewer, with quality lagers in its own country but lacklustre copies in Britain. It has owned no pubs, but, with its modern Northampton brewery now added to Allied's already under-capacity sites, worries about brewery closures remain. The Romford keg brewery has already ceased production and Allied's lager plant at Wrexham still looks vulnerable. The company's biggest ale brand is the heavily promoted Tetley Bitter, but Ind Coope Burton Ale has been much less successful of late.

On the pub front, the company is keen to keep its local brewery image. Though the Tetley Pub Company now manages the former Joshua Tetley and Tetley Walker pubs, the traditional brewery liveries still decorate the pubs, as they do in the South-East, where Ind Coope Retail runs the former pubs of Friary Meux, Benskins, ABC and Halls. In London, Taylor Walker is complemented by the small Nicholson's chain of upmarket pubs, and the Ansells trade-mark is very prominent in the Midlands and South Wales. However, many former Allied pubs have been sold to regional breweries and pub chains, and over 700 have been leased by Pubmaster (with the Allied beer tie still in place).

ALLOA	**Carlsberg-Tetley Alloa Ltd., Alloa Brewery, Whins Road, Alloa, Clackmannanshire, Central FK10 3RB. Tel. (01259) 723539**

The company's Scottish arm, established in 1810, which was taken over by Archibald Arrol in 1866. It fell to Ind Coope & Allsopp's in 1951, becoming part of Allied in the 1961 merger. Less than a third of Alloa pubs sell real ale, but some offer Maclay and Caledonian beers as guests.

Archibald Arrol's 80/-*	(OG 1041, ABV 4.4%) A full-flavoured beer with dry hop character.

FURGUSONS	**Carlsberg-Tetley Brewing Ltd., Furgusons Plympton Brewery, Valley Road, Plympton, Plymouth, Devon PL7 3LQ. Tel. (01752) 330171**

Set up in the Halls Plympton depot in 1984, this brewery's business has expanded rapidly over the last four years and continues to grow. It now offers three ales of its own for sale to Ansells pubs in the area and to free trade in the South-West.

Dartmoor Best Bitter	(OG 1037, ABV 3.9%) Mid-brown-coloured, malty bitter with hop bitterness in both taste and finish.
Dartmoor Strong	(OG 1043, ABV 4.6%) A pale brown, fruity and sweet-tasting beer with a fruity aroma.
Cockleroaster	(OG 1058, ABV 6%) Around Christmas only. An amber-coloured, full-bodied beer. Smooth and well balanced, yet slightly sweet-tasting, with a strong, multi-flavoured finish.

HP&D	**Holt, Plant & Deakin Ltd., Dudley Road, Wolverhampton, W. Midlands, WV2 3AF. Tel. (01902) 450504**

This division trades under the name of Holts, but do not confuse it with Manchester's Joseph Holt brewery. This is a Black Country company set up in 1984 and now running 23 traditional pubs, all serving real ale. Holts Mild and Bitter are brewed by Tetley Walker in Warrington.

Entire	(OG 1043, ABV 4.4%) An amber, hoppy beer with an aromatic bouquet and a powerful bitter aftertaste that can be astringent.
Deakin's Downfall	(OG 1060, ABV 6.1%) A full-bodied, fruity, malty winter ale.

IND COOPE	**Ind Coope Burton Brewery Ltd., 107 Station Street, Burton upon Trent, Staffs. DE14 1BZ. Tel. (01283) 531111**

The major brewery in the group which resulted from the merger of the adjoining Allsopp's and Ind Coope breweries in 1934. It currently has a capacity of two and a half million barrels a year and brews eight real ales for the South and the Midlands, providing beer for the Ansells, Ind Coope Retail, Taylor Walker and Nicholson's trading divisions. These 'local' beers are derived from two mashes: ABC, Friary and Taylor Walker from one, Benskins and Nicholson's from the other. Lumphammer (OG 1039) is brewed for the Worcestershire-based Little Pub Co. chain.

For Ind Coope Retail:

ABC Best Bitter*
(OG 1035, ABV 3.5%) A light, refreshing bitter, owing much of its character to dry hopping.

Benskins Best Bitter
(OG 1035, ABV 3.5%) A predominantly hoppy beer, which occasionally has an astringent aftertaste. Can be thin, when any malt and fruit characteristics are lost. Otherwise, it's a pleasant, suppable pint.

Friary Meux Best Bitter
(OG 1035, ABV 3.5%) Malt just dominates over hops in the aroma and flavour of this beer, and a strange, fruity flavour lurks in the background.

Ind Coope Burton Ale
(OG 1047, ABV 4.8%) Full of malt, fruit and hop flavours, which are also present in the aroma. Bitterness comes through in the aftertaste.

For Ansells:

Ansells Bitter
(OG 1035, ABV 3.5%) A pale brown, malty bitter, balanced by hoppiness. Bittersweet aftertaste.

Ansells Mild
(OG 1035.5, ABV 3.2%) A dark brown, malty beer with hints of roast caramel and sweetness. Well-balanced aftertaste.

For Taylor Walker and Nicholson's:

Nicholson's Best Bitter*
(OG 1035, ABV 3.5%)

Taylor Walker Best Bitter*
(OG 1035, ABV 3.5%) Light, malty bitter.

JOSHUA TETLEY
Carlsberg-Tetley Brewing Ltd., Joshua Tetley & Son, PO Box 142, The Brewery, Leeds, W. Yorks. LS1 1QG. Tel. (0113) 2435282

Yorkshire's best-known brewery, founded in 1822 by maltster Joshua Tetley. The brewery site covers 20 acres and includes a brewhouse opened in May 1989 to handle the increased demand for Tetley Bitter, though versions of both Tetley Bitter and Mild are also brewed at the Tetley Walker plant in Warrington, with no point of origin declared on the pump clips. A new £6 million visitor centre and museum, Tetley's Brewery Wharf, opened in spring 1994.

Mild
(OG 1032, ABV 3.2%) Red/brown in colour, with a light hint of malt and caramel in the aroma. A rounded taste of malt and caramel follows, with balancing bitterness, then a generally dry finish. A smooth, satisfying mild.

Bitter
(OG 1035.5, ABV 3.6%) An amber-coloured standard bitter with a faint hoppy aroma. A good, refreshing, smooth balance of hop, bitterness and grain in the mouth, finishing with a long, dry aftertaste.

Imperial*
(OG 1042, ABV 4.1%)

TETLEY WALKER
Tetley Walker Ltd., Dallam Lane, Warrington, Cheshire WA2 7NU. Tel. (01925) 31231

Brewery founded by the Walker family in 1852 which merged with Joshua Tetley in 1960 and currently brews Tetley Walker, Peter Walker, HP&D and Greenalls brands. The Tetley Mild and Bitter brewed here are versions of the beers from Tetley's Leeds brewery but are sold with identical pump clips. In the *Good Beer Guide* pub section we state Tetley Walker instead of Tetley when we are aware that the beer comes from Warrington and not Leeds. Occasional beer: Wild Rover (OG 1055, ABV 5.6%, brewed for Tetley's in-pub beer festivals and sold under various names).

Tetley Dark Mild (OG 1032, ABV 2.9%) A smooth, dark, malty mild with balanced roast and caramel flavours, and a hint of fruit and liquorice. Some dryness.

Walker Mild (OG 1032, ABV 2.9%) A smooth, dark mild with fruit and hints of caramel, roast and bitterness. The malty aftertaste quickly gives way to a faint dryness.

Tetley Mild (OG 1032, ABV 3.2%) A smooth, malty mild with some fruitiness and bitter notes. The aftertaste is malty, with a little dryness. A refreshing, darkish mild.

Walker Bitter (OG 1033, ABV 3.3%) A light, refreshing, well-balanced bitter with some hop and a little fruit.

Walker Best Bitter (OG 1036, ABV 3.3%) A bitter, fruity beer with a dry finish. Reasonably hoppy but hardly a best bitter.

Tetley Bitter (OG 1036, ABV 3.6%) A fruity session beer with a dry finish. Bitterness tends to dominate malt and hop flavours. Sharp, clean-tasting and popular.

Walker Winter Warmer (OG 1060, ABV 5.8%) Brewed November-February. A smooth, dark and sweet winter ale, with a strong, fruity flavour, balanced to some degree by a bitter taste and the dry character of the finish. Improves with age as sweetness declines and other flavours emerge. At its best, it is dangerously drinkable.

For HP&D:

HP&D Bitter (OG 1036, ABV 3.4%) Brewed not to give offence: pale, sweet, malty and brown.

HP&D Mild (OG 1036, ABV 3.4%) An innocuous mild that doesn't trouble the tastebuds. Dark brown, sweet and malty.

For Greenalls:

Greenalls Mild (OG 1032, ABV 3.1%) A dark, malty mild with a faint malt and fruit aroma. Quite fruity, with hints of roast, caramel and a little bitterness.

Shipstone's Mild* (OG 1034, ABV 3.4%)

Greenalls Bitter (OG 1036, ABV 3.8%) A well-balanced beer which is quite fruity and well-hopped, with a good, dry finish.

Davenports Traditional Bitter* (OG 1037, ABV 3.9%)

Shipstone's Bitter* (OG 1037, ABV 4%)

Thomas Greenall's Original Bitter (OG 1045, ABV 4.4%) A smooth, malty and well-hopped premium bitter, fairly fruity and bitter.

COURAGE

Courage Ltd., Ashby House, 1 Bridge Street, Staines, Surrey TW18 4TP. Tel. (01784) 466199 Fax. (01784) 468131

Since 1991, Courage, owned by Foster's of Australia, has been a brewer without pubs. Indulging in a pubs-for-breweries swap with Grand Metropolitan (Watney's), as a means of avoiding the full implications of the 1989 Beer Orders, it divested itself of all its pub estate, gaining at the same time all Grand Met's breweries and giving itself 20% of all UK beer production. The ex-Courage pubs, together with most of Grand Met's pubs, were amalgamated into Inntrepreneur Estates (see Pub Groups) for leasing out on long contracts to existing tenants or other businessmen. These pubs are obliged to take Courage beers until 1998, though this agreement may well continue beyond this time.

The brewery closures feared when the deal was announced have yet to materialise, though the future of the old Webster's brewery in Halifax is still in some doubt. Webster's Choice has already been killed off by the heavy promotion of Directors, and all non-production staff have been transferred to John Smith's in Tadcaster. Nationwide, 700 jobs have been phased out in the last year. Courage has also sold off the Ruddles brewery (see Independents) to Dutch lager giants Grolsch, and Ushers of Trowbridge is now independent, thanks to a management buy-out (again see Independents). The company operates keg beer plants in Mortlake and on the outskirts of Reading, and owns the Beamish & Crawford brewery in Cork, Ireland.

BRISTOL

Bristol Brewery, Counterslip, Victoria Street, Bristol, Avon BS1 6EX. Tel. (0117) 9297222

The former Georges brewery (established 1788), and now Courage's only real ale brewery in the South. Growing demand for cask beer has resulted in expansion at this plant in recent years, with Best and Directors very well promoted nationally but Bitter Ale sales confined mostly to the West Country and South-East Wales. However, the three beers are all diluted versions of the same original high-gravity brew.

Bitter Ale

(OG 1032, ABV 3.3%) A pale, light-bodied bitter, with a delicately hoppy, bitter, grainy malt taste. A dry bitter finish and a hoppy aroma.

Best Bitter

(OG 1039, ABV 4%) A pale brown bitter with a balance of bitter hops, grainy malt (sometimes fruit), and a slight sweetness. The aroma is hoppy; the finish is bitter and dry, with some hops.

Directors

(OG 1046, ABV 4.8%) A well-balanced, red/brown malty ale, with hops and fruit in the nose. The similar taste has a faint fruitiness, and develops into a bitter, dry finish.

JOHN SMITH'S

John Smith's Brewery, Tadcaster, N. Yorks. LS24 9SA. Tel. (01937) 832091

A business founded at the Old Brewery in 1758 and taken over by John Smith (brother of Samuel Smith—see Independents) in 1847. The present brewery was built in 1884 and became part of the Courage empire in 1970. John Smith's Bitter is Courage's best known ale, thanks to extensive television advertising. Bottle-conditioned beer: Imperial Russian Stout ⊕ (OG 1098, ABV 10%), a famous export beer which is now only occasionally brewed.

Bitter

(OG 1039, ABV 3.8%) Copper-coloured beer with a pleasant mix of hops and malt in the nose. Malt dominates the taste but hops take over in the finish. The brewery's quality control for this beer is excellent. Widely available nationally.

Magnet

(OG 1040, ABV 4%) A well-crafted beer, almost ruby coloured. Hops, malt and citrus fruit can be identified in the nose and there are complex flavours of nuts, hops and fruit, giving way to a long, malty finish.

OG stands for Original Gravity, the reading taken before fermentation of the amount of fermentable material in the brew. It is a rough indicator of strength. More reliable is the ABV (Alcohol by Volume) rating, which gives the percentage of alcohol in the finished beer.

FOUNTAIN HEAD	**Fountain Head Brewery, Ovenden Wood, Halifax, W. Yorks. HX2 0TL. Tel. (01422) 357188**

The original Samuel Webster brewery, merged by Watney in 1985 with Wilson's of Manchester, a move which saw the closure of Wilson's own brewery. Webster's Yorkshire Bitter appeared to be threatened by the Grand Met deal, as Courage were already committed to John Smith's Bitter, but the Halifax brew has proved surprisingly resilient and still benefits from a sizeable advertising budget. It may be the one beer to survive if Courage do close the Halifax brewery. Already Wilson's Mild has been contracted out to Morland (see Independents).

Webster's Green Label Best	(OG 1034, ABV 3.2%) A faint, hoppy aroma, with a little fruitiness at times. Some sweetness in the malty taste, and a bitter finish. A boy's bitter.
Wilson's Original Bitter	(OG 1036, ABV 3.5%) A fairly thin, golden beer with a malty and fruity aroma and a flowery hop flavour, which can be very bitter at times. Malty overtones in taste and finish.
Webster's Yorkshire Bitter	(OG 1037, ABV 3.5%) A disappointing beer with a faintly malty and fruity aroma (sometimes metallic). Often very bland in taste to offend no-one but it can have a good, fresh, hoppy-bitter flavour and finish.

GUINNESS

Guinness Brewing (GB), Park Royal Brewery, London NW10 7RR. Tel. (0181) 965 7700 Fax. (0181) 963 0801

No real ale—sad words with which to begin a description of one of the world's great breweries. The last naturally-conditioned beer, the bottled Guinness Original, was discontinued in April 1993, despite loud protests from beer-lovers. This was a strange move, especially at a time when both stouts and bottle-conditioned beers were attracting so much interest. Guinness Original is still on sale, but only in a brewery-conditioned, pasteurised version, which lacks the complexity and freshness of the bottle-conditioned beer. However, the stronger Foreign Export Stout, a beer sold all over the world, has at last been reintroduced to British pubs (though, yet again, this is not a bottle-conditioned beer).

All Draught Guinness sold in the UK is keg. In Ireland, Draught Guinness (OG 1038, brewed at Arthur Guinness, St James's Gate, Dublin 8) is not pasteurised but is served with gas pressure. Canned 'Draught' Guinness is pasteurised and produces its tight, creamy head by use of a small plastic sparkler at the bottom of the can.

SCOTTISH & NEWCASTLE

Scottish & Newcastle Beer Production Ltd., Scottish & Newcastle PLC, Abbey Brewery, 111 Holyrood Road, Edinburgh, Lothian EH8 8YS. Tel. (0131) 556 2591 Fax. (0131) 556 4571

The 1960 merger between Scottish Brewers Ltd. (the former Younger and McEwan breweries) and Newcastle Breweries Ltd. has had a major influence on the British brewing industry. Though it avoided classification as a 'national' brewer—and the guest beer law which applies to such brewers—by selling off enough pubs to dip below the 2,000 pub threshold, S&N has now soared back amongst the giants by purchasing the Chef & Brewer group from

Grand Metropolitan. This acquisition of 1,600 pubs has increased S&N's estate to around 3,500 houses. As a consequence, all S&N tenants and leaseholders are now free to take a guest real ale of their own choosing. S&N also continues to have a massive presence in the free trade (particularly through McEwan and Theakston brands and the infamous Newcastle Brown Ale), and also dominates many free houses through the loan-tie system of offering financial loans in return for beer sales.

The company currently operates five breweries, including a keg beer plant in Manchester, but the closure of its Matthew Brown subsidiary in Blackburn in 1991, despite earlier assurances that the brewery was 'sacrosanct', still rankles drinkers. Fears grew for Theakston, too, when S&N began to produce Theakston beers at the Tyne Brewery in Newcastle, and, today, most of Theakston's production comes from Newcastle.

FOUNTAIN	**Fountain Brewery, 159 Fountainbridge, Edinburgh, Lothian EH3 9YY. Tel (0131) 229 9377**

The Scottish production centre, formerly the home of William McEwan & Co. Ltd, founded in 1856. Its beers are sold under two separate names—McEwan and Younger, depending on the trading area, but such is the promotion of Theakston products that the futures of 70/-/Younger Scotch Bitter and No. 3 remain in doubt.

McEwan 70/- or Younger Scotch Bitter*	(OG 1036, ABV 3.7%) A well-balanced, sweetish brew, becoming more and more rare. Often sold cheaply in Wetherspoon pubs.
McEwan 80/- or Younger IPA*	(OG 1042, ABV 4.5%) Malty and sweet-flavoured, with some graininess and a dry finish.
Younger No. 3*	(OG 1042, ABV 4.5%) Rich and dark.

TYNE	**Tyne Brewery, Gallowgate, Newcastle upon Tyne, Tyne & Wear NE99 1RA. Tel. (0191) 232 5091**

The home of Newcastle Breweries Ltd., formed in 1890 as an amalgamation of five local breweries. In recent years it brewed no real ale, until most of Theakston's production was transferred here (see Theakston, below), but no indication is given at the point of sale or in advertising that Theakston beers are brewed in Newcastle (for tasting notes, see Theakston). A new cask beer, Newcastle Exhibition, has been added in the last year.

Theakston Mild Ale	(OG 1035, ABV 3.5%)
Theakston Best Bitter	(OG 1038, ABV 3.8%)
Newcastle Exhibition*	(OG 1040, ABV 4.4%)
Theakston XB	(OG 1044, ABV 4.5%)
Theakston Old Peculier	(OG 1057, ABV 5.6%)

HOME	**Home Brewery, Mansfield Road, Daybrook, Nottingham NG5 6BU. Tel. (0115) 9675030**

Founded in 1875 and acquired by S&N in 1986, Home's tied estate offers real ale in 180 of its 400 pubs and the brewery enjoys extensive free trade in the Midlands and the North. It now also brews the beers from the closed Matthew Brown brewery in Blackburn and these are still sold in 184 of the 403 Matthew Brown pubs in the North-West. Home Mild (OG 1036, ABV 3.6%), however, is now contract-brewed at Mansfield (see Independents), and there are real worries about its future.

The Nationals

Matthew Brown Dark Mild*	(OG 1030.5, ABV 3.1%)
Matthew Brown Bitter*	(OG 1034, ABV 3.5%)
Home Bitter	(OG 1038, ABV 3.8%) A beer with little aroma. The flavour balances malt and hops well, with a smooth, initial taste and a lingering, dry, bitter finish. Golden/copper in colour.

THEAKSTON	**T&R Theakston Ltd., Wellgarth, Masham, Ripon, N. Yorks. HG4 4DX. Tel (01765) 689544 Fax. (01765) 689769**
	Company formed in 1827 and based at this brewery since 1875. Theakston became part of S&N when its parent company, Matthew Brown, was swallowed up. More than £1 million has been spent on this brewery in the last few years, reflecting the 'national' status its brews have been given by S&N. Although Theakston itself runs just ten tied houses, the free trade is enormous and, consequently, most of Theakston's production now takes place in Newcastle. The same pump clips are used for Masham and Newcastle beers, so the consumer is still not told whether the beer actually comes from Theakston's brewery. Occasional beers: Hogshead Bitter (OG 1040, ABV 3.9%), Masham Ale (OG 1065, ABV 6.5%).
Mild Ale	(OG 1034, ABV 3.5%) A rich and smooth mild ale with a good liquorice taste. Dark amber in colour, with a mix of malt and fruit in the nose and a delicious hoppy aftertaste.
Best Bitter	(OG 1038, ABV 3.8%) A light drinking bitter with little body or aftertaste. Hoppiness rapidly declines, leaving a low bitterness and little to remember.
XB	(OG 1044, ABV 4.5%) A good drinking bitter, with hop and fruit character, and a smooth, slightly creamy aftertaste.
Old Peculier	(OG 1057, ABV 5.6%) The mostly highly acclaimed of the Theakston range. A rich, complex beer with a fruity aroma and a well-balanced taste of roast malts and mature dryness. The mouth-feel is smooth, assertive and rich.

WHITBREAD

The Whitbread Beer Company, Whitbread PLC, Porter Tun House, Capability Green, Luton, Beds. LU1 3LS. Tel. (01582) 391166 Fax. (01582) 397397

Whitbread's name is synonymous with brewery closures. Having destroyed the likes of Strong's of Romsey, Wethered of Marlow, Fremlins of Faversham, Chester's of Salford and Higsons of Liverpool, the most recent plant to feel the axe was Sheffield's Exchange Brewery, which closed in 1993, despite great investment in recent years. Ironically, at the same time, Whitbread has been putting large sums of money into promoting its cask ale portfolio, and the retail side of the company has turned a number of pubs into 'alehouses' to support this initiative. Boddingtons Bitter, purchased along with the Strangeways Brewery in 1989, and Flowers Original have been the major beneficiaries, though the new Porter was also well publicised initially. There have also been some noteworthy special brew promotions, involving limited edition beers brewed in Cheltenham and Castle Eden, and culminating in

---

The tankard symbol indicates the *Good Beer Guide Beers of the Year*, finalists in the *Champion Beer of Britain* contest held at the *Great British Beer Festival* at Olympia in August 1994.

'The Beer Thinkers', an initiative based on single varietal hop brews, to encourage drinkers to discern the difference between hop varieties and to think more about the beer they are drinking. The first brew was Glorious Goldings. In addition to the cask ale breweries, the company also operates keg beer factories in Magor in Gwent and Samlesbury in Lancashire.

Whitbread's 4,600 pubs are controlled by two divisions: Whitbread Inns (managed houses) and Whitbread Pub Partnerships (pubs leased out, usually on 20-year terms). Each group has about 2,300 pubs.

BODDINGTONS	**Strangeways Brewery, PO Box 23, Strangeways, Manchester M60 3WB. Tel. (0161) 828 2000**

Brewery established in 1778 whose Bitter has long been one of Britain best-known traditional beers. Whitbread acquired the brewery when the Boddingtons company, which had already taken-over and closed Oldham Brewery, retreated to pub owning and other leisure enterprises. Whitbread is pushing Boddingtons Bitter relentlessly nationwide and it now takes up 90% of the brewery's already expanded production capacity.

Boddingtons Mild (OG 1032, ABV 3%) A thin, dark mild with a sweet caramel and malt flavour, and a short aftertaste. It has now disappeared from many tied houses.

OB Mild (OG 1032, ABV 3%) Copper-red in colour, with a malty aroma. A smooth roast malt and fruit flavour follows, then a malty aftertaste.

Boddingtons Bitter (OG 1034.5, ABV 3.8%) A pale beer in which the grainy malt, hop and bitter character can be spoiled by a rather cloying sweetness.

OB Bitter (OG 1037.5, ABV 3.8%) Pale beer with an aroma of malt and fruit. The flavour is malty and bitter, with a bittersweet tinge and a dry, malty finish.

CASTLE EDEN	**Castle Eden Brewery, PO Box 13, Castle Eden, Hartlepool, Cleveland TS27 4SX. Tel. (01429) 836007**

Originally attached to a 17th-century coaching inn, the old Nimmo's brewery (established in 1826) was purchased by Whitbread in 1963. It actually stands in County Durham, despite the Cleveland postal address, and now produces some of Whitbread's better quality beers. Winter Royal, once brewed by Wethered of Marlow, has arrived here after a time at Gale's in Horndean, as have the Higsons beers from Sheffield—all helping to secure the future of this small brewery. Eden Bitter has been added to the range, and further new products are expected. Rymans Reserve (OG 1039, ABV 4.2%) was brewed for Whitbread's Beer Thinkers promotion in June 1994.

Higsons Mild (OG 1032, ABV 3.4%) A fruity, dark mild with some roast malt and a hint of caramel. Fairly bitter and dry. A great improvement on the Sheffield product, but why pretend it's Higsons?

Eden Bitter* (OG 1037, ABV 3.6%)

Higsons Bitter (OG 1037, ABV 3.7%) An unremarkable but refreshing, well-balanced bitter with a dry aftertaste and a hint of sulphur on the nose. Like the Higsons Mild, an improvement, but nothing like Higsons used to be.

Beers marked with an asterisk have not been tasted by official CAMRA tasting panels. However, some of these beers do carry brief descriptions derived from limited samplings or other sources, and can be used for rough guidance.

The Nationals

Castle Eden Ale	(OG 1040, ABV 4.2%) A rich bitter with well-developed hop character, solid body and a creamy taste. Sulphur can appear when fresh, but in balance with hops and some roast malts.
Old Dambuster*	(OG 1043, ABV 4.6%) A seasonal beer which is now produced throughout the year.
Whitbread Porter	(OG 1052, ABV 4.6%) A deservedly proud beer, rich in coffee and liquorice flavours. Very smooth and well-balanced, with an impressively rich, dry aftertaste. Now only available February–May.
Winter Royal	(OG 1055, ABV 5.5%) The former Wethered winter ale. A rich, fruity and full-flavoured beer with a malty palate, tasting even stronger than its gravity suggests.

FLOWERS	**The Flowers Brewery, Monson Avenue, Cheltenham, Gloucestershire. GL50 4EL. Tel. (01242) 261166**
	Brewery established in 1760 by banker John Gardner, which became the Cheltenham Original Brewery when rebuilt in 1898. It merged in 1958 with Stroud Brewery to form West Country Breweries Ltd. and was acquired by Whitbread in 1963. The Flowers brewing operation and title were transferred from Stratford-upon-Avon in 1968. In recent years it has become the centre for Whitbread cask ale in the South, absorbing the Wethered, Strong and Fremlins production as these breweries were closed. Wethered Bitter (see McMullen), Pompey Royal (see Gale's) and Strong Country Bitter (see Morrells) have since been contracted out to other breweries, while Fremlins Bitter has been joined at Cheltenham by Royal Wessex Bitter (for Devenish/Greenalls), Bentley's and Trophy (following the closure of Exchange brewery). The new Summer Ale was reasonably successful when introduced in 1993, and several one-off brews have followed.
West Country Pale Ale (WCPA)	(OG 1030, ABV 3%) Hoppy in aroma, but not as distinctive as it used to be. Light, refreshing and hoppy, with a clean, dry finish.
Fremlins Bitter*	(OG 1035, ABV 3.5%)
Summer Ale*	(OG 1035, ABV 3.6%) Available in summer only.
Flowers IPA	(OG 1035.5, ABV 3.6%) Pale brown, with little aroma, perhaps a faint maltiness. Moderately dry taste and finish, but no discernible hoppiness. Thin and uninspiring.
Whitbread Best Bitter*	(OG 1035.5, ABV 3.6%) Also available in keg form.
Bentley's Yorkshire Bitter*	(OG 1036, ABV 3.8%)
Trophy Bitter*	(OG 1036, ABV 3.8%)
Flowers Original	(OG 1044, ABV 4.5%) Hoppy aroma and hops in the taste, with some malt and a hint of fruit. A notably bitter finish.
	For Greenalls:
Royal Wessex Bitter*	(OG 1039, ABV 4%)

OG stands for Original Gravity, the reading taken before fermentation of the amount of fermentable material in the brew. It is a rough indicator of strength. More reliable is the ABV (Alcohol by Volume) rating, which gives the percentage of alcohol in the finished beer.

ASCOT ESTATES LTD
Bury House, 31 Bury Street, London
EC3A 5AR.
Tel. (0171) 815 0805 Fax. (0171) 815 0808

Pub-owning company established as Belhaven Inns (a division of Control Securities) in 1987 with 68 pubs. The number rose to over 600 but has now been reduced to 540, spread across most of the country. Of these, 278 are tenanted, with the remaining 262 being leased out on 20-year contracts. Beers are supplied by Courage and Carlsberg-Tetley.

BEARDS OF SUSSEX LTD
Diplocks Way, Hailsham, E. Sussex
BN27 3JF.
Tel. (01323) 847888 Fax. (01323) 440661

Former brewing company which opted out of production in 1959. It currently runs 32 traditional pubs in Sussex, which can sell any beers from the company's wholesaling division. Over 40 breweries feature on the list and the choice is increasing.

BODDINGTON PUB COMPANY
West Point, 501 Chester Road, Manchester
M16 9HX.
Tel. (0161) 876 4292 Fax. (0161) 876 4260

Famous Manchester brewing name which sold its Strangeways and Higsons breweries to Whitbread in 1989. It now runs 475 pubs in the North-West, 275 managed and the rest tenanted, including 24 Henry's Tables pub restaurants. The pubs sell Whitbread Cask Collection beers, as well as Tetley, John Smith's and Theakston brews, plus Cains beers in the Liverpool area. There is also a selection from the group's Guest Ale Club and some pubs have been designated 'Boddingtons Ale Houses'.

CAFE INNS PLC
3 St Thomas's Road, Chorley, Lancs.
PR7 1HP.
Tel. (01257) 262424 Fax. (01257) 260497

Company established in 1986 and now running 130, mostly tenanted pubs in the North-West. Fifty-one of the pubs are leased from Burtonwood and are operated under the Vantage Inns banner, a company jointly owned by Café Inns and Burtonwood. These pubs stock Burtonwood beers. The other pubs sell beers from Bass and S&N (Matthew Brown).

CENTRIC PUB COMPANY LTD
Pub group established with the leasing of 200 pubs from Bass in 1992. However, its pubs, in the Midlands and the North-West, were acquired by Gibbs Mew in summer 1994.

CENTURY INNS LTD
Belasis Business Centre, Coxwold Way,
Billingham, Cleveland TS23 4EA.
Tel. (01642) 343426 Fax. (01642) 345603

Company formed in 1991 by Camerons employees with the purchase of 185 pubs from Bass. The intention was to establish a pub estate for a buy-out of the Camerons brewery, but this was scuppered by Brent Walker. The number of pubs now stands at 301, one managed and the rest traditionally tenanted (three-year agreements), with pubs located down the north-eastern side of the country, from Teesside to Lincolnshire. Beer sales are still mostly confined to Bass products, with some Courage, Carlsberg-Tetley and S&N beers, though the expected switch to more managed pubs may, strangely, allow some outlets to take guest beers from smaller breweries.

CHEF & BREWER GROUP LTD
The managed house division of Grand Metropolitan PLC, operating 1,600 pubs and pub-restaurants, which has now been sold to Scottish & Newcastle (see Nationals).

CM GROUP LTD
Magnet House, Station Road, Tadcaster,
N. Yorks. LS24 9JF.
Tel. (01937) 833311 Fax. (01937) 834236

Eighty-strong pub chain in North-East England, expanded from ten in 1992. Most of the pubs have been leased from Whitbread, with half tenanted, half managed. No guest beers are available to managers or tenants, with supplies coming from Whitbread, Courage, S&N and Carlsberg-Tetley.

CONQUEST INNS LTD
The Old Vicarage, 10 Church Street,
Rickmansworth, Herts. WD3 1BS.
Tel. (01923) 711118 Fax. (01923) 711128

Company set up to obtain 59 pubs from Bass in May 1994, backed by Jersey's Ann Street brewery. About half the pubs are in London, with small pockets of houses in Sussex, the Midlands and East Anglia. Beers come from Bass and Courage, but tenants (on three-year agreements) have no guest beer rights.

JT DAVIES
7 Aberdeen Road, Croydon, London
CR0 1EQ.
Tel. (0181) 681 3222 Fax. (0181) 760 0390

Wine merchant now controlling 29 tenancies and six managed houses in the South-East. Its main suppliers are Bass, Courage, Fuller's and Harveys.

DAVY'S OF LONDON LTD
59–63 Bermondsey Street, London SE1 3XF.
Tel. (0171) 407 9670 Fax. (0171) 407 5844

Long established (1870) wine merchants which has been opening wine bars and ale and port houses in the City since 1965, taking previously unlicensed properties (largely basements) and creating a Dickensian, sawdust, nooks and crannies type of establishment. One beer is sold: Davy's Old Wallop (ABV 4.8%), a re-badged brew of undeclared origin. Amongst its 50 outlets, the company also owns one pub, the Spotted Dog in Barking, and the White Hart hotel in Exeter.

DEAN ENTERTAINMENTS LTD
Dean House, Victoria Road, Kirkcaldy, Fife KY1 2SA.
Tel. (01592) 200417 Fax. (01592) 269501

Scottish-based company owning 44 pubs (nine managed, the rest tenanted), two hotels and three discos in the Fife and Tayside area. Many of the pubs came from Tennent Caledonian, whose beers are the only ones on sale. No guest beers are allowed. The tenanted side of the company has been ear-marked for expansion.

JA DEVENISH PLC
A former brewery whose 540 pubs were acquired by Greenalls in 1993 (see Greenalls).

DISCOVERY INNS
Unit 502, Discovery House, Worle Parkway, Worle, Weston-super-Mare, Avon BS22 0WA.
Tel. (01934) 520400 Fax. (01934) 520401

Company founded in 1992 and now running 222 pubs which it picked up from Whitbread, mostly on a freehold basis. The pubs are offered out on three-year tenancies but all guest beer rights have been taken away and only a limited choice from Whitbread's portfolio, with some Bass, Courage and regional brewers' beers, is offered to tenants. Most of the pubs are in the West Country and South Wales, with others in the North and London.

ENTERPRISE INNS LTD
Friars Gate, Stratford Road, Solihull, W. Midlands B90 4BN.
Tel. (0121) 733 7700 Fax. (0121) 733 6447

Midlands-based company founded in 1991 with the purchase of 372 pubs from Bass. The total now stands at 469, over half run on a 21-year lease basis and the remainder tenanted, with beers provided by Bass, Carlsberg-Tetley, Courage and Wolverhampton & Dudley. Licensees are not allowed to buy beers outside the company. The pubs are situated in the Midlands and the North.

SIR JOHN FITZGERALD LTD
Café Royal Buildings, 8 Nelson Street, Newcastle upon Tyne, Tyne & Wear NE1 5AW.
Tel. (0191) 232 0664 Fax. (0191) 222 1764

Long-established, family-owned, property and pubs company, dating from the end of the last century. Its pubs convey a 'free house' image, most offering a decent choice of cask beers. All 30 pubs (28 managed, two tenanted) are located in the North-East.

GRAY & SONS (CHELMSFORD) LTD
Rignals Lane, Galleywood, Chelmsford, Essex CM2 8RE.
Tel. (01245) 475181 Fax. (01245) 475182

A brewery which ceased production at its Chelmsford brewery in 1974 and which now supplies its 49 Essex pubs with beers from Greene King (IPA, Rayments Special and Abbot Ale) and Ridleys (Mild, plus one other) instead.

GREENALLS GROUP PLC
Wilderspool House, Greenalls Avenue, Warrington, Cheshire WA4 6RH.
Tel. (01925) 651234 Fax. (01925) 444734

Former brewing giant which destroyed many fine independent breweries before turning its back on brewing in 1991. On a 1980s rampage, Greenalls stormed the Midlands, taking over and closing the Wem, Davenports, Simpkiss and Shipstone's breweries. Since the closure of its own Warrington brewery, Greenalls brands have been brewed by Carlsberg-Tetley. The company further demonstrated its contempt for brewing and pub traditions by bulldozing the famous Tommy Ducks pub in Manchester under the cover of night in 1993, ignoring local planning legislation. Following its acquisition of Devenish in the same year, the company now operates 1,068 tenancies and 870 managed houses. Another 112 pubs are leased out on seven-year contracts. The Devenish beers, Cornish Original (brewed by Redruth) and Royal Wessex (brewed by Whitbread) can be found in the former Devenish estate, alongside other Whitbread beers. Guest beers across the country include Tetley Bitter, Stones Best Bitter and, in a few outlets, ales from Cains, Adnams, Greene King, Young's and Coach House.

GROSVENOR INNS PLC
The Old Schoolhouse, London Road, Shenley, Herts. WD7 9DX.
Tel. (01923) 855837 Fax. (01923) 857992

Group running 37 pubs in the South-East, over half of which are leased from Inntrepreneur or other companies and are tied to Courage beers. The other pubs take beers from Whitbread, Fuller's and Wadworth, as well as Courage. Once known as Cromwell Taverns, it is now a publicly-quoted company and plans to develop its estate, establishing more of its Slug & Lettuces (currently 12 pubs). David 'Firkin' Bruce has also joined the board to develop a subsidiary company of free house catering outlets, Belcher's Pubs Ltd.

HEAVITREE BREWERY PLC
Trood Lane, Matford, Exeter, Devon EX2 8YP.
Tel. (01392) 58406 Fax. (01392) 411697

West Country brewery which gave up production in 1970 to concentrate on running pubs. The current estate (largely in Devon) stands at 114: 11 managed, and the rest tenanted or leased out (mostly on 21-year contracts). The pubs are tied to taking beers from Whitbread, Bass and Eldridge Pope.

INN BUSINESS LTD
Woodrow Farm, Wiggington, Tring, Herts HP23 6HT. Tel./Fax. (01442) 891508

Company running 79 pubs (four managed, 75 on one-year, tied tenancies), most obtained from Whitbread. The pubs (which have an emphasis on catering) cover two locations, the northern Home Counties and the South Coast, and there is still a strong Whitbread beer presence, though some Bass, Harveys and Banks & Taylor beers are also sold.

THE INNKEEPER GROUP PLC
Mobbs Miller House, Christchurch Road, Northampton NN1 5NE.
Tel. (01604) 33700 Fax. (01604) 21867

Established in June 1993, a company with around 300 managed houses across the country, including 160 pubs in East Anglia and London obtained in a merger with Molyneux Leisure. The main suppliers are Courage and Whitbread.

INNTREPRENEUR ESTATES LTD
Mill House, Aylesbury Road, Thame, Oxfordshire OX9 3AT.
Tel. (01844) 261526 Fax. (01844) 261332

The pub-owning company formed by Courage and Grand Metropolitan as part of the pubs-for-breweries swap in 1991. In the deal, Courage bought up all Grand Met's (Watney's) breweries, with most of Courage's pubs taken over by Inntrepreneur (330 went directly to Grand Met, which has since sold them to Scottish & Newcastle). Inntrepreneur has led the way with the long lease (20 years) as a replacement for the traditional

tenancy. As a result, many former Courage tenants have left the trade. The company currently operates around 6,500 pubs, 4,250 of which it is allowed to keep tied, under the Government's Beer Orders. The others (some leased to other pub groups) became free houses on 1 November 1992. The tied pubs will take Courage beers until 1998, after which they will be free.

MARITIME TAVERNS LTD
Fryern House, 125 Winchester Road, Chandler's Ford, Eastleigh, Hampshire SO5 2DR.
Tel. (01703) 255116 Fax. (01703) 251615

A subsidiary of John Labatt (UK) Ltd., operating 150 pubs across southern Britain. Most pubs are tenanted, though ten are managed. Licensees (tenants and managers) have a choice from the Whitbread and Bass beer lists, plus beers direct from Gale's, Fuller's and Brains, if the pub falls within those brewers' distribution areas.

MARR TAVERNS LTD
156 Tooley Street, London SE1 2NR.
Tel. (0171) 403 1140 Fax. (0171) 403 2891

Group owning 200 pubs and aiming at over 700 by the end of the decade. Nearly all pubs (most in South-East England and South Wales) are tenanted on traditional three-year contracts, but there are no guest beer rights at present. Beers are supplied by Courage and Bass, plus some local suppliers.

MERCURY GROUP
Mercury House, Amber Business Village, Amington, Tamworth, Staffs. B77 4RP.
Tel. (01827) 68461 Fax. (01827) 310530

Company running 115 pubs through its Mercury Taverns division and managing another 80 pubs as Mercury Leisure. Most pubs have come from Bass, which, together with Carlsberg-Tetley, supplies the beer.

PARAMOUNT PLC
St Werburghs Chambers, Godstall Lane, Chester, Cheshire CH1 2EP.
Tel. (01244) 321171 Fax. (01244) 317665

Ambitious company founded in 1987 as Silver Bear, a games manufacturing company, becoming Paramount in 1988 when it began acquiring pubs. The company is now part-owned by Greenalls (25%), Burtonwood (20%) and Bass (10%), and most of its 107 outlets were purchased from these three operators and S&N. Paramount is also a partner in Real Inns (66 pubs) with Labatts, and manages 50 pubs for Whitbread under the Wirral Taverns name. The pubs are centred within 100 miles of Chester and nearly all are leased out on long contracts. Licensees are encouraged to sell cask ale, but are restricted to the Burtonwood, Bass and Whitbread lists. Wirral Taverns offer the Whitbread portfolio.

Pub Groups

PUB MANAGEMENT CO. LTD
First Floor, North Barn, Tempest Court,
Broughton Hall Business Park, Skipton,
N. Yorks BD23 3AE.
Tel. (01756) 792717 Fax. (01756) 798613

Company running 69 pubs in Yorkshire, on a
mixture of short leases and tenancies, with
one managed house. Formed in 1992, with
the purchase of 32 Bass pubs and 38 Allied
pubs, the company is still aiming for 100 pubs
in the next three years. All beers sold come
from the Carlsberg-Tetley list.

PUBMASTER LTD
Greenbank, Hartlepool, Cleveland
TS24 7QS.
Tel. (01429) 266699 Fax. (01429) 278457

Company formed in 1991 to take over the pub
estate of Brent Walker (ex-Camerons and
Tolly Cobbold pubs). In 1992, 734 houses
were leased from Allied, and 174 from
Whitbread, and other acquisitions have been
made from Bass. Pubmaster currently runs
2,000 pubs across the country, over 1,900
tenanted. Its most famous trading name is
Tap & Spile, a chain of around 30 traditional
alehouses offering an excellent choice of
beers. The other Pubmaster pubs stock beers
from Bass, Carlsberg-Tetley, Whitbread and
some regional independents. Pubmaster
shares control of 170 Maple Leaf Inns with
Labatts.

RANDALLS VAUTIER LTD
PO Box 43, Clare Street, St Helier, Jersey
JE4 8NZ.
Tel. (01534) 887788 Fax. (01534) 888350

Brewery which had produced no real ale for
some time but which stopped brewing
altogether in September 1992. It now runs 29
pubs on Jersey which sell beers from Bass,
Whitbread and Marston's. Not to be confused
with Randalls of Guernsey.

REGENT INNS PLC
Northway House, 1379 High Road,
Whetstone, London N20 9LP.
Tel. (0181) 445 5016 Fax. (0181) 446 0886

Company founded in 1980 and now owning
42 managed pubs in London and the Home
Counties. Some of the 'foodier' pubs have
been sold, but other outlets have been
acquired. The pubs are allowed to preserve
their individual identities and a wide range
of beers is sold.

RYAN ELIZABETH HOLDINGS PLC
Ryan Precinct, 33 Fore Street, Ipswich,
Suffolk IP4 1JL.
Tel. (01473) 217458 Fax. (01473) 258237

This company's 52 pubs in East Anglia
(bought from national brewers) are leased to
individual operators on 35-year contracts.
Most are free, but around 20% have a tie to
Bass or S&N. A breakaway company,
Elizabeth Hotels (currently running six
pubs), was formed in 1991.

SCORPIO INNS LTD
Zealley House, Greenhill Way, Newton
Abbot, Devon TQ12 3TB.
Tel. (01626) 334888 Fax. (01626) 332081

Pub group formed in 1991. After initially
managing pubs in Plymouth for Grand Met,
it obtained over 100 houses from Whitbread
on short leases, bringing the number of pubs
controlled to 122, all now tenanted out.
Despite being 'free of tie', these pubs stock
Whitbread lagers and keg beers, plus a Whitbread cask ale. A guest beer from a short list
of well-known brands is also available to
tenants. Pubs are located in South Wales, the
Bristol and Hereford areas and along the M4
corridor to Swindon.

SMITHINNS PLC
Bridge House, Station Road, Scunthorpe,
Humbs. DN15 6PY.
Tel. (01724) 861703 Fax. (01724) 861708

Six-year-old company operating 32 managed
pubs in Yorkshire, Humberside and northern
Lincolnshire. Eleven pubs are leased from big
brewers and tied to their products, with the
others selling beers from national and certain
regional brewers. There are plans to develop
the Honest Lawyer mini-chain of pubs (three
outlets) which offer at least seven ales.

STAND INN SERVICES
21 Queen Anne's Place, Bush Hill Park,
Enfield, London EN1 2QB.
Tel. (0181) 360 5377 Fax. (0181) 360 6563

Chain of more than 70 pubs in the Home
Counties, over half on six-year leases from
Whitbread. Supply arrangements are in place
with Whitbread, Bass, Carlsberg-Tetley and
Shepherd Neame, and the company has now
opened its first ale house-style pub, the Barrel
& Beef in Hemel Hempstead, which sells a
wide range of beers and regional dishes.

SYCAMORE TAVERNS LTD
1 Guildford Street, Chertsey, Surrey
KT16 9BG.
Tel. (01932) 571545 Fax. (01932) 571562

Company formed in 1992 and operating 275
traditionally-tenanted pubs nationwide. The
stock originally came from Allied (308 pubs),
but the estate has now been rationalised.
Tenants are allowed a guest beer from the
Bass and Courage lists, though the main supplier is still Carlsberg-Tetley.

TOM COBLEIGH PLC
Phoenix House, Oak Tree Lane, Mansfield,
Notts. NG18 4LF.
Tel. (01623) 21414 Fax. (01623) 28255

Company established in 1991 with two pubs.
Since then the estate has grown to 80, two-
thirds tenanted, the remainder managed. The
pubs, which conform to the company's
slogan of 'unspoilt pubs for nice people', are
located in Yorkshire, Humberside and the
north-eastern Midlands. The tenanted pubs
were acquired from Whitbread, though these
are signed as belonging to The Nice Pub

Company. Licensees choose beers from a head office range of 36 national and regional ales from eight brewers, with Marston's, Whitbread, Bass and Courage the main suppliers.

TRENT TAVERNS LTD
PO Box 1061, Gringley on the Hill, Doncaster, S. Yorks. DN10 4ED. Tel. (01777) 817408 Fax. (01777) 816487

Company set up by a former S&N employee. Its 60 pubs in the Midlands (mainly in Warwickshire and Hereford & Worcester) are leased from Whitbread and sell only beers from the Whitbread and S&N lists.

JD WETHERSPOON ORGANISATION PLC
735 High Road, North Finchley, London N12 0BP. Tel. (0181) 446 9099 Fax. (0181) 446 9324

Ambitious London-based group which opened its first pub in 1979 and went public in 1992. It currently owns 77 pubs in and around the capital, all managed, and is looking to add about 20 pubs a year to its stock (including outside London, in places like Birmingham, Reading and Norwich). Many of the pubs are conversions from shops, including ex-Woolworth stores, and common names are JJ Moon's and other 'Moon' titles. No music is played in any of the pubs, all offer no-smoking areas and food is served all day. There are five standard beers available to licensees: S&N Theakston Best, XB and Younger Scotch, Courage Directors and Wadworth 6X, with Greene King IPA and Abbot Ale, and Morland Old Speckled Hen also sometimes seen. Additional guest beers are sold at weekends.

WHARFEDALE TAVERNS LTD
Croft House, Audby Lane, Wetherby, W. Yorks. LS22 4DN. Tel. (01937) 580805 Fax. (01937) 580806

Company set up in 1993 by former Tetley employees to lease 90 pubs from that company. The pubs are traditionally tenanted (three-year agreements), and the main beer range still comes from Carlsberg-Tetley, with guest beers supplied by S&N. The pubs are situated mostly in West and South Yorkshire, and on the east coast.

WHITE ROSE INNS PLC
Chantrell Road, 1 Chantrell Court, The Calls, Leeds LS2 7HA. Tel. (0113) 2461332

Group with 35 tenancies and two managed houses in Yorkshire. The main supplier is Carlsberg-Tetley.

JAMES WILLIAMS (NARBERTH)
7 Spring Gardens, Narberth, Dyfed SA67 7BP. Tel. (01834) 860318 Fax. (01834) 860358

Privately-owned concern, founded in 1830 and operating 51 pubs in Dyfed (all tenanted). Tenants can choose selected beers from Brains, Crown Buckley and Felinfoel, as well as from the Bass, Carlsberg-Tetley, Courage and Whitbread lists.

YATES WINE LODGES LTD
Peter Yates House, Manchester Road, Bolton, Gtr. Manchester BL3 2PY. Tel. (01204) 373737 Fax. (01204) 388383

Company founded in Oldham in 1884 and now running 50 pubs from Scotland to London. Beers are mainly from Courage and Bass, with some Cains ales in Liverpool.

Other notable chains (operated by, or divisions of, brewing companies or pub groups):
Artist's Fare (Morland)
Beefeater (Whitbread)
Bert's Bars (Alloa)
Bill Bentley's Wine Bars (Young's)
Brewers Fayre (Whitbread)
Calendars (Allied)
Exchanges (Taylor Walker)
Firkin (Carlsberg-Tetley)
Fork & Pitcher (Bass)
Harvester (Forte)
Hedgehog & Hogshead (Grosvenor Inns)
Henry Molyneux's Fine Ale and Dining
   Establishments (Innkeeper Group)
Henry's Café Bars (Greenalls)
Henry's Tables (Boddington Pub Group)
High Street Taverns (Grosvenor Inns)
Hogshead Ale Houses (Whitbread)
Honest Lawyer (Smithinns)
Hudsons (Greenalls)
JJ Moon's (Wetherspoon)
King's Fayre (Greene King)
Lacon Inns (Adnams)
Landlord's Table (Mansfield)
Maple Leaf Inns (Pubmaster/Labatts)
Maxwells (Taylor Walker)
Milestone Restaurants and Taverns
   (Wolverhampton & Dudley)
Millers Kitchen (Greenalls)
Mr Q's (Allied)
Nice Pub Company (Tom Cobleigh)
Pizza Hut (Whitbread)
Quincey's (Greenalls)
Real Inns (Labatts/Paramount)
Roast Inns (Greenalls)
Shakespeare Ale Houses (Forte)
Slug & Lettuce (Grosvenor Inns)
T&J Bernards (S&N)
Tap & Spile (Pubmaster)
TGI Friday (Whitbread)
Toby Restaurants (Bass)
Tut 'n' Shive (Whitbread)
Vantage Inns (Burtonwood/Café Inns)
Wirral Taverns (Paramount)

The Beers Index

The Beers Index is the quick guide to the most popular beers of Britain. If you want to know who brews Abbot Ale or Zetland Best Bitter, the answers are in the following pages, together with page references to the breweries section, where you can find out more about each brew. Beers only sold in one outlet or with a very limited availability have not been included. Some breweries' and wholesalers' beers are brewed under contract by other producers. Where this is the case, the names in brackets reveal the actual brewing company.

The Beers Index

The Beers Index

The Beers Index

The Beers Index

The Beers Index

Tollyshooter *Tolly Cobbold* 491
Tom Brown's Best Bitter *Goldfinch* 443
Tom Hoskins Porter *Hoskins & Oldfield* 454
Tom Kelly's Christmas Pudding Porter, Stout *Hoskins & Oldfield* 454
Tommy Todd Porter *Thomas McGuinness* 462
Top Dog Stout *Burton Bridge* 423
Top Hat *Burtonwood* 423
Topsy Turvy *Berrow* 416
Torchlight *Little Avenham* 461
Total Eclipse *Rising Sun* 480
T'Owd Tup *Dent* 433
Town Crier *Hobsons* 451
Treacleminer Bitter *Hanby* 447
Triple X Pale Special *William Clark* 428
Trojan Bitter *Nene Valley* 469
Trooper *Marston Moor* 464
Trophy *Whitbread* 512
Trotton Bitter *Ballard's* 413
Trudoxhill *Ash Vine* 412
TT *Berrow* 416
Turvey Bitter *Nix Wincott* 469
Twelve Bore Bitter *Freetraders (King & Barnes)* 458
Twelve Days *Hook Norton* 452
2B *Arkell's* 412
Two Bays Best Bitter *William Clark* 428
Two Henrys Bitter *Nix Wincott* 470
200 *Palmers* 473
Two Pints Best Bitter *Cropton* 431
2XS *Banks & Taylor* 414
Tyke Bitter *Oak* 471

UB40 *Uley* 493
Uncle Igor's *Ross* 481
Union Bitter *Nene Valley* 469

Valiant *Bateman* 415
Varsity *Morrells* 468
Vassilenski's Black Russian *Hanseatic (McMullen)* 463
Vectis Venom *Burts* 424
Velvet Stout *Reepham* 478
Ventnor Premium Ale *Burts* 423
Very Important Pint *Lloyds* 461
Vice Beer *Bunces* 422
Victory Ale *Bateman* 415
Victualler's Choice *Lincolnshire Steam* 459
Viking *Rudgate* 482
Village Bitter *Archers* 411
VIP *Lloyds* 461
Vixen Velvet *Lloyds* 461
VPA *Burts* 423
Vulcan Bitter *Featherstone* 437

Wake Ale *Gibbs Mew* 442
Walker Best Bitter, Bitter, Mild, Winter Warmer *Carlsberg-Tetley* 506
Wallop *Whitby's* 497
Wood 498
Wassail *Ballard's* 413
Waverley 70/- *Harviestoun* 449
WCPA *Whitbread* 512
Webster's Green Label Best, Yorkshire Bitter *Courage* 508
Wenceslas Winter Warmer *Elgood's* 435
West Country Pale Ale *Whitbread* 512
Wethered Bitter *Whitbread (McMullen)* 463
Whapweasel *Hexhamshire* 450
Wharfedale *Goose Eye* 444
Wheat Beer *Hop Back* 453
Kelham Island 457
Wheat Dragon *Snowdonia* 485
Wherry Best Bitter *Woodforde's* 499
Whistle Belly Vengeance *Summerskills* 488

Whistlemas *Beer Engine* 415
White *Enville* 435
White Adder *Mauldons* 465
White Boar *Village Brewer (Hambleton)* 447
White Dolphin *Hoskins & Oldfield* 454
White Shield *Bass* 502
Wicked Widget *East-West Ales (Brewery on Sea)* 420
Wild *Ballard's* 413
William Butler's Black Country Ale *Bass* 503
William French *Scott's* 483
Willie Warmer *Crouch Vale* 432
Wilson's Original Bitter *Courage* 508
Wilson's Original Mild *Courage (Morland)* 468
Wiltshire Stonehenge Bitter *United Breweries* 493
Wiltshire Traditional Bitter *Gibbs Mew* 442
Winky's Winter Warmer *Nix Wincott* 469
Winky Wobbler *Nix Wincott* 470
Winter Blotto *Franklin's* 440
Winter Royal *Whitbread* 512
Winter Warmer *Big Lamp* 416
Clark's 428
Goddard's 443
St Austell 483
Walker (Carlsberg-Tetley) 506
Young's 501
Winter Wobbler *Jolly Roger* 456
Witchfinder Porter *Ridleys* 479
Wobbler *Gribble* 445
Wobbly Bob *Oak* 471
Woblle *Whitby's* 497
Wonderful *Wood* 498
Woodham IPA *Crouch Vale* 431
Worth Best Bitter, Bitter, Porter *Commercial* 429
Worthington Best Bitter, Dark *Bass* 503
Worthington White Shield *Bass* 502
Wreckage *Titanic* 491

XB *Bateman* 415
Holden's 452
Mole's 467
Theakston (Scottish & Newcastle) 509
XL *Holden's* 452
XL Bitter *Burton Bridge* 422
Xmas Herbert *North Yorkshire* 470
Xpired *Lichfield* 459
XSB *Sutton* 488
XX Dark Mild *Greene King* 444
XX Mild Ale *Harveys* 449
XXX *Batham* 415
Donnington 433
XXXB *Bateman* 415
XXXD *Gale's* 442
XXXX *Harveys* 449
XXXX Mild *St Austell* 482
XXXX Porter *Ringwood* 479

Yakima Grande Pale Ale, Porter *West Coast* 496
Yankee *Rooster's* 480
Yardarm Special Bitter *Cook's* 430
Yeomanry Bicentenary Ale *Arkell's* 412
Yeoman Strong Ale *Oakhill* 471
Yorkshire Brown, Porter *North Yorkshire* 470
Younger IPA, No.3, Scotch Bitter *Scottish & Newcastle* 509
Yule Fuel *Hadrian* 446

Zetland Best Bitter *Village Brewer (Hadrian)* 446

READERS' RECOMMENDATIONS
Suggestions for pubs to be included or excluded

All pubs are surveyed by the local branches of CAMRA. If you would like to draw their attention to a pub already featured, or any you think should be featured, please fill in the form below (or a copy of it) and send it to the address indicated. We also welcome letters, if readers feel strongly about pub entries.

Pub Name:

Address:

Reason for recommendation/criticism:

Pub Name:

Address:

Reason for recommendation/criticism:

Your name and address:

Please send to: GBG, CAMRA Ltd., 34 Alma Road, St Albans, Herts. AL1 3BW

CAMRA BOOKS AND GIFTS

CAMRA produces a wide range of books and other items to complement the *Good Beer Guide*. The major titles are listed below, but a full catalogue of CAMRA products (including local guides) is available on request. Tear out or copy this form for ease of ordering.

All prices include UK postage and packing.

	Quantity	Price each	Amount
GUIDES			
Good Beer Guide to Belgium and Holland (Totally revised edition)		£9.99	
Good Beer Guide to Munich and Bavaria		£8.99	
CAMRA Guide to Good Pub Food		£9.95	
OTHER TITLES			
CAMRA Guide to Home Brewing		£6.99	
Brew Your Own Real Ale at Home		£6.99	
Cellarmanship		£2.95	
Called to the Bar (CAMRA: the first 21 years)		£6.99	
Real Ale Drinker's Almanac		£6.99	
OTHER PRODUCTS			
CAMRA Tie		£6.50	
CAMRA Lapel Badge		£2.25	
CAMRA T-shirt (white: M, L, XL, XXL – state size)		£6.50	
'Real Ale Masterclass' 30 minute video with Roger Protz		£12.95	
		Total	£

Please send to CAMRA Ltd., 34 Alma Road, St Albans, Herts. AL1 3BW (cheques made payable to CAMRA Ltd. must accompany all orders). Allow 28 days for delivery. To place a credit card order, phone (01727) 867201 and ask for the Products Secretary.

Name	
Address	
	Post Code

INSTRUCTIONS TO YOUR BANK TO PAY DIRECT DEBITS

Please complete parts 1 to 4 to instruct your bank to make payments directly from your account.

Return the form to Campaign for Real Ale Limited, 34 Alma Road, St Albans, Herts. AL1 3BW

To the Manager

_____ **Bank**

_____

_____

1 Please write the full postal address of your bank branch in the box.

2 Name(s) of account holders(s)

_____

Address _____

_____

_____ Post Code

3 Account number

Banks may refuse to accept instructions to pay direct debits from some types of account.

Direct debit instructions should only be addressed to banks in the United Kingdom.

CAMRA Computer Membership No. (for office use only)

0	0					

Originator's Identification No.

9	2	6	1	2	9

4 Your instructions to the bank, and signature.

- I instruct you to pay direct debits from my account at the request of Campaign for Real Ale Limited.
- The amounts are variable and are to be debited annually.
- I understand that Campaign for Real Ale Limited may change the amount only after giving me prior notice.
- PLEASE CANCEL ALL PREVIOUS STANDING ORDER INSTRUCTIONS IN FAVOUR OF CAMPAIGN FOR REAL ALE LIMITED.
- I will inform the bank in writing if I wish to cancel this instruction.
- I understand that if any direct debit is paid which breaks the terms of this instruction, the bank will make a refund.

Signature(s) _____

_____

Date _____

CAMRA - FREE MEMBERSHIP!

You've read the book, now join the Campaign!

ONCE AGAIN, we are offering *Good Beer Guide* readers the chance to sample CAMRA membership at no expense and with no obligation. For three-months', no strings, trial membership, just fill in the direct debit form overleaf, sign the application form below and pop them in the post to us (photocopies will do). If, after the three months are up, you do not wish to remain a CAMRA member, simply write to us returning your membership card and you will owe nothing.

■ As a CAMRA member (even for these three months), you will be able to enjoy generous discounts on all CAMRA products (including the *Good Beer Guide*) and you will receive the highly-rated monthly newspaper, *What's Brewing*, to keep you up to date with events in the pub and brewing world. You will also obtain the CAMRA members' handbook, packed with useful facts and figures about real ale, and will be able to take advantage of free or reduced-price membership at many beer festivals.

■ As a CAMRA member you can help to save pubs and breweries, enjoy local social events and brewery trips, and assist with surveying for the *Good Beer Guide* and other CAMRA activities.

■ If you do not want to take up this offer, but wish to join anyway, just fill in the application form below and return it to us with a cheque for your first year's subscription. Do not fill in the direct debit form. To pay by credit card, contact the Membership Secretary on (01727) 867201.

■ Join CAMRA and protect your pleasure. Over 40,000 members can't be wrong!

- -

■ Full membership £12; ■ Joint husband and wife membership £14;
■ Life membership £120/£140

Please delete as appropriate:

☐ I/We wish to take advantage of the trial membership,
and have completed the instructions overleaf.

☐ I/We wish to become members of CAMRA.

☐ I/We agree to abide by the memorandum and articles of
association of the company.

☐ I/We enclose a cheque/p.o. for £   (payable to CAMRA Ltd.)

Name(s) _____

Address _____

_____

_____

Signature(s) _____

CAMRA Ltd., 34 Alma Road, St Albans, Herts. AL1 3BW